MONTGOMERY WARD & CO.

1894-95

CATALOGUE & BUYERS GUIDE

No. 56.

EDITED BY JOSEPH J. SCHROEDER, JR.

DBI BOOKS, INC., Northfield, Ill.

INTRODUCTION

"Write what you want, enclose the money, tell where to send and we do the rest. Easiest thing in the world."

So exhorted this catalogue, and thus furthered a merchandising revolution that has influenced —at least indirectly—the lives of almost every American born in the last 100 years. By "eliminating the middleman" Montgomery Ward brought the necessities of life to rural America at substantial savings, and rural America responded by returning to Ward's for everything from spectacles (test your own sight—page 198) to coal (in gondola car lots, 12-18 tons, so plan to "pool" with your neighbors).

Aaron Montgomery Ward was born in Chatham, New Jersey in 1843 and was raised in Niles, Michigan where he attended public school until he was 14. He served briefly as an apprentice, then worked in a barrel stave factory and as a laborer in a brickyard. At the age of 19 he moved to St. Joseph, Michigan to take a job as clerk in a general store for five dollars a month and board. Here Ward's merchandising talents first manifested themselves, as in only three years he rose to manager of the store and $100 a month salary.

St. Joe apparently wasn't large enough for Ward's ambitions, so in the spring of 1865 he joined the newly formed Chicago firm of (Marshall) Field, Palmer and Leiter where he was paid $23.08 every two weeks. Here Ward spent two valuable years, after which his merchandising education was further expanded by travels in the rural circuit for a St. Louis dry goods wholesaler. Here Ward learned first hand the problems and dissatisfactions that plagued purchasers who lacked access to the competitive markets of the big cities, and saw the opportunity for a potentially profitable business.

Returning to Chicago in 1870, Ward spent two more years on State Street with a dry goods firm, C. W. Pardridge, and by 1872 had saved up $1600 to invest in his dream. His brother-in-law, George R. Thorne, put up another $800, thus, with a capital of only $2400, Montgomery Ward & Co. was founded. The company's first quarters was a single room over a livery stable just north of the Chicago River, and its first catalogue a single sheet listing only dry goods.

From the beginning the new company paid its way, but its big break came in 1873-74 when the newly formed National Grange selected Montgomery Ward & Company to help stock their cooperative stores throughout the country. This fortunate relationship was maintained for some time, and all of Ward's early catalogues carry the statement, "Official Supply House to the Grange," or words to that effect in a prominent place on the outside (see our back cover). This extra business provided the impetus that Ward's needed, with more and more items being added to each new issue of the company's rapidly growing catalogue.

From one page in 1872 the catalogue had reached 72 pages by 1874, still simply listing the merchandise available. Catalogue Number 17, Fall 1876, was a diminutive $3\frac{1}{2}$ x $5\frac{1}{2}$ inches but boasted 136 pages—a few of them (listing trunks) with woodcuts. The Fall and Winter Catalogue of 1878, Number 23, was only up to 144 pages—but they were 6 x 9 inch pages and heavily illustrated.

It wasn't until the summer of 1881 with Number 29 that Ward's catalogue finally reached "standard" $8\frac{1}{2}$ x 11 inch page size, though with only 176 pages. The following year the page count reached 240, and in seven years (1889) this had more than doubled to 488 pages—and annual sales had reached a million dollars. The 1894-95 catalogue, which incidentally was issued the year that Sears, Roebuck & Co. first began to offer a serious threat to Ward, contained 600 pages of the many things that kept the rural American happy and functioning.

"Our claim that this catalogue opens the large markets to you is no idle boast. Where else can you find so much? As a genuine guide to prices, it has no equal."

As a genuine guide to the America of the 1890's, Montgomery Ward's catalogue has no equal, either. Here you will find tools for farm, home or business; clothes for work, play or church on Sunday. Water pumps and wagon trees, furniture, pocket watches, musical instruments and baby buggies, roofing paper and patent medicines are all neatly listed for easy ordering.

Starting on page 307 the equestrian of Grand-father's day would find harness, crops, quirts and whips, blankets and curry combs. The toys that are pictured and described on pages 219 through 234 will undoubtedly delight present day collectors even more than they did the children for whom they were intended. The patriot's attention is called to the notation in the flag listing on page 486, since "a 6 foot flag is the smallest that 44 stars can be put on."

"For Guns and Sporting Goods, we are head-quarters. Remember this."

Sportsmen of the era did, with Ward's comprehensive selection from the products of Parker, Remington, Winchester, Ithaca, L. C. Smith, Charles Daly, Greener (from England), and even Daisy in shotguns and rifles; Colt, Smith & Wesson, Hopkins and Allen, Stevens, and a dozen or more Saturday Night Specials from which to choose a pistol or revolver.

The pre-TV pastime of reading was also well taken care of by Ward's, with page after page of books for almost every taste. Louisa May Alcott and Horatio Alger, Jr. rub shoulders with Dumas, Dickens, Goethe, Washington Irving, Longfellow, Twain, Shakespeare, and Peck's "Bad Boy."

"Are you an electrician or engineer? We can supply you with the best books on these subjects."

Reminders for the professional man are sprinkled here and there throughout the catalogue,

along with the admonition, "do not pay agents big prices for books before consulting us."

"There never was a better year to buy."

After all, Ward's guaranteed satisfaction and assured the would-be customer that "our employees are instructed to do as they would be done by." The friendly image was further enhanced by the statement, "We are always glad to have folks call at our store when in Chicago. Free reading and writing room, free parcel check room and information bureau at your service," appear prominently on the inside front cover.

But enough of this—the real pleasure in this book is to be found starting on the next page. If you are looking for something in particular, the very complete index at the back will help you—otherwise you can simply open it at random and we give you *our* guarantee that you won't be disappointed.

Joseph J. Schroeder, Jr.
Glenview, Illinois
February, 1977

Joseph J. Schroeder, Jr. is the editor of the 1908 Sears Roebuck & Co. catalogue replica, a replica of the Marshall Field and Company 1896 catalogue and is the co-author of System Mauser, a pictorial history of the Mauser pistol. He has written a number of articles for technical electronic publications, firearms magazines and books. He, his wife Janet, and their two children make their home in Glenview, Illinois, where he operates his own business as a technical consultant and writer in the electronics field.

During the World's Fair

MORE THAN 285,000 out-of-town visitors called at our store to see what it looked like. They came from every county in the U. S., and the recent increase in our business would seem to indicate that they were pleased with our establishment and our ways of doing business.

We are always glad to have folks call at our store when in Chicago. Free Reading and Writing Room, Free Parcel Check-room and Information Bureau at your service.

If you see it in the Guide, it's so.

Small orders receive the same care and attention as large ones.

HALF A MILLION DOLLARS A MONTH. THIS IS THE VOLUME OF OUR BUSINESS. THERE MUST BE A REASON FOR IT. STUDY OUR WAYS AND PRICES.

WE'VE BEEN A QUARTER OF A CENTURY IN THE MAIL ORDER BUSINESS (INVENTED IT IN FACT.) TRADE IS INCREASING AS FAST NOW AS AT ANY TIME IN OUR HISTORY.

Many an honest dealer has to charge you much more for goods than we do, simply because he has paid too much for them himself. Ignorance is less provoking than dishonesty, but it costs you just as much.

As large buyers, as cash buyers, as buyers who have all the markets of the world to choose from, we are not liable to pay too high a price for our goods, which accounts for our ability to save you 20 per cent. on your yearly purchases.

Remember that in these days of perfected mail, freight and express service, the mail order business has no terrors. It is generally easier to order a bill of goods from Chicago than to go into five or six stores and buy them. Distance counts for nothing, except time, and that you are paid for by the saving effected.

Try and get into the habit of thinking about the goods that you will need two or three weeks hence. This plan will double the advantages of buying away from home.

Montgomery Ward & Co.
CHICAGO

Twenty-five Stenographers at your service. Write us on any subject. We are always glad to answer letters.

Insure your mail shipments. See remarks on page 1.

It requires a force of 750 clerks to conduct our business. As we can only prosper by fair dealing, our employees are instructed to do as they would be done by. Under this golden rule we have built up a business of which we are justly proud. We invite a careful perusal of this catalogue, and ask an investigation as to our reputation in the past, and our ability to perform what we promise in the future. We refer to any citizen of Chicago, and particularly to the First National Bank of Chicago, Ill. Capital, six million dollars.

111 to 116 Michigan Avenue, CHICAGO.

Montgomery Ward & Co.

Catalogue and Buyers' Guide.

FALL AND WINTER 1894—95.

Montgomery Ward & Co.,

111, 112, 113, 114, 115 AND 116 MICHIGAN AVENUE, CHICAGO, ILL.

Please Read Remarks and Rules Before Ordering.

FOR INDEX SEE PINK PAGES IN MIDDLE OF BOOK.

REMARKS.

Our business was organized in 1872 to meet the wants of the Patrons of Husbandry, from whom we then received our main support. We did not, however, refuse the patronage of any person, knowing that the more goods we handled the cheaper we could sell them.

Our goods, with few exceptions, are sold in quantities to suit the purchaser at prices quoted.

We employ no agents or traveling collectors.

The prices we quote are for goods in our store. All expenses for transportation of both goods and money must be paid by the purchaser.

We cheerfully answer inquiries.

All orders sent us from previous catalogues will be filled from Catalogue No. 56 until 57 is issued. Values are subject to the fluctuations of the market, without notice to the purchaser.

NOTICE—Our Catalogues are issued early in March and September of each year. Please preserve this copy until March 1, 1895, then write us for No. 57, inclosing 15 cents for postage or expressage (we send catalogue by express when we can do so to advantage).

All claims must be made within 10 days after receipt of goods.

To conduct our business in a successful and satisfactory manner, it is necessary to have certain rules to govern our movements. We therefore, in order to prevent all misunderstanding, invite your careful attention to the following:

RULES FOR SHIPMENT OF GOODS.

Freight Shipments.

RULE 1. We will ship goods by freight to ANY ONE if money accompanies the order. Orders from officers of Granges, Farmers' Alliances, or other organizations, must be accompanied by satisfactory references or cash.

For prudential reasons we are obliged to ADHERE STRICTLY TO THE ABOVE.

We will ship goods by freight to our own address and collect the bill through your banker, if sufficient money is sent us with the order to cover freight charges. Be sure you give us the name and location of your bank.

Our responsibility ceases when we have obtained a receipt in good order from the transportation company.

We make claims on the Transportation Companies for loss or damage of goods in transit, if reported to us, but such claims are for your benefit, not ours.

Freight must be prepaid to points which have no agent. Where there is an agent it is not necessary as there is no difference in charges.

We make no charge for cartage. When it is necessary to use cases for packing an order, we charge same at cost.

When sending money with order allow a nominal sum for cases, if goods are of a character requiring cases for packing. This charge varies from 5c. to 50c., according to the size and kind of case. If you send too much we will refund the difference, or omit some article if not enough.

Express Shipments.

RULE 2. Goods will be sent by express, C. O. D. (collect on delivery) when, in our opinion, the articles ordered are suitable. Value, bulk, weight, class, distance, etc., will determine our acceptance or refusal of all such orders. We will not send C. O. D. for amounts under $5.00. To insure the certain shipment of goods by express C. O. D., sufficient money should at least be sent to pay all possible transportation charges. We guarantee that goods shipped by us shall be as represented and of full value, and if not satisfactory we will exchange for other goods or refund the money paid for them, at the option of the purchaser.

No goods will be sent by Express to points off a railway, unless paid for. Express and Freight rates from Chicago to any point can be obtained of the local agent or by writing to us. We use cases or boxes for express shipments only when necessary to secure safety of contents.

No. 56, 6th Edition, November, 1894. **See Pink Pages for Index.**

Goods shipped by Express C. O. D. can be examined at the Express office, in presence of agent. Please do not abuse this privilege by disarranging the goods or occupying too much of the agent's time. While we are willing that the purchaser shall examine the goods, and be satisfied that they are as ordered before paying for them, the Express companies and their representatives dislike the trouble, annoyance and risk attending it, and the privilege is extended to you on condition that it is not abused.

We repeat that we will guarantee all packages to contain the goods ordered and of full value.

Mail Shipments.

RULE 3. Postage on goods by mail is 1 cent per ounce, or fraction thereof, being 16 cents per pound. No one package must exceed 4 lbs., but any number of packages may be sent to the same address, weighing 4 lbs. or less each. Packages can be sent by registered mail for 8 cents per package extra. We would advise insuring all mail shipments, as the insurance fee is usually less than the cost of registering, and in case of loss the shipment is duplicated.

We positively require cash in advance for goods and postage. Send enough and we will return the amount overpaid, if any. The invoice or bill will generally follow the goods within two days. Sometimes, when the amount is small and the account is balanced, we do not send the bill.

Explosives, poisonous or inflammable articles are unmailable. Sharp pointed instruments and glass, such as, Needles, Knives, Pens, Lantern Slides, etc., can go in mailing cases at an extra cost of from 5 to 10 cents. Liquids may be inclosed in vials, packed in wooden boxes, as provided in U. S. Postal Laws. Allow from 5 to 25 cents for liquid cases. We are constantly sending large quantities of goods by mail to all parts of the country, and with very few exceptions goods reach their destination.

All goods sent by mail are at purchaser's risk unless insured. We can assume no responsibility after goods are deposited in postoffice. We advise insuring everything of value.

Insure Your Mail Packages.

We have perfected a plan of Postal Insurance and will, until further notice, insure mail packages *when so instructed* for 5 cents for each package of $5.00 or under in value, 10 cents for packages valued at from $5.00 to $10.00, and 5 cents for each additional $5.00 in value. If you want your packages insured be sure to write "Insure" on your order, and inclose the insurance fee. Prompt notification of failure to receive packages is necessary to secure adjustments.

After reading the foregoing Rules, BE SURE to say HOW you want your goods shipped, whether by Freight, EXPRESS or MAIL.

How to Order.

Commence your order similar to the sample heading on page 2, following the order of directions as there given, *and always say at the top of the order how much money you inclose;* also read our rules regarding the shipment of goods. Write your name, P.O. address, shipping point, etc., PLAINLY. It is best to make Express orders exceed $5 in value, and freight orders exceed 100 lbs. in weight. *We often refuse to ship small orders, as the cost of transportation would consume your profit.* We desire that our goods shall cost you LESS under all circumstances than you can possibly obtain them through any other source. To equalize or reduce the cost of transportation, we advise the sending of club orders. ANY ONE can get up a club. Your Freight or Express Agent can usually give you the rate per 100 lbs. from Chicago. If you have questions to ask, or wish to refer to other matters, write your communication on a separate sheet of paper, give your P. O. address, and sign your name in full. Do not ask questions on sheet used for orders, as our Corresponding and Order departments are in different parts of the building, consequently such questions may not receive attention. (See cash discounts, page 2.)

All goods guaranteed as represented or money and charges refunded.

DISCOUNTS FOR CASH.

RULE 4. DISCOUNT FOR CASH.—Until further notice we will allow the following discounts, *when money accompanies the Order.* *AND IN NO OTHER CASE:*

On orders amounting to $ 10.00 and up to $ 25.00, 1 per cent. discount.
On orders amounting to 25.00 and up to 50.00, 2 per cent. discount.
On orders amounting to 50.00 and up to 100.00, 3 per cent. discount.
On orders amounting to 100.00 and up to 150.00, 4 per cent. discount.
On orders amounting to 150.00 and upward   5 per cent. discount.

On orders for groceries, amounting to $25.00 and over, we allow 2 per cent. discount (except on sugar, which is *net* in all cases).

These discounts will not be allowed unless sufficient money is sent to pay the *WHOLE ORDER*, and will in no case be allowed on C. O. D. orders.

Our object is to treat it as a *Cash Sale*, and close the transaction at one entry, thus saving trouble and expense of keeping an account; therefore be sure to send enough. If you send too much we will refund the balance with the bill. If any balance is due you not convenient to refund in stamps, we will send it in the form of a treasurer's draft, or in some form simply and easily negotiated. We do not refund or claim balances of less than 5 cents. We particularly desire every one to make inquiries about us before sending us an order.

OUR RESPONSIBILITY.

To those unacquainted with us, our ability and willingness to perform our part of the contract, we refer you to any resident or business house of this city, and, by permission, to the First National Bank of Chicago, the largest bank in America—capital and surplus six million of dollars.

Always inclose stamps for reply when writing TO ANY ONE for references.

We do not wish to be classed with the numerous swindlers of our city, and particularly desire every person to make inquiry about us before giving us an order. If this plan is always followed, honest men will be supported, and swindlers die out.

(Our financial standing can be ascertained of any of the commercial agencies or of any reputable bank in America.)

HOW TO SEND MONEY.

It is perfectly safe to send money in the following manner, viz.: Bank Draft, Postal Money Order, or Express Money Order, and in cash by Express, charges prepaid, because in case of miscarriage the loss will be made good.

NOTICE.—Drafts or Checks on Aberdeen, Atlanta, Atchison, Albany, Baltimore, Buffalo, Bismarck, Cincinnati, Columbus, Ohio; Cleveland, Denver, Des Moines, Duluth, Detroit, Dubuque, Fargo, Indianapolis, Kansas City, Lincoln, Neb., Louisville, Milwaukee, Minneapolis, Mitchell, S. Dak.; Omaha, Philadelphia, Pittsburg, Portland, Ore., St. Paul, St. Louis, St. Joseph, Mo., San Francisco, Sioux City, Sioux Falls, Toledo, Troy, Topeka, Washington, Yankton, will be received at par. On other towns we deduct the banker's charge for collection and exchange, which varies from 10c. to 50c., according to amount and distance.

☞ Orders accompanied by individual checks on local banks will be delayed until checks are collected. Expense of collection will be charged.

We will not be responsible for currency or coin sent by open mail nor for money sent in Registered Letters, although we consider this last method practically safe if they are carefully sealed. We advise the use of two envelopes—one within the other. When sending a Postoffice Money Order, disregard instructions on back and inclose it in your letter with order for goods.

When gold or silver becomes worn so as to be light weight, it is only worth what it will bring as bullion, which is about 10 per cent. less than its face value. Do not send us worn and defaced coins and expect to get its face value. Defaced 5c. coins have no value.

NOTICE.—We do not care to take postage stamps, but to accommodate our customers who live where there is no Postal Money Order office where it is difficult to make change in currency, we will accept them for amounts under $5.00. From points where Postal Money Order and express offices are established, we will not accept stamps in larger amounts than $1.00, except at a discount of 3 to 3 per cent.

We recommend the Express Money Order as a system of remitting, because it is safe, simple and economical. There is no use of sending money or stamps where access can be had to an Express office.

NOTE.—Do not send Money or Stamps in a letter by open mail. Many such letters never reach their destination, and we are often blamed for it. Always when possible send money by some of the forms mentioned above.

RETURNING GOODS.

Parties desiring to return goods bought of us and sent as ordered must do so immediately on receipt of them. We are perfectly willing to make exchanges or refund the money, but if the goods are as represented by us, the return charges must be paid by the purchaser. Goods used or damaged after leaving our hands cannot be returned unless by special agreement.

Extract from U. S. Postal Laws: "All packages of merchandise sent through the mails must be so wrapped or enveloped that their contents may be readily examined by postmasters, without destroying the wrapper." Tie the packages firmly with twine, but do not seal.

NEVER SEAL packages returned by mail, or enclose written matter, as by doing so it subjects the whole to double letter postage (4 cents per ounce) and the sender thereof to a fine of $10.00, provided parties to whom it is addressed refuse to pay extra postage. When packages of merchandise are returned to us sealed, or contain written matter, we shall deduct the extra amount of postage paid by us from the value of the goods returned.

When you send goods by mail, write your name and address, AND NOTHING ELSE, ON THE OUTSIDE of the parcel, or enclose a PRINTED CARD only. Send letter of instruction by mail, but DO NOT INCLOSE IT IN PACKAGE WITH GOODS. For rates of postage, see Rule 3, page 1.

Never return goods by freight unless the weight exceeds 25 lbs., nor by express unless the weight is under 25 lbs. Before returning goods write us for instructions. When you return goods by express or freight, put your letter of instructions, if possible, inside the package. Be sure to give the invoice number of all goods returned; this will save us lots of trouble.

All claims for damages, shortage, etc., must be made within 10 days after receipt of goods.

NOTE.—We decline to be held responsible for delays, errors, etc., in adjusting accounts for goods returned to us without the name and address of the sender on the outside. Our business is much too large for us to identify anything unless plainly marked.

SPECIAL CATALOGUES.

We publish a large number of special catalogues, for which see inside rear cover.

SAMPLES.

We make no charge for samples of dry goods, and for that reason we request you when writing for them, to be very explicit in stating exactly what is wanted, giving Catalogue Number when possible, if not, the width, price, quality, color, etc., so that we can send you just what you need, instead of a great lot of samples that are of no use to you and cost us considerable money.

HOW IT PAYS

To get up club orders. Please observe that we allow a discount for cash when money accompanies the order. The discount is rated according to amount of goods purchased. (See Rule 4.) Now suppose you want $40 worth of goods and you can persuade your neighbors to club with you. The following will illustrate the profit.

Your order	$40.00	
Neighbor A	17.00	his share of discount, 17c.
Neighbor B	9.00	his share of discount, 00c.
Neighbor C	30.00	his share of discount, 60c.
Neighbor D	8.00	his share of discount, 00c.
Neighbor E	20.00	his share of discount, 20c.
Neighbor F	6.00	his share of discount, 00c.
Neighbor G	26.00	his share of discount, 52c.
	$156.00	$1.49

You get 5 per cent. discount on $156.00, which is $7.80, and pay out $1.49 to your neighbors, leaving you a profit of $6.31, to say nothing of what you saved by getting the goods at our prices. This would pay well for an evening's work. Your neighbors would gain, as well as yourself, in the reduced proportionate freight charges.

In making the above estimate, it is supposed no groceries are ordered, as the discount on groceries is 2 per cent. on amounts over $25.00, excepting sugar (no discount on sugar). If the above order is for $100.00 worth of dry goods and $56.00 worth of groceries (no sugar), then the discount would be 5 per cent. on $100.00 and 2 per cent. on $56.00. It pays to buy of us on any terms.

SAMPLE HEADING FOR ORDER.

We inclose one order blank in each Catalogue sent you, and will furnish more on application, free. It is not absolutely necessary to have these blanks, but they are a great convenience and prevent many mistakes. If you do not happen to have any handy, try to conform to the sample heading here given, to prevent error:

MESSRS. MONTGOMERY WARD & CO.,

111 to 116 Michigan Avenue, CHICAGO, ILL.

Please Send to
Name ....
Postoffice ....
County ....
State ....

How to be shipped (See rules in Catalogue, page 1).........

Inclosed please find $..............

The following articles are selected from Catalogue No.......................Grocery List No.................

State here the amount of money sent and whether Draft, Express Money Order, Postal Order, Postal Note, Currency or Stamps.
(Always mention number of Catalogue or Grocery List from which order is taken.)

No. of Article in Catalogue.	Quantity.	ARTICLES WANTED.	SIZES, COLORS, etc.	PRICE.	TOTAL AMOUNT.

DESCRIPTIVE ILLUSTRATED PRICE LIST.

FALL AND **No. 56.** WINTER 1894.

Montgomery Ward & Co.

111 TO 116 MICHIGAN AVENUE, - - CHICAGO, ILL.

ALL GOODS IN THIS PRICE LIST SOLD SUBJECT TO THE FLUCTUATIONS OF THE MARKET.

SEE PINK PAGES FOR INDEX.

DRESS GOODS DEPARTMENT.

Note: Ladies will find our Dress Goods Department fully abreast of the times in the assortment of fashionable weaves and shades. We are direct importers of foreign made dress goods, and our stock reflects the latest approved ideas of fashion designers in the great European centers of production.

In domestic goods we handle only the productions of the best known mills, from whom we buy direct. Samples are always cheerfully sent upon request. We only ask that such requests be as specific as possible. Indefinite orders necessitate the sending of large quantities of samples for which there is no need and which means considerable expense to us, both in goods used and additional postage.

A special piece price will be found quoted on many of our lines. We were induced to adopt this feature owing to the numerous inquiries which we receive from merchants, clubs and individuals, asking for special quotations on large quantities. It costs us less to do business when we do not have to unroll, measure and cut goods. What we save in cost of handling, and often more, we are willing to allow to those of our customers who buy their goods in original packages. Where piece prices have been omitted we will be glad to quote same upon request. If you cannot use a full piece perhaps a neighbor would be glad to take part of it, and in this way both can make a saving.

Under no circumstances will we allow "piece prices" where we cut goods.

Colored Alpaca, Cashmere, Henrietta, Serge, Etc.

Special attention is directed to the fact that *our prices have all been revised and reduced*, or where no change appears in price a better quality is substituted for the original line. We have taken advantage of the existing low markets, with the result that our purchases have been made at the lowest prices ever known, the benefit of which we offer to our patrons.

5 Alpaca, single fold, 22 inches wide, half wool, wears well, looks well, and don't cost much. Colors: Slate, gray, tan, golden brown, medium brown, seal brown, purple, royal blue, myrtle, cardinal, garnet, wine, navy or black; also staple mixture in brown, light gray or medium gray. Per yard.......... $0.08¼
Full piece of about 50 yards, 8¼ cents per yard.

8 Union Cashmere, light, medium or dark slate, olive, medium blue, medium brown, seal, tan, golden brown, cardinal, garnet, myrtle, navy or black, 21 inches wide, single fold. Per yard.... .09
Full piece of 50 yards, 8¾ cents per yard.

10 Pacific Mohair Cashmere, 22 inches wide, single fold, in mixtures only of dark and medium shades of brown or gray, in light, medium or dark shades. These goods are well known, and are always worn by certain middle-aged and elderly ladies who have a preference for quiet colors. Per yard.......... .09½
Full piece of about 50 yards, 9 cents per yard.

12 English or Union Cashmere, double fold, 27 inches wide. This is a staple goods, and universally worn. We can furnish all the fashionable fall and winter shades, with the exception of light or evening shades. These are not made in this quality. Colors: Wine, garnet, cardinal, navy blue, myrtle green, slate, mahogany, tan, light brown, medium brown, seal or black. Per yard.......... .12
Full piece of about 50 yards, 11¾ cents per yard.

NOTE—Nos. 5, 8 and 10 and 12 are not made in cream, white or evening shades.

14 Henrietta Cloth, double fold, width 36 inches. This is a new production in cotton, made from the best stock, and woven to show a fine and distinct twill, almost equal in appearance to a fine French Henrietta. We have it in a complete new range of colors, including all the fashionable shades to be worn this season. Colors are: Cream, pink, light blue, nile green, canary, purple, silver gray, slate, medium blue, tan, old rose, sapphire, cardinal, wine, medium brown, dark brown, navy blue, bronze, myrtle green or black. *This black is perfectly fast color and will not crock.* Per yard.......... .13
Full piece of about 50 yards, 12¼ cents per yard.

18 Cashmere, double fold, 36 inches wide, all wool filling. All the fashionable colors, among which are the following: Drab, gray, dark slate, sapphire blue, navy, olive green, myrtle, cardinal, garnet, wine, tan, golden brown, medium plum, heliotrope, sage green, hussar blue, old rose, seal brown, purple, black, marine blue, light blue, pink or cream. Per yard.......... .20
Full piece of about 50 yards, 19¼ cents per yard.

20 English Cashmere, finest quality, double fold, 36 inches wide. We can furnish all seasonable shades. For colors, see No. 18. Per yard.......... .25
Full piece of about 50 yards, 24¼ cents per yard.

Dress Goods—Continued.

23 Cashmere Serge, reversible, strictly all wool; 45 inches wide, equal to anything retailed at 60 cents. We have all the fashionable shades, light or dark navy blue, sapphire blue, tan, golden brown, medium brown, seal brown, myrtle green, cardinal, garnet, wine, slate, gray, old rose, sage, cream or black. Experts pronounce this the cheapest and best serge ever offered. Per yard.......... $0.44

24 Cashmere, all wool, Henrietta finish, 38 inches wide, double fold. This cloth has never been sold heretofore for less than half a dollar. Colors: Navy, plum, medium blue, cream, light blue, pink, nile green, sage, bronze, mahogany, seal, dark brown, golden brown, medium brown, myrtle, tan, cardinal, garnet, wine, old rose, sapphire, gobelin, heliotrope, beige, olive, purple, black, gray or slate. Per yard.......... .40

25 Cashmere, all wool, Henrietta finish, 45 inches wide. Colors: Navy blue, sapphire blue, plum, wine, garnet, cardinal, olive, myrtle green, golden brown, medium brown, seal brown, tan, old rose, slate, gray or black. Per yard.......... .48

26 Imported French Henrietta, all wool, 40 inches wide, finest quality, in the following colors; Old rose, reseda, nile, heliotrope, lavender, eminence purple, light blue, pink, cardinal, scarlet, white, cream, seal brown, medium brown, golden brown, bronze, black, olive, myrtle, navy blue, gray, tan, slate, wine, mahogany, salmon, gobelin, sapphire, and all other seasonable colors. We would like to have you compare these goods with what others sell at seventy-five cents. Per yard.......... .68

28 Colored Henrietta, 45 inches wide, all wool, a fine finished, cloth, made in all the fashionable street shades for this season. Tan, golden brown, seal, medium brown, cardinal, heliotrope, olive, wine, myrtle, old rose, navy, sapphire, slate, blue black or jet black. No delicate or evening shade made in this quality. Per yard.......... .59

30 Imported French Henrietta, all wool, 46 inches wide, double fold, superior quality. Colors: Navy blue, hussar blue, marine blue, sapphire blue, peacock blue, eminence purple, prune, olive, mahogany, golden brown, reseda or sage green, bronze or seal brown, tan, beige, castor, myrtle green, old rose, cardinal, garnet, wine, light pink, lavender, medium gray, slate, white, cream, light blue, and all other seasonable shades. The leading city houses sell this quality for $1.00 per yard. Our price, per yard.......... .78

32 India Cashmere, 50 inches wide, made of finest wool, twilled on both sides, highest finish, and made in all the fashionable street shades, as follows: Myrtle, navy blue, seal, dark brown, slate, gobelin, tan, sage, old rose, wine, heliotrope or black. The extreme width of the goods makes it economical to buy, as a few yards makes a dress. Per yard.......... .88

Albatross.

36 Albatross cloth, all wool, light and thin, like Nun's veiling, only not so hard twisted wool, has a soft crepe-like appearance. Much used for party, wedding or graduating dresses. Colors: Cream, pink, light blue, nile, light gray, slate, navy, brown, tan or black. Width, 38 inches. Per yard.......... .45

French Serges.

40 French Serge, all wool, 38 inches wide, our own importations and the handsomest low priced, pure wool serge in the market. We pride ourselves on the value we give. Everybody now wears serge. We have the following seasonable shades; Slate, medium gray, cardinal, garnet, wine, marine blue, navy blue, golden brown, seal brown, tan, bronze, myrtle, reseda (a new grayish green) sapphire blue, hussar blue, purple, helitrope, cream or black. Per yard.......... $0.47

42 Superfine French Serge, all wool, 46 inches wide. This is a very fine, beautifully finished cloth, and will give excellent wear. Serges are now used for all occassions. We can furnish all the fashionable shades as quoted in No. 40. Per yard.......... .67

Serges are reversible and can be made up either side out, which is an advantage in making over a dress.

BLACK GOODS.

Black Cashmeres and Henriettas.

We are direct importers of these goods. They come from the hands of the best dyers and finishers in the world and are unsurpassed for durability and color. Always state whether jet or blue black is wanted. Union or cotton warp goods is only made in blue black, that shade being the most serviceable in these grades.

Per yard.

50 Union Cashmere, black, 22 in. wide.......... $0.09
51 Black Cashmere, 27 inches wide, half wool, double fold.......... .12
52 Black Cashmere, double-fold, 32 in. wide, all wool filling.......... .17
54 Black, Double Fold Cashmere, 36 in. wide, cotton warp, all wool filling.......... .22
56 Henrietta, black union, 36 in. wide.......... .30
58 Henrietta, black union, 36 in. wide.......... .36
60 Henrietta, black, all wool, 38 in. wide, double fold.......... .39
62 Henrietta, black, all wool, 38 in. wide, double fold.......... .45
64 Henrietta, black, all wool, 38 in. wide.......... .55
66 Henrietta, black, all wool, 38 in. wide.......... .67
68 Henrietta, black, all wool, 38 in. wide.......... .78
70 Henrietta, black, all wool, 38 in. wide.......... .85
72 Henrietta, black, all wool, 38 in. wide.......... .95
73 Henrietta, all wool, blue black or jet black, 45 inches wide.......... .48
74 Henrietta, all wool, 46 in. wide, blue black or jet black.......... .59
76 Henrietta, blue or jet black, all wool, 46 in. wide.......... .89
78 Henrietta, fine and heavy, Drap d'Ete finish, blue or jet black, 46 in. wide.......... 1.15

Ecroyd's Silk Warp Henriettas.

Per yard.

80 Black Henrietta, Silk Warp, 39 inches wide, double fold.......... $0.87
82 Black Henrietta, Silk Warp, finer quality, 39 inches wide, double fold.......... .98
84 Black Henrietta, Silk Warp, 39 inches wide, double fold.......... 1.12½
86 Black Henrietta, Silk Warp, 46 inches wide, double fold, finer quality.......... 1.20
87 Black Henrietta, Silk Warp, 39 inches wide, double fold, superfine quality.......... 1.30

Rare Bargain in Brocades.

980 Black Brocaded Silk Velvets; width 19 inches, medium and small designs, rich in color and style. Many velvets will be worn this season for wraps and trimmings, hence this lot which we purchased at much under their value should attract unusual attention from close buyers. The price at which we offer them until sold is about ¼ their actual value. Per yard......$0.37½
For full piece of about 32 yards, 37½ cents per yard.

VELVETS AND VELVETEENS.

Royal Silk Finish Velveteens, Black.

Per yard.
982 Black Velveteen, 17½ inches wide..........$0.25
Price for full piece of about 36 yards, 5 per cent. less than cut-piece price on all velveteens.
984 Black Royal Velveteen, 18 inches wide...... .35
986 Black Royal Silk Finish Velveteen, 22 inches wide.......................... .50
988 Black Royal Silk Finish Velveteen, 22 inches wide.......................... .60
990 Black Royal Silk Finish Velveteen, heavy, 22 inches wide.......................... .75

Black Velutina.

A heavy, lustrous Velveteen, made by an improved process, and the nearest approach to a Lyons all silk velvet in appearance that has ever been produced.
992 Black Velutina, 24 inches wide..........$0.90
994 Black Velutina, heavy, 26 inches wide...... 1.30

Colored Velveteens, Silk Finish.

Velvets and Velveteens are to be much used for fashionable trimmings. We have all desirable shades.
1000 Silk Finish, Colored Velveteens. A good value for low price; width 18 inches; colors as follows: Cream, pink, beige, moss olive, bronze, myrtle, sky blue, azure blue, royal blue, navy, gray, dark slate, gobelin, old rose, peacock blue, gold, golden brown, Havana brown, medium or seal brown, mahogany, cardinal, garnet, wine, saphire or purple. Per yard..................$0.23
1002 Colored Velveteen, silk finish, 20 inches wide Can furnish all colors as in 1000. Price per yard.......................... .35
1004 Colored Velveteens, silk finish, 22 inches wide. For colors see 1000. Per yard.......... .50

Moleskin.

1020 White Moleskin, for painting, fancy work, etc., 26 inches wide, fine and heavy, not made in colors. Per yard..........................$1.75

Black Silk Velvets.

NOTE—We do not cut any black or Colored Velvets on the bias. All velvets, silks, etc., are cut straight only.
1024 Black Silk Velvets.

Width,	18 in.	18 in.	18 in.	18 in.	18 in.	18 in.
Per yd..	75c	$1.00	$1.25	$1.50	$1.75	$2.00

Price for full piece of about 25 yards, 5 per cent less than for a cut-piece on all velvets.

Colored Silk Velvets.

Velvets are now very fashionable for dresses or trimmings. Our stock is so complete we can usually match any sample or furnish any color made. Per yard
1030 Colored Silk Velvets, 18 inches wide in the following colors: Cream, white, pink, light blue, cardinal, garnet, myrtle, coach green, golden brown, lilac, mahogany, old rose, reseda, heliotrope, prune or black, medium brown, seal brown, moss olive, drab, purple, navy, marine, terra cotta, sapphire, peacock blue or claret...$0.75
1032 Colored Silk Croise Velvet, 18 inches wide, all colors as above.......................... 1.00
1034 Colored Silk Croise Velvet, 19 inches wide, colors as in 1030.......................... 1.25

Silk Plushes.

Mottled Finish.

Per yard.
1054 Mottled Silk Plush, 18 in. wide; colors as follows: nile, lavender, old gold, serpent, reseda, scarlet, cardinal, garnet, wine, claret, navy, olive, bronze, sapphire, mahogany, prune, heliotrope, myrtle, brown, castor, copper, gobelin, gold brown..........................$0.75
1056 Mottled Silk Plush, 18 inches wide. We have all the colors in 1054 (except evening or light shades) given above, and the new shades as fast as dyed. Per yard.......................... 1.00
1058 Mottled or Marbelized Silk Plush, 24 inches wide. We have the following shades only in this width and will have no more when sold: Cadet blue, reseda (a gray or sage green) gray, old rose, gobelin blue, sapphire blue, peacock blue, myrtle green, gold, mobogany, cardinal, navy, medium brown or black. Per yard....... 1.00
1070 Silk Seal Plush in brown only; width 24 inches. Used for jackets, capes, etc. Price, per yard.......................... 2.25

PRINT DEPARTMENT.

Autumn and Winter Styles.

1100 Best American Standard Prints; new fall styles and colors, small and medium floral designs, sprigs, vines, leaves, dots and geometrical patterns on grounds of navy, golden or dark brown, green, sapphire blue or wine. We also have striped effects in same colors. This number includes such well-known makes as Garner's, Gloucester, Hamilton, Merrimac, Allen, Cocheco, etc. We will sell these goods in *any cut length desired*, but limit single orders to 5 full pieces. Pieces average about 55 yards. These goods being offered at such an extremely low price, we are obliged to place a limit on single orders, as our contracts call for but a limited quantity. Customers residing at distant points are, therefore, assured that their orders will be filled. Price per yard $0.03½
1102 Fast Color Prints in small figures, red and white, or pink and white checks or plaids. Per yard.......................... .05
Price for full piece about 50 yards, same.
1104 Full Standard Print, in dark brown and white small apron checks, very neat, and will not show dirt. Per yard.......................... .05
Price for full piece about 50 yards, same.
1106 Frock Prints, very small figures, in pink, buff or purple. Per yard.......................... .06
Price for full piece about 50 yards, 5¾ cents.
1108 Hair-Line Striped Prints, fast colors in purple and white, and pink and white. Per yard.......................... .06
Price for full piece about 50 yards, 5¼ cents per yard.
1110 Oil prints, green ground, yellow and black small figures; canary, with red and black small figure; red ground, with yellow and black figure. Per yard .... .07
Price for full piece about 50 yards, 6⅞ cents per yard.

Shepherd Checks.

1118 Black and White Shepherd Checked Print. Checks run from pin checks up to those a half-inch square. All fast colors and all perfectly printed. Just the thing for aprons, dresses and children's wear. Per yard.... ....$0.06
Price for full piece, of about 50 yards, 5¾ cents per yard

New Fancy Dress Prints.

Fall and Winter Styles.

1122 Mercedes Dress Prints, new styles. Colors predominating are brown, black, green, cardinal, wine, sapphire or black. Small and medium figures. Floral effects or stripes in harmonizing colors. Per yard..........................$0.05
Price for full piece of about 52 yards, 4⅞ cents per yard.
1126 Windsor Prints, new fancy dress styles, 25 inches wide. Small and medium figures on solid color grounds. Brown, sapphire, green, wine, cardinal or navy. Checked and mottled grounds in same colors with shaded figures of green and heliotrope; also cobweb effects. Per yard.......................... .06
Full piece of about 50 yards, 5¾ cents per yard.
1127 Navy Blue Fancy Prints, entirely new, 25 inches wide. Navy blue grounds, with small and medium floral and set figures; figured stripes, stars, dots and dashes in cardinal or gold. Per yard.......................... .06
Full piece of about 50 yards, 5½ cents per yard.

Garnet Foulards.

1129 Garnet Foulard Prints, 25 inches wide. A new line; very neat and stylish. Solid garnet colored grounds, with small foulard silk pattern in white, such as dots, dashes, stars and crescent, floral designs and stripes; colors fast. Per yard..........................$0.05¾
Full piece of about 50 yards, 5½ cents per yard.

Simpson's Gray Printed Novelties.

1136 Simpson's Silver Gray Prints, with small and medium figures in mixed quiet colorings. Predominating effect in gray with just enough color to relieve the sombre effect, very neat and pretty. Per yard..........................$0.06
Full piece of about 55 yards, 5¾ cents per yard.

Simpson's Fast Black Printed Novelties.

1137 Simpson's Fast Black Prints, 25 inches wide, solid black grounds with handsome small and medium designs in bright new colorings. Among the effects now shown are dots, stars, darts, dashes, oblong spots, etc in red, blue, pink, green, gold or heliotrope. Vine patterns, in mixed colors. Hair line stripes in gold or green, floral stripes in mixed colors. Per yard..$0.06
Full piece of about 50 yards, 5¾ cents per yard.

DRESS LININGS.

Your dresses will wear better, fit better and you will save money by patronizing our Lining Department. A new convenience—Lining Sets. See quotations, page 13.

Turkey Red Dress Prints.

1138 Turkey Red and Black Oil Prints, turkey red ground with small or medium figures of black, also black stripes or bars and small or medium polka dots. Per yard. $0.06
Price for full piece, about 50 yards, 5¾ cents per yard.
1140 Cardinal and Black Wool Checks, small plaids or fine mixtures of black on cardinal grounds, fast colors: exceedingly attractive for children's dresses; printed in exact imitation of wool goods. Per yard.......................... .06
Price for full piece, about 50 yards, 5¾ cents per yard.
1144 German Percale in Turkey Red. Checks, plaids or stripes of white, fast color. Extra strong cloth. Width 30 inches. Per yard..... .09
Price for full piece, about 44 yards, 8¾ cents per yard.
1148 Extra Wide Turkey Red Fancy Prints, 31 inches wide, cloth fine and strong, fast color. Red ground with medium or large size white figures or stripes. Per yard.......................... .11
Price for full piece, about 45 yards, 10¾ cents per yard.

Flannel Print.

A New Production.

1150 Flannel Print, 26 inches wide. The cloth very firm and is teazled or closely napped, so as to exactly resemble the fine French figured flannels. It is only made in cardinal grounds, over which are printed small or medium black figures, vine tracings or small polka dots. Per yard..........................$0.06½
Price for full piece of about 43 yards, 6¼ cents per yard.

Indigo Blue Prints.

1160 Indigo Blue Prints, solid blue grounds, figured, dotted or striped with white; width 25 inches. Per yard..........................$0.05
Price for full piece of about 50 yards, 4¾ cents per yard.
1162 Plain Indigo Blue Print Cloth, no figures; width 25 inches. Per yard.......................... .05
Price for full piece of about 50 yards, 4¾ cents per yard.
1164 Blue and Gold Indigo Prints, small and medium figure or stripes of gold on indigo blue ground. Per yard.......................... .06
Price for full piece of about 50 yards, 5¾ cents per yard.
1166 Dutch Blue Print, 28 inches wide, polka dots, medium or small figures or stripes in white or gold, checks in white only. Per yard .. .09
Price for full piece of about 50 yards, 8¾ cents per yard.
1167 Plain or solid Indigo Blue Print Cloth, quality as above; width 28 inches. Per yard.... .09
Price for full piece of about 50 yards, 8¾ cents per yard
1168 Dutch Indigo Print, 31 inches wide, white figured stripes, checks. Per yard.......... 10½
Price for full piece of about 43 yards, 10¼ cents per yard.
1170 German Extra Heavy Indigo Blue Print, 33 inches wide, solid blue ground, with figures, stripes or bars of white. Per yard.......... .12½
Price for full piece of about 50 yards, 12¼ cents per yard.

Extra Wide Print.

1172 Golden Eagle Cloth, an extra fine wide print cloth, in solid black ground, with vines and floral designs in heliotrope, cardinal, gold and blue combinations; width, 32 inches Per yard..$0.09
Full piece of about 50 yards, 8¾ cents per yard.
1174 Extra Wide Costume Print, very fine, fast colors; width, 32 inches. Designs are all new. Ground or predominating colors are: Black with gold, black with white or black with heliotrope, navy ground with white gold or light blue. Designs are floral effects, stripes and set figures, medium or small. Per yard.......................... .10
Full piece of about 50 yards, 9¼ cents per yard.

Shirting Prints.

1180 Shirting Prints, white ground, with figures black, red, blue, brown, black and red or black and blue. Checks in black only Stripes in black, blue or red and cheviot effects and sporting patterns for boys' waists in combinations of black and red or black and blue. Per yard....$0.04
Full piece of about 50 yards, no less per yard.
1182 Fine Percale or Cambric, 31 inches wide. Adapted for men's and boys' shirts, shirt waists, ladies' and children's dresses and aprons. Styles are stripes or polka dots of white on pink or light blue ground; small floral figures in black, blue or red on white ground. Per yard....... 08½
Full piece of about 50 yards, 8¼ cents per yard.

We sell more Sewing Machines than any other house in the world.

Why?

. . . See Our Prices . . .

Black and White Prints.

1186 Black ground, with small, medium or large designs. Hair line stripes or figured stripes of white on black. Patterns are new, neat and pretty. Per yard.......... $0.06
Full piece, about 50 yards, 5¾ cents per yard.

Silver Gray Prints.

1188 Silver Gray Grounds, with small, medium or large designs, stripes or plaids, in black, gray and white. Very genteel and serviceable. Per yard.......... $0.06
Full piece, about 50 yards, 5¾ cents per yard.

Bed Quilt, Comforter or Robe Prints.

1190 Comforter Print, high colors, fancy large patterns. Regular width. Per yard.......... $0.04½
Full piece, about 50 yards, 4¼ cents per yard.
1192 Riverpoint Robe Prints, black ground with red figures, or red ground with white or gold figures. Per yard.......... .05
Full piece of about 50 yards, 4⅞ cents per yard.
1194 Portsmouth Comforter Prints, patterns mostly large, bright colors; cloth good and firm. Per yard.......... .06
Full piece of about 50 yards, 5¾ cents per yard.
1196 Hamilton Twilled Drapery, also for Comforters; wears splendidly. Colors bright and clear. Per yard.......... .06¾
Full piece of about 50 yards, 6½ cents per yard.
1198 Russian Turkey Red, Robe Print, black figures on red ground, medium sized designs. Per yard.......... .07
Price full piece of about 50 yards, 6¾ cents per yard.
1200 Pacific Comforter Print, absolutely fast colors, made in large handsome designs, bringing out beautiful color effects. Medium and dark colors predominating. Per yard.......... .07
Price full piece of about 50 yards, 6¾ cents per yard.
1202 Washington Oil Prints, black ground with red figure. Red or green ground with black and white figure, or navy with black and white figures. Fast colors. Per yard.......... .08
Price full piece of about 50 yards, 7¾ cents per yard.

Tabby Cats.

1210 Tabby Cat Prints. No home complete without a cat. Each half yard of cloth is printed in three pictures. Front, back and feet with outlined margin for cutting. These pictures are to be cut out, sewed together and stuffed with sawdust or cotton, and the result is a life size Maltese tabby cat in sitting position. The most natural thing of the kind ever produced. Every yard contains two cats. Also have same goods with kittens, 8 to the yard. Price per yard...... $0.13½

Indestructible Dolls.

1212 A printed Cambric heavier and stronger than the cats. Each half yard contains 1 complete doll, front and back, printed in perfect imitation of fine bisques, same color tints. This doll will stand any amount of hardship and will please the little ones immensely. Price per yard....... $0.13½

Drapery Prints.

1220 Merrimack or Cocheco Cretonne for Drapery lambrequins or furniture covering, 32 inches wide; large and medium designs in light, medium and dark colors; no stripes. *Notice our price*.......... .11
Price for full piece of about 33 yards, 10¼ cents per yard.
1222 Cameo Drapery, 30 inches wide, in handsome patterns and rich colorings. Cloth is good and strong, and woven in rep or twilled effects. They will drape beautifully. Designs are medium or large, and highly artistic in shadings. Colors of ground work: Tan, black, brown, navy, wine, cream, golden brown or slate. Per yard.......... .12
Price for full piece of about 50 yards, 11 cents per yard.

ALLIANCE BRAND

UNBLEACHED, YARD WIDE, SHEETINGS.

Nos. 1, 2, 3 and 4.

Manufactured for and sold only by Montgomery Ward & Co. We also control the sale of "Monitor" and "Purity" fine bleached sheetings, yard wide. The above brands are highly recommended for domestic uses. They are sold by the bolt only, 25 yards to a bolt. The small piece idea originated with us, and allows the consumer to buy cottons in original mill lengths, thereby saving the merchants' percentage for cost of cutting.

Solid Colored Print.

Per yard

1230 Plain colored prints in the following colors; Cardinal, orange, gray, medium brown, seal brown, light or dark green, dark blue, scarlet, tan, black or medium blue. 25 inches wide $0.05
Price for full piece of about 50 yards 4⅞ cents per yard.
1232 Plain oil turkey red prints, 25 in. wide.... .05
Price for full piece of about 50 yards 4⅞ cents per yard.
1234 Plain turkey red oil prints, 25 in., better grade.......... 07
Price for full piece of about 50 yards 6¾ cents per yard.
1236 Plain turkey red oil prints, 31 in. wide.... .10
Price for full piece of about 40 yards 9 cents per yard.
1238 Plain turkey red oil prints, 36 in. wide.... .12
Price for full piece of about 50 yards, 11¼ cents per yard.
1240 Twilled turkey red oil prints, 36 inches, plain color.......... .15
Price for full piece of about 50 yards, 14½ cents per yard.

Oil Prints.

1242 Oil prints in orange, blue or green, 24 in. wide, plain colors only.......... $0.06
Price for full piece of about 54 yards, 5⅞ cents per yard.

National Decoration Bunting.

We handle large quantities of Decoration Buntings, and are particularly well prepared to supply large orders. Entertainment and Decoration committees will save money by sending to us for their supplies.

1246 Print Cloth, similar to Bunting, printed in red, white and blue stripes, with stars, 21 inches wide. Per yard.......... $0.04½
Price for full piece of about 65 yards, 4¼ cents per yard.
1248 Red, white or blue bunting, 25 inches wide. Plain solid colors, for festooning or draping. In ordering always specify the colors wanted. Per yard.......... .04
Full piece, about 55 yards, 3⅞ cents per yard.
1250 Tri-color bunting, width 25 inches, striped in wide bands of red, white and blue, plain, no stars. Per yard.......... .05
Full piece, about 50 yards, 4¾ cents per yard.
1252 Flag bunting, 28 inches wide, made with 2 or 4 flags to the yard. Price per yard.......... .06
Price for full piece of about 53 yards, 5¾ cents per yard.
For solid colored bunting in national and other fancy colors, see No. 350.

DOMESTICS.

ANY GOODS NOT QUOTED HERE WILL BE FURNISHED AT LOWEST MARKET PRICE AND SAMPLES MARKED WITH WIDTH AND PRICE, SENT ON APPLICATION.

Large contracts which we have made with leading manufacturers this season are on a much lower and more favorable basis than ever before. This will be more readily appreciated by referring to the *extraordinarily low prices* we are now enabled to quote on well known *Standard Cottons. If low prices are an inducement, we should beyond doubt have your trade on Domestics.*

Unbleached Sheeting.

For Brown Sheeting by the small pieces see Nos. 1450 to 1453. Per yard.
1305 Standard LL Unbleached Sheetings, 36 inches wide. We handle the following well-known brands: Aurora, Badger, Atlantic, Harper. Full pieces average about 60 yards. Price per yard, any quantity.......... $0.04¼
NOTE: LL Sheetings average about 4 yards to the pound.
1307 Unbleached Sheetings, 36 inches wide; strong and heavy. Buck's Head, Honest Width, or Triumph brands. Full pieces average about 60 yards. Per yard for any quantity.......... .04⅞
These sheetings average about 3¼ yards to the pound.
1310 Extra Heavy Unbleached Sheetings. 36 inches wide, Atlantic "A" or Indian Head brands. These sheetings average about 55 yards to the piece, and weighs 2⅞ yards to the pound. Single orders limited to 1 bolt.......... 05
The above prices are subject to fluctuations of the market, and are not guaranteed beyond the present stock, which is limited to 100 bales of each grade.

Fine Unbleached Shirtings and Sheetings.

About 56 yards to a piece.

For Brown Sheeting by the small piece see No. 1450 to 1453. Per yard.
1312 Fine Brown Cotton, 36 inches wide, Tioga.......... $0.04¼
1314 Fine Brown Cotton, 36 inches wide, Salisbury.......... .05
1318 Fine Brown Cotton, 36 inches wide, Pepperell "R".......... .05½

Sheetings—Continued.

Per yard.
1320 Fine Brown Cotton, 36 inches wide, Lockwood.......... $0.06
1322 Fine Brown Cotton, 39 inches wide, Pepperell "E".......... .06¾
1324 Fine Brown Cotton, 40 inches wide, Dwight Star.......... .08

Unbleached Pepperell Sheetings Extra Wide.

The Pepperell Mills Wide Sheetings, while not woven as fine, close or hard as some others, are universally used by hotels, hospitals and the U. S. Government, as their experience teaches that a cloth woven hard is worn out more in washing in trying to get it clean and white than one slightly coarser.

These are fine enough for most any trade, wear splendidly, will not crack, and wash easily.

Width given is exact. Per yard.
1340 Brown Pepperell Sheetings, fine, 45 inches wide.......... $0.09
Full piece of about 45 yards, 8¾ cents per yard.
1342 Brown Pepperell Sheetings, fine, 48 inches wide.......... .10
Full piece, about 45 yards, 9¾ cents per yard.
Per yard.
1344 Brown Pepperell Sheetings, fine, 58 inches wide.......... $0.12½
Full piece, about 45 yards, 12 cents per yard.
1346 Brown Pepperell Sheetings, fine, 68 inches wide.......... .14
Full piece, about 45 yards, 13½ cents per yard.
1348 Brown Pepperell Sheetings, fine, 80 inches wide.......... 16
Full piece, about 45 yards, 15½ cents per yard.
1350 Brown Pepperell Sheetings, fine, 88 inches wide.......... .18
Full piece, about 45 yards, 17½ cents per yard.

Drilling.

1360 Unbleached Drilling, 29 in. Per yard .. $0.06¾
Price for full piece of about 40 yards, 6 cents per yard.
1362 Unbleached Drilling, best, 29 in. Per yard, 07
Price for full piece of about 30 yards, 6¾ cents per yard.
Drilling in use for pockets, for lining pants, etc.

Boat Sail Drill.

1364 Twilled Sail Drill, 29 in. wide, unbleached, weight between 6 and 7 ozs. to the yard. Much used. Woven strong. Per yard.......... $0.08
Price for full piece of about 60 yards, 7¾ cents per yard.

Unbleached Pequot White Sheetings.

While for general wearing qualities the Pepperell Sheetings are undoubtedly the most satisfactory medium priced cottons on the market, there has been for some time a growing demand from many of our customers for a finer and heavier quality. We have therefore, after a careful comparison of leading brands, selected the Pequot Sheetings as being superior to all others for uniformity of thread, fineness of weave, weight and general combination of qualities, which are essential in first-class sheetings.

1370 Unbleached Pequot Sheeting (⁵⁄₄) 45 ins. Per yd. wide.......... $0.11½
Full piece of about 48 yards, 11 cents per yard.
1371 Unbleached Pequot Sheeting, (⁶⁄₄) 54 inches wide.......... .13½
Full piece of about 48 yards, 13 cents per yard.
1372 Unbleached Pequot Sheeting (⁷⁄₄) 58 inches wide.......... .15
Full piece of about 48 yards, 14½ cents per yd.
1373 Unbleached Pequot Sheeting (⁸⁄₄) 68 inches wide.......... .17½
Full piece of about 48 yards, 16¾ cents per yd.
1374 Unbleached Pequot Sheeting (⁹⁄₄) 80 inches wide.......... .20
Full piece of about 48 yards, 19 cents per yard.
1375 Unbleached Pequot Sheeting (¹⁰⁄₄) 88 inches wide.......... .22
Full piece of about 48 yards, 21 cents per yard.

Bleached Pequot Pillow Casing.

1378 Bleached Pequot Pillow Casing, 42 inches wide. Per yard.......... $0.11½
Full piece of about 48 yards, 11 cents per yard.
1379 Bleached Pequot Pillow Casing (⁵⁄₄) 45 inches wide. Per yard.......... .12½
Full piece of about 48 yards, 12 cents per yard.
1380 Bleached Pequot Pillow Casing 50 inches wide.......... .13½
Full piece of about 48 yards, 13 cents per yard.

Bleached Pequot Wide Sheetings.

1382 Bleached Pequot Sheetings (⁶⁄₄) 54 inches wide.......... $0.15
Full piece of about 48 yards, 14½ cents per yard.
1383 Bleached Pequot Sheetings (⁷⁄₄) 63 inches wide.......... .17½
Full piece of about 48 yards, 16¾ cents per yd.
1384 Bleached Pequot Sheetings (⁸⁄₄) 72 inches wide.......... .20
Full piece of about 48 yards, 19 cents per yard.
1385 Bleached Pequot Sheetings (⁹⁄₄) 81 inches wide.......... .22
Full piece of about 48 yards, 21 cents per yard.
1386 Bleached Pequot Sheetings (¹⁰⁄₄) 90 inches wide.......... .25
Full piece of about 48 yards, 24 cents per yard.

All lines of merchandise very generally reduced in price.

Linings—Continued.

1760 Soft-finished Cambric, black one side, white the other; 27 inches wide $0.07
Price for full piece of about 50 yards, 6¾ cents per yard.
1762 Paper Cambric, double fold, in black, brown, drab or slate; 36 inches wide .... .06
Price for full piece of about 53 yards, 5¾ cents per yard.
1764 Paper Cambric, double fold, in high colors, red, pink, white, light blue, dark blue or green; 36 inches wide .... .07
Price for full piece of about 54 yards, 6¾ cents per yard.

Farmers' Satin and Italian Cloth.

Per yard.
1766 Farmers' Satin, black, 27 inches wide... $0.25
Full piece of about 50 yards, 23½ cents per yd.
1768 Farmers' Satin, black; 27 inches wide...... .50
Full piece of about 50 yards, 48 cents per yard.
1770 Farmers' Satin, black; 54 inches wide..... 1.00
Price for full piece of about 54 yards, 95 cents per yard.
1772 Farmers' Satin, black; 54 inches wide...... 1.25
Price for full piece of about 50 yards, $1.14 per yard.
1774 Farmers' Satin, black; 54 inches wide..... $1.40
Price for full piece of about 40 yards, $1.30 per yard.
1776 Farmers' Satin, 27 inches wide, fine quality; colors, navy blue, bottle green, old gold, wine, tan, golden brown, light blue, medium blue, dark brown and scarlet $0.40
Full piece of about 28 yards, 37 cents per yard.

Fine Fancy Sateen Linings.

1780 Fancy Sateen Lining, 36 inches wide, made in drab or slate, with small fancy figures printed in fast colors. Per yard........ $0.19
Full piece of about 50 yards, 18 cents per yard.
1782 Extra Fine Sateen Lining, 38 inches wide, black on one side, tan and drab on other, over which is printed neat designs in fast colors. This class of linings is now much used. Per yard .25
Full piece of about 50 yards, 24 cents per yard.

Silesias.

For waist linings and tailors' use, 36 inches wide.
1790 Fernwood Silesia, made in black and all staple shades. A very good lining, much better than usually sold at ten cents. Per yard....... $0.08
For full piece of about 60 yards, 7¾ cents per yard.
1792 Silesia, in plain colors, good and firm..... $0.10
Price for full piece of about 60 yards, 9 cents per yard.

Silesias—Continued.

1794 Silesia, fine quality, all colors. We recommend this grade........ $0.15
Price for full piece of about 60 yards, 14 cents per yd.
1796 Fast Black Silesia, 36 inches wide........ $0.16
Price for full piece of about 55 yards, 15 cents per yard.
1798 Silesia, black one side, white the other, or drab one side and black the other .... .16
Full pice of about 58 yards, 15 cents per yard.
1800 Silesia, light colored stripe or fancy pattern .20
Full piece of about 60 yards, 19 cents per yard.
1802 Silesia, fancy check, stripes or figures, medium colors........ .15
Price for full piece of about 60 yards, 13½ cents per yard.
1804 Silesia, fancy colored, checked one side, black the other........ .20
Full piece of about 45 yards, 19 cents per yard.

Percaline.

A soft waist lining now much used. While light in weight, it is firm and does not stretch, and is preferred to any other lining by ladies who have their dresses tightly fitted; owing to its light silky texture it does not make bulky seams or enlarge the size of the dress waist. Per yard.
1806 Percaline, Moire silk finished, all colors, 36 inches wide........ $0.12½
Full piece of about 55 yards, 12 cents per yard.

Linings for Stiffenings.

For bottoms of dresses, collars and cuffs and tailors' use.
Linings of this class are in great demand owing to the present styles of wide bottom, flared or bell-shaped skirts.

Per yard.
1810 Wigan, black, gray, brown or white, similar to crinoline, but stiffer, with less body than canvas; 33 inches wide........ $0.07½
Full piece of about 55 yards, 7 cents per yard.
1811 Grass Cloth, a very light weight, wiry stiffening much used for skirts and interlinings for large sleeves now so fashionable. It keeps the latter in shape without noticeably increasing the weight. Colors, gray, brown, black or natural tan. Per yard........ .08
Full piece of about 30 yards, 7¼ cents per yard.
1812 Padding, a stiff glazed lining for bottoms of dresses, in black, cream brown or slate; 27 inches wide 12
Price for full piece of about 66 yards, 11½ cents per yard.

Linings—Continued.

1813 Elastic canvas, good quality, used for skirt stiffening. Black, brown or gray; width 25 inches. Per yard........ $0.12
Full piece of about 50 yards 11¼ cents per yard.
1814 Linen Canvas, French elastic, the best lining for bottoms of dresses; it retains its stiffness longer than any other lining; no dress can set well without it; colors: white, natural linen, brown, gray or black. Medium grade. Per yard. .15
Price for full piece of about 50 yards 13 cents per yard.
1816 Linen French Elastic Canvas, better quality than the above........ .20
Price for full piece of about 50 yards, 19 cents per yard.
1818 A New Crinoline, gray striped, elastic finish, 25 inches wide. Especially adapted for use in present style skirts........ .10
Full piece of about 50 yards, 8¾ cents per yard.
1820 Crinoline, 20 inches wide, for lining collars, cuffs, etc., in black, brown, slate, or white. Per yard........ .08
Full piece of 12 yards 80 cents per piece.
1822 Crinoline, width 33 inches; black, brown, slate or white, extra heavy........ .12
Price for full piece of about 30 yards, 11½ cents per yard.
1824 Black Barred Crinoline, 33 inches wide... .13
Price for full piece of about 30 yards, 12 cents per yard.
1826 Tailors' Canvas, natural color only........ .15
1827 Tailors' Canvas, natural color only, better than above........ .18
1828 Imitation Hair Cloth, gray striped, width 17 inches, for skirt stiffening. This is a new light weight stiffening made of elastic cotton in exact imitation in color and texture of the imported hair cloth and costs very much less. Price per yard........ .15
Price for full piece of about 45 yards, 13½ cents per yard.
1830 Gray Hair Cloth, 16 inches wide........ .35
Price for full piece of about 65 yards, 30 cents per yard.
1832 Buckram, similar to wigan, 24 inches wide, put up in rolls, in black or white only. Per yard........ .12
Price for full piece of about 8 yards, 85 cents.

Serge Coat Lining.

1840 Mohair Serge Lining, 32 inches wide. Black or brown only. Per yard........ $0.55

WHITE GOODS DEPARTMENT.

We make a specialty of *White Goods*. Our purchases are of such a magnitude each season that we are enabled to offer extraordinary values in each line. Write us for samples and compare qualities with what other houses sell. We feel safe in asserting that no other house which reaches and is accessible to the consumer can compete with the values we give in foreign and domestic white goods.

Apron and Skirting Lawns.

Made with broad band, fancy open work, satin stripes and imitation hemstitching borders on one side of goods, for bottom of skirts, aprons, etc.

1852 Plain White Apron or Skirting Lawn, width 39 inches. A clean, strong cloth of even weave, has wide border composed of three double bands or six single bands, lace openwork with eight-inch imitation hem-stitched hem at bottom. Per yard........ $0.10
Full piece, about 54 yards, 9 cents per yard.
1854 White Flouncing Lawn, 39 inches wide, with two wide bands of black at bottom. Per yard........ .10
Full piece, about 54 yards, 9 cents per yard.
1856 White Apron or Skirting Lawn, 40 inches wide, a smooth sheer lawn with broad band borders in three styles, even narrow sateen stripes, medium broken or uneven sateen stripes or wide uneven sateen stripes. Stripes are woven to have the appearance of tucking. Per yard........ .12
Full piece, about 55 yards, 11 cents per yard.
1858 White Fine Lace Checked Apron Lawn, width 40 inches; has broad border and hem of white sateen stripes separated by lace work, two styles, narrow or wide stripes in border. Per yard........ .15
Full piece of about 55 yards, 14 cents per yard.
1860 Fine White Apron or Flouncing Lawn, 40 inches wide. With border composed of even or broken satin stripes separated by several rows hem-stitched open work. A very handsome lawn. Per yard........ .15
Full piece of about 55 yards, 14 cents per yard.
1862 Apron or Skirting Lawn, width 40 inches. This is an exceedingly fine and sheer quality. Similar to Bishop Lawn. The border is composed of two wide sateen stripes, imitation of tucking, separated by band of fine corded lace open work. The prettiest apron lawn you ever saw. Per yard........ .20
Full piece of about 55 yards, 18¾ cents per yard.

Hemstitched Apron and Flouncing Lawns.

When we say hemstitched we don't mean machine drawn work in imitation of it, but real hemstitching that will wash and look as well after as before. Each knot is tied the same as in the finest handkerchiefs, and will wear just as well. Width given includes hem, the width of which is afterward also given. These goods are made for fine trade.

Per yard.
1866 Misses' or children's Hemstitched Apron or Flouncing Lawn, 27 inches wide, width of hem 3 inches. Lawn is good and fine, smoothly woven and strong........ $0.15
Full piece of about 30 yards, 14 cents per yard.
1868 Ladies' White Hemstitched Apron or Flouncing Lawn, 37 inches wide, with 5-inch hem. Good lawn, and at the price should be a rapid seller .... .20
Price for full piece of about 30 yards, 19 cents per yard.
1870 Hemstitched Flouncing or Skirting Lawn, 44 inches wide, with folded edge. Hem 10 inches deep. A fine lawn, and have but small quantity to sell. Per yard........ .30
Full piece of about 54 yards, 28 cents per yard.

Black Hemstitched Lawn.

1872 Black Hemstitched Flouncing Lawn, width 42 inches; width of hem, 6 inches. Per yard........ $0.35
Price for full piece of about 30 yards, 32 cents per yard.

Drapery or Curtain Fabrics.

1880 Figured Silkaline, 36 inches wide, large floral designs in exact imitation of drapery silks. Very pretty for inexpensive mantel drapes, curtains, sofa pillows, head rests, etc.; also used for covering fine quilts. Colors are nile green, olive, white, light blue, old rose, gold or orange. Per yard $0.08
Full piece of about 60 yards, 7¼ cents per yard.
1886 Plain Vestibule Drapery, also called silkaline, because of its close resemblance to silk drapery. It is 30 inches wide, solid colored and in the following shades only: Old rose, orange, lemon or reseda. Its uses: Lining for heavy winter window curtains, for book cases, covering for bureau cushions, toilet sets, lining of transoms, window curtain drapery, and its peculiar silk-like finish makes it adapted to dress purposes. Per yard........ .14
Full piece of about 50 yards, 13 cents per yard.

Harness, Halters and Strap Work—We can save you lots of money on these goods.

1888 Figured Vestibule Silkaline or Drapery, width 30 inches. Same goods as No. 1886. New conventional design in beautiful artistic colorings, pretty for curtains, draperies, coverings, for sofa pillows or fine comfortables. Ground tints are white, tan, gold, pink, robin's egg blue or red. Per yard...... $0.15
Full piece of about 50 yards, 14 cents per yard.

Drapery-Dotted Swiss.

1900 Imported Figured White Swiss Muslin, for curtains and drapery, two styles, small lappet squares or square and cross. Width 30 inches. For sash, curtains, or in place of the more expensive lace curtains, it is very pretty. Per yard. $0.15
Full piece of about 50 yards, 14 cents per yard.
1904 Imported White Dotted Swiss Drapery, 34 inches wide. New importations. Swiss lappet spots, small, medium or large. (The largest size is smaller than a quarter dollar piece, smallest about size of peas.)
Price per yard .... .16
Full piece of about 50 yards, 15 cents per yard
1906 Imported Curtain Swiss, white with woven coin spots and pretty side border, tape effect, width 30 inches; will make dainty and stylish wash curtains. Price per yard........ .15
Full piece of about 50 yards, 14¼ cents per yard.

Drapery—Continued.

1908 Imported Cream White Swiss Drapery, with colored coin spots in blue, gold or mahogany. Spots are size of quarter dollar and arranged in clusters of four. Width, 36 inches. Price per yard................................$0.20
Full piece of about 50 yards, 19 cents per yard.

1910 New Imported Drapery Swiss, all white. 36 inches wide; designs are small and are in leaded stained glass effects, being outlined with fine raised cords. Some patterns have center of lace open work. Price per yard.............. .22
Full piece of about 50 yards, 20 cents per yard.

1911 Plain White Organdie, very stylish, and much used now for ruffled window curtains. It washes perfectly, and is very serviceable; width is 48 inches. This fabric is also extensively used for white dresses. Price per yard............ .18
Full piece of about 40 yards, 17 cents per yard.

Scarf Embroidery or Bureau Scrim

1912 Embroidery Scrim, 18 inches wide, fast edges. Can be used plain or worked with worsted, silk, linen or cotton, and with or without ribbons in or under open work at sides. Makes a very cheap, easily washed, lasting tidy or scarf. Per yard.........$0.15
1914 Scarf Scrim, 18 inches wide, selvedge edges, plain center, as above, but it has more open work at the sides. Center can be worked, left plain or threads drawn to make design wanted. Two rows open work each side. Per yard $0.20
1916 Cream, 18 inches wide, with coarse mesh in center, two rows of tied openwork at each side, hemstitched selvedge edge of finer scrim. Makes pretty fancy work. Per yard............ .25
1918 Cream Scrim, 18 inches wide; will wash and iron perfectly. Made in two patterns: Fine scrim in center, one row of three-inch openwork and heavy thread pattern at either side; heavy hemstitched selvedge edge, with three rows of openwork and heavy thread design in center; patterns look like hand-work; very pretty. Per yard............................ .30
1920 Deep Cream Embroidery Scrim, 19 inches wide, with hemstitched parted openwork and bands of light blue, gold or pink, on both sides. Please state which color you want................. .32
1922 Bolting Cloth Embroidery Scrim, 18 inches wide, fine as silk. Has exquisite tied openwork in center of two twilled bands separated by delicate hemstitching on both edges. The center is plain, edges fast. This is an extra rich pattern, and will make very dainty art work with the proper needle work and taste displayed..... .42

Plain Curtain Scrim.

1926 Plain Scrim, cream color; width 36 inches, makes good looking but inexpensive curtains for bed rooms, etc. Per yard...................$0.12
Full piece of about 40 yards, 11¼ cents per yard.
1928 Plain Curtain Scrim, fine quality, cream color; width 36 inches; will wear and wash well. Nice for curtains, splashes, tidies, etc. Per yard............................ .25
Full piece of about 40 yards, 23¼ cents per yard.

Fast Black Wash Goods.

These goods are all absolutely fast black—will not crock nor grow rusty after repeated washing. Will stand all ordinary acid tests, and are not rotted in dyeing. For a light weight, cool dress nothing is more serviceable and generally satisfactory. We have a splendid line of patterns. Samples will be cheerfully sent upon request.

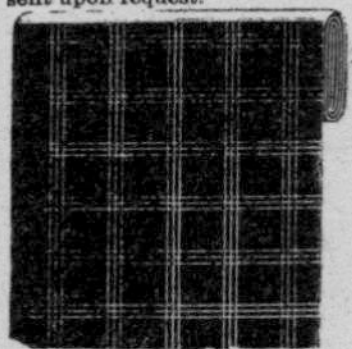

1930 Fast Black even and broken Plaid Lawn,28 inches wide; four patterns. Per yard..........$0.10
Full piece of about 50 yards, 9¼ cents per yard.
These cuts do not properly represent the goods. The designs are much enlarged to plainly show patterns.

1936 Fast Black Hemstitched, checked and Plaid Lawn, 28 inches wide. Five patterns, small, medium and large. Good cloth, good styles. Per yard........$0.15
Full piece of about 50 yards, 14 cents per yard.

Wash Goods—Continued.

1938 Fast Black Hemstitched Lawn in five designs, narrow, medium and wide stripes. Width 28 inches. The cloth is extra close and firm, and the hemstitching an exact imitation of that done by hand.........$0.16
Full piece of about 50 yards, 15 cents per yard.

Plain Black India Linen.

While called linen, it is not, but resembles lawn, and is made from a fine grade of Sea Island cotton, carefully and evenly spun, and taking on a soft, silky finish. Ours are bright black, fast colors; will not crock, and we know upon comparison with others will be found cheap.

Per yard.
1960 Plain Black India Linen, 29 in. wide......$0.10
Prices for full piece of about 24 yards, 9¼ cents per yard.
1964 Plain Black India Linen, 30 in. wide...... .15
Price for full piece of about 24 yards, 14 cents per yard.
1966 Plain Black India Linen, 30 in. wide...... .17
Price for full piece of about 24 yards, 16¼ cents per yard.
1968 Plain Black India Linen, 30 in. wide...... .23
Prices for full piece of about 24 yards, 21¼ cents per yard.
1970 Plain Black India Linen, 32 in. wide...... .33
Price for full piece of about 24 yards, 31 cents per yard.

Nainsooks.

We take especial pride in our Nainsooks; our sales are so large, our purchasing power so great, that we are enabled to offer exceptional values.

Plain White Nainsooks.

Per yard.
1980 Plain Nainsook, fine and sheer, 31 inches wide............................$0.12
Price for full piece of about 20 yards, 11 cents per yard.
1982 Plain Nainsook, fine and sheer, 31 inches wide............................ .15
Price for full piece of about 20 yards, 14 cents per yard.
1984 Plain Nainsook, fine and sheer, 36 inches wide............................ .20
Price for full piece of about 20 yards, 18 cents per yard.
1986 Plain Nainsook, fine and sheer, 36 inches wide............................ .25
Price for full piece of about 20 yards, 23 cents per yard.

Open-work Striped Nainsooks.

Long-Fold.

1990 White Lace Striped Nainsook; width 27 inches,fine open lace work in three widths of stripes, narrow, medium or wide. Price per yard,$0.08
For full piece of about 50 yards, 7½ cents per yard.
1994 White Lace Striped Nainsook, width 27 inches, finer cloth than above, three styles. They are, medium even stripe, medium broken stripe with 4 rows open work, wide broken stripe, 6 rows open work. Per yard.........$0.10
For full piece of about 55 yards, 9¼ cents per yard.
1996 White Lace Stripe Nainsook, width 27 in. a fine sheer lawn of even finish, stripes are in 3 styles, narrow, medium or wide; lace openwork separates the lawn. Per yard................ .14
For full piece of about 55 yards, 13 cents per yard.

Satin Striped Nainsook.

Bookfold.

2000 White Satin Striped Nainsook width 27 inches, a good looking cloth at a low price. We have four styles. Hair line, fine double line, medium herring bone, even stripe or broken herring bone stripe. Per yard.... $0.10
For full piece of about 24 yards, 9¼ cents per yard.

Nainsooks—Continued.

2002 White Satin Striped Nainsook, finer than above; width, 26 inches, 3 styles, fine hair line stripe, narrow herringbone, even stripe, or medium broken or uneven herringbone stripe. Per yard............................$0.12
Full piece, about 24 yards, 11¼ cents per yard.
2004 White Satin Striped Nainsook; width 26 inches. A fine quality, one that will wear and wash well. Come in four styles; hair line stripe, fine broken stripe, narrow, even or medium size broken herringbone stripe. Per yard........ .15
Full piece, about 24 yards, 14 cents per yard.
2006 Extra Fine White Satin Striped Nainsook; width, 27 inches; fine, clear bleach and superior satin finish. Comes in four styles. Hair line stripe, narrow single line stripe, narrow single herringbone or broken herringbone stripe. Per yard............................ .20
Full piece of about 24 yards, 18 cents per yard.

Checked White Nainsook.

Longfold.

2010 Nainsook Checks, 25 in. wide, and in five patterns; small, medium and large. Did you ever buy one so low before? At the price, the cloths and patterns are surprisingly good; a leader for price. Per yd.......$0.04½
Price for full piece of about 50 yards, 4¼ cents per yard.
2012 Checked and Plaid Nainsook, 25 inches wide; checks are small, and the plaids are medium and small. Comparison of prices will show we are headquarters for white goods. . $0.06
Price for full piece of about 50 yards, 5½ cents per yard.

Bookfold.
2014 White Nainsook, Checks and Plaids; width, 25 inches. Have five different styles; pin check, small dice check, small bar checks. One inch even plaid, composed of fine satin lines or double line; one inch plaid. Per yard...........$0.08
For full piece of about 24 yards, 7¼ cents per yard.
2016 White Nainsook Checks and Plaids; width, 27 inches. A good quality at a popular price. Have five styles; pin check, small dice check, medium dice check, ¾-inch satin bar plaid or three line inch plaid. Per yard................ .10
For full piece of about 24 yards, 9¼ cents per yard.
2018 Fine Nainsook Checks and Plaids, 28 in. wide, 4 patterns. Pin check, small dice check, small single bar check, or 1-inch broken line plaid. Per yard.......................... .15
Price for full piece of about 24 yards, 14 cents per yard.
2020 Extra fine Nainsook Checks and Plaids, width, 30 inches. A handsome cloth, one that will wear and retain its fine finish after repeated washings. Comes in four patterns; Pin check, small dice check, small single satin bar check, or 2 inch broken satin line plaid. Per yard.... .20
For full piece of about 24 yards, 18 cents per yard.

White Victoria Lawns.

These goods are woven the same as India Linens, but are not so thin or sheer.
2030 White Victoria Lawn, 25 inches wide. Not cheese cloth because low-priced, but made of even threads, smoothly woven, well bleached and strong. Your merchant cannot buy it for any less. Per yard........................$0.05
Price for full piece of about 24 yards, 4¼ cents per yard.
2032 White Victoria Lawn, 26 inches wide; has the qualities of the above number; made by the same mill, but finer. Don't judge the quality by the price; buy one, or send for samples, then you will buy. Per yard................ .06
Price for full piece of about 50 yards, 5¼ cents per yard.
2034 White Victoria Lawn, 30 inches wide, better.............................. .08
Price for full piece of about 24 yards, 7 cents per yard.
2036 White Victoria Lawn, 30 inches wide. A very good seller........................ .10
Price for full piece of about 24 yards, 9½ cents per yard.
2038 White Victoria Lawn, 32 inches wide; well liked.............................. .12
Price for full piece of about 24 yards, 11 cents per yard.
2040 White Victoria Lawn, 32 inches wide; very fine weave and excellent finish. Per yard...... .15
Price for full piece of about 24 yards, 14 cents per yard.
2042 White Victoria Lawn, 36 inches wide; a highly finished, clean and sheer lawn, free from all specks or imperfections so often found in such goods. Per yard................... .18
Full piece of about 24 yards, 16¾ cents per yard.

. Write your name and Address on package returned to us if you want it to have attention; send letter of instructions by mail; do not put it in package.

Union Linen Red Bordered Covers.

Same styles as preceding Nos. Cheapest cloths made.

2884 Size, 50x60 inches (½). Each $0.49
2885 Size, 50x70 inches (1/12). Each .... .60
2886 Size, 50x78 inches (1/12). Each .... .69
2887 Size, 50x88 inches (1/12). Each .... .74
2888 Size, 50x98 inches (1/12). Each .... .89
2889 Size, 50x105 in. (1/12). Each .... .95

Bleached Fringed Table Cloths.

Bleached Linen Fringed Cloths, handsome brocaded Damask center patterns with rich Damask border. Fringe all around. We believe they are the best, low priced bleached cloths in the market. They are in three sizes as follows:

Each.
2890 Size 58x65 inches $1.00
2892 Size 58x88 inches 1.35
2894 Size 58x100 inches 1.65

All Linen Bleached Cloths.

These cloths are made in Austria, are woven from fine bleached yarns and have the soft feeling peculiar to Austrian linens. No starch used. They come in broken dice patterns and are fringed all round.

Each.
2900 Size, 61x68 inches $1.00
2902 Size, 61x83 inches 1.25
2904 Size, 61x100 inches 1.50

Bleached Colored Bordered Cloths.

Same manufacture as the plain. Same class of goods. Border is in lines, making a noticeable but not conspicuous edging. Colors: Red, pink, buff, blue; fringe on all sides. All linen.

Each.
2908 Size, 58x66 inches $1.10
2910 Size, 58x84 inches 1.35
2912 Size, 58x100 inches 1.60

Austrian Hand Tied Open-work Bleached Linen Table Cloths.

Our prices will not exceed present cost to import. We incite special attention to this line.

2916 All pure linen, bleached table cloth. Austrian manufacture Queen's Household design. Has two rows of hand tied drawn open work 6 inches apart, forming border all round with fine knotted fringe and double plated heading on all sides; size, including fringe, 62x86 inches. Each...... $1.98
2918 Bleached Knotted Fringed Openwork Table Cloth, exactly same as above size, including fringe. 62x100 inches.
Each $2.47

Table Cloth and Napkin Sets.

Each Set in a Box.

All linen colored Border Fringed Table cloth, size 65x66 inches and 12 all linen colored border fringed napkins; size 17¼x18 inches. We can furnish borders of red, blue, yellow, salmon, gold or plain white. These goods are our own importation and are very cheap.
2920 Each set comes put up in a neat box. Price per set...... $2.25
2921 Same as above Cloth 63x85 in. Napkins 17x17. Each........ $2.67
2922 Same as above, cloth, 64x101 inches; napkins, 17¼x18 inches. Each.................. $3.00

INSURE YOUR PACKAGES.—Mail packages may be insured against loss by paying a fee of 5 cents for each $5.00 in value. Write "Insured Mail" on your order, enclose the money, and we will do the rest.

Table Cloths—Continued.

Colored border. All linen Table Set. Has fine damask cloth, fringe all around, with fast colored border of light blue, red, pink, gold or plain white, and 12 fringed napkins with colored borders to match cloth.
2924 Cloth, size, 62x64; napkins, 14¾x15½ inches. Price per set $2.67
2925 Cloth, size, 66x85; napkins, 14¾x15½ inches. Price per set $3.00
2926 Cloth, size, 63x99; napkins, 15x15½ inches. Price per set $3.50

All linen, openwork, Colored Border Table set. Damask is fine, colors are fast and patterns are new. As cut shows, it has two rows of open work on cloth, fringed all around, brocaded in center. Napkins have colored borders to match cloth. Colors: Red, light blue, pink, gold or plain white.
2928 Cloth 63x84 in., napkins 15x15½ in. Per set..... $3.50
2929 Cloth 75x100 in., napkins 15x15½ in. Per set...... $4.00

2931 All Linen Table Set. Cloth and Napkins fringed all around. Colors red, gold, light blue, pink or white. Size of Cloth 59x82 inches. Napkins 15x15 inches. Per Set.... $2.10
2932 All Linen Table Set, same quality and colors as above; size of cloth 59x98 inches. Napkins 15x15 in. Per Set.... $2.40

Turkey Red Damask.

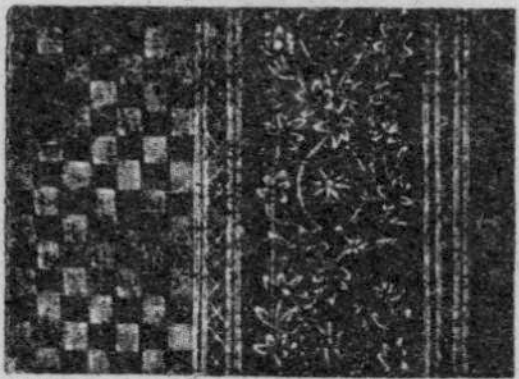

Sold by the yard; made in squares, stripes, and fancy patterns with borders. Per yard.
2940 Turkey Red and White Damask, 50 inches wide, best in America for the price.............. $0.18
Price for full piece of about 27 yards, 17¼ cents per yard.
2944 Turkey Red and White Damask, 56 inches wide........................ .25
Price for full piece of about 27 yards, 24 cents per yard.
2946 Turkey Red and White Table Damask, 57 inches wide, fast colors, handsome designs. This Damask is a leader with us and we believe it to be the best cloth ever sold at this price.......... .33
Price for full piece of about 27 yards, 31½ cents per yard.
2947 Solid Cardinal Brocaded Damask, 58 inches wide, border of same color or brightened with lines of white or black.
Per yard........................ .38
For full piece of about 30 yards, 36 cents per yard.

Turkey Red Damask—Continued.

2948 Turkey Red and White Table Damask, 58 inches wide, fast colors, oil boiled................ $0.40
Price for full piece of about 27 yards, 39 cents per yd.

• 2952

2950 Cardinal and White Fancy Checked Damask, 58 inches wide. Very sightly goods. Colors absolutely fast.. $0.37½
Price for full piece of about 27 yards, 36¼ cents per yard.
2952 Imported Turkey Red Damask, absolutely fast color. New styles which we think the prettiest ever shown. Grounds are all in red and white fine mottled effects, called brainwork (see illustration), over which are arranged handsome designs in solid red, forming a bold relief. Width, 58 in.
Per yard.................... $0.50
For full piece of about 50 yards, 47½ cents per yard.
2954 Turkey Red and White Figured Damask, 58 inches wide, warranted oil colors, perfectly fast................ $0.55
Price for full piece of about 27 yards, 53 cents per yard.

Turkey Red Damask, Fancy Colored Border.

2960 Imported Turkey Red and green Damask, 58 inches wide, with green border 8 inches wide. Oil colors, perfectly fast. Flowered or dice patterns........................ $0.45
Price for full piece of about 27 yards, 43 cents per yard.
2962 Imported Turkey Red and green Damask, 58 inches wide, with flowered or Grecian border 8 inches wide, of green; patterns are either block or floral and are warranted absolutely fast colors........................ .50
Price for full piece of about 27 yards, 48 cents per yard.
2964 Imported Turkey Red and green Damask, 58 inches wide, with green flowers or blocks; has an 8 in. border of red and green, with lines of black. Dice or fancy pattern. Perfectly fast colors........................ .60
Price for full piece of about 27 yards, 57 cents per yard.

Half Bleached Union Table Linen.

Half Bleached Union Linen Table Cloth, in square or dice pattern. Squares are made small, medium or large and broken dice effects. Where low-priced goods will answer, these are the best you can get. They are made in three widths. We have all patterns in all widths.

Per yard.
2970 Union Table Linen, 46 inches wide...... $0.19
Price for full piece of about 43 yards, 18½ cents per yard.
2972 Union Table Linen, 50 inches wide...... .23½
Price for full piece of about 43 yards, 22¼ cts. per yard.
2974 Union Table Linen, 54 inches wide...... .26
Price for full piece of about 43 yards, 23¼ cts. per yard.
2976 Union Table Linen, Dice or broken square pattern. German manufacture, 67 inches wide.
Per yard........................ .49
For full piece of about 45 yards, 47½ cents per yard.

All Linen Half Bleached Table Linen.

Patterns are even or broken squares. Cloth is all linen and well woven for hard wear and frequent washings.

Per yard.
2980 Half Bleached Dice Linen, 56 inches wide. Per yard.................... $0.36
For full piece of about 43 yards, 34¼ cents per yard.
2982 Half Bleached Dice Linen, 58 inches wide. Per yard.................... $0.50
Price for full piece of about 43 yards, 47½ cts. per yard.

Extra Heavy German Table Linen.

This cloth has no dressing in it, but is made with a wash finish. Patterns are even or broken dice or squares. It is made more especially for hotels and restaurants, where a cloth receives frequent washing and hard usage.

Per yard.
2986 Heavy German Table Linen, 54 inches wide........................ $0.40
Price for full piece of about 43 yards, 38 cents per yard.
2988 Heavy German Table Linen, 58 inches wide........................ .50
Price for full piece of about 43 yards, 49 cents per yard.

⁂ All orders are filled from the latest Catalogue. We shall, whenever possible, on orders from old Catalogues, give the nearest we have, and wish to explain that we change our quotations so as to be able to give the latest styles and better values.

Red Bordered Half Bleached Table Linen.

Patterns are even or broken dice. Cloth is good and will thicken slightly after washing, and also become whiter. Per yard.

2992 Half Bleached Table Linen, red border, 55 inches wide......... $0.35
Full piece of about 43 yards, 34 cents per yard.

2994 Half Bleached Table Linen, red border, 58 inches wide......... .50
Full piece of about 43 yards, 48 cents per yard.

Half Bleached Linen Damask.

Differs from the above in that the patterns are not in squares, but in figures, floral designs, etc., with a woven side border. Per yard.

3000 Half Bleached 54-inch Damask, all linen.. $0.32
3002 Half Bleached 56-inch Damask, all linen.. .40
3004 Half Bleached 58-inch Damask, all linen, better than the above......... .50
3006 Cream Damask, very fine, all linen, 67 inches wide......... .60

Bleached Damask.

Bleached table linen is so much used we have taken great care to present only those we could recommend for width, finish, wear, pattern and bleach. We believe it to be to your interest to buy your linen of us. Many of the patterns are confined to us; not shown elsewhere. Per yard.

3020 Bleached Union Damask, 54 inches wide $0.29½
Full piece of about 25 yards, 28½ cents per yard.

3022 Bleached All Linen Damask, 54 inches wide......... .40
Full piece of about 25 yards, 38¼ cents per yard.

3024 Bleached All Linen Damask, 62 inches wide......... .47
Full piece of about 25 yards, 46 cents per yard.

3026 Bleached All Linen Damask, 62 inches wide, better......... .56
Full piece of about 25 yards, 55 cents per yard.

3028 Bleached All Linen Damask, 63 inches wide, still better......... .75
Full piece of about 25 yards, 72 cents er yard.

3030 All Linen Bleached Imported Satin Table Damask, elegant patterns, 68 inches wide. We pride ourselves on the value we give......... .85

3032 Pure Linen White Satin Damask, 72 inches (two yards wide), beautiful patterns......... 1.00

Fine Bleached Table Damask with Napkins.

New special designs with napkins to match, either ⅝ or ¾ sizes.

3040 Bleached All Linen Satin Finished Damask; width, 68 inches; special designs. Per yard......... $1.00

3041 Fine Bleached Damask Napkins; size, 20x20 inches; same quality and design as No. 3040 Damask. Per dozen......... $2.35

3042 Large and Fine Bleached Damask Dinner Napkins; size, 24x24 inches; same quality and pattern as above napkins and damask. We recommend the above goods where fine and perfect service is desired. Per dozen......... $3.40

Irish Bosom Linen.

For Shirt Bosoms, Collars, Cuffs, etc. Per yard.

3060 Irish Linen, 36 inches wide......... $0.28
Price for full piece of about 22 yards, 27 cents per yard.

3062 Irish Linen, 36 inches wide, better......... .35
Price for full piece of about 22 yards, 34 cents per yard.

3064 Irish Linen, 36 inches wide......... .40
Price for full piece of about 22 yards, 38 cents per yard.

3066 Irish Linen, 36 inches wide......... .60

All lines of merchandise very generally reduced in price.

Butchers' Linen.

Used for re-enforcing shirt bosoms, embroidery, drawn work, etc. Per yard.

3068 Unbleached Butchers' Linen, 36 inches wide......... $0.25
Price for full piece of about 24 yards, 24 cents per yard.

3070 Unbleached Butchers' Linen, 40 inches wide......... .27
Price for full piece of about 24 yards, 26 cents per yard.

3074 Unbleached Butchers' Linen, 40 inches wide......... .37
Price for full piece of about 24 yards, 36 cents per yard.

3078 Bleached Butchers' Linen, 29 inches wide .25
Price for full piece of about 25 yards, 24 cents per yard.

3080 Bleached Butchers' Linen, 29 inches wide .30
Price for full piece of about 24 yards, 29 cents per yard.

3082 Bleached Butchers' Linen, 36 inches wide .35
Price for full piece of about 24 yards, 33 cents per yard.

3084 Bleached Butchers' Linen, 40 inches wide .40
Price for full piece of about 24 yards, 38 cents per yard.

Brown Linen Drilling.

Per yard.

3090 Brown or Unbleached Linen Drilling, twilled, good weight; for men's clothing, etc.; width 26 inches......... $0.25

White Cotton Table Felting.

It is also called silent cloth, as when placed under the table cloth it dulls the sound of placing china on the table, makes the cloth look whiter, does not allow hot dishes to spoil the finish of the table, and is universally used when perfect table service is desired. We have it in cream white only. Per yard.

3094 Table Felting, white only, double napped, good weight, 54 inches wide. Per yard......... $0.35

3096 Table Felting, double napped, thick, and soft, 54 inches wide. Alabama XX......... .50

3098 Table Felting, 66 inches wide, extra thick, and soft, double napped, Howard......... .65

WOOLEN DEPARTMENT.

In this department we carry a large and varied assortment of ladies' heavy weight and extra width *Dress Goods, Jacket cloths, Cloakings, Men's and Boys' Cassimeres* and *Corduroys*. As we purchase all of these goods direct from manufacturers and in very large quantities, we can always save our customers "the middlemen's profit," and often more.

Tricot Suitings.

3200 Tricot Suiting 50 inches wide, part wool. Six yards makes a dress. This cloth we consider one of the cheapest dress fabrics, width and quality considered, that we have ever offered. Colors: Brown, navy or myrtle, quantity is limited. Price while they last; per yard.. $0.22½
Full piece of about 53 yards, 21½ cents per yard.

Ladies' Cloth.

Fall and Winter shades for Dresses, Wraps, etc.

3204 Ladies' Cloth, 50 inches wide, fine Union wool mixtures. A nicely finished cloth, good weight and one that will give satisfactory wear. Colors are medium gray mixture, light brown, tan, navy, wine, black or myrtle. Per yard..... $0.35
Full piece of about 50 yards, 32 cents per yard.

3206 Ladies' Cloth, fine, closely woven, perfect finish, absolutely all wool, 50 inches wide, for fashionable and durable dresses. We claim for this cloth that it is far superior in quality and finish to any half dollar ladies' cloth on the market. Buy a pattern and compare it with others. Colors: Slate, black, light navy, dark navy, garnet, electric blue, brown, light brown, beige, cardinal, wine, myrtle, sapphire, olive, plain gray, old rose, tan, seal brown, also mixtures in light gray, medium gray, dark gray, light or dark brown mixtures; also illuminated mixtures in brown or blue. Per yard......... .45
Price for full piece of about 50 yards, 43 cents per yard.

3210 Extra Fine Habit Cloth, 52 inches wide, all wool, very heavy, handsomely finished, new shades. This cloth will compare favorably with any 90 cent cloth in the market. Write for samples before purchasing elsewhere. Colors: Tan, slate, light gray, old rose, seal brown, golden brown, myrtle, medium brown, sapphire blue, navy blue, wine, black; also mixtures in dark iron gray, medium gray, light gray, light or medium brown. Per yard......... .65
Full piece of about 50 yards, 63 cents per yard.

HOUSEKEEPING LINENS.

No line offers better profits to small dealers. We import direct from European manufacturers, and are in a position to save you money. Send us a trial order and be convinced.

Broadcloths.

New Shades for Fall and Winter.

NOTE:—Broadcloths will be very extensively used for ladies' dresses, wraps, etc. It is a fabric that is unusually durable and elegant for out-door gowns.

Our lines have been selected with great care. They are manufactured especially for us, and we believe to be unapproachable in values.

3212 All Wool Broadcloth, 50 inches wide, twilled back and rich glossy face; finish is in the weave, not put on with rollers and sizing; colors are seal brown, tan, beige, myrtle, garnet or wine, old rose, purple, sapphire blue, slate, light gray, navy blue or black. Per yard......... $0.80

3214 Columbia Fine Broadcloth, all wool, superb lustrous finish, 52 inches wide; 6 yards makes a handsome dress. Colors are seal brown, medium brown, golden brown, light tan, dark tan, bronze, wine, marine or light navy, dark navy, silver gray, medium gray, slate, old rose, purple, cardinal or black. Per yard......... 1.00
We claim this cloth to be equal to any sold elsewhere at $1.50.

3216 Imported Broadcloth, very fine, all wool, 54 inches wide. Colors: Seal, medium or golden brown, black, fawn, tan, wine, myrtle, navy slate, bronze, purple, white or cream. Per yard......... 2.00

Storm Serge.

The popularity of Storm Serge does not diminish. No other fabric yet produced combines the wearing qualities and styles of this cloth. Suited, as it is, to wear on nearly all occasions, no woman's wardrobe is quite complete without a Storm Serge dress. The width of these goods also makes them economical.

3220 All worsted Storm Serge, 50 inches wide, a good cloth, made from extra long combed wool. Colors as follows: Black, light navy, dark navy or myrtle green. Per yard......... $0.60

3222 French all Worsted Storm Serge, a splendid heavy cloth, fine and firm, made from hard twisted wiry wools, an original and perfect wear resisting serge. Colors are: myrtle, navy or black; width 50 inches. Per yard......... .75

Silk and Wool Mixed Costume Cloth.

This cloth is especially designed for fashionable trade. Many ladies who display quiet taste in dress selections, but do not always want plain goods, will find this fabric peculiarly suited to their wants. It is firm and well woven. Very wide, so that a few yards suffices for a dress, and will make up attractively either plain or velvet trimmings.

3232 Silk and Wool Mixed Suiting, 50 in. wide, small checked effects in the following mixtures: Brown and gold, wine and gold, green and gold, drab and gold, or gray with blue and gold. Also plain mixtures, pepper and salt style in gray and white, brown and white, blue and white, wine and white or blue and gold. Per yard......... $0.68

Fancy Wool Suitings.

For tailor-made street gowns.

3234 Fancy Wool Suiting, 50 inches wide, entirely new, and the handsomest wide cloth shown this season. It is made from twisted wools of contrasting colors, so as to produce a fine seeded effect; color combinations are black and gold, wine and black, navy and gold, black and red, olive and gold, turquoise blue, black and gold. Per yard......... $0.80

Covert Cloth Suiting.

The newest cloth for ladies' tailor-made costumes.

3236 Covert Cloth Suiting, all wool, 50 inches wide; a handsome cloth, strong and heavy. Covert cloth is woven from wool of two contrasting colors, which form a fine mixture effect. The back of the cloth is in contrasting color to the face, and is often used as a trimming. We have the following combinations: Light and dark gray mixture, blue and gold, olive and myrtle, light grayish brown, light and dark brown, dark blue and gray, tan and seal. Per yard......... $0.69

Heavy Woolens, Cloakings, Overcoatings, Etc.

Per yard.

3240 Old Homestead Cloaking, 27 in. wide, quite heavy. Plaided, striped or checked in tan and light brown or dark colors, also diagonal effects in dark colors. Needs no lining. Not made of fine wool, but will wear well......... $0.40
Price for full piece of about 50 yards, 36 cents per yard.

3242 Scotch Mixed Cloaking, heavy weight, 56 inches wide. We bought a job lot of them and cannot furnish more when these are sold. The styles are all good, being pretty, stylish and durable. They come in pinhead checked ground with dark colored bourette threads over the surface, in gray and black, or tan and brown, very pretty. Price per yard, while the lot lasts .75

Diagonal Jacket Cloth.

A job to close.

3243 Diagonal Jacket Cloth, 50 inches wide; also used for heavy dresses; a very strong and handsome cloth; weight about 14 ozs. to the yard. Colors are tan or gray mixtures. Present actual value $1.00 per yard. Price while they last......... $0.47½

Ready made Wrappers and Tea Gowns. A new and stylish line at prices to suit your pocket. See our quotations.

Bleached Cotton Flannel.

Per yard.
4520 Bleached Cotton Flannel, width 24 inches..........................$0.06½
Price for full piece of about 58 yards, 6¼ cents per yard.
4522 Bleached Cotton Flannel, width 26 inches, per yard..........................08½
Price for full piece of about 58 yards, 8¼ cents per yard.
4524 Bleached Cotton Flannel, width 26 inches .10
Price for full piece of about 57 yards, 9½ cents per yard.
4526 Bleached Cotton Flannel, width 28 inches..........................12
Price for full piece of about 55 yards, 11¼ cents per yard.
4528 Bleached Cotton Flannel, heavy weight, width 28¼ inches..........................14
Price for full piece of about 55 yards, 13¼ cents per yard.

Cotton Flannel—Continued.

4530 Bleached Cotton Flannel, width 29½ inches, extra heavy..........................$0.15½
Price for full piece of about 54 yards, 15 cents per yard.

Colored Cotton Flannel or Drapery Plushes.

Used for Portieres, Wall Hangings, Linings, etc.

Per yard
4550 Colored Cotton Flannel, old gold, medium and navy blue, olive, wine, cardinal, scarlet, drab or brown, 23½ inches..........................$0.09
Price for full piece of about 54 yards, 8½ cents per yard.
4554 Colored Cotton Flannels, high colors, blue, scarlet, garnet, brown, slate, pink, drab and gold, 27 inches..........................12½
Price for full piece of about 55 yards, 11¼ cents per yard.

Drapery Plushes—Continued.

4556 Heavy Cotton Plushes, 28 inches wide: plain colors: Cardinal, scarlet, wine, pink, claret, blue, drab, slate, brown, old gold...$0.15
Price for full piece of about 55 yards, 13 cents per yard.

Fancy Colored Cotton Plush.

4560 Colored Cotton Flannel, black striped or checked with scarlet, old gold checked with black, width 27 inches..........................$0.10
Price for full piece of about 56 yards, 9¼ cents per yard.

Use the William Clark Co.'s "N-E-W" Six Cord Spool Cotton.

LADIES' AND CHILDREN'S SUIT DEPARTMENT.

Ready Made Wrappers and Tea Gowns; dresses made to order. Styles absolutely correct and up to date.
NOTE.—We can not furnish samples of wrappers or other ready-made garments. Samples of any garments which we quote to measure and make up in our custom department will be cheerfully sent upon request.
SPECIAL.—*We can make to order any dress shown in the Standard Fashion Catalogue.* Samples of dress materials and any information desired will be furnished upon request.
Write for our Special Dressmaking Catalogue No. E, mailed free of charge.
See our Special Catalogue E for rules for measurement.
Ready made wrappers, gowns and dresses are made in the following scale of sizes only:
Bust, 32 in. Length, 54 in. Bust, 38 in. Length, 58 in.
Bust, 34 in. Length, 56 in. Bust, 40 in. Length, 58 in.
Bust, 36 in. Length, 56 in. Bust, 42 in. Length, 58 in.

5610

5600 Ladies' Ready Made Wrappers, made of dark prints; new styles; lined waist, belt, full sleeves, wide ruffle over shoulders and forming pointed yoke.
Each..........................$0.59
Per doz..........................6.65

5602 Ladies' Ready Made Wrappers, made of indigo blue prints, small and medium figures, lined waist, large sleeves, belt, wide ruffle over shoulders and forming yoke.
Each..........................$0.69
Per doz..........................7.85

5604 Ladies' Ready Made Wrappers, made of fast black prints, medium and small white figures and stripes, lined waist, belt, large sleeves, wide ruffle over shoulders and forming yoke, Wateau back.
Each..........................$0.85
Per doz..........................9.75

5600

5602-4-6

5606 Ladies' Ready Made Wrappers, made of best American indigo blue prints, same style as above.
Each..........................$0.85
Per doz..........................9.75

5608 Ladies' Ready Made Wrappers, made of best quality American indigo blue or fast black and white prints, lined waist, large sleeves, belt, wide cape ruffle over shoulders, Wateau back, ruffle and collar trimmed in narrow feather stitching.
Each..........................$0.98
Per doz..........................11.25

5608

5611

5610 Ladies' Ready Made Wrappers, made of high grade novelty chintz, black grounds with small neat floral designs in colors, lined waist, belt, Wateau back, large sleeves and wide cape ruffle over shoulders, trimmed with handsome 2-inch cream lace, the prettiest garment ever made for the price.
Each..........................$1.25
Per doz..........................14.25

5611 Ladies' Ready Made Wrappers, made of best quality American indigo prints, dark grounds with neat white figures, blue, collar and cuffs of plain indigo blue cloth trimmed with narrow fancy braid in blue and white, has lined waist, belt, full front and Wateau back and shoulder ruffles.
Each..........................$1.25
Per dozen..........................14.25

5612

5612 Ladies' Wrappers, made of high grade novelty chintz; black grounds with small figures or dots in white or colors, such as gold, blue, etc., lined waist, belt, Wateau back, large sleeves, wide ruffle over shoulders forms pointed yoke, ruffle trimmed with two rows white rickrack braid.
Each..........................$1.10
Per dozen..........................12.80

5614-16

5614 Ladies' Wrapper, made of Domett outing flannel in narrow stripes; medium colors, lined waist, belt, full back, large sleeves and wide ruffle over shoulders, forming yoke.
Each..........................$1.40
Per dozen..........................16.25

5616 Ladies' Ready Made Wrapper, made of plain fast black Henrietta sateen, lined waist, belt, Wateau back, large sleeves, wide ruffle over shoulder, forming yoke. Same style as above.
Each..........................$1.45
Per dozen..........................16.85

5618 Ladies' Wrappers, made of cashmere de laine in dark grounds with floral stripes in bright contrasting colors, entirely new; has lined waist, belt, Wateau back, leg of mutton sleeves, circular ruffle.
Each..........................$1.50
Per dozen..........................17.45

5618-20-22-24

5620 Ladies' Ready Made Wrappers, made of new dark striped ginghams; same style as above.
Each..........................1.50
5622 Ladies' Ready Made Wrappers, made of printed flannelette; handsome figured stripes in dark colors. New goods. Same style as above. Each..........................1.50
5624 Ladies' Ready Made Wrappers made of cashmere flannelette; fleeced back, dark grounds printed in bright mixed floral and Persian designs. Style same as above. Each..........................1.89

5626

5626 Ladies' Ready Made Wrappers, made of dark figured sateen; black grounds with small bright printed designs, lined waist, belt, Wateau back: new cape front trimmed with cream lace inserting, large sleeves.
Each..........................$1.75

Ladies' Wrappers—Continued.

5627 Ladies' Ready Made Wrappers, made of medium and dark colored Persian striped flannelette, cashmere twilled surface with fine soft fleece on inside; lined waist; wide ruffle over shoulder, tapering to waist line in front and back; large drop sleeves and belt. Each................$1.50

5627

5628

5628 Ladies' Ready Made Wrappers, made of English cashmere; half wool. Colors: Navy blue, cardinal, wine or black; lined waist, full Wateau back, loose front held to form with small strap, large drop sleeves, embroidered collar and two rows embroidery, scroll design worked in the material the entire length of front. Each................$3.50

5629 Ladies' Ready Made Wrappers, made of half worsted brocaded suiting, ruffle of the same material forms yoke front and back, large sleeves with ruffle at elbow; Wateau pleat from yoke; lined waist. Colors: Navy blue, tan, cardinal, light gray, brown, wine, myrtle or black. Each......$2.75

5630   **5632-34**

5630 Ladies' Ready Made House Wrappers, made of striped English flannelette, medium colors, pointed yoke and full back, held to the form with belt of the same material, revere front, raised shoulders, full ruffled sleeves. Each.....$2.25

5632 Ladies' Ready Made House Wrappers, made of fast black Henrietta sateen, full back and front shirred at collar, lined waist, raised shoulders. Each....................... 2.25

5634 Ladies' Ready Made Wrappers, same style as above, but made of small figured or striped black and white sateen. Each 2.50

Ladies' Tea Gowns.
Made to measure.

5650   **5652**

5650 Ladies' Tea Gowns, made of best English cashmere, black, cardinal, wine, navy or sapphire blue, full front and back, lined throughout, large gathered sleeves, wide revere front, worsted braid trimming on collar, reveres and sleeves. Each.............$5.00

5652 Ladies' Tea Gowns, made of best English cashmere, black, wine, cardinal, navy or sapphire blue, light blue or pink, lined throughout, tight fitting waist in back with Wateau pleat from yoke, loose front, leg of mutton sleeves, epaniets shoulders and ruffle across front and back. Each................ 5.00

5654 Ladies' Tea Gown, made of all wool reversible serge, fine twill, lined throughout, has large puff sleeves, wide ruffle and collar trimmed with narrow silk ribbon, full Wateau pleats in back from collar. Colors: Cardinal, wine, navy blue or black, or any other seasonable colors. Each......................$6.50

5656 Ladies' Tea Gown, made of new illuminated twill suiting, lined throughout, has large sleeves, close fitted back and loose front held to figure with half belt, velvet butterfly front and collar trimmed with tinsel braid. Colors: Wine, cardinal, navy, myrtle, brown or tan. Each $6.75

5558 Ladies' Tea Gown, made of fine French Henrietta, lined throughout handsomely shirred front and back, ruffled collar full coat sleeves with ruffle shirred in arm hole, full Wateauback, full front trimmed with silk ribbon to match. We can furnish all seasonable shades. Ea......$9.00

Children's and Misses' Dresses.

5680 Little Girls' Dresses, made of best staple gingham; small checks in navy blue, brown, or pink, with white; yoke of white all over tucking; trimming of white Hamburg edging. Ages, 2 yrs., 3 yrs., 4 yrs., 5 yrs. Each..............................$0.69

5682 Little Girl's Dress, made of small checked baby flannel, in pink, light blue, tan, scarlet or gray. The dantiest fabric you ever saw. Round yoke, wide circular ruffle, full bishop sleeves.

Ages—	1 yr	2 yrs.	3 yrs.	4 yrs.	5 yrs.	6 yrs.
Price—	$0.75	$0.95	$1.00	$1.10	$1.20	$1.30

5684 Little Girl's Dress, made of printed flannelette, in scarlet and black only. Small neat designs in black on scarlet grounds; full front with girdle, wide sash at back, full bishop sleeves; girdle, cuffs, collar and bottom of skirt trimmed in all wool black hercules braid.

Ages—							
2 yrs.	3 yrs.	4 yrs.	5 yrs.	6 yrs.	7 yrs.	8 yrs.	9 yrs.
Price—
$1.25	$1.35	$1.45	$1.55	$1.75	$1.95	$2.15	$2.35
Age, 10 years, $2.50

5686 Little Girls' Dress, made of English cashmere, half wool, wide pointed ruffle over shoulders to waist line forming V front and back; lined throughout; full bishop sleeves, cuffs, collar and ruffle in fancy silk braid, made in all seasonable colors.

Ages— 2 years.	4 yrs.	6 yrs.	8 yrs.	10 yrs.	12 yrs.
Price, $1.75	$1.90	$2.15	$2.45	$2.80	$3.15	$3.50

5688 Little Girls' Dress, made in same style as above, but of fine finished, all wool flannel suiting; lined waist only.

Ages— 2 yrs.	4 yrs.	6 yrs.	8 yrs.	10 yrs.	12 yrs.
Prices, $1.90	$2.20	$2.50	$3.00	$3.50	$3.65

5692 Misses' Dress, made of English Cashmere, half wool, lined throughout, has round yoke formed by wide military cape ruffle extending across shoulders, full balloon sleeves, empire belt, collar, cuffs, ruffle, and bottom of skirt trimmed with wooled hercules braid. We can furnish all seasonable colors.

Ages—	12 yrs.	13 yrs.	14 yrs.	15 yrs.	16 yrs.
	$5.00	$5.25	$5.50	$5.75	$6.00

5694 Misses' Dress, same style as above, made of fine all wool serge. All the staple and new shades.

Ages—	12 yrs.	13 yrs.	14 yrs.	15 yrs.	16 yrs.
	$6.00	$6.25	$6.50	$6.75	$7.00

5696 Misses' Dress, made of new novelty suiting, wool bourette effects, combinations of dark colors intermixed. Waist is made over fitted lining. Three box pleats are formed of the material in the back and front below a shapely yoke of velvet in shade to harmonize with goods. Epaulets above shoulders ripple prettily over the leg-of-mutton sleeves, narrow belt, new gored skirt. Color effects are in brown, green, wine or gray.

Ages—	12 yrs.	13 yrs.	14 yrs.	15 yrs.	16 yrs.
Price—	$5.50	$5.75	$6.00	$6.25	$6.50

Ladies' Newport Suits.
See note under department heading for scale of sizes.

5700 Ladies' Newport Suit, ready made, consists of jacket and skirt to be worn with shirt waists. Jacket is made with Tuxedo back, large leg-o'-mutton sleeves, wide revers in front, double stitched seams, inside seams bound, gored skirt, very full and wide, deep corded hem at bottom. Made of good looking and serviceable water repellent cloth, in navy blue or black. Per suit........$4.90

5702 Ladies' Newport Suit, same style as above. Made of strong repellent cloth. Collar, cuffs and bottom of skirt trimmed with black worsted hercules braid. Colors, black or navy blue only. Per suit........$5.50

5704 Ladies' Newport Suit, same style as above. Made of heavy all-wool storm serge, trimmed with two rows of folded satin rhadame on collar, cuffs and bottom of skirt. Colors: Black or navy blue only. A stylish and splendid wearing suit. Per suit.......................$5.95

Ladies' Suits—Continued.

5706 Ladies' Newport Suit, same style as 5700, made of the new and fashionable covert cloth suitings, all-wool, wide double stitched edges, very rich and dressy, light and dark mixtures; tans, grays, browns or blues. Per suit........ $8.00

5708 Ladies' Newport Suit, same style as 5700, made of fine all wool broadcloth, high finished; collar, cuffs and bottom of skirt trimmed with narrow fold of moire silk; very elegant. Colors: Black, brown, light or dark navy blue.
Per suit... 8.50

5710 Ladies' Newport Suit, same style as above, made of cotton warp serge, firm and heavy. Navy blue only. Per suit........................ 8.25

5712 Ladies' Dress Skirt, new gored back, very wide; much used with blouse or shirt waists. Same material as 5710. Price, each............ 1.05

Ladies' Ready Made Waists.

Can be worn with any kind of dress skirt.
Sizes: 32, 34, 36, 38, 40, 42, 44 inches bust measure.

5750 Ladies' W a i s t, made of striped cotton flannel, medium colors, has pointed yoke formed by wide ruffle, extending over shoulders; large sleeves, belt, unlined.
Each...............$0.60
Per dozen........ 6.90

5752

5752 Ladies' Blouse Waist, made of navy blue repellent cloth, fine and heavy large sleeves, square yoke bordered with double row of serpentine braid; lined throughout, gathered full at yoke and belt. Each.......................$1.50
Per dozen... 17.00

5754 Ladies' Waist, made of half wool cashmere. Colors: Cardinal, wine, n a v y or black; lined throughout; large sleeves epaulets on shoulders, double row of black serpentine braid across front, single row around collar and belt. Each...$1.50
Per dozen, $17.00

5754

5756 Ladies' Waist, made of fine all wool repellent flannel in garnet, navy blue, gray or black; lined throughout, wide circular ruffle forming yoke and epaulets on shoulder; ruffle and collar trimmed in fancy worsted braid belt and large sleeves.
Each...$2.00
Per doz.23.00

WASHING MACHINES.

No Lady will appreciate a good Washer until she has tried one. We advise her to try an Anthony Wayne or Western Star. See Index for Quotations.

Ladies' Laundered Shirt Waists.

Very stylish and popular.
Our stock includes a hundred different styles suited to all tastes.

5760 Ladies' Laundered Shirt Waists, pleated front and full back, with belt made from printed percale in stripes, dots, figures and checks. Ground colors are pink, light blue, heliotrope light gray or white. Each waist put up with full sets studs for front and cuffs.
Each..............$0.98
Per dozen......11.50

5762 Ladies' Laundered Shirt Waists, full back from yoke, pleated front and back, made from fine percale better quality than above. Styles are figures, figured stripes or hair line stripes of pink, blue or black on white, white hair line stripes on pink or blue grounds, plain chambray effects in pink or blue. Each waist put up with full set studs. Each...........................$1.25
Per doz..14.25

5764 Ladies' Laundered Shirt Waists, same style as above, made of fine percale in dark navy blue or bright Turkey red grounds with fine white stripes. Each.....................................$1.50
Per dozen...17.25

Ladies' Unlaundered Shirt Waists.

Ladies' waists are worn with any or all kinds of skirts. They can be washed and laundered and always kept looking fresh. Weight from 5 to 9 ounces each.

5780 Ladies' Shirt Waists, made of good quality prints, small figures or stripes, with ruffled front and belt; raised shoulders.
Each......................$0.35
Per dozen......... 3.75

5782 Ladies' Shirt Waists, Indigo blue print, with small dots, plaited and ruffled front, raised shoulders, large sleeves.
Each......................$0.50
Per doz.............. 5.40

5784 Ladies' Shirt Waists, made of plain Chambray or hair line prints in pink, blue or heliotrope, large bishop sleeves, double ruffle down front; plaited front and back, raised shoulders, with belt.
Each......................$0.75
Per dozen........ 8.10

5786 Ladies' Shirt Waists, made of fine fast black plain sateen, large sleeves, ruffle down front, box pleat front and back; belt.
Each......................$1.00
Per dozen......10.80

5788 Ladies' Shirt Waists, made of fine fast black and white striped sateen, narrow hair line effects; wide cape, ruffle from collar to belt, pleated front; large sleeves. Each...............78
Per dozen....... 8.10

5790 Ladies' Shirt Waists, made of plain fast black sateen, fine knife plaited ruffle down front, around collar and cuffs; large sleeves and belt.
Each......................$.75
Per dozen........ 8.10

5792 Ladies' Shirt Waists, plain fine black sateen, double ruffle down front; plaited front and back, raised shoulders, with belt.
Each......................$1.00
Per dozen...... 10.80

Ladies' Unlaundered Shirt Waists—Continued.

5800 Ladies' Shirt Waists. Imported White Lawn, six plaits in front and back, embroidered cuff bands; and embroidered hemstitch collar, raised shoulders, with belt.
Each..................$0.90
Per dozen......... 9.72

5802 Ladies' Shirt Waists, made of fine White Cambric, plaited front and back, knife-plaited ruffle on collar, sleeves and down front, turn down collar, raised shoulders, with belt.
Each..................$0.90
Per dozen......... 9.72

5804 Ladies' Shirt Waists Imported White Lawn, fine plaited front and back, sailor collar with ruffle, ruffled front and back, raised shoulders.
Each..................$1.00
Per dozen...... 10.80

Jerseys and Blouse Waists.

☞ Be sure to send bust and waist measure. (Measure over bust close under arms.)
Ladies' sizes, 32 to 44; no odd sizes. Jerseys weigh 6 to 13 ounces, according to size and quality.
NOTE.—Jerseys are a close fitting garment, and are intended to stretch to fit the form.

Ladies' and Misses' Jersey Jackets.

Prices reduced to close out this line.

5810 Children's or Misses' Worsted Jersey Jackets. Colors: Cardinal, navy blue and black; sizes, 22, 24 and 26 bust measure.
To close, each......................................$0.19

5812 Ladies' Extra Fine Black Worsted Jersey Jackets, elegantly braided all over front, back, cuff and around bottom, double row of buttons and silk braid on front. French coat back, very stylish and dressy.
Each, until sold.....$1.98

5814 Ladies' Fine All-Worsted Cream White Jersey Blouse, a job to close, only a few left; yoke front and back trimmed on collar and around yoke with white worsted and silk braid. Each..........................$0.49

BOOK DEPARTMENT.

(Books bought on special order cannot be returned.) *No books taken back or exchanged if sent as ordered.* All prices quoted are for books in our store, charges for transportation to be paid by purchaser. Those wishing to have books sent by mail will find the approximate amount required for postage in addition to cost of book appended to each quotation or else in a table under the general heading under which the book is classed.

We give below a table showing about size in inches of the different books on our list. These measurements sometime vary, but will serve to give a general idea of the dimensions of any of our books.

16 mo..............4x6½ in. Royal 8 vo..7½x10 in. 12 mo.............4½x7¼ in. Quarto....8⅛x10½ in. 8 vo.........6½x9 in. Imp. Quarto..12x9 in.

(*In ordering books give name and number.*) Any books not found in this department we will be pleased to furnish upon application, school books included. Send 5 cents for postage for special complete Illustrated Book Catalogue.

We also issue, free, a complete medical book catalogue, complete rural book catalogue and complete educational (school book) catalogue. Send for them.

INDEX.

Visiting, Regret, Correspondence and Wedding Cards.

This line of cards only embraces the correct styles now in use.

Prices for printing Visiting Cards, one Name:

25 Cards	50 Cards	100 Cards	300 Cards
$0.25	$0.35	$0.50	$0.75

Wedding, Regret and Correspondence:

100 Cards	300 Cards	500 Cards
$1.50	$1.75	$2.00

Prices for Plain Cards.

	Per Pkg. of 25 Cards.	Per Box of 300 Cards.
6000 **Visiting Cards**, plain white, 4 ply, very stylish, (HT) size 3¼x1⅛	$0.06	$0.55
6001 Same as 6000, size 3⅛x1⅞ (HC)	.07	.75
6002 Same as 6000, size 3⅜x1⅞ (HX)	.08	85
6003 Same as 6000, size, 4x2 (HA)	.09	.95
6004 Same as 6000, size 4¼x2¼ (HM)	.10	1.05
6005 Same as 6000, size 3x2 (CB)	.11	1.15
6006 Same as 6000, size 3¼x2¼ (CE)	.12	1.25
6007 Same as 6000, size 3½x2⅛ (CR)	.13	1.35
6010 **Visiting Cards**, 8 ply, plain white Bevel edge (HT). Very latest, size 3x1⅜	.07	.75
6011 Same as 6010, size 3¼x1⅞ (CX)	.08	.85
6012 Same as 6010, size 3½x2 (CH)	.09	.95
6013 Same as 6010, size 3⅜x2¼ (CA)	.10	1.05
6014 Same as 6010, size 4x2½ (CE)	.11	1.15
6015 Same as 6010, size 2x3 (CB)	.12	1.25
6016 Same as 6010, size 3¼x2¼ (CE)	.13	1.35
6020 **Visiting Cards**, 8 ply, White Cards with Gold Bevel edges, neat and stylish, size 3x1⅜ (CT)	.08	.85
6021 Same as 6020, size 3¼x1⅞ (CX)	.09	.95
6022 Same as 6020, size 3⅛x2 (CA)	.10	1.05
6023 Same as 6020, size 3⅜x2¼ (CA)	.11	1.15
6024 Same as 6020, size 4x2½ (CM)	.12	1.25
6025 Same as 6020, size 2x3 (CB)	.13	1.35
6026 Same as 6020, size 3⅜x1 (CE)	.14	1.45
6028 **Visiting Cards**, with notched Bevel border, 8 ply, a novelty, size 3x1⅜ (CH)	.09	.95
6029 Same as 6028, size 3¼x1⅞ (CX)	.10	1.05
6030 Same as 6028, size 3½x2 (CH)	.11	1.15
6031 Same as 6028, size 2x3 (CB)	.12	1.25
6032 Same as 6028, size 3¼x2¼ (CE)	.13	1.35
6035 **Visiting Cards**, pure white, the very latest and best, put up in boxes of 25 cards and 25 envelopes to match, size of cards 3½x2	.25	Per Dz. boxes. $2.70
6036 Same as 6035 in box with envelope, size 3½x2½	.35	3.00

	Per Pkg. of 25 Cards.	Per Box of 300 Cards.
6037 **Mourning Cards**, 25 in package, with ⅛ inch Black Border, size 2x3¼	$0.10	$1.05
6038 Same as 6037, size 2½x3½	.11	1.15

⁂ **No one enjoys eating from chipped or cracked dishes—Why not get a new set? Prices low.**

Wedding, Correspondence and Regret Cards.

	Per Pkg. of 25 Cards.	Per Box of 100 Cards.
6040 Plain White 3 ply cards (C90) 25 in box with envelopes to match, size 4½x3½	$0.14	$0.45
6041 Same as 6040 with gold edge in box with envelopes (C91)	.15	.52
6042 Plain White Bevel edge (CAH) Cards, 25 in box with envelopes to match, size 4½x3¼	.28	.96
6043 Same as 6042 with gold edge cards (CAX)	.30	1.05
6044 Ragged Edge Bevel Cards, 25 in box with envelopes, size 4½x3½ (CAM)	.33	1.10
6045 Same as 6044 with gold edges (CAB)	.36	1.28
	Box of 100	Per 1000
6048 Large Double Cards to fold in center, size open 4½x6¾. Bevel notched edges, a beautiful wedding card (CAEH)	$0.90	$7.50
6049 Same as 6048 with fancy notched border red and gold	1.00	8.50

Fancy Memorandums.

This line numbers 6060 to 6072; embraces entirely new goods, separate and distinct from styles heretofore sold by us. (*Not How Cheap But How Good.*)

	Each.	Per Doz.
6060 American Russia leather lined limp covers, ruled faint, 60 leaves, size 2½x3¾ (A1.)	$0.50	$5.50
6061 Same as 6060. Indexed with cover stamped visits (AE)	.55	6.00
6062 American Russia, ruled faint, 60 leaves with pencil attached. (Stamped Visits), size 2½x3¾ (A7.)	.65	7.00
6063 Same as 6062. Stamped Cash Account, without pencil (A8.)	.55	6.00
6064 American Russia (A9.) Ruled faint, 60 leaves, stamped engagements.	.50	5.40
6065 American Russia, 60 leaves, indexed, stamped visiting list, with pencil attached, size 3x4 (A 25.)	.70	7.75
6067 American Russia, 60 leaves, ruled dollars and cents. Size 3⅝x5. Stamped cash account (A 44.)	.75	8.25
6068 Same as 6067, stamped engagements with printed heading (A 47.)	.75	8.25
6069 Same as 6067. Stamped household expenses (A 48.)	.75	8.25
6070 American Russia, 60 leaves. Size 3⅝x5⅜. Indexed and stamped addresses (A 52.)	.80	8.75
6071 Same as 6070, faint ruled, plain, 96 leaves, (A 54.)	.90	9.50
6072 Genuine Seal, leather binding, leather lined. Size 2¼x4⅜. Cross Bar Ruling	.75	8.25

"The Standard Diaries" for 1895.

No. 67.

These Diaries are made with blank spaces for either one day, two days, or three days to the page, and contain spaces for recording weather, thermometer and correct almanac anywhere in U. S., cash account, bills payable and receivable, addresses, and in the ladies' sizes (18 mo. and 12 mo.) calls and letters received and answered. They also contain information which may be of great use at any moment.

They are thus equally valuable as reference books or as record or daily memorandum books, and the finer styles are pocket books also; supplying three very useful things in one. They also contain information which may be of great use at any moment; Population of States and principal cities, weights and measures, legal weights of all kinds of grain, value of gold and silver coins, presidents of the United States, postal rates, business law in daily use, etc., etc., and antidotes for poisons and what to do in case of accidents, etc.

Send for illustrated catalogue and price list

Memorandums.

Numbers 6074 to 6081 all open on end.

	Each.	Per doz.
6074 Red leather vest pocket memorandum, size 2¼x4¼ (V-C. H. B. R.) 40 leaves, green edges, quadrille ruling	$0.07	$0.75
6075 Red leather memorandum, 60 leaves, ruled for $ and cts., green edges, size 3⅝x6 (V—CH EA)	.13	1.45

Harness, Halters and Strap Work—We can save you lots of money on these goods.

Blank Books—Continued.

6287 Our Leader. Full Bound Sheep with Russia ends and bands, flat opening, containing 300 leaves of superior quality paper. Ruled in Journals, Cash, Day Books, Records, S. E. and D. E. Ledgers. Best book made. Our special price, each..$1.60
Per dozen........................18.50

Manifold Letter and Note Book.

Size 8½x10.

6290 Manifold Letter Books. A sheet of carbon paper is placed between two leaves, and the letter is written with a stylus or lead pencil; when finished the lower leaf is torn off and the upper remains as a copy. Each book is furnished with carbon, paper and stylus with directions for using. Indexed books have patented ready reference extension index.

Style.	No.	Size.	No. Leaves.	Price.
Pocket Size....	(I)	4x7	200	$0.60
Note Size.......	(c)	5½x8½	100	.60
Note Size.......	(H)	5½x8½	200	.95
Note Size.......	(a)	5½x8½	300	1.20
Large Note...	(aX)	6 x9½	300	1.35
Large Note...	(aB)	6 x9½	paged and indexed 500	2.00
Letter Size....	(M)	8½x11	200	1.35
Letter Size....	(B)	8½x11	paged and indexed 300	2.00
Letter size....	(E)	8½x11	paged and indexed 500	2.35
Letter Size....	(R)	8½x11	paged and indexed 500	2.15
Note Size......	(P)	7 x10	paged and indexed 300	1.50

6291 Made of all tissue paper for those who desire to use their own note and letter heads.

Note Size.....	(O)	7 x10	paged and indexed 500	2.00

Atlases, Latest Editions.

6295 New Rand, McNally & Co.'s Pocket Atlas of the World. Containing county maps of all States and Territories in the United States, and the Provinces of the Dominion of Canada, together with descriptive, statistical and historical matter pertaining to each, and indexed lists of their counties, population, etc.; also colored skeleton maps of the continents showing all countries of the world. Retail price, each......$0.25
Our price...........................18
Per dozen.......................... 1.90
Postage each, extra, 4c.

New Handy Atlas.

6297 This new atlas contains county maps of the United States and Dominion of Canada in colors, also descriptive, statistical and historical matter pertaining to each State or Province; indexed list of all counties with area and population; a ready reference list alphabetically arranged of all towns and villages, with population of 1890, also colored maps of all countries of the world, with diagrams, etc. Bound in limp cloth. 382 pages, size 5⅛x8.
Retail price..................$1.00
Our price...............$0.70 Postage.............. .10

Montgomery Ward & Co.'s New Home and Library Gazetteer and Indexed Atlas of the World, 345 pages.

6298 Containing complete 1890 census population of every city, town and incorporated village in the United States, alphabetically arranged, and all information relative to same. Authentic. Containing the latest colored indexed maps of every State and Territory in the United States, every province of Canada, and every country in the world, together with historical, descriptive, and statistical information pertaining to each, embellished with 125 colored maps, 368 elegant illustrations, 612 colored statistical diagrams, 89,700 towns, villages and hamlets. Size, when closed, 11½x14¼ inches. Complete in one volume. Atlases comparing with this would retail for not less than $5.00 to $10.00. Bound in the best English cloth, gold side stamp.
Our price.......................................$2.25
Bound in half Morocco, gold side stamp. Our price.. 2.75
Weight, 104 ounces. Postage 55 cents extra.

School, Family and Library Globes.

A copy of the Globe Manual will accompany each Globe.

The Manual gives explanation of the terms used in geography and astronomy, and the phenomena of mathematical geography, including temperature and ocean currents, and forty-five problems on the use of globes, with rules and illustrative examples; also several valuable tables.

6300

6300 Our new eight inch globe (C. T. M.) mounted on a beautiful nickel plated stand, inclined axis absolutely correct. Manufacturer's price $8.00.
Our price....... $4.00

6301 New Plain Terrestrial twelve inch globe 23 inches in height, mounted on a nickel plated stand, guaranteed correct. Manufacturer's price $15.00.
Our price.......$5.00

6301

6302 Full meridian library globe, twelve inch, mounted on a polished nickel stand 23 inches in height guaranteed absolutely correct. Manufacturer's price $20.00 Our price $7.00.

6302

6304

6304 Our best full mounted globe twelve inches in diameter, twenty-three inches in height mounted on a beautiful nickel plated stand guaranteed absolutely correct, manufacturer's price $25.00 Our price...............$9.00

Rand, McNally's Latest Maps.

6306 A large map of the world, with a special map of the United States, England and Wales, and Germany and Norway and Sweden. Comprehensive diagrams of mountains and rivers, and alphabetically arranged compilation describing every country in the world, and its location indexed. The only reversible map showing Rand, McNally & Co's latest general map of the United States, size 66x46. Bound with tape, sticks, top and bottom, ready to hang on the wall. Our special prepaid price.............$0.90
Per dozen...10.00

6307 **State Maps.** Folded neatly into pocket size. We have maps of every State and Territory in the United States without exception. In ordering *be sure and give name of State and Territory wanted.* Each..15
Per dozen.... ....1.60
By mail, extra, each...................................02

POCKET MAPS OF FOREIGN COUNTRIES.

Series 6310.

	Each.
Afghanistan, indexed, board cover................	$0.18
Africa, 21x28 inches, with an inset map, on an enlarged scale, of the Suez Canal..............	.52
Alaska, 50x28 inches........................	.70
Argentine Republic, Chile, Paraguay, and Uruguay (new) 21x28 inches..................	.52
Asia, 21x14 inches..............................	.35
Australia and New Zealand, 21x14 inches, with plans of Sydney and Port Jackson..............	.35
Austro-Hungarian Monarchy, 21x14 inches, with plan of Vienna............................	.35
Belgium and The Netherlands, 21x14 inches, with plan of Brussels, Index to cities, towns, etc.....	.35
Brazil and Guiana (new), 21x28 inches.........	.52
British Columbia, 14x21 inches..............	.35
Central America (new), 28x21 inches...........	.52
China, 21x14 inches..............................	.35
China, Farther India, and Indian Archipelago, indexed, board cover..........................	.18
Colombia and Venezuela (new), 28x21 inches....	.52
Cuba, 21x14 inches..............................	.35
Denmark, 14x11 inches, with Northern portion of the German Empire, comprising Schleswig-Holstein and Lauenburg..........................	.35
Egypt and the Egyptian Soudan, paper cover.....	.18
England and Wales, 21x14 inches, with Index to cities, towns, etc..............................	.52
Europe, 21x14 inches..............................	.35
France, 21x14 inches, with plan of Paris, Index to cities, towns, etc..............................	.52
Germany (new), 35x28 inches, with Index to cities, towns, etc..............................	.70
Greece and the Ionian Islands, 21x14 inches.....	.35
India, Indo-China, and Farther India, 21x14 inches, with plans of Calcutta and Bombay.....	.35
Ireland, 21x14 inches, with Index to cities, towns, etc..............................	.52
Italy, 21x14 inches..............................	.35
Japan, in two sheets, 21x14 inches each.........	.52
Mexico (new), 28x21 inches......................	.52
North America, 21x14 inches, showing the West India Islands and Central America............	.35
Oceanica, 21x14 inches..........................	.35
Palestine, 21x14 inches, with plats showing environs of Jerusalem, journeyings of Christ, and sketch showing divisions into tribes	.35

Maps—Continued.

	Each.
Persia and Afghanistan, 14x11 inches.........	$0.35
Peru and Bolivia (new), 28x21 inches........	.52
Russia (European), 21x14 inches............	.35
Scotland, 21x14 inches, with Index to cities, towns, etc..............................	.52
South America (new), 28x21 inches..........	.52
Spain and Portugal, 21x14 inches, with plans of Madrid and Lisbon..........................	.35
Sweden and Norway, 21x14 inches.............	.35
Switzerland, 21x14 inches....................	.35
Turkey in Asia (Asia Minor) and Transcaucasia 21x14 inches..............................	.35
Turkey in Europe, 21x14 inches...............	.35
West Indies, 18x14 inches....................	.35

On above maps, postage extra, 5c.

Rand, McNally & Co.'s New Large Scale Wall Maps.

Series 6311.

Sent to any address, charges prepaid upon receipt of prices quoted.

STATE.	Size.	Scale to 1 inch.	* Half Mount'd	* Full Mount'd
CALIFORNIA & NEVADA	34x46	18 miles	$1.50	$2.25
COLORADO...........	36x26	12 "	1.25	2.25
FLORIDA.............	36x48	10 "	......	2.25
ILLINOIS.............	35x55	8 "	1.50	2.50
INDIANA.............	28x42	8 "	1.25	2.25
INDIAN TERRITORY...	34x26	12 "	......	1.50
IOWA................	48x36	8 "	1.25	2.25
KANSAS..............	56x32	8 "	1.25	2.25
MICHIGAN............	41x58	8 "	1.50	2.50
MINNESOTA...........	40x56	8 "	1.25	2.25
MISSISSIPPI.........	51x58	7 "	1.25	2.25
MISSOURI............	48x40	8 "	1.25	2.25
MONTANA.............	38x25	16 "	1.00	1.75
NEBRASKA............	61x34	8 "	1.50	2.50
NEW ENGLAND STATES	41x58	10 "	......	3.00
NEW MEXICO TY......	30x26	18 "	......	1.50
NEW YORK............	34x31	10 "	......	2.25
NORTH DAKOTA........	50x36	8 "	1.50	2.50
OHIO................	51x44	6 "	1.50	2.50
PENNSYLVANIA........	40x25	8 "	......	2.25
SOUTH DAKOTA........	52x36	8 "	1.50	2.50
TENNESSEE...........	58x24	9 "	......	2.25
TEXAS...............	63x46	15 "	......	4.00
UNITED STATES.......	66x46	45 "	....	4.00
WASHINGTON..........	60x41	8 "	1.50	2.50
WEST VIRGINIA.......	44x38	7 "	......	2.50
WISCONSIN...........	41x58	8 "	1.25	2.25

Globe Series of School Maps.

Series No. 6312.

PRICES OF WALL MAPS.	SIZE.	PRICE.
Western Hemisphere..............	41x58 inches.	$3.60
Eastern Hemisphere..............	41x58 "	3.60
North America...................	41x58 "	3.60
South America...................	41x52 "	3.60
United States, Canada and Mexico,	41x58 "	4.50
Europe..........................	41x52 "	3.60
Asia............................	41x52 "	3.60
Africa..........................	41x52 "	3.60

The above maps forwarded to any address by mail or express upon receipt of price quoted.

How to Kill Time in Chicago.

6314 The Stranger's Guide to the World's Fair City. Where to go and how to get there, with map and illustrations of all public buildings, etc. Any one who intends to visit the greatest city on earth should have this book.
Our special price...............................$0.15
Postage 05

Montgomery Ward & Co.'s New Indexed Map of Chicago.

6315 Guaranteed the latest and best, printed in colors. Price...................................$0.04
Per dozen...40
Postage each.......................................02

Dictionary Holders.

Harvard.

Noyes.

Noyes Holders.

Perfectly adjustable to any height or angle and is pivoted to turn any angle. Suitable for holding dictionaries, bibles, albums or large books of any kind.

6317 All iron, bronzed and nickel-plated, polished walnut case, four legs on casters. Has book rack below to hold 8 or 10 volumes—a great convenience.
Retail price, each.... $4.00 Our price..........$2.60

6318 All wire, level top, no pivot or casters, light and strong. Folds up for shipment.
Retail price, each.... $3.00 Our price..........$1.45

Harvard Holders.

Are durable and practicable. The sides are operated by double acting springs, the book being firmly clamped while closed and resting on a level surface when open. The adjustment to books of different sizes, and the inclination to any angle, are effected by a single screw.

6320 Complete with casters and revolving book shelf, all nickel plated finish. Retail price........$8.00 Our price........$3.95

6321 Same as No. 6320, finished in black japan. Retail price........$5.50 Our price........$2.60

6322 Same as 6321 in finish, without shelf or castors. Retail price........$4.00 Our price........$2.05

6323 Same as 6320, finished in antique copper, suitable for office or parlor. Retail price........$8.00 Our price........$3.80

WORKS OF REFERENCE.

American Encyclopaedic Dictionary.

6325—An entirely new accurate, practical and inexhaustive work of reference to all the words in the English Language, with a full account of their origin, meaning, pronunciation and use. Edited by Robert Hunter, A. M., F. G. S. Containing 250,000 words, or 160,000 more than the Webster International. A complete encyclopædia and dictionary combined. 2,000 illustrations.

It gives over 50,000 important cyclopædic subjects not given in any of the standard cyclopædias. It is the embodiment of many dictionaries in one, embracing Botany, Chemistry, Mineralogy, Zoology, Anatomy, Law, Medicine, Electricity, etc. It is also complete as a classical and biblical dictionary, and is a perfect glossary of the English language. Well and durably bound, as follows:

Cloth per set of 4 Volumes, *complete*............$6.50
½ Morocco per set of 4 Volumes, *complete*........8.50
Library Sheep " " " , *complete*........9.50
Total weight of 4 volumes 28 lbs. Sample pages on application.

Alibone's Quotations.

6326 Complete in three volumes. A valuable work for every home, library and academy, containing POETICAL QUOTATIONS covering the entire field of British and American poetry, from Chaucer to Tennyson, with copious indices. Both authors and subjects alphabetically arranged.

PROSE QUOTATIONS, from Socrates to Macaulay, with indices; authors, 544; subjects, 571; quotations, 8,810.

GREAT AUTHORS of all ages. Being selections from the prose works of eminent writers, from the time of Pericles to the present day. By S. Austin Alibone, LL. D. Set of three volumes, complete..........$6.00
Any volume, separate..........2.10
Postage, each..........24

Ayres', Alfred, Works.

6327 The Orthoepist, a pronouncing manual, containing about three thousand five hundred words, including a considerable number of the names of foreign authors, artists, etc., that are often mispronounced. 18mo.
Retail price..........$1.25
Our price..........90
Postage, extra, 10c.

6329 The Verbalist, a manual devoted to brief discussions of the right and wrong use of words. 18mo. Retail price $1.25. Our price..........90
Postage, extra, 10c.

Business Correspondence.

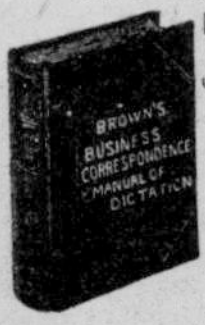

6330 Brown's Business Correspondence and Manual of Dictation, for the use of Teachers and Students of Stenography and Typewriting, containing selected letters of actual correspondence in Banking, Insurance, Railroad and Mercantile Business; a chapter on Punctuation, Spelling and Use of Capital Letters; together with a full and complete Spelling List of 27,000 words. Our price..........$0.75
Postage, extra 12c.

Cruden's Complete Concordance.

6331 Complete Concordance of the Holy Bible (unabridged edition). Large 8vo. Cloth.........$1.00
Full leather..........1.85
Postage, extra, 32c.

Cushing's Manual.

6332 Of Parliamentary Practice, being rules for conducting business in deliberative assemblies. Cloth, 16mo..........$0.35
Postage, extra, 4c.

Chambers' Encyclopaedia.

Special attention given to American subjects. The New Chambers' Encyclopædia.

6334 Twenty years later than any encyclopædia in the market. New type, new subjects, new illustrations, new maps. A complete dictionary of art, science, history, literature, fable, mythology, biography, geography, etc. Handsomely illustrated with maps and numerous wood engravings.

Specimen pages sent on application.
Complete in Sets: Ten volumes:
Cloth..........$21.00
Sheep..........28.00 Half Morocco...... $31.50
Weight, 50 lbs.

Book-keeping at a Glance.

6335 By Expert J. T. Brierly. A simple and concise method of practical book-keeping, with instructions for the proper keeping of books and accounts, and numerous explanations and forms used in a commercial business, showing an entire set of books, based upon actual transactions; how to take off a trial balance sheet, and finally close and balance accounts. 144 pages. Size 2¾x5. Russia leather. Retail price..........$0.50
Our price..........38
With patent index..........50
Postage, extra, 5c.

Chamber's Encyclopædia.

A library of universal knowledge for the people, being a complete reprint of the Edinburgh and London edition of Chambers' Encyclopædia, with very large additions upon topics of special interest to American readers, and giving American statistics of population down to and including the census of 1890, containing more than 27,000 specially prepared articles giving pointed, practical, explicit and most interesting and instructive information.

6338 Red and Gold Edition. Bound in blue cloth with stampings on side and back in red ink and gold. Retail price..$10.00. Our price..........$6.50

6251 Popular Edition. Bound in brown cloth with gold title on back. Retail price, $7.00. Our price..........4.50

Chamber's English Literature.

6339 4 volumes. Cloth. 12mo.
Per set 4 volumes..........$3.00
Postage..........48

Crabb's English Synonyms.

6340 Explained in alphabetical order, to which is added an index to the words. Illustrated by G. Crabb.
Retail price $1.25; our price..........$0.88
Postage, extra..........12

Conklin's Handy Manual.

(New Edition 1894, containing full census of 1890.)

6342 Conklin's Handy Manual and Atlas of the World, by Professor Conklin, of Hamilton University. A full description of every country in the world; 440 pages of information, facts, calculations, receipts, processes, rules, business forms, legal items, etc., over 2,000 subjects of value. Conklin's Manual in limp cloth. Each......$0.15
Per dozen..........1.65
Conklin's Manual in stiff cloth, gold embossed, library style.
Each..........$0.30
Per dozen..........3.25
Extra by mail: Limp..........03
Cloth..........05
Can be furnished in German at same prices.

Coffin's Interest Tables.

6343 Interest tables at ½, 1, 2, 3, 3½, 4, 4½, 5, 6, 7, 8 and 10 per cent. per annum. By John Coffin. Best book in print on this subject.
Retail price $1.00. Our price..........$0.75
Postage 10c. extra.

Cassell's Latin Dictionary.

6344 Latin-English and English-Latin, by J. R. Beard, D. D. Cloth. 12mo. 892 pages.
Retail price $1.50; our price..........$1.05
Postage, extra..........14

Drill Tactics.

LATEST EDITIONS.

6346 **Government Edition.** Infantry drill regulations, approved by the President Oct. 3, 1891. These books were printed with those ordered by the war department for issue to the army.
Paper..........$0.26
Leather..........65
Postage extra, 6c.

Duffey's Ladies' and Gentlemen's Etiquette.

6347 A complete manual of the manner and dress of American society. Retail price..........$1.50
Our price..........1.05
Postage..........12

Dick's Encyclopædia.

6348 DICK'S ENCYCLOPÆDIA OF PRACTICAL RECEIPTS AND PROCESSES, containing 6,422 practical receipts on all subjects. By Wm. B. Dick. 607 pages, royal octavo. Price, cloth..........$3.50
Bound in sheep, an ornament to any library $4.50. Extra by mail..........35

Encyclopædia Britannica.

6349 **Encyclopædia Britannica.** 30 large octavo volumes (Allen Reprint) 25 volumes Encyclopædia Britannica and 5 volumes American Supplement. This new reprint edition includes all of the American copyrighted articles, and is the only word for word, page for page, volume for volume, reprint, unaltered from the original ever published. Over 1,500 contributors, 20,500 pages, 8,000 illustrations, etc
Single volumes, green silk cloth..........$1.25
Full set, 30 vols., green silk cloth..........35.00
Single Volume, ½ Russia..........1.45
Full set, 30 vols., ½ Russia..........42.00
Single volumes, ½ Russia Extra..........1.65
Full set, 30 vols., ½ Russia Extra..........48.00
Postage on single volumes..........28
In ordering single volumes, always state what volume or volumes are wanted.
Set of 30 vols. weighs 125 lbs. packed in box.

Experimental Science.

6350 Experimental Science by George M. Hopkins; this book is full of interest and value for teachers, students and others who desire to impart or obtain a practical knowledge of physics. 740 pages, over 680 illustrations, elegantly bound in cloth. Fourteenth edition revised and enlarged.
Retail price..........$4.00
Our price..........3.10
Postage 40 cents extra.

English-Swedish and Swedish-English Dictionary.

6351 Full explanations of all words. Bound in half leather. Each..........$1.25
Postage extra, 10 cents.

English and Dano-Norwegian Dictionary.

6353 New stereotype edition, revised and improved, half Russia binding. Each..........$1.50
Postage, 10 cents extra.

Do not send money in a letter by open mail. Many such letters never reach their destination, and we are often blamed for it. **See page 2 for information on this point.**

Edison's Handy Encyclopædia.

New Census Edition of 1891-92.

6354 Of general information a universal atlas, edited by Thos. F. Edison. Much in little. Five hundred and twelve pages of closely printed matter. A reference encyclopædia, contains a million facts of great value to everyone, also a compilation of practical facts on practical subjects.
Bound in limp cloth.
Each $0.15
Per dozen 1.65
   Cloth covers, embossed titles
library style. Each........$0.30
Per dozen 3.25
Postage, each, limp .... .03
Library .... .04

Encyclopædia of Quotations.

6356 A treasury of wisdom, wit and humor, odd comparisons and proverbs. Authors, 931; subjects, 1,893; quotations, 10,299. Compiled and arranged by Adam Woolever. Royal octavo, cloth, gilt.
Retail price $1.75
Our price 1.00
Postage, extra .... .32

Flowers.

6357 Their language, poetry, sentiment, etc. *Red-line edition.* 18mo. Cloth, beveled gilt edges. Retail price $1.25
Our price .... .88
Postage .... .10

Everybody's Guide to Music.

6358 With illustrated chapters on singing and the cultivation of the voice; full and explicit helps to the piano and organ; complete dictionary of musical terms. By Josiah Booth. pp. vi, 176. Square 18mo. cloth.
Retail price $0.75
Our price .... .55
Postage, extra, 4c.

Fallow's, Rt. Rev. Samuel,

6359 100,000 Synonyms and Antonyms; or Synonyms and Words of Opposite Meaning, with an appendix. 16mo, cloth. Retail price $1.00
Our price .... .70
Postage, extra .... .12

Favorite Illustrated Dictionary.

6360 A Dictionary of the English language, from the best authorities, 32,000 words and phrases, 670 illustrations. Retail price..... $0.25
Our price .... .12
Per dozen 2.25
Postage, 3 cents.

Good Manners.

6362 A Manual of Etiquette. *Red-line Edition.* Square 18mo. Cloth, gilt edges.
Retail price $1.25
Our price .... .38
Postage, extra, 10 cents.

Gaskell's Compendium of Business Forms.

6363 Educational, social, legal and commercial, embracing self-teaching penmanship, book-keeping, laws, etiquette, agricultural, mining, receipts, etc. By G. A. Gaskell; 935 pages; cloth. This edition has been revised and enlarged by Loomis T. Palmer, making it a complete encyclopædia of reference. Also contains beautiful illustrations throughout.
Subscription price $6.00
Our price 2.80
Postage .... .48

Gaskell's Penmanship.

6364 Gaskell's Complete Compendium of Elegant Writing, comprised in a new series of twenty beautiful copy slips for self-instruction; one large plate of fancy and ornamental penwork, and a book of instruction complete in a packet. Our price per set............ $0.25
Postage .... .04

Gaskell's Guide to Writing, Pen Flourishing, Lettering and Letter Writing.

6365 With Gems from American and European penmen, and portraits and sketches, being a complete Self-Teaching Guide to plain and artistic work of every description possible for the use of the pen. By G. A. Gaskell. Profusely illustrated with original plates expressly for this book. Our price $0.60
Postage .... .12

Hill's Manual.

6366 Of Social and Business forms, a guide to correct writing and approved methods in speaking and acting in the various relations of life. New enlarged edition. Illustrated and corrected to date. By Thos. E. Hill, author of Morals and Manners, Hill Banking system, etc
Subscription price............. $6.00
Our price 1.95
Postage .... .45

How to Pronounce 10,000 Difficult Words.

6367 An authoritative hand-book of words in common use. There are few persons whose education is so complete as to insure the correct pronunciation of all the words met with in daily reading. Czar, Boucicault, Isolate, Balmoral, Boulanger, Coup d' etat, etc, are cases in point. These words with very many others of the same kind will be found in the book. The aid offered to the reader or speaker by it is very great, It also contains an extended list of words often incorrectly pronounced.
By F. M. Payne; 128 pages, bound in Russia, indexed. Retail price 50c. Our price 38c. Postage, extra, 3c.

Masson's New French-English and English-French Dictionary.

6369 Of the French language, uniform with above, giving new words recently introduced in French.
Retail price $1.00. Our price $0.70
Per dozen 8.00
Mail, 15 cents extra.

Mythology.

6370 **Manual of Mythology.** By Alex. S. Murray. For the use of schools, art students and general readers. Founded on the works of Petiscus, Preller and Welcker. With 45 plates on tinted paper, representing nearly 100 mythological subjects. Crown, 8vo. Our price $1.45
Postage, 16c. extra.

New Webster Vest-Pocket Dictionary.

6371 An entirely new and original compilation from the famous Webster's great work. Its size and general make-up are such as to render this beautiful little book for ready reference in Spelling, Meaning of Words, Correct Pronunciation, Synonyms, Irregular Verbs and Habitual Mistakes. Simple, Practical, Invaluable. It includes the Gazetteer of the World. Something new and especially useful.
Limp cloth, retail price $0.25
Our price .... .15
Per dozen 1.65
Full Morocco, indexed, retail price .... .50
Our price .... .30
Per dozen 2.25
Postage, each .... .04

Size 5¼ x 2¾.

Nuttall's Standard Dictionary of the English Language.

6373 Handiest Lexicon in the world. In large crown 8vo; 832 pages.
PRINCIPAL FEATURES: New, clear type, 100,000 references containing all new words introduced into common parlance, science and literature. It is an etymological dictionary, giving derivations and meanings of all root words. It is illustrated, contains tables of pronunciation of classical, geometrical and scriptural names and for scholastic and home use is undoubtedly the handiest dictionary extant.
Cloth, retail price $1.50
Our price .... .75
Same, with pat. index 2.00
Half Morocco, indexed .... .78
Postage, each .... .20

Popular Handbooks. Series No. 6374.

	Retail price	Our price
Cavendish on Whist	$0 50	$0 35

Etiquette. By Agnes H. Morton, B. O. Cloth binding	50	35
Correspondence. By Agnes H. Morton B. O. Cloth binding	50	35
Handbook of Pronunciation. By John H. Bechtel. Cloth binding	50	35
Punctuation By Paul Allardyce. Cloth binding	50	35
The Debater's Treasury. By Wm. Pittenger. Cloth binding	50	35
Oratory. By Rev. Henry Ward Beecher. Cloth binding...........	50	35
Quotations. By Agnes H. Morton, B. O. Cloth binding	50	35
Practical Synonyms. By John H. Bechtel. Cloth binding	50	35
The Art of Conversation. By J. P.	50	35
Mahafly. Cloth binding	50	35

Any of the above 9 books, postage 5c. each.

Parson's Laws of Business.

6375 For all the states and territories of the Union and the Dominion of Canada, with forms and directions for all transactions. New revised edition, 8vo., cloth, 866 pages.
Subscription price, $3.75. Our price ... $2.39
Sheep .... $2.65. Postage, extra. .30

Popular American Dictionary.

6378 Illustrated. A Complete Library in itself. Contains beside the dictionary proper a mass of information never before gathered within the compass of one volume. Revised from latest and best English and American authorities. 18mo, cloth, embossed sides and back.
Retail price $1.00
Our price .... .30
Per dozen 3.25
Extra by mail .... .10

Reed's Rules.

6379 The latest recognized book of Parliamentary law for every one in any way connected with societies, clubs or organizations of any kind. By Thos. B. Reed, ex-speaker of the House of Representatives. Cloth, 18mo. Retail price, $0.75. Our price ... $0.52
Full Seal Leather .... .88
Postage, extra, 6c.

Roberts' Rules of Order.

6380 For Deliberative Assemblies. By Lieut. Col H. M. Roberts, Corps of Engineers, U. S. A. 168th thousandth. Pocket size. Cloth $0.55
Postage, extra, 6c.

Ropp's Commercial Calculator.

6381 Contains a new system of commercial tables, also a practical arithmetic for the merchant; all for practical purposes, in which is embodied the shortest and simplest rules, easy, interesting tables, a new process for adding long columns, explanations to nearly all tables in both English and German. The tables of wages, interest, grain, log and lumber are worth many times the price of the work. No. C paper. Each $0.12
Per dozen 1.75
No. H. Leatherette. Each, $0.35. Per dozen.. 3.50
No. A Morocco. Each .... .70. Per dozen.. 7.50
No. M Kid. Each .... .90. Per dozen.. 9.50
Postage, each, 6c.

Reference Books. Series 6382.

National Standard History of the United States. By Everit Brown.
National Standard Encyclopædia.
Law Without Lawyers. By Henry B. Corey.
Dictionary of American Politics. By Everit Brown and Albert Strauss.
What Everyone Should Know. By S. H. Burt.
Readers. Reference Hand-Book. By H. C. Faulkner and W. H Van Orden.
Writers' Reference Handbook. By Jennie T. Wandle and H. C. Faulkner.
Etiquette, Health and Beauty By Francis Stevens and Francis M. Smith.
Cyclopædia of Natural History. By Charles C. Abbott.
Why, When and Where. By Robert Thorne, M. A.
National Standard Dictionary, Illustrated; containing 40,000 words.
All are handsomely bound in cloth, large, 12mo.
Retail price $1.00. Our price, each $0.65
Postage, each .... .15

Roget's Thesaurus of English Words and Phrases.

6383 New edition, revised and enlarged by the author's son, J. L. Roget. Crown 8vo. cloth.
Retail price.........$2 00 Our price..............$1.40
Postage 16 cents extra.

Stamp Albums.

6385 **Mekeel's Postage Stamp Album of the World** is acknowledged to be the standard album. Its latest edition that has just been placed on sale is receiving the support of stamp collectors the world over.

This album contains spaces for the famous Columbian series now in use, a feature not included in any other album, and also provides for all other stamps issued to date. The illustration at the left gives a good idea of its general appearance, and the album measures 9x12 inches. It is printed in four styles, as follows:

No. 1—Half bound, cloth and boards..............$1.05
No. 2—Full cloth, black and gilt.................. 1.75
No. 3—Full cloth, black and gilt, with stubs...... 2.45
No. 4—Extra, full leather, stubs and gilt edges... 5.25
Postage, extra.. .42

Scientific American Encyclopædia of Receipts.

6386 Beautifully bound in cloth with gold title stamps, large print, and fully illustrated. Notes and queries 1,200 receipts and 680 pages, a careful compilation of most useful receipts and replies published in the Scientific American for the last fifty years. 675 pages. Cloth, retail price $5.00
Our price............................ 3.65
Postage, 40 cents.

Smith's Bible Dictionary.

6387 Comprising antiquities, biography, geography, natural history, etc., with numerous illustrations and maps. A history of books of the Bible, also containing Cruden's complete concordance and 4,000 questions and answers on the New and Old Testaments. Cloth, marbled edges.
Retail price, cloth.........$2.50
Our price, cloth........... 1.05
Retail price, sheep......... 3.00
Our price, sheep........... 1.60
Postage, 28c. extra.

Smith-Peloubet Dictionary.

6388 Dictionary of the Bible. Comprising its antiquities, biography, geography, natural history and literature. Edited by William Smith, LL.D. Revised and adapted to the present use of Sunday-school teachers and Bible students. By Rev. F. N. and M. A. Peloubet. With eight colored maps and 440 engravings on wood, 8vo.

	Retail price.	Our price
Cloth, extra	$2.00	$1.40
Full Sheep	3.00	2.10

Postage, extra, 20c.

Wessely's Spanish Dictionary.

6390 New pocket Spanish-English dictionary, 12 mo. Cloth............$0.55 Postage, extra, 10c.

Wessely's Italian Dictionary.

6391 New pocket dictionary of the Italian and English language, 12 mo. Cloth..$0.55 Postage, 10c

Webster's International Dictionary

The New Webster.

6394 The authentic Webster's Unabridged Dictionary, comprising the issues of 1864, '79 and '84, all still copyrighted, is now thoroughly revised and enlarged, under the supervision of Noah Porter, D. D., LL. D., of Yale University, and as a distinguishing title bears the name, Webster's International Dictionary. This last revision is by far the most complete that the work has ever undergone during the sixty-two years that it has been before the public, every page being treated as if the book was now published for the first time.

In addition to the Dictionary of Words, with their pronunciation, alternative spellings, etymology, and various meanings, illustrated by quotations and numerous engravings, there are several valuable appendices, comprising: A pronouncing gazeteer of the world. Vocabularies of Scripture, Greek, Latin and English proper names. A dictionary of the noted names of fiction. A brief history of the English language. A dictionary of foreign quotations, words, phrases, proverbs, etc. A biographical dictionary with 10,000 names. A classified selection of illustrations (filling 82 pages), etc., etc.

Library Sheep Binding.	Retail price........	$10.00
" " "	Our price..........	8.50
" " "	Indexed...........	9.25

Postage extra, $1.08.

Reprint of Webster's Unabridged Dictionary of the English Language.

6395 Noah Webster's Dictionary of the English language. The copyright having expired enables us to furnish the reprint. Pronunciations exhibited by the divisions of words into syllables, by accentuation or by general rules. Revised and enlarged by Chauncey A. Goodrich, professor in Yale College, to which has been added an appendix of 10,000 words and 1,500 illustrations, with pronouncing vocabularies of scripture, classical and geographical terms and a dictionary of mercantile and legal terms. Substantially bound in sheep with embossed sides, marbled edges.
Our price, only $1.68. With patent Index......$2.25
Postage 68 cents extra.

Webster's Every Man His Own Lawyer.

6396 A compendium of business and domestic law and equity; comprising the rights and wrongs of individuals. A handy guide in all law and business transactions and negotiations. Civil and commercial relations of everyday life. The special laws of every state and territory in the United States, 12mo., cloth, gilt. Library.
Our price, only...$0.75
Postage .... .13

Word-Book of Synonyms.

6397 Of the English Language. By Thos. P. Peabody. The most complete in the English language. 12mo. Cloth...............................$0.30
Postage, 6 cents.

Young's Analytical Concordance to the Bible.

6398 Containing every word in alphabetical order, arranged under its Greek or Hebrew original, with the original meaning of each, and pronunciation. With the latest information on Biblical Geography and Antiquities, etc. By Robert Young, LL. D. Quarto. Retail price, $5.00. Our price.............................$3.75
Postage, 48c. extra.

Zahner's New German-English and English-German Dictionary.

6400 A Dictionary of the English-German and German-English, arranged in separate parts. By Carl Zahner. Contains pronunciations, definitions, etc. Illustrated, 462 pages, finely bound, leather backs, gilt stamp. Large crown, 8vo.
Retail price......................$1.00
Our price............................ .70
Per dozen........................... 8.00
Postage, each...................... .15
The best dictionary made for the price.

MEDICAL BOOKS.

We list below only a partial list of family medical books which are all standard on the subjects they treat. (Doctors and students will find it profitable to have our special medical book catalogue.) Free upon request.

Dr. Foote's Plain Home Talk.

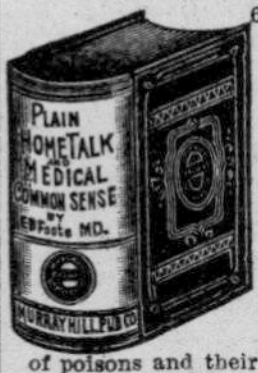

6405 If you want to know all about the human body, in health and disease, nature's secrets revealed, how life is perpetuated, health maintained, disease induced, death delayed, how to marry your own mate, and transmit wealth of health to posterity, read the most popular, comprehensive and useful book treating of medical, social and sexual science. An appendix of great practical utility made up of over 200 prescriptions or receipts for Acute and Chronic Disorders Common to Adults and Children, a complete table of poisons and their antidotes; illustrated by over 20 beautiful colored lithographs.
Popular Edition, retail price $1.50 Our price...$0.85
Standard " " " 3.25 " " 1.35
Postage 14 and 18 cents extra.
6406 Same printed in the German language at same prices.

New Physician.

6407 Gunn & Jordan's Newest Revised Physician, being the first new domestic physician or home book of health by John C. Gunn, M. D., originally as enlarged and now issued with renewed copyright to the author, who prepared the large additions made to it during the six years from earliest publications. Johnson H. Jordan, M. D. Large octavo, 1200 pages. Bound in leather with marble edges.
Subscription price.........$6.00
Our price........................ 4.00
Postage .... .36
Can be furnished in the German language at same price.

Ladies' Medical Guide.

6409 By S. Pancoast, M. D., instructor, counselor and friend, explaining nature and mystery of reproductive organs in both sexes. Handsomely bound in cloth. Containing 682 pages, with working chart, showing all external parts of the human body. Also hundreds of other illustrations.
Subscription price.......$2.50
Our price...................... 1.60
Full Morocco............... 1.90
Postage........................ .19

Cowan's Science of New Life.

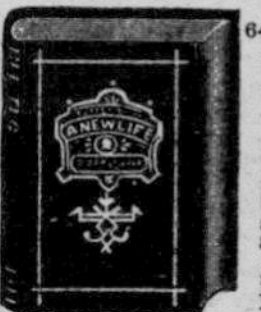

6410 By John Cowan, M. D. A book well worth possessing by every thoughtful man and woman. The "Science of a New Life" has received the highest testimonials and commendations from leading medical and religious critics; 400 pages; 100 illustrations.
8 vo. English cloth, gilt side and back stamps...............$2.05
8 vo. leather, sprinkled edges, ... 2.40
½ Morocco................. 2.75
Postage extra............... .24

Science of Life.

6411 By Prof O. S. Fowler; containing chapters on manhood, womanhood and their relations. Love, laws, power, selection or mutual adaption, courtship, married life and perfect children, male vigor and female health and beauty perpetuated. 1050 pages, cloth.
Subscription price......$3.75
Our price.................. 1.95
Full Morocco............. 2.15
Postage .... .26

Human Science.

6412 Uniform with above by same author. Physiology, phrenology, etc.
Subscription price.....................................$3.75
Our price.. 1.95
Postage, extra... .26
Full Morocco.. 2.15

Physical Life of Woman.

6414 By George H. Napheys, A. M., M. D. Advice to the Maiden, Wife and Mother. A new edition, revised to the latest date, with a life of the author. This is the only work on the delicate topic of woman recommended for popular reading by the most distinguished physicians, eminent divines, prominent educators, leading medical journals, and the press generally.
Subscription price, cloth..$2.00
Our price........................ .80
Postage.......................... .12

Hand-Book of Popular Medicine.

6415 Uniform with above, embracing the anatomy and physiology of the human body; instructions for nursing the sick; home gymnastics, the domestic treatment of ordinary diseases and accidents of children and adults. 12mo. cloth, gilt back and side.............................$0.80
Postage .... .12

Transmission of Life.

6416 Uniform with "Physical Life of Woman." Counsels of the nature and hygiene of the masculine functions. New edition, revised and enlarged. Large 12mo, cloth, gilt back and side...$0 80
Postage... 12

TRAPPING AND ANGLING.

Gibson's Camp Life in the Woods.

6711 Camp life in the woods, and the tricks of trappers and trap making. Containing comprehensive hints on camp shelter of all kinds, boat and canoe building, and valuable suggestions on trappers' food, etc. Valuable recipes for the curing and tanning of fur skins, etc. By W. Hamilton Gibson. 300 pages. Illustrated by the author. 16 mo. cloth $0.75
Postage, extra .... .10

The Trappers' Guide.

6712 By S. Newhouse. A manual of instruction for capturing all kinds of fur-bearing animals and curing their skins. Illustrated. Cloth.
Retail price .... $0.50. Our price $0.38
Postage .... .05

Hunter and Trapper.

6713 The best modes of Hunting and Trapping are fully explained, and Foxes, Deer, Bears, etc., fall into his traps readily by following his directions. By Halsey Thrasher, an old and experienced sportsman. Cloth, 12mo.
Retail price .... $0.75. Our price $0.55
Postage .... .08

Brown's Taxidermist's Manual.

6715 A New and Improved Edition. The standard guide for the collection and preservation of specimens of birds, animals, reptiles, etc.; fully illustrated. Cloth, 12mo. Retail price ... $1.00
Our price .... .75
Postage .... .08

Batty's Practical Taxidermy and Home Decoration.

6716 By Joseph H. Batty. An entirely new and complete as well as authentic work on taxidermy—giving in detail full directions for collecting and mounting animals, birds, reptiles, fish, insects, and general objects of natural history. 125 illustrations. Cloth, 12mo.
Retail price $1.50
Our price 1.10
Postage, extra .... .10

The Amateur Trapper and Trap-Maker's Guide.

6717 A complete treatise on the art of trapping, snaring and netting; containing directions for constructing the most approved traps, snares, nets and deadfalls; and the most successful baits for attracting all kinds of animals, birds, etc.; with their special uses in each case; also practical receipts for preparing skins and furs for market, and for tanning them, with instructions for stuffing specimens of birds and animals in the most natural manner. Illustrated, 16mo, paper cover $0.35
Bound in boards, cloth back .... .50

The Taxidermist's Manual.

6718 Containing complete instructions in the art of taxidermy, with directions how to prepare, mount and preserve all kinds of birds, animals and insects. By Graham Allen. Profusely illustrated.
Large 16mo $0.18

The Hunter and Angler.

6719 A handy manual of hunting, trapping and angling, with valuable hints in regard to guns, rods, game, fish and baits; including instructions for the care and medical treatment of dogs. Illustrated.
Large 16mo $0.18

BIRDS.

Key to North American Birds.

6721 Third Revised Edition. By Elliott Coues, M.A., M.D., Ph. D. It contains a concise account of every species of living and fossil bird at present known on the continent north of the boundary line between Mexico and the United States, including Greenland. Illustrated with over 500 wood engravings. 1 vol., royal octavo, vellum cloth. Retail price $7.50
Our price 6.85

Our Own Birds.

6722 A familiar natural history of the birds of the U. S. By Wm. L. Baily; beautifully illustrated.
Retail price $1.25
Our price .... .88
Postage, extra .... .10

Murphy's American Game Bird Shooting.

6723 This work on game birds is written ent rely from a sportsman's standpoint, being intended not only to describe their haunts and habits, but also the various methods employed in this country and Europe for bagging them. Cloth.
Retail price $2.50. Our price $1.85
Postage .... .14

Nest and Eggs of North American Birds.

6724 By Oliver Davie. Fourth edition. Illustrated. Cloth. 455 pages, with index.
Retail price $2.00. Our price $1.45
Postage .... .14

Hints and Points for Sportsmen.

6726 Compiled by "Seneca." This compilation comprises six hundred and odd wrinkles and suggestions for the shooter, fisherman, dog owner, yachtman, canoeist and camper.
Retail price $150. Our price $1.10
Postage .... .10

Woodcraft.

6727 By Messmuk. 140 pages on this subject.
Our price $0.75
Postage .... .10

FISHING.

Book of the Black Bass.

6729 Comprising its complete scientific and life history, together with a practical treatise on angling and fly-fishing, and a full description of tools, tackle and implements. By James A. Henshall, M. D. Illustrated. Cloth, 470 pages.
Retail price .... $3.00 Our price $2.25
Postage .... .14

Practical Trout Culture.

6730 By J. H. Slack, M. B. A useful and practical work showing how the farmer may grow crops in his pond just as he does in his fields. Illustrated. Cloth, 143 pp. Price $0.70
Postage 10

Fishing With the Fly.

6732 Fifteen full page colored plates illustrating over 100 flies. New edition, 335 pages.
Our price only .... $2.10 Postage $0.14

Fly Fishing and Fly Making.

6733 By J. H. Keene, with plates of actual material for making flies. 159 pages. Cloth $1.25
Postage .... .10

American Game and Fishes.

6734 By G. O. Shields, and 19 other standard authorities on this subject. 8 vo. 580 pages. Cloth. Retail price .... $2.50 Our price $1.75
Postage .... .22

A. B. C. of Carp Culture.

6735 A treatise on the German, or European Carp, by Root, Miller and Finley. 8vo. Paper $0.23
Postage, extra .... .04

CANOEING AND CAMPING.

Canoe and Boat Building.

6739 A Complete Manual for Amatures. Containing plain and comprehensive directions for the construction of Canoes, Rowing and Sailing Boats and Hunting Craft. By W. P. Stephens, Retail price $2.00. Our price $1.45
Postage, 16c.

Practical Boat Building for Amateurs.

6740 By Adrian Neison. Cloth. This is Part I. of the foregoing, bound separately. Cloth, 106 pages.
Retail price .... $1.00. Our price $0.80
Postage, 10c.

Canoe and Camp Cookery.

6742 A practical Cook Book for Canoeists Corinthian Sailors and Outers. By Seneca. Cloth, 96 pages.
Retail price $1 00
Our price .... .75
Postage, 10c.

Canvas Canoes and How to Build Them.

6743 By Parker B. Field. With a plan and all dimensions. 48 pages. Retail price $0.50
Our price .... .38
Postage, 3c.

The Sailing Boat.

6744 Practical instructions for its management, together with "Nautical Vocabulary," "Weather Indications," and "Rules for Sailing Boat Matches." By C. E. Prescott. Pocket edition. Flexible cloth. 12mo.
Retail price $0.25
Our price .... .18
Postage, 4c.

The Oarsman's Manual.

6745 Containing practical instructions in rowing and sculling for amateurs and professionals. By W. Beach. Illustrated. Large 16mo.... $0.18
Postage, 3c.

Dick's Yachting and Sailing.

6747 Containing practical instructions in all that pertains to the construction, rigging and management of all kinds of yachts. Illustrated. 12mo. Cloth, gilt $0.50
Postage, 6c.

How to Camp Out.

6748 By Gould. Cloth, 16mo. Price $0.55
Postage, 8c.

Camping and Camp Outfits.

6749 A manual of instruction for young and old sportsmen. By G. O. Shields ("Coquina"). Contains practical points on how to dress for camping trips; what to carry, how to select camp sites. Thirty illustrations. 12mo., 200 pages; cloth. Retail price $1.25
Our price .... .88
Postage, 10c.

DOGS.

Dogs of Great Britain, America and Other Countries.

6751 Enlarged and revised. Cloth, 12mo. $1.45
Postage .... .12

Diseases of Dogs.

6752 Hugh Dalziel. The author is one of the first British authorities on dogs. 116 pp.
Paper $0.40
Postage .... .04

Training vs. Breaking.

6753 By S. T. Hammond. This is a book for dog owners, who by its directions can successfully train their hunting dogs. 163 pages. Cloth $0.88
Postage .... .08

The Spaniel and Its Breaking.

6754 By F. H. F. Mercer. Cloth. Illustrated.
Price $0.88
Postage .... .08

American Book of the Dog.

6755 The origin, development, utility, breeding, training, deseases and kennel management. By G. O. Shields. 8 Vo., 700 pages. Cloth $2.45
Postage 26 cents.

First Lessons in Training.

6756 With points and standards of all breeds of dogs. Paper, 106 pages. Price $0.40
Postage 4 cents.

Scientific Education of Dogs for the Gun.

6757 By "H. H." The results of thirty-seven years practical experience. 220 pages. Cloth $2.25
Postage .... .12

Modern Training.

6759 Handling and Kennel Management. By B. Waters. Illustrated. Cloth, 373 pages. Retail $2.00, our price $1.45. Postage 14 cents.

Altemus Library.

6762 Altemus Library. All beautifully bound in half crushed levant with guilt tops, handsomely printed on calendered paper, large clear type. A most beautiful holiday and gift book.
Retail price $1.50
Our price .... .92
6763 Presentation Cloth Edition. Each $0.52
Postage, each .... .08

Sesame and Lilies, Ruskin.
Pleasures of Life, Ludbock;
Bacon's Essays.
Thoughts, Marcus Aurelius Antoinus.
Discourses, Epictetus.
Emerson's Essays, First Series.
Emerson's Essays, Second Series.
Cranford ...... Mrs Gaskell.
Imitation of Christ .... Thomas A'Kempis.
Vicar of Wakefield .... Goldsmith.
Chesterfield's Letters.
Idle Thoughts of an Idle Fellow .... Jerome
Tales from Shakespeare .... Charles and Mary Lamb
Natural Law in the Spiritual World .... Drummond
Addresses .... Drummond
Evolution of Man .... Drummond
My Point of View .... Selections from Drummond
The Scarlet Letter .... Hawthorne
Representative Men .... Emerson
My King and His Service .... Havergal
Reveries of a Bachelor .... Ik. Marvel
House of the Seven Gables .... Hawthorne
Dream Life .... Ik. Marvel
Rab and His Friends, Marjorie Fleming, etc. .... Brown
Essays of Elia .... Lamb
Sartor Resartus .... Carlyle
Heroes and Hero Worship .... Carlyle
Ethics of the Dust .... Ruskin
A Window in Thrums .... J. M. Barrie
Mosses from an Old Manse .... Hawthorne
Twice-Told Tales .... Hawthorne
Uncle Tom's Cabin .... Stowe

American Statesmen. Series No. 6764.

Bound Uniform in cloth 12 mo.
Retail price each $1.25
Our price each .... .88
A series of biographies of men famous in the political history of the United States.

Daniel Webster.	By Henry Cabot Lodge.
Albert Gallatin.	By John Austin Stevens.
James Madison.	By Sidney Howard Gay.
John Adams.	By John T. Morse, Jr.
John Marshall.	By Allan B. Margruder.
Samuel Adams.	Bp J. K. Hosmer.
Thomas H. Benton.	By Theodore Roosevelt.
Henry Clay, 2 vols.	By Carl Schurz.
Patrick Henry.	By Moses Coit Tyler
Gouverneur Morris.	By Theodore Roosevelt.
Martin Van Buren.	By E. M. Shepard.
George Washington, 2 vols.	By Henry Cabot Lodge.
Benjamin Franklin.	By John T. Morse, Jr.
John Jay.	By George Pellew.
Lewis Cass.	By AndrewC. McLaughlin
John Quincy Adams.	By John T. Morse, Jr.
Alexander Hamilton.	By Henry Cabot Lodge.
John C. Calhoun.	By Dr. Von Holst.
Andrew Jackson.	By Prof. W. G. Sumner.
John Randolph.	By Henry Adams.
James Monroe.	By D. C. Gilman.
Thomas Jefferson.	By John T. Morse, Jr.
Abraham Lincoln, 2 vols.	By John T. Morse, Jr.

Postage, each $0 10

American Commonwealths. Series No. 6766.

A series of Histories of the Commonwealths of the United States, with maps. Edited by Horace E. Scudder. Bound in silk cloth, gilt tops, large type, etc.

Virginia .... By John Eston Cooke.
Oregon .... By William Barrows.
Maryland .... By William H. Browne.
Kentucky .... By N. S. Shaler.
Michigan .... By T. M. Cooley.
Kansas .... By L. W. Spring.
California .... By Josiah Royce.
Tennessee .... By James Phelan.
New York .... By E. H. Roberts, Vol. 1
New York .... By E. H. Roberts, Vol. 2
Connecticut .... By Alex Johnson.
Missouri .... By Lucien Carr.
Indiana .... By J. P. Dunn, Jr.
Ohio .... By Rufus King.
Vermont .... By Rowland E. Robinson.
New Jersey .... By Austin Scott.
Pennsylvania .... By Wayne MacVeagh.
Illinois .... By E. G. Mason.
South Carolina .... By Edward McCrady, Jr.
Our price............$0.88
Postage extra each............12

Alcott's, Louisa M., Stories, Series No. 6768.

"Miss Alcott is the benefactor of households".

Little Men.
Little Women.
Eight Cousins.
Jack and Jill.
Work.
Moods.
Life Letters and Journals.
Hospital Sketches.
Modern Mephistopheles.
Rose in Bloom.
Jo's Boys.
Old Fashioned Girl.
Under the Lilacs.

Each 12mo. Cloth. Retail price, each $1.50
Our price, each............98
Postage.............12

Comic Tragedies.

6769 Written by "Jo" and "Meg," and acted by the "Little Women," with a foreword by "Meg." Portraits of Jo and Meg, and a view of the house in which they lived. 16mo., cloth. Uniform with Miss Alcott's books. Retail price.......$1.50
Our price............98

Alcott's Garland Series. Series No. 6770.

A Garland for Girls. Proverb Stories.
Silver Pitcher's. Spinning Wheel Stories.
Retail price, each $1.25
Our price, each............88
Postage.............12

Aunt Jo's Scrap Bag Series. Series No. 6771.

My Boys.
Cupid and Chow-Chow.
My Girls.
Jimmie's Cruise in the Pinafore.
An Old Fashioned Thanksgiving.
Shawl Straps.
16mo., cloth.
Retail price, each............$1.00
Our price, each............70
Set of 6 vols 4.10
Postage, each............08

Arthur's, T. S., Works. Series No. 6773.

(Temperance Series.)
Durably bound in cloth, 12mo., 12 volumes, containing:
The Wedding Guest. Our Homes.
Words of Cheer. Grappling with the Monster.
Cast Adrift. Mother's Rule.
Woman to the Rescue. Friends and Neighbors.
Danger. The True Path.
Saved as by Fire.
Three Years in a Mantrap.
Retail price, per set $6.00
Our price 3.25
Single volumes, each............88
Postage, each, per volume............10

Ten Nights in a Bar Room.

6774 Ten Nights in a Bar Room; And What I Saw There. By T. S. Arthur. A new edition in large type of this famous book, 12mo. Illustrated. Retail price.....$1.25
Our price............84
Postage............10
6775 Home Stories. 6 vols. Sold only in sets.
Sowing the Wind.
Hidden Wings.
At Home.
Not Anything for Peace.
The Peace Makers.
After a Shadow.
Price $2.00

Abbott's, Willis J., American Wars

6777 "The Blue Jackets of 1776." A history of the navy. 32 full page illustrations. Large 4to. Cloth.
Retail price............$2.00
Our price, only............1.25
6778 "The Blue Jackets of 1812." A history of the naval battles of the second war with Great Britain, to which is prefixed an account of the French war of 1798, with 32 illustrations, by W. C. Jackson, and 50 by H. W. McVickar. A new edition, large 4to. Cloth.
Retail price............$2.00
Our price, only 1.25
6779 "The Blue Jackets of 1861." A history of the navy in the American Rebellion; with many full page pictures of great interest. A new edition, 4to., cloth. Retail price............$2.00
Our price, only 1.25
6780 "The Battle Fields of 1861." The initial volume of a History of the land forces of the War for the Union, with many illustrations. 4to, cloth. Retail price......$2.00 Our price only..$1.25
6781 "Battle Fields and Camp Fires." The second volume of the History of the Land Forces in the War for the Union, fully illustrated by W. C. Jackson, 4to, cloth. Retail price............$2.00
Our price 1.25
6782 "Battle Field and Victory." The third volume of the History of the land force in the War for the Union, 4to, cloth. Retail price $2.00
Our price, only 1.25
Postage on above six, each............25

Abbott's American Pioneers and Patriots Series. Series No. 6785.

By John S. C. Abbott. A series illustrating the early history and settlement of our country.

George Washington.
Kit Carson.
LaSalle.
Miles Standish.
Paul Jones.
Peter Stuyvesant.
Benjamin Franklin.
Captain Kidd.
Columbus.
Daniel Boone.
David Crockett.
De Soto.
Each in one volume, 12mo. Illustrated.
Per volume $0.75
Our price, each............10
Per set of 12 vols 8.00

Alger, Horatio, Jr.'s Popular Juvenile Books for Boys.

12mo. Cloth. Illustrated.
6786 Ragged Dick Series. 12mo. Cloth.
Ragged Dick.
Fame and Fortune.
Mark, the Match Boy.
Rough and Ready.
Ben, the Luggage Boy.
Rufus and Rose.
Set of six volumes $5.25
Single volumes, each............88
6787 Tattered Tom Stories. 12mo. cloth. First Series. Illustrated.
Tattered Tom. Phil the Fiddler.
Paul the Peddler. Slow and Sure.
Set of four volumes............$3.50
Single volumes, each............88
6788 Tattered Tom Stories. 12mo. cloth. Second Series. Illustrated.
Julius. Sam's Chance.
The Young Outlaw. The Telegraph Boy.
Set of four volumes............$3.50
Single volume, each............88
6789 Campaign Series. 12mo. cloth. Illustrated.
Frank's Campaign. Paul Prescott's Charge.
Charley Codman's Cruise.
Set of three volumes $2.50
Single volumes, each............88
6790 Luck and Pluck Series. 12mo. cloth. First Series. Illustrated.
Luck and Pluck Strong and Steady.
Sink or Swim. Strive and Succeed.
Set of four volumes............$3.50
Single volume, each............88
6791 Luck and Pluck Series. 12mo. cloth. Second Series. Illustrated.
Try and Trust. Risen from the Ranks.
Bound to Rise. Herbert Carter's Legacy.
Set of four volumes............$3.50
Single volume, each............88
6792 Brave and Bold Series. 12mo. cloth. Illustrated.
Brave and Bold. Shifting for Himself.
Jack Ward Wait and Hope.
Set of four volumes............$3.50
Single volume, each............88

Juvenile Books—Continued.

6793 Pacific Series. 12mo. cloth. Illustrated.
The Young Adventurer. The Young Explorer.
The Young Miner. Ben's Nugget.
Set of four volumes............$3.50
Single volume, each............88
6794 Atlantic Series. 12mo. cloth. Illustrated.
Young Circus Rider Hector's Inheritance.
Do and Dare. Helping Himself.
Set of four volumes............$3.50
Single volumes, each............88
6795 Way to Success Series. 4 vols. 12mo. cloth.
Bob Burton. The Store Boy.
Luke Walton. Struggling Upward.
Set of four volumes............$3.50
Single volumes, each............88
6796 New World Series. By Horatio Alger, Jr.
Digging for Gold. Facing the World.
In a New World.
Set of three volumes, $2.50. Single volumes, each $0.88
Postage extra, per vol. 10
6798 Only an Irish Boy. By Horatio Alger, Jr. 12mo............$0.88
6800 Victor Vane. By Horatio Alger, Jr. 12mo..$0.88

Arabian Nights' Entertainments.

6802 Translated from the Original Arabic by Edward William Lane. Handsomely illustrated with one hundred and fifty illustrations. Revised and enlarged edition. Royal octavo. Cloth.
Retail price............$2.00
Our price 1.40
Postage, 33c. extra.

Alger Series For Boys. Series 6804.

A series of Spirited stories for boys, by popular writers. Each Illustrated, uniform in size, bound in handsome cloth binding.
Retail price each $1.00
Our price, each............52
Postage, each 10 cents extra.

Adrift in the Wilds. By Edward S. Ellis.
The Boy Cruisers, By St. George Rathborne.
Budd Boyd's Triumph. By William P. Chipman.
Captain Kidd's Gold. By James Franklin Pitts.
Captured by Apes. By Harry Prentice.
The Castaways. By James Otis.
Dan, the Newsboy. By Horatio Alger, Jr.
The Errand Boy. By Horatio Alger, Jr.
Frank Fowler, the Cash Boy. By Horatio Alger, Jr.
Guy Harris, the Runaway. By Harry Castlemon.
The Island Treasure. By Frank H Converse.
Jaunt Through Java. By Edward S. Ellis.
Joe's Luck. By Horatio Alger, Jr.
Julian Mortimer. By Harry Castlemon.
Lost in the Canon. By Alfred R. Calhoun.
Roy Gilbert's Search. By William P. Chipman.
A Runaway Brig. By James Otis.
Search for the Silver City. By James Otis.
The Slate-Picker. By Harry Prentice.
Tom Temple's Career. By Horatio Alger, Jr.
Tom Thatcher's Fortune. By Horatio Alger, Jr.
Tom, the Bootblack. By Horatio Alger, Jr.
Tom, the Ready. By Randolph Hill.
Tony, the Hero. By Horatio Alger, Jr.
The Train Boy. By Horatio Alger, Jr.
The Treasure Finders. By James Otis.
A Young Hero. By Edward S. Ellis.

Burnham, Clara Louise, Works. Series No. 6805.

	Retail price.	Our price.
12mo, cloth.		
Young Maids and Old.	$1.50	$1.05
Next Door............	1.25	.88
No Gentlemen............	1.25	.88
A Sane Lunatic............	1.25	.88
Miss Bagg's Secretary............	1.25	.88
Mistress of Beech Knoll............	1.25	.88

Postage, each, 10c extra.

Buffalo Bill, From Prairie to Palace.

6807 Compiled by John M. Burke, by authority of General W. F. Cody (Buffalo Bill). Profusely illustrated. The title of this book tells something of the wide range of interest covered by its 275 pages. Illustrated paper cover............$0.35
Handsome cloth binding 75

Dickens' Works.

6911 New Columbus Edition, 15 volumes, large type, good paper, 12mo. cloth. Retail price....$5.00
Our price..............................3.75

Deland, Margaret, Works.

6913 Beautifully bound in cloth, 12mo.
The Old Garden.
John Ward, Preacher.
Sidney (A Novel).

	Retail price, each	Our price
	$1.25	.88
Our price, extra		.10

Davis, Richard Harding, Works.

6914 Each 12mo, cloth extra.

	Retail price.	Our price.
Our English Cousins	$1.25	$0.88
West From a Car Window	1.25	.88
Rulers of the Mediterranean	1.25	.88
Van Bibber, and others	1.00	.70
Postage, extra, 12 cents each.		

Evans, Augusta J., Works.
Series 6917.

Almost every one is familiar with this author's writings, the books are all durably bound in cloth with gold trimmings; size 5¼ x 7¼; large type and good paper.

Beulah, Inez, Macaria, Retail price each, $1.75 Our price... $1.26
St. Elmo Vashti, Infelice, At the Mercy of Tiberius. Retail price, $2.00. Our price, each... $1.35
Postage, each..............................14

Ely, Prof. R. T., Works.

6918 Labor Movement in America. All 12mo., cloth binding. By Prof. Richhard T. Ely.
Retail price..............................$1.50
Our price..............................1.05
6919 Problems of To-Day. A Discussion of Tariff, Taxation and Monopolies. By Prof. Richard T. Ely. 12mo. Revised and enlarged edition.
Retail price..............................1.50
Our price..............................1.05
6920. Social Aspects of Christianity. By Prof. R. T. Ely. Retail price..............................90
Our price..............................65
6921 Taxation in American States and Cities. 12mo.
Retail price..............................1.75
Our price..............................1.23
Postage, each..............................12
6922 Socialism and Social Reform. By Prof. Ely. 12mo. Cloth.
Retail price..............................1.50
Our price..............................1.05
Postage, extra, 12c.

Emerson, R. W., Works.

6923–2 vols. Cloth, 12 mo.
Representative Men.
Nature, Addresses and Lectures.
Retail price..............................$2.00
Our price..............................1.05
Postage..............................24

Emerson's Essays.

6924 (Ralph Waldo) printed from new plates on fine laid paper and tastefully bound in uniform style, in two volumes.
Essays, First Series complete.
Essays, Second Series complete.
Per set of two volumes, gilt
top..............................$0.94
Half calf..............................1.95
Postage, extra..............................28

6925 Avon Edition of Emerson's Essays, 2 volumes, cloth.
12 mo..............................$0.38
Postage..............................20

Emerson's Complete Works.

6926 Complete works of Ralph Waldo Emerson, with portraits. 12 volumes, 12mo.; gilt top. Per set..............................$14.60

Emerson's Handy Volumes.

6928 Beautiful 12mo. edition, containing Emerson's Essays, 1st and 2nd volumes and Representative Men, bound in vellum cloth, with gold stampings. 3 volumes in box to match..............................$0.78
Postage, extra, 22c.

Eliot, George, Works.

6930 New Library Edition, 8 volumes. Illustrated, large type, 12mo., cloth. Gilt tops (complete).
Retail price..............................$8.00
Our price..............................4.25

Eliot's Works.

6931 New Standard Edition, 8 volumes. Large type, Ornamental, Cloth. 12mo. (complete).
Retail price..............................$5.50
Our price..............................3.00
Half calf..............................8.00

Eliot's Works.

6932 New Popular Edition, 6 volumes. 12mo.
Cloth..............................$1.25

Eggleston, Edward, Works.
Series 6935.

(illustration: THE HOOSIER SCHOOL-BOY, Edward Eggleston)

	Retail price.	Our price.
Roxy. Illustrated. 12mo.	$1.50	$1.05
The Circuit Rider. Illustrated. 12mo.	1.50	1.05
The End of the World. Illustrated. 12mo.	1.50	1.05
The Graysons. 12mo.	1.50	1.05
The Hoosier Schoolmaster. Illustrated. 12mo.	1.25	.88
The Mystery of Metropolisville. Illustrated. 12mo.	1.50	1.05
The Hoosier Schoolboy. Illustrated. 12mo.	1.00	.70
Queer Stories for Boys and Girls. 12mo.	1.00	.70
The Faith Doctor. 12mo.	1.50	1.05
Postage, extra, 12c.		

Ewing (Juliana Horatio) Works.
Series 6937.

Six to Sixteen.
A Flat-Iron for a Farthing.
A Great Emergency, and Other Tales.
Mrs. Overtheway's Remembrances and Other Tales.
Jan of the Windmill.
Jackanapes and Other Tales.
We and the World.
Melchoir's Dream.
Lob-Lie-by-the-Fire.
9 vols., 12 mo. Illustrated..............................$2.50
Single volumes, each....$0.30. Postage, each...10

Ellis, Edward S., Works.

6938 Log Cabin Series. By Edward S. Ellis, 5 volumes, 12mo. cloth.
Camp Fire and Wigwam.
Footprints in the Forest.
Lost Trail.
Set of 5 Volumes............$2.50
Single volumes, each..............................88
6939 Deerfoot Series. By Edward S. Ellis, 3 volumes, 12mo. cloth.
Hunters of the Ozark.
Camp in the Mountains.
The Lost War Trail.
In set of 3 volumes..............................$2.50
Single volumes, each..............................10
6940 Boy Pioneer Series. By Edward S. Ellis, 3 volumes, 12mo. cloth.
Ned in the Block House.   Ned in the Woods.
Ned on the River.
In sets of 3 volumes..............................$2.50
Single volumes, each..............................88
6941 Wildwood Series. By Edward S. Ellis, 12mo. cloth.
Through Forest and Fire. On the Trail of the Moose. Across Texas.
Set of 3 volumes...$2.50   Single volumes, each...$0.88
6942 Wyoming Series. By E. S. Ellis.
Wyoming.   Storm Mountain.
Cabin on the Clearing.
3 volumes, 12 mo. cloth..............................$2.50
Single volumes, each..............................88
6944 Bear and Wilderness Series. By E. S. Ellis.
River Fugitives.   Wilderness Fugitives.
Lena—Wingo the Mohawk.
3 volumes, complete..............................$2.50
Single volumes, each..............................88
6945 War Whoop Series. By Lieut. Jayne, (E. S. Ellis.)
Lost in the Wilderness.   The Cave in the Mountain.
In the Pecos Country.
Per set of 3 volumes..............................$2.50
Single volumes, each..............................88
6946 Great Cattle Trail. By Ed. Ellis. 12mo...$0.88
Postage, extra, on Ellis' books, per vol. 10c.

Ebers, George, Works.

6949 Beautiful cloth binding, printed on super-calendered paper and from new plates.
Homo Sum.   Egyptian Princess.   Uarda.
Joshua.   Bride of the Nile.   Only a Word.
The Emperor.
Sold only in sets of 7 volumes. Retail price...$8.00
Our price..............................$8.00   Postage..............................72
6950 George Ebers' Works. Popular Edition, 4 volumes, cloth, 12 mo....$2.48   Postage..............................44

Elsie, Books, The
Series 6952.

(illustration: THE ELSIE BOOKS)

By Martha Finley, in 18 volumes, 12mo. cloth.
Elsie Dinsmore.
Elsie's Girlhood.
Elsie's Holiday at Roselands.
Elsie's Womanhood.
Elsie's Motherhood.
Elsie's Children.
Elsie's Widowhood.
Grandmother Elsie.
Elsie Yachting with the Raymonds.
Elsie's Vacation.
Elsie at Viamede.
Elsie's New Relations.
Elsie at Nantucket.
The Two Elsies.
Elsie's Kith and Kin.
Elsie's Friends at Woodburn.
Christmas with Grandma Elsie.
Elsie and the Raymonds.
Elsie at Ion.
Elsie at the World's Fair.
Retail price, each...$1.25   Our price, each...$0.75
Postage..............................10
Complete set of 20 volumes..............................14.50

Books—Continued.

(illustration: Elsie Dinsmore)

6953 Quarter Century Edition of the famous Elsie Dinsmore. By Martha Finley. 16mo. Bound in cloth, decorated in ink and silver, a beautiful present for girls.
Retail price..............................$0.75
Our price..............................40
Postage, extra..............................08

Full Watered Silk Edition.
Series 6956.

Consisting of twenty-one volumes of the best works in English and American Fiction. Beautifully printed on fine paper, and bound in full watered silk gold stamping, gilt edges, silk headbands, ribbon marker, rich linings. Each of the volumes contain a photogravure and a photogravure title page.
Retail price, per volume, boxed..............................$1.50
Our price, each..............................75
Postage, extra, 10c.

Blackmore, R. D.	Lorna Doone. Vol. I.
Blackmore, R. D.	Lorna Doone. Vol. II.
Brown, Dr. John	Rab and His Friends
Drummond, Henry	Greatest Things in the World, and other Addresses.
Eliot, George.	Ramola. Vol. I.
" "	Ramola. Vol. II.
" "	Mill on the Floss. Vol. I.
" "	Mill on the Floss. Vol. II.
Hawthorne, Nathaniel.	House of the Seven Gables.
" "	Scarlet Letter.
" "	Mosses from an Old Manse.
" "	Twice Told Tales. Vol. I.
" "	Twice Told Tales. Vol. II.
Muluck, Miss.	John Halifax. Vol. I.
Muluck, Miss.	John Halifax. Vol. II.
Sewall, Anna.	Black Beauty.
St. Pierre, Benardinde.	Paul and Virginia.
Tennyson, Lord.	The Princess.
Warner, Susan.	Wide, Wide World. Vol. I.
Warner, Susan.	Wide, Wide World. Vol. II.
Yonge, Charlotte M.	Book of Golden Deeds.

Fireside Series for Girls.
Series 6958.

(illustration: FIRESIDE GIRLS)

A carefully selected series of books for girls, written by authors of acknowledged reputation; will win the hearts of all girl readers. Esther. By Rosa Nouchette Carey. Illustrated.
A World of Girls: The Story of a School. By L. T. Meade. Illustrated.
The Heir of Redcliffe. By Charlotte M. Yonge. Illustrated.
The Story of a Short Life. By Juliana Horatio Ewing.
A Sweet Girl Graduate. By L. T. Meade. Illustrated.
Our Bessie. By Rosa Nouchette Carey. Illustrated.
Six to Sixteen: A Story for Girls. By Juliana Horatio Ewing. Illustrated.
The Dove in the Eagle's Nest. By Charlotte M. Yonge. Illustrated.
Giannetta: A Girl's Story of Herself. By Rosa Mulholland. Illustrated.
Jan of the Windmill: A Story of the Plains. By Juliana Horatio Ewing. Illustrated.
Averil. By Rosa Nouchette Carey. Illustrated.
Alice in Wonderland and Alice through a Looking Glass. 2 vols. in one. By Lewis Carroll. Illustrated.
Merle's Crusade. By Rosa Nouchette Carey. Illustrated.
Girl Neighbors; or, The Old Fashion and the New. By Sarah Tytler. Illustrated.
Polly: A New Fashioned Girl. By L. T. Meade. Illustrated.
Aunt Diana. By Rosa N. Carey. Illustrated.
At the Back of the North Wind. By Geo. McDonald.
A Chaplet of Pearls. By Grace Aguilar.
Days of Bruce. By Grace Aguilar.
Water Babies. By Rev. Chas. Kingsley.
Uniform cloth binding.
Retail price. Each...$1.00   Our price. Each...$0.52
Postage, each extra, 12 cents.

*** SHEETING IN 25 YARD LENGTHS. A feature originating with us. See our Domestic Department for information.

When ordering goods shipped by mail, be sure to allow money for postage. If you send too much we will refund balance.

Fleming, May Agnes, Novels.
Series 6960.

Guy Earlscourt's Wife.
A Wonderful Woman.
A Terrible Secret.
A Mad Marriage.
Norine's Revenge.
One Night's Mystery.
Kate Danton.
Silent and True.
Maud Percy's Secret.
The Queen of the Isle.
Edith Percival (new).

Heir of Carlton.
Carried by Storm.
Lost for a Woman.
A Wife's Tragedy.
A Changed Heart.
Pride and Passion.
Sharing Her Crime.
A Wronged Wife.
The Actress' Daughter.
The Midnight Queen.

12mo. cloth. Retail price $1.50
Our price, each 98
Postage 12

Famous African Explorers and Adventurers.

6961 2 volumes, cloth, 12mo. Per set (2 volumes) $0.75
Postage 24

Famous Frontiersmen, Pioneers and Scouts.

6962 A thrilling narrative of the lives of Boone, Crawford, Gisty, Finney, McCullough, Wetzel, Kenton, Clark, Brady, Crockett, Houston, Carson, California Joe, Wild Bill, Texas Jack, Buffalo Bill and Certain Jack, including Custer's last fight and Cook's recent campaign; 550 pages, illustrated. Bound in cloth, with gold stamps.
Our special price $0.75
Postage 20

Finley Books, The.
Series 6963.

By Martha Finley, 12mo, cloth.

Old Fashioned Boy.
Wanted, a Pedigree.
The Thorn in the Nest.
Signing the Contract.
Casella.
Our Fred.
All are bound in beautiful cloth with gold emblematic title stamps, large print and calendered paper. Retail price $1.25
Our price 75
Postage 10

Fielding, Henry, Works.

6965 New Edition of Tom Jones in two Volumes, 12mo, Cloth. Retail price $1.50
Our price 75
Postage 24 cents extra.

Fairmont Sets.
Series 6968.

Comprising standard and fast-selling classics, beautifully bound in half Russia, in boxes or match. Retail price, each, per set of 3 vols. $3.00.
Our price, each, per set of 3 vols. $2.00.
Set No. 1 contains: Pleasures of Life, Tales from Shakespeare and Sesame and Lilies.
Set No. 2 contains: Bacon's Essays, Thoughts of Marcus Aurelius and Discourses of Epictetus.
Set No. 3 contains: Emerson's Essays 1st, Emerson's Essays 2nd, and Representative Men.
Set No. 4 contains: Cranford, Reveries of a Bachelor and Vicar of Wakefield.
Set No. 5 contains: Dream of Life, Scarlet Letter and House of Seven Gables.
Set No. 6 contains: Sartor Resartus, Chesterfield's Letters and Heroes and Hero Worship.
Postage, per set extra, 22c.

Golden Gleams of Thought.

6970 Thoughts from the Words of Leading Orators, Divines, Philosophers, Statesmen and Poets. By Rev. S. P. Linn. Handsomely bound in silk cloth with gold edges. Retail price $1.50
Our price 1.05
Postage, 14c. extra.

Golden Poems.

6971 By British and American authors, edited by Francis F. Browne. Uniform binding with Golden Gleams of Thought. Retail price $1.50
Our price 1.05

Grote's Greece.

6972 4 vols., silk cloth binding, new plates, large print, calender paper. Retail price $6.00
Our price 3.00
Half calf binding 3.98
Postage 66

Goethe, J. W. Von, Works of.

6973 5 vols. Illustrated 12mo., cloth, gilt top..$5.00
5 vols. illustrated., 12mo., half calf, gilt top...7.50
I. Autobiography of Goethe.   IV. Faust and Dramatic
II. Wilhelm Meister's Ap-   Works.
prenticeship and   V. Poems of Goethe,
Travels.   Phigenia, Torquato Tasso, etc.
III. Elective Affinities, Sorrows of Werther, Travels in Italy.

Guizot's France.

6974 8 vols., cloth, (best edition). Retail price.$12.00
Our price 6.25
Half calf binding 7.95
Postage 96

Guizot's England.

6976 4 vols. Retail price $6.50
Our price 3.00
Half calf binding 4.20
Postage 55

Greenwood, Grace, Works.

6977 These works are handsomely bound and illustrated, 12mo, cloth. "Stories of My Childhood." "History of My Pets."
Retail price each ..$1.50   Our price each...$0.75
Postage, each 10

Goethe's William Meister.

6978 2 volumes; cloth. 12mo.
Per set, 2 volumes $1.50
Postage 24

Goethe's Faust and Dramatic Works.

6980 2 volumes; cloth. 12mo.
Per set, 2 volumes $1.50
Postage 24

Grant and His Travels.

6981 2 volumes; cloth, 12mo. Per set (2 vols) ..$0.75
Postage 24

Grant's Memoirs.
2 Vols.

ORIGINAL EDITION.

6982 Personal Memoirs of U. S. Grant, with portraits, maps, etc., 2 volumes, 1231 pages. Cloth and gilt.
Subscription price $7.00
Our price 3.25
Postage 50 cents extra.
Subscription price in sheep, library binding ...10.00
Our price 4.50
Postage, 50c. extra.

Green's History of the English People.

Please note that we do not sell less than a full set.

6984 History of the English People. By John Richard Green. Printed from new plates, large clear type, 5 volumes, large 12mo., cloth.
Publishers' price $6.00
Our price 2.90
Half calf, 5 vols 4.95
Postage 48

Short History of the English People.

6985 By John R. Green, with colored maps and tables. 12mo., cloth $1.05
Postage extra 19

Gibbon's Roman Empire.

6986 History of the Decline and Fall of Roman Empire. By Edward Gibbon. With Dean Milman's notes complete. New edition, containing over 2,000 pages. 5 Volumes, 12mo., cloth.....$2.50
6 Volumes, 12mo., half calf 6.00
6987 Gibbon's Roman Empire. New Vellum Cloth Edition gilt tops, 5 Volumes, large type 2.15
6989 Popular Edition. Gibbon's Roman Empire. 5 Volumes, 12mo., Cloth 1.75

Hawthorne, Nathaniel, Works.
Price.

6991 Scarlet Letter. 16mo., cloth, red and white $0.32
6992 House of the Seven Gables. 16mo., red and white cloth 22
6993 A Wonder-book for Girls and Boys. 16mo. red and white cloth...23
6994 Mosses from an Old Manse. 16mo., red and white cloth....22
6995 The Snow Image, and Other Twice-Told Tales. 16mo., red and white cloth 22
6996 Twice Told Tales. 16mo., red and white cloth 22
6997 Blithdale Romances. 16mo. red and white cloth 22
6998 Marble Faun. By Nathaniel Hawthorne 12mo., cloth, gilt top.
Retail price ......$2.00   Our price ...1.45
Postage, 12 cents extra.
6999 Hawthorne's Works. 12mo., cloth, Library Style, 5 volumes. Retail price 3.00
Our price per set of 5 Volumes 1.75
Postage, extra 65

Marble Faun.

7000 Beautiful 2 volume holiday edition of Marble Faun, by Hawthorne. Retail price...$6.00
Our price 4.35
Postage, 24 cents extra.

Hawthorne's Works.

7001 New Beautiful 16mo. presentation edition containing Scarlet Letter, Twice Told Tales, Mosses from and Old Manse and House of Seven Gables. Red and white vellum cloth with box to match. Per set of 4 volumes.....$0.98
Postage extra 30 cents.

Habberton, John, Works.

7002 Helen's Babies, by Jno. Habberton. Cloth, 16mo. new edition. Retail price $0.75
Our price 35
Postage, extra 09

Holmes, Mrs. Mary J., Novels.
Series 7005.

Daisy Thornton.
Chateau D'Or.
Darkness and Daylight.
Hugh Worthington.
Cameron Pride.
Rose Mather.
Ethelyn's Mistake.
Millbank.
Edna Browning.
West Lawn.
Lena Rivers.
Mildred.
Forest House.
Madeline.
Marguerite (New).
Homestead on the Hillside.
Cousin Maude.
Meadow Brook.
Dora Deane.
Gretchen (New).
Christmas Stories.

Marian Gray.
Edith Lyle.
Queenie Hetherton.
Bessie's Fortune (New).
English Orphans.
Tempest and Sunshine.
Retail price, each $1.50
Our price, each...$0.98.   Postage.....12

Harland, Marion, Works.
Series 7006.

Alone.
Nemesis.
Ruby's Husband.
Phemie's Tempt'n The Empty Heart.
Helen Gardner.
Husbands and Homes

Hidden Path.
Miriam.
At Last.
From My Youth Up
Jessamine
Moss Side.
Sunny Bank.
My Little Love.
True as Steel.

Retail price, per volume $1.50
Our price 98

Holland, Dr. J. C., Complete Works.
Series 7007.

New edition with the author's latest revisions. In 16 volumes.
The Mistress of the Manse.
Puritan's Guests, and other Poems.
Titcomb's Letters to Young People.
Plain Talks on Family Subjects.
Concerning the Jones Family.
Every Day Topics (Second Series).
Seven Oaks.
Lessons in Life.
Kathrina.
Gold Foil.
Miss Gilbert's Career.
The Bay Path.
Arthur Bonnicastle.   Every Day Topics. (First
Bitter Sweet.   Series.)
                          Nicholas Minturn.
Bound in English cloth, small 12mo. Sold in separate volumes......................$0.88
Or in sets of 16 volumes 13.75
Postage, per volume, extra 10

Holland's Poetical Works.

7008 The Complete Poetical Writings of Dr. J. G. Holland. With illustrations by C. S. Reinhart, C. J. Griswold, and Mary Hallock Foote, and a portrait by Wyatt Eaton. From new stereotype plates. 8vo. handsome cloth binding.
Retail Price $3.50
Our price ....$2.38.   Postage, 14 cents extra.

MacDonald, George, Works.
Series 7121.

With illustrations on wood and steel. Being the first collected uniform edition of the author's writings; 23 vols., 12mo, cloth.

Annals of a Quiet Neighborhood.
The Seaboard Parish.
Guild Court.
Alec Forbes of Howglen.
Robert Falconer.
The Vicar's Daughter.
Paul Faber, Surgeon.
Thomas Wingfold, Curate.
Wilfred Cumbermede.
Sir Gibbie.
St. George and St. Michael.
What's Mine's Mine.
Phantastes.
The Portant.
David Elginbrod.
Adela Cathcart.
Malcolm.
The Marquis of Lossie.
Warlock o' Glenwarlock.
Mary Marston.
Weighed and Wanting.
Donal Grant.
Stephen Archer.
There and Back.

Retail price, each.....$1.50   Our price......$0.95
Postage, extra...... .12

Napoleon Bonaparte, Memoirs of.
7123 By Bourrienne, his private secretary; to which are added an account of the important events of the hundred days of Napoleon's surrender to the English, and of his residence and death at St. Helena. Beautifully bound and illustrated. 4 vols. Cloth. Retail price.....$5.00
Our price...... 3.45
Postage, 50 cents extra.

Napoleon and His Marshals.
7124 By Headley. 2 vols. 12mo. Cloth.........$1.00
Postage................ .24

Napoleon Bonaparte.
7125 By Jno. S. C. Abbott, illustrated maps and portraits on steel, 2 Volumes, 8 Vo.
Retail price.........$7.00
Our price...... 5.00

Olive Optic's Standard Books.
All of the following series are handsomely bound in cloth, 12mo, and illustrated.

7126 Blue and Gray Series.
Taken by the Enemy.
A Victorious Union.
Stand by the Union.
Fighting for the Right.
On the Blockade.
Within the Enemy's Lines.
6 volumes, per set.........$5.85
Each, per volume......... .98

7127 Army and Navy Series.
Soldier Boy.
Sailor Boy.
Young Lieutenant.
Brave Old Salt.
Yankee Middy.
Fighting Joe.
6 volumes, cloth......... 5.85
Single volume, each......... .98

7128 Yacht Club Series.
Little Bobtail.
Dorcas Club.
Coming Wave.
Money Makers.
Yacht Club.
Ocean Born.
6 volumes, cloth......... 5.85
Single volumes, each......... .98

7130 Young America Abroad Series.
Dikes and Ditches.
Outward Bound.
Red Cross.
Down the Rhine.
Palace and Cottage.
Shamrock and Thistle.
6 volumes complete......... 5.85
Single volumes, each......... .98

7131 Young America Abroad, 2d Series.
Cross and Crescent.
Isles of the Seas.
Northern Lands.
Sunny Shores.
Up the Baltic.
Vine and Olive.
6 volumes complete, per set......... 5.85
Single volumes, each......... .98

7132 All Over the World Series.
A Missing Million.
A Young Knight Errant.
A Millionaire at Sixteen.
Strange Sights Abroad.
4 volumes complete......... 3.40
Single volume, each......... .87
Postage on any Optic Book, 12 cents each extra.

Paine, Thomas Works.
7135 Age of Reason. 12mo. cloth.........$0.40
Postage 4 and 10c......... .16
7136 Rights of Man. 12mo cloth......... .40
Postage extra......... .16
7137 Theological Works of Thos. Paine, containing Age of Reason, Examination of the Prophecies, Letters to Bishop Llandoff, etc., 12mo, cloth. Retail price......... 1.50
Our price......... .75
Postage......... .12
7139 Political Works Complete, Containing Rights of Man, Common Sense and the Crisis, 12mo.
Retail price......... 1.50
Our price......... .75
Postage extra......... .12

** Our next Catalogue will be sent only to those who send us 15 cents for postage.

We have an Educational Catalogue, quoting all adopted school books, specially designed for teachers and students. (Free.)

Pansy Books.
Series 7140.

Among the substantial reasons of the great popularity of the "Pansy Books" is their truth to nature and to life. All are handsomely bound in English silk cloth with gold embossed title stamps, and contain large bold type and calendered paper.

Aunt Hannah, Martha and John.
Chautauqua Girls at Home.
Christie's Christmas.
Crissy's Endeavor.
Divers Women.
Echoing and Re-echoing.
Eighty-Seven.
Endless Chain (An).
Ester Ried.

Modern Prophet.
Man of the House.
New Graft on the Family Tree (A).
One Commonplace Day.
Pocket Measure (The).
Profiles.
Ruth Erskine's Crosses.
Randolphs (The).
Sevenfold Trouble (A).
Sidney Martin's Christmas.
Spun from Fact.
Stephen Mitchell's Journey.
Those Boys.
Three People.
Tip Lewis and His Lamp.
Twenty Minutes Late
Wise and Otherwise.
Wanted.

Ester Ried Yet Speaking.
Four Girls at Chautauqua.
From different Standpoints
Hall in the Grove (The).
Her Associate Members.
Household Puzzle.
Interrupted.
John Remington, Martyr.
Judge Burnham's Daughters.
Julia Ried.
King's Daughter (The).
Little Fishers and Their Nets.
Links in Rebecca's Life.
Miss Dee Dunmore Bryant.
Mrs. Solomon Smith Looking On.
Modern Exodus (A).
Only Ten Cents.

Retail price, each.........$1.50
Our price......... .98
Ordering in lots of 10, at one time, 95c each.
Postage, each, 10c. extra.

Pansy Books.
Series 7141.
Cunning Workmen.
Dr. Dean's Way.
Grandpapa's Darlings.
Miss Priscilla Hunter.
Mrs. Dean's Way.
What She Said.
Bound in extra cloth, 12mo.
Retail price, each.........$1.25
Our price, each......... .85
Postage......... .09

Phelps, Elizabeth Stewart, Works,
Series 7145.

The Gates Series, 3 vols. cloth, 12 mo.
	Retail price.	Our price.
The Gates Ajar.	$1.50	$1.05
Beyond the Gates.	1.25	.88
The Gates Between.	1.25	.88
Per set of three volumes.	4.00	2.75
Postage each 12c.

Gypsy Books.
7146 Gypsy Brenton. Gypsy's Cousin Joy. Gypsy's Sowing and Reaping. Gypsy's Year at the Golden Crescent.
4 vols., 16mo, cloth, each.........$0.65
Or in set, boxed......... 2.50

Poetical Works.
Red Line Poets.
Series 7147.

Our new line of beautiful Red Line Poets are the best bound, best paper and largest print. All are handsomely bound in cloth with gold edges.
Retail price, each.........$1.25
Our price, each......... .48
In lots of 10 or more, each......... .45

Arnold Edwin.
*Aurora Leigh.
Ayrton.
Beauties of Shakespeare.
British Female Poets.
*Browning (Mrs.)
*Browning (Robt.)
*Bryant (W. C.)
*Burns.
*Byron.
Calverly.
Campbell
Chaucer.
*Childe Harold.
Christian Year.
Coleridge.
Cook, E. Eliza.
Cowper.
Crabbe.
*Dante.
Dryden.
Emerson.
*Eliot (Geo.)

*Lay of the Last Minstrel
*Longfellow, Early Poems
*Lowell. Early Poems.
*Lucile.
Macaulay.
*Marmion.
*Meredith (Owen.)
*Milton.
*Moore.
Motherwell.
Mulock (Miss.)
*Odyssey.
Ossian.
Paradise Lost.
Pilgrim's Progress.
*Poe (Edgar A.)
Poetry of Flowers.
Poetry of Love.
Poetry of Passion.
Poetry of Sentiment.
Poets of America.
Pope.
Praed.

Series 7147—Continued.

*Familiar Quotations.
Famous Poems.
*Favorite Poems.
*Faust (Goethe.)
Freeman's Poems.
*Gems 1001.
*Goethe's Poems.
Golden Treasury.
*Goldsmith.
Gray (Thomas.)
Greene Marlowe & Johnson.
Half Hours with Poets.
Halleck, Fitz-Greene.
Heber Bishop.
Heine.
*Hemans.
Hubert.
*Hood.
Holmes.
*Hugo (Victor.)
*Illiad (Homer's)
Hugoldsby Legends.
Irish Humorous Poems.
Irish Melodies.
*Jean Ingelow.
*Keats.
Kingsley (Chas.)
*Lady of the Lake.
*Lalla Rookh.

*Proctor.
*Red Letter Poems.
Religious Poems.
Rogers.
Rossetti (Dante G.)
*Schiller.
*Scott.
Scottish Poems.
*Shakespeare.
Shelley.
Shipton (Anna.)
Smith, Alex.
Songs Household.
Songs Sacred.
Southey.
Spanish Ballads.
Spencer.
Surf and Wave.
Swinburne.
Tasso.
*Tennyson.
Thackary.
Thompson.
Tupper.
Virgil.
War Songs.
Wesley.
White Kirke.
*Whittier (J. G.) Early
Willis.   [Poems.
*Wordsworth.

Beautiful Edition of Woodbine Poets.

7148 Any of the above Red Line Poems marked * can be furnished in beautiful padded binding with full gold edges; suitable for presentation purposes.
Retail price, each.........$1.50
Our price, each......... .95
Lots of 10 at one time......... .90
Postage, each......... .12

Poets' Presentation Edition
Series 7150.

Consisting of fifteen volumes of the best poets. Beautifully printed on fine paper and bound in parti-colored cloth. Elaborately embossed from a new design in genuine gold. Gilt tops. ribbon markers. All of the volumes contain photogravures and photogravure title pages.
Retail price, each.........$0.75
Our price, each......... .42
Postage, each extra......... .08

Arnold, Sir Edwin.........Light of Asia
Aytoun, Wm. Edmunston....Lays of the Scottish Cavaliers.
Browning, Robert.........Selections.
Byron, Lord.........Childe Harold's Pilgrimage.
Longfellow, Henry W.........Earlier Poems.
Lowell, James Russell.........Earlier Poems.
Macaulay, Lord.........Lays of Ancient Rome.
Meredith, Owen.........Lucile.
Moore, Thomas.........Lalla Rookh.
Poems, Edgar Allan.........Poems.
Scott, Sir Walter.........Lady of the Lake.
Tennyson, Lord.........Princess
Tennyson, Lord.........Idylls of the King.
Tennyson, Lord.........In Memoriam.
Whittier, John Greenleaf.........Poems.

Westminster Edition of Poets.
Series 7155.

New Cover Design, beautifully decorated in white, gold and colors. Full gilt edges. Each book in a box with printed wrappers. 12mo.
Retail price, each.........$1.25
Our price, each......... .75

Browning (Mrs.)
Browning (Robert)
Bryant.
Burns.
Byron.
Eliot.
Familiar Quotations.
Favorite Poems.
Golden Treasury.
Goldsmith.
Hemans.
Ingelow.
Lady of the Lake.
Lalla Rookh.
Longfellow (Early Poems.)
Lowell.
Lucile.
Meredith.
Milton.
Moore.
Proctor.
Red Letter Poems.
Scott.
Tennyson.
Whittier (Early Poems.)
Postage each, extra, 12 cents.

The Children's Book of Poetry.

7156 Compiled by Henry T. Coates. With nearly 200 illustrations. The most complete collection of poetry for children ever published, quarto.

	Retail price.	Our price.
Cloth extra, gilt edges	$3.00	$2.10

Beautiful Illustrative Octavos.

7158 Bound in flexible leather. All are superbly illustrated. Each one volume complete.

Christmas Carol. By Dickens.
Hanging of the Crane. By Longfellow.
Snow Bound. By Whittier.
Dream of Fair Woman. By Tennyson.

Retail price, each	$2.00
Our price, each	1.40
Postage, each 12 cents.	

The Cow Boy Poet.

7159 Ranch Verses by the Poet Ranchman (Larry Chittenden) containing 190 pages of bright, sparkling poetry, and which has received the highest indorsement from our leading critics; handsomely bound in cloth and illustrated.

Retail price	$1.50
Our price	1 05
Postage 10c extra.	

Household Edition of Poets.
Series 7160.
Complete Editions.

The volumes are of convenient size, good type and desirable for private and library use. Illustrated, 12mo, cloth binding.

Aldrich.	Emerson.
Harte (Bret.)	Holmes.
Lowell.	
Meredith.	Taylor.
Tennyson.	Whittier.
Carey.	

Retail price, each	$1.50
Our price, each	1.00

Wilcox, Ella Wheeler, Poems.

7162 Ella Wheeler Wilcox Poems; over 300,000 copies have been sold.

Poems of Passion, 12mo., cloth. Handsomely illustrated; cloth binding.

Retail price	$1.00
Our price	.65

Poems of Pleasure, 12mo.

Retail price	$1.00
Our price	.66

Maurine, and other Poems.

Retail price	$1.00
Our price	.66
Postage, each	.10
3 vol. set in box	1.85

Any of above can be had in presentation binding, full white vellum, for $1.10 each.

World's Greatest Poems.

7163 Each bound in flexible leather, in a box.
Visions of Sir Launfal, by Lowell.
Building of the Ship, by Longfellow.

Retail price	$1.50
Our price	1.05
Postage, each, 10 cents.	

Family Poets.
Series 7165.
Complete Editions.

Beautifully bound in cloth and illustrated. 8 vo.
Longfellow.
Tennyson.
Lucile.
Whittier.
George Eliot.
Mrs. Browning.
Golden Treasury.
Robert Browning.
Lowell.
Holmes.
Princess.
Ingelow.
Burns.
Lalla Rookh.
Favorite Poems.
Red Letter Poems.

Retail price, each	$2.00	Our price, each	$1.40
Postage, each, 14 cents.			

Whitman, Walt, Poems by.

7167 Leaves of Grass, by Walt Whitman, in one volume; comprises all the author's poetical works down to 1892; large 8vo, cloth top, cloth.

Retail price	$2.50
Our price	1.45
Postage	.18

Poems of Passion, by Ella Wheeler, Wilcox.

7168 New 16 mo. edition; illustrated. A beautiful presentation edition.

Retail price	$0.75
Our price	.50
Postage, extra	.08

NEW EDITION OF THE POETS.
Embossed Leather, New Style.
Series 7170.
Complete Edition.

Our Octave Poets, padded sides, burnished yellow edges. The handsomest, most unique and desirable edition ever offered at the remarkably low price. Large royal 8vo, in the following Complete Works: Byron, Burns, Hemans, Josephus, Moore, Milton, Shakespeare, Scott.

Retail price of this edition is $3.50 per volume.	
Our price per vol.	$1.80
Postage	.30

Encyclopaedia of Poetry.

7172 Fireside Encyclopaedia of Poetry, collected and arranged by Henry T. Coates. Twenty-eighth edition, enlarged and thoroughly revised, and containing portraits with fac-similes of their handwriting.

Each poem has been given complete, and great care has been taken to follow the most authentic and approved editions of the respective authors.

Here will be found the most important poems by prominent authors, besides other poems of note and popularity.   Retail price of above

Imperial 8vo; cloth extra; gilt side and edges	$5.00	$3.50
Half calf, gilt	7.50	5.25
Full morocco, antique; gilt edges	7.55	5.25

Olive Edition of Poets.
Series 7173.

All are handsomely bound in Genuine Embossed Persian Leather, stamped in gold, with full round gold edges, and are without a doubt the finest line ever offered by us for presentation purposes.

Moore.
Mrs. Browning.
Scott.
Bryant.
Robert Browning.
Whittier.
Jean Ingelow.
Lalla Rookh.
Longfellow.
Lucile.   Milton.
Byron.
Burns.
Shakespeare.
Lady of the Lake.
Tennyson.

Retail price, each	$3.50	Our price each	$1.95
Postage, each			.14

Parkman Francis' Works.

7174 The California and Oregon Trail. A work depicting Indian life and adventures in the Rocky mountains and prairies of the West. Cloth, gilt top. Retail price | $1.50

| Our price | $0.75. Postage, extra | .14 |

Plutarch's Lives of Illustrious Men.

Langshorne's translation. Texts and notes complete, with index. Large type, good paper, and tastefully bound.

7175 Four volumes, 12mo. Cloth, gilt, in box	$2.20
Bound in half calf	3.75

7176 Popular Edition. Three volumes, 12mo. Ornamental cloth | 1.76

Prescott, Wm. H., Works.

7178 New Popular Edition. Illustrated. 16 vols. complete, 12mo, cloth Retail price | $16.50
Our price | 11.50

7179 Conquest of Mexico. 3 vols. 12mo. cloth. Classic Edition | 1.05

7180 Conquest of Mexico. Popular Edition. 2 vols. 12mo, cloth | .75

7181 Conquest of Peru. Classic Edition. 2 vols. 12mo. cloth | .90

7182 Conquest of Peru. Popular Edition. 2 vols. 12 mo. cloth | .75

7183 Ferdinand and Isabella, Classic Edition. 3 vols. 12mo, cloth | 1.05

7184 Ferdinand and Isabella. Popular Edition. 2 vols. 12mo, cloth | .75

7186 Prescott's Reign of Philip II, 3 vols. 12mo. cloth. Retail price, $3.75. Our price | 2.60

7187 Prescott's Reign of Charles V. 3 vols. cloth. 12mo. Retail price, $3.75. | 2.60

Peck, Geo. W., Works.

7190 Peck's Bad Boy and His Pa, and Bad Boy and the Groceryman. Complete in one volume, beautifully illustrated, handsomely bound in cloth. Size 8¾x8¾, 368 pages.

Retail price	$1.50
Our price	.88
Same in paper binding	.35
Postage, extra	.10

7191 Peck, 12 mos.   Each Bound in cloth.
Bad Boy and his Pa.   Bad Boy and the Groceryman
Peck's Irish Friend.   Peck's Sunshine.
Peck's Boss Book.
Peck's Bad Boy.

Retail price, each	$0.50
Our price	.25
Postage, each, extra	.10

"Peep-O'Day" Series.

7193 Peep-of-Day Series.

Line Upon Line.   Peep-of-Day.
Precept Upon Precept.

Three volumes in set, cloth bound, 16mo. Price per set only	$0.65
(Retail price of above, $1.50.)	
Postage, 20 cents.	

7194 Best Way Series, 3 volumes, cloth, uniform with Peep-of-Day. | .65
Postage, 20 cents.

7195 Stories of History, 6 volumes, cloth, very beautiful for children. Per set. | .83
Postage, 50 cents.

7196 Stories of Travel, 6 volumes, uniform with Stories of History. Per set | .83
Postage, 50 cents.

Roe, Edward P., Works.
Series 7198.

Barriers Burned Away.
What Can She Do.
Opening of a Chestnut Burr.
Near to Nature's Heart.
From Jest to Earnest.
A Knight of the XIXth Century.
A Face Illumined.
A Day of Fate.
Without a Home.
His Sombre Rivals.
A Young Girl's Wooing.
An Original Belle.
Driven Back to Eden.
Nature's Serial Story.
He Fell in Love With His Wife.
The Earth Trembled.
Miss Lou.
Taken Alive.
The Home Acre.
Success With Small Fruits.

12 mo. cloth. Retail price, $1.50	
Our price	.93
Postage	.12
19 volumes complete	17.00

Barriers Burned Away.

7199 By E. P. Roe. New presentation edition. 16mo. Cloth Red and White.

Retail price	$0.50
Our price	.30

Opening of a Chestnut Burr.

7200 Same binding and style as "Barriers Burned Away." | $0.30
Postage, each, 8 cents.

Ruskin, John, Works.

7201 Complete Works of Jno. Ruskin handsomely bound in 13 volumes. Cloth. Gilt tops. Large type, colored and other illustrations.

Retail price, per set	$13.00
Our price, per set	8.90
Same, bound in half calf	19.00

7202 Ruskin's Stones of Venice. 2 volumes; cloth, 12 mo.
Per set, 2 volumes | 2.10
Postage 22 cents.

7203 Ruskin's Modern Painters. 3 volumes; cloth. 12mo.
Per set, 3 volumes | 2.95
Postage 36 cents.

Rambaud, Alfred, Works.

7205 History of Russia from the earliest times to 1877. 2 volumes. 12mo. Cloth. Retail price | $1.00
Our price | .79
Postage, 12 cents extra.

Reade, Chas., Novels.
Series 7207.

Perilous Secret.
A Woman Hater.
Love Me Little, Love Me Long.
The Cloister and the Hearth.
It is Never Too Late to Mend.
Peg Woffington, etc.
Good Stories.
A Simpleton and the Wandering
Heir.
Put Yourself in His Place.
Hard Cash.
Foul Play.
White Lies.
Griffith Gaunt.
A Terrible Temptation.
Illustrated. 12mo, Cloth.

Per volume............$0.52 Postage...........$0.10
7209 Complete Works of Chas. Reade, in 8 large
12mo. volumes, cloth........................ 8.25

Rawlinson, George C., Works.

	Retail price.	Our price.
7210 Seven Great Monarchies of the Ancient Eastern World. Standard Edition, with 7 maps and 760 illustrations; 3 vols., 12mo., 3 vols., 12mo, cloth....	$4.00	$2.80
Popular Edition 3 vols. 12mo, half calf.	4.00	2.80
7211 Ancient Egypt. Students' Edition, with numerous illustrations. 2 vols. 8vo	3.00	1.80
7213 Popular Edition. 2 vols., 12mo, Half calf	3.00	2.00
7214 Complete Works, comprising "The Ancient Monarchies," "Ancient Egypt," "Religions of the Ancient World," and "Historians' Evidence—Egypt and Babylon," Standard Edition, with maps and illustrations, 7 vols., 12mo....	9.25	6.60
Add for postage 10 per cent. extra.		

Rollin, Charles, Works.

7218 Rollin's ancient history of the Egyptians, Carthaginians, Assyrians, Babylonians, Medes and Persians, Macedonians and Grecians, 4 vols. 12mo. Cloth...$3.00 Half calf 4.00
7219 Popular Edition Rollin's Ancient History. 4 vols., 12mo.....$1.95 Postage, each........ .46

Ridpath, Jno. Clark, Works.

7220 History of the United States, from Aboriginal times to the present day; embracing an account of the Aborigines, the Norsemen in the new world, discoveries by Spaniards, English and French. Planting of settlements, growth of colonies, struggle of liberty, establishment of the Union, the civil war, centennial of independence, and recent annals of the Republic; brought down to the year of 1891. Illustrated with charts, portraits and diagrams. Large 8vo. 782 pages. Subscription price, $4.00.
Our price............ $2.75
7222 Large cheap edition, same contents as above. Retail price........$3.00
Our price............ 1.50 Postage, each.... .50

Riley, James Whitcomb, Works.
Series 7224.

Neighborly Poems.
Sketches in Prose and occasional verses.
Afterwhiles, poems dialect and serious.
Pipes, O'Pan, five sketches and fifty poems.
Rhymes of Childhood, 101 poems.
Flying Islands of the Night.
Above each 12mo, cloth, gilt top.
Retail price each....$1.25 Our price....$0.88
Postage, extra, each................ .10

Poems Here at Home.

7226 A new book by James Whitcomb Riley, 12mo. cloth. Retail Price............$1.50
Our price............$1.05 Postage, extra..... .10

Stowe, Harriet Beecher, Works.

7229 Uncle Tom's Cabin. New edition, 12 mo., handsomely bound in two colors, cloth.
Retail price............ $0.50
Our price............ .18
Postage............ .07
7230 Fine 2 volume illustrated edition; a beautiful present.
Bound in silk cloth............ $2.85

Other Stowe Books.
Series 7231.

Bound in English silk cloth.
Agnes of Sorrento. Pearl of Orr's Island.
The Mayflower. Dred (Nina Gordon).
Oldtown Folks. A Minister Wooing.
My Wife and I. Poganuc People.
We and Our Neighbors. Uncle Tom's Cabin.
Retail price........$1.50 Our price........$1.05
Postage, each................ .12

Stretton, Hesba, Works.
Series 7232.

12mo cloth.
Through the Needle's Eye.
In Prison and Out.
Cobwebs and Cables.
Carols.
Bede's Charity.
David Lloyd's Last Will.
Hester Morley's Promise.
Doctor's Dilemma.

Retail price............$1.00 Our price......$0.70
Postage, each................ .12

Stevens, Ann S., Works.

7234 All are well bound and printed, 12 mo. cloth
Soldiers' Orphans A Noble Woman.
Doubly Wise. Fashion and Famine.
Gold Brick. The Heiress.
Mabel's Mistake. Mary Derwent.
Norston's Rest. The Old Homestead.
Palaces and Prisons. Bertha's Engagements.
Retail price................ $0.60
Our price................ .27
Complete set of 9 volumes................ 2.25
Postage, each, 10c. extra.

Schiller, Frederick, Works.

7235 Complete Works of Schiller. Illustrated. 4 volumes, 12 mo. Cloth. Containing:
The Thirty Years' War. Historical Dramas.
Romances and Dramas. Poems and Essays.
Retail price per set. $6.00 Our price........ $4.00
Same bound in half calf................ 6.00

Southworth, Mrs. E. D. E. N., Works.
Series 7236.

Durably bound in cloth, 12mo.
Ishmael, or in the Depths.
Ishmael, or the Depths From.
Bridal Eve.
Bride of Llewellyn.
Curse of Clifton.
Deserted Wife.
How He Won Her.
The Lost Heiress.
Love's Labor Won.
Lost Heir of Linlithgow.
Allworth Abbey.
Discarded Daughter.
Fair Play.
Fatal Marriage.
The Fortune Seeker.
Gypsy's Prophecy.
Mystery of Dark Hollow.
A Noble Lord. Maiden Widow.
Retribution. Missing Bride.
Vivia, or the Secret Power. The Motherlaw.
Artists' Love. Phantom Wedding.
Beautiful Fiend. Prince of Darkness.
Bride's Fate. Haunted Homestead
Changed Brides. Spectre Lover.
Christmas Quest. Three Beauties.
Cruel as the Grave. Tried for Her Life.
Family Doom. The Two Sisters.
India, or Pearl. Victor's Triumph.
Lady of the Isle. Widow's Son.
Retail price, each....$0.50 Our price........$0.27
Complete set of 40 volumes................ 10.00
Postage, extra, each................ .10

Hidden Hand.

7237 By Mrs. E. D. E. N. Southworth, Cloth, 12mo. Retail price................ $1.25
Our price................ .60
Postage, 10 cents extra.

Shakespeare's Complete Works.
Handy Complete Edition.

7239 Complete, 3 Volume Edition. Illustrated, good clear type, printed on extra paper, vellum cloth, 12 mo., gilt top, leather label.
Retail price................ $4.00
Our price................ 1.85
Postage................ .36

New Cabinet Edition.

7240 Shakespeare's Complete Works. Large type edition, 8 vols., 16 mo., by J. Talfourd Blair, fully illustrated, bound in English cloth, red edges, in box uniform with binding.
Our price................ $4.00
Bound in French Morocco, gilt edges........ 6.75
Weight, 7 pounds.

Shakespeare's Works.

7241 New 4 volume 12mo., edition complete, large type and illustrated. Cloth, 4 vols. $1.50
Half calf, 4 vols................ 3.98

Shakespeare's Complete Works.

7243 Large 8vo. edition, large type and illustrated. Retail price, $3.75. Our price........$1.23
Postage, extra................ .38

Shakespeare.

7244 Handy Volume Edition. Complete in 13 volumes, with glossary, green cloth, red edges and maroon cloth, orange edges. In a cloth box.
Retail price, $7.50. Our price................ 3.98

The Ariel Shakespeare.
STUDENT'S EDITION.
Series 7248.

It would seem difficult to find place for another edition of Shakespeare, but the Ariel edition will be found to differ in so many respects from any other edition that it is thought no justification is needed for its existence. The distinctive features of the edition are as follows:
Each play is in a separate volume.
The size of the volume is 3¼x5 inches and about a half inch in thickness—of comfortable bulk for the pocket.
The page is clearly printed from an entirely new font of brevier type.
The text is complete and unabridged, and conforms to the latest scholarly editions.
As illustrations, the charming designs by Frank Howard (first published in 1833), five hundred in all, have been effectively reproduced, making a series of delicate outline plates.
16mo., cloth.

The Tempest. King John.
A Midsummer Night's Richard II.
  Dream. Henry IV. (First Part).
The Merchant of Venice. Henry IV. (Second Part).
As You Like It. Henry V.
Much Ado About Nothing. Richard III.
Twelfth Night. Henry VIII.
The Winter's Tale. The Two Gentlemen of
Hamlet.   Verona.
Othello. The Merry Wives of Windsor.
Macbeth.   sor.
King Lear. Measure for Measure.
Romeo and Juliet. The Comedy of Errors.
Anthony and Cleopatra. Love's Labor Lost.
Henry VI. (First Part). Taming of the Shrew.
Henry VI. (Second Part). All's Well that Ends Well.
Henry VI. (Third Part). Cymbeline.
Troilus and Cressida. Pericles.
Coriolanus. Poems.
Titus Andronicus. Sonnets.
Timon of Athens. Glossary, and index of characters, etc.
Retail price, each 50c.; Our price.... $0.30
Complete set of 40 volumes............ 11.00
Postage, each, extra, 5c.

Subscription Books.
Series 7250.

We desire to call your attention to our special line of finely illustrated and attractive publications which our agents are selling throughout the country for from $3.00 to $5.00 each.
Our price, each....$0.98

Story of the Wild West. By Buffalo Bill.
Columbus and Columbia. A complete History of the United States. By Jno. Clark Ridpath and Jas. G. Blaine.
Footprints of the World's History. By Jno. Clark Ridpath.
Story of Man. By J. W. Buel.
Heroes of the Dark Continent, and How Stanley Found Emin Pasha.
Life and Work of James G. Blaine.
Exile Life in Siberia. By J. W. Buel.
The Living World. A complete Natural History. By J. W. Buel.
Sea and Land. By J. W. Buel.
The World's Wonders, as seen by great tropical and Polar explorers. By J. W. Buel.
Heroes of The Plains. Wild Bill, Buffalo Bill and all famous scouts.
United States Secret Service. By Gen. Lafayette Baker.
Pictorial History of the Civil War. A full account of our late war.
Pictorial History of the U. S. By James D. McCabe.
Stanley's Story, or Through the Wilds of Africa. By Col. Fletcher.
Museum of Wonders, or Curiosities of the Whole World.
Barnum's Wild Beasts, and Reptiles of the World. By P. T. Barnum.
King of Mysteries, or Adventures at the Frozen North. By Col. Feather.
Postage, each, extra, 32 cents.

Sue, Eugene, Works.

7255 Wandering Jew. Library Edition. 2 volumes. 12mo. Cloth
Retail price, $1.50. Our price................ $0.75
7256 Wandering Jew. Columbus Edition. 2 volumes................ .40
7258 Mysteries of Paris. Library Edition. 2 volumes. 12mo. Cloth................ .75
7259 Mysteries of Paris. Columbus Edition. 2 volumes, 12mo. Cloth................ .40

Sheridan's Troopers on the Border.

7260 Being an account of a winter's campaign on the plains with General Sheridan. By Randolph DeB. Keim. With portrait and seven full-page illustrations. 12mo. full gilt back and side.
Retail price..............$1.00
Our price.................. .70
Postage, extra, 10c.

Sheridan, Gen. Philip H., Personal Memoirs of.

	Retail price.	Our price.
7261 With steel and wood portraits of Sheridan and his famous generals. 2 vols., 8vo. Cloth.....	$6.00	$4.00
Sheep....	8.00	5.34

Postage, extra, 62c.

Smiles, Samuel, Works. Series 7264.

Bound in cloth, 12 mo.
Self Help.
Character.
Duty.
Thrift.
Life and Labor.
Retail price, per set.....$3.75
Our price.................. 2.25
Single volumes, each....... .50
Postage, each.............. .10

Stockton, Frank R., Works.

7265 Stories of the Three Burglars. 16 mo., cloth, in green and silver.
Retail price...............$0.60
Our price.................. .35
Postage.................... .08
7267 The Great War Syndicate. 12 mo.
Price, cloth...............$0.70
Postage.................... .10

Stockton's Novels.

7268 Cloth. 12mo. Illustrated.
The Late Mrs. Null.   Christmas Wreck.
The Lady or the Tiger.   Rudder Grange.
Rudder Grangers Abroad.   House of Martha.
Retail price, each....$1.25   Our price, each....$0 88
Postage, extra............ .10

Smith, F. Hopkinson, Works.

7269 Col. Carter of Cartersville. By F. Hopkinson Smith. Illustrated by E. W. Kemble. The author of this book has created a great sensation among critics. Bound in two colors, cloth.
Retail price...............$1.25
Our price.................. .88
Postage, extra............ .08

Sidney, Margaret, Books. Series 7270.

Margaret Sidney divides with Louisa M. Alcott and Mrs. Burnett the honors of having depicted the most charming child-life with which modern literature is acquainted. Each square 12mo., cloth.
Five Little Peppers and How They Grew.
Five Little Peppers Midway.
Five Little Peppers Grown Up.
Retail price, each.....$1.50   Our price, each....$1.00
Set of 3 volumes..................... 2.90
Postage, each..................... .12

Sherman's Memoirs.

7272 Memoirs of General W. T. Sherman, written by himself, to which are added chapters completing his life, and including his funeral obsequies. Prepared by W. Fletcher Johnson, Esq., and carefully reviewed by Maj. Gen. O. O. Howard, U. S. A.. Illustrated; contains full page portraits of the author and other prominent generals; 2 volumes, 8vo; 853 pages, bound in silk cloth. Subscription price........$6.00
Our price................. 3.00
Postage, extra............ .50

Sketch Book.

7273 An entirely new 16mo. edition of the Sketch book, by Washington Irving. Large type and handsomely bound in vellum cloth.
Retail price...............$0.75
Our price.................. .30
Postage, extra............ .08

Scott, Sir Walter, Works. Waverly Novels.

7277 An entirely new large type edition of Waverly Novels, red vellum cloth, leather labels, gilt tops, 24 volumes, sold in single volumes or complete set.
Ivanhoe.
Guy Mannering.
The Heart of Mid-Lothian.
The Bride of Lammermoor and a Legend of Montrose
Anne of Geierstein.
Chronicles of the Canongate.
The Fortunes of Nigel.
Quentin Durward.
Redgauntlet
The Pirate.
The Betrothed.
The Fair Maid of Perth.
Waverly.
Black Dwarf and Old Mortality.
The Monastery.
The Abbot.
Kenilworth.
Count Robert of Paris.
The Antiquary.
Rob Roy.
Peveril of the Peak.
St. Roman's Well.
The Talisman, and Castle Dangerous.
Woodstock.
Retail price per vol., $1.00; Our price per vol. $ 0.50
Complete set of 24 volumes..................11.00

Waverly Novels.

7279 Standard Edition. 12 volumes. 12mo. cloth, gilt tops..................$6.25

Waverly Novels.

7280 Popular Edition. Library Edition. 12mo. cloth, 12 volumes..................$ 4.50
Half calf..................12.00
7281 Waverly Novels. Columbus Edition. 12 volumes, 12mo cloth.................. 3.60

Tales of a Grandfather.

7282 Or History of Scotland. By Sir Walter Scott; 4 volumes, 12mo cloth, gilt top.
Retail price...............$4.00
Our price.................. 2.20

Taine's English Literature.

7283 New Standard Library Edition. 4 vols., cloth, 12mo, gilt tops..................$4.75

Tess of the D'Urbervilles.

7284 A Pure Woman, Faithfully Presented. By Thomas Hardy. Illustrated. Crown 8 vo.
Retail price...............$1.50
Our price.................. 1.05
Postage, extra, 12 cents.

Twelve Decisive Battles.

7286 Of the War. A history of the Eastern and Western campaigns in relation to the actions. 520 pages. Illustrated. Cloth..................$2.35
Postage..................... .26

Trowbridge, J. T., Novels. Series 7287.

A new uniform edition, all handsomely bound in silk cloth, with gold title stamps. Large, bold type, etc.
Coupon Bonds.
Cudjo's Cave.
The Drummer Boy.
Farewell's Folly.
Martin Merrivale, His (X) Mark.
Neighbor Jackwood.
Neighbor's Wives.
The Three Scouts.
Per volume................$1.10
Postage..................... .12

Jack Hazard Series. Series 7289.

By J. T. Trowbridge. Six volumes. 12mo., cloth.
Jack Hazard and His For-   A Chance for Himself.
tunes.   Doing His Best.
Fast Friends.   Lawrence's Adventures.
The Young Surveyor.
Per set of six volumes, only...............$5.25
Per volume, separately................... .85
Postage, each..................... .12

The Electrical Boy.

7290 Or The Career of Richard Greatman and George Greatthings. By Prof. John Trowbridge, of Harvard University. Illustrated. 16mo., cloth. Retail price...............$1.50
Our price.................. 1.00
Postage, 12 cents extra.

Ten Years a Cowboy.

7291 Ten years a Cowboy. The story, romance and adventure of life on the plains, with the varied experiences as a cowboy, stock owner, rancher, etc., finely illustrated with many full-page illustrations. 470 pages.
Cloth.....................$0.50
Paper covers............... .15
Postage, 12 and 4 cents.

Taylor's Views Afoot.

7292 Of Europe Seen with Knapsack and Staff. By Bayard J. Taylor. Well illustrated. Printed on fine laid paper, and bound tastefully in fine English cloth, gilt top, large 12mo.
Retail price...............$1.00
Our price, only........... .52
Postage................... .12

Thackeray, Wm. Makepeace, Works.

7295 Standard Edition. 10 volumes, 12mo cloth, illustrated. Retail price..................$9.00
Our price................. 6.00
Half calf..................10.00
7296 Popular Edition. 10 volumes, illustrated, 12mo cloth. Retail price................. 7.50
Our price................. 4 10
7297 Columbus Edition. 10 volumes, 12mo. cloth.
Retail price................. 5.00
Our price................. 3.10

Thompson, Judge D. P., Works.

7298 Containing, Green Mountain Boys and Locke Amsden; 2 volumes, 12mo. cloth.
Retail price...............$1.50
Our price.................. .75

TWAIN, MARK, BOOKS. Series 7300.

All bound in fine English silk cloth, with gold title stamps, printed on super-calendered paper with large print, and containing numerous beautiful illustrations.

	Retail price.	Our price.
Tom Sawyer.....Cloth	$2.75	$1.60
Small Edition. "	1.00	.70
Innocents Abroad.... "	3.50	1.98
Tramp Abroad "	3.50	1.98
Huckleberry Finn..... "	2.75	1.60
Small Edition "	1.00	.70
Prince and Pauper.... "	3.00	1.75
Small Edition. "	1.00	.70
Connecticut Yankee.... "	3.00	1.90
Library of Humor "	3.50	1.98
Roughing It "	3.50	1.98
Sketches "	3.00	1.75
Small Edition. "	1.00	.70
Gilded Age. "	3.50	1.98
Stolen White Elephant... "	1.25	.88
Life on the Mississippi. "	3.50	1.98
American Claimant. "	1.50	1.05
Tom Sawyer Abr "	1.00	1.05
Million Dollar Note... "	1.00	.70

N. B.—Postage.... $1.60, $1.75 and $1.98 books, 24c.; on 75c. books, 1 .

Tourgee's Popular Novels.

7301 By Judge Albion W. Tourgee. 12mo. Cloth. Fully illustrated.
A Fool's Errand.   Bricks Without Straw
Hot Plowshares.   A Royal Gentleman.
Figs and Thistles.
Retail price, each..................$1.50
Our price, each..................... 1.05
Postage, each..................... .12

Fool's Errand.

7302 New 16mo. Red and White Edition. Cloth.
Retail price...............$0.50
Our price.................. .35
Postage.................... .08

Art of Wing Shooting.

7303 A practical treatise on the use of the shot gun, illustrating by sketches and easy reading how to become a crack shot. By Wm. Bruce Leffingwell.
12 mo. cloth..................$0.70
Paper covers................. .35
Postage, extra, cloth $0.10; paper $0.04.

All goods sent by mail at purchaser's risk. We can assume no responsibility after goods are deposited in postoffice. We advise insuring everything of value. See page 1.

Arabian Nights.

7378 The best tales from the 'Arabian Nights,' arranged for the young by Helen Marion Burnside, and illustrated by 12 full page color plates by W. and F. Brundage. Certainly the handsomest edition of this most interesting work ever issued. Heavy board covers; illuminated. Size 8x10. Quarto. Retail price $1.50; our price......$1.00

7379 Same as above, bound in cloth with rich gold stamping on cover. Gold edges. Retail price $2.00.
Our price......$1.35
Postage, 26c.

Year. Book of American Authors.

7380 American Literature selected and edited by Ida Scott Taylor. Containing 366 pages. Highly colored and artistic illustrations by C. Klein. Bound in white cloth, gold stamping side and back; gilt top. Size 5x9. Retail price $1.50; our price......$1.00
Postage 12c.

Black Beauty.

7381 A new and handsome illustrated edition of this famous and interesting story of a horse. Richly bound in cloth with red band and gold stampings. Retail price $1.50 our price 80c. Postage extra 18c. This book should be read by everybody who rides, drives, or cares for horses

World's Fair Photographs.

7382 A grand collection of art pictures of 160 full page views; size 11x13, taken from the original photographs of all the principal buildings of the Fair and Midway Plaisance; each view is described authentic and accurate. Cloth, quarto. Retail price $3.00.
Our price...$1.30
Postage 30c extra

New Editions of Art and Gift Books.

The Finest Editions Ever Placed on the Market.
THE DORE BIBLE GALLERY.

7383 A complete pictorial summary of Biblical Narrative from Genesis to Revelations, containing one hundred full-page illustrations by Gustave Dore. Arranged in chronological order and accompanied by descriptive explanations. The illustrations are unequaled. The work will be found equally acceptable to either Protestants or Catholics. Bound in cloth with full gold edges. Retail price...$3.50
Our price......1.00
Bound in full Morocco......2.25

7384 Cloth, same as above, in the German language. Retail price............4.00
Our price............1.80
Our price, each............2.25

By anticipating your wants and sending an order large enough to go by freight (100 lbs.) you will save money. The larger the order the more you will save.

The Life of Christ.

7385 The Life of Jesus Christ. By Canon Farrar, D. D., F. R. S., Archdeacon of Westminster. Illustrated with a large number of full-page engravings by Gustave Dore and others; also reproductions in original oil colors of famous paintings by Raphael, Rubens and other great painters. 500 pages, 8x11 inches. Bound in extra fine cloth.

Publisher's price......$2.75   Our price......$1.00

Dante's Inferno.

7386 Poetry and Art, with seventy-five full page illustrations by Gustave Dore. Translated from the original by Henry Francis Cary, M. A. Edited by H. C. Webb, A. M.; a book worthy of its subject. The printing and binding are the finest. Royal quarto; size 9½x12 inches. Bound in extra fine English cloth, emblematic design, full gilt, gold edges. Price...$1.05
Full Morocco, gold edges.
Price............$2.25
Postage............38

Bible Stories.

7387 By Russell H. Conwell, pastor of "The Temple," Phila. (The largest church in America.) Contains Bible stories from Genesis to Revelations, told in a simple manner, including the stories of Bible heroes. Over 200 full-page illustrations and 12 colored plates. Cloth. Retail price...$1.50
Our price............1.25
Postage............30

Milton's Paradise Lost.

7388 A masterpiece of poetry and art, embellished with FIFTY superb full page engravings by Gustave Dore. Edited by Henry C. Walsh, A. M. The type, printing and costly binding combined, make this the most elegant, attractive and valuable art publication of the day. Royal quarto; size 9½x12 inches. Bound in extra fine English cloth, emblematic design, full gilt gold edges...$1.05
Bound in full morocco gold edges......$2.25
Postage............38

Tennyson's Idylls of the King.

7390 New Edition. Embellished with 37 magnificent full page engravings by Gustave Dore, the renowned French artist. Brilliant rays of fairy romance from the lights of genius. The Poet Laureate gives new interest to the old and hoary legends handed down from the days of the early bards. Imperial quarto; size 11x14½ inches. Bound in extra fine English cloth. Emblematic design, full gilt, good edges. Retail price......$7.00
Our price............$2.95   Postage......52

Dante's Purgatory and Paradise.

7391 Translated from the original of Dante's Alighieri and illustrated with designs of M. Gustave Dore with critical and explanatory notes.
Retail price......$2.50
Our price, cloth......1.05
Postage............38
Full Morocco......2.25

Ancient Mariner.

7392 Ancient Mariner, by Coleridge. New edition; embellished with 46 full page engravings by the renowned artist, Gustave Dore; edited by Henry C. Walsh, A. M. No one can read the poem without being the wiser and better for it. A masterpiece of art and an ornament to any home. Large imperial quarto; size 11x14½ inches.
Bound in extra cloth, full gilt. Retail price......$6.00
Our price............2.95
Postage............22

Paul and Virginia.

7394 By Bernadin De Saint Pierre. This well known story fully illustrated with numerous full-page engravings, on highly calendered paper, with gold edges. Bound in fine English cloth. Emblematic designs in gold, silver and ink. Quarto size.
Retail price, cloth......$3.00
Our price............1.05
Bound in full morocco......1.85
Postage............28

Hell Up to Date.

Something altogether new! The humorous hit of the age!

7396 The journey of R. Palesco Dante, newspaper correspondent, through the Infernal Regions, as reported by himself. Illustrated by Art Young. Dante's famous drawing illustrating Dante's "Inferno" are familiar to everybody, and it is, perhaps, for this reason that Art Young's clever book appeals so readily to all who see it. The illustrations will wring from the most critical the admission that here we have a decided addition to the wealth of American humor. The text describes an imaginary trip to the domain of Satan. Popular edition, small quarto, in extra silk cloth binding.
Retail price............$1.00
Our price............37
Postage, extra............17

The Pilgrim's Progress.

7397 By John Bunyan. Illustrated with 100 engravings. This is highly attractive as well as very valuable. Bound in extra fine English cloth, emblematic design in gold, silver and ink. Gold edges.
Retail price......$2.50
Our price............79
Bound in full morocco............1.85
Postage............28

Child's History of England.

7398 (New) A Child's History of England, by Charles Dickens, embellished with 75 engravings by the eminent historical illustrators. A. DeNeuville, Gilbert Bayard and others. Size 5x10. Magnificently bound in fine English cloth with gold edges.
Retail price............$3.50
Our price............30
Postage............30

Robinson Crusoe.

7400 Robinson Crusoe, by Daniel DeFoe. This edition has just been published regardless of expense: 120 illustrations by Walter Paget. Size 7¼x9¾.
Retail price........................$3.50
Our price.......................... 1.05
Postage.............................. .36
N. B.—We guarantee this book to be the largest and best edition of Robinson Crusoe ever published.

Picturesque Washington.

7401 A souvenir of American capital; beautifully illustrated throughout; over 300 pages, bound in fine silk cloth with white edges.
Retail price.........$2.50
Our price.............. 1.00
Postage................ .14

Picturesque West.

7402 Uniform with Picturesque Washington. Covering the country west of the Missouri River. Over 300 pages; elegantly illustrated. Bound in fine English cloth, and side stamp.
Retail price..$2.50
Our price only...................................... 1.00
Postage.. .14

Glimpses of the World.

7403 Glimpses of the World, a portfolio of photographs of the mervelous works of God and man; prepared under the supervision of the distinguished traveler John L. Stoddard. Containing 549 elaborate views of all parts of the world. Size, 12 x 14; 600 pages; weight, 8¼ lbs. Cloth binding, stamped in gold. Retail price.............................$6.50
Our price.. 2.98
Half Morocco...................................... 3.50
Full Russian....................................... 3.95
Postage, extra..................................... .72
7404 Large Cheap Edition Stoddard Glimpses, cloth.. 1.25

Around the World in Eighty Minutes.

7406 Containing 106 photographs, size 5⅜x7 inches, of the most prominent views in the world, with an entertaining and instructive description of each view by W. S. Walsh. This work is superior in mechanical execution to anything of the kind ever made, and is sold at about one-third the price asked for work of inferior quality; 224 pages.

	Retail price	Our price.
Illuminated Paper Covers..........	$0.50	$0.38
Fine English Cloth and Silver.....	1.00	.70

Postage extra, 10 cents.

Adventures of Don Quixote De La Mancha.

7407 Translated from the French of Miguel De Cervantes Saavedra, by Charles Jarvis, Esq., memoir of Cervantes and a notice of his works, 800 beautiful engravings, 100 full page plates in tint, illustrated by Gustave Dore and Tony Johannot. Beautiful cloth binding, gold edges.
Retail price..$4.00
Our price.. 2.25
Postage extra, 34 cents.

Famous Paintings of the World.

7408 A grand collection of the most famous paintings of the world reproduced in half tone illustrations, containing over 300 pages; size 10 x14. Durably bound in the best English silk cloth. Retail price....................................$5.00
Our price.. 2.65
Postage, 36 cents extra.

Harness, Halters and Strap Work—We can save you lots of money on these goods.

Sights and Scenes of the World.

7410 The greatest public buildings, temples and churches men have reared; the gigantic ruins of past ages; the homes of celebrated people; perfect photographs of places where notable events have taken place; the most beautiful paintings, statuary, obilisks and monuments; the wonderful things in nature of mountain, lake and desert, from the poles to the equator; in short, a grouping of the most interesting things the earth affords to look upon. Beautiful cloth binding, size 11¼x14¼, containing nearly 700 pages; 350 illustrations. Retail price..........$6.50
Our price... 2.60

Bible Pictures and Stories.

7411 Nearly one hundred of the most important incidents of sacred history are grouped in this attractive volume, forming a chronological panorama of the Holy Bible that is both instructive and interesting. The work cannot fail to instill into the young mind a love and desire for greater knowledge of the Holy Book itself. Although Bible pictures and stories are primarily intended for the young, it is full of interest for those more advanced in years. Elegant heavy paper, extra large type; fine English cloth binding; emblematic design in gold and ink.
Size 7x8¾ inches. Retail price.......................$1.25
Our price.............$0.70 Postage, extra........ .18

America Illustrated.

7412 A perfect panorama of American scenery. Full of splendid illustrations. Imperial quarto. Edited by J. David Williams. The purpose of this work is to make people acquainted with superb creations of nature.
Publisher's price..$2.00
Our price............ 1.00
Postage................ .20

Egypt Illustrated.

7413 Egypt fully illustrated with full page, engravings, sketches, etc., showing all points of interest all through Egypt and the Holy Land on heavy tinted paper with gold edges, bound in fine English cloth, extra gilt and colors. Size 9¼x12 in.
Our price..........$1.00
Postage............. .30
Publisher's price.. 2.50

Ireland Illustrated.

7414 Edited by Richard Lovett, M.A.; fully illustrated with pen and pencil sketches, maps, engravings, etc. Any Irishman or others who wish to see the beautiful lakes of Killarney should have this book. On heavy tinted paper, with gold edge. Bound in fine English cloth, extra gilt and colored side title: boxed. Sizes 9¼x12 in.
Retail price........$2.50
Our price............ 1.00
Postage............... .30

Germany Illustrated.

7416 Germany fully illustrated with numerous engravings, sketches, etc., on heavy tinted paper with gold edges. Bound in fine English cloth, title in extra guilt and colors. Size 9¼x12 in. Boxed. This book shows beautiful scenery up the Rhine, Black Forest, Northern Germany. The Tyrol, Eastern Alps, etc.
Retail price ...$2.50
Our price........ 1.00
Postage........... .30

India Illustrated.

7417 India fully illustrated with numerous full-page engravings, sketches, etc., on heavy tinted paper with gold edges. Bound in fine English cloth. Size, 9¼ x12 inches. Revised and enlarged by Prof. Edward P. Twing, M. A., member of the Royal Asiatic Society.
Retail price.......$2.50
Boxed Our price. 1.00
Postage............. .30

Europe Illustrated.

7418. Edited by F. K. Warren, R. B. S. Illustrated with numerous full page engravings and wood engravings by the best artists. This book is the best and cheapest ever published which shows Europe as it is. Large 4to. cloth, extra gilt edges. Retail, $2.50
Boxed, each........ 1.00
Postage............... .20

England Illustrated.

7419 Printed from new plates on fine laid paper, bound in cloth. Large 8vo.; size, about 9¼x 12 inches. Beautifully illustrated with over 200 engravings of all places of note in England.
Retail price $3.00
Our price only............ 1.00
Postage .... .20

Palestine Illustrated.

7420 Large 8vo, size about 9¼x12 inches, bound in fine cloth, fully illustrated and printed on laid paper from new plates. This work shows all journeys through Palestine, its scenery, rivers mountains, etc. The only complete work ever published.
Retail price............$2.00
Our price only........... 1.00
Postage .... .20

Scotland Illustrated.

7421 This beautiful illustrated book of Scotland has just been published at an enormous expense, and contains views of all principal Scotland scenery. Handsomely bound in fine English cloth with gold emblematic designs and full gold edges.
Retail price..........................$3.00
Our price............................ 1.00
Postage .... .20

California Illustrated (New).

7422 Handsomely bound in fine English cloth with full gold edges, size 9x12. Showing all points of interest in beautiful full page engravings, large new type and super-calender paper.
Retail price....................$3.00
Our price.......................... 1.00
Postage .... .20

History of the United States.

7510 A work in words of one syllable. It brings out the main points of American history, from the landing of Columbus to the present time. Quarto, 118 pages. Board covers, with colored illustrations.
Retail price, each.......$1.50
Our price............ .60
Postage, extra.......... .24

Grimm's Household Fairy Tales.

7511 A large quarto of 284 pages, 8¼x10¼ inches, containing over one hundred illustrations in black by that clever artist, R. Andre, together with a beautiful colored frontispiece. It is bound in elegantly covered board covers.
Retail price, each........$1.50. Our price.....$0.60
Postage, extra..................................... .24

Half Hours With the Bible.

7512 An epitome of the histories contained in the Old and New Testaments; 350 pages. Royal 16mo. One hundred and fifty illustrations.
Retail price.. ....$1.50. Our price........$0.60
Postage.. .24

Happy Hours Series.

7513 A favorite line of 128 page Juvenile books, specially illustrated throughout, beautiful board covers in colors; size 7¾x10.
Happy Hours, Christmas Cheer, Merry Moments, Little Folks' World, Little Playmates, Children's Delight, Comrades, Home Stories, Alice's Adventures in Wonderland.
Retail price each............ $0.60
Our price each.................. .22
Per dozen assorted............... 2.40
Postage each extra 10 cents.

Mother Goose Series.

7515 All charmingly illustrated; containing 64 pages. Beautiful lithographed covers; size 8x10. Mother Goose Melodies, Facts and Fancies, Jolly Jingles from Mother Goose, Mirth and Melody, Idle Chat, Mother Goose Favorites, Girlhood's Golden Days, Childhood's Days, Fun and Frolic, Mischief, Play Days, Forward March, Youthful Yarns, Blossoms, Bible Pictures, Book of Animals.
Retail price each...............................$0.50
Our price each......$0.16 Per dozen assorted.. 1.75

Playtimes Series.

7516 All bound in varnished colored illustrated covers. 50 pages of illustrations and stories; size 7½x9½.
Playtime Primer.
Picture Lessons.
Easy Word Story Book
Mother Goose A B C Book.
Rhymes and Chimes from Mother Goose.
Mother Goose Nursery Rhymes.
Retail price, each......$0.25. Our price..........$0.10
Per dozen assorted................................ 1.00
Postage, each.. .07

Pleasant Picture Series.

7518 Bound in illustrated board covers, containing 16 pages of illustrations and verse. Size, 7½x9¼.
Sparkles of Joy.
Baby Boy's Book.
Little Words of Wisdom.
Pretty Pets.
Happy Thoughts.
Pleasant Pictures.
Gee Whoa.
Merry Lads and Lasses.

Precocious Piggy.	Kitty's Rescue.
Reynard the Fox.	Robber Kitten.
Alice Alphabet.	Tot, Tom and Toby.
Rosy Cheeks.	Curly Locks.

Retail price, each .....$0.25. Our price........$0.07
Per dozen assorted.................................. .75

Picture Gallery.

7519 **Montgomery Ward & Co.'s Picture Gallery for Young Folks.** Handsomely illustrated with charts containing simple drawing lessons, embellished with children's poems, delightful anecdotes, moral stories, etc.; bound in boards; lithograph covers. Size, 8¼x6 inches.
Each........................$0.12
Per doz..................... 1.25
Postage...................... .05

World's Best Juveniles.

7521 The books in this line are handsomely bound in heavy board covers, varnished, colored and illustrated; average thickness; over 300 pages; beautifully illustrated. Size, 8x10.
Woods Natural History.
Young Folks History of England.
Grimm's Fairy Tales.
Arabian Nights.
Our Young Folks at Home and Abroad.
Robinson Crusoe.
Young Folks Companion, or Chatterbox for '93.
Æsop's Fables.
Gulliver's Travels.
Mother Goose, complete.
Retail price, each...$1.00
Our price, each....$0.38 Per dozen assorted... 4.25
Postage, each, 18 cents.

Boys' and Girls' Series.

7522 Charming Stories, beautifully illustrated; average number of pages 200. Extra fine lithographed covers. Size 8x10.
Boys' Best Book.
Boys' Book of Adventures.
Girls' Best Book.
Girls' Book of Treasures.
Boys' and Girls' Annual.
Youth's Golden Days.
Travelers' Tales.
Retail price, each..............$0.75
Our price, each.................... .30
Per dozen, assorted.............. 3.25
Postage, each, extra 16 cents.

Toy Books.

7523 A nice little series of popular stories, 8vo. 12 pages. Six full-page illustrations. Printed in two colors. Stories printed in large type

Dame Trot and Her Cat.
Little Bo-Peep.
Sing-a-Song of Sixpence.
The Five Little Pigs.
Old Mother Goose.
Old Woman who Lived in a Shoe.
The Three Bears.
My First Alphabet.

Three Little Pigs.	Rip Van Winkle.
Diamonds and Toads.	Aladdin, or the Wonderful Lamp.
Jack and the Bean Stalk.	Ali Baba, or the Forty Thieves.
The Babes in the Wood	Jack the Giant Killer.
Robinson Crusoe.	
Story of Robin Hood.	

Paper, illustrated covers. Each......................$0.01
Per dozen.. .10
Per gross.. 1.10

Farm Yard A B C.

7524 A picture A B C book, appropriately filled with animated views of farm life, showing cattle, poultry, pigs, etc. Illustrated paper covers.
Each...$0.02
Per doz.. .20

Alphabet Series.

7525 This series consists of our newest and best A B C books, reduced in size, and one entirely new book. They are all handsomely printed in colors. Illustrated paper covers.

Mother Goose.
Adventures of A B C and other Little People.
Apple Pie A B C.
Merry Alphabet.
Jolly Animal A B C.
Every Baby's A B C.

Little Boys' and Girls' A B C.	Alphabet and Funny Pictures.
Noah's Ark A B C.	The Three Young Crows.
Cinderella, or the Little Glass Slipper.	The Babes in the Wood.
The House that Jack Built.	Tom Thumb.

Each $0.05
Per dozen, assorted.. .50
Per gross, assorted.. 5.75

Home Series.

7526 A very select assortment of famous old nursery stories. Varied contents. New and superior edition, with two-thirds page illustrations, printed in oil colors. Showy covers.
Dolly's Party.
Dolly's Adventures.
Topsy.
The Last of the Mohicans.
My Baby Dolly.
Dolly at the Seaside.
Rock-a-Bye-Baby, and other Rhymes.
Jack Spratt, and other Rhymes.
Pippin Hill, and other Rhymes.

Little Bo-Peep, and other Rhymes.	Picture Alphabet.
Jack and Jill, and other Rhymes.	Young Folks' Painting Book.
The Little Maid, and other Rhymes.	Little Dot's Painting Book.
A. B. C. of Animals.	Jap Dollie.
The Home Primer.	My Dollie.

Each..............$0.08. Per dozen, assorted...$0.85

Elephant Series.

7527 New edition, new covers, and pretty books added to the assortment, making the series one of the best on our list.
Alphabet of Animals.
Alphabet of Birds.
Frog Frolics.
E. Elephant, Esq.
Monkey Tricks.
Doggie Pranks.
Apple Pie A. B. C.
Doggie's Doings.
Playful Pussy.
The Daisy Chain.

Daisy Painting Book.	Donkey Days.
Here We Are Again.	Birds and Beasts.
Our Animal Friends.	One, Two, Three.
Day in the Country	Dicky Birds.
Mail Cart.	Baby's Letter.

Each...............$0.10. Per dozen, assorted.$0.95

Mother Goose Melodies; or Rhymes, Chimes and Jingles. Complete—Colored.

7528 Contains three hundred and twenty-six melodies and stories, with one hundred illustrations in colors. Royal, 16mo. 132 pages. Handsome stiff covers, in colors
Retail price, each............$0.60
Our price......................... .38

Aunt Louisa's Big Picture Books.

7530 Comprising some of the best and most popular toy books. They are elegantly printed in oil colors, on good paper.
Alphabet of Country Scenes.
Doings of the Alphabet.
Henny Penny.
Jack and the Beanstalk.
Red Riding Hood.
Robinson Crusoe.
A Merry A B C.
Our Zoo at Home.
Childhood's Happy Days.
Our Own Sailor Dolly.
Mr. Punch and his Tricks.

Drummer Boy.	Dolly's Lovers.
Kriss Kringle.	Dorothy Dumps and the Yellow Bird.
Merry Little Maid.	From a Merry Little Maid.
Through the Alphabet.	From the Realm of Story Land.
Scenes from Showland.	Crust and Crumbs.
Rip Van Winkle.	A New Book.
Tit, Tiny and Tittens.	Jap Dollie.
Three Little Kittens.	Mr. Toyman.
Three Christmas Boxes.	Pretty Poll's Painting Book.
Visit to the Menagerie.	Behind the Bars.
Yankee Doodle.	
Reynard the Fox.	
The Bible Alphabet.	

Each..$0.18
Per dozen assorted.. 2.00

Round the World Series.

7531 14 pages with colored and monochrome illustrations. Four kinds assorted in dozens. Size 9½x12½.

Our Village.	The Dog that would a Soldier be.
The Cat's Courtship.	Sketches at the Zoo.
Adventures of A B C.	Twelfth Night Revels.
Little Sunbeams.	Come to Our Circus.
Mixed Pickles.	Scenes from Showland.
Let Me Look.	Our Annimal Kingdom.
Happy Faces in Many Places.	

Each..$0.30
One dozen assorted.. 3.25

Linen Books.

All numbers from 7533 to 7538 are printed on linen cloth in colors.

Little A B C Book.

7533 A showy little Alphabet Book at a very modest price. Each letter is illustrated with a common object, having beneath it a name for a spelling lesson. Each $0.04
Per dozen.. .35

Pleasewell Series.

7534 A collection of Fairy and other wonderful stories that have been household joys for many generations; 8vo, 16 pages and 6 illustrations in each. Printed in colors.

The Three Little Kittens
The Five Little Pigs.
The House that Jack Built.
The Old Woman and her Pig.
Dame Trot and Her Cat.
Mother Hubbard and her Dog.
Little Pets A. B. C.

Each..$0.08
Per dozen... .85

Little Folks' Series.

7536 Favorite old Nursery Stories, selected for their special excellence. Newly illustrated and enlarged. Six full-page pictures, elegantly printed in colors. Covers in colors and very handsome.

Cinderella.
Red Riding-Hood.
Babes in the Wood.
Jack and the Bean Stalk.
Puss in Boots.
The Three Bears.
Tom Thumb. Goody Two-Shoes.
A B C of Animals. Every Baby's A B C.
Boys' and Girls' A B C Noah's Ark A B C.
Mother Goose.
Each....$0.18
Per dozen, assorted....1.90

Cock Robin Series.

7537 Superbly illustrated, each having six full-page pictures, in oil colors, together with eight pages of reading. The covers have elegant pictures on both front and back, and are varnished.
Bo Peep, Mother Goose Melodies.
Tommy Tucker, Mother Goose Melodies.
Old King Cole, Mother Goose Melodies.
Cock Robin. Tom Thumb.
Goody Two Shoes. Old Woman and Pig.
Little Pigs. House that Jack Built.
Apple Pie. A B C Merry Alphabet.
Child's First Book. Jolly Animal A B C.
Child's Home A B C.
Each....$0.25
Per dozen assorted....2.75

Ten Little Niggers Series.

7538 Our best illustrated series beautifully printed in colors, average size 10x12.
Soldiers A B C.
Ten Little Niggers.
Mother Goose Melodies.
Our Baby's A B C.
Frogs and Mice.
Each....$0.38
Per dozen, assorted....4.25

STANDARD RELIGIOUS WORKS.

Rev. J. H. Ingraham's Works.

7545 All beautifully bound in cloth, 600 pages. 12 mo.
Throne of David.
Pillar of Fire.
Prince of the House of David.
Each....$1.05
Postage....12

Moody's Books.

7546 Moody's Gospel Sermons delivered in Europe and America, including his Bible Readings, etc. Cloth. 12mo. 2 volumes....$1.00
Postage....24

7547 Moody's Anecdotes and Illustrations, 21 pages, as related by D. L. Moody in his revival work. Cloth. 12mo....$0.50
Postage....12

Endeavor Doin's Down to the Corners.

7548 By Rev. J. F. Cowan. Square 12mo. Illustrated.
A delightfully realistic account by "Brother Jonathan Hayseeds" of the Christian Endeavor work in a country village.
Price....$1.05

Ecce Homo.

7549 A Survey of the Life and Work of Jesus Christ. By J. R. Seeley, M. A. 16mo....$0.70
Postage, each, 10 cents.

Peloubet's Notes.

7551 And questions on international Sunday-school lessons, for '94-95.
Retail price....$1.25
Our price....88
Postage....10

Murray, Rev. Andrew.

7552 12mo. Cloth.

	Retail price.	Our price.
Abide in Christ	$1.00	$0.75
Believe in Christ	1.25	.90
Children for Christ, The	1.25	.90
Holy in Christ	1.00	.75
Like Christ	1.00	.75
New Life, The	1.00	.75
Spirit of Christ, The	1.25	.90
With Christ in the School of Prayer	1.00	.75

Postage, each, 10 cents.

Spurgeon, Rev. Chas. H., Works.

Series 7553.

	Retail price.	Our price.
Feathers for Arrows, 12mo	$1.00	$0.70
Spurgeon's Gems, 12mo	1.00	.70
The Golden Alphabet, 12mo	1.00	.70
My Sermon Notes, 4 vols., in box, 12mo	4.00	2.80
Gleamings Among the Sheaves, 18mo, gilt top	.60	.48
All of Grace. 16mo	.50	.35
According to Promise. 16mo	.50	.35
Twelve Christmas Sermons. 8vo	.50	.35
Twelve New Year Sermons. 8vo	.50	.35
Twelve Sermons on the Resurrection. 8vo	.50	.35
Twelve Striking Sermons. 8vo	.50	.35
Twelve Soul Winning Sermons. 8vo	.50	.35

Add for postage 10 per cent. extra.

World's Congress of Religions.

7554 Edited by Prof. C. M. Stevens, Ph. D., with introduction by Rev. H. W. Thomas, D. D., containing a full and correct account of the gathering of religious leaders from every country at the World's Fair. Fully illustrated.
Paper covers....$0.35
Silk cloth....75

Havergal, Francis Ridley, Works.

7556 My King and His Service. New 16mo edition. Vellum cloth.
Retail price....$0.50
Our price....35

Havergal 32mos.

7557 Beautifully bound in cloth.
Retail price, each....$0.25
Our price, each....18

Little Pillows. Kept for the Master's Use.
Morning Bells. Loyal Responses.
Morning Stars. My King.
My Bible Studies. Royal Bounty.
Royal Commandments. Royal Invitation.
Postage, each....03

Abiding Series.

7559 Ornamental cloth, 32mos.
Abiding. Peace.
Confiding. Rest.
Retail price, each 50c Our price, each....$0.38
Per set....1.40
Postage, each, extra....03

Smith, Hannah W., Works.

Christian Secret.

7560 **Christian's Secret of a Happy Life.** By Hannah Whitall Smith. New and enlarged edition. Cloth. 12mo. Price....$0.53
Postage....10

7561 **The Open Secret**; or, the Bible Explaining Itself. 12mo. Cloth. Retail price, $1.00 Our price. $0.70
Postage....10

7562 **Every-Day Religion**; or, the Common-Sense Teaching of the Bible. By Hannah Whitall Smith. 12mo. Cloth....$0.70
Postage....10

Between the Lights.

7563 Thoughts for the Quiet Hour. By Fanny B. Bates. 12mo. Cloth....$0.88
Postage....12

Daily Text Book.

7565 Beautifully printed in two colors. 64mo. cloth extra, gilt edges.
Daily Bread (Our). Daily Guide (Our).
Daily Duty (Our) Daily Light (Our).
Daily Food (Our). Daily Portion (Our).
Retail price, each...$0.25 Our price....$0.15
Per set of 6 volumes....83
Postage, extra, each 3c.

Prentiss, Elizabeth, Works.

7566 Stepping Heavenward. Cloth, 12mo. It is a story of life and faith, with the charm of naturalness and human sympathy. This makes it acceptable, as well as pure, strong and helpful. Retail price..$1.00
Our price....85

Aunt Jane's Hero. 12mo., cloth....$0.85
Flower of the Family. 12mo., cloth....85
Home at Greylock. 12mo., cloth....85
Pemaquid. 12mo., cloth....85
Urbane and His Friends. 12mo., cloth....85
Postage, each, 10c. extra.

Beautiful Tree of Life.

7567 One of the most poetic and charming pictures in the whole Bible is that portion of scripture in Revelation above quoted, describing the Tree of Life; 512 pages, 100 illustrations, 8vo., cloth. Retail price....$2.00
Our price....75
Postage, 22c. extra.

Royal Road.

7568 A new work by Marian Harland; 12mo. cloth....$1.05
Postage, 12c extra.

Why We Went.

7569 A new book by Jno. Habberton, author of Helen's Babies; 12mo., cloth.
Retail price....$1.50 Our price....$1.05
Postage, extra, 12c.

Divinity Classics.

7571 Containing Addresses, by Drummond; Imitation of Christ, by A'Kempis; and My King and His Service, by Havergal. Beautiful presentation edition, white and lavender vellum cloth in box to match. 16mo., 3 vols.
Per set of 3 volumes....$0.88
Postage, extra, 26 cents.

Drummond, Henry, Works.

NEW SCIENTIFIC WORK.

7573 **The Ascent of Man.** By Henry Drummond, F.G.S. In this new work an attempt is made to tell in a plain way a few of the things which science is now seeing with regard to the "A cent of Man." Though its standpoint is evolution and its subject man, this book is far from being designed to prove that man has relations, compromising or otherwise, with lower animals. Its theme is "ascent," not "descent." 12mo., cloth.
Retail price....$2.00. Our price....$1.40
Postage, extra, 16 cents.

7574 **Natural Law in the Spiritual World.** 16mo., blue cloth, silver stampings, yellow edges.
Retail price....$0.75 Our price....40
Postage, 8 cents.

7575 **My Point of View.** By Prof. Henry Drummond. A beautiful presentation edition; bound in white vellum, with designs in silver, and silver top. Retail price....75
Our price....52
Postage, 8 cents.

7576 **Addresses.** By Prof. Henry Drummond. Four books bound in one volume. Half blue vellum. Each....22
For full white vellum, silver stamping, each....52
Postage....08

7577 **Cup of Loving Service.** Presentation binding, same as above....75

7578 **Pax Vobiscum.** Presentation binding....75

7579 **What is a Christian.** A talk on books....27

Talmage Books.

7583 **"The Beautiful Story,"** by T. DeWitt Talmage. This is the companion book to the Bible History of all sacred events recorded in the Bible. Handsomely bound in cloth with silver and gold stampings.
Subscription price....$3.50
Our price....1.20
Postage....36

7584 **The New Beautiful Story.** By J. W. Buel and T. DeWitt Talmage, the great companion book to the Bible. 600 pages, beautifully illustrated. 8vo., cloth. Retail price $3.50. Our price....$1.40
Postage, extra, 24 cents.

7585 **The Pathway of Life.** By T. DeWitt Talmage, containing 576 pages, 300 illustrations, and numerous colored plates. 8vo., cloth.
Retail price....$3.50. Our price....1.20
Postage, extra, 30 cents.

7586 **From Manger to Throne.** by T. DeWitt Talmage. A companion book to above. Subscription price....$3.75 Our price....1.40
Postage, 32 cents.

7587 **Ready! Aye, Ready!** and other addresses, by T. DeWitt Talmage, 16mo., white vellum cloth, stamped in s lver. Retail price....1.00
Our price....25
Postage....08

7588 **From the Pyramids to the Acropolis.** Sacred Places through Biblical Spectacles. Bound uniform with Ready! Ay, Ready....25
Postage....08

7589 **Night Scenes of City Life.** By T. DeWitt Talmage. Cloth, 12mo. Retail price....75
Our price....35
Postage....10

7591 **Traps for Men.** By T. DeWitt Talmage. Cloth, 12mo. Retail price....75
Our price....35
Postage....10

7592 **Sermons in the Holy Land.** By T. DeWitt Talmage. Retail price....75
Our price....35
Postage....10

7593 **Crumbs Swept Up..** By T. DeWitt Talmage. 12mo., cloth....52
Postage....12

7594 **Wedding Ring.** By T. DeWitt Talmage. 12mo., cloth....35
Postage....10

7595 **Woman.** Her Power and Privileges. By T. DeWitt Talmage. 12mo., cloth....35
Postage....10

7596 **Battle for Bread.** By T. DeWitt Talmage. 12mo., cloth....$0.35 Postage....10

Hymnals.

7756 Hymnals, 48mo, 3⅜x2⅜ inches, boards, white edges. Each $0.24
7757 Hymnal, French seal, broken glass design, size, 3½x5¼, red under gold edges, large type. Each 1.50
7758 Hymnals, French seal, sizes 5x7¼, broken glass design, pica type, red under gold edges. Each 2.05
7759 Hymnals, grain cloth, size, 5x7½, pica type, plain edges. Each .... .75

Prayer Books and Hymnals.

7760 Japanese Seal, limp round corners, gold edge size, 2⅝x3⅜. Each $0.75
7761 Prayer and Hymnal French seal, limp, round corners, gold edges and gold cross $1.00
7762 Prayer and Hymnal French pebble grain, limp, round corners, red under gold edges, gold roll $1.50
7763 Prayer and Hymnal Syrian Levant, limp, red under gold edges, gold roll, blind ties. Each $2.00
N. B.—All above Prayers and Hymnals are minion type books.

Catholic Prayer Books.

(In English.) Each.

7765 Catholic Prayer Book, 48mo, black cloth binding, white edges $0.16
7766 Catholic Prayer Book, same as above. Bound in French calf, limp, round corners, gold edges .... .45
7767 Catholic Prayer Book, 32mo, bound in arabesque, with gilt center and edges .... .40
7769 Catholic Prayer Book 32mo, bound in French seal, with stamp and gilt edges, round corners .... .75
7780 Catholic Prayer Book, manual of prayer for use of the Faithful, with Epistles and Gospels, the Mass and Stations of the Cross. Bound in fine Persian, padded sides, gilt cross and title, red under gold edges; large type. Price, each 1.50
7781 Catholic Prayer Book, with all approved devotions for the Church and home, with Epistles and Gospels for all Sunday and Holy days of the year; bound in German calf, limp, gilt filled gilt title and monogram on side, round corners, red under gold, solid edges, large type. Each.. 2.50
7782 Vest Pocket Catholic Prayer Book, 32mo, long for the vest pocket; bound in fine Persian flexible leather, red under gold edges. Each, only .... .70
7783 Combination Set, Key of Heaven and Epistles and Gospels. Bound in fine Persian, duplex, red under gold edges, 32mo, only 2.50
7784 Combination Set, Key of Heaven, H. C. A. H., 2 vols. in a fine French kid case with handle; books are bound in a smooth French kid, red under gold edges 3.00

Catholic Prayer Books.

(In German.)

7785 Fuerer Zum Himmel, 32mo $0.40
7787 Fuerer Zum Himmel, 32mo, bound in embossed leather, gilt edges .... .75
7789 Fuerer Zum Himmel, 32mo, bound in fine Russia, round corners, gilt edges, boxed 1.25

French Prayer Books.

7790 **French Catholic Prayer Books.** Bound in very handsome binding, gilt edges; our special price 1.50

Greek Testament.

7791 **Greek Testament.** With Lexicon and Supplement. By Gulielmi Greenfield. Second American Revised Edition, with Lexicon and Supplement, giving various readings adopted by the English and American revisers, 1881, and other valuable information, 24mo. Cloth .... .55
Postage .... .10

Family, Pulpit and Reference Bibles.

7795 Bible. Imitation Leather, full gilt side, panel design, gilt edges. Printed on fine white paper, pica type, marginal references. Contains the King James Version of the Old and New Testaments; map of Palestine in colors; life of our Lord and Savior, illustrated; numerous full page Dore and other engravings; new and beautiful marriage certificate and family record; index to Holy Bible; tables of Scripture weights, measures and coins, and alphabetibal table of proper names. Size, 10¼x12⅜. Retail price $3.00
Our price 1.25

Bibles—Continued.

7796 Bible. Bound in American morocco, London antique gold side and back title; comb edges, cloth joints, containing same contents as Bible No. 7605 and in addition Smith's Bible Dictionary. Size, 10½ x12⅜ (No. 3). Retail price... $4.25
Our price 1.85

7797 Quarto Family Bible, containing the Old and New Testament, with revised version of the New Testament appended. History of the Books of the Bible, illustrated, complete Bible analysis. Concordance, Psalms in meter. Profusely illustrated with numerous full page Dore and other engravings, marriage certificates and family record in gold and colors. Bound in padded American Morocco, full gilt edges, gilt side title, cloth joints (6¼). Price $2.90
Same with nickel clasp $3.15

7798 Bible. American morocco; new arabesque design, gold title on side and back; marbled edges. King James version Old and New Testament, 12 full page Dore engravings, colored maps, life of our Lord, etc. Apocrypha, Concordance and Psalms, revised New Testament and family record. Contains also same as 7795. Price, each $2.30
Same Bible with nickel clasp..... 2.50

7800 Bible. French Morocco; wine color, antique raised panel sides, gold title on side and back, gold corners, gold edges. Contains also same as 7797 and in addition illuminated plate.
Extra fine Family Record.
Life of our Lord.
Scenes in the Life of Christ and Apostle Paul.
Scenes in Jerusalem, Egypt, Assyria.
Customs, arts and sciences.
Religious rites and emblems.
Wanderings of the Israelites, Idols and Idolatry of the Ancients and Scenes in Palestine, fully illustrated. Price each $3.25
Same Bible with nickel clasp 3.50

7801 American Calf, basket pattern, soft padded sides, round corners, gold side and back title, squares rolled with gold, gilt edges, cloth joints. Printed on fine white paper, pica type, marginal references. Contains the King James version of the Old and New Testaments, with the revised version of the New Testament appended, and in addition thereto the Apocrypha. Concordance, Psalms in meter, Smith's Bible Dictionary, with 700 illustrations, history of the religious denominations of the world, illustrated, numerous full page Dore and other engravings; steel and chromatic plates; handsome marriage cirtificate and family record in black and gold; chronological index; tables of scripture measures, weights and coins, and alphabetical table of proper names........ $3.45
Same bible with nickel clasp 3.70

Bibles—Continued.

7802 Bible. Containing the Old and New Testament, King James' version, Apocrypha, concordance and Psalms; Revised New Testament, steel plate frontispiece, illuminated plate, 14 full page Dore engravings, fine family record and colored maps, Smith's Bible Dictionary with over 700 illustrations, parables of our Lord; full page engravings described; bound in American morocco, calf finish, full gilt massive paneled sides, gold edges. Price $3.68
Same Bible with nickel clasp 3.88

7803 Bible. French Morocco. A beautiful design, soft padded sides, round corners, squares rolled with gold side and back stamps, gilt edges. Contains King Jame's version of the Old and New Testaments appended Concordance and Psalms in metre, Smiths Bible Dictionary, Bible Analysis, Family Records. Marriage Cirtificate. Illustrated with numerous Dore engravings.
Retail price $8.50
Our price 5.05
Same Bible with nickel clasp........ 5.45

7805 Bible containing the King James version of the Old and New Testament, with 12 full page engravings, col'd maps, life of our Lord, Apocrypha, Concordance and Psalms, revised New Testament, Bible Dictionary illustrated, 112 pages, steel plate frontispiece and fine Family Record. Bound in pebble German morocco, new scroll design, gold title and edges.. $4.25
Same Bible with nickel clasp $4.50

7806 Bible, containing the Old and New Testament, Apocrypha, Concordance and Psalms, Revised New Testament printed on super calendered paper, 2 steel engravings, 24 full page Dore engravings, 2 illuminated plates, extra fine Family Record and Smith's Bible Dictionary, illustrated, 112 pages. Bible History, and Analysis, illustrated, 72 pages. Illustrated Cyclopædia, illustrated, 96 pages. Complete Instructor and Guide, illustrated, 54 pages. Parables of Our Lord, illustrated, 32 pages. Pebbled Persian morocco, new ornamental scroll design embossed, gold title and edges, squares rolled in gold, covers round cornered... $6.25
Same Bible with fine nickel clasp 6.65

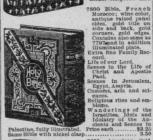

7807 Bible, printed marginal references. Contains the King James Version of the Old and New Testaments, with the Revised Version of the New Testament appended, and in addition thereto the Apocrypha; Concordance and Psalms; Smith's Bible Dictionary, new edition, illustrated with seven hundred engravings; Bible History and Analysis, illustrated; Cyclopædia of the Bible. Marriage Certificate in black and gold. German Morocco, basket pattern, unique design, soft padded sides, round corners, squares rolled with gold, gold edges $5.25
Same Bible with clasp 5.50

Bibles—Continued.

7809 Containing the authorized version Old Testament and parallel New Testament. Large quarto size 12½-10¼. Ours is the only edition having both versions of the New Testament in parallel columns. Numerous Biblical illustrations in black and colors; history of the Bible; marriage certificate and family record; maps, etc. All of our editions contain a new pronouncing dictionary of nearly 4,000 scriptual proper names, giving their derivation and meaning, and the passage where they first occur. Bound in French morocco, padded sides, round corners, gold edges. Price, each...$2.95
Same Bible, with nickle clasp........................ 3.25

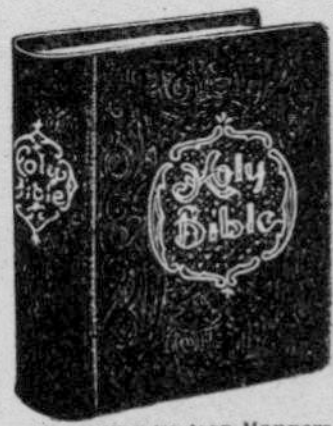

7810 Bible. This magnificent edition of the Holy Bible was made in London. The plates were cast from clear, open pica type. Contains the Old and New Testaments, Apocrypha Concordance, Psalms in metre, revised version of the New Testament appended, Smith's Pronouncing Bible Dictionary, new edition, with seven hundred illustrations, Bible Analysis, illustrated with numerous engravings, Bible History, seventy-four pages. Illustrated Cyclopædia of the Bible, embracing Eastern Manners and Customs, Animals of the Bible, Plants, Flowers, and Fruits of the Bible Wanderings of the Israelites, Idols and Idolatry of the Ancients, Jewish Worship Explained, Countries and Nations of the Bible, Palestine, Canaan or the Holy Land, City and Environs of Jerusalem, Life of our Lord and Saviour Jesus Christ, Missionary Journeys of St. Paul, Prophecys of the Bible, Dictionary of Names, Symbolical Language of the Scriptures, Coins of the Bible. Profusely illustrated with numerous new and original illuminations. fine steel line engravings, colored maps, family record and marriage certificate in colors, etc. Gallery of Bible illustrations and the parables of our Lord illustrated with full-page engravings and fully described. Bound in Turkey morocco, new ornamental scroll design, Gold title and edges. Retail price $12.00. Our price..$9.00
Same Bible with heavy nickle clasp.............. 9.50

New Parallel Bibles.

The Authorized and the Revised Versions of both Old and New Testaments in Parallel Columns. Line for Line, upon each page, Large Quarto size 12¼x10¼. Two Bibles in one volume.

All Bibles numbering from 7812 to 7824 are Parallel.

7812 Bible bound in imitation leather paneled gold sides, comb edges contaning new pronouncing dictionary of proper names concordance to scriptures. Ten line and sixteen full line engravings marriage certificate and family records. Retail price $3.50.
Our price.....$1.98

7813 Bible. Grained American Morocco padded sides, round corners,gold edges. Ten line and sixteen full-page Dore engravings. A complete concordance to the Holy Scriptures. Map of Palestine in colors. Marriage certificate and family record. The revisers' preface to Old and New Testaments, and the readings and renderings preferred by the American committee of revisers: a chronological index to the Bible, giving years when remarkable events occurred and the passages wherein they are recorded; a history of the Bible; a summary of its contents; a chapter upon Evangelists and Deacons; and many other valuable aids and helps to Bible students.......................$3.75
Same with nickel clasp........................ 4.10

Bibles—Continued.

7814 The authorized and the revised version of both Old and New Testaments, in parallel columns, line for line, upon each page. Larger type than any other parallel Bible. Nearly 200 pages more of Bible text. People's Family Edition (312). Two steel line and 32 full-page Dore engravings: Smith's Pronouncing Bible Dictionary (600 illustrations); a complete Concordance to Old and New Testaments; brilliantly illuminated Scripture text; map of Palestine in colors; Marriage Certificate and Family Record in black and gold; gallery of 72 Scripture illustrations; 16 portraits of founders chronological tables; the harmony of the four gospels, etc., etc. Large quarto size. 12½x10¾. Two Bibles in one volume. American morocco, raised panel, gold title and gold edges. Each.........$4.30
Same with nickel clasp............................ 4.70

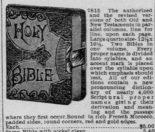

7815 The authorized and the revised versions of both Old and New Testaments in parallel columns, line for line, upon each page. Large quarto size- 12¼x10¼. Two Bibles in one volume. Every proper name is divided into sylables, and an accent mark is placed over the syllable upon which emphasis should rest. All of our editions contain a new pronouncing dictionary of nearly 4,000 Scriptural proper names giving their derivation and meaning and the passage where they first occur.Bound in rich French Morocco, padded sides, round corners, red and gold edges.
Each...$5.00
Same Bible with nickel clasp.......................... 5.40

7817 The Authorized and the Revised Version of both old and New Testaments in parallel columns, line for line, upon each page. Two Bibles in one volume. Larger type than any other Parallel Bibles. Nearly 200 pages more of Bible texts Superfine family edition. Enlarged size, 12¾x10¾. 2,000 pages. Over 1,000 illustrations. In these Bibles both the text and the collateral features are printed within rules. The pages are one-half inch longer and three-eighths wider than those in any other.Parallel Bible. Fine super-calendered paper is used. Containing twelve magnificently executed full page illustrations of Bible scenes from steel line plates. The subjects have been selected from the greatest masterpieces of sacred art. The Parables of our Lord, illustrated with ten full-page engravings, thirty-four full-page Dore engravings. Sixteen lithographic maps of Holy lands. Two beautiful illuminated Scripture texts. Smith's Pronouncing Bible Dictionary, (600 illustrations); a complete Concordance. Customs, Chronological Tables, Marriage Certificate and Family Record, etc. French morocco, London antique, padded sides, round corners; solid red under gold edges. NEW DESIGN. $6.50
Same with heavy nickel clasp............................ 7.00

Superfine Family Edition, Gilt Edged.

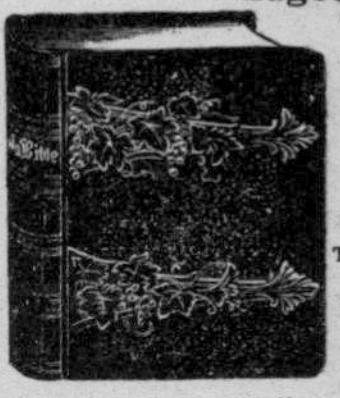

7818 Levant Morocco, London antique, super extra cushion bevel solid edges, red under gold round corners. New design. Size 12¾x10¾. (*Best Bible made*) Containing twelve magnificently executed full-page illustrations of Bible Scenes from steel line plates.
The subjects have been selected from the greatest masterpieces of sacred art. The plates have been engraved especially for us by the best artists in this country.
The Peerless Hormann Gallery or New Testament Illustrations, 24 full-page monochromatic plates.
The Parables of our Lord, illustrated with ten full-page engravings. Thirty-four full-page Dore engravings.
Colored Lithograph Maps of Holy Lands.
Smith's Pronouncing Bible Dictionary (600 illustrations); a complete Concordance; four thousand questions and answers upon Old and New Testaments for use of teachers and students; History of the Books of the Bible, illustrated by forty-eight full-page engravings; gallery of ninety-six Scripture illustrations; sixteen portraits of Founders or eminent heads of Religious Denominations; the Lives of Apostles and Evangelists; Christ and His Kingdom, illustrated; forty views of Palestine from photographs; Coins and Gems, illustrated; Manners and Customs; Chronological Tables; Marriage Certificate and Family Record, etc. Retail price.............................$24.00
Our price.. 13.00
Same, with extra fine clasp.......................... 13.75

7819 Bible contains the Self-Pronouncing Text of the authorized (King James) and Revised Versions of the Old and New Testaments, arranged in parallel columns, line for line. Two colored and sixteen full-page Dore engravings, a complete concordance to the Holy Scriptures, maps of the Holy Land, and numerous biblical illustrations. Psalms of David in meter, chronological index to the Holy Bible, giving years when remarkable events occurred and passages wherein they are recorded, history of the Holy Bible, a summary of its contents, and many valuable aids and helps to bible students; marriage certificate and family record. Imitation of leather, arabesque, paneled, full gold sides, gilt edges.....................$1.85
Same Bible, with clasp................................ 2.10

7820 Bible contains the authorized King James and Revised Versions, arranged in parallel columns; good, clear type; white paper; full-page engravings. Size 10¼x12¼. Contains, also, the same as bible No. 7819. Bound in American morocco, arabesque, paneled, comb edges.
Retail price.......$3.50
Our price.......... 2.10
Same Bible with clasp............. 2.35

7821 Bible contains same as No. 7819, and in addition two colored and 16 full-page Dore engravings; a complete concordance to the Holy Scriptures, maps of the Holy Land and biblical illustrations. Psalms of David in meter, chronological index. History of the Bible. Valuable helps to bible students; marriage certificate etc. Handsomely bound in American morocco, raised panel, full gold edges, gold sides and back. Size 10½x12¼.
Retail price.........$6.50
Our price.. .... 3.90
Same Bible with clasp...................................... 4.15

Real Hand Made Torchon Laces, All Linen.

8080 Torchon Linen Edge, ⅝ to ¾ inch, heavy.
Per yard........$0.06
Per 12 yards..... .65

8082 Torchon Linen Edge, 1 inch, heavy.
Per yard.......$0.07
Per 12 yards.... .75

	Per yard	Per 12 yards.
8083 Torchon Linen Edge, 1¼ inch, heavy..................	$0.09	$1.00
8085 Torchon Linen Edge, 1¼ inch, finer......................	.11	1.20

8087 Torchon Linen Edge, 2¼ inch, heavy
Per yard...............$0.11
Per 12 yards 1.20

8089 Torchon Linen Edge, 2 inch, finer.
Per yard............$0.14
Per 12 yards.......... 1.40

	Per yard.	Per 12 yards.
8092 Torchon Linen Edge, 3¼ inch, heavy.............	$0.14	$1.50

	Per yard.	Per 12 yds.
8097 Torchon Linen Edge, ⅞ inch, very fine..........	$0.18	$1.95
8098 Torchon Linen Edge, 1⅛ inch, extra fine..........	.20	2.15
8100 Torchon Linen Edge, 1½ inch, extra fine........	.25	2.75

	Per yard.	Per 12 yds.
8103 Torchon Linen inserting heavy thread to match heavy edges. 1 inch wide..................	$0.08	$0.85
8105 Torchon Linen Inserting, heavy, to match above heavy edges, 1½ inch............................	.11	1.20
8110 Torchon Linen Inserting, fine, 1 inch to match 8097, 8098 and 8100..........................	.17	1.85

8115 Torchon Linen Edge, heavy thread. See cut, 3½ to 4 inch.
Per yard.....$0.17
Per 12 yards...1.85

8118 Torchon Linen inserting to match 8115, 4 inch.
Per yard.....$0.17
Per dozen... 1.85

Silk Lace Chiffon.

8122 All Silk Lace Chiffon (4 inches), silk embroidered edge, and one row silk embroidery above the edge. Note the colors: Black, white, cream, beige, brown, cardinal, sky blue, nile green, gray, lavender or heliotrope, navy blue and maize or corn. Per yard..................$0.20

8125 Silk Chiffon, with silk embroidered edge and heavy embroidery in all colors. Width, 3¾ to 4¼ inches. See cut. Per yard............$0.32

*** Write your name and Address on package returned to us if you want it to have attention; send letter of instructions by mail; do not put it in package.

Butter Color Laces.

8128 Vandyke point lace, butter color, new. See cut.

Width.............	3¼ in.	5 in.	6¼ in.	8 in.
Per yard.............	$0.12	$0.16	$0.20	$0.27
Per 12 yards........	1.30	1.65	2.15	2.90

Silk Lace Edgings.

(8140)

8140 Point d'Ireland Black Silk Lace, in five widths to match

Width..	3¼ in.	4¼ in.
Per yard.	$0.13	$0.16

5 in.	6¼ in.	8¼ in.
$0.20	$0.24	$0.35

8145 Black Silk Bourdonne Lace, on heavy net.

Width.............	3⅜ in.	5 in.	6½ in.	9¼ in.
Per yard..........	$0.18	$0.28	$0.35	$0.50

Silk Spanish Lace.

8154 Black Silk Lace, cheap quality and pattern.
Width.. 2¼ in.
Per yard.. $0.08
Per 12 yards.. .85

8157 Cream Silk Lace, same quality as above, 8154.
Width...2⅝ in.
Per yard.. $0.10
Per 12 yards.. 1.10

Black Chantilly Lace Edgings.

8165 Black Silk Chantilly Lace Edging.

Width.......	3 in.	3¾ in.
Per yard...	$0.10	$0.13
Width....	4¾ in.	5¼ in.
Per yard...	$0.15	$0.18

8171 Cream Silk Chantilly Lace.
Width.................. 4¼ in.
Per yard $0.18
Per 12 yards.......... 1.95

*** Read pages 1 and 2 before ordering goods. You obtain a discount by sending money with order. Send money by Express, Draft on Chicago or New York, Post Office Money Order, or Registered Mail.

Silk Laces.

8177 Black Guipure Chantilly Lace.

Width.	Per Yard.
3½	$0.17

Chantilly Lace Flouncing and Full Skirting.

Per yard.

8194 Black Silk Chantilly Lace Flouncing, 40 to 43 ins. wide.....$1.00

8198 Black Silk Chantilly Lace Flouncing, 40 to 43 inches......$1.40

All Over Spanish Guipure Lace.

8252 Black Silk Spanish Guipure Lace, 14 inches.
Per yard..............$0.75
27 inches, per yard.. 1.50

Black Silk Scarfs.

Special line black silk Spanish lace scarfs, all with purled edges, at about one-half their real value. We quote until sold as they cannot be duplicated.

	Each.
8275 Black silk lace scarfs, 6x54 inches........	$0.35
8277 Black silk lace scarfs, 7½x56 inches......	.40
8279 Black silk lace scarfs, 7½x58 inches.......	.50
8281 Black silk lace scarfs, 9½x70 inches.......	.60
8283 Black silk lace scarfs, extra quality, 8x56 inches...	.70
8285 Black Silk Lace Scarfs, extra quality and size, 10½x76 inches..................................	.80
8287 Black Silk Lace Scarfs, extra quality and size, 12x74 inches..................................	1.00
8290 Black All Silk Chantilly Lace Scarfs, very fine, purled edges all around; size 13x94 inches.	2.00

Silk Lace Scarfs.

8292 Cream Spanish All Silk Lace Scarfs. Until sold...$1.50

Silk Lace Fichus.

Special value in black; see quotations below.

8294 Spanish Lace Fichus, cream, all silk. Each, until sold...................................$1.00

8296 Black Silk Spanish Guipure Lace Fichus, purled edges all around; length 53 inches by 12 inches at center; at one-half value. Each...... 50

Ladies' Silk Ties.

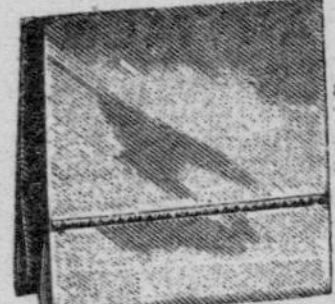

8300 Japanese (washable) Silk Ties, 5x35 in. drawn hemstitch. Each.............$0.20
8303 Japanese (washable) Silk Ties; 6x39 in.; drawn hemstitch. Each.............$0.25
NOTE.—Colors in above: pink, light blue, navy, cardinal, Nile green, yellow, cream and black.

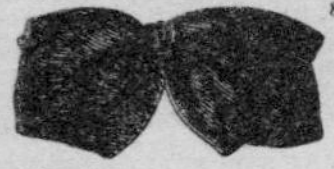

8315 Ladies' or Children's Surah Silk Bows; solid colors: Black, cream, nile green, pink, blue, orange, brown, tan, navy, cardinal and heliotrope, all with elastic ribbon for putting on readily. Each..............$0.25
Per Dozen 2.70

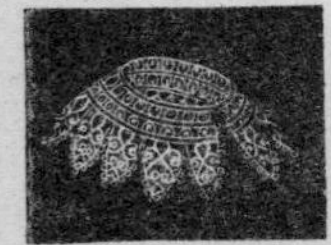

Lace Collars.

8328 Aplique Openwork Lace Collars. Each.............. $0.12
Per dozen.......... 1.25

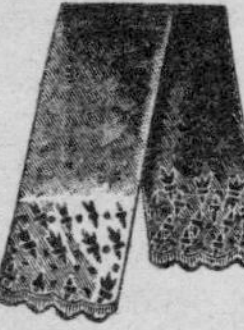

White and Colored Mull Ties.

8372 White Mull Ties, with scalloped and embroidered ends, 4⅜ and 5 in. wide. Each................ $0.10
Per dozen............ 1.00
8381 Fine White Mull Ties, with colored embroidery. Each.............$0.18
Per dozen............ 1.95

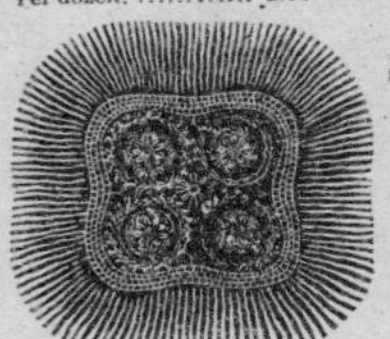

A Bargain.

8390 Hand Crocheted Tidies. Size 18x18 to outside of fringe. Size inside of fringe, 11 x 11. These tidies are worth 50c. at retail, but our price will be 20 cents each until sold, or $2.25 per dozen.

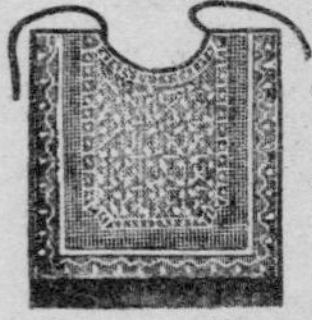

Children's Feeders.

8392 Heavy Cotton Feeders, fancy printed designs, fast colors. Size 11x14. Each...............$0.08
Per doz.............. .85
8395 Damask linen feeders fancy colored borders, fringed at bottom. Size 11½x15. Each...............$0.12
Per dozen.......... 1.25

Baby Bibs.

8420 Honey Comb Bibs with bound edge. Each..................$0.04
Per doz................ .37

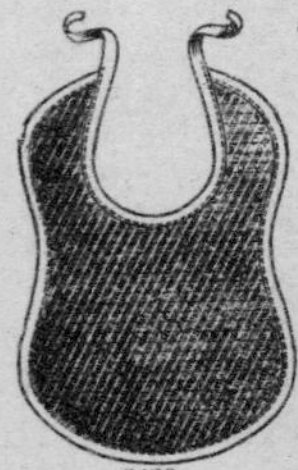

8420

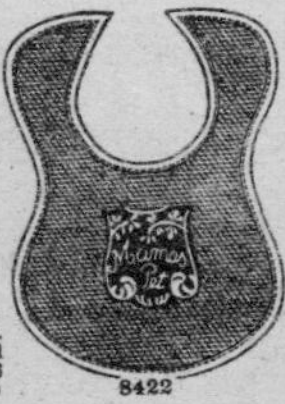

8422

8422 Honey Comb Bibs. Bound edge and colored medallion. Each....$0.06
Per doz............... .60

Bibs—Continued.

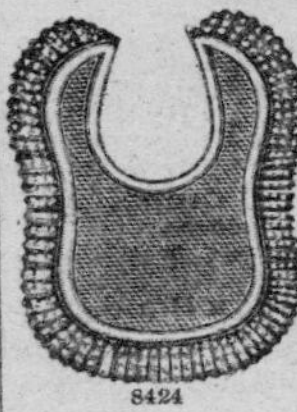

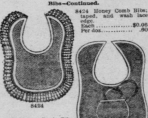

8424

8424 Honey Comb Bibs; taped, and wash lace edge. Each..............$0.06
Per doz.............. .60

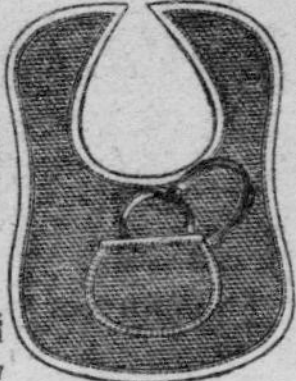

8426

8426 Honey Comb Bibs; bound edge, with bound pocket and bone ring. Each................$0.07
Per doz.............. .75

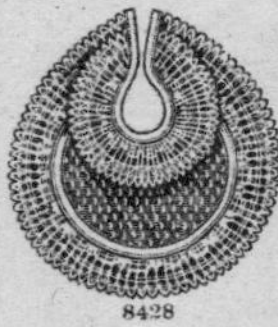

8428

8428 New Round Pattern Bibs: figured pique-fleeced on back, lace edge. Each...............$0.09
Per doz.............. .95

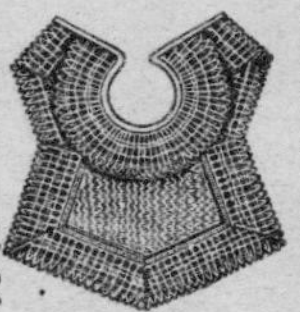

8430

8430 New Pattern Bibs; fancy cloth fleeced back, lace edge. Each.............. $0.09
Per doz............. .95

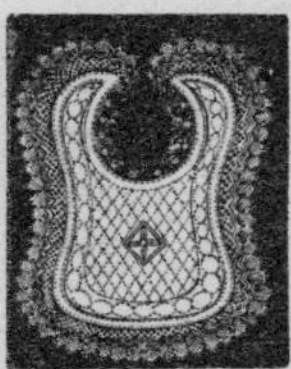

8432

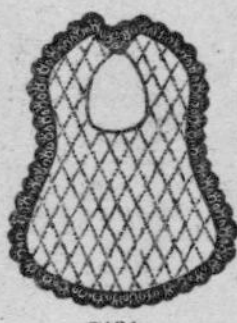

8434

8432 Quilted Bibs with wash lace edge. Each..........................$0.10
Per doz.......................... 1.05
8434 Fine Imported Bibs; hand made; quilted and padded; wash lace edge. Each.......... .18
Per doz.......................... 1.95

White Cambric and Suisse All Over Embroidery.

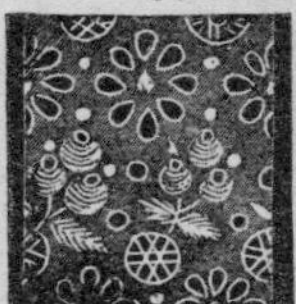

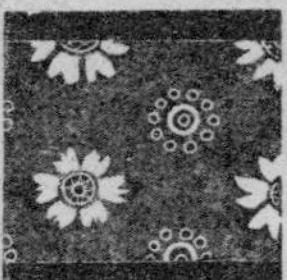

All our Cambric and Suisse Embroidery for yokes, sleeves and children's garments 22 inches wide. Price governs work and quality.

8504 All Over Embroidery. Per yard............$0.35
8507 Cambric All Over Embroidery. Per yard. .50
8514 Cambric All Over Embroidery. Per yard. .75
8518 Cambric All Over Embroidery. Per yard. 1.00
8530 Suisse All Over Embroidery, 23 inches wide.......... .30
8533 Suisse All Over Embroidery, 23 inches wide.......... .50
8536 Suisse All Over Embroidery, 23 inches wide.......... .75
8538 Suisse All Over Embroidery, 23 inches wide.......... 1.00

*** And the kitchen furnishings! A treat for a woman to give an order there—Anything—Everything.

Colored Embroideries.

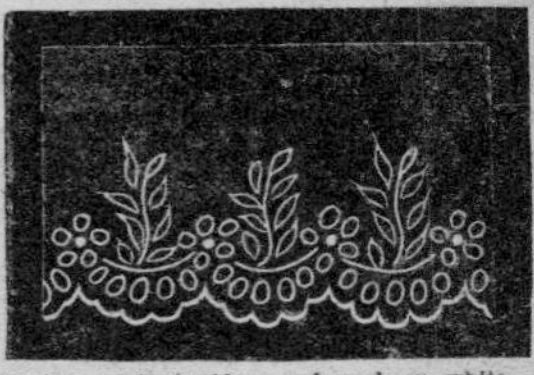

8570 Colored Embroidery, red work on white cloth, ½ inch, per yard..........$0.05
8572 Colored Embroidery, blue work on white cloth, ½ inch, per yard.......... .05
8574 Colored Embroidery, white work on red cloth, ½ inch, per yard.......... .05
8576 Colored Embroidery, white work on blue cloth, ½ inch, per yard.......... .05

White Embroidered Edges.

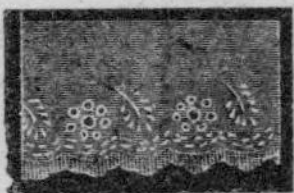

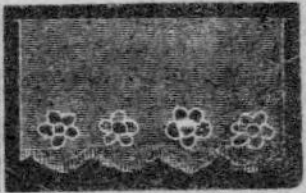

8578 White Embroidery, assorted openwork patterns

Width.........	1 in.	1½	2	3½	4½
Per yard......	6c.	7c.	10c.	12c.	15c.

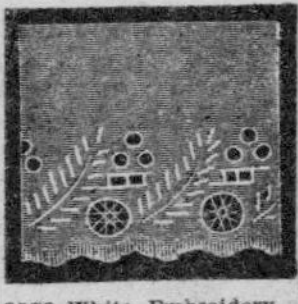

8579 White Embroidery, 8 inch work on 17 inch cloth. Per yard....$0.32

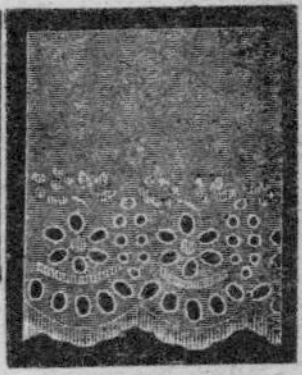

8585 White Embroidery, 5 to 5½ inches, nice work on 10 and 11 inch cloth. Per yard....... $0.33

Hamburg Embroidered Edgings on Good Cloth.

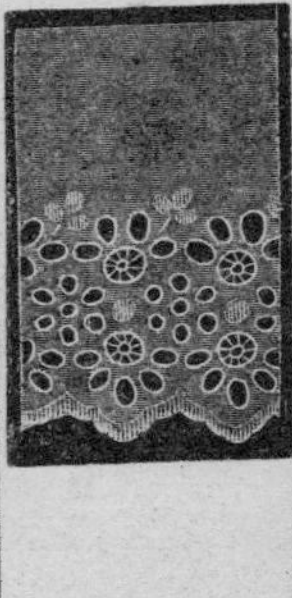

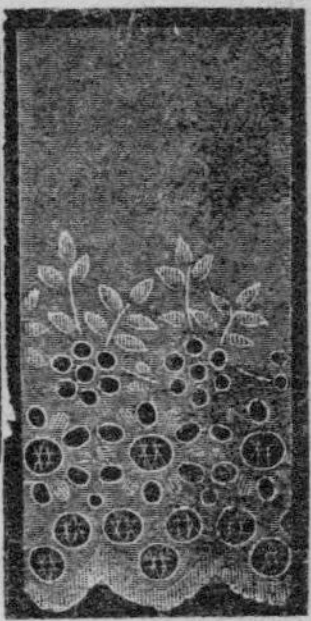

8600—

Width........	⅜in.	½	¾	1	1⅛	1¼	1¾	2
Per yard.....	3c.	5c.	7c.	8c.	9c.	10c.	12c.	13c.
Width.......	2½	3	3½	4	5			
Per yard.....	14c.	18c.	20c	30c	32c.			

Hamburg Embroidered Insertings

8610—

Width, inch..........	⅜	½	¾	1	1⅛	1¾	2
Per yard.............	4c.	5c.	7c.	9c.	12c.	16c.	19c

We quote width of embroidery, not cloth.

*** Write your name and Address on package returned to us if you want it to have attention; send letter of instructions by mail; do not put it in package.

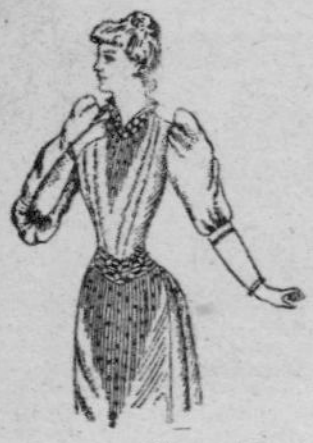

Bead Fronts and Stomachers.

9425 Black Cut Bead Stomacher. Size, 15 in. wide by 14½ in. long. Each $1.00
9430 Black Cut Bead Stomacher. Size, 16 in. by 16 in. Each $1.25

New Bead Yokes.

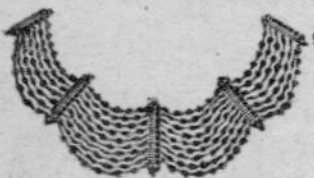

9432 Black Jet Bead Yokes. To be worn as shown on figure or at back as well as front. Each..............$1.10

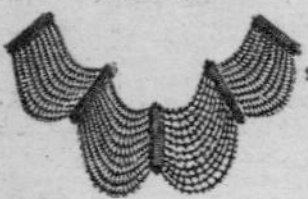

9434 Black Yokes, jet beads and spangles, with 5 crossbars. Each.............$1.50

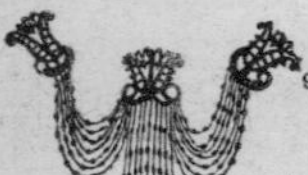

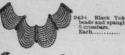

9436 Black Yokes. Cut beads, large and small. Each $1.40

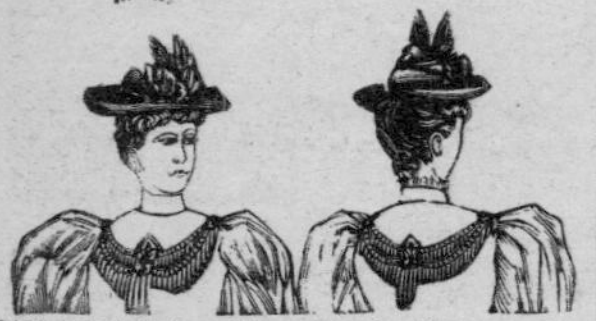

9438 Black Yokes. Fine cut beads. Cut shows front and back view. Each $2.30

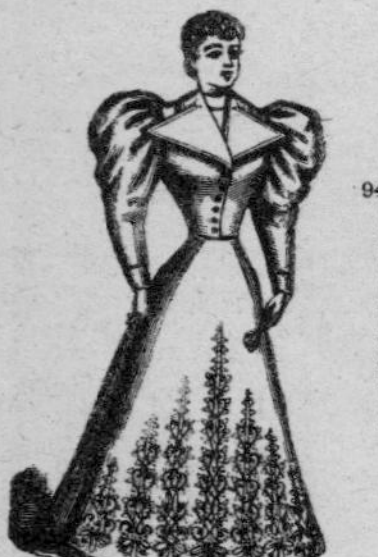

9439 Special Skirt Set, made of fine cut beads; seven (7) pieces, the center one 19 inches deep, two 14 inches, two 10 inches and two 6 inches. This is especially rich and entirely new. Per set of 7 pieces $3.25
Black only.

Black and Colored Bead Sets.

Note the reduction in prices. We quote only until sold.
9440 Colored Bead Sets, 5 pieces, in bronze and wine only. Per set..............................$0.60
Postage...13
9445 Black Italian Cut Bead Sets, with large oblong beads, making a very rich set; 5 pieces. Per set..............................$1.69

***** It will be a favor to us (and perhaps to your friends) if you will place, where they will do the most good, any duplicate Catalogues or advertising matter which you may receive from us.**

Zouave Sets.

Note the low prices to close.
9450 Black Italian Cut Bead, two pieces. Zouave set. See cut of lady showing set as it will appear when worn. Per set..............$0.90
9455 Black Satin and Silk Cord, two-piece (2 piece Zouave set). See cut. Per set..............$1.00

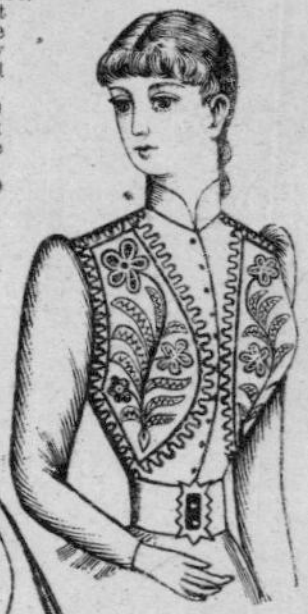

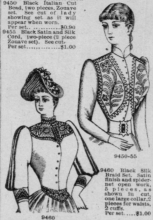

9450-55

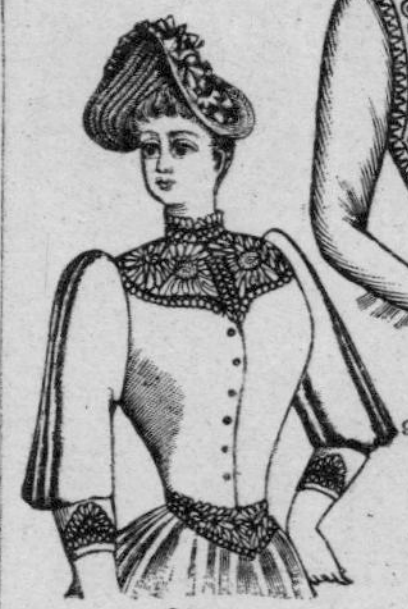

9460

9460 Black Silk Braid Set. Satin finish and spider-net open work, 5 pieces, as shown in cut, one large collar, 2 pieces for waists, 2 cuffs. Per set.....$1.00

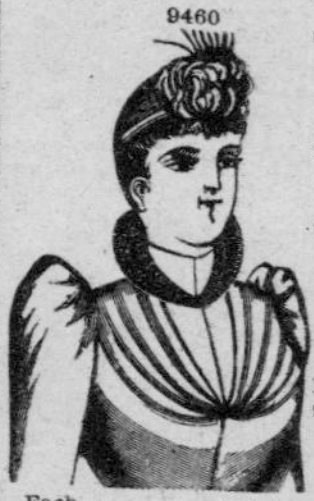

9465 De Medici Collars, real steel points. Can be worn standing, as shown in cut, or flat down. Steel color only. Each..............$0.75
9470 De Medici Collar, black cut beads; see cut. Black only. Each..............$1.00
9475 De Medici Collars. Extra quality cut black beads; see illustration on figure. Black only. Each..............$1.25

Bead Panels, Job.

Note the prices until sold.
9494 Black Italian Bead Panels, with cut beads, 4 inches at top, 7½ inches at bottom, 36 inches long. Postage, 21 cents. Each..............................$0.99
9496 Job Lot Solid Bead Panels, in colors only, as follows: Medium and dark brown and dark blue. Postage, 18 cents. Each..............$0.75

Astrakhan Cloth Band Trimming.

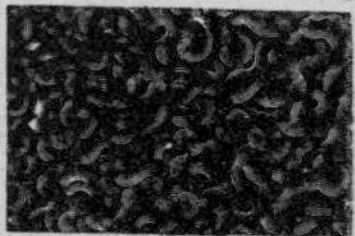

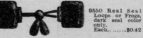

9540-42

Extra quality.

9540 Astrakhan Cloth Band Trimming, fine quality; black only.

Width,	1 in	1½ in.	2 in.	3 in.	4 in.
Per yard	20c.	24c.	30c.	42c.	45c.

9542 Astrakhan Cloth Band Trimming, fine quality; chinchilla or white and gray mixed.

Width	1 in.	1½ in.	2 in.	3 in.
Per yard	15c	20c.	24c.	43c.

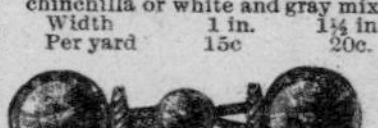

9545 Real Seal Loops or Frogs; dark seal color only. Each........$0.22

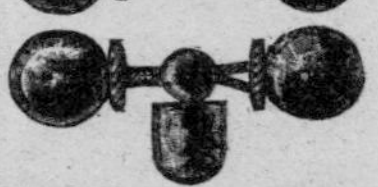

9548 Real Seal Loops or Frogs, dark seal color only. Each.......$0.30

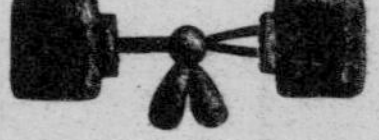

9550 Real Seal Loops or Frogs, dark seal color only. Each.........$0.42

Meyenburg Silk Fur Trimmings.

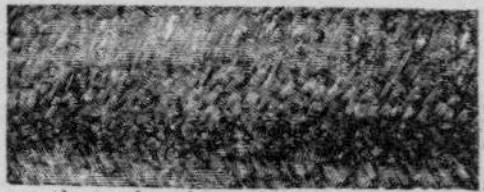

Are uniformly one shades not affected by water do not spot, are moth proof, and are of one quality, and that the best.
9554 Silk for piping, round, ⅜ in. wide, for edging or trimmings on any garment, ready to sew on. light or dark beaver color.
Per yard..............$0.25. Per 12 yards.......$2.70

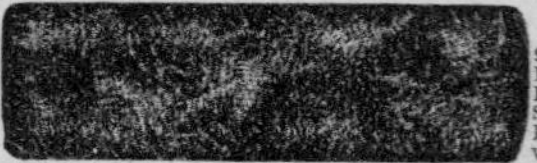

9558—Flat Band Silk Beaver Trimming, light or dark beaver color.

Width	½ in.	¾ in.	1 in.	1½ in.	2 in.	3 in.
Per yard	$0.13	.16	.21	.29	.44	.62
Per 12 yards	1.45	1.75	2.25	3.10	4.90	6.90

9562—Royal Shaded brown silk piping ⅜ inch, round.
Per yard..............$0.25 Per 12 yards..... 2.75
9564 Royal Shaded Brown, Silk Band Trimming, dark center shaded to light.

Widths	¾ in.	1 in.	1½ in.	2 in.	3 in.
Per yard	$0.18	.25	.33	.54	.75

9566 Shaded Mink Silk Beaver Piping, ⅜ inch, round. Per yard....$0.25. Per 12 yards......$2.75
9568 Shaded Mink Silk Beaver Band Trimming, dark center stripe, shaded to light.

Width	¾ in.	1 in.	1½ in.	2 in.	3 in.
Per yard	$0.18	.25	.33	.54	.75

Fur Trimmings.

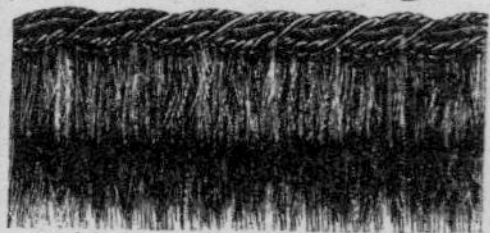

9580-84

9580 Black Coney fur edging with silk gimp heading; width 1½ inch (see band trimming to match.)
Per yard..............$0.15. Per doz..........$1.60

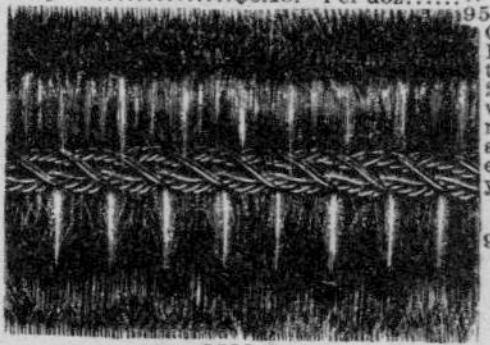

9582-6

9582. Black Coney Fur band trimming 2¼ inches wide, to match above edge. Per yard 25c.
9584 Gray Coney fur edging with silk gimp heading; width 1½ inch (see band trimming to match). Per yard 25c.
9586 Gray Coney fur band trimming 2¼ inches wide, to match above gray edge. Per yard......$0.40

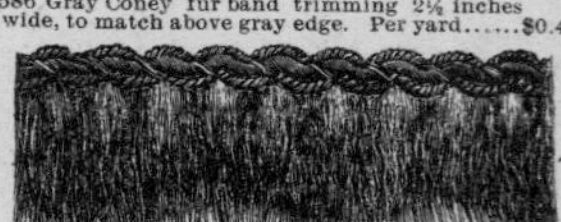

9590 Fur edging, with silk gimp heading, dark brown, imitation martin. Width 1½ in. Per yd.$0.25
9592 Fur edging, as above, natural opossum, light with darker tipped edge, width 1½ to 2 in. Per yard..............................$0.35

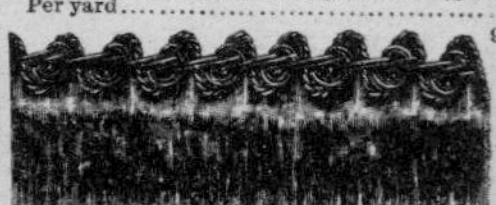

9594 Fur Edging as above, brown nutria (imitation beaver); width 1½ inch.
Per yard..............................$0.40
9596 Fur edging, as above, real martin, 2 in. wide. Per yard.............................75
9598 Fur edging, as above, real mink, 1 in. Per yd. .75
9600 Fur edging, as above, silver fox. Per yard. . .45

Swan's Down.

WHITE ONLY.

	Per yard.	Per doz.
9612 Swan's Down, No. 1, ¾ in., unlined	$0.25	$2.70
9614 Swan's Down, No. 2, 1 in., unlined	.35	4.05
9616 Swan's Down, No. 3, 1¼ in., unlined	.50	5.40
9618 Swan's Down, No. 4, 1½ in., unlined	.65	7.00
9620 Swan's Down, No. 1, ¾ in. lined	.35	3.75
9622 Swan's Down, No. 2, lined 1 in.	.45	4.80
9624 Swan's Down, No. 3, lined, 1¼ in.	.55	6.00
9626 Swan's Down, No. 4, 1½ in. lined	.65	7.25

Fur Trimmings.

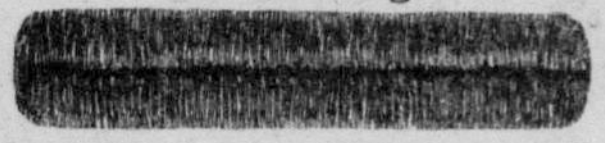

N. B.--All fur trimmings sold are manufacturers' measurement in width.

9640 Black unlined Coney, first quality.

Width	1 in.	2 in.	3 in.	4 in.
Per yard	$0.12	.24	.36	.48
Per doz yds.	1.25	2.50	3.75	5.00

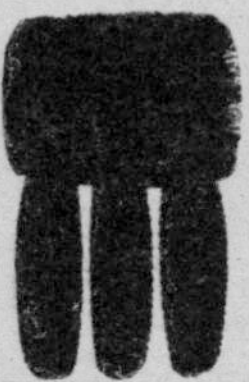

9646 Gray Coney Fur, unlined, first quality, light or dark.

Width	1 in.	1½	2 in.	3 in.
Per yd.	$0.19	.29	.39	.57

9650 Black Hare Fur Trimming, padded and lined, full width, about 9 in., 6 in. tails; width of fur about 3 in.; until sold; see cut. Per yd. $1.25

NOTE.--We can supply any of the finer and more expensive furs. Write for prices, giving width and color, and state quality desired.

Fur Trimmings—Continued.

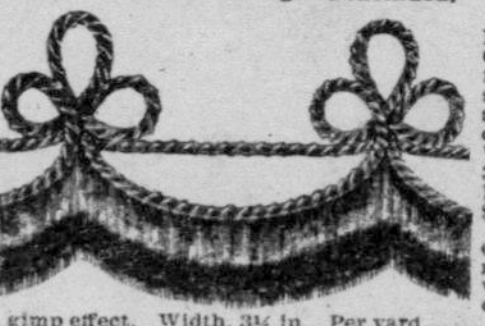

9660 Black Coney fur with silk cord and gimp effect. Width, 3½ in. Per yard, $0.50.

9662 Gray Coney fur, with silk cord and gimp effect. Width, 3½ in. Per yard $0.60

9664 Brown Coney fur with silk cord and gimp effect. Width, 3½ in. Per yard .75

9666 Blue Hare Coney fur with silk cord and gimp effect. Width, 3½ in. Per yard .75

9668 Electric dark seal Coney fur with silk cord and gimp effect. Width, 3½ in. Per yard .75

Fur Trimmings.

PLAIN BAND.

9670 Natural Opossum, satin lined.

Width.	1 in.	2 in.	3 in.
Per yard.	$0.45	$0.90	$1.35

9672 French Seal (pulled Coney), satin lined.

Width.	1 in.	2 in.	3 in.	4 in.
Per yard.	$0.55	$1.10	$1.65	$2.20

9674 Imitation Mink (blended muskrat), lined.

Width.	1 in.	2 in.	3 in.
Per yard.	$0.35	$0.75	$1.15

9676 Nutria (Imitation Beaver), satin lined.

Width.	1 in.	2 in.	3 in.	4 in.
Per yard.	$0.60	$1.20	$1.85	$2.40

9678 Natural Raccoon, lined.

Width	1 in.	1½ in.	2 in.
Per yard	$0.65	$0.98	$1.30

We have an Educational Catalogue, quoting all adopted school books, specially designed for teachers and students. (Free.)

Fur Trimmings—Continued.

	Width 1 in.	Width 2 in.	Width 3 in.
9680 Black Opossum, satin lined. Per yard	$0.65	$1.30	$2.00
9682 Genuine Black Astrakahn, satin lined. Per yard.	.65	1.30	2.00
9686 Gray Krimmer, satin lined. Per yard	.75	1.50	2.25
9694 Genuine Beaver Fur, dark, satin lined. Per yard.	1.25	2.50	3.75
9696 Genuine Beaver Fur, light, satin lined. Per yard.	1.50	3.00	4.50
9698 Genuine Mink Fur, satin lined. Per yard	1.50	3.00	4.50

9704 White Angora Fur, 7 to 8 inches wide, extra heavy, with white satin padded lining. Per yard $0.50
Per doz 5.40

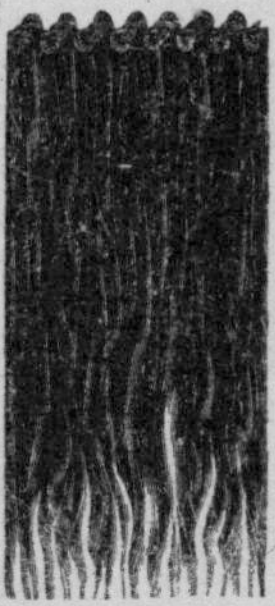

9705 Plain Black Angora Fur, with black silk gimp heading, width 6 to 7 in. Per yard $0.35

9710 Plain White Angora Fur, white silk gimp heading, width 6¼ to 7½ in. Per yard $0.35

9715 Angora Fur, upper part white, with blue gray tipped ends, and gray silk gimp heading to match. Width 6 to 7 in. Per yard $0.35

9720 Angora Fur, upper part white, with brown or amber tipped ends, and silk gimp heading to match. Width 6 in. Per yard $0.35

BUTTON DEPARTMENT.

Jet Dress Buttons.

9800

9805

	Per Doz.	Per Gross.
9800 Black Ball Cut Jet Dress Buttons	$0.04	$0.40
9805 Black Ball Cut Jet Dress Buttons larger	.05	.50
9808 Black Cut Jet Ball Dress Buttons, one size larger than 9805	.06	.65

9287

9829

9831

Cuts are exact size of Buttons.

	Per Doz.	Per Gross.
9827 Fine Jet Buttons, polished smooth edges	$0.05	$0.50
9829 Fine Jet Buttons, polished, smooth edges	.05	.50
9831 Fine Jet Buttons, polished, smooth rim edge	.05	.50

9833

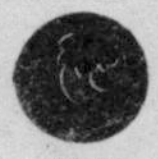

9836

9838

Cuts are exact size of Buttons.

	Per Doz.	Per Gross.
9833 Fine Jet Buttons, dull polished, smooth rim edges	$0.05	$0.50
9836 Fine Jet Buttons, polished points in crescent	.05	.50
9838 Fine Dull Jet Buttons, polished points	.05	.50

Fancy Metal Dress Buttons.

9880

9880 Metal Dress Buttons in all colorings. No black. Per doz $0.05
Per gross .50

9883 New Metal Dress Buttons in assorted tints and black. Per doz $0.08
Per gross .75

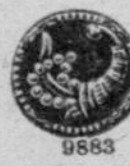

9883

9889

9889 New Metal Dress Buttons in assorted tints and black. Per dozen $0.08
Per gross .75

9895 New Bright Steel Dress Buttons, with cut steel points; a high grade button similar to No. 9900. Per dozen $0.25
Per gross 2.50

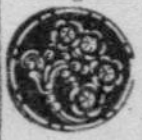

9900 New Metal Dress Buttons, in assorted tints, with four cut steel points; a high grade button. Per dozen $0.25
Per gross 2.50

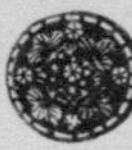

9930

9930 Fine French Dress Buttons, with 5 cut steel points, in new shadings. No black. Per doz $0.25
Per gross 2.75

9935

9935 Fine Metal Dress Buttons, in all the new shades, and black. Per doz $0.22
Per gross 2.25

Black and Colored Crochet Buttons.

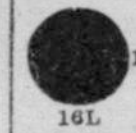

16L

10000 Black and Colored Ball Crochet Buttons with metal shank, 16 line; see cut. Per dozen $0.25. Per gross $2.60

18L

10009 Black Crochet Button, flat with fancy centers.

	18L	20L	22L
Per dozen	$0.24	$0.28	$0.30
Per gross	2.25	2.75	2.95

18L

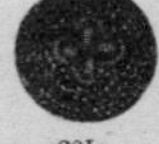

20L

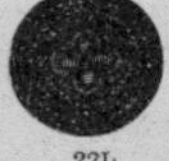

22L

10015 Black Crochet Button, flat, with fancy centers.

	18L	20L	22L
Per dozen	$0.30	$0.32	$0.34
Per gross	3.00	3.25	3.50

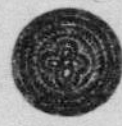

18 L

20L

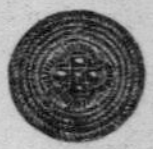

22L

10019 Black Crochet Buttons, half oval, beaded centers.

	18L	20L	22L
Per dozen	$0.30	$0.32	$0.35
Per gross	3.10	3.25	3.50

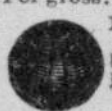

10025 Black Ball Crochet Silk Buttons. 16L
Per dozen $0.30
Per gross 3.20

10031 Black Ball Crochet Silk Dress Buttons, Beaded center. 18L
Per dozen $0.33
Per gross 3.30

Silk Dress Buttons.

10035 Silk Tailor Buttons, black and colors, 22 line. Per dozen $0.08
Per gross .75

Button Molds.

10045 Button Molds, small to large. Per gross, 10 cents to $0.50

Colored Vest, Coat and Cloak Buttons.

(We sell any quantity.)

10047 Black Lasting Button, iron back.

Line	22	30	38
12 dozen for	$0.35	$0.50	$0.65

10049 Black Lasting Button, silk back.

Line	22	30	38
12 dozen for	$0.75	$1.00	$2.00

	Per doz.	Per gross.
10051 Black Worsted Diagonal Buttons, stripe, 24 line, see cut 10247	$0.08	$0.75
10053 Black Worsted Diagonal Buttons, stripe, 30 line, see cut 10247	.10	1.00
10056 Black Worsted Diagonal Buttons, 38 line, 1 inch	.14	1.40

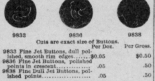

Safety Pins—Continued.

10524 Same as 10520-10522.

No. 3.

Per dozen......$0.03.   Per gross......$0.31

10525 Large Safety Sensible Blanket Pin, 4 in. long. The heaviest, best finished and most practical blanket pin made, nickel-plated, put up ½ dozen on card, ½ gross in box. Each......$0.04
Per dozen......$0.40.   Per gross......$4.00

Hat and Shawl Pins.

10541 Hat pins, steel, with black heads, 6 in. long. Per dozen......$0.04   Per gross......$0.35
10543 Shawl or Belt Pins, black, large heads.
Per dozen......$0.03.   Per gross......26
10547 Shawl Pins, fancy heads, steel chains,
Per pair......08
Per pair......75

Hair Pins.

10555 Hairpins, crimped or straight, 8 papers to a bundle.
Per bundle......$0.02
Per package of 10 bundles......$0.13

10557 Invisible Hairpins, about 50 in a box.
Per box......$0.08   Per doz. boxes......30
10560 Hairpins, wood cabinet, contains 50 hairpins per box, 4 cts. per dozen boxes, 40c. until sold.

10562 New Countess Hairpin in wood cabinet, 60 assorted pins.
Per box......$0.04
Per dozen......40

No. 7 CRIMPED Hair Pins

10565 Package Hairpins, 16 small boxes containing 20 crimped hairpins, each, or 320 in package.
Per package......$0.14
Per dozen......1.50

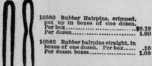

10567— Our Solid Metal Gilt Box of 100 assorted hairpins. Pr. bx.$0.06
Per dozen bxs......$0.65

10569—Unique Cabinet. A combination put up in convenient and attractive form. 100

10567 assorted   10569
hairpins, 100 toilet pins, 30 black pins and 4 jet shawl or belt pins. Each......$0.09
Per dozen......95

Rubber Hairpins.

10580 Rubber Hairpins, crimped, put up in boxes of one dozen.
Per box......$0.10
Per box......1.00
10582 Rubber hairpins straight, in boxes of one dozen. Per box......10
Per dozen boxes......1.00

When ordering goods shipped by mail, be sure to allow money for postage. If you send too much we will refund balance.

Hairpins—Continued.

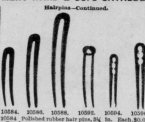

10584. 10586. 10588. 10592 10594. 10596.
10584 Polished rubber hair pins, 3¼ in. Each.$0.03
Per doz......28
10586 Polished rubber hair pins, 4¼ in. Each..03
Per doz......35
10588 Polished rubber hair pins, 5 in. Each......05
Per doz......45
10592 Polished twist top rubber hair pins, 3½ in. Each......04
Per doz......38
10594 Fancy rubber hair or braid pin, 3 in. Each......04
Per doz......38
10596 Fancy rubber hair or braid pin, 3½ in. Each......05
Per doz......50

Hair Crimpers.

10600 Common Sense Hair Crimpers made of lead with woven covers, 12 in. package 2 in. 3 in.
Per pkg. 3c.   4c.
Per doz. pkg.30c.   40c.
10602 Duplex Hair Crimpers, nickel plate
Per pair......$0.02
Per dozen pairs......20

10602

Thimbles.

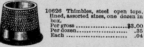

10622 Silver plated thimbles, in round box, glass tops, closed ends; put up one dozen in a box, assorted sizes.
Per gross......$1.30
Per doz......12

10624 Sterling plated Thimbles, one dozen closed tops, in box, assorted sizes.
Per gross......$3.25
Per dozen......35
Each......03

10626 Thimbles, steel open tops, lined, assorted sizes, one dozen in box.
Per gross......$3.00
Per dozen......35
Each......04

10630 Steel Thimbles, electro-silver lined, closed tops. Each......03
Per box of 3 dos......75
Per gross......2 60
10632 Rubber Thimbles, closed, assorted sizes.
Each......10
Per doz......1.08

10635 Aluminum Thimbles, one each in wood box. Each......$0.05
Per doz......45
Per gross......4.50

N. B.—For silver and gold thimbles see jewelry department.

Cuff Holders.

10660 The Paris Cuff Holder, with lever button, very practical. Per pair$0.10
Per dozen......1.00
Per gross......10.50
10665 The Wizard Cuff Holders improved, nickel plated.
Per pair......$ 0.12
Per doz......1.20
Per gross......12.00

Necktie Holders.

10670 The Standard Tie Holder, nickel plated, small and neat.
Each, 3 cts., 2 for 5 cts.
Per doz......18
10671 The Excelsior Men's Drawer Supporters, very simple, hooking to pants band; nickel plated.
Per pair......$0.05
Per 12 pairs......50

10670   10671

Patent Coat Collar Spring.

SAVES the wear on button holes, which disfigures a coat so quickly.

10678 Patent Adjustable Coat Collar Spring. The spring is made from best oil-tempered steel, formed to fit the coat under the collar. By its use the coat collar and lapels always retain their shape.
Each......$0.08
Per dozen......75
Per gross......7.50
Postage......04

Tape Measures.

	Each.	Per doz.
10680 Imitation Linen Tape Measure. 60 inches long	$0.02	$0.08
10683 Tape Measures, ½ inch wide, 60 inch long, figured on both sides	.04	.30
10686 Tailor's Tape Measures, double stitched, 60 in. long, figured on both sides	.08	.75

Needles.

T. HARPER'S PATENT PRO BONO BURNISHED GOLD EYED SHARPS Nos 5 to 10

10733 Harper's Best Needles, in patent wrappers, cloth stuck, oval eyes, sharps, the finest quality that can be manufactured, except the gold-eyed, solid sizes 1, 2, 3, 4, 5, 6, 7, 8, 9, 10, and assorted 1 to 5, 3 to 9, 4 to 8, and 5 to 10. 40 papers for $1.25; 10 papers for 38c., 1 paper for 4c.
10735 Harper's Best Gold-Eyed Needles, in patent wrappers, cloth stuck, sharps. The very finest quality that can be manufactured; solid numbers 1, 2, 3, 4, 5, 6, 7, 8, 9 and 10, and assorted sizes same as in 10733. 40 papers for $1.50; 10 for 45 cents; 1 for 5 cents. Give numbers wanted.

Lightning Needles.

Sewing Made Easy.   A New Idea.

The Lightning   Needle.

TRADE   MARK

Being tapered from the center to the eye forces itself through the fabric without effort. Try it and you will like it.

10740 The Lightning Hand Sewing Needles, one push sufficient to pass the entire needle through the fabric. The eyes of the 8, 9, 10 are as large as those found in 5, 6 and 7 of other makes, enabling the user to do better and finer sewing, permitting a coarser thread to be used in a fine needle. We quote in Sharps (long) only. Sizes 1, 2, 3, 4, 5, 6, 7, 8, 9, 10, 11, 12, 5 to 10, 4 to 8, 3 to 9, 1 to 6. Per paper......$0.04
Per 10 papers......35
Per 40 papers (1000 needles)......1.25

Henry Milward & Sons Calyx-Eyed Needles.

Kratz's Patent
No. 5221-84

This needle is made to meet a want patent to every one, namely, a needle that will thread without the annoying process of passing the end of the cotton through the eye. The cotton is slipped through a slit above the eye, as shown by the accompanying sketch. Invaluable for failing sight.

10744 Milward's Calyx-Eyed Needles: 10 needles in a paper, 100 papers to the thousand. Solid sizes. Nos. 3, 4, 5, 6, 7, 8 and 9. Assorted sizes, 3 to 9, 4 to 8, 5 to 9; in a paper only.

Per paper	$0.07
10 papers	.60
1,000 needles	5.00

10746 Glover's Needles, solid sizes, Nos. 1, 2, 3, 4, 5, 6, 7, 8. Per paper ..... .08
Per 10 papers ..... .75
Per 40 papers or 1,000 needles .. 2.75

10750 Steel Knitting Needles, best quality in packages of 3 dozen, Nos. 12 to 20, No. 12 being very coarse, Per set of five needles ..... .04

10751 Steel Knitting Needles, in sets of five, in wooden case. See cut. Per set ..... .04
Per dozen ..... .40

10753 Double Long Cotton Darning Needles, 5 in paper, assorted 1 to 5. Per paper ..... .02
Per 3 papers ..... .05
Per 12 papers ..... .16

10754 Large Wool Darning Needles 5 in paper, 14 to 18.
Per paper ..... .02
Per 3 papers ..... .05
Per 12 papers ..... .16

10755 Darning Needles, per box of 10 papers, come solid numbers in a paper and are assorted as follows: 1, 14; 2, 15; 3, 16; 4, 18; 2, 17; No. 14 being the coarsest and No. 18 finest; per box of 10 papers, 250 needles, assorted as above, 33c; per paper, not assorted, 4c.

10761

10761 The Excelsior Needle Case contains five papers good English Needles (sharps and 15 assorted single needles, tape darners, etc.) cambric stuck. Retail price 25c. Our price, each $0.08
Per dozen ..... $0.75. Per gross 5.50

10762 Imperial Toilet Case, large 3 fold Size closed 4½x7 inches Contains 160 fine cloth stuck sewing needles (4 papers) besides an assortment of 40 varieties of all other large needles, bonnet, hat, shawl, and 96 white pins, a total of 238 useful articles Each $0.18
Per dozen ..... $1.50 Per gross 16.50

10774 Our Climax Needle Case, size, closed 2¼x4 inches, in fancy assorted leatherette cases.

Contains—
Sewing needles	80
Darning needles	10
Glove needles	1
Packing needles	1
Carpet sharps	3
Double long	2
Yarn	2
Betweens (tailor)	25
Crewel	5
Tapestry	2
Surgeon	1
Bodkin	2
Chenille	4
Millinery	10

Total 150 best Harper's Gold-eyed Needles. Quantity and quality considered, this is the cheapest needle case in market.
Each $0.50
Per dozen 5.50

10778 Fine Needle Box, with 6 papers best gold eyed, English needles with 9 large assorted needles, on satin cushion. Each $0.50
Per dozen 5.50

Emery Bags.

10780 Emery Bag for polishing needles.
Each $0.09
Per doz. ..... .95

Globe Combination Revolving Spool Holder.

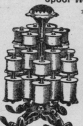

10790 Contains holders for 30 spools of thread and plush pin cushion, so constructed that spools can quickly be put on or taken off. The above device is certainly a household necessity. Almost every family has enough thread, white, black, colored—and buttonhole twist—to fill the spool holder, which is nicely polished and nickel plated and will prove itself an ornamental and useful household necessity.
Each $0.90
Per dozen 9.00
Postage 36c.

10800 Knitting Companion or Spool Holder, for ladies' use in knitting, crocheting and sewing. Each holder on fancy card, with printed instructions. Each $0.05
Per dozen ..... .50
Per gross 5.50

10800   10805-10810

10805 Ladies' Sewing Companion, bright pewter metal, 5x5, one in box, has mirror, plush pincushion, four spoolholders, etc. Each $0.06
Per dozen, Per $0.65. Per gross 6.00

10810 Ladies' Sewing Companion, frame made, of aluminum alloy, 7 inches high, 5 inches wide silk velvet needle and pin-cushion, mirror 2¾ inches square, 2 rings for thimbles, 4 arms for spools, 2 hooks for shears and scissors; a very useful household article. Each ..... .15
Per dozen, $1.50. Per gross 15.00

Wire Sleeve Supporters, Arm Bands and Garters.

10836 Patent Duplex Ventilated Men's Arm Bands or Ladies' Garters, fine nickeled steel wire one pair in box
Each, $0.10. Per dozen $0.95
Postage ..... .04

Hose Supporters.

10855 Men's Elastic Web Garters, plain webs; see cut; per pair $0.10
Per dozen ..... .95

10860 Men's Silk Garters, fine, one pair in box (see cut). Black, white and assorted colors. Per pair $0.25
Per dozen 2.70

10864 Men's Silk and Satin Paris Garter, in colors and black. One pair in a box. Very fine.
Per pair $0.35
Per dozen 3.75

10865 Ladies' Lisle Elastic Frill Edge Garters, silk bows. One pair in box. Per pair $0.25

10864 Per dozen $2 60

Garters—Continued.

10870 Ladies' Silk Garters, extra fine, with satin bows, in black, white and assorted colors; one pair in box.
Per pair $0.45
Per dozen 4.50

10865-70

Improved Button Clasp Hose Supporters.

The button fastener is the simplest and best. Never cuts the stocking, never slips or lets go, has no stitching. Our supporters are made of Lisle Elastic in black and white.

10900 Babies' Single Strap Supporter.
Per pair $0.07
Per dozen ..... .70

10902 Babies' Double Strap Supporters
Per pair $0.09
Per dozen ..... .90

10904 Misses' Two Strap Supporters
Per pair $0.10
Per dozen 1.00

10906 Young Ladies' Two Strap Supporters.
Per pair $0.12
Per dozen 1.15

	Per pair.	Per doz.
10908 Ladies' Two Strap Hose Supporters	$0.13	$1.25
10910 Ladies' Belts with Hose Supporters	.18	1.95
10913 Ladies' Shoulder Braces with hose supporters	.23	2.40
10915 Misses' Shoulder Braces with hose supporters	.18	1.95
10917 Children's Shoulder Braces with hose supporters	.17	1.75

10931 Ladies' Black or White Sateen Combination Belt, with hose supporters and points for safety belt; size 24 to 54 in. (see cut). Each $0.25
Per dozen 2.65

10931

10932 Ladies' Suspenders for supporting skirt.
Per pair $0.10
Per dozen 1.00

10935 Ladies' faultless Serviette supporter, made of soft sateen with a rubber band across hips. Meets with universal approval.
Sizes are every inch from 22 to 36; ask for one inch larger than your exact waist measure.
Each $0.25
Per dozen 2.75

10936 The faultless serviette or absorbent health napkin; economical, comfortable, healthful. Recommended by physicians and fast superseding bird's-eye linen, more absorbent, antiseptic, no washing, burned after using, invaluable while travelling, cheaper than laundrying, medium size. Sold by the package of 1 doz. only.
Per dozen $0.50
Extra, by mail ..... .12

Daisy Hose Supporters.

10937 Child's Shoulder Hose Supporters, in black, white and drab, with bright metal clasp. No. 1, age 1 to 3; No. 2, age 3 to 5. Try them and you will like them.
Per pair $0.16
Per dozen 1.65

10937—Nos. 1 and 2.

Belts—Continued.

13017 Black Velvet Belt, cloth lined, two inches wide; fancy oxidized buckle. Each...........$0.15
Per dozen... 1.50
Postage 8 cents.

13035 Our Leader in Ladies' Belts. Smooth calf solid leather belt, two inches wide; black, red or tan; fancy oxidized buckle. Each.........$0.10
Per dozen... 1.00
Postage 8 cents.

Ladies' "Empire" Belts.
Always Mention Waist Measure When Ordering Belts.

13044—Fancy embossed Fine Calf "Empire" Belt with pinked and perforated edge; 3½ inches wide; tan or black; similar to cut; shield strap and nickeled buckle. Weight packed, 10 ounces. Each.........$0.45
13046 Black Velvet "Empire" Belt. 3 inches wide; shield strap and buckle. Weight packed, 10 ounces. Each.........$0.33

Ladies' Bodice Belts.
Always Mention Waist Measure When Ordering Belts.

13048 Grain leather Adjustable Bodice Belt, black or tan; silvered slide, oxidized buckle. Each.........$0.20 Per dozen.....$2.25
Postage 10 cents.

13052 Fine Black Velvet Adjustable Bodice Belt, black buckle and finely polished black horn slide. Closing price, each.........$0.26
Postage, 10 cents.

Ladies' Double Bodice Belts.
Mention Waist Measure when Ordering Belts.

13060 Black Velvet Double Bodice Belt, with cord lace; black buckles. *Mention size wanted or order will be delayed.* Each.........$0.25
Per dozen... 2.70
Postage, 10 cents.

Belts—Continued.

13070 Fine Calf "Diamond" Double Bodice Belt with ten steel point ornaments; square buckle. 24 to 30 inches only. Tan or black. *Mention waist measure to avoid delay in filling order.* Weight packed, 10 ounces.
Each.........$0.47

13072 Fancy Embossed Fine Calf Double Bodice Belt, with pinked and perforated edge, square buckles, tan or black, 24 to 30 inches only. *Mention waist measure to avoid delay in filling order.* Weight packed, 10 ounces. Each.........$0.47

13076, 13078 and 13082.
13076 Fine Calf Sash Belt with two square nickeled buckles; tan only; 24 to 30 inches. Weight packed, 8 ounces. Each.........$0.45
13078 Seal Grain Calf Sash Belt with two square buckles; black only; 24 to 30 inches. Weight packed, 8 ounces. Each.........$0.45

Men's Leather Belts.
13082 Men's Fine Calf Sash Belt, tan only; two rings and square buckle. Lengths up to 42 inches. *Mention waist measure* when ordering. Weight packed, 10 ounces. Each.........$0.60

13084 and 13086
13084 Men's Fine Lizard Grain Calf Belt, with leather covered buckle and rings; tan only; lengths up to 42 inches. *Mention waist measure* when ordering. Weight, packed, 10 ounces. Each.........$0.50
13086 Men's Solid Calf Ring Belt, two inches wide, tan only; lengths up to 42 inches. *Mention waist measure* when ordering. Weight, packed, 10 ounces. Each.........$.33

Ladies' Shopping Bags.
NOTICE.—We are out of all bags not quoted in this catalogue, and cannot obtain them, as they are no longer manufactured, and we will be obliged to substitute from our present stock on all orders for bags selected from former catalogues.

13101 Ladies' Shopping Bag, of fancy embossed seal grain, cloth, leatherette, bound all around with silk gimp cord, two leather handles, sixteen top with drawing strings; 9 inches wide. Weight packed, 15 ounces. Each.........$0.50

Shopping Bags—Continued.

13103 Ladies' Shopping Bag, of seal grain cloth, leatherette, bound all around with silk gimp cord, one large and 2 small outside pockets with oxidized catches; sixteen top with drawing strings; 2 leather handles; 10½ in. deep, 10¼ inches wide. Weight packed, 16 ozs. Each.........$0.75

13105 Ladies' Shopping Bag, of seal grain leather and ends, two leather handles; sixteen top with drawing strings; size 10 x 10 x 2¾. A handsome and roomy bag. Weight packed, 18 ounces. Each.........$1.00

13108 Ladies' Shopping Bag of seal grain leather with rounded bottom and ends, large gusseted outside pocket with oxidized catch; two leather handles; sixteen top with drawing strings. Size 10 x 10 x 2¾. A stylish, handsome and roomy bag. Weight packed, 20 ozs. Each.........$1.25

13113 "Boston" Shopping Bag, fancy embossed leather with 12 steel point ornaments; kid sides; repp silk top, lined with cambric, silk gimp drawing strings, 9 inches deep, 8 in. wide. Weight packed, 12 ounces. Each.........$0.90

13116 Shopping Bags, extra fine calf, Suede finish, pinked edges, silk stitched all around; size, 8¾ x 11½ inches, with silk gimp drawing cords. Colors: Mouse (or drab), purple, seal brown, black. Handsome and very durable. Weight, 5 oz. Each.........$0.93
13117 Shopping Bags, extra fine calf, Suede finish; size 9½ x 12¾ inches; otherwise same as 13116. Weight, 6 oz. Each.........$1.40
13118 Shopping Bags, extra fine calf, Suede finish, pinked edges, silk stitched all around; size, 8¼ x 11½ inches, silk gimp drawing cords; No. 5C, mouse color, with fine stripe, imitating corduroy; No. 6C, mouse color with dark hollow polka dots. Very handsome, stylish and durable. Weight, 5 oz. Each.........$1.65
13116-17-18

Ladies' Chatelaine Bags.
13122 Misses' Chatelaine Bag, of black lizard grained leather with oxidized frame with bell catch, nickel chains and bell hook; size 4 x 4. Weight, packed, 5 ounces. Each.........$0.25

13124 Ladies' Chatelaine Bag of seal grained leather; size 5½ x 5; black japanned riveted frame with nickeled spring catch, leather straps and belt hook. Weight packed, 10 ounces. Each.........$0.50

Chatelaine Bags—Continued.

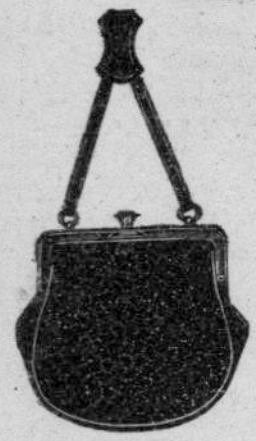

13125 Ladies' Chatelaine Bag of black lizard grained leather, cloth lined; size 5½x5½; black riveted frame with patented nickeled catch, leather covered belt-hook and straps. Weight, packed, 11 ounces.
Each......................$0.65

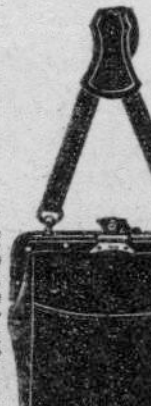

13127 Ladies' Chatelaine Bag of seal grained leather, with outside pocket, black riveted frame with patented nickeled catch; size 5¾x5¼; inside pocket, leather lined, leather covered belt-hook with swinging ring, leather straps. Weight, packed, 9 ounce.
Each..........................$0.80

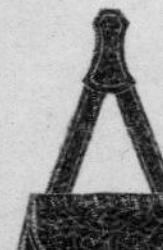

13128 Ladies' Cleopatra Bag of seal grained leather with flap and oxidized catch; gusseted all around; size 5½x5¾; leather covered belt hook, leather straps; inside pocket; cloth lined. Weight packed, 10 ounces. Each............$1.00

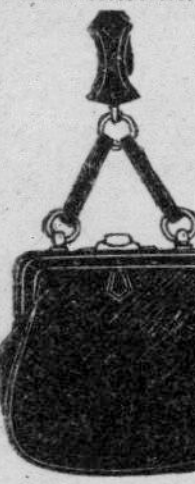

13129 Ladies' Chateline Bag of fine Vienna calf leather, with leather covered riveted frame, nickeled spring catch; size 5½x5½; leather lined; inside pocket; leather covered belt-hook with swinging ring; leather straps. Weight packed, 11 ounces.
Each......................$1.50

Ladies' Pocket Books.

NOTICE.—Our pocket books are selected from the best makes in the country, and we are prepared to offer the latest and best styles and qualities in the market at very reasonable prices.

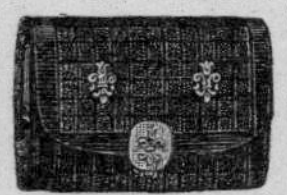

13133 Embossed Morocco Grain Leather with silvered catch and two ornaments on flap; leather-faced; coin-pocket with snap frame and four regular pockets. Size 2¾x4 inches.
Each $0.25
Postage 4c.

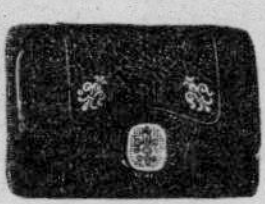

13139 Seal Grain Leather with embossed band, two silvered ornaments and catch; leather faced, four regular pockets and coin-pocket with nickel snap frame. Size 2¾x4⅜ in.
Each......................$0 45

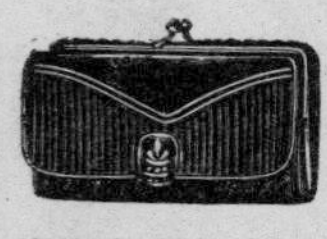

13145 Seal Grain Leather with fancy embossed fine calf flap; oxidized catch, outside card pocket and coin pocket with fancy nickeled frame; two regular pockets under flap; size, 2¾x 4½ inches.
Each..... .....$0.50

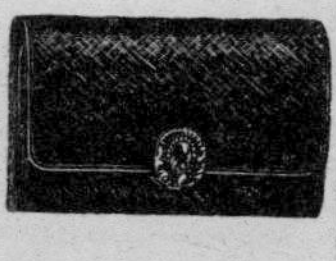

13149 Colored Grained Calf Leather, with silvered catch; leather faced and lined, four regular pockets and coin pocket with nickeled snap frame; size 2¾ x4½ inches.
Each............$0.65
Postage........ .05

Pocket Books—Continued.

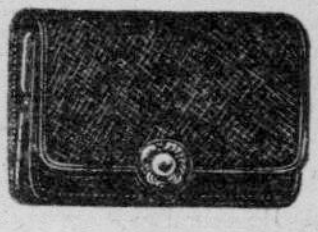

13153 Colored Grained Calf Leather, with silvered catch; outside card pocket; leather lined; flap faced with smooth calf; three regular pockets and coin pocket with fine nickeled snap frame. Size 2¾x 4½ inches (362-A)
Each...............$0.85
Postage, 4 cents.

Ladies' Combination Pocket Books.

13158 Seal Grain Leather, card pocket in flap, coin pocket with snap frame and three regular pockets; size 3x4½ inches. Weight packed 3 oz.
Each.............$0.25

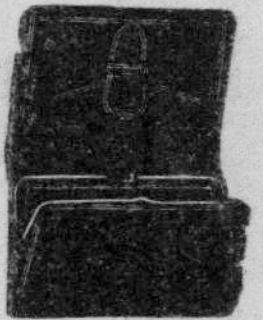

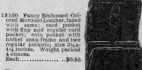

13160 Fancy Embossed Colored Morocco Leather, faced with same; card pocket with flap and regular card pocket; coin pocket with nickel snap-frame and two regular pockets; size 3½x-4½ inches. Weight packed 4 ounces.
Each................ ..$0.55

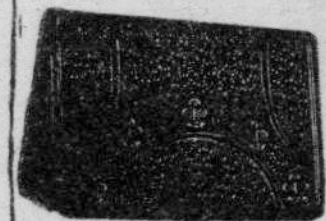

13162 Embossed Seal grain leather, with five silvered ornaments; two card pockets, two regular pockets and coin pocket with snap frame. Size 3⅛x4½ inches.
Each $0.65
Postage............... .04

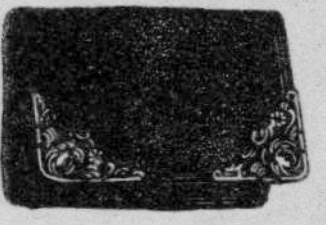

13164 Real Seal Leather with oxidized corners; leather faced; one card pocket with flap and regular card pocket; coin pocket with snap frame and two regular pockets; size 3½x4½ inches. Weight packed 4 oz.
Each..............$0.75

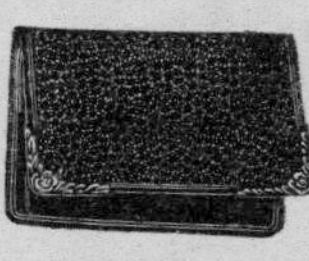

13166 Fine Genuine Seal Leather, with genuine sterling silver corners; leather faced; card pocket with flap and one regular card pocket, coin pocket with nickeled snap frame and two regular pockets.
Size, 3x4½ inches.
Weight packed, 4 oz.
Each...............$1.10

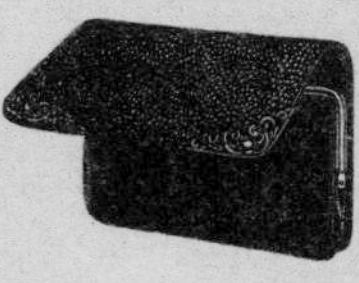

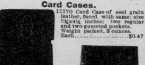

13168 Extra Fine colored Vienna Calf Leather, with genuine sterling silver corners; faced with smooth calf; card pocket with flap and one regular card pocket; coin pocket with nickeled snap frame and two regular pockets; size 3x 4½ inches.
Weight packed 4 oz.
Each...$1.30

Card Cases.

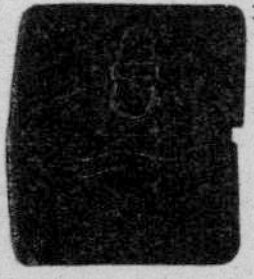

13170 Card Case of seal grain leather, faced with same; size 2¾x4½ inches; two regular and two gusseted pockets. Weight packed, 3 ounces.
Each..........................$0.47

13172 Card Case, fine grained colored Persian goat leather, faced with same; size 2¾x 4½ inches; two gusseted pockets. Weight packed, 3 oz.
Each.....................$0.55

Card Cases—Continued.

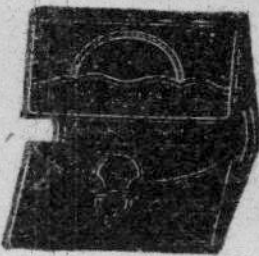

13174 Card Case of pebbled grain leather; vest pocket size, 2⅝x4½; leather faced and lined; one regular and two gusseted pockets, and three stamp pockets. Weight packed, 3 ounces.
Each......................$0.50

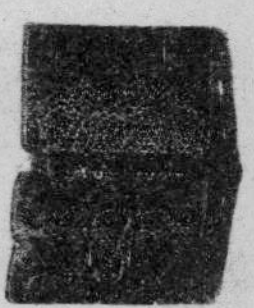

13176 Card case of fine Morocco leather, faced with same; leather and cloth lined; size, 3x4½ inches: one regular and two gusseted pockets, and three stamp pockets. Weight, packed, 3 ounces.
Each.... ....$0.75

Men's Flap Books.

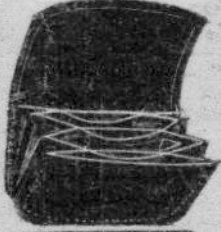

13181 Men's Flap Book of fine, smooth calf, bound and stitched all around, leather faced; four regular and three small, all leather pockets. Size 2⅝x4½. Weight packed, 4 ounces.
Each.........................$0.50

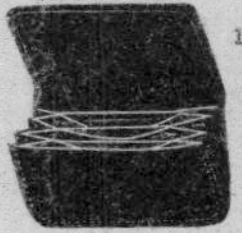

13183 Men's Flap Book of Real Russia Leather, bound and stitched all around; leather faced flap; four regular and three smaller all leather pockets. Size 2⅝x4¼ inches. A very handsome and durable book. Weight packed, 4 ounces.
Each.........................$0.60

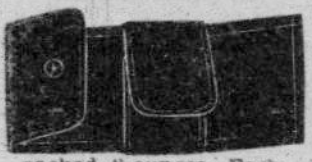

13186 Men's Bill Holder or Boodle Book, of morocco grained leather, faced and lined with leather; two flaps for holding bills. Size, closed, 2⅞x3¼ inches; button lock on flap. Weight packed, 3 ounces Each $0.40

Men's Strap Books.

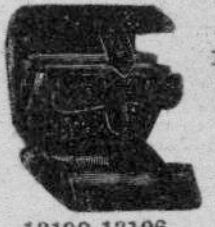

13190 Colored Morocco Leather size 2⅝x4¼ inches; leather faced; three small and four regular *all leather* pockets, bound and stitched and bill fold. Weight, packed, 4 ounces. Each............ $0.55

13190-13196

13192 Extra Fine Calf, size 2⅝x4⅝ inches, leather faced; four regular and three smaller *all leather* pockets, bound and stitched bellows style; card pocket and bill fold with flap and tuck strap. Each...........................$0.95
Postage, 4c.

13196 Men's Fine Morocco Leather Strap Book; size 2¾x4½ inches; leather faced and lined; *coin-pocket with nickeled snap-frame* and five regular pockets; drop bill fold with flap and tuck strap. Weight, packed, 4 ounces. Each.......$0.95

Men's Sheep and Calf Books.

Natural Colors.

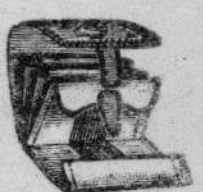

13207 Sheep (calf finish) stamped, size 2¾x4¾, stitched all around, leather faced flap, cloth lined, 4 pockets and bill fold. Weight packed, 3 ounces.
Each.............................$0.17

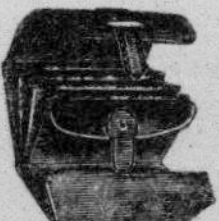

13208 Heavy Sheep calf finish, size 2¾x4¾, stitched all around; leather faced, cloth lined; *coin pocket* and four regular pockets and bill fold. Weight, packed, 4 ounces. Each...................$0.25

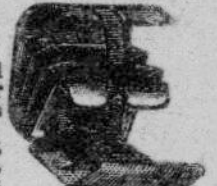

13212 Calf, stamped, silk stitched all around; size 2⅝x4½; leather faced flap, leather lined, 4 pockets and bill fold, with strap.
Each..............................$0.35
Per dozen........................ 3.80
Extra by mail, each........... .05

Hair Brushes—Continued.

13444 Black, All Bristle Hair Brush, hard rubber back. See cut. Each, $0.45. Per dozen......$4.75 Brush weighs 8 ounces.

13446 Hair Brushes, Florence hard rubber backs, fine white Russia bristles.

Assorted designs, similar to cut.
Each......$0.55   Per dozen......$6.00
Brush weighs 8 ounces.

13448 Hair Brushes, Florence hard rubber backs, large size, fine white Russia bristles. See cut.
Each......$0.75   Per dozen......$8.10
Brush weighs 8 ounces.

13450 Florence Hair Brush extra fine white Russian Okatka bristles.

15 row, carved back and handle, 9¼ in. long.
Each brush in a box......$1.00

Cloth Brushes.

13452 Cloth Brush, black center, with outside row of black and white bristles, redwood back. Weight, packed, 3 ozs.
Each......$0.25
Per dozen......$2.50

13474 Cloth Brushes, all white bristles, white satin wood back. A fine brush. Weight, packed, 8 ounces.
Each......$0.50
Per dozen......$5.40

13476 Hat or Cloth Brush, white horse-hair, 6 rows, plush back; small size, 5¼ inches long. Weight, packed, 5 oz.
Each......$0.25
Per dozen......2.50

Flesh and Bath Brushes.

13490 Long Curved Flesh Brush, *for dry use* (not for water); alternate rows of black and white bristles; light satinwood back. Weight packed. 10 ounces. Each......$0.50
Per dozen......$5.25
Leiner's Patent Combined Bath and Flesh Brushes, guaranteed for wet or dry use. Superior friction brushes made from select bristles woven into twisted wire; very durable and popular.

13493 Leiner's Bath and Flesh Brush, metallic back, curved handle, which may be detached and reversed; web strap on back for use without handle. Weight, packed, 10 ounces.
Each......$0.48   Per doz......$5.32

13497 Leiner's Bath and Flesh Brush, long and curved, with three rows of superior bristles. Weight, packed, 12 ounces. Each......$0.80
Per dozen......8.60

Perfection Corn File.

13498—The greatest thing on the market for a speedy and painless removal of corns. A practical, perfect remedy. Can be operated by any child. No danger of blood poisoning or lock-jaw. Made of genuine African Salamander skin, and truly antiseptic.
Price each......$0.20   Per dozen......$1.75
Per gross......21.00
Give it a trial.

Tooth Brushes.

HINTS IN REGARD TO THE CARE OF TOOTH BRUSHES.
Never lay a wet brush away, but put it upright in an open dish.

A new brush should be soaked in cool water about twenty minutes before using the first time.

If some of the bristles begin to work up in use, do not draw them out, but trim them off, and your brush will last longer.

Bristles will be injured if brushes are put away wet, and left for several days to dry. For the same reason the backs split and the brushes become offensive to the smell, and discolored.

Tooth Brushes are not expensive. It is wiser to throw an old brush away than be annoyed in trying to make it last a while longer.

Tooth brushes should be selected according to requirements of the individual. A soft brush used with much pressure would break down the bristles, while a stiffer brush would stand the wear.

Note.—For Tooth Soap and Powder, see Index.

13500-02   13510   13514   13512   13506

13500 Tooth Brushes, good, cheap brush.
Each......$0.06   Per dozen......$0.65
Weight per dozen, 12 ounces.
13502 Tooth Brushes, good.
Each......$0.10   Per dozen......1.00
Weight, per dozen, 14 ounces.
13504 Tooth Brushes, fine quality.
Each......$0.15   Per dozen......1.50
Weight, per dozen, 15 ounces.
13506 Tooth Brushes, superior quality.
Each......$0.18   Per dozen......1.95
Weight, per dozen, 17 ounces.
13510 Tooth Brushes, standard M. W. & Co., warranted, extra fine.
Each......$0.25   Per dozen......2.60

13512

13512 Tooth Brushes, Florence dental plate, extra quality, for cleaning artificial teeth.
Each......$0.28   Per dozen......$3.10
Weight, per dozen, 16 ounces.
13514 The "Prophylactic" Tooth Brush; a perfect cleanser of the teeth; is constructed upon principles of dental science, the bristles being in separate and distinctly pointed tufts, that they may be forced *between* the teeth as well as to cleanse the surface. Directions for use are given with each brush.
Each......$0.29   Per dozen......3.10
Weight, per dozen, 16 ounces.

13516 Folding Pocket Tooth Brush, all bristle brush.
Each......$0.25
Per doz......2.60

Nail and Hand Brushes.

13520   13530   Each.   Per doz.

13520 Hand Brushes, 4 rows, imported fiber, hardwood back, 4 inches in length; also useful in house cleaning, kitchen work, etc......$0.04 $0.40
Weight, per dozen, 20 ounces.
13524 Nail Brushes, 6 row, all white bristles, horse back......15   1.50
Weight, per dozen, 16 ounces.
13526 Nail Brushes, 8 row, all white bristles......20   2.00
Weight, per dozen, 18 ounces.
13530 Nail Brushes, 5 row, all white bristles, with wings. See cut......25   2.60
Weight, per dozen, 22 ounces.

Shaving or Lather Brushes.

For shaving soap see Index.

          Each. Per doz.
13542 Plunger Shaving Brushes, good quality bristles......$0.10 $1.00
13544 Shaving Brushes, larger, all bristles......15   1.50
13546 Shaving Brushes, good quality, all bristles......25   2.50

13551 Shaving Brush, medium size, fine quality of pure badger bristles, oval end; assortment of handles in box of half dozen. Weight (per box) packed 20 ounces. Each $0.40 Per dozen......4.25

13554 Shaving Brush, large size, fine white bristles, 2¾ inches long, square cut; black hard rubber handle. Weight, packed, 3 ounces.
Each......$0.50
Per dozen......5.35

Barbers' or Furniture Dusters.

13558 Barbers' Dusters, all white horse hair; full length 9 inches weighs 4 ounces.
Each......$0.45
Per dozen......4.80

Dust or Counter Brushes.

13563 Counter Brush, all bristles, gray center, black coloring.
Each......$0.25
13563-6   Per doz......2.65
13566 Dust Brushes, American bristles, plain handles. Each. Per dozen......$4.90
Dust brushes weigh 5 ozs. each.

Turkey Feather Dusters.

           Each. Per doz.
13570 10 inches......$0.22 $2.35
13574 12 inches......30   3.00
13578 14 inches......36   3.60
13580 15 inches......40   4.30
13582 16 inches......45   4.80
Weight, 9 to 12 ounces.

Feather Dusters.

13585 Body Feather Duster, 8 inch handle and 6 inch feathers.
Each......$0.10
Per dozen......1.00
Weight, 6 ounces.
13588 Body Dusters, full and soft 10 inch handle and 7 inch feathers.
Each......$0.15
Per dozen......1.65
Weight, 8 ounces.

The woven down duster, flat, not round, has no equal; double faced, soft, downy wiper that gathers up the dust and when filled with dust can be taken from the room and beaten out in a moment.

13585-88   13591-94

13591 (No. 1) Duster, 8 inch handle, all dark down, 7x9 inch, double faced brush.
Each......$0.75
Per dozen......7.50
Weight, 6 ozs.
13594 (No. 2) 16 inch handle, duster 8x11, all dark down, same as No. 1. Weight, 8 ounces.
Each......96
Per dozen......8.75

⁎.⁎ ERRORS.—We make them; so does everyone, and we will cheerfully correct them if you will write to us. Try to write us good-naturedly, but if you cannot, then write us any way. Do not let an error pass unnoticed, or complain to your friends or neighbors about it. We want an early opportunity to make right any mistakes that may occur.

Blacking Brushes.

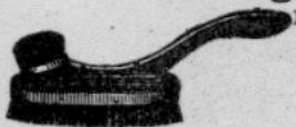

13600 Blacking Brush, mixed bristle; a good brush.
Each $0.15
Per dozen 1.50
Brush weighs 8 ounces.

13604 Blacking Brush, all bristle, a good one.
Each $0.25
Per dozen 2.50

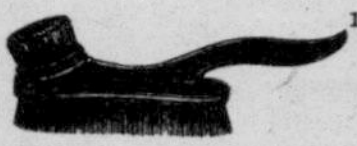

13608 Blacking Brush, all bristle, large, full and heavy.
Each $0.50
Per dozen 5.40
Brush weighs 14 ozs.

Blacking Sets.

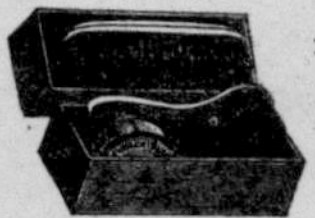

13610 Blacking Set, in neat box; polisher, dauber and box of blacking.
Each $0.25
Per dozen 2.65
Set weighs 11 ounces.

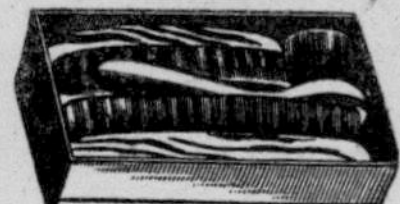

13614 Blacking Set in box; has bristle polisher, mud brush and dauber.
Each $0.45
Per dozen. 4.80
Postage.... .14

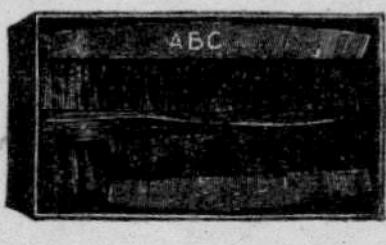

13618 Shoe Blacking Set, containing polisher, mud brush and dauber of good quality, with polished antique oak solid backs. Weight, packed, 16 ounces.
Each $0.50
Per dozen.. 5.40

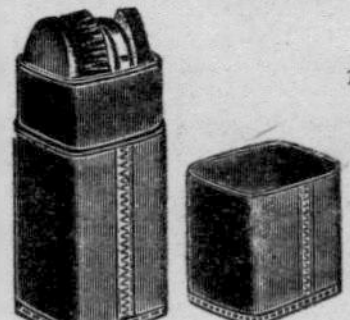

13621 Shoe Blacking Set, stitched sole leather case, upright telescope style; size, 6⅞ x 3¼ x 2⅜ inches; containing polisher, dauber and box of blacking. Weight, packed, 12 ounces. Our special price, each $0.55

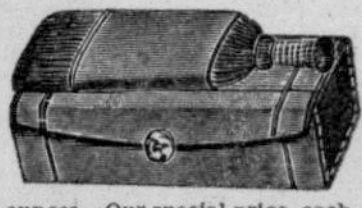

13623 Shoe Blacking Set, stitched sole leather case; size, 7x3x2½ inches, with whisk broom on cover; oxidized catch; contains polisher, dauber and box of blacking. Weight, packed, 20 ounces. Our special price, each $0.75

13625 "Sunshine" Shoe Blacking Set, contains the perfect "Sunshine" polisher (No. 13627), dauber and box of blacking in stamped cloth case, and is intended for consumers of good goods. Weight, packed, 20 oz. Our special price, each $0.85

Shoe Polishers.

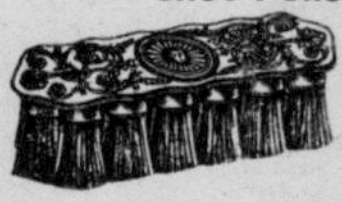

13627 Sunshine polisher, solid mass of fine elastic bristles, 1½ inches long, same as in set 13625.
Each $0.60
Per dozen 6.85
Brush weighs 11 ozs.

13625-27

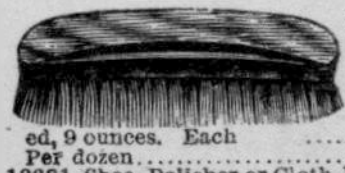

13629 Shoe Polisher or Cloth Brush, made of all pure gray bristles, long stock, with polished cherry back. Weight, packed, 9 ounces. Each $0.48
Per dozen 5.15

13631 Shoe Polisher or Cloth Brush of all black bristles, with polished hardwood back. Weight, packed, 8 ounces.
Each $0.20
Per dozen 2.10

Blacking Daubers.

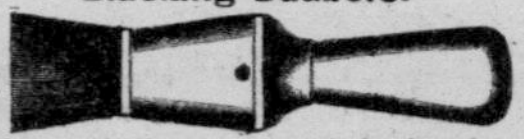

13633 Blacking Dauber, stencil brush style, made of pure black bristles, with metal ferrule, light hardwood handle. Weight, packed, 4 ounces Each $0.10
Per dozen 1.00

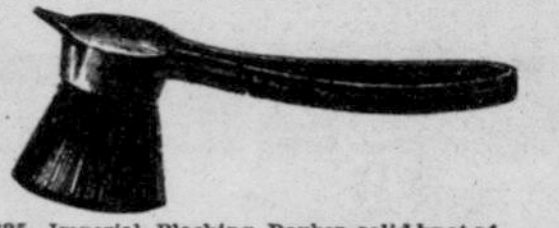

13635 Imperial Blacking Dauber, solid knot of pure black bristles, securely set in tinned iron handle, with mud-scraper. Wt., packed, 5 ozs.
Our special price, each $0.10
Per dozen 1.00

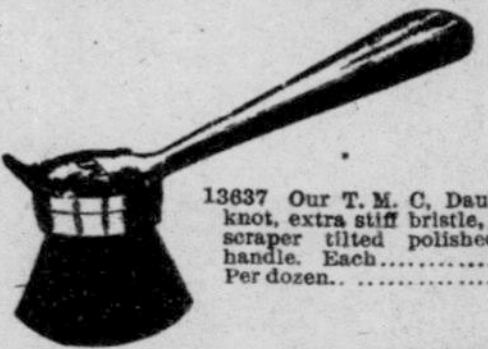

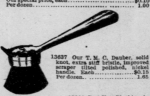

13637 Our T. M. C. Dauber, solid knot, extra stiff bristle, improved scraper tilted polished, nickel handle. Each $0.15
Per dozen 1.65

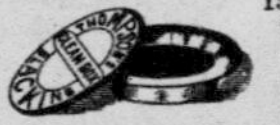

13639 Best Shoe Blacking in a perfect box. No soiled fingers, no tight covers, no wasted blacking. See cut.
Small size per box $0.05
Per dozen .... .50
Box weighs 4 oz.

Paint Brushes.

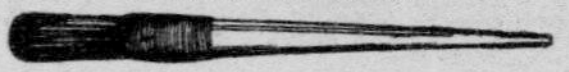

13685 French Sash Tools, all white bristles, short ferrule, wire bound, a fair jobbing brush. Length of bristles 1⅜ to 2 in.

Manufacturers' number	2	4	6	8
Price, each	$0.03	$0.04	$0.06	$0.08
Per dozen	.30	.45	.60	.85

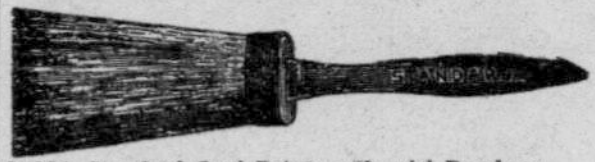

13691 Standard Oval Paint or Varnish Brushes; our cheap, all white brush, wire bound, a good jobbing brush.

Manufacturers No.	6	4	2	3-0	6-0
Each	$0.10	$0.16	$0.23	$0.43	$0.73

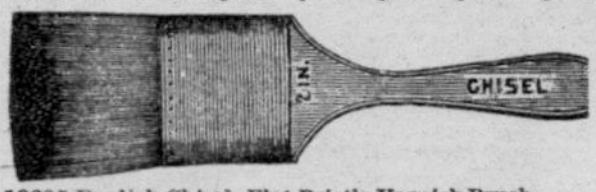

13695 English Chisel, Flat Bristle Varnish Brushes in tin, chisel point, polished handles.

Size	1 in.	1½ in.	2 in.	2½ in.	3 in.
Price each	$0.08	$0.12	$0.16	$0.23	$0.28
Per doz	.80	1.20	1.65	2.35	2.95

13696 Extra Chisel, Bristle Flowing Varnish Brush, white French bristles, tin bound; a good jobbing brush.

	1 in.	1½ in.	2 in.	2½ in.	3 in.
Price each	$0.15	$0.23	$0.30	$0.38	$0.45

Per set of five, one of each size $1.40

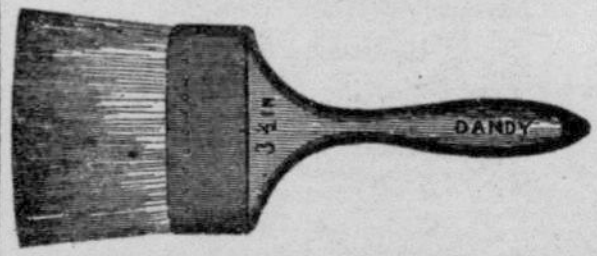

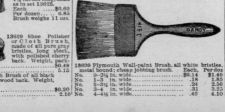

13699 Plymouth Wall-paint Brush, all white bristles, metal bound; cheap jobbing brush.

	Each.	Per doz
No. 0-2½ in. wide	$0.14	$1.40
No. 1-3 in. wide	.18	1.85
No. 2-3½ in. wide	.24	2.50
No. 3-4 in. wide	.31	3.25
No. 4-4½ in. wide	.40	4.10

Paint Brushes—Continued.

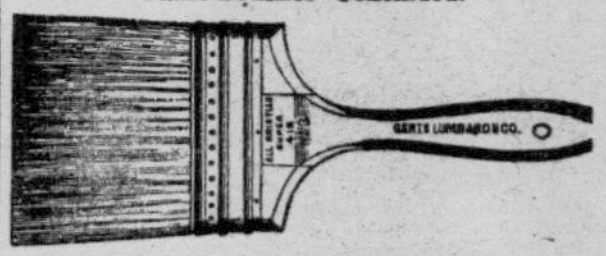

13703 Superior Wall Paint Brush; our best brass bound flat paint, made of selected white bristle, very heavy and warranted.
No. 0—3 in. wide $0.43
" 2—4 " " .... .76
" 4—5 " " 1.20

13705 Superior Wall Brush, same as above, 13703, but longer stock.
No. 6—3½ in. wide. Long stock .... .80
No. 7—4 " " " " 1.05

13710. O. K. Stucco Flat Paint Brush, long all white Russia bristles; leather bound; stained handle and strap.

	Each.	Per doz.
No. 25, 3 in. wide	$0.90	$10.00
No. 30, 3½ in. wide	1.15	12.75
No. 35, 4 in. wide	1.45	15.75
No. 40, 4½ in. wide	1.75	19.00

"B" Whitewash Brushes.

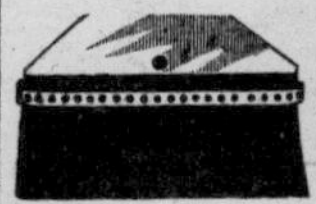

13713 A good brush for rough outside work, leather bound; gray middle, white outside.

Manufac'rs' Nos.	5	6	7	8	9	12
Width	6¼	6¾	7¼	7¾	8¼	9½
Price, each	$0.25	$0.30	$0.35	$0.45	$0.50	$0.68
Weight, ounces	7	9	10	11	13	15

13715 Dandy Whitewash Heads, metal bound, all white bristles. Each.
No. 0. 6 in $0.27
No. 5. 8 in .... .53
No. 7. 9 in .... .68

13717 Standard Whitewash Heads, brass bound, white outside, mixed center; a durable family brush.
No. 7, 7 in $0.40
No. 8, 8 in .... .50
No. 10, 9 in .... .80

13720 Gem Whitewash Brush; our best brass bound brush; all white Russia bristles; very heavy; warranted. Each.
No. 0, 7 inches wide $0.63
No. 1, 8 inches wide .... .83
No. 3, 8½ inches wide 1.33
No. 20, 9 inches wide 2.15

Calcimine Brushes.

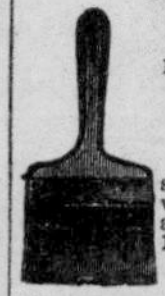

13723 Standard Calcimine Brushes, an all white bristle brush, for family use, brass bound.
6 inch, each $0.80
8 inch, each 1.35
Keep your brushes in a cool place, and soak them well before using. Never put whitewash brushes in newly slaked lime, as it will rot the bristles. Weight 15 and 16 oz.

13725 Extra Calcimine Brushes, our standard white or yellow Russia bristle brush, brass bound, warranted.
8 inch, 5½ inch bristle, each $3.00

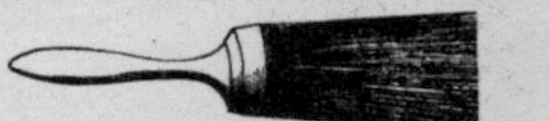

13730 Painters' Dusters, all black bristles, No. 14
Each $0.45

13732 Paper Hangers' Smoothing Brushes, white bristles, two rows, 10 in wide., No. 2. Each.... .80

13734 Paper Hangers' Patented Smoothing Brush and Roller Combined, No. 20, 10 inches wide. 2 rows bristles, roller on one end of handle.
Each 1.20

13736 Paper Hangers' Paste Brush, 7 inches wide, all white bristles, metal bound.
Each 1.25

Graining Combs.

13738 American Leather Graining Combs.
Per set $0.55

13739 Taylor's English Steel Graining Combs.
Per set $1.25

Note.—We are prepared to supply Floor and Carpet Brushes, Cobweb Brushes; Oblong, Round or Pope's Eye Window Brushes. Prices and descriptions upon application.

COMBS.

13745 Pure Aluminum Dressing Comb, coarse and fine, 7½ inches long, 1½ inches wide, highly polished, very light, strong and durable.
Each..$0.75

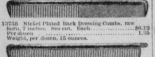

(13749 and 13751).

13749 Paragon Metallic Dressing Comb, nickel plated, coarse and fine, 1 inch wide, 5½ inches long. Weight, per dozen, 14 ounces.
Each..$0.05
Per dozen.. .50
13751 Paragon Metallic Dressing Comb, 1 inch wide, 6½ inches long. Weight, packed, 16 ounces.
Each..$0.06
Per doz... .65

Raw Horn Dressing Comb With Metallic Back.

13755 Nickel-Plated Back Dressing Combs, raw horn, 7 inches. See cut. Each..............$0.12
Per dozen.. 1.25
Weight, per dozen, 15 ounces.

13760 Nickel Plated Back Hotel Comb, raw horn. All coarse. See cut. Each................$0.12
Per dozen.. 1.25
Weight, per dozen, 15 ounces.

Raw Horn Barber Combs.

13762 Polished Horn Barber Combs. All coarse. 7 inch, ¾ inch teeth. Each................$0.10
Per dozen.. .90
Weight per dozen, 7 ounces.
13764 Polished Horn Combs, coarse and fine. See cut. Each...........................$0.10
Per dozen.. .90

Celluloid Combs.

13768 Celluloid Dressing Comb, 7 inch; 1 inch teeth, in blue, red, pink and white. Each.....$0.09
Per dozen.. .90
Weight per dozen, 9 ounces.

Rubber Dressing Combs.

Lengths	6 in.	7 in.	8 in.
Closing price, each	$0.06	$0.07	$0.08
Closing price, per doz	.65	.75	.85
Weight, per doz	14 oz.	15 oz.	16 oz.

13775 Hard Rubber Dressing Comb, 1½ inches wide; heavy, plain flat back.

Length	7 in.	8 in.
Each	$0.07	$0.08
Per dozen	.72	.85
Weight per dozen	10 oz.	12 oz.

13778 Hard Rubber Dressing Comb, 1½ inches wide, heavy curved back.

13781 Atlantic India Rubber Dressing Combs, 8 inches. See cut. Weight, per dozen, 16 ounces.
Each..$0.10
Per doz... .96

13783 Atlantic India Rubber Dressing Combs, 8 inches. See cut. Weight, per dozen, 16 ounces.
Each..$0.12
Per doz... 1.10

13785 Hard Rubber Dressing Comb, 1¾ inches wide, heavy curved quill back; length, 8 inches. Weight, per dozen, 16 ounces. Each..........$0.12
Per dozen.. 1.25

13787 Hard Rubber Dressing Comb, 1⅜ inches wide, wide fancy back; length, 8 inches. Weight, per dozen, 16 ounces.
Each..$0.12
Per dozen.. 1.30

13789 Goodyear Extra Heavy Rubber Dressing Combs, 8 inches. Weight, per dozen, 16 ounces.
Each..$0.20
Per doz... 2.10

13790 Fine High Grade Dressing Combs, grailed teeth. Weight, per dozen, 17 ounces.
Each..$0.25
Per doz... 2.70

13798 Dressing Combs, rubber, toilet.
Each..$0.35
Per doz... 3.75
Weight, per dozen, 26 ounces.

13805 Slant Barber Combs, fine quality, rubber, unbreakable; length, 7½ inches. Weight, per dozen, 8 ounces. Each...........................$0.13
Per dozen.. 1.20

Rubber Pocket Combs.

13807 Hard Rubber Pocket Comb, ¾ inch wide, curved back, coarse and fine, length, 4 inches; in leatherette slide case. Weight, per dozen, 5 ounces. Each...........................$0.05
Per dozen.. .50

13809 Hard Rubber Pocket Comb, of superior quality and finish, length, 4½ inches; in sliding case. Weight, per dozen, 6 ounces.
Each..$0.10
Per dozen.. .95

We want you to know that we are Manufacturers of Ready-Made Wrappers,

TEA GOWNS AND DRESSES.

We also make Dresses to order in most fashionable styles. Our Dressmakers are experts in their line which insures superior style and finish for all of our garments.

Write for Dressmaking Catalogue No. E.

Unbreakable Combs.

13812 Siamese Folding Pocket Comb of unbreakable hard rubber, coarse and fine; length, closed, 3¾ inches. Weight, per dozen, 6 ounces. Each..................$0.12 Per doz...........$1.15

13816 Rubber Pocket Comb, 4½ inches long, in leatherette slides; very neat pocket comb for hair or mustache. Weight per dozen, 5 ounces. Each......$0.12
Per dozen.. 1.10

13822 Unbreakable Rubber Dressing Comb; none better; 7 inch. Weight, per dozen, 12 ounces.
Each..................$0.16 Per dozen...........$1.65

13825 Unbreakable Rubber Dressing Comb, all coarse, 1½ inches wide, length 8 inches. Weight, per dozen, 16 ounces. Each...........$0.16
Per dozen.. 1.65
The above lines of unbreakable combs are especially recommended for service and cheapness.

13826 Superior quality fine tooth India rubber Combs. Each......$0.08
Per doz. .85

13830 Unbreakable fine tooth Rubber Combs, fine; see cut. Each......$0.10
Per doz. 1.10

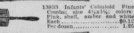

13833 Infants' Celluloid Fine Combs; size 4½x1½; colors: Pink, shell, amber and white. Each......$0.12
Per doz. 1.25

13836 Fine Rubber Combs, one side fine, the other coarse; see cut. Each......$0.08
Per doz. .85
Weight per doz. 6 ounces.

Hard Rubber Circle Combs.

13846 Unbreakable Rubber Circle or Round Comb, ribbed top. Weight per dozen, 9 ounces. Each......$0.08
Per dozen. .85

13849 Unbreakable Round Combs, rubber; weight per dozen, 9 ounces.
Each.............$0.12
Per doz. 1.10

Combs—Continued.

13852 Hard Rubber Combination Side and Round Comb, curved back. Weight, per dozen, 9 ounces.
Each $0.10
Per doz. .. 1.00

Celluloid Combs.

13854 Circle or Round Combs, celluloid, in colors; blue, red, shell and white, plain tops.
Each $0.06
Per doz. .... .55

13858 Circle or Round Combs, celluloid, fancy back in shell color only. Each $0.09
Per dozen .... .95

Goodyear's Hard Rubber Syringes.

(Postage 3 to 5 cents each.)

13890 Urethral (or male), capacity ⅜ oz.
Each $0.20
Per doz. 2.15

13892 Urethral (or male, safety point, capacity ⅜ oz. Each $0.50
Per doz. 2.15

13894 Urethral (or male) capacity ¼ oz.
Each $0.25
Per doz. .... .50

13896 Urethral (or male), safety point, capacity ¼ oz.
Each $0.30
Per doz. 3.00

13901 Ear syringe capacity 1 oz.
Each $0.70
Per dozen 7.00

13903-05 Vaginal syringe, capacity 1 oz.
Each $0.45
Per dozen 4.50

13905 Vaginal syringe, capacity ½ oz. Each .... .60
Per dozen 6.00

13907 Goodyear Infant Syringe, capacity one ounce; soft rubber bulb with hard rubber infant's rectal pipe. Weight packed, 4 oz.
Each $0.20
Per dozen 2.00

13909 Eye, Ear, Ulcer and Abcess Syringe, capacity one ounce; injection tube is made of very soft and flexible rubber, and will not injure or pain the inflamed part. Weight packed, 2 ounces. Each $0.20
Per dozen 2.00

Challenge Bulb Syringes.

13910 Our Challenge Bulb Syringe, 3 hard rubber pipes, infant, rectal, and large vaginal syringe, made from fine Para stock, and we challenge comparison for actual value.
Each $0.50
Per dozen 5.40

Goodyear Bulb Syringes.

13928 Enterprise Crown Syringe, with two nasal pipes. A good, cheap Syringe
Each $0.40
Per doz. .09
Postage. .09

Syringes—Continued.

13933 The Metropolitan Crown Syringe, hard rubber fittings, three hard rubber pipes in neat box; see cut.
Each $0.65
Syringe weighs 9 ounces. Per dozen. 5.75

13935 Goodyear Crown Syringe, constructed of the best quality of dark soft rubber, with hard rubber infant, rectal and vaginal pipes and improved vaginal irrigator, in wood box. Weight packed 12 oz. Each $1.00
Per dozen $10.25

13940 "English" Breast Pump, one lip box Weight packed, 8 oz. Each $0.25
Per dozen 2.75

Continuous Flow Syringes.

All intermittent syringes inject more or less air, which is invariably drawn back into the tube while the bulb is expanding and re-filling, and is often painful and dangerous. These syringes have a steady and continuous flow, which can be gentle or strong at the easy control of the user. High medical authorities indorse them as being safe, easy to operate and perfect in cleanliness, durability and efficiency. First-class goods made of the finest Para rubber, and Warranted reliable in every respect.

13944 "Omega" No. 4 Syringe (continuous flow), hard rubber vaginal and rectal pipes; no screw threads; valves secured from loss; pipes attached by inserting in soft rubber socket. Packed in octagon box. Weight packed, 9 ounces. Each $0.75

13946 "Omega" No. 3 Syringe (continuous flow), hard rubber vaginal, rectal and infant pipes; noiseless sinker. Improved method of coupling bulb and tubing that secures valves from loss. Packed in oval box. Weight packed, 9 ounces. Each $1.00

13948 "Alpha E" Syringe, (continuous flow), has no screw threads or washers, therefore cannot leak; injecting tubes being attached by an improved soft rubber joint socket; hard rubber infant, rectal and vaginal pipes; in cloth case. Weight packed, 12 ounces. Each $1.50

13950 "Alpha D" Syringe (continuous flow), fitted without extra large valve chambers; hard rubber infant, rectal, vaginal and nasal pipes, and improved Vaginal Irrigating Spray; noiseless and non-corrosive sinker and; packed in neat cloth case. Weight packed, 13 ounces. Each $1.75

Female Syringe.

13952 "Tyrian" Female Syringe, for cleansing the vaginal passages of all discharges; especially adapted for injections of hot water; the liquid being driven from the syringe when bulb is compressed and drawn back into it on relaxing the pressure, thus giving an opportunity to thoroughly wash the diseased parts. Capacity eight ounces. Made of one piece of Soft rubber, with removable hard rubber shield. Having no valves or connections cannot get out of order. Weight, packed, 13 oz. Each $1.25

The Ladies' Syringe.

13954 Ladies' Syringe is the only PERFECT vaginal syringe in the world. Constructed upon the principle of Injection and Suction (a plan generally admitted by the medical profession as the only correct and efficient one); it cleanses the passages of all discharges perfectly. It is very easily cleaned. During the injections not a drop of fluid need be spilled on clothing, etc. Consists simply of one piece of fine soft rubber. Full instructions for use with each syringe. Weight, packed, 17 ounces. Each $2.50

Syringes—Continued.

13956 "Perfection" Fountain Syringes, made from pure rubber, with hard rubber connections, hard rubber vaginal, rectal and infant pipes, and vaginal irrigator, about six feet pure rubber tubing, with shut-off.
Price each.
2 Quarts $0.90
3 Quarts 1.00
4 Quarts 1.10
Per dozen.
2 Quarts $9.60
3 Quarts 10.50
4 Quarts 11.65

Combination Water Bottle and Fountain Syringe.

First class goods, made from Pure Rubber of high grade; perfect in durability and all other respects, and guaranteed to give satisfaction.

13959 "Perfection" Combination Water Bottle and Fountain Syringe, fitted with hard rubber connection, bent vaginal and nasal pipes, and vaginal irrigator, six feet pure rubber tubing, with shut-off attachment. Packed in strong black cloth box.

Capacity. Price each.
2 Quarts $1.50
3 Quarts 1.60
4 Quarts 1.70
Postage, 23 to 30c. ea.
Capacity. Per dozen.
2 Quarts $15.00
3 Quarts 15.75
4 Quarts 16.50

Challenge Hot Water Bottles.

13965 Challenge Hot Water Bottles, pure rubber, high grade goods. Note our prices.
Capacity. Price each. Per doz.
2 Quarts .... $0.75 .... $7.50
3 Quarts .... .80 .... 7.75
4 Quarts .... .85 .... 8.13
Postage, 18 to 25 cents.

Goodyear Crown Water Bottles.

(Hard Rubber Stopper.)

13963 Goodyear Crown Water Bottles, hard rubber stopper. These are pure rubber and warranted. Fountain Syringe Attachments quoted below will fit these water bottles.
Capacity. Price each. Per doz.
2 Quarts .... $1.15 .... $10.75
3 Quarts .... 1.20 .... 11.75
4 Quarts .... 1.30 .... 12.50

Note.—See Fountain Syringe Attachments No. 13967 which fit water bottles No. 13963.

Fountain Syringe Attachment.

13967—Fountain Syringe Attachment for above water bottles No. 13963 has hard rubber connection attached to 6 feet of fountain syringe tubing, a shut-off and set of pipes (hard rubber); cannot spill in any portion, either hanging or on shelf or mantel.
Per set $0.95
Per dozen 10.80

Note—We are prepared to supply Spize Hot Water Bottles; Head Water Bags; Spinal, Throat and Head Ice Bags; Ice or Water Caps, Soft Rubber Urinal Bags for male or female, day or night use; Round and Oval Soft Rubber Bed Pans; Stomach Tubes, and will quote prices of same upon application.

Sealing Wax.

15595 Sanford's No. 2 Red Express Sealing Wax 4 four-ounce sticks to pound, or 8 two-ounce sticks to pound. Per (4 oz.) stick........$0.12
Per (2 oz.) stick........ .06
Per pound (either size)........ .35

15597 Sanford's Green Express Sealing Wax; 4 or 8 sticks to the pound box. Per(4 oz.)stick.... .12
Per (2 oz.) stick........ .06
Per pound (either size)........ .35

Initial Seals.

15599 Initial Seal for Sealing Wax, length, 2½ inches, black enameled handle, nickeled metal die with rustic initial letter.
Our special price, each........$0.10
Per dozen........ 1.00

Inkstands.

15601 Flint Glass, with metal screw cap, for use in writing desks.
Each........$0.07
Per dozen........ .75
Weight, 3 ounces.

15601

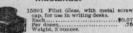

15605 Crystal Glass, 1⅝ inches square, with hinged silvered tops; weight, packed, 12 ounces.
Each........ $0.20 Per dozen........ 2.00

15607 Crystal Glass, *Rope Pattern*, 2 inches square, with hinged silvered tops. Weight, packed, 14 ounces.
Until sold. Each, $0.25
Per dozen........ 2.70

15605 15607

15621 Practical or Common Sense Inkstand. No evaporation, no spilling of ink. Same style as safety inkstand, but without cork in bottom.
Weight, packed, 18 ounces.
Each........$0.12
Per dozen........ 1.20

15623 "*Sterling*" Automatic Inkstand, saves 75 per cent. in ink, or more than its cost, in six months; seals ink from atmosphere and prevents evaporation; will not overflow, delivers ink to the pen in perfect liquid form; has no plugs to be adjusted and no detachable parts to be mislaid or lost.
Weight, packed, 20 ounces.
Our special price, each.$0.40

15625 Inkstand, enameled finish, 4½ inches high, with revolving "Star" bottle, heavy flint glass. Weight, packed, 19 ounces.
Each........$0.20
Per dozen........ 2.10

15629 Inkstand. Double, enameled finish, 4½ inches high, with two revolving "Star" bottles, heavy flint glass.
Weight, packed, 28 oz.
Each........$0.35
Per dozen........ 3.75

15631 Inkstand, fancy embossed silvered metal base with tray for pens, and twisted wire pen rack, crystal glass ink well with cap of silvered metal; 2½ inches high; base, 5x3⅝ inches. Weight, packed, 12 ounces. Each........$0.20
Per dozen........ 2.10

When ordering goods shipped by mail, be sure to allow money for postage. If you send too much we will refund balance.

Inkstands—Continued.

15633 Inkstand. Enameled finish, 5½ inches high, white crystal ink bottle with hinged cap, pen rack and envelope holder. Weight, packed, 44 ounces.
Each........$0.32

15635 Inkstand, rolled steel base, pen-rack and hinged cover, nickel plated and highly polished, with pressed crystal glass ink bottle; 2¾ inches high; 3⅝ inch base. Weight, packed, 15 ounces.
Each........$0.45

15639 Inkstand, maroon finish, iron base and pen-rack, with rope pattern crystal glass sponge cup and two ink-wells, with fancy iron caps; 3½ inches high; base, 9¾x4⅛ inches. Weight, packed, 4½ pounds. Too heavy to go by mail.
Each........$0.50

Pocket Inkstands.

FOR TRAVELERS' AND TOURISTS' USE.

15646 Lignum Vitæ Wood Inkstand with screw top, 2 inches high 1¼ inches in diameter; leakage impossible, polished.
Weight, 3 ounces. Each........$0.12
Per dozen........ 1.25

15650 Inkstand covered with fine grade of leather, double spring covers, silvered finish inside; 1⅝ inches in diameter. Weight, packed, 3 ounces. Our special price, each........$0.30

Paper Clips.

"Ever-Handy" Paper Clips, for holding together notes, receipts, invoices, letters and memoranda of every description, made from best spring steel and brass, double strength.

15653 "Ever Handy" Paper Clip, small size, with jaws 1½ inches wide.
Each........$0.04
Per dozen........ .40

15655 "Ever-Handy" Paper Clip, medium size, with jaws 2½ inches wide Each........$0.06
Per dozen........ .60

Board Clips.

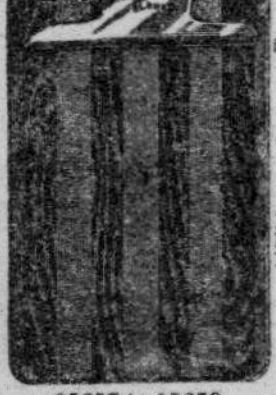

15657 to 15659

Striped wood board, nickeled clip, with brass wire spring, improved metal shoulder for papers to square against, and metal eye to hang up by. The best made and finished board clip on the market.

	Each.	Per doz.
15657 Note Size...	$0.28	$3.05
15658 Letter Size.	.31	3.35
15659 Cap Size....	.34	3.65

Paper Files.

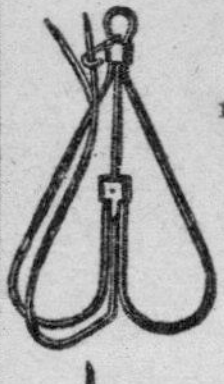

15665 Hanging Paper File, tinned wire back and hook with protected point. Weight, packed, 9 ounces.
Each........$0.04
Per doz........ .40

15667 Jumbo Standing Paper File, 4 inch lacquered iron base, wire 8 inches long. Weight, packed, 9 ounces. Each........$0.07
Per dozen........ .75

PEN RACKS.

15672 Keep's Patent Perfection Spiral Pen Rack, each coil permanently but loosely held by loops in base, thus preventing springs from being weakened or displaced by use; size 6½x1¼x1⅛ inches. Weight, packed, 3 ounces. Each........$0.08
Per dozen........ .80

Wooden Rulers.

15685 Spencerian Script Ruler, a heavy maple ruler 1⅜ inches wide, 15 inches long, divided into eighths of inches; copies of penmanship printed on both sides of ruler. Suitable for school or office use. Weight per dozen, packed, 2 lbs.
Each........$0.04
Per dozen........ .40

15687 Spencerian Script Ruler, with inlaid brass edge; length 15 inches; otherwise same as 15685. Weight, packed (per dozen), 2⅛ lbs.
Each........$0.08
Per dozen........ .85

Scholars' Companions.

15700 Whitewood Box Scholars' Companion; furnished with lead pencil, pen, penholder, slate pencil and six inch-wood ruler. Weighs 3 oz.
Each........$0.03
Per dozen........ .30

15703 and 15705.

15703 "Magic Hingeless" Scholars' Companion, highly polished basswood box with three compartments and lock and key. 8¼x2⅜x1⅛ inches.
Weight, packed, 6 ounces. Each........$0.05
Per dozen........ .45

15705 "Magic Hingeless" Scholars' Companion, furnished with rubber eraser, lead pencil, slate pencil, penholder and pen; otherwise same as 15703. Weight, packed, 7 ounces.
Each........$0.08
Per dozen........ .75

15707 "Magic Hingeless" Scholars' Companion, highly polished hard-wood body *with inlaid butternut top;* three compartments for fittings; lock and key. 8¼x2⅜x1⅛ inches. Weight, packed, 6 ounces.
Each........$0.08
Per dozen........ .75

15709 "Combination Lock" Scholars' Companion, hard-wood box, with three compartments; sliding cover fastened by combination lock on end of box. A favorite with scholars. Each........$0.08
Per dozen........ .75
Postage........ .06

Scholars' Companions—Continued

15712 The Scholars' Combination Carry-all: combining book-clamp, 12-inch ruler and scholars' companion; hardwood, nicely finished, with stout leather straps and buckle. Suitable for use by boy or girl. Weight, packed, 9 ounces.
Each $0.20
Per dozen 2.00

Chalk Crayons.

15715 White Chalk Crayons, round; one gross in box. Weight 2½ pounds.
Per box $0.07
Per dozen boxes .... .70

15717 Colored Chalk Crayons, round; one gross assorted colors a box. Weight, 2½ pounds.
Per box (five gross).................. .30

15719 Enameled Colored Chalk Crayons, 12 pieces assorted colors in slide box. Weight, packed, 5 ounces.
Per box $0.04
Per doz boxes .... .40

15721 "Alpha Dustless Crayon" makes a firm clean mark; will not soil hands or clothing, nor scratch or glaze the board; it is DUSTLESS and will not injure the throats of teachers and pupils. It is durable and will last six times as long as common chalk crayons. Weight per box, 4 lbs. Per box (one gross)............ $0.55
Per dozen boxes 6.90
We do not sell less than a box of Chalk Crayons.

Blackboard Erasers.

15725 "Star" Dustless Eraser, made of lasting set on edge; holds the dust and can be easily cleaned. *The best low-price eraser in the market.*
Each $0.05
Per dozen .... .45
Postage .... .04

15727 Acme Dustless Eraser, all wool felt cut across the thread set on edge; cleans the board thoroughly, gathers and holds the dust and can be easily cleaned. Weight, packed, 4 ounces.
Each $0.08
Per dozen .... .80

15729 Cheney's Dustless Eraser, colored felt, firmly secured to block, a substantial eraser. Weight, packed, 3 ounces. Each............ $0.04
Per dozen .... .40

Portable Blackboards.

15735 Portable Blackboard of cloth with best black liquid slating surface on both sides, mounted on rollers with hook and rings complete for hanging.

No.	Size.	Each.	No.	Size.	Each.
1A.	2x2 ft.	$0.60	7A.	4x4 ft.	$2.25
2A.	3x3 ft.	1.30	8A.	4x5 ft.	2.75
3A.	3x4 ft.	1.75	9A.	4x6 ft.	3.25
4A.	3x5 ft.	2.25	10A.	4x7 ft.	3.85
5A.	3x6 ft.	2.75			

15737 Portable Blackboard of hylo-plate, slated both sides, with ash frame; for use on wall, easel or table.

No.	Size.	Each.	No.	Size.	Each.
1B.	2x3 ft.	$3.00	4B.	3½x5 ft.	$6.40
2B.	3x4 ft.	4.15	5B.	4 x6 ft.	8.25
3B.	3x4½ ft.	5.25			

NOTE.—We can supply Blackboard Slating; Slated Cloth and paper for blackboards; reversible portable blackboards, mounted; pointers for map or blackboard; school directors, officers or teachers' registers and record books. Prices quoted on application.

By anticipating your wants and ordering large enough to go by freight (100 lbs.), you will save money. The larger the order the more you will save.
8—5th

School Bags.

15743 School Bags, Burlap embroidered with colored braid; with pocket; 11¼x14 inches. Weight packed,5 ounces
Each $0.08
Per doz .... .80

15745 Waterproof School Bags; made of enameled cloth, with flap and leather shoulder strap. Weight, packed, 5 ounces.
14 in........ 8c $0.85
16 in........ 10c 1.05

15747 Open Work School Bags; made of netted macramé cord, with colored stripes, a very desirable bag. 16 inches wide. Weight, packed, 5 ounces.
Each $0.16
Per doz 1.75

15749 School Bag, brown duck bound and stitched all around, large pocket 6 inches deep across front of bag; flap fastens with buckle and strap; grain leather shoulder strap with buckle; size 9½x3½x14 with 2½ inch gusset, making a very roomy bag. Weight, packed 6 ounces.
Each $0.18
Per dozen 1.90

Slate Sponges.

15758 Sponges for cleaning school slates, fair size, medium in texture, bleached and cleaned.
Per dozen $0.08
Per gross .... .80

School Slates With Wood Frames.

"Hyatt" patent Wire Bound School Slates combine strength, lightness, durability and uniformity of finish of surface; being wire-bound *they cannot come apart*, and machine-smoothed they present an absolutely even writing surface, free from ridges.

Size.	Each.	Per doz.	Weight Each.
6x9	$0.04	$0.42	18 oz.
7x11	.05	.48	22 oz.
8x12	.06	.60	25 oz.

15760

TOYS FOR THE CHILDREN.

Our line of toys and games consists of all the latest articles upon the market. Prices very low this season. See pages 219 to 234.

"Hyatt" Noiseless Slates.

Strength, lightness and durability combined. Best quality slate with perfectly finished even writing surface, free from ridges. Frame is *wire bound* cannot come apart and covered with fine bright red (fast color) wool felt, securely fastened.
15762 "Hyatt" Noiseless Slate, single.

Size	Each	Per dz.	Weight Each.
6x9	$0.08	$0.80	18 oz.
7x11	.10	1.05	23 oz.
8x12	.12	1.25	26 oz.

15764 "Hyatt" Noiseless Slate, double, hinged with strong webbing, firmly riveted to frames.

Size.	Each.	Per doz.	Weight Each.
7x11	$0.20	$2.10	40 oz.
8x12	.24	2.50	46 oz.

15768 Hyatt "Peerless" Noiseless Slate with non-erasable *colored lines* on one side, produced by patent process which leaves slate surface perfectly smooth and even; felt covered wire bound frame; size, 6x9 inches. Weight, packed, 18 ounces.
Each $0.12
Per dozen 1.25
We will quote special prices for large quantities.

Silicate Book Slates.

Superior quality, strongly made, bound in fine black cloth covers. Superior slate surface *for the slate pencil*. For school or office use.

	Size.	Ea.	Per dz.
15772 6 surfaces,	5x8½	$0.25	$2.70
6	"	.35	3.80

Silicate Book Slates, neatly and strongly bound in fine cloth, with superior IVORINE SURFACE *for the lead pencil*; for the pocket.

		Size.	Each.	Per doz.
15775	6 surfaces..........	3x5	$0.15	$1.60
	.10	3½x5½	.25	2.70

Writing Desks.

15823 Butternut Desks (*for juveniles*), varnished; top beveled, paneled, and has black and gilt center ornament, beveled extension base,flannel lined, furnished with screw top inkstand; size, 11x7½x2½, weight, 28 ounces. Each........... $0.40

15825 Quartered Oak Desk, beveled edge, paneled top with gilt and black ornaments; inside folds beaded and lined with colored flannel; furnished with inkstand, size, 12x8x3½. Weighs 55 ounces. Each.................... $0.80

15829 Walnut Top Writing Desk, with gilt corner, band and center ornaments; bevel edge, inside folds beaded and lined with colored flannel, furnished with inkstand, Size, 11½x8x4. Weight, packed, 4 pounds. Each............ $1.05

Chess Men.

16264 French Wood Chess Men, black and white, in white wood boxes. Per set...$0.45
Postage 10c.

16268 Fine Boxwood Chess Men, *Staunton Pattern*, black and white polished; in dove-tailed polished hardwood box, with sliding cover. Weight, packed, 18 oz.
Per set $1.00

Dice.

No. 1.

No. 3.

No. 7.

16271 Bone Dice.
No. 1. $\frac{5}{16}$ inch. Per dozen $0.06
Postage .... .02
No. 3. ⅜ inch. Per dozen .... .11
Postage .... .03
No. 7. $\frac{9}{16}$ inch. Per dozen .... .20
Postage .... .05

No. D 1.

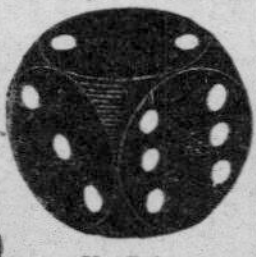

No. D 3.

No. D 2.

16275 Black Diamond Dice, made of black composition with white enameled sunken dots, rounded corners.
No. D 1, ½ inch. Per dozen $0.15
Weight, packed, 3 ounces.
No. D 2, ⅝ inch. Per dozen .... .30
Weight, packed, 4 ounces.
No. D 3, ¾ inch. Per dozen .... .45
Weight, packed, 7 ounces.

16276 "Celluloid" Poker Dice, representing ace, king, queen, jack, ten and nine spots; ivory finish celluloid. PERFECT GOODS. Set of five pieces in box. Weight, packed, 4 oz.
Per set $0.65

Dice Cups.

16279 Heavy Solid Sole Leather Dice Cup. Natural color, securely stitched, medium size.
Each $0.18
Per dozen 1.85
Postage, 4 cents.

Cribbage Boards.

16291 Le Count's Cribbage Board, polished, nickeled metal plate with drilled holes; stained whitewood base with compartment containing six cribbage pins. Size, 2¼x9¾ inches. Weight, packed, 17 ounces. Our special price, each....$0.50

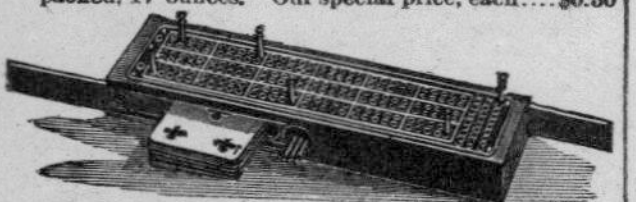

16295 Le Count's Patent Cribbage Board, polished, nickeled metal plate with three double rows drilled holes, to score for three or six players; base of polished black walnut with compartments for two packs of cards and one containing nine steel cribbage pins. Size, 2⅞x10¼ inches. Weight, packed, 20 ounces.
Our special price, each $1.00

All goods sent by mail at purchaser's risk. We can assume no responsibility after goods are deposited in postoffice. We advise insuring everything of value. **See page 2.**

Poker Chips.

16341 Composition Poker Chips, ivory finish, warranted not to chip or warp, 1¼ inches in diameter, 100 in box assorted as follows: 50 white, 25 red, 25 blue. Weight, packed, 25 oz.
Per box of 100 ....$0.30
Per 1000 .... 2.75

16345 Composition Poker Chips, ivory finish, first quality, warranted not to chip or warp; 1¼ inches in diameter; 100 in box, assorted as follows: 50 white, 25 red, 25 blue. Weight, packed, 28 ounces. Per box of 100 ....$0.35
Per 1000 .... 3.00

16351 Decorated Poker Chips, for playing "Penny Ante," 100 in box, assorted as follows: 50 white of numeral 1, 25 red of numeral 5, 25 blue of numeral 10. Size, 1⅛ inches.
Weight, per box (100), 28 ounces.
Per bx of 100.$1.20
Per 1000 .... 10.75

16355 "Lily" Design Poker Chips, 1⅛ inches in diameter; 100 chips in box, assorted as follows: 50 white, 25 blue, 25 red. Can supply in no other assortment of colors unless ordered in lots of 1000 or more; will then be assorted as desired. Weight (per box) packed, 28 ounces.
Per box of 100.$1.20
Per 1000. .. ..10.75

16358 "Bull's Head" Design Poker Chips, 1⅛ inches in diameter; 100 chips in box, assorted as follows: 50 white, 25 blue, 25 red. Cannot supply in any other assortment of colors unless ordered in lots of 1000 or more; may then be assorted as desired. Weight (per box), packed, 28 ounces.
Per box of 100.$1.20
Per 1000......10.75

Poker Sets.

16363 Polished Antique Oak Box, rounded top and corners, silvered catch and hinges, cover and box flannel lined contains 60 poker chips, 1¼ inches in diameter, and pack of enameled playing cards. Size, 6¼x4¼x1⅛. Weight packed, 26 ounces.
Our special price—
Each $0.85

16367 Polished Antique Oak Box, with rounded top and corners, silvered catch and hinges, cover and box lined with flannel, contains 100 poker chips in assorted colors, 1¼ inches in diameter, and pack of enameled playing cards. Size, 7½x5x2. Weight, packed, 38 ounces.
Our special price, each $1.10

Game Counters.

16371 Game Counters of ivory finish celluloid, 3x1$\frac{3}{16}$ inches, two wheels, one for games and one for points, one pair in pebbled paper sliding box. Our special price.
Per box (one pair) $0.25
Per dozen 2.70

Playing Card Boxes.

16378 Playing Card Box, made from English sole leather, telescope style, securely stitched, russet color, for one pack of cards. Size, 4x3x1. Weight, packed, 3 oz.
Our special price, each $0.25
Per dozen 2.70

Duplicate Whist Sets at Popular Prices.

16390 "Tokalon" Duplicate Whist Set; consists of four slide boxes, suitably marked for each player, each box having three divisions, and each division will hold three hands, or a complete pack of cards; dividers of a separate color for each player; score-cards and directions for playing in each set. Size 8½x5x4¼. Weight, packed, 24 ounces.
Our special price, per set $0.40
Extra score cards for 16390, 100 in package.
Per package .... .40

16393 "Tokalon" Duplicate Whist Set, complete for 12 hands; four Russia red leatherette boxes (as shown in illustration), each fitted with movable card-board dividers, score-cards, counters and directions for playing in box size, 11¼x5¾x4¼ inches. Weight, packed, 38 ounces. Our special price, per set. .$0.80

16396 "Tokalon" Duplicate Whist Set, complete for 12 hands; four colored English silk cloth boxes (as shown in illustration) in large pebbled black cloth box, with telescope cover stamped in gold; furnished same as 16393. Weight, packed, 44 ounces. Our special price, per set 1.60
Extra score cards for 16393 and 16396, 100 in package. Per package .... .80

Playing Cards.

Important Notice.

The Government by the new Tariff Law has enacted an Internal Revenue Tax on Playing Cards, which accounts for the change in prices of these goods.

Our playing cards are of the best standard makes and will commend themselves by the following distinguishable features: Excellence of stock, artistic and accurate printing, superior slip, finish and cutting; designs of faces and backs from sketches by prominent artists. Incomparable jokers, all original designs, artistic and handsome decoration of pack boxes and wrappers.

16443 "Owl" No. 00, round corners, assorted backs, double indexed, lowest price ever named on playing cards of any description.
Per pack, $0.08 Per dozen packs $0.84
Per 12 dozen packs 8.50

16447 Steamboat, No. 9. The best steamboat card made, a variety of calico, star and plaid backs. All face cards printed in four colors.
Per pack, $0.09. Per dozen packs 1.00
Per gross packs 11.50

16452 "Fauntleroy," No. 29. New and novel, small sized (1⅝x2¼ in.) playing cards with **enameled ivory finish.** A variety of backs representing the principal characters in the story—"Dick," "Mr. Hobbs," "Dearest" and "The Earl."
Per pack .... .13
Per dozen packs 1.40
Per gross packs 16.00

***** No one enjoys eating from chipped or cracked dishes—Why not get a new set? Prices low.**

Playing Cards—Continued.

16456 "Rambler," No. 22, superior quality; "Aluminum" surface and waterproof finish; new and appropriate backs; printed in red, blue, etc. A very popular card.
Per pack........ $0.13
Per dozen packs........ 1.40
Per gross packs........ 16.00

16458 "Bicycle," No. 808, superior ivory enameled finish; numerous popular and appropriate backs. Largely used by card players throughout the world. Per pack........ .17
Per dozen packs........ 1.85

16464 ANGEL BACK "Club," No. 75, second quality; manufactured of PURE LINEN STOCK *expressly for club use.* Per pack........ .22
Per dozen packs........ 2.40

16467 "Boston," No. 55, fine linen stock, double enameled and waterproof high slip finish; new and beautiful backs. Each pack sealed in an inside wrapper, in cloth case, stamped in gold.
Per pack........ .31
Per dozen packs........ 3.45

There never was a better year to buy.

Playing Cards—Continued.

16474 El Dorado Gold Edges, No. 49, variety of illuminated backs, tints and rich gold leaf bronze, exquisitely put up in gold coin tuck box, printed in color and rich gold bronze. The daintiest card in the market. Per pack........ $0.37
Per dozen packs........ 4.15

16480 "AMERICAN SKAT," No. 2, with German faces and modern American indexes; best quality, double enameled, highly finished, fancy backs in red and blue. Thirty-six cards in pack, size 2¼x3⅜, longer and narrower than the regular size and *superior to imported cards* for "SKAT," *the leading German game,* and all games where not more than 36 cards are used.
Per pack........ .30
Per dozen packs........ 3.25

16489 "WHIST," No. 175, French size, 2¼x3½ inches; made from pure linen stock, extra enameled; expressly for "*Whist,*" "*Bezique,*" "*Penuchle,*" "*Poker,*" "*Sixty-Six,*" "*Solitaire,*" and all games where more than five cards are dealt to the hand; handsomely designed backs; each pack in sealed wrapper, in cloth case stamped in gold. Per pack........ .35
Per dozen packs........ 3.50

Playing Cards—Continued.

16491 "TREASURY," No. 89, for clubs and exacting players desiring perfect cards; contains the finest selected linen stock, is gauged to standard thickness with cutting and margins accurate and true; each pack in wrapper and in enameled cloth case. Per pack........ $0.57
Per dozen packs........ 6.25

16494 Barcelona, Spanish playing cards, for playing Mexican Monte; 48 cards to pack.
Per pack........ .40
Per dozen packs........ 4.00

16499 Hand-painted Celluloid Playing Card Case, contains pack of gold-edge enameled playing cards of good quality; each put up in cardboard box. Weight, packed, 6 ounces.
Each........ $0.30
Per doz........ 3.25

STAMPED AND FANCY GOODS DEPARTMENT.

Stamped Linen Squares.

16500 Stamped linen squares stamped in newest assorted designs, ready for outlining or embroidering.
Size...5 in., 7, 9, 12.
Each.$0.03, .04, .06, .09.
Size..15 in., 18, 20, 24.
Each.$0.12, .18, .30, .35.
Size..27 in., 32, 36.
Each.$0.50, .55, .65.

16502 Hemstitched Linen Squares, fine quality, with drawn work edges and corners, stamped in new designs. (See cut.)
Size..12 in., 18, 24, 30,
Each.$0.25, .45, .60, 1.00

The 5, 7 and 9 inch squares are suitable sizes for doylies; 12, 15, 18, 20, 24 and 27 in. for center pieces; 30, 32 and 36 in. for table covers and lunch cloths.

Table Covers.

16503 White Cotton Drill Table Covers, one yard square, stamped in colors, to be outlined or embroidered with different colors of linen embroidery thread. (See 16508.)
Each....$0.25

Sofa Cushion Covers.

16504 White Cotton Bedford Cord Cushion Covers, 22 in. square, stamped in colors, to be worked as above.
Each........ $0.40

Doylies.

16506 White Cotton Drill Doylies, stamped in colors, to be worked as above. Size, 9x9 in. Each.... $0.06
12x12 in. Each........ .12

16508 Linen Embroidery Thread, in colors for working above covers etc. Per skein........ .03
Per dozen skeins........ .30

When this thread is ordered for working above articles, we select suitable shades to match colors of stamping. It takes about twelve skeins to work table cover and about six for cushion cover.

16512 Linen Fringe for finishing edge of table covers. Comes in plain white also in white with green, white with yellow and white with brown.
Per yard........ $0.08

Stamped Tray Cloths.

New Assorted Designs.

16520 Stamped Tray Cloths, white cotton duck, 18x27 in.
Each...... $0.10

16522 Stamped and Fringed Tray Cloths, all linen, 19x25 in.
Each...... $0.18

16524 Stamped and Fringed Tray Cloths, all linen momie, 19x27 in.
Each........ $0.30

16526 Stamped Tray Cloths, white linen, fine quality. 19x27 in. Each.. $0.35

16528 Stamped and Fringed Tray Cloths, all linen momie, 19x29 in. Each........ $0.40

16530 Stamped and Fringed Tray Cloths, open work, all linen momie, 20x30 in. Each........ .45

16532 Hemstitched Tray Cloths fine quality linen with drawn work edges and corners, stamped in assorted new designs. See cut 16502 for illustration 18x27 in. Each........ .55

Stamped Splashers.

16534 Stamped Splashers, white cotton duck; size 18x28 inches. Each........ $0.10

16536 Stamped Splashers, plain linen, fringed; size 19x32 inches. Each........ .18

16538 Stamped Splashers, plain linen, with row of open work; fringed; size 19x32 inches.
Each........ .25

16540 Stamped Splashers, all linen momie, scalloped with knotted fringe; size 19x32 inches.
Each........ .32

16542 Stamped Splashers, all linen momie, open work in center and corners; fringed; size 17x31 inches. Each........ .38

16544 Stamped Splashers, all linen momie, open work all around; fringed; size 19x32 inches.
Each........ .40

Stamped Fringed Linen Scarfs.

16550 Stamped and Fringed Scarfs, plain linen.

Size.	Each.
16x54 in.	$0.25
16x72 in.	.35

16552 Stamped and Fringed Scarfs, plain linen, with row of open work on both ends.

Size.	Each.
16x54 in.	$0.32
16x72 in.	.40

16554 Stamped Linen Momie Scarfs, scalloped ends with knotted fringe.

Size.	Each.
16x54 in.	$0.35
16x72 in.	.45

16556 Stamped Linen Momie Scarfs, open work center and sides, knotted fringe.
Size 16x54 inches. Each........ $0.45
Size 16x72 inches. Each........ .58

Stamping Outfits.

We have the perforated stamping patterns in the latest designs, also liquids for stamping. We design monograms and special patterns to order. We have (3) three stamping outfits, the finest in the market. See quotations following.

In each of these outfits can be found designs suitable for any kind of embroidery. There are no two patterns alike in these three outfits.

16629 Stamping outfit No. 4 contains 22 patterns and one complete alphabet, with box of powder. Each........ $0.45
Postage........ .12

16633 Stamping outfit No. 1 contains 75 patterns and one complete alphabet and one box of powder. Each........ .85
Postage........ .15

16643 Stamping outfit No. 2 contains 40 patterns and one complete alphabet but larger designs and letters than No. 16633, and one box of powder. Each........ .85
Postage........ .15

16658 Liquid for stamping black.
2 oz. bottle, each........ .12
5 oz. bottle, each........ .25
Cannot go by mail.

16661 Stamping Powder, white and blue.
Per box........ .12

Stamping Patterns.

16668 We furnish special patterns to order, but as the variety is great we cannot describe them. Prices range from 5 to 75 cents each. Give a full and clear description of your wants and we will send you good value for your money, and allow three to five days to complete them.

In ordering, give style of pattern, STYLE you prefer, and PURPOSE of its use.

We sell more SEWING MACHINES than any other house in the world.

Why?

. . . See our Prices . . .

GLOVE DEPARTMENT.

We do not warrant kid gloves. Carelessness in fitting on will ruin any glove. To insure satisfaction the glove must be put on with great care the first time remembering that the more you pull the tighter the glove will become. Put the fingers in first, smooth by rubbing from the tips of the fingers (never push between the fingers), then rub the thumb on and push the glove up. Never take hold of the top of the glove. By observing the above, gloves will fit better and wear longer.

N. B. In ordering gloves, especially kid, be sure always to give color and size wanted. **To determine your size measure closely around the hand across the knuckles.** If sizes of kid gloves are sent as ordered and have been tried on, *they will not be exchanged.*

17019 Norma Ladies' Kid Gloves, with 4 large white pearl buttons; embroidery to match color of glove; colors, black, brown, tan, mode and slate. Per pair.......$1.10

17021 Empress Kid Gloves, with 4 large pearl buttons, which match color of glove and embroidery in same color; colors, black, brown, tan, mode, slate, red, blue and green. Per pair.......$1.25

17023 Franconia, real French kid gloves, with four large white pearl buttons and embroidery to match color of glove; colors, black, brown, tan, mode, slate, red, blue and green. Per pair.......1.50

17025 La Tosca, four Button Kid Gloves, quoted only until sold in the following colors and sizes; Cream color, size, 5¾. Tan color, sizes 7¾, and 8. Brown sizes 7¾. Gray, sizes 6, 7¼, 7½, 7¾ and 8. Black, size 6; also four button suede in black, sizes 6 and 6¼. Brown, sizes 6, 6¼ and 6¾ and gray, size 7. Per pair.......75

Ladies' Hook Gloves.

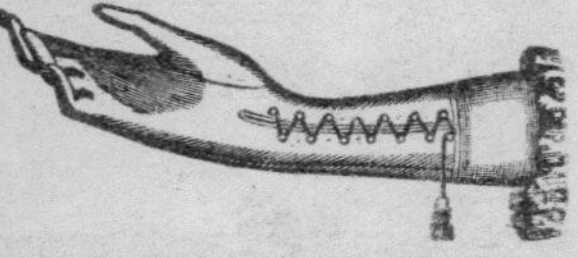

17030 Duchess Kid Gloves, five-hook, Foster lacing, with embroidery to match color of glove; colors, black, brown, tan, mode and slate. Per pair.......$0.95

17034 Duchess Kid Gloves, seven-hook Foster lacing; embroidery to match color of glove; colors, black, brown, tan, mode and slate. Per pair 1.10

17038 La Reine Kid Gloves, five-hook Foster lacing; embroidery to match color of glove; colors, black, brown, tan, mode, slate, blue, red and green. Per pair.......1.35

17042 La Reine Kid Gloves, seven hook Foster, lacing, embroidery to match color of glove. Colors: Black, brown, tan, mode and slate. Per pair.......1.55

Ladies' Undressed Kid Gloves.

17052 Ariadne Kid Gloves, five-hook Foster lacing suede, embroidery to match color of glove; colors, black, brown, tan, mode and slate. Per pair.......$1.10

17056 Richmond Kid Gloves; 5 hook Foster lacing, Suede; embroidery to match color of glove. Colors: Black, brown, tan and slate. Per pair.......1.25

Undressed Mousquetaire Kid Gloves.

17070 Ariadne 8-button length Suede Mousquetaire, with 3 buttons at wrist, and embroidery to match glove. Colors: Black, brown, tan, mode, slate, white, blue, cardinal, pearl and pink. Per pair.......$1.35

17072 Seville, 12-button length Suede Mousquetaire. Colors: Black, tan, mode, cardinal, pink, lemon, light blue and pearl. Per pair.......$2.60

17076 Seville, 16-button length Suede Mousquetaires. Colors: Black, gray, pearl, white, lemon, cardinal, light blue and pink. Per pair.......3.10

17078 Seville, 20-button length Suede Mousquetaire. Colors: Black, tan, gray, pearl, white, lemon, cardinal, light blue and pink. Per pair.......3.50

17080 Belsaire, 12-button length Suede Mousquetaire; white only Per pair.......1.75

17082 Bellaire, 16-button length Suede Mousquetaire; white only. Per pair.......2.25

Biarritz Gloves.

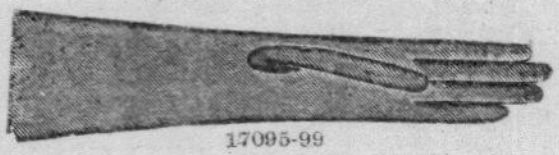

17095-99

17095 Biarritz, 6-button length closed wrist Mousquetaire, partly white stitching and partly embroidery to match color of glove. Colors: Black, brown, tan, slate, red, blue, green, white and pearl Per pair.......$0.95

17099 Chamois, 6-button length Mousquetaire. Colors: White and yellow. Per pair.......95

Ladies' Gauntlet Gloves.

17104 Ladies' Gauntlet Undressed Mocha; good weight, nice for driving. Colors: Tan, brown and black. Per pair..$1.10

17108 Ladies' Gauntlet Dressed Kid Gloves, one button. See cut. Colors: Brown, tan and reddish tans; sizes 6 to 7¾. Per pair.......$1.25

17110 Ladies' Mocha Gauntlet, 2button. See cut. Colors: Brown, tan, black. Sizes, 6 to 7½. Per pair.......$1.50

17108 17110

Ladies' Lined Gloves and Mittens.

Per pair.

17119 Ladies' Kid Gloves, plush lined; trimmed with coney fur and patent button at wrist.......$1.00

17123 Ladies Kid Gloves, plush lined, beaver wrist fur, and patent button at wrist.......1.25

17125 Ladies' Sack Gloves, fine kid, lined, deep fur cuffs, black and brown. Per Pair.......1.48

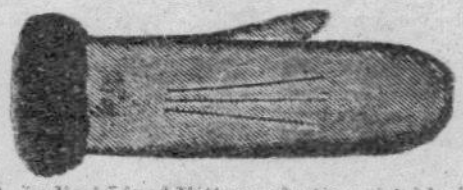

17130 Ladies' Lined Mittens, elastic wrist, black and brown. Per pair.......$0.50

17132 Ladies Kid Mittens, plush lined, fur wrist and button.......1.00

17136 Ladies' Kid Mitten, plush lined, trimmed with fur.......1.20

17140 Ladies' Fine Kid Mittens, plush lined, with deep fur cuffs; sack style.......1.48

Children's Mitts.

17142 Children's Kid Mittens, plush lined, fur top, with button. Per pair.......$0.50

17144 Children's Mocha, lined Mitts, one button, fur top. Per Pair.......0.60

Men's Kid Gloves.

In Tans, Browns and English Reds.

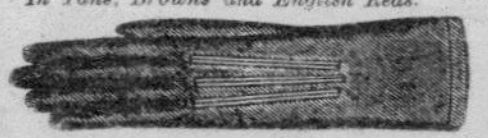

Per pair.

17148 Men's Kid Gloves, stitched backs and tops. (10).......$1.00

17151 Men's Fine Dress Kid Gloves, Pique back 1.35

Ladies' Jersey Gloves.

	Per pair.	Per doz.
17155 Ladies' Fast Black Gloves, pointed backs, length 12 inches.......	$0.15	$1.65
17157 Ladies' Jersey Gloves, silk embroidered backs. Colors: Slates, tans, browns.......	.15	1.65
17162 Ladies' Jersey Gloves in tans only; fine lisle silk pointed backs, length 13 inches.......	.22	2.40

Ladies' Taffeta Gloves.

	Per pair.	Per doz.
17164 Ladies' Black Taffeta Silk Gloves, pointed backs, length 12 in.	$0.30	$3.20
17167 Ladies' Taffeta Silk Gloves, in tan shades, pointed backs, length 12 inches.......	.30	3.20

Ladies' Gauntlet Gloves.

	Per pair.	Per doz.
17172 Ladies' fast black Gauntlet Gloves, Berlin lisle.......	$0.25	$2.70
17174 Ladies' Gauntlet Gloves, Berlin lisle, tan shades.......	.25	2.70
17176 Ladies' fast black Gauntlet Gloves, silk bound cuffs.......	.33	3.60
17179 Ladies' Gauntlet Gloves, silk bound cuffs, tan shades.......	.33	3.60
17181 Ladies' Black Taffeta Silk Gauntlets, pointed backs.......	.43	4.60
17183 Ladies' Colored Taffeta Silk Gauntlets, pointed backs, in tans and browns.......	.43	4.60

Ladies' Pure Silk Gloves.

	Per pair.	Per doz.
17185 Ladies' Pure Silk Black Gloves, fine silk pointed backs.......	$0.50	$5.40
17187 Ladies' Pure Silk Black Gloves, fine silk pointed backs, in 4, 5 and 6 button lengths.......	.65	7.00

Kayser Patent Finger Tipped Gloves, either silk or cashmere; have a guarantee ticket in each pair, that entitles the customer to a new pair *Free*, if the tips wear out before the gloves.

17189 Kayser Pure Silk Gloves. These are 3 ply at finger ends, and are guaranteed not to wear out at finger ends first. Sizes, 6 to 8½. Per pair.......$0.85

17191 Kayser Two Thread, black only; cashmere gloves, with patent 3-ply finger tips, silk fourchettes between the fingers. Per pair, 43, 50 and 85 cents.

Ladies' and Children's Winter Gloves.

	Per pair.	Per dz. pair.
17267 Children's Cashmere Gloves; all wool, assorted, dark colors and black..	$0.25	$2.70
17271 Ladies' Solid Black Berlin Fleece Lined Gloves; length, 12 in.......	.20	2.15
17274 Ladies' All Wool Black Cashmere Gloves; length, 12 inches.......	.20	2.15
17277 Ladies Fine Cashmere Gloves; black only, silk pointed backs.......	.32	3.50

Ornaments for Fancy Work.

Silk and chenille or plush tufts in fancy colors for fancy work. Cuts are from ½ to ¾ size of goods. No blacks except in No. 17351 tufts.

17351 Silk Ball Tufts ⅝ in. in diameter, all colors.

Each.......$0.02
Per dozen.......15

17351

17353 Fancy Silk Pompons, 2¼ in. long, all colors. Each.......$0.04
Per dozen.......43

17353

Ornaments—Continued.

17355

17355 Silk Pompons, assorted colors, 1¼x2½ in. Each $0.06
Per dozen .... .65

17359 Tassel for fancy work in the new shades; length, 6 inches. Each $0.04
Per dozen .... .40

17359

17363 17367

17363 Fancy Silk Pompons; 2 inches long. Each $0.04
Per dozen .... .43

17367 Fancy Silk Pompons; with two drops; length 2½ inches. Each $0.04
Per dozen .... .43

Fancy Cords.

17375—77

17375 Madrid fancy cord, silk chenille and tinsel; for fancy work, all colors and black, white and cream. Per yard $0.06
Per dozen yards .... .60

17377 Fine Berlin Combination Silk Chenille and gold Tinsel Cord. Very handsome for all kinds of fancy work and as a fancy trimming cord for costumes, etc. See cut. Black and colors. Per yard .... .08
Per dozen .... .85

Fancy Materials for Embroidery.

17380 Kismet or frosted Tinsel thread, 12 balls in box, in plain colors; gold, silver, canary, blue, pink, steel, gold, dark and light copper, light blue, green, red, fancy blue, yellow, copper, etc. Per ball $0.02
Per dozen balls 20

17382 Arrasene for embroidery in all colors, put up in bunches of 12 skeins. Per bunch .... .15
Per dozen 1.50

17384 Chenille for embroidery in all colors, put up in bunches of 12 skeins. Per bunch (No. 1) .20
Per dozen bunches 2.00

17386 Ribbosene or Braidene for embroidery, white and colors, put up in bunches of 12 skeins. Per bunch .... .20

SAMPLE OF WORK.

17388 Twilled Lace Thread for crocheting, knitting and all kinds of fancy work; it is unequaled by any crochet thread in the market. We have it in all numbers from 20 to 100 in both white and ecru. The twill is a new feature, giving a much better appearance to the work than the common three and six cord threads now in use. A trial will satisfy you as to the superiority over all others. No. 20, 30, 40, 50, 60, 70, all 200 yards, on each spool; we can supply samples. If you are interested send for them. Per spool $0.05
Per box (10 spools) .... .45

Gold Threads for Embroidery.

17390 Imitation Gold Thread, 12 yards in a bunch. Per bunch $0.15

17392 Frosted Gold Thread, 12 yards in a bunch. Per bunch .... .15

17394 Crochet Gold Thread. Per ball .... .11

17396 Washable Gold Thread, sizes 7, 8, 9. Per skein .... .05

17398 Washable Gold Cord. Per skein .... .05

17399 Japanese Gold Thread, fine. Per skein .... .11

17400 Japanese Gold Thread, medium. Per skein .... .15

17401 Japanese Gold Thread, coarse. Per skein. .20

Spangles.

17402 Gold or Silver Spangles. Sizes ¼ to ⅜ in. Per ounce $0.14

Embroidery Hoops.

17406 Embroidery Hoops, 4, 5, and 6 inches in diameter. Per pair $0.05
7 to 12 inches Per pair .... .06

17408 Rubber Tatting shuttles, finely polished. Each $0.15
Per dozen 1.50

Fancy Towel Holders.

17410 Towel Rings in ebony, rosewood, mahogany and antique oak. Large, each $0.10
Per dozen 1.00

17412 Towel Ring. Consists of polished hardwood ring with brass chain and hook. Price, without towel,
Each, large, ... $0.12
Per dozen 1.20

Pin Cushion Novelties.

17416 White Metal Basket with plush cushion; see cut; Each $0.12
Postage 5c.

17418 White Metal Bootee with plush cushion; see cut, Each $0.12
Postage 4c.

17420 White Metal Shoe with plush cushion; see cut. Each $0.12
Postage, 6c.

17422 White Metal Slipper with plush cushion, length 5¼ in.; see cut. Each $0.20
Postage, 8c.

17424 White Metal Slipper with plush cushion, length 4 in.; see cut. Each .... .12
Postage, 5c.

Fans.

		Each.	Per. doz.
17452	Palm Leaf Fans	$0.02	$0.20
17453	Japanese Folding Fans, decorated	.08	.25

17464 Ning Po Fans. See cut. A fine braided fan, quite unique in style. The natural and new shades of colors. Each. $0.10

17466 Open.

Closed.

17466 Telescope Fans, inclosed in an imitation cigar. Each .... $0.15 Per dozen $1.50

17487 The Pencil Patent Fan, Telescope handle; colors red, tan and white.
Each $0.15
Per dozen 1.50

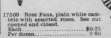

17509 Rose Fans, plain white cambric with assorted roses. See cut opened and closed.
Each $0.25
Per dozen 2.60

Fans—Continued.

17510 New Fatinitza Cloth Fan; fancy shape, folding; size open, 10x10; 9½ inch stick. Colors Tan, black, red. Weight, 3 ounces. Each $0.15
Per dozen 1.50

WALL PAPER? Yes—any color, any width—with border to match—prices will astonish and please—samples free.

HAIR GOODS.

When ordering, send samples of hair, as hair goods cannot be returned except to be exchanged for another shade of the same quality.

Drab, red, gray and golden shades in switches, curls, waves, frizzes, etc., will be charged 25 to 50 per cent. extra.

N. B.—Be sure you understand what you are ordering before sending for hair goods, as they can not be returned. In ordering send sample of shade wanted, free from oil, folded up in a paper, pinned to your order and marked "Sample," to avoid any mistake.

La Toska Bang.

17530 La Toska Bang. Ladies who do not require large, heavy front will find this a little gem, light and fluffy, ventilated foundation. Each, until sold $1.25

Feather Bang.

17536 Feather Bang, new fluffy bang of fine natural curly hair. See cut. Each $2.50

17575 Princess Bang, made of natural curly hair on weft; a popular bang, being light and easily attached, Each $0.50

Emma Wave.

17581 Emma Wave, invisible hair lace foundation, natural curly hair, 3 in part, 12 in. from side to side. Each, until sold $3.00

17618 Kid Hair Curlers, neat and nice for curling the hair; 12 in package.

Length	3½ in.	4 in.	4½ in.
Per package	$0.06	$0.08	$0.10

Ostrich Tips—Continued.

17996 Black Prince of Wales Ostrich Tips Per bunch of two..........$0.43
17998 Black Prince of Wales Ostrich Tips Per bunch of two..........$0.69

Black Ostrich Half Plumes.

18000 Black Ostrich Half Plumes, single. Each..........$025
18002 Black Ostrich Half Plumes, single. Each..........$0.42
18004 Black Ostrich Half Plumes, single. Each..55c., 68c. and 85c.

Jetted Ostrich Tips.

18006

18008

18006 Black Ostrich Tips with Aigrettes, jetted. Per bunch of three........$0.35
18008 Black Ostrich Tips, Prince of Wales, jetted. Per bunch of two..........$0.45

10810

18012

18010 Black Ostrich Tips, Princess, with Aigrettes, jetted. Per bunch of three, ...$0.55
18012 Black Ostrich Tips, with Aigrettes and six (6) jetted tips. Per bunch..$0.75

Cocque Feathers.

18022

18014 Cocque Feathers, 7 in a bunch; black only Per bunch..........$0.15
18016 Bunch of Six Fine Cocque Feathers, with jetted edges; black only. Per bunch..........$0.22
18018 Bunch of Ten Fine Cocque Feathers, with jetted edges; black only. Per bunch..........$0.25
18020 Ornament of Three High Cocque Feathers, grouped with six curved ones; jetted edges; black only. Per bunch..........$0.25
18022 Bunch of Fourteen Fine Jetted Cocque Feathers; black only. See cut. Per bunch..........$0.45
18026 Bunch of Five Cocque Feathers, in assorted colors, with spangled edges. .... .15
18028 Bunch of Five Cocque Feathers, in assorted colors; same style as 18026, larger; spangled edges. Per bunch.......... .30

Birds.

18030 Small Black Birds, plain; 5 in. Each..$0.15
18032 Small Black Birds, new style; edges of wings tipped with spangles; in green, gold, red, yellow, blue Each..........$0.25

18034 Small Black Birds; fine quality; fancifully jetted Each..........$0.25
18036 Small Black Birds; fine quality; wings edged with jet; fancy jetted tail feather ornament. Each..........$0.30
18038 Small Black Birds; fine, with long, narrow tail feathers and wings Each..........$0.35
18040 Small Black Birds; heavily jetted wings; full bunch of jetted aigrettes. See cut. Each..........$0.40
18042 Black Birds with spangled wings and aigrettes; arranged with two colored jetted quills which may be had in either yellow, green, blue tan, red or brown Each..........$0.65

Ornaments—Continued.

18044

18044 Bird Ornament; two fine birds, heavily spangled, ornamental tail feathers. Colors: yellow, green, navy, red and tan See cut. Each..........$0.70
18046 Black Birds: fine glossy black, heavily jetted wings and tail feathers Each..........$0.75

18048 Black Birds; fine glossy black jetted wings, ornament and aigrettes. See cut. Each..........$0.80

18057

Quills.

18050 Black Quills, pointed tops. Each..........$0.02
18053 Natural Quills, square tops; black, white and all colors. Each..........$0.04
18055 Bunch of three quills, with jetted square tops. Colors: Red, navy, brown, tan, yellow, green and white. Per bunch..........$0.15

18057 Bunch of two fine quills, heavily jetted, black only. See cut. Each..........$0.22
18059 Bunch of three high, square top quills with three short ones, all jetted edges; colors, cardinal, navy, tan, brown, white and black. Per bunch..........$0.25
18061 Bunch of fine quills, dove-tailed points with jetted edges; *black* only Per bunch..........$0.30

Wings.

18063 Black Stiff Wings, 9 inches long. Each..........$0.12
18065 Large Stiff Wings, fine quality, in shaded effects; colors, lemon, orange, nile and changeable pinks. Each..........$0.25
Per pair.......... .50

Aigrettes.

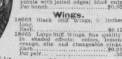

18067 Fancy Stiff Aigrettes, eight pieces in a bunch, four plain, four spangled; colors, brown, red, navy, green and yellow. See cut. Per bunch..........$0.12
18069 Fancy Stiff Aigrettes, nine pieces in bunch, same style as 18067; black only. Per bunch..........$0.12
18071 Ostrich Aigrettes, fine quality; colors, red, light blue, pink, navy and tan. Five in bunch. Per bunch..........$0.25

Feather Ornaments.

18073 Bunch of twelve fine cocque feathers with pompon tuft, similar to cut; assorted colors. Each..........$0.15
18075 Bunch of six fine quills with spangled edges, pompon tuft; assorted colors. Each..........$0.20
18077 Pompon of fine feathers with bunch of soft aigrettes and spangled feathers; assorted colors. Each..........$0.25
18079 Pompon of fancy curled feathers, combined with ostrich; colors, cream and light blue with black. Each..........$0.20

18081 Fancy ornament of two quills and ostrich feather pompon; colors: pink and yellow, combined with black. Each...$0.26
18083 Fancy bird's wing with quills; assorted colors combined with black. Each..........$0.26
18086 Ornament of two fancy bird's wings with jetted tops and three jetted pompons; assorted colors. Each..........$0.25
18088 Ornament of fancy bird's wings, with bunch of fine jetted quills; colors, red, green, brown, navy and tan, combined with black, also in plain black. Each..........$0.30

Ornaments—Continued.

18090 Large Feather Ornament; two wings, three quills and pompon, all spangled; assorted colors. Each.......... $0.30
18092 Small Feather Ornament, suitable trimming for bonnets and toques; consists of two small black jetted wings, with jetted aigrettes and three colored pompons in either yellow, green, navy, red or tan. Each.......... .30

18094 Ornament of fancy stiff and curled-feathers; colors red, green, brown, navy, tan and black See cut. Each..........$0.30
18096 Ornament of fine quality curled gauze feathers in large broad bow or butterfly design; spangled in colors to match; assorted colors. Each..........$0.35
18098 Ornament of fine white cocque feathers, ostrich aigrette and two imitation butterflies on spiral wire until sold. Each..........$0.35
18102 Ornament of fine Peacock feathers, beautiful natural colors, until sold. Each.......... .35

18105

18105 Pompon, three fine feather tufts, with bunch of jetted quills, assorted colors combined with black. See cut. Each..........$0.38
18107 Large Feather Ornament; two high quills, two wings, pompon tufts and spangled aigrettes, assorted colors. Each..........$0.38
18109 Gauze Feather Ornament; full bunch of fine quality jetted and spangled gauze feathers, assorted colors and black. Each. $0.40
18111 Pompon; fine gauze feathers, with jetted tips and bunch of jet aigrettes; comes in black only. Each..........$0.50
18114 Ornament of Fancy Wings; centers of black jets, outside tipped in colored spangles; green, yellow, red, gold or navy. Each..........$0.50
18116 Ornament of Two Small Ostrich Tips, spangled; two high jetted quills; assorted colors and black. Each.......... .55
18118 Fine quality pure white feather ornament, three quills, breast and aigrettes until sold. Each.......... .75
18120 Fur Novelty, small head with three pompons; come in black or white. Each.......... .52

Orange Blossoms.

18275 Orange Blossoms, Bridal Sets, fine quality wax blossoms with buds and green leaves; each set contains wreath, ear drops, spray pin and bouquet. Each..........$1.50, $2.00 and $3.00
18280 Orange Blossom Sprays, fine wax blossoms with buds and leaves. Each..........50, 75 and 1.00
18285 Orange Blossom Bouquets, same as above. Small. Each.......... .15
18290 Confirmation Wreaths, white. Each.......... .20
18295 Confirmation Bouquets, white. Per spray .08
Per bunch of 2 sprays.......... .15

Buckles.

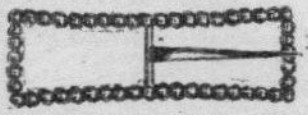

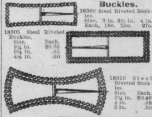

18300 Steel Riveted Buckles.

Size,	3 in.	3½ in.	4 in.
Each,	18c.	23c.	27c.

18305 Steel Riveted Buckles,

Size.	Each.
2¼ in.	$0.35
3¼ in.	.45
4¼ in.	.60

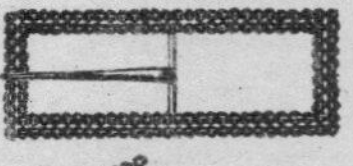

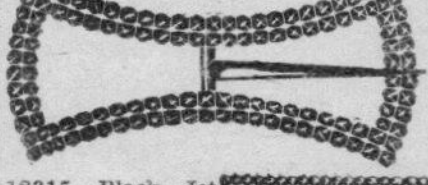

18310 Steel Riveted Buckles.

Size.	Each.
3¼ in.	$0.40
4 in.	.45
5 in.	.50

18315 Black Jet Riveted Buckles. Size..........3¾ in. Each....... $0.40

18320 Jet Buckles.

Width.	Each.
2⅛ in.	$0.20
3⅛ in.	.25
4⅛ in.	.29

Buckles—Continued.

18325 Large Gilt Buckles, ornamented with steel. Size...... 5 in. Each..... $0.25

18330 Steel Slides, riveted. Size 4¼ in. Each, $0.45

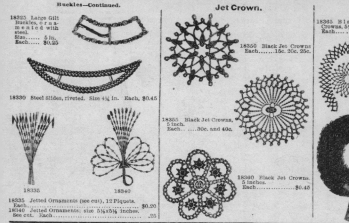

18335   18340

18335 Jetted Ornaments (see cut), 12 Piquets. Each...$0.20
18340 Jetted Ornaments; size 5½x5¼ inches. See cut. Each.................................. .25

Jet Crown.

18350 Black Jet Crowns Each.......15c. 20c. 25c.

18355 Black Jet Crowns, 5 inch. Each.. ....30c. and 40c.

18360 Black Jet Crowns. 5 inches. Each..................$0.45

Jet Crowns—Continued.

18365 Black Jet Crowns, 5½ inch. Each..... ...$0.75

18375 Jet Crown and Band, for hat trimming. Each..................$0 75

Feather Collars

18380 Ostrich Feather Collars, black only. Each................$1.25
18385 Ostrich Feather Collars, black only. Each.................$4.00
18390 Ostrich Feather Collars, black only; very fine. Each.................$5.00
18395 Ostrich Feather Collars, black only; very fine. Each.................$6.50

MILLINERY DEPARTMENT.

We invite the attention of our customers to this department. We can furnish any style of trimmed or untrimmed Hats in any desired quality or cost; see illustrations and quotations following. We also carry in stock a full line of Ribbons, Fancy Flowers, Wreaths, Sprays, Ostrich Tips, Plumes, Birds, Jetted Ornaments, Aigrettes, etc., etc. A reasonable charge will be made for trimming, from 15c. to 75c. These prices are for the work only. Any made Hat or Bonnet made or trimmed to order cannot be returned or exchanged.

Sailor Hats

Each.
18540 Sailor Hats, cashmere crown, brim and band. Colors: Navy, brown, ecru and black; 3 in. brim...................................$0.35

Each.
18542 Sailor Hats, velvet crown, cashmere brim and band. Colors: Navy, brown, ecru and black; 3 in. brim.................................$0.45

Each.
18544 Sailor Hats, satin crown, cashmere brim, ribbon band and bow. Colors: Navy, brown, tan and black; 3 in. brim.................$0.50

Each.
18546 Newport, satin crown, cashmere rim, ribbon band and bow.....................$0.45
Silk plush crown, cashmere rim, ribbon band and bow............................... .80
Wool felt, trimmed with ribbon band.......... .80
Wool felt, finer, trimmed with ribbon band; colors same as above....................... 1.00

Each.
18548 Knox High Crown Sailor, satin crown, cashmere rim, ribbon band...............$0.65
Wool Felt, trimmed with ribbon band .... .80
Wool Felt, finer, trimmed with ribbon band.... 1.10
Same colors as above.

Each.
18551 Promenade Wool Felt, trimmed with ribbon band and bow........................$0.80
Wool Felt, finer, trimmed with ribbon band and bow.................................. 1.00
Untrimmed Wool Felt............................ .75
Colors: Brown, navy, ecru and black.

Wide Rim Flats.

Each.
18555 Hyde Park Ladies' Flat. Colors: Brown, navy, ecru and black.
Wool Felt..................................$0.60
Wool Felt, finer.............................. .72
Fur Felt.................................... 1.50

Each.
18562 May Queen Child's Flat. Colors: Brown, navy, ecru and cardinal.
Wool Felt..................................$0.60
Wool Felt, finer.............................. .72
Fur Felt.................................... 1.50

18566 Riddle. English Wool Felt, for misses and children. Colors: Navy, brown, tan, cardinal and butter color. Each..................$0.60

WATCH DEPARTMENT.

Men's 18 Size Solid 14-K Gold Stem Wind Watches, with Elgin, Hampden or Waltham Movements.

Prices of Elgin Watches in Solid Gold Cases.

No.	Style A or B	Style C or D	Style E or F
18800 A 7 Jewel Gilt (96 or 73) movement	$67.10	$42.35	$30.05
18801 An 11 Jewel Gilt (10 or 74) movement	68.47	43.72	31.42
18802 An 11 Jewel Nickel (102 or 43) movement	68.75	44.00	31.70
18803 A 15 Jewel Gilt, G. M. Wheeler, patent regulator, movement	70.95	46.20	33.90
18804 A 15 Jewel Nickel, G. M. Wheeler, patent regulator, movement	71.50	46.75	34.45
18805 A 15 Jewel Gilt, H. H. Taylor or 123 or 125, patent regulator, adjusted, movement	73.70	48.95	36.65
18806 A 15 Jewel Nickel, H. H. Taylor, patent regulator, adjusted, movement	75.90	51.15	38.85
18807 A 17 Jewel Gilt, B. W. Raymond, patent regulator, adjusted, D. S. dial, movement	78.10	53.35	41.05
18808 A 17 Jewel Nickel, B. W. Raymond, patent regulator, adjusted, D. S. dial movement	80.30	55.55	43.25

Style A, Raised Ornaments, Large Diamond in Center. Weight, 55 pwt. 14-K Solid Gold. Case without movement, $62.70.

Style B, 14-K Solid Gold Box Joint Case. Weight, 58 pwt. Raised Ornaments, large Diamond in Horse's Eyes. Case without movement, $62.70.

Prices of Waltham Watches with Solid Gold Cases.

No.	Style A or B	Style C or D	Style E or F
18809 A 7 Jewel Gilt (1) movement	$67.05	$42.30	$30.00
18810 An 11 Jewel Gilt (3) movement	68.45	43.70	31.40
18811 An 11 Jewel Nickel (3) movement	68.70	43.95	31.65
18812 A 15 Jewel Gilt P. S. Bartlett, patent regulator, movement	70.90	46.15	33.85
18813 A 15 Jewel Nickel P. S. Bartlett, patent regulator, movement	71.45	46.70	34.40
18814 A 15 Jewel Gilt P. S. Bartlett, patent regulator, adjusted, D. S. dial, movement	73.10	48.35	36.05
18815 A 15 Jewel Nickel, P. S. Bartlett, patent regulator, adjusted, D. S. dial, movement	73.65	48.90	36.60
18816 A 17 Jewel-Gilt (25) patent regulator, adjusted, D. S. dial, movement	75.85	51.10	38.80
18817 A 17 Jewel, Gilt, Appleton Tracy, patent regulator, adjusted, D. S. dial, movement	78.05	53.30	41.00
18818 A 17 Jewel Nickel, 35 or Appleton Tracy, patent regulator, adjusted, D. S. dial, movement	80.25	55.50	43.20
18819 A 17 Jewel Crescent St. Nickel, patent regulator, adjusted, D. S. dial, movement	84.70	59.95	47.65
18819½ The New 17-Jewel Waltham Vanguard, Gold Settings, gold, patent regulator, full adjusted, double sunk dial. Highest grade 18 size Waltham movement ever made.	95.70	70.95	58.65

Style D. 50 pwt., 14-K Solid Gold Case. $37.95.

Prices of Complete Hampden Watches in Solid Gold Cases.

No.	Style A or B	Style C or D	Style E or F
18820 A 7-Jewel gilt movement	$67.00	$42.25	$29.95
18821 An 11-Jewel gilt movement	68.40	43.65	31.35
18822 An 11-Jewel nickel movement	68.65	43.90	31.60
18823 A 16-Jewel, nickel, No. 44 or 64 "Dueber" movement patent regulator	71.40	46.65	34.35
18824 A 17-Ruby Jewel, nickel, No. 43 or 63 "J. C. Dueber," movement, adjusted patent regulator, D. S. Dial	75.80	51.05	38.75
18825 A 17-Ruby Jewel, nickel, No. 47 or 67 "J. C. Dueber Special" movement, adjusted patent regulator, D. S. Dial	79.15	54.45	42.10
18826 A 17-Ruby Jewel, nickel, Dueber "New Railway" movement, fully adjusted, gold patent regulator, D. S. Dial	80.20	65.45	53.15
18827 A 17-Ruby Jewel, nickel, Dueber, "Special Railway" movement fully adjusted, gold patent regulator, D. S. Dial	101.20	76.45	64.15

Prices of Montgomery Ward & Co's Special Guarantee Watches in Solid Gold Cases.

No.	Style A or B	Style C or D	Style E or F
18828 A 16-Ruby Jewel, nickel movement, named "Montgomery Ward & Co., Extra 16 Jeweled."	$77.70	$52.95	$40.65
18829 A 20-Ruby Jewel, nickel movement named "Montgomery Ward & Co., Extra Railroad Timer."	112.70	87.95	75.65

The Montgomery Ward & Co. Special Guarantee Movements are made especially for us and are the best value for the money in the market. Each movement of this brand is accompanied by Our Special Guarantee Certificate.

For Men's 16 Size Solid Gold Watches, see page 139.

Style A.

Style C. 50 pwt Solid 14-K Gold Case $37.95

Style E. Solid 14-K Gold Case........ $25.65

Style F. Solid 14-K Gold Case........ $25 65

Men's 18 Size, 14K, Gold Filled, Stem Wind, Watches. Guaranteed for 20 Years.

Prices of Complete Elgin Watches in Either of these Boss, 20-Year Guarantee, 14K Gold Filled, 18 Size, Box Joint Cases.

No.		Hunting Case.	Open Face. Case.
18850	A 7-Jewel Gilt (96 or 73) move't..	$21.45	$19.80
18851	An 11-Jewel Gilt (10 or 74) move't..	22.83	21.18
18852	An 11-Jewel Nickel (102 or 43) movement.	23.10	21.45
18853	A 15-Jewel Gilt G. M. Wheeler, Patent Regulator, movement	25.30	23.65
18854	A 15-Jewel Nickel G. M. Wheeler, Patent Regulator, movement	25.85	24.20
18855	15-Jewel Gilt H. H. Taylor or 123 or 125, Patent Regulator, Adjusted, movement.	28.05	26.40
18856	A 15-Jewel Nickel H. H. Taylor or 123 or 125, Patent Regulator, Adjusted, movement	30.25	28.60
18857	A 17-Jewel Gilt B. W. Raymond, Patent Regulator, Adjusted, double sunk dial, movement	32.45	30.80
18858	A 17-Jewel Nickel B. W. Raymond, Patent Regulator, Adjusted, double sunk dial, movement	34.65	33.00

Style M. Case only. Htg., $17.05. O. F., $15.40.

Style N. Case only. Htg., $17.05. O. F., $15.40.

Prices of Complete Waltham Watches in either of these Boss, 20-year guarantee, 14K gold filled, 18 size, box joint cases.

No.		Hunting Case.	Open Face. Case.
18859	A 7-Jewel Gilt (1) movement.	$20.35	$19.25
18860	An 11-Jewel Gilt (3) movement.	21.73	20.68
18861	An 11-Jewel Nickel (3) movement.	22.00	20.90
18862	A 15-Jewel Gilt, P. S. Bartlett, patent regulator, movement.	24.20	23.10
18863	A 15-Jewel Nickel, P. S. Bartlett, patent regulator, movement.	24.75	23.65
18864	A 15-Jewel Gilt P. S. Bartlett, patent regulator, adjusted, double sunk dial, movement.	26.46	25.30
18865	A 15-Jewel Nickel P. S. Bartlett, patent regulator, adjusted, double sunk dial, movement.	26.95	25.85
18866	A 17-Jewel Gilt, No. 25, patent regulator, adjusted, double sunk dial, movement.	29.15	28.05
18867	A 17-Jewel Gilt Appleton Tracy, patent regulator, adjusted, double sunk dial, movement.	31.35	30.25
18868	A 17-Jewel Nickel Appleton Tracy or 85, patent regulator, adjusted, double sunk dial, movement.	33.55	32.45
18869	A 17-Jewel Nickel Crescent St., patent regulator, adjusted, double sunk dial, movement.	37.95	36.85
18870	The Vanguard. New Waltham movement, 17 jewels, in gold settings, gold patent regulator, full adjusted, abmolutely finished. Highest grade 18 size Waltham movement ever made.	48.95	47.85

Style O. Case only. Htg., $15.95. O. F., $14.85.

Style P. Case only. Htg., $15.95. O. F., $14.85.

Prices of Complete Hampden Watches in either of these Dueber 14K gold filled 20-year guarantee cases.

No.		Hunting Case.	Open face Case.
18871	A 7-Jewel Gilt "Exp. Bal." Movement	$19.80	$18.70
18872	An 11-Jewel Gilt "Exp. Bal." Movement	21.17	20.07
18873	An 11-Jewel Nickel "Exp. Bal." Movement	21.45	20.35
18874	A 16-Jewel, nickel, No. 44 or 64, "Dueber" movement, patent regulator.	24.20	23.10
18875	A 17-Ruby Jewel, nickel, No. 43 or 63, "J. C. Dueber" movement, adjusted, patent regulator, D. S. Dial.	28.60	27.50
18876	A 17-Ruby Jewel, nickel, No. 47 or 67, "J. C. Dueber Special" movement, adjusted, patent regulator, D. S. Dial.	31.90	30.80
18877	A 17-Ruby Jewel, nickel, Dueber "New Railway" movement, fully adjusted, gold patent regulator, D. S. Dial	42.90	41.80
188.8	A 17-Ruby Jewel, nickel, Dueber "Special Railway" movement, fully adjusted, gold patent regulator, D. S. Dial.	53.90	52.80

Prices of Montgomery Ward & Co.'s Special guarantee watches in these Dueber 14K filled 20-year guarantee cases.

No.		Hunting Case.	Open face Case.
18879	A 16-Ruby Jewel, nickel movement, named Montgomery Ward & Co., Extra 16-Jewel.	$30.40	$29.30
18880	A 20-Ruby Jewel, nickel movement, named "Montgomery Ward & Co., Co., Extra Railroad Timer."	65.40	64.30

Style T. Case only. Htg., $15.40. O. F., $14.30.

Style U. Case only. Htg., $15.40. O. F., $14.30.

Dust Proof Screw Bezel and Back Stem Wind Watches.

Fabys Dust Proof Cases are the strongest and most durable cases made. The Monarch Cases, styles N2, P2 and U2, are 14k gold filled, warranted 21 years. Montauk Cases, styles O2, T2 and A3, are 10k filled, warranted 15 years.

Style N2.   Case only.   14k filled $8.80

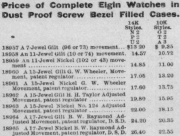

Style O2.   Case only.   10k filled $4.95

Prices of Complete Elgin Watches in Dust Proof Screw Bezel Filled Cases.

	14K Styles. N 2 P 2 U 2	10K Styles. O 2 T 2 A 3
18957 A 7-Jewel Gilt (96 or 73) movement.....	$13 20	$ 9.35
18958 An 11-Jewel Gilt (10 or 74) movement..	14.57	10.72
18959 An 11-Jewel Nickel (102 or 43) movement	14.85	11.00
18960 A 15-Jewel Gilt G. W. Wheeler, Movement, patent regulator	17.05	13.20
18961 A 15-Jewel Nickel G. W. Wheeler Movement, patent regulator	17.60	13.75
18962 A 15-Jewel Gilt H. H. Taylor Adjusted Movement, patent regulator	19.80	15.95
18963 A 15-Jewel Nickel No. 124 Adjusted Movement, patent regulator	22.00	18.15
18964 A 17-Jewel Gilt B. W. Raymond Adjusted Movement, patent regulator, D.S.D.	24.20	20.35
18965 A 17-Jewel Nickel B.W. Raymond Adjusted Movement, patent regulator, D.S.D.	26.40	22.55

Prices of Complete Waltham Watches in Dust Proof Screw Bezel Filled Cases.

	14K Styles. N 2 P 2 U 2	10K Styles. O 2 T 2 A 3
18966 A 7-Jewel Gilt No. 1 Movement.......	$13.15	$9.30
18967 An 11-Jewel Gilt No. 3 Movement	14.55	10.70
18968 An 11-Jewel Nickel No. 3 Movement..	14.80	10.95
18969 A 15-Jewel Gilt P. S. Bartlett Movement, patent regulator.................	17.00	13.15
18970 A 15-Jewel Nickel P. S. Bartlett Movement, patent regulator	17.55	13.70
18971 A 15-Jewel Gilt P. S. Bartlett Adjusted Movement, patent regulator, D.S. Dial.....	19.25	15.40
18972 A 15-Jewel Nickel P. S. Bartlett Adjusted Mov't. patent reg., D. S. Dial..	19.75	15.90
18973 A 17-Jewel Gilt No. 25 Adjusted Movement, patent regulator................	21.95	18.30
18974 A 17-Jewel Gilt Appleton Tracy Adj. Mov't, patent regulator, D. S. Dial........	24.15	20.30
18975 A 17-Jewel Nickel Appleton Tracy Adj. Mov't, patent regulator, D. S. Dial.......	26.35	22.50
18976 A 17-Jewel Crescent St., Adj. Mov't, patent regulator, D. S. Dial.............	30.80	26.95
18977 The Vanguard New Waltham Mov't, 17 Jewels in gold settings, gold patent regulator, full adjusted, elaborately finished.....	41.80	37.95

Prices of Complete Hampden Watches in Dust Proof Screw Bezel Filled Cases.

	14K Styles. N 2 P 2 U 2	10K Styles. O 2 T 2 A 3
18978 A 7-Jewel Gilt Exp. Bal. Mov't.......	$13.10	$9.25
18979 An 11-Jewel, Gilt Exp. Bal. Mov't.....	14.55	10.65
18980 An 11-Jewel, Nickel Exp. Bal. Mov't..	14.75	10 90
18981 A 16-Jewel, Nickel, No. 44 or 64 "Dueber" movement, patent regulator..	17.50	13.65
18982 A 17-Ruby Jewel, nickel, No. 45 or 63 "J. C. Dueber" movement, adjusted patent regulator, D.S. Dial..............	21.90	18.05
18983 A 17-Ruby Jewel, nickel, No. 47 or 67 "J. C. Dueber" Special movement, adjusted, patent regulator, D. S. Dial......	25.30	21.45
18984 A 17-Ruby Jewel, nickel, "Dueber New Railway" movement, fully adjusted, gold patent regulator, D. S. Dial..........	36.30	32.45
18985 A 17-Ruby, Jewel, nickel, "Dueber Special Railway" movement, fully adjusted, gold patent regulator, D. S. Dial.........	47.30	43.45

Prices of Complete Montgomery Ward & Co.'s Special Guarantee Watches in Screw Bezel Cases.

	14K Styles. N 2 P 2 U 2	10K Styles. O 2 T 2 A 3
18986 A 16-Ruby Jewel, nickel movement named "Montgomery Ward & Co. Extra 16-Jeweled."	$23.80	$19.95
18987 A 20-Ruby Jewel, nickel, movement named "Montgomery Ward & Co. Extra Railroad Timer."	58.80	54.95

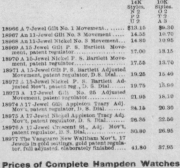

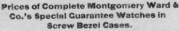

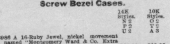

Style T2.   Case only.   10k filled $4.95

Style A3., Case only.   10k filled $4.95

Style P2.   Case only.   14k filled $8.80

Style U2.   Case only.   14k filled $8.80

MONTGOMERY WARD & CO.'S CATALOGUE No. 56.
SPECIAL BARGAINS IN MEN'S STEM WIND WATCHES.

137

Every watch on this page is quoted at a specially low price. They are leaders with us and only the large quantity we sell enables us to quote such low prices.

$4.75   Leader.

18988 Solid Silver Hunting Case, beautifully engraved, fitted with 11-jewel nickel movement, micrometer expansion balance, stem wind and set, highly finished and accurately regulated, making the most elegant gentleman's watch ever sold for such a low price. In addition to watch we include a double strand full length coin silver chain (see cut above), ornamented with large, finely chased slide. We engrave initials on the chain slide and also on the watch when so ordered.
Our price, complete... ....$8.50

18989 This 16 size open Face Stem Wind and Stem Set, Straight Line Lever Movement, is jeweled in the escapement, is well finished, and at the price is very desirable; watch case is solid metal (called Silverine). Brought to high polish, which it will retain like Sterling Silver. Watch is fully guaranteed satisfactory value at the price, or money refunded.
Price...$4.75
Price in a beautifully engraved silver case.... 8.75

18990 Solid Silver 5 oz. Hunting Case, large 18 size stem wind and set, fitted with 11 jewel, Waltham, Elgin or Hampden movement, expansion balance, stem wind and set, perfectly regulated and warranted to keep accurate time, and a solid silver double strand chain. See cut above.
Price of watch and chain complete ...$15.75

A Howard   Watch
for $27.50.

18991 An 18 size, American made movement, jeweled in the escapement, stem wind and set, of A1 timekeeping quality, fully warranted, cased in a silverine open face case, making a splendid watch for the price. This is positively the best value ever offered $5.00
18991A A similar movement in hunting style, silverine case...........................$6.00

18992 Elegant Boss 14k Filled Hunting Case, with solid gold bow, crown and joints; warranted for 20 years; fitted with genuine Howard Full Jewel Patent Regulator, stem wind and set movement, fully guaranteed. This quotation is a special one which will be withdrawn soon as the limited supply of these watches is disposed of. Price only. $27.50
With engraved case....................... 29.50

18893 Genuine Waltham Stem Wind and Stem Set, 11 Jewel, Movement, WARRANTED; in a Dueber's Patent Gold Filled, Louis XIV or Box Joint Case. Elegantly engraved, accompanied by manufacturer's guarantee for 20 years. This watch would be good value at $35.00.
Our special price.... ....$16.50

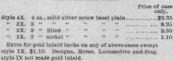

18 Size Stem Wind, Solid Silver, Silveroid and Silver Filled Watches.
Waltham Screw, Bezel and Solid Back Cases.

Styles 4X and 3X have gold ring around stem and gold reflectors inside bezel.

Price of case only.

Style 4X. 4 oz., solid silver screw bezel plain	....	$2.35
" 3X. 3 " " " " "	....	.. 8.25
" 2X. 3 " filled " " "	....	3.30
" 1X. 3 " nickel " " "	....	1.10

Extra for gold inlaid backs on any of above cases except style 1X, $1.10. Designs, Horse, Locomotive and Stag, style IX not made gold inlaid.

Fahys Screw Bezel and Back Cases.

Style 4W. 4 oz., solid silver screw B. & B. plain	....	$5.77
Style 3W. 3 oz., " " " " "	....	4.67
Style 2W. 3 oz., filled " " "	....	3.30
Style 1W. 3 oz., ore " " "	....	.85
Style W. 3 oz., " " " " engraved	....	1.35

Extra for gold inlaid backs on any of above cases except 1W and W, $1.10.

Style 4X, Gold Inlaid................$10.45.

Style 4W, Gold Inlaid................$6.87.

For prices of these cases with movements see table below.

Style 4S. Silver 4 oz., Htg. Case only	....$7.42.
Style 3S. 3 " " " "	.... 6.05.

Style 4R. Silver 4oz., Htg. Case only	....$6.87.
" 3R. " 3 " " "	.... 5.50.

Style 8V. Silveroid o. f. 18 size, plain case only	..$0.85
" 2V. " 18 " Eng. Stag "	.. 1.35
" 1V. " Htg. 18 " plain "	.. 1.50

We can furnish open-face silverine cases, style of No. H 2, page 135, for 25c. more than price of plain case.

Prices of Elgin, Waltham and Hampden Watches Complete.	Style 1W or 3 V	Style 1X	Style W or 2 V	Style 1V	Style 2X or 2W	Style 3W	Style 3R	Style 4W	Style 3S	Style 4R	Style 4S	Style 3X	Style 4X
18994 7 Jewel, gilt, Elgin, Waltham or Hampden	$ 5.22	$ 5.50	$ 5.75	$ 5.90	$ 9.07	$ 9.90	$10.17	$10.45	$11.27	$11.82	$12.65	$13.75
18995 11 " " " " "	6.62	6.87	7.12	7.27	9.08	10.44	11.27	11.54	11.52	12.64	13.19	14.02	15.12
18996 15 " " G. M. Wheeler, Elgin or No. 15 Waltham gilt	9.10	9.35	9.60	9.75	11.55	12.92	13.75	14.02	14.30	15.12	15.67	16.50	17.60
18997 15 Jewel, nickel, G. M. Wheeler, Elgin, No. 15 nickel Waltham, or No. 64 Hampden	9.65	9.90	10.15	10.30	12.10	13.47	14.30	14.57	14.85	15.67	16.22	17.05	18.15
18998 15 Jewel, gilt, adj. 125 Elgin, P. S. Bartlett, Waltham or Nos. 49 Hampden	11.30	11.55	11.80	11.95	13.75	15.12	15.95	16.22	16.50	17.32	17.87	18.70	19.80
18999 15 Jewel, nickel, adj. 124 Elgin or P. S. Bartlett, Waltham	11.85	12.10	12.35	12.50	14.30	15.67	16.50	16.77	17.05	17.87	18.42	19.25	20.35
19000 17 Jewel, nickel, adj. No. 25 Waltham or 17 jewel Hampden, J. C. Dueber	14.05	14.30	14.55	14.70	16.50	17.87	18.70	18.97	19.25	20.07	20.62	21.45	22.55
19001 17 Jewel, gilt, B. W. Raymond, Elgin or Appleton, Tracy & Co., Waltham 17 Jewel	16.25	16.50	16.75	16.90	18.70	20.06	20.90	21.17	21.45	22.27	22.82	23.65	24.75
19002 17 Jewel, nickel, B. W. Raymond, Elgin or Appleton, Tracy & Co., Waltham	18.45	18.70	18.95	19.10	20.90	22.26	23.10	23.37	23.65	24.47	25.02	25.85	26.95
19003 17 Jewel, nickel, Crescent Street Waltham	22.85	23.10	23.35	23.50	25.30	26.66	27.50	27.77	28.05	28.87	29.42	30.25	31.35
19004 17 Jewel, nickel, New Railway Hampden	28.25	28.60	28.85	29.00	30.80	32.16	33.00	33.27	33.55	34.37	34.92	35.75	36.85
19005 17 Jewel, nickel, Vanguard, Waltham	33.85	34.10	34.35	34.60	36.30	37.66	38.50	38.77	39.05	39.87	40.42	41.25	42.35
19006 17 Jewel, nickel, Special Railway Hampden	39.35	39.60	39.85	40.00	41.80	43.16	44.00	44.27	44.55	45.37	45.92	46.75	47.85

SPECIAL BARGAINS IN WATCHES.

19007¼ This handsome oak case, with mirror back, silver trimmings and lock and key, given with Nos. 19007 and 19008 watch bargains. Price of case alone $1.00

19007 Our "Lady Grange" Bargain. An elegant 14k solid gold case, fitted with our 16 jewel nickel expansion bal. Breguet hairspring, stem wind and set, adjusted movement, the "Lady Grange." This movement is accompanied by our special guarantee certificate and is warranted when properly regulated to run within 50 seconds per month. The outfit includes a beautiful solid gold Victoria chain, and a handsome oak case, silver trimmed, with lock and key, as shown in illustration. Price only $27.00

19008 A New Special Bargain in Ladies' Watches. Dueber 14k filled case, guaranteed 20 years; elegant star and vermicelli engraving, exactly like illustration, fitted with a 13 jewel nickel U.S. Waltham movement, stem wind and set. A beautiful roll plate chain and elegant oak box, silver trimmed, with lock and key as shown in illustration. Price only.............$16.00

19010 Ladies' Open Face Crescent, 14k gold filled case, fitted with Waltham movement, stem wind and set. Price each...................$9.90
19011 Same as above, but engraved case. Price each 11.00

19009 Boys' Nickel Watch. This is a first-class article, guaranteed to keep good time. Movement is stem wind and set.
Price with nickel case $3.50
Price with solid silver case 4.50

19012 Ladies' Solid Silver, Engraved Open Face stem wind and set Chatelain Watch, nickel cylinder movement.
Price, each $7.00
19013 Same movement in plain nickel case. Price each 4.25

The postage on a watch is 8 cents. See page 1 for Mail Insurance.

We charge for engraving initials 2½c per letter for script, 5½c for Old English

19014 Mens' 16 Size 14k Solid Gold Case, fitted with 11 jewel Elgin, Waltham or Hampden movement, stem wind and set. Price each.....................$31.00
19014½ Same with full jewel movement. Price each..............................$33.50

19015 A new size in watches—12 size. Just the thing for gentlemen who want a small size watch, or ladies who prefer a size larger than regular. This 14k filled 20-year guarantee case, plain or engraved, with 11 jewel Elgin, Waltham or Hampden movement, stem wind and set. Price $16.75

19016 Men's 16 Size 14k Solid Gold Case, fitted with 11 jewel Elgin, Waltham or Hampden movement, stem wind and set. Price each...........................$30.50
19016½ Same with full jewel movement. Price each...............................$33.00

LADIES' 6 SIZE 14K SOLID GOLD STEM WIND WATCHES.
For Prices With Elgin, Waltham or Hampden Movements See Table Below.

Style B3. 2 Diamonds, 3 Rubies, any name, furnished in one week's time. Case only. $27.30

Style C3. Raised ornaments, 1 Diamond. Case only, $28.00.

Style D3. Fancy engraved, 1 Diamond. Case only, $25.00.

Style E3. Plain polished, 1 Diamond. Case only, $24.00.

Style F3. Heavy Raised Ornaments, Case only, $24.00.

Style G3. Fancy Engraved. Case only, $20.00.

Style H3. Fancy Engraved. Case only, $22.50.

Style J3. Fancy Engraved. Case only, $20.00.

Style K3. Fancy Engraved. Case only, $22.50.

Style L3. Fancy Engraved. Case only, $19.00.

Style M3. Fancy Engraved. Case only, $19.00.

Style N3. Fancy Engraved. Case only, $19.00.

Catalogue No.	Prices of Complete Watches.	Style B3	Style C3	Style D3	Styles E3 & F3	Styles H3 & K3	Styles J3 & G3	Styles L3 M3 N3
19027	A 7-Jewel Gilt Exp. Bal. Elgin, Waltham or Hampden Mov't...........	$32.25	$33.02	$29.95	$28.95	$27.45	$24.95	$23.95
19028	An 11 " " " " or " " "	33.63	34.40	32.10	31.10	29.60	27.10	26.10
19029	An 11 " " Nickel " " " " "	34.18	34.95	31.88	30.88	29.38	26.88	25.88
19030	An 11 " " " " " " Jewels in Settings	35.00	35.77	32.70	31.70	30.20	27.70	26.70
19031	A 13 " " " " " " " "	35.55	36.32	33.25	32.25	30.75	28.25	27.25
19032	A 15 " " " " " " " "	38.30	39.07	36.00	35.00	33.50	31.00	30.00
19033	A 16 " " " " " " " "	39.30	40.07	37.00	35.96	34.45	31.95	30.95
19034	A 17 " " " " " " " "	49.30	50.07	47.00	46.00	44.50	42.00	41.00
19035	A 15 " " " " Montgomery Ward & Co.'s Mov't with Special Guarantee Certificate	35.30	36.00	33.00	32.00	30.50	28.00	27.00
19036	A 16-Jewel Nickel Chronometer Bal., Montgomery Ward & Co.'s Mov't, with Special Guarantee Certificate................	42.30	43.00	40.00	39.00	37.50	34.95	33.95

Montgomery Ward & Co. Movements are made to run. They are the best value we can offer.   We send a written guarantee with each movement, and every purchaser is insured satisfaction.

LADIES' 6 SIZE SOLID 14K GOLD STEM WIND WATCHES.

For Prices with Elgin, Waltham or Hampden Movements, See Table Below.

Style O3. Fancy Engraved.
Case only, $18.50.

Style P3. Fancy Engraved.
Case only, $18.50.

Style T3. Raised Ornaments.
Case only, $16.00.

Style U3. Fancy Engraved.
Case only, $18.50.

Style A4. Fancy Engraved.
Case only, $15.00.

Style B4. Fancy Engraved.
Case only, $14.50.

Style C4. Fancy Engraved.
Case only, $14.50.

Style D4. Fancy Engraved.
Case only, $14.50.

Style E4. Fancy Engraved.
Case only, $13.00.

Style F4. Fancy Engraved.
Case only, $13.00.

Style G4. Fancy Engraved.
Case only, $12.50.

Style H4. Fancy Engraved.
Case only, $12.00.

Complete Prices of Watches.

Catalogue Number.		Style. H 4	Style. G 4	Styles. E 4 F 4	Styles. D 4 C 4 B 4	Style. A 4	Style. T 3	Styles. U 3 P 3 O 3
19037	A 7-Jewel, Gilt, Expansion Balance, Elgin, Waltham or Hampden Movement	$16.95	$17.45	$17.95	$19.45	$19.95	$20.95	$23.45
19038	An 11-Jewel, Gilt, Expansion Balance, Elgin or Waltham Movement	18.32	18.82	19.32	20.82	21.32	22.32	24.82
19039	An 11-Jewel, Nickel, Expansion Balance, Elgin or Waltham Movement	18.87	19.37	19.87	21.37	21.87	22.87	25.37
19040	An 11-Jewel, Nickel in Settings, Expansion Balance, Waltham or Hampden Movement	19.70	20.20	20.70	22.20	22.70	23.70	26.20
19041	A 13-Jewel, Nickel in Settings, Expansion Balance, Elgin Movement	20.25	20.75	21.25	22.75	23.25	24.25	26.75
19042	A 15-Jewel, Nickel in Settings, Expansion Balance, Elgin, Waltham or Hampden Movement	23.00	23.50	24.00	25.50	26.00	27.00	29.50
19043	A 16-Jewel, Nickel in Settings, Expansion Balance, Hampden Movement	24.10	24.60	25.10	26.60	27.10	28.10	30.80
19044	A 17-Jewel, Nickel in Settings, Expansion Balance, Elgin, Waltham or Hampden Movement	34.00	34.50	35.00	36.50	37.00	38.00	40.50
19045	A 15-Jewel, Nickel in Settings, Expansion Balance, Montgomery Ward & Co. Movement with Special Guarantee Certificate	20.00	20.45	20.90	22.45	22.95	23.95	26.45
19046	A 16-Jewel, Nickel Chronometer Balance, Montgomery Ward & Co. Movement, with Special Guarantee Certificate	27.05	27.55	28.05	29.55	30.05	31.05	33.55

Our Special Holiday Jewelry Catalogue sent free upon request.

Watchmakers' Tools, Materials and Supplies.

Having had many calls for watchmakers' tools we have decided to add a selection of these goods to our already large and varied assortment. Lack of space will allow us to illustrate but a few of the most useful and desirable, and even these illustrations we have had to reduce to the smallest possible space. However, we will furnish goods of standard make and size and of the very best quality. Price we guarantee as low as any and in some instances below the market. If articles desired are not illustrated or quoted, allow market price and give accurate description of same and we will furnish. When ordering material, always send samples if possible, if not, fully describe size and make of watch or clock for which parts are intended. When placing orders for small articles in this line, where price indicates, you will save both time and trouble by making a remittance of sufficient funds to cover all possible charges. We always refund any balance these may be in your favor.

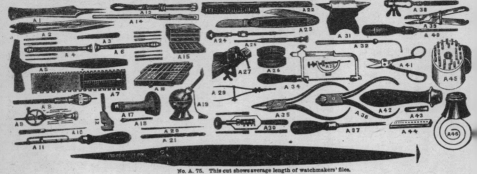

No. A. 75. This cut shows average length of watchmakers' files.

Our New Lathe for Watchmakers Use.

18 EXTRA CHUCKS

MAINSPRING PUNCH

Jeweling Tool.

Our New Improved Lathe.

With Index Pointer and Latch.

This Lathe is by far the best made for the price in the market. They are made with hardened spindles and bearings; the bed is made of steel, giving it a fine, high polish, and free from all imperfections. We warrant them to be perfect in every part; nickel-plated; the cone is made of steel with three steps, with INDEX POINTER and latch at cone as shown in cut, with rubber knob on the end; the tailstock is provided with hard taper center, hardened and ground; the bed can be raised to suit the operator and can be removed with ease.

Length of bed, 10 inches. Bed to center. 1¼ inches.

Lath complete with 18 extra chucks. Price $22.00
Counter Shaft extra............ 3.00
Foot Wheel   " 3.60
No. A 160 Improved Mainspring Punch.... 1.25
No A 175 Complete Jeweling Tool (see cut) 1.50
Silver Plating Liquid, a good thing. See quotations A 146, this page.

Watch and Clock material cannot be exchanged. Always send sample of part wanted. Outer end of mainspring, with one inch of spring, will always bring the right kind.
Silver and Gold Solution for Plating without a Battery. See No. A 146 and 147.

No. 73. F	O. No. A. 75.	R. No. A 71.	M. No. A 7.	S. Cuts F, O, R, M, and S. show width and shape, length as above.	No. A 95.—Each 20c.

No.			No.	
A 50	Alcohol Cups.................each	$0.35	A 71	Files, small, round and square........each $0.12
A 31	Anvil (jeweler's)...............each	.75	A 73	Files, flat, regular..................each .35
A 53	Blow Pipes, common brass..........each	.25	A 76	Files, rounding and entering..........each .35
A 52	Blow Pipes, nickel plated with ball...each	.50	A 77	Files, screw bend...................each .35
A 23	Bench Knife (jeweler's), with case		A 7	Gauge Mainspring...................each 1.00
	opener......................each	.50	A 79	Gauge, Degree, nickel-plated, with rule, each 1.00
A 55	Buffs, Chamois, or Felt, round or flat, each	.30	A 5	Hammers, according to size........each .40 to .75
A 22	Brushes, best bristle, watch or clock, each	.50	A 81	Hammers' Handles, ebony...........each .65
A 59	Burnishers, jewel and other...... .25 to	.75	A 83	Hands, Watch, per pair, 10c. per doz. pair .50
A 10	Broaches, Stub's best quality, assorted		A 85	Hands, 2d. each, per pair, 10c: per doz. pair .50
	sizes from No. 75 to 40....per dozen	1.00	A 85	Hands, Clock, per pair, 5c ; per doz. pair .42
A 3	Broach Handle.....................each	.10	A 17	Handles, adjustable, for graver or small
A 16	Broaches, Swiss joint............per dozen	.25		files........................each .15
A 16	Cabinet, for small material........each	1.50	A 42	Handles, adjustable, for medium files each .25
A 15	Cabinet, for large material........each	4.50	A 87	Jeweling Tools, Swiss, in box........each 1.50
A 20	Calipers, Pinion, plain............each	.25	A 89	Jeweler's Cement, per bottle........each .25
A 61	Calipers, regular brass............each	.30	A 91	Jewel Pin Setter...................each .88
A 63	Calipers, nickel plated, with bar and		A 43	Jewel Bottle.......................each .03
	screw,.....................each	.65	A 93	Keys, Watch, common...........per dozen .25
A 40	Clock Screwdriver.................each	.28	A 95	Keys, Watch, wind any watch (see cut) each .20
A 37	Clock wire bender.................each	.20	A 97	Keys, Watch, for bench use..........each .50
A 65	Counter Sinks, per set of three...........each	1.00	A 99	Keys, Clock, iron or brass..........each .10
A 67	Counter Sinks, per set of six...........each	2.00	A 19	Lamps, Alcohol, patented, large......each 1.75
A 6	Counter Sinks, adjustable handle, per		A101	Lamps, Alcohol, faceted glass........each .88
	set.........................each	.75	A103	Mainsprings, Watch, each 25c....per doz 1.75
A 26	Cups, Oil, for watch or clock......each	.20	A105	Mainsprings, Clock, 1 day..........each .15
A 18	Drills, common...............per dozen	.36	A107	Mainsprings, Clock, 8 day..........each .45
A 21	Drills, Morse, Twist, assorted.....per dozen	1.25	A100	Oil, Watch or Clock, per bottle......each .20
A 53	Drills, Stock, common.............each	.50	A111	Oiler, Watch.......................each .15
A 69	Drill Bow, to use with above......each	.65	A113	Oil Stone, best Arkansas, in box....each 1.00
A 24	Drill Stock, patent spiral..........each	.65	A 13	Pin Slide, common medium...........each .35
A 67	Counter Sinks, patent guard........each	2.00	A 38	Pin Vise, hollow handle............each .75
A 6	Drill Stock, adjustable............each		A 27	Pin Vise, nickel plated, patented....each 1.25
A 46	Eyeglasses, Watchmakers' common....each	.30	A146	Plating Solution, silver, per bottle....each 1.00
A 46	Eyeglasses, Watchmakers' with coil		A147	Plating Solution, gold, per bottle....each 2.50
	spring.......................each	.50		

No.		
A 12	Punch, mainspring, English........each	$0 75
A117	Punch, mainspring, Swiss (3 punches)	
	each........................	1.25
A 45	Punches, set of 24, with hollow stake,	
	in hardwood box, per set......	1.25
A 35	Pliers, round, square or snipe bill....each	1.25
A 36	Pliers, Stub's best side cutting........each	1.00
A 37	Pliers, cutting, regular Swiss........each	.65
A 33	Shears and Wire Cutters...........each	.25
A 40	Screw Holder and Driver combined....each	.75
A 25	Screw Driver, Watch...............each	.25
A 4	Screw Driver, Watch, adjustable, 4	
	sizes, per set................	.60
A 1	Second Hand Holder, nickel plated ...each	.40
A 44	Stake, Riveting, hard steel.........each	.25
A 34	Saw Frame, Swiss, extra quality,	
	nickel plated.................	1.10
A121	Saws for above................per doz	.15
A123	Saw Frames, Stubs'...............each	1.75
A125	Saw Blades, Stubs'................each	.25
A127	Soldering, copper.................each	.25
A129	Soldering fluid, per bottle.........each	.25
A131	Solder, Silver................per package	.50
	Solder, gold.................per package	.50
A 30	Screw Stock and Dies, Per set........	3.00
A105	Tweezers, fine medium or heavy....each	.35
A 2	Tweezers and hand raiser...........each	.45
A 39	Tongs, 2 hole, hand...............each	.40
A133	Vise, jewelers', 1½ in. jaw........each	1.75
A133	Vice, amateur....................each	.40
A135	Watch Glasses..............each, fitted	.10
A130	Watch Glasses, per ¼ dozen of one No....	.20
A141	Watch Glasses, assorted, per gross.....each	.20
A143	Watch Glasses, thick flat..........each	.20
A155	Watch Glasses, thick flat, per dozen....	.40

DIAMOND DEPARTMENT.

We illustrate on this and the following page the newest and most desirable styles of Diamond Jewelry. Our Diamonds are guaranteed to be perfect, pure white stones. Prices are the lowest, consistent with good quality, and we willingly refund money on any article which fails to come up to expectation, if it is returned at once.

APPROXIMATE SIZES OF STONES.

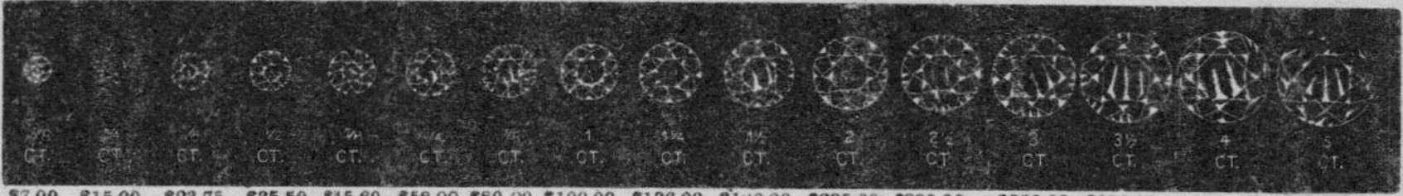

$7.00 $15.00 $23.75 $35.50 $45.60 $58.00 $80.00 $100.00 $136.00 $190.00 $235.00 $290.00 $350.00 $390.00 $450.00 $675.00

19150 Roman Coil Brooch, ⅜k Diamond center. $13.50.

19151 ⅜k. Diamond, $27.00.

19152 2 ¼k. Diamonds, $37.50.

19153 Elegant Pearl and Diamond Brooch or Necklace Pendant; can be worn either way. $48.00.

19154 ¼k. Diamond. Price, $18.75.

19155 3/16k. Diamond. Price, $13.75

19156 Roman Leaf Brooch, Diamond center. Price, $11.50

19157 ⅛k. Diamond. Price, $11.75

19158 ⅛k, Diamond. Price, $10.50

19159 Brooch or Pendant, Pearls and Diamond in center Price $31.50

19160 ⅜k. Price per pair $12.00

19161 Diamond center. Price, $9.00

19162 Diamond center. Price, $10.25

19163 ¼k. Price per pair, $10.50

19164 ¼k. Price per pair, $17.50

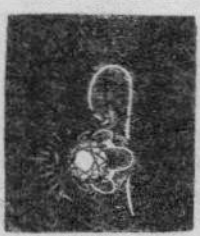

19165 ½k. Price per pair, $35.00

19166 ¾k. Price per pair, $44.00

19167 1k. Diamond. Price per pair, $69.00

19169 Locket, 2 pictures, Diamond. Price, $10.75.

19170 Raised gold head and whip, 3 Diamonds. Price, $14.74

19171 Plain satin finish, 1 Diamond. Price, $9.25

19172 1 picture locket, 8 Diamonds. Price, $15.00

19173 Raised Horse shoe and Horse head, set with 4 real diamonds, 2 pictures. Price $10.50

19174 ⅝k. Diamond. Price, $40.00

19175 ⅛k Diamond. Price, $16.00

19176 ⅛k. Diamond. Price, $16.50

19177 1/16k. Diamond. Price, $6.75

19178 3/16k Diamond complete. $12.50

19179 Colored enamel pansy, Diamond center, scarf pin, $5.50

19180 Coil Scarf pin, Diamond center. Price $5.00.

19181 Rope twist scarf pin, Diamond center. Price, $5.75

19182 Diamond link cuff buttons. Price per pair $12.50.

19183 Diamond cuff buttons. Price per pair $9.00

19184 ⅛k. Diamond. Price, $9.25

19185 3/16k. Diamond Price, $12.00

MEN'S ROLL PLATE VEST CHAINS. FULL REGULAR LENGTH.

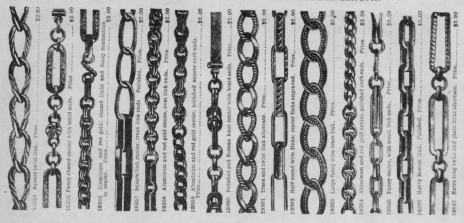

18354 Square twist link. Price............ $2.00
18355 Fancy chased center with braid ends. Price..... $2.00
18356 Aluminum and red gold; chased links and fancy connection in center. Price........ $2.00
18357 Square link center, trace link ends. Polished. Price.... $2.00
18358 Aluminum and red gold center, oval link ends. Price.... $2.00
18359 Aluminum and red gold center, polished square curb ends. Price.... $2.00
18360 Polished and Roman knot center with braid ends. Price.... $2.00
18361 Trace and twist link alternate. Price.... $2.00
18362 Half round wire links; center links engraved. Price.... $2.00
18363 Large fancy wire link. Price.... $3.00
18364 Aluminum and red gold center, polished curb ends. Price.... $2.00
18365 Fancy center, with small link ends. Price.... $2.00
16599 Heavy Boston link. Polished. Price.... $3.00
18607 Extra long twist and plain link alternate. Price.... $2.00

Men's Roll Plate Vest Chains. Warranted to Outwear any Chain of the same price.

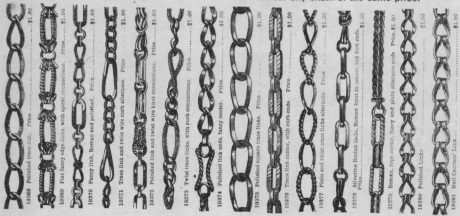

19388 Polished trace link. Price.... $1.00
19369 Flat fancy edge links, with spiral connections. Price.... $1.00
19370 Fancy link, Roman and polished. Price.... $1.00
19371 Trace link and twist wire curb alternate. Price.... $1.00
19372 Polished link and twist wire knot connections. Price.... $1.00
19373 Twist trace links, with curb connection. Price.... $1.00
19374 Polished link ends, fancy center. Price.... $1.00
19375 Polished square trace links. Price.... $1.00
19376 Trace link center, with curb ends. Price.... $1.00
19377 Plain and twist trace links alternate. Price.... $1.00
19378 Silvertine Boston links, Roman knot in center, red link ends. Price.... $1.00
19379 Roman, rope center, fancy and plain alternate ends Price. $1.00
19380 Polished Links.... $1.00
18381 Malt Carriers' Link.... $1.00

Aluminum Vest Chains.
Light as wood. Strong as steel. Never tarnish.

19382 Aluminum.. $1.25

19383 Aluminum.. $1.25

19384 Aluminum.. $1.25

Pony, or Boys' Size Roll Plate Chains.
8¼ inches long with drop piece for charm.

19385 Polished Links.................................... $1.00

19386 Twist Links....................................... $1.00

19387 Rope Pattern, gold and platinum finish......... $1.00

18388 Open Curb, gold and platinum finish............ $1.00

All chains on this page are full length, 12 inches, except the Boys' chains.

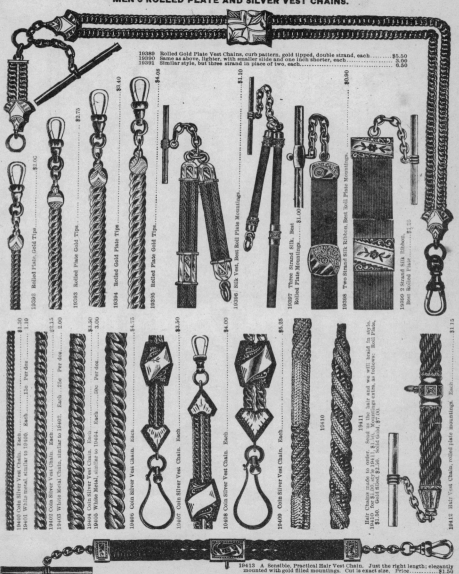

19389 Rolled Gold Plate Vest Chains, curb pattern, gold tipped, double strand, each...........$5.50
19390 Same as above, lighter, with smaller slide and one inch shorter, each....................3.00
19391 Similar style, but three strand in place of two, each....................6.50

$3.40

$4.08

$2.75

$1.10

$0.90

$3.00

19392 Rolled Plate, Gold Tips.................$2.00

19393 Rolled Plate Gold Tips

19394 Rolled Gold Plate Tips

19395 Rolled Plate Gold Tips

19396 Silk Vest, Best Roll Plate Mountings.

19397 Three Strand Silk, Best Roll Plate Mountings................$1.00

19398 Two Strand Silk Ribbon, Best Roll Plate Mountings.

19399 2 Strand Silk Ribbon, Best Rolled Plate................$1.25

$1.30
$2.15
$3.50
$4.75
$3.50
$4.00
$5.25
$1.15

1.10 Per doz.
2.00 Per doz.
3.00 Per doz.

19400 Coin Silver Vest Chain. Each............$1.30
19401 White metal, similar to 19400. Each........15c Per doz.

19402 Coin Silver Vest Chain. Each...............$2.15
19403 White Metal Chain, similar to 19402. Each....25c Per doz.

19404 Coin Silver Vest Chain. Each...............$3.50
19405 White Metal, similar to 19404. Each........80c Per doz.

19406 Coin Silver Vest Chain. Each

19407 Coin Silver Vest Chain. Each

19408 Coin Silver Vest Chain. Each

19409 Coin Silver Vest Chain. Each

19410

19411

Hair Chains made to order. Send us the hair and we will braid in style, 19410 for $1.00, style 19411, $1.50. Mountings extra, as follows: Roll Plate, $1.50. Gold filled, $2.50. Solid Gold, $7.00.

19412 Hair Vest Chain, rolled plate mountings. Each.

19413 A Sensible, Practical Hair Vest Chain. Just the right length; elegantly mounted with gold filled mountings. Cut is exact size. Price............$1.50

All chains on this page, except No. 19413, are full regular length.

BEST ROLLED PLATE NECKLACES AND BRACELETS.

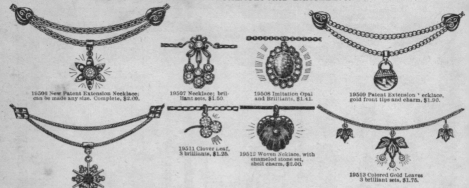

19506 New Patent Extension Necklace; can be made any size. Complete, $2.00.

19507 Necklace; brilliant sets, $1.50.

19508 Imitation Opal and Brilliants, $1.41.

19509 Patent Extension Necklace, gold front tips and charm, $1.90.

19511 Clover Leaf, 3 brilliants, $1.25.

19512 Woven Necklace, with enameled stone set, shell charm, $2.00.

19513 Colored Gold Leaves 3 brilliant sets, $1.75.

19510 Patent Extension Necklace, ruby set.......$3.25

19514 A beautiful, showy article with 5 large imitation Rubies and Olivines, $2.30.

19515 Gold Front Cross, complete, $1.35.

19516 Plain Link Chain, with 3 plain polished heart charms, $1.38.

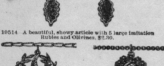

19517 Colored Gold and enameled pendant, complete, $2.25.

19518 Fine Cameo, encircled, with brilliants, complete, $1.50.

19519 Barrel Link Chain with heart pendant, $1.15.

19520 Geneva Link Chain with enameled and stone set pendant.
Price complete......$2.25
Pendant only.......1.05

19521 Colored Gold Wreath with turquoise sets, complete, $1.95.

19523 Necklace, with 17 fine brilliants.... $2.00

19522 Woven Chain, with 8 fine brilliants $2.10

19526 Gold Filled Bracelet, lock and key, $3.00
19527 Similar to above, solid silver........3.25
19528 Similar to above, solid gold...........15.00

19524 Bracelet, adjustable as to size.   Price........$0.50

19529 Gold Filled Bracelet, lock and key.......Each.
19530 Similar to above, solid silver........$2.75
19531 Similar to above, solid gold.......2.90
........13.50

19525 Rolled Plate, Garnet and Brilliant Bracelet,
Each...$1.30

19532 Gold Filled Bracelet, with lock and key. Each. $3.10
19533 Similar to above, but solid silver....3.35
19534 Similar to above, but solid gold.......16.00

MONTGOMERY WARD & CO.'S CATALOGUE No. 56.   159

LADIES' AND MEN'S SET RINGS, BEST QUALITY SOLID GOLD.

We illustrate below the largest and finest line of set rings we have ever shown. All the mountings are best quality solid gold. Among the ladies' rings are several with olivene settings. This is very popular stone of a pale green color and affords a beautiful contrast when set with pearls and other stones. Nos. 19540 to 19547 are gents rings, sizes 6 to 12. Nos. 19548 to 19587 are ladies' rings. Sizes 3½ to 8½, extra large sizes, cost extra.

19540 Emblem Ring, Masonic, Odd Fellows, K. of P., etc.: 6 Diamonds, $7.90. Same with 12 Diamonds. $14.00

19541 Any Initial, 12 Diamonds, $13.50

19542 Any Initial, 6 Diamonds, $7.80

19543 Any Initial, Gold Letter, no Diamonds, $5.00

19544 Men's Tiger Eye Set Ring. Price, $4.25

19545 Men's Glove Ring, Sardonyx set. Price, $5.35

19546 Men's Tiger Eye Set, Carved Shank, $5.75

19547 Men's Real Carbuncle, Plain Durable Shank, $6.00

19548 Marquise Style, Emeralds and Pearls. Price, $4.50

19549 Marquise Style, Ruby and Pearls. Price, $3.50

19550 Marquise Style, Olivene and Pearls. Price, $4.00

19551 6 Garnets and 3 Moonstones. Price, $4.55

19552 5 Diamond Stars and 7 Emeralds. Price, $9.00

19553 Rubies, Emeralds and Pearls. Price, $4.30

19554 Rubies, Emeralds and Pearls. Price, $5.25

19555 Rubies, Emeralds and Pearls. Price, $5.50

19556 Olivene Center and 6 Pink Topaz. Price, $3.75

19557 Ruby Center and 6 Pearls. Price, $4.75

19558 4 Rubies, 4 Pearls. Price, $5.00

19559 Amethyst and Pearls. Price, $6.00

19560 Olivenes, Topaz and Pearls. Price, $4.35

19561 Moonstone Center and 6 Pink Topaz. Price, $3.70

19562 Pearl Center and 6 Pink Topaz. Price, $3.65

19563 2 Rubies and 2 Pearls. Price, $2.25

19564 2 Rubies and 2 Moonstones. Price, $3.25

19565 1 Opal and 2 Rubies. Price, $3.85

19566 4 Sapphires and 4 Pearls. Price, $4.10

19567 Emerald and Pearls. Price, $2.50

19568 2 Heart-Shape Rubies, 3 Pearls. Price, $3.00

19569 Emerald, Rubies and Pearls. Price, $3.90

19570 Emerald or Garnet. Price, $1.50

19571 Flat Band, Assorted Sets. Price, $2.00

19572 Garnet and Pearls. Price, $2.17

19573 Olivene Center 4 Pink Topaz. Price, $3.95

19560A Moonstone and 6 Olivenes. Price, $3.25

19561A Pearls, Emeralds and Rubies. Price, $5.00

19562A Turquoise and Pearls. Price, $2.60

19563A Diamond cut Olivene. Price, $3.00

19564A Fine Solitaire Pearl. Price, $7.75

19565A Epworth League, Enameled Top. Price, $1.50

19566A Christian Endeavor, Enameled Top. Price, $2.50

19574 Opal, Ruby and Emerald. Price, $3.75

19575 Opal and 2 Rubies. Price, $3.60

19576 3 Fine Opals. Price, $3.50

19577 3 Large Opals. Price, $7.00

19578 Solitaire Opal. Price, $6.50

19579 1 Fine Opal. Price, $7.00

19580 Solitaire Opal. Price, $4.00

19581 Diamond Cut Amethyst. Price, $3.40

19582 Moonstone. Price, $4.40

19583 Moonstone. Price, $2.10

19584 5 Pearls. Price, $8.25

19585 Single Pearl. Price, $7.25

19586 Single Small Pearl. Price, $4.10

19587 Single Small Pearl. Price, $3.80

Misses' Rings Size 4 to 7 only.

19588 2 Emeralds, 2 Pearls. Price, $2.00

19589 Turquoise and Pearls. Price, $2.90

19590 2 Rubies and 1 Pearl. Price, $1.85

19591 Amethyst or Garnet. Price, $1.90

19592 Single Ruby. Price, $1.50

19593 Ruby and Pearls. Price, $1.25

19594 Emerald and Pearls. Price, $1.75

BEST QUALITY SOLID GOLD BAND RINGS.

The price of these rings is governed entirely by the weight; the higher the price the heavier the ring. Some of the cuts make one ring look heavier than others at the same price, but the actual weight is in proportion to the price.

19600 Sizes, 6¼ to 11. Price.....$3.60

19601 Sizes 6¼ to 10½. Price...$2.50

19602 Sizes, 6¼ to 11. Price.......$3.50

19603 Sizes, 6¼ to 11. Price................$2.43

19605 Sizes, 6¼ to 11. Price.......$2.60

19606 Sizes, 6¼ to 11. Price.$3.00

19607 Sizes, 6¼ to 11. Price...........$3.20

19608 Sizes, 6¼ to 11. Price......$2.75

19609 Sizes, 6¼ to 11. Price...$2.60

19610 Sizes, 6¼ to 10¼. Price..$2.10

19611 Sizes, 6¼ to 11. Price...$2.80

19612 Sizes, 6 to 10. Price...$1.88

19613 Sizes, 6¼ to 11 Price. ...$2.00

19614 Sizes, 6¼ to 11. Price......$2.85

19615 Sizes, 6 to 10½. Price....$1.90

19616 Sizes, 6¼ to 11. Price.. $2.45

19617 Sizes, 6¼ to 11. Price.$1.95

19618 Sizes, 6¼ to 11. Price. $2.05

19619 Sizes, 6¼ to 11. Price.. $2.30

19620 Sizes, 6¼ to 11. Price.. $1.90

19621 Sizes, 6¼ to 11. Price.. $1.84

19622 Sizes, 6¼ to 11. Price....$2.20

19623 Sizes, 6¼ to 11. Price....$2.15

19624 Sizes, 6 to 10¼. Price..$1.65

19625 Sizes, 6¼ to 11. Price...$1.97

19626 Sizes, 6¼ to 11. Price ...$1.84

19627 Sizes, 6 to 10. Price....$1.40

19628 Sizes, 6 to 10. Price....$1.35

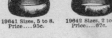

19629 Sizes, 6 to 10¼. Price....$1.78

19630 Sizes, 6¼ to 11. Price ...$2.15

19631 Sizes, 6 to 10. Price....$1.30

19632 Sizes, 6 to 10. Price....$1.72

19633 Sizes, 6¼ to 11. Price....1.94

19634 Sizes, 5¼ to 9. Price....$1.05

19635 Sizes, 3 to 6½. Price..65c.

19636 Sizes, 3 to 8. Price....85c.

19637 Sizes, 6 to 10. Price....$1.25

19638 Sizes, 5 to 8. Price ... 88c.

19639 Sizes, 6¼ to 11. Price....$2.25

19640 Sizes, 6 to 10. Price....$1.50

19641 Sizes, 5 to 8. Price....95c.

19642 Sizes, 2 to 5. Price....67c.

19643 Sizes, 3 to 6½. Price..68c.

19644 Sizes, 0 to 4. Price......54c

19645 Sizes, 1 to 5. Price.....58c.

19646 Sizes, 1 to 5. Price.....55c.

19647 Sizes, 0 to 4. Price.....60c.

19648 Sizes, 0 to 5. Price....65c.

19649 Sizes, 0 to 3. Price...50c.

Children's Set Rings, Sizes 0 to 5.

19650 Garnets and Pearls. Price.90c.

19651 Garnets and Pearl. Price $1.05

19652 Garnets and Pearl. Price.95c.

19653 Turquois and Pearl. Price.$1.10

19654 Garnet Set. Price..$1.00

19655 Garnets and Pearls. Price.$1.25

19656 Garnet, Pearl & Turquois. Price$1.05

19657 Turquois and Pearls. Price.$1.30

A Plain Solid 18k Gold Ring is the Proper Thing for a Wedding Ring.

Multiply the No. of pwt. by the cost per pwt. which will give the cost of ring complete.

Flat — Flat. — Flat. — Oval. — Oval. — Oval. — Oval.

7 pwt. — 5 pwt. — 3 pwt. — 7 pwt. — 5 pwt. — 3 pwt. — 1¼ pwt.

19658 Flat 18k Solid Gold Bands, per pennyweight $1.00
19659 Flat 16k Solid Gold Bands, per pennyweight .... .90
19660 Flat 14k Solid Gold Bands, per pennyweight .... .80
19661 Flat 10k Solid Gold Bands, per pennyweight .... .60
19662 Plain Oval 18k Rings, per pennyweight $1.00
19663 Plain Oval 16k Rings, per pennyweight .... .90
19664 Plain Oval 14k Rings, per pennyweight .... .80
19665 Plain Oval 10k Rings, per pennyweight .... .60

NOTE.—Plain Rings as above are not furnished lighter than 3 pwt., except at advance upon pennyweight price of 30c per pwt.

Plain 18k Gold Filled Rings,- See Illustrations above.

Similar in appearance to Nos. 19658 and 19662; wear for years like solid gold.

19666 Plain 14k Gold Filled, Oval, size of 7 pennyweight, each $2.00
19667 Plain 14k Gold Filled, Oval, size of 5 pennyweight, each 1.55
19668 Plain 14k Gold Filled, Oval, size of 3 pennyweight, each 1.25
19669 Plain 14k Gold Filled, Oval, size of 2 pennyweight, each .... .75
19670 Extra Quality Flat Gold Filled, size of 7 pennyweight 3.00
19671 Extra Quality Flat Gold Filled, size of 5 pennyweight 2.25
19672 Extra Quality Flat Gold Filled, size of 3 pennyweight $1.85
19673 Extra Quality Plain Oval Gold Filled, size of 7 pennyweight 2.62
19674 Extra Quality Plain Oval Gold Filled, size of 5 pennyweight 2.00
19675 Extra Quality Plain Oval Gold Filled, size of 3 pennyweight 1.62
19676 Extra Quality Plain Oval Gold Filled. Child's size of 1¼ pennyweight .... .75

In ordering Rings be sure to send Finger Size. See Ring Gauge on Page 148.

BEST QUALITY ROLLED GOLD PLATE RINGS.--Always send size.

19680
Mason's Emblem.
$0.75

19681
Fine Intaglio cut stone. $1.00

19682
Gents' Black Cameo
$0.70

19683
Gold Stone Set.
$0.75

19684
Tiger eye Stone. Fancy Setting. $0.48

19686
Carbuncle Garnet.
$0.80

19687
5 Carat. $0.75

19688   5½ Carat. $0.80

19689
Three Brilliants, Chased Setting. $0.60

19690
Three White Stone Brilliants, $0.75

19691
Fine Solitaire Brilliant.
$0.78

19692
Faceted Setting, one Brilliant. $0.75

19693
Fine Solitaire Brilliant.
$0.50

19694
Misses' Brilliant Set. $0.40

19695
Three Brilliants.
$0.42

19696
Emerald and Brilliants.
$1.00

19697
Ruby and Brilliants.
$0.65

19698
Ruby and Brilliants, $0.57

19699
Good Finish, plain wedding style, each 3c; per doz. 25c

19700
Misses' Friendship Ring. $0.25

COIN SILVER RINGS. Good Style and Finish. Always Send Size.

19701
Coin Silver. Double Hearts. $0.18

19702
Gold Hands.
$0.55

19703
Silver Shield Top.
$0.30

19704
Silver Shield Top.
$0.65

19705
Silver Gold Top.
$0.85

19706
Plain Silver.
$0.40

19707
Sterling Silver. Stone Set Eyes. $1.34

SOLID GOLD LOCKETS AND CHARMS.—Prices Each.

These goods are all of standard quality gold and are priced upon the cost of production. Price therefore can safely be taken as an indication of Real Value.

19708
Fine Roman Pendant, Diamond Set. $10.50
19709 Same without Diamond. $6.50

19710
Two Picture Locket, Raised Colored Gold Ornamentation.
$6.00

19711
Two Pictures, Raised Ornamentation.
$6.25

19712
Two Pictures, Raised Colored Ornamentation. Very Handsome.
$6.50

19713
Two Pictures, Raised Rococo Edge, Real Diamond. $7.75

19714
Two Pictures, Handsome Engraving, Real Diamond. $6.04

19715
Two Pictures, Rococo Edge, Real Diamond. $6.25

19716
Fine Polished Engraved Locket for Two Pictures, ⅟₁₆k Diamond in Center. $7.50

19717
Fine Polished Engraved Locket for Two Pictures, ⅟₁₆k Diamond in Center, $7.25

19718
Satin Finish Chased Locket for Two Pictures, ⅟₁₆k Diamond in Center. $7.00

19719
Raised Gold Flowers, K. of P. Emblem Two Pictures. $7.25. Can furnish Masonic or Odd Fellows at same Price

19720
Beautifully Engraved Locket for Two Pictures.
$4.25

19721
Fine Engraved Front Locket for Two Pictures.
$4.00

19722
Satin Finish Chased Locket for Two Pictures.
$4.50

All of these Lockets have plain back where initial or any emblem can be engraved for slight extra charge.

SOLID GOLD LOCKETS AND CHARMS.

Many of the lower priced lockets quoted below, although known as solid gold and sold as such by all jewelers, have the backs strengthened inside with silver solder. We guarantee all to wear as well as any locket made.

19724. Heart Locket. Diamond set. $10.50
19725. Same without Diamond. $7.00

19726. Extra quality. Diamond set. $7.50

19727. Gold Locket Engraved. 2 pictures. $3.50

19728. Bright Engraved Locket. 2 pictures. $2.95

19729. Satin Chased Locket. 2 pictures. $3.00

19730. Hand Engraved Charm, $3.00

19731. Odd Fellows' Locket. Enameled in colors. 2 pictures. $4.40. K. of P. or Masonic, same price.

19732. Raised Gold Birds and Flowers. 2 pictures. $3.55

19733. Roman Chased Locket. 2 pictures. $3.45

19734. Bright Engraved Locket. 2 pictures. $1.95

19735. Bright Engraved Locket. 2 pictures. $1.90

19736. Bright Engraved Locket. 2 pictures. $2.23

19737. Satin Finish Locket. Diamond set. $3.09
19738. Same without Diamond. $2.00

19739. Satin Finish Locket. Diamond set. $3.95
19740. Same without Diamond. $2.05

19741. Engraved Locket. 2 pictures. Diamond set. $4.80

19742. Gold Star Pendant. Pearl sets. $1.88

19743. Fancy Gold Pendant. Sapphire and Pearls. $2.45

19744. Gold Pendant. Pearl set. $1.75

19745. Roman Charm. Ruby, Pearl and Sapphire. $2.15

19746. Roman Heart Charm. Pearl sets. $2.26

19747. Roman Chased Charm. Pearl set. $1.75

19748. Roman Heart Charm. Pearl. $1.25

19749. Roman Heart Charm. Diamond set. $3.00

19750. Engraved Heart Locket. 2 pictures. $3.35

Best Rolled Plate Lockets and Charms.

19751. Aluminum. Heavily Gold Plated; light and durable. Garnet eyes. $1.25

19752. Aluminum. Heavy Gold Plated. Garnet eyes $1.15

19753. Aluminum. Heavy Gold Plated Garnet eyes. $1.30

19754. Gold Filled Locket. 2 pictures. $1.55

19755. Chased and Engraved Locket. 1 picture. 75c

19756. Filled Locket. 2 pictures. Brilliant set. $1.27

19757. Filled Locket. 2 pictures. $1.37

19758. Gold Filled Locket. 2 pictures. $1.67

19759. Chased Locket. 1 picture. $0.78

19760. Stone Set. 1 picture. $1.15

19761. Fine Intaglio. Seal Charm. $0.68

19762. Horse Shoe Charm. $1.54

19763. Fine Roman Locket. 6 Brilliants. 1 picture. $1.42

19764. Raised Wreath. 1 picture. $0.84

19765. Satin Finish. 1 picture. $0.73

19766. Filled Locket. 2 pictures. $1.00

19767. Engraved. 1 picture. $0.79

19768. A perfect practical Compass. Warranted. $1.20

19769. Crystal Charm. $0.92

MONTGOMERY WARD & CO.'S CATALOGUE No. 56.
BEST QUALITY ROLL PLATE LOCKETS AND CHARMS.

163

19770
Rolled Plate Pearl
Handle Revolver.
Each, 40c.

19771
Fancy Stone Set Locket.
Each, $1.20

19772
Fine Rolled Plate Charm.
Each, 59c.

19773
Rolled Plate Locket.
Each, 63c.

19774
Fancy 4 Color Stone.
Each, 95c.

19775
Fancy Stone Set 1
Picture Locket.
Each, 85c.

19776
Gold Side Fancy Stone
Set, 1 Picture Locket.
Each, $1.18

19777
Fancy Edge Stone
Set, 2 Pictures, 75c.

19778
Real Crystal Ball Charm.
Each, $1.03

19779
Compass Charm.
Each, $1.25

19780
Raised Gold Dogs, 1
Picture, $1.56

19781
Crystal Ball.
Each, 64c.

19782
Rolled Plate, gold sides.
Each, $1.30

19783
Fancy Stone Set
Locket. Each, 80c.

19784
Fancy Rolled Plate,
Stone Eyes. Each, 55c.

19785
Fancy Gold Plate,
2 Picture Locket.
Each, 65c.

19786
Rolled Plate Opera
Glasses, World's Fair
Views. Each, 65c.

19787
Fancy Center, Plain
Edge. Each, 50c.

19788
Black and Gold
Stone Charm.
Each, 97c.

19789
Fancy Gold Side 2
Picture Locket.
Each, 64c.

19790
Fancy 3 Color Stone.
Each, 95c.

19791
Raised Colored Gold, 1
Picture Locket, 90c.

19792
Rolled Plate Stone Set.
1 Picture. Each, 80c.

19793
Roman Stone Set.
1 picture. Each, 78c

19794
1 Picture Chased Stone
Set Locket. Each, 81c.

19795
Pearl Horn Charm.
Each, 68c.

19796
4 Colors. Barrel Charm
Each, 95c.

19797
Rolled Plate Locket.
2 pictures. Each, 60c.

19798
Extra Quality.
Each, $1.35

19799
Each, 67c.

19800
Stone Set Locket.
Each, 88c.

19801
Fine Roman Locket, 6
Brilliants, 1 Picture.
Each, $1.49

19802
Love Locket, 1 Picture,
Brilliant Set.
Each, 91c.

19803
Bunch Cigars, Gold
Stone. Each, 50c.

49804
Fancy Colored Gold,
1 Picture Locket.
Each, 60c.

19805
Plow, Two Colors. Each, $1.25

19806
Roman Color, Garnet Eyes.
Each, $1.00

19807
Book Locket, 2 Pictures.
Each, 98c.

19808
Roman Heart Locket,
1 Picture. Each, 63c.

19809
Roman Finish, Garnet
Eyes. Each, 50c.

19810
Stone Base.
Each, $1.25

SOLID GOLD AND ROLL PLATE ENAMELED CHARMS—Enameled in Appropriate Colors.

Nos. 20473, 20486, 20475 and 20476 are engraved. Nos. 20474 and 20485 raised colored gold. All others are enameled.

20470 Masonic.
Roll Plate $1.00
Solid Gold 3.25

20471 Masonic
Keystone. Solid
gold $4.50
Roll plate 1.25.

20472 Masonic
Keystone. Roll
plate top $0.85,
solid gold top.
$1.50.

20473 Masonic.
Roll plate 75c.
Solid gold $2.25

20474 Masonic
locket, 2 pictures,
solid gold only,
raised emblem $6.50,
K. P. or Odd Fellow
same price.

20475 Masonic.
Roll plate $1.15,
Solid gold 3.50

30476 Masonic.
Roll plate 75c.
Solid gold $3.00

20477 Knight
Templar. Solid
gold $18.00.
Roll plate 4.00.

20478 K. of P.
Roll Plate $1.25.
Solid Gold 7.00

20479 K. of P.
Roll Plate $1.75
Solid Gold $9.50

20480 K. of P.
Roll Plate $3.75
Solid Gold 16.00

20481 K. of P.
Roll Plate $0.75
Solid Gold 8.00

20482 K. of P.
Roll Plate $1.20
Solid Gold 3.50

20483 K. of P.
Roll Plate $0.90
Solid Gold 2.00

20484 Odd Fellows,
Roll Plate $1.75
Solid Gold 9.00

20485 Odd Fellows,
locket, 2 pictures,
raised emblem
Solid Gold only $7.75.

20486 Odd Fellows,
Solid Gold $3.50
Roll Plate 1.10

20487 Odd Fellows,
Solid Gold $3.00
Roll Plate 1.00

20488 Odd Fellows,
Roll Plate $0.95
Solid Gold 2.00

20489 A. O. U. W.
Roll Plate $0.90
Solid gold 3.75

20490 Masonic and
Odd Fellows,
Roll Plate $1.25
Solid Gold 4.00

20491 Royal Arcanum
Roll Plate $1.35
Solid Gold 5.00

20492 I. O. F.
Roll Plate $1.00
Solid Gold 4.25

20493 Woodmen
Roll Plate $1.05
Solid Gold 4.00

20494 G. A. R.
Roll Plate $2.75
Not made in gold.

20495 P. O. S. of A
Roll Plate $1.10
Seild Gold 5.00

20496 Jr.O.U.A.M.
Roll Plate $1.15
Solid Gold 5.70

20497 Sr. O.U.A.M
Roll Plate $1.25
Solid Gold 5.00

20498 Foresters
Roll Plate $1.00
Solid Gold 3.50

20499 Jr. A.M.
Mechanics'
Roll Plate 75c.

20500 Gold plate
and pearl, any
emblem. $1.00.

20501 Grand Army Charm,
rolled plate, enameled
in colors, $1.00.

20502 K. of P.
Roll Plate,
$1.50

20503 Epworth
League, Roll
Plate. 80c.

20504 Any Emblem,
Pearl and Roll
Plate, $1.50.

We are prepared to furnish estimates and designs for society badges, jewelry and medals of all kinds upon application.

SHELL HAIR PINS WITH SOLID GOLD, SILVER AND PLATED TOPS.

Prices, Each.

20510
Shell Pin. Sterling Silver Raised Ornaments. Cut full size. $0.90

20511
Shell Pin. Sterling Silver Raised Ornament. Cut one-half size. $1.75

20512
Fine Filigree Work Sterling Silver Top. Cut one-half size. $2.35

20513
Shell Prongs. Silver plated Top. Cut one-half size. $0.55

20514
Shell Pin. Sterling Silver Raised Ornament. Cut one-half size. $1.50

20516
Shell Prong. Gold Plated Head. Very showy. Cut one-half size. $1.60

20517
Shell Pin. Solid Gold Raised Ornament. Cut one-half size. $3.75

20518
Shell Pin. Solid Gold Raised Ornament. Cut one-half size. $4.00

20519
Shell Pin. Silver Plated Raised Ornament. Cut one-half size. $0.64

20520
Shell Pin. Sterling Silver Raised Ornament. Cut one-half size. $1.45

20521
Shell Pin. Sterling Silver Top. Cut one-half size. $2.50

20522
Shell Pin. Sterling Silver Raised Ornament. Cut full size. $0.75

20523
Shell Pin. Sterling Silver Raised Ornament. Cut one-half size. $1.25

20524
Shell Prong. Gold Plate Head. Very handsome. Cut one-half size. $1.50

20525
Shell Prong. Gold Plate Top. Cut one-half size. $0.80

20526
Shell Pin. Sterling Silver Raised Wreath. Cut one-half size. $1.35

20527
Silver Plated Raised Ornament. Cut one-half size. $0.80

20528
Shell Prongs. Silver Plated Top. Cut one-half size. $0.50

20529
Shell Prongs. Gold Plated Top. Cut one-half size. $0.48

20530
White metal, gilded and lacquered, warranted not to tarnish. Price, $0.75

20531
Roman color top with polished points of good rolled gold Length 5½ inches. $0.25

20532
Rolled gold point, with silver hilt handle and guard. $0.55

20533
Rolled plate. Set with brilliants. $0.48

MONTGOMERY WARD & CO.'S CATALOGUE No. 56.
HAT AND HAIR PINS. Price, Each.

20535
Rolled Gold Hat Pin, length 6 inches. Price, 50c.

20536
Sterling Silver Hat Pin. Price, 60c.

20537
Sterling Silver Hat Pin. Price, 30c.

20538
Sterling Silver Enameled Hat Pin. Price, 50c.

20539
Sterling Silver Hat Pin. Price, 80c.

20540
Best Gold Plate Hat Pin. Price, $1.00.

20541
Sterling Silver Hat Pin. Price, 40c.

20542
Tinted Moonstone Hat Pin. Price, 25c.

20543
Shell (imitation) Hair Pin. Length 3 inches. Each, 3c. Per doz., 25c. 20544. Similar, smaller and lighter. Price, 1c.

20545
Real Tortoise Shell. Length 4 inches. Price, 50c.

20546
Smooth plain top, good and strong. Length 5 inches. Each, 9c; doz. $1.00.

20547
Fancy sawed top, good shape and finish. Length 6 inches. Each, 10c; doz. 90c.

20548
Strong Heavy Twist Pin. Length 5 inches. Each, 25c.

20549
Fancy Top Shell Side Combs. Per pair, 50c. 20550. Imitation. Per pair, 20c.

20551
Plain Top Side Combs. Per pair, 18c. 20552. Imitation. Per pair, 10c.

20553
Real Tortoise Shell Pin. Price, 90c.

20554
Imitation Shell. Length 5 inches. Price, 25c.

20556
Fine Imitation Shell. Length 5½ inches. Price, 20c.

20557
Extra Fine Imitation Shell Pin. Length 5½ inches. Price, 35c.

20558
Fine Shell Imitation. Beautiful design. Length, 6 in. Price, 30c.

20559
Fine Shell Imitation; handsome goods. Length, 6 in. Price, 28c.

Why buy imitations when you can get the real article at so low a figure?

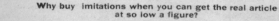

20560
Real Tortoise Shell. Regular length 6 inches. Price, $1.50.

20561
Very Fine Shell Substitute. Handsome as an $8.00 article. Length 6½ inches. Price, 48c.

20562
Real Tortoise Shell; plain, rich, elegant. Length 5½ inches. Price, $1.00.

20563
Choice Pattern. Imitation Shell Pin. Length 5 inches. Price, 20c.

20564
Real Shell Back Combs; Plain and Rich. Dimensions, 3x3½. Price, $1.60.

FOUNTAIN PENS.

Note—Fountain Pens are rapidly superceding all other styles and kinds for practical use. The best value will be found in **Montgomery Ward & Co.'s Special "The Best,"** manufactured especially for us. GIVE THEM A TRIAL. *They are fully guaranteed,* and we refund money if they fail to give satisfaction.

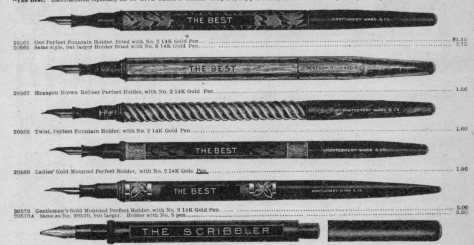

20565 Our Perfect Fountain Holder, fitted with No. 2 14K Gold Pen..$1.10
20566 Same style, but larger Holder fitted with No. 5 14K Gold Pen...2.75

20567 Hexagon Brown Rubber Perfect Holder, with No. 2 14K Gold Pen. Price..........................1.50

20568 Twist, Perfect Fountain Holder, with No. 2 14K Gold Pen..1.60

20569 Ladies' Gold Mounted Perfect Holder, with No. 2 14K Gold Pen.......................................1.90

20570 Gentlemen's Gold Mounted Perfect Holder, with No. 2 14K Gold Pen..............................2.00
20570A Same as No. 20570, but larger. Holder with No. 5 pen...3.50

20571 The Scribbler Fountain Pen. We offer to our patrons under this title a fountain pen which will equal in quality, beauty and durability any fountain pen ever manufactured at a low price. The cut gives a very faint idea of its appearance. The barrel is made of purest Para Rubber, with best Rubber Cap. Pen is perfect in shape, not flattened out, and is made of solid gold, guaranteed to assay not less than 14K. Price 65 cents. If not as represented above in every particular, your money will be promptly refunded. Cost of mailing is only 2 cents.

The P. S. Fountain Pen.

20572 The P. S. Fountain Pen, best hard rubber holder, fitted with Gillott's fine point, or Esterbrook stub pen. This article is reliable, in fact the only one that we know of made to hold steel Pens. Price each...................$0.35

Ward's Stylographic Pen.

20573 Ward's New improved Stylographic Pen, plain barrel. Price..........................$0.80
Wirt Fountain Pen. Regular size. Each............2.25

Independent Stylographic Pen.

20574 The celebrated Independent Stylographic Pen, made of best quality hard rubber. Platinum point and needle, alloyed with iridium, not affected by any kind of ink. Will not leak or blot and are always ready for use. Each...................................$0.75

Note—We make a specialty of repairing fountain pens and replacing missing parts. Send pen to us with 75 cents, and we will repair and refund balance of money with pen. This method saves time and correspondence.

GOLD AND SILVER MOUNTED PENS AND PENCILS.

ILLUSTRATIONS ARE TWO-THIRDS SIZE.

20575 New Patent Reversible Gold Pen and Screw Extension Pencil, length 5½ in., fitted with No. 4 gold pen. Each..................$3.00

20575.

20575½ Same as above, but made of Sterling silver, handsomely chased and oxidized, fitted with No. 4 gold pen. Each.......................3.32

20576 Twist Pearl Holder mounted with antique chased rolled gold plate and fitted with No. 2 pen. Each, with case..........................2.82
20576½ Similar to above, but pearl of different twist, fine Sterling Silver holder, chased and oxidized, No. 4 pen. Each, with case.......3.50

20576.

20577 Handsome Antique Chased Gold Plated Tablet Pencil, length 4½ inches. Each............................1.05
20578 Same sized pencil as above, twisted Sterling silver. Each....................1.25

20577.

20579 Sterling Silver Twisted and Hand Chased Tablet Extension Pencil, length 3¾ inches. Price each..............................95
20580 Same as above, gold plate. Price, each.....................78

20579.

20581 Magic Pencil, length extended 3¾ inches, gold plated, handsomely chased; barrel covered with old knotted ivory, length of barrel 1¼ inches. Price, each 1.65

20581.

20582 New and very elegant pattern. Sterling silver holder, twist, antique chased and oxidized, fitted with No. 4 gold pen, length 7 inches, with case. Each...................4.00
20583 Similar to above, but different style twist, and ornamentation, No. 4 pen, total length, 7 inches. In case, each.....................3.75

20582.

20584 Pure Aluminum (Non tarnishable). A very light and elegant article. Price without pen......................50

20586 Similar style, fine quality Rolled gold Holder, fitted with Best No. 3 gold Pen. Price..........................2.60

Plush Cases for Pens, 75c. Each.

GOLD PENS, HOLDERS, PENCILS, ETC.

In this line of goods we are able to give unusual good value at prices quoted, as we have large quantities of these goods made especially to our order; the pens are of 14k gold, and known as diamond pointed; the mountings are best 14k plate, and will wear a lifetime. Nos. 20587 to 20594 are all cased in neat satin lined boxes at price quoted. Postage on cased goods, 4 to 6c. extra

20587   Fine Pearl Holder, best rolled plate mountings, 14k Pen, No. 1 or 2. Fitted into satin-lined case as shown by No. 20600. Price each, **$1.65.**

20588   No. 3, 14k Pen. Best rolled plate mountings, fine pearl holder. Fitted in case similar to No. 20600. Price each, **$1.90.**

20589   No. 4, 14k Pen. Fine Pearl Holder, best rolled plate mountings. Fitted in case similar to No. 20600. Price each, **$2.15.**

20590   No. 5, 14k Pen. Fine Pearl Holder, best rolled plate mountings. Fitted in case similar to No. 20600. Price each, **$2.50.**

20591   No. 4 Pen. Fine Pearl Holder, solid sterling silver mountings, handsomely chased. Fitted in case similar to 20600. Price each, **$2.25.**
20592   Same as above, with No. 5 Pen. Price each, **$2.45.**

20593   No. 5 Pen. Ebony Desk Holder, rolled plate mountings. Fitted with leather covered satin lined box. Price each, **$1.48.**

20594   No. 4 Pen. Ebony Desk Holder, rolled plate mountings. Fitted in leather covered satin lined box. Price each, **$1.25.**

20595   No. 4 Pen. Black Enameled Holder, rolled plate mountings, screw pencil in end. Price each, **$1.75.**

20596   No. 4 Pen. Rolled Plate Telescope Holder, closes to vest pocket size. Price each, **$1.45.**
20597   No. 5 Pen, otherwise same as above. Price each, **$1.75.**

20598   No. 5 Pen. Fine Chased Rolled Plate Holder; combination screw pencil. Price each, **$1.75.**

20599   Men's Propelling and Repelling Pencil; gold trimmed; takes full size and length of lead. A business pencil. Each **$0.35.**

20600   Antique Chased Gold Plate Holder; Handle of knotted ivory, fitted with No. 2 gold pen, and furnished with Morocco, satin lined case, total length, 7 inches.   Each................**$1.90**
20601   Similar to above, old knotted ivory holder, mounted in Sterling silver, handsome antique chasing, fitted with No. 4 gold pen, morocco case.   Each..................... 2.00

20602   Assorted colors, Twist Pearl Holder, mounted in fine rolled gold plate, and fitted with No. 3 gold pen. Length of above, 7 inches. Price, in morocco case, each.....................**$1.90**

20603   A perfect Fountain Pen. Pearl holder, Gold mounted, fitted with a No. 1 gold pen. Price, **$6.00.** An elegant holiday or birthday gift.

Gold Pens repointed and repaired. Send pen and 42c; this will cover expense if pen can be repaired at all.

GOLD PENS.   (CUTS FULL SIZE.)

PRICES EACH.

Nos.	1	2	3	4	5	6	7
20604 14k........	$0.65	$0.75	$0.82	$1.05	$1.18	$1.55	$1.85
20605 10k........			.50	.60	.80	.90	

10k pens not made smaller than No. 3.

Cut full size.

20606   Magic Screw Pencil, sterling silver mountings, elegantly chased and oxidized stone set. Come in assorted patterns. Prices each...**$1.38**

20607   Rolled Plate Magic Pencil, elegantly chased. Price, **$0.83**

20608   Sterling Silver, chased and oxidized.   Stone in head of snake. Each. **$2.68**

20609   Sterling Silver, gold mounted, assorted designs. Price, each.......**$1.00**

20610   Rolled Plate Magic Pencil, ebony mounting.................Price, each,**$0.50**

20611   Rolled Plate, Magic Chased Pencil, finely chased. Price, each...**$0.75**

20612   Rolled Plate Screw Pencil, vest pocket size. Price each, **$0.30.** Per doz....................................**$3.00**

Cut one-half size.

20613   Rolled Plate Tooth Pick, with solid gold pick. Price, each, **$0.28.**   Per doz.......................**$3.00**
20613A   No. 20613 Toothpick in leather case............... .40

For Fountain and Stylographic Pens see preceding page. Plush Cases for any of above 75c. to $1.50,

GOLD HEAD CANES, THIMBLES AND SILVER NOVELTIES.

20700

20700 An extra quality 14k Gold Filled Cane Head, the top plate solid gold, handsomely chased and warranted for 20 yrs. Stick is ⅜ inch ebony. Price $13.50

Cuts are ⅛ Size.

20701 Superior Quality Gold Head Cane, latest pattern and finest quality of chasings; a cane that will last a lifetime; ⅜ inch ebony stick. Price.........$20.00

(Always send size.)

20702 A Fifteen Year Guaranteed Gold Filled Head, handsomely chased; 1 inch ebony stick. Price.........$10.00

NOTE.—We furnish Gold Headed Canes, any size from ⅜ in. to 1⅛ in. at are reduced proportionate prices; satisfactory value guaranteed.

This cut is exact size; other cuts size. 20703 Gold Filled Head (cut is exact size) handsomely chased; ⅜ in. ebony stick. Price.........$2.50

SILVER THIMBLES.

20704 Aluminum, Very light, 10c.
20705 Silver, 25c.

20706 Silver, better quality, 33c.

20707 Silver Chased Fancy patterns, 45c.

20708 Silver, extra quality, ornamental band, 55c.

20709 Silver, gold band, assorted chasings, $1.00.

20710 14k Solid Gold, each, $4.00.
20710½ 10k Solid Gold, each, $3.12

20711 Plain Gold filled, each, 82c
20711½ Same, Solid gold, $2.90.

20712 Fancy Octagon, gold filled assorted chasing each, $1.40.

GOLD FILLED THIMBLES.

20713 Solid Sterling Silver Match Box.........$3.50

20714 Solid Sterling Silver Match Box.........$2.00

20715 Quadruple Silver Plated Match Box, with frog enameled in colors; very neat.........$0.90

20716 Quadruple Silver Plated Match Box, shell pattern chased.........

20717 Ladies' Sterling Silver Trimmed Belt; finest silk web, assorted colors.........$2.50

20718 Ladies' Sterling Silver Trimmed Belt, finest silk web, assorted colors.........$2.00

20719 Ladies' Sterling Silver Trimmed Belt, finest quality of Silk Web Belt, assorted colors....$1.90
20720 Same but silver plated.................. 1.10

20721 Silk Elastic Garter, with solid silver clasps. Per pair........$3.25

20722 Silk Elastic garter, with solid silver clasps. Per pair........$3.00

20723 Sterling Silver Umbrella Clasp.........$0.35

20724 Sterling Key Chain, 17 inch $2.25

20725 Silk Elastic Garters, with solid silver clasps. Per pair........$2.00
20726 Garters similar to above, but plated, per pair.........

20727 Silk Elastic Garters, solid silver clasps. Per pair.................$2.25
20726 ....$0.85

20728 Sterling Silver Veil Clasp; very Useful.................60c.

20729 Sterling Silver Key Ring. ....80c.

PICTURE FRAMES, PIN TRAYS, PAPER CUTTERS AND ALUMINUM GOODS.

The little articles on this and the preceding page are very suitable for inexpensive Birthday and Holiday gifts, Eucher prizes, etc.

20740
Cabinet Photo Frame.
Gilded and beautifully Enameled in colors; 10 in. High. $2.00

20741
Cabinet Frame. Silver Plated and Enameled in colors. 7¼ in. high. $1.00

20742
Cabinet Frame. Silver Plated and Enameled in colors. 6 inches high. $0.80

20743
Card size Photo Frame. Silver Plated and Enameled in colors. 4½ inches high. $0.80

20744
Silver Plated Pin Tray. $0.35

20745
Silver Plated Jewelry Tray. $0.40

20746 Gold Plated and Enameled Handle Paper Cutter. Length, 5¼ inches. $1.00

20747 Silver Plated and Enameled Handle Paper Cutter. Length, 6 inches. $0.50

20748 Sterling Silver Handle, Pearl Blade Book Mark. $1.25

20749 Sterling Silver Glove Buttoner. $0.60

20750 Sterling Silver Handle, Pearl Blade Book Mark and Paper Cutter. $1.30

20751 Fine Steel Cutting Blades, mounted with sterling silver handles These are choice articles for holiday gifts $2.90

20752 Pearl Book Mark and Paper Cutter $0.50

20753 Pearl Paper Cutter, 5 inches long. $0.80

20754 Sterling Silver Book Mark. $0.55

Tea Ball.   Sugar Bowl.   Sugar Shaker.   Syrup Pitcher.   Cup.   T. P. Holder.   Bon Bon.

20755
Pure Aluminum, Tea Ball, total length, 7 in. Ball 1½ in. dia. Each, $0.50.

20756
Pure Aluminum Sugar Bowl Satin and Polished Finish. Height 5 inches. Each, $2.00.

20757
Pure Aluminum Chased and Polished. Height 4½ inches. Each, $1.25.

20758
Pure Aluminum Syrup Pitcher, Bright Polished. Height 6 inches. Each, $1.75.

20759
Child's Cup. Satin and Polished finished. Height 3 inches. $0.75

20760
Pure Aluminum Match or Tooth Pick Holder. Silver finish; height 2¾ inches. $0.50

20761
Pure Aluminum fancy edge, twist wire handle; dimensions 4x5 inches. Each, $0.85.

Mustard Cup.

Salt Cup.   Ink Well.   Ash and Card Tray.   Candle Stick.   Nut Tray.   Salt and Pepper.   Tea Strainer.

20762
Pure Aluminum; diameter, 2 in. Each, $0.25

20763
Patent Fountain Ink Well. Non-tarnishable and unbreakable; looks like silver. Each, $0.50

20764
Pure Aluminum Ash Tray; diam. 5 in. Rope edge, fancy satin finish. Each, $0.75

20765
Pure Aluminum Candle Stick; dimensions, 2¾ x 4 inches. Each, $0.65.

20766
Pure Aluminum Nut or Bon-Bon Tray; diameter, 4 inches. Each, $0.55

20768
Aluminum Cover and Spoon; Cup and base is glass. Each, $0.75

20769
Fine Finish, like silver; height 4 in. Salt or Pepper. Each, $0.65

20770
Pure Aluminum Tea Strainer, fine silver finish; size 1½x2. Each, $0.50

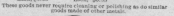

These goods never require cleaning or polishing as do similar goods made of other metals.

Candle Stick.   Funnel.   Match Holder.

20771
Pure Aluminum, handsome as silver. Each. Height 6 inches. $0.75 Height, 8 inches. 1.45

20772
Pure Aluminum, mirror polish. Each.
3 inch............. $0.50
4 inch............. .68
5 inch, with strainer, .75

20773
Pure Aluminum Match or Tooth Pick Holder, satin finish; height 2¼ inches. Each.....$0.52

20774
Aluminum. Each, $0.10

20775
Mirror Polish. Aluminum. Diameter 5 in Each, $0.70

20776
Aluminum, Price, $0.87

SOLID STERLING SILVER FLAT WARE. Guaranteed 𝔐 Fine.

Tipped. **Louvre.** **Waverly.** **Engraved.**

Louvre Coffee Spoon.

20804 Plain Bowl, per dozen..$7.50. 20805 Gold Bowl, per dozen $9.50

Waverly Coffee Spoon.

20806 Plain Bowl, per dozen....$7.25 20807 Gold Bowl, per dozen....$9.25

Engraved Coffee Spoon.

20808 Plain Bowl, per doz ....$ 8.00
20809 Gold Bowl, per doz................................ 10.00

Waverly Oyster Fork.
20811 Price, Each....$1.05
Louvre pattern same price.

Waverly Cream Ladle.
20800 Cream Ladle, Each......$ 3.20
20801 Medium Ladle, Each......10.40
20802 Soup Ladle, Each....... 14.75
20803 Gravy Ladle, Each...... 4.90
Louvre pattern same price.

20810 Waverly Dinner Knife, Sterling Silver Handle. Per doz.....................$34.00

All Goods on this page are Sterling Silver, $\frac{925}{1000}$ Fine.

Waverly Butter Knife.
20812 Plain Blade. Each ...$2.70
20813 Gold Blade. Each ... 3.25
20814 Gold Engraved Blade,
Each........................ 3.50
Louvre pattern same price.

Louvre Sugar Tongs.

20815 Large size. Each......$2.75 20816 Small size. Each......$2.25

Prices of Tipped, Louvre and Waverly Flat Ware.

Tea Spoons, 6 oz.....Per doz.$	6.60
Tea Spoons, 8 oz.....Per doz.	8.80
Table Spoons, 18 oz. Per doz.	19.80
Medium Forks, 18 oz. Per doz.	19.80
Dessert Spoons, 14 oz. Per doz	15.40
Dessert Forks, 14 oz. Per doz.	15.40
Sugar Shells. Each..........	1.70
Butter Knives. Each........	2.70

Waverly Sugar Shell.
20817 Plain Bowl ....Each. $1.70
20818 Gold Lined Bowl .... Each. 2.00
20819 Gold Lined Engraved Bowl .... Each. 2.25
Louvre Pattern Same Price.

For price of engraved pattern add to price of Waverly $1.50 per doz. for Tea Spoons; $2.25 per doz. for Dessert Spoons and Forks; $2.50 per doz. for Table Spoon and Forks; 25c each for Butter Knives and Sugar Spoons.

THE CELEBRATED ROGER BROS. "1847", FLAT WARE.

Sold by jewelers the world over as the best plated ware made. Compare our prices with your jeweler's, and notice how much you can save by ordering from us.

20900	Solid Crucible Steel Knives, plain or frosted, 9 inches long, hand burnished, triple plate Per dozen $3.40
20901	Forks to match. Per dozen 3.40
20902	Dessert knives to match, 7¼ inches long. Per dozen 3.20
20903	Dessert Forks to match 3.20
20904	3 piece Carving Set to match 3.50

20905	Table Knives, arabesque handles, like or similar to cut, bright finish.
	triple plate. Per dozen $4.25
20906	Forks to match. Per dozen 4.30
20907	Three-piece Carving set to match 4.50
20908	Fruit Knives to match, per set (6) 1.75
20910	Nut Picks to match, per set (6) 1.50

20911	Quadruple Plate on Nickle Silver, Hollow Handle, arabesque, bright finish knives. Per dozen $6.00
20912	Forks to match. Per dozen 6.00
20913	Three-piece Carving set to match 6.00

Patterns.	Tea Spoons.			Table Spoons.			Dessert Spoons			Medium Forks			Dessert Forks.		
	Extra plate. Per doz	Shell plate. Per doz	Triple plate. Per doz	Extra Plate. Per doz	Shell plate. Per doz	Triple plate. Per doz	Extra plate. Per doz	Shell plate. Per doz	Triple plate. Per doz	Extra plate. Per doz	Shell plate. Per doz	Triple plate. Per doz	Extra plate. Per doz	Shell plate. Per doz	Triple plate. Per doz
20914 Tipped...	$2.48	$3.96	$4.95	$7.86	$4.37	$6.71	$4.07	$7.89	$4.40	$6.73					
20915 Shell.....	2.77	4.21	5.45	8.41	4.96	7.29	5.45	8.42	4.91	7.30					
20916 Portland.	2.79	4.23	5.47	8.43	4.98	7.31	5.44	8.44	4.92	7.34					
20917 Savoy.....	2.80	4.25	5.49	8.45	5.00	7.35	5.46	8.47	4.93	7.35					
20918 Columbia.	2.82	4.27	5.51	8.47	5.02	7.37	5.49	8.40	4.94	7.38					

Patterns.	Butter Knives.	Sugar Shells.	Pickle Forks.	Coffee Spoons	Mustard Spoons.
	Extra or Standard Plate	Extra or Standard Plate.	Extra or Standard Plate.	Extra or Standard Plate.	Extra or Standard Plate.
20919 Tipped........	$0.48 each	$0.40 each	$0.32 each	Not made.	$0.22 each
20920 Shell.........	.50 each	.44 each	Not made.	$3.75 doz.	.33 each
20921 Portland.....	.51 each	.45 each	$0.46 each	3.77 doz.	.35 each
20922 Columbia....	.52 each	.47 each	Not made.	3.79 doz.	.36 each
20923 Savoy........	.53 each	.49 each	Not made.	3.80 doz.	.38 each

Tipped.   Shells.   Savoy.   Portland.   Columbia.

We illustrate below a few fancy pieces of the famous "Rogers Bros. '1847'" Brand. We can furnish either of these articles in any of the four fancy pattern shown above.

	Fancy Pieces. Standard Plate. Each.	
20924	Pie Knife, any fancy pattern	$2.08
20925	Cake Knife, any fancy pattern	2.08
20926	Cream Ladles, any fancy pattern	.85
20927	Gravy Ladle, any fancy pattern	1.25
20928	Berry Spoons, any fancy pattern	1.15
20929	Sugar Tongs, any fancy pattern	1.00
20930	Salt Spoons, any fancy pattern	.21
20931	Soup Ladles, any fancy pattern	2.51
20931¼	Oyster Forks, any fancy pattern. Perdz	4.10

Butter Knife. Cut ⅝ size.

20932   Columbia Butter Knife, triple plate. Each $0.75

Coffee Spoon. Cuts full size.

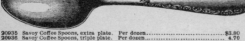

20933   Primrose Coffee Spoons, extra plate. Per dozen $3.75
20934   Primrose Coffee Spoons, triple plate. Per dozen 4.75

20935   Savoy Coffee Spoons, extra plate. Per dozen $3.80
20936   Savoy Coffee Spoons, triple plate. Per dozen 4.70

We Charge for Engraving Initials
2½c. per Letter for Script; 5½c for Old English.

Sugar Spoon, ⅝ size.

20937   Columbia Sugar Shell, triple plate. Each $0.65

Cut full size.

20938   Portland Salt Spoon, extra plate. Each $0.31

Cut full size.

20939   Embossed Small Sugar Tongs, made in embossed pattern only. Each $0.75
20940   Sugar Tongs, larger size, any fancy pattern. Each 1.00

MONTGOMERY WARD & CO.'S GUARANTEED FLAT WARE.

These goods are made for us especially by one of the largest factories of America. They are stamped with our name and the makers are under forfeit to keep the quality up to our standard, which is the very best it is possible to produce. By making contracts for large quantities of these goods we are enabled to place them with our customers at prices much lower than any of the standard brands of plated ware. Each principal package of forks, spoons, etc., contains our "Guarantee Certificate," which authorizes the purchaser to return any ware bearing our name in case it should not prove as represented in every particular, and we will refund money or replace the goods.

Length, 9 inches.

20950 Montgomery Ward & Co's Extra Crucible Steel Knife, extra quality triple plate. Hand burnished, polished or satin finished handles, making positively the best knife offered at the price. Per dozen...$2.95

20951 Forks to match. Made of Solid Nickel Silver and extra heavy plated. Per dozen...2.95

NOTE.—These goods are put up in a handsome box bearing our name and trade-mark; also a guarantee that they will give perfect satisfaction or money will be refunded. If you want the best for your money, order them.

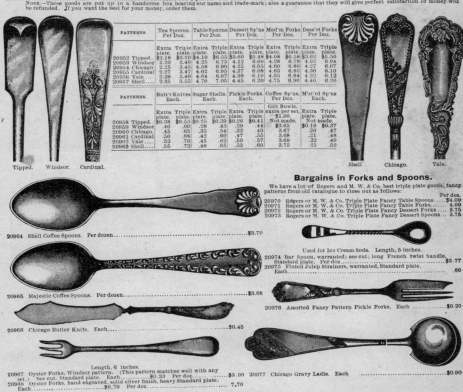

PATTERNS.	Tea Spoons. Per Doz.		Table Spoons. Per Doz.		Dessert Sp'ns Per Doz.		Med'm Forks Per Doz.		Dess'rt Forks Per Doz.	
	Extra plate.	Triple plate.	Extra plate.	Triple plate.	Extra plate.	Triple plate.	Extra plate.	Triple plate.	Extra plate.	Triple plate.
20952 Tipped..	$2.18	$3.20	$4.10	$6.55	$3.60	$5.48	$4.08	$6.58	$3.62	$5.50
20953 Windsor	2.20	3.40	4.25	6.75	4.12	6.00	4.28	6.78	4.02	6.04
20954 Chicago	2.25	3.45	4.58	6.90	4.25	6.05	4.60	6.80	4.27	6.07
20955 Cardinal	2.27	3.47	4.62	6.95	4.37	6.08	4.63	6.82	4.30	6.10
20956 Yale	2.29	3.49	4.64	6.97	4.39	6.10	4.65	6.84	4.32	6.12
20957 Shell	2.35	3.55	4.70	7.05	4.45	6.20	4.75	6.90	4.40	6.20

PATTERNS.	Butt'r Knives Each.		Sugar Shells. Each.		Pickle Forks. Each.		Coffee Sp'ns. Per Doz.		M'st'rd Sp'ns Each.	
	Extra plate.	Triple plate.	Extra plate.	Triple plate.	Extra plate.	Triple plate.	Gilt Bowls, extra per set, $1.00.		Extra plate.	Triple plate.
20958 Tipped...	$0.38	$0.55	$0.25	$0.39	$0.26	$0.41	$3.65	Not made.	$0.19	$0.37
20959 Windsor	.40	.60	.28	.43	.29	.44	3.65		.20	.47
20960 Chicago.	.45	.65	.35	.54	.32	.49	3.67		.21	.48
20961 Cardinal	.50	.68	.42	.60	.47	.55	3.68		.22	.49
20962 Yale	.52	.70	.45	.62	.50	.57	3.69		.25	.52
20963 Shell....	.55	.72	.48	.65	.53	.60	3.75			

Tipped. Windsor. Cardinal.

Shell. Chicago. Yale.

Bargains in Forks and Spoons.

We have a lot of Rogers and M. W. & Co. best triple plate goods, fancy patterns from old catalogue to close out as follows:

Per doz.

20970 Rogers or M. W. & Co. Triple Plate Fancy Table Spoons....$4.00
20971 Rogers or M. W. & Co. Triple Plate Fancy Table Forks...... 4.00
20972 Rogers or M. W. & Co. Triple Plate Fancy Dessert Forks.... 3.75
20973 Rogers or M. W. & Co. Triple Plate Fancy Dessert Spoons.. 3.75

20964 Shell Coffee Spoons. Per dozen....................$3.70

Used for Ice Cream Soda. Length, 5 inches.

20974 Bar Spoon, warranted; see cut; long French twist handle. Standard plate. Per doz..$3.77
20975 Fluted Julep Strainers, warranted. Standard plate. Each...60

20965 Majestic Coffee Spoons. Per dozen....................$3.68

20976 Assorted Fancy Pattern Pickle Forks. Each $0.20

20966 Chicago Butter Knife. Each.....................$0.45

Length, 6 inches.

20967 Oyster Forks, Windsor pattern. (This pattern matches well with any set.) See cut. Standard plate. Each........$0.33 Per doz.........$3.00
20968 Oyster Forks, hand engraved, solid silver finish, heavy Standard plate. Each....................................$0.70 Per doz.......... 7.70

20977 Chicago Gravy Ladle. Each $0.90

PANAMA SILVER.—A New Discovery in Precious Metal.

Panama Silver. The metal of the century. It is solid and not plated, and will not tarnish when exposed to the atmosphere.

Forks, spoons, butter knives and sugar shells now made of the new metal are superior to silver plated goods in point of non-tarnishing, and are equal to sterling silver for durability.

For hotel, restaurant and family use, Panama silver tableware is without a parallel.

We guarantee them to wear longer than any other metal goods made. As there is no plate to wear off, any silver powder, polish, chalk or electroine can be used to clean them.

In constant use they retain a beautiful white color very much like our coin silver, and might readily be mistaken for it.

They are put up in neat packages, each one bearing our brand and trade mark, which we consider a sufficient guarantee as to their quality.

Price List of Panama Silver.

Per doz.

20978 Teaspoons, Windsor pattern $1.50
20979 Dessert spoons, Windsor pattern 2.50
20980 Tablespoons, Windsor pattern 3.00
20981 Medium Forks, Windsor pattern 3.00

Each.

20982 Sugar Shells, Windsor pattern $0.21
20983 Butter Knives, Windsor pattern .... .21

Purchasers of these goods, not finding them perfectly satisfactory, may return them in exchange for other goods, or we will refund the purchase price.

They are made only in Windsor patterns, as shown in illustration marked "Windsor," on this page.

SILVER PLATED FANCY PIECES.
Made by the **Most Reliable Manufacturers.**

21000 Monarch Sugar Spoon and Butter Knife in satin
lined box...$1.30
Any fancy pattern same price.

21001 Shell Pie Knife, in satin lined box...................$2.10
Any fancy pattern pie knife same price.

21002 Shell Cream Ladle in satin lined box $1.00
Any fancy pattern Cream Ladle same price.

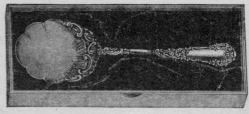

21108 Yale Berry Spoon, in plush lined case................$1.25

21109 Yale Child's Set of three pieces: knife,
fork and spoon. Heavy A 1 plate on best
White metal. Put up on elegant colored lithograph cards like cut. Each set in paper case.
Per set...$1.95
Savoy, Portland or Shell (1847) Child's Sets
same price.

21109

21110 Three pieces, Chicago Pattern; in fine
silk plush case, A 1 goods. Per set.........$2.25
21111 Child's Sterling Silver Fork and Spoon,
with Pearl Handle Knife, all in plush case.
Per set..$7.50

21003 Child's knife, fork, spoon, napkin ring and cup, in satin lined case
Cup is nickel, gold lined........$1.25

21004 6 Steel Nut Picks in
paper case $0.33

21112 Fancy Fork and Spoon, plain steel knife,
in satin lined box......................................$0.65
21113 Child's Set, 3 pieces in box.................. .25

21005 Nut Cracker and 6 picks
in plush case.............$1.25.

21106 Set of six Nut Picks and one Cracker
in Aluminum tray, very neat and pretty.
Price..$1.00.

21114 Nut Cracker and 6 Picks in case.
Heavy Silver Plate.....................$1.75

21007 Nut Cracker, in satin lined box. Each..$0.90.

21100 These 3 illustrations are
samples of a large line of solid
sterling silver souvenir spoons,
coffee size; some gold lined
bowls, some with photos of
Columbus in bowl, and other
World's Fair souvenirs. We do
not agree to furnish any special
pattern, but all are handsome, and
worth twice the price we ask.
While they last, 68c.

"Standard" Silver Plated Ware.

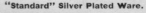

This ware is known as fine White Metal, silver plated, and is fair ware at
the low price quoted.
21115 1 package (6) Tea Spoons; per package ....$0.25. Postage.........$0.06
21116 1 package (3) Table Spoons; per package .. .25. Postage........... .06
21117 1 package (3) Medium Forks; per package .25. Postage........... .06

FIRST QUALITY QUADRUPLE SILVER PLATED WARE— QUALITY GUARANTEED.

21120   Quadruple Plate Tea Set, 6 pieces, including waiter, $35.45; without waiter, 5-piece set, $25.45.
21121   Coffee, 9½ inches, $6.60.   21122—Tea, 7½ inches, $5.75.   21123—Sugar, 6¼ inches, $4.55.   21124—Cream, 4¼ inches, $4.30.   21125—Spoon, 4½ inches, $4.20
Coffee holds 3½ pints; Pitcher and Spoon Holder are gold-lined.

21130   Tea, $5.50.   21131   Spoon Holder, $4.00.   21132   Sugar, $4.25.   21133   Cream, $4.10.   21134   Coffee, $6.25.
Coffee holds 3½ pints; 8 inches high; other pieces in proportion.   Cream and Spoon gold-lined.

21135   Tea, $4.00.   21136   Cream, $2.75.   21137   Sugar, $3.00.   21138   Spoon Holder, $2.70.   21139   Coffee, $4.50.
Coffee, 8½ inches, 3½ pints capacity.   Spoon Holder and Cream Pitcher gold-lined.

21140   Coffee, $4.00.   21141   Spoon Holder, $2.00.   21142   Sugar, $2.50.   21143   Cream, $2.00.   21144   Tea, $3.50.

21145   Elegant Embossed Crumb Tray and Scraper, $3.00.
21146   Cream, $3.85.
21147   Spoon to match, $3.90.
21148   Sugar, $3.80.
21149   Coffee, $5.75.
21150   Tea to match, $5.25.
Coffee, 8½ inches, 3½ pints.   Cream and Spoon gold-lined.
Syrup Pitchers and Butter Dishes to match above shown on pages 189 and 190.

EXTRA PLATE SILVERWARE.

Under this heading we quote a line of goods not up to the regular Quadruple Plate Goods, but a line that is well made, one that with reasonable care will last for many years. The styles are all of the latest and most desirable. For prizes, or for occasional use they are unsurpassed.

Caster.

21291 Extra Plate Caster, 5 bottles; height, 15 inches. A beauty at the price; looks as well as a $6.00 caster.
Each.....................$0.90

Caster.

21292 Extra Plate 5 Bottle Caster; height, 15in. Heavier base and better bottles than No.21291.
Each.................$1.50

Caster.

21293 Elegant Extra Plate, 5 Bottle Caster. Height, 17 in. Beautiful bottles, with call-bell in handle.
Each....................$2.75

Water Set.

21294 Extra Plate Water Set; chased cup, gold lined. Height, 19 in. Set complete........$7.50

Pickle Caster.

21295 Extra Plate Pickle Caster, tongs attached. Height, 11½ inches.
Each................$1.00

Syrup.

21296 Triple Plate with extended base. Height 5½ inches. Price....$1.25

Sugar.

21297 Combination Sugar Bowl and Spoonholder for 12 spoons. Height, 6¼ inches. Price, without spoons, $1.38

Berry.

21298 Large Fruit Stand glass dish; extra plate frame and base. Height, 8 inches. Each....$1.25

Berry.

21299 Large Glass Fruit Dish, Metal frame, extra plate, Height, 6¼ inches. Each.........$1.50

Cake.

21300 Beautiful Cake Basket. Height, 10 inches. Each...................$1.50

Butter.

21402 Extra Plate Butter Dish; chased. Height, 7½ inches. Each $1.25

TRIPLE PLATE 4-PIECE TEA SET.

Satin Finish, Elegantly Chased.

Tea Pot.

21304 Height 9 inches. Price.....$2.75

Sugar Bowl.

21306 Height 6 inches. Price.......$1.85

Spoon Holder.

21308 Height 4 inches. Price...$1.65

Creamer.

21310 Height, 3½ inches. Price......$1.62

Sugar.

21312 Fancy Colored Glass Sugar Bowl in Silver plated frame with sugar shell attached. Price, $1.35

Butter.

21314 Extra Butter Dish; Height, 6 inches, chased. Price $1.35

TEA SET, FOUR PIECES.

Coffee.

21318 Height, 6 inches. Price.....$2.25

THORNE'S SILVER POLISH, Dry, Per Box $0 10

Sugar.

21320 Height, 4½ inches. Price.....$1.30

TRIPLE PLATE.

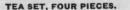

21316 Triple Plate 4-Piece Tea Set, Sugar Bowl not shown, complete, $7.00 Each piece separate $1.75

Spoon Holder.

21321 Height, 4½ inches. Price ...$1 05

Creamer.

21322 Height, 4 inches Price $1.00

21323 13 inch Waiter only $2.75 Will hold a 4-piece tea set

CLOCK DEPARTMENT.

We warrant every Clock we sell to keep good time.

Bee Time
Nickel Clocks.

23000 Cut ¼ size. One day time. Ansonia make; dial is 2 inches in diameter, with bevel ed glass; the smallest clock made that keeps good time.
Price............$0.85
Postage, extra.... .09

23000

Bee Alarm.

23001 Same size as No. 23000, but with alarm; the smallest alarm clock made in the country; warranted to give satisfaction; dial 2 inches.
Price............$1.25
Postage, extra.... .12

23001

Progressor.

Please note price—compare with your retail jeweler. A better alarm clock for the money cannot be produced.
23002 Dial is 4 inches.
Price............$0.57
Postage, extra...... .25
23003 Same clock, with calendar attachment.
Price $0.80

23002

Sure-Call Alarm.

23004 The best alarm clock made. Will not fail to wake you up. Rings for over a minute. Dial is 2 in., height 4½ in. Nickel or Gilt finish; fine movement; cut steel pinions; double roller escapement.
Price............$1.50
Postage .... .24

23004

Electric Alarm.

23005 Double telephone bells. Rings for three minutes. Fine adjusted movement, cut steel pinions, double roller escapement. A very accurate timepiece. Height 5½ inches; dial 2 inches. Nickel or gilt finish.
Price............$3.00
Postage........ .30

23005

The Liberty Alarm.

23006 Our Bronze Clock bargain, fitted with Ansonia-Waterbury or New Haven movement, with or without alarm and calendar. Height, 10½ inches; width of base 10 inches, total weight, ready for shipment, about 15 lbs. Elegant finish, perfect time-piece.
Price, only $2.00

13—6th

Cupid's Dart.

23007 A Handsome Ornament as well as a good timekeeper, finished in silver or bronze, with fancy dial. Height, 6 inches, Ansonia movement, dial 2 inches.
Price.........$3.20
Postage, extra .26

23007

Frolic No. 2.

23008 Another handsome little clock in Silver or Bronze finish. 2-inch fancy dial; Ansonia movement. Warranted a good timepiece. Height 7½ inches.
Price.........$3.00

23008

Magic.

23009 This is one of the prettiest and most graceful little clocks ever made. It comes in Silver or Bronze finish; has 2-inch fancy dial. Ansonia movement. A good timepiece and a beautiful ornament. Height, 9¾ inches.
Price............$3.25

23009

Croquette.

23010

23010 Another style of Ansonia fancy Silver and Bronze finish clock. A good timekeeper; 2-inch fancy dial. Height, 8¼ inches.
Price $3.25

The Countess.

23011 The Countess. A perfect Stem Wind Watch, good movement, made by the Waterbury Clock Co. Stem Wind and set, porcelain dial, fancy embossed case. Dial 1¼ in. Same diameter as an ordinary Men's Size Watch. Can be hung up or carried in the pocket; warranted to keep time. Price...... $1.50
23011½ Same as above, but winds from back.
Price............$1.25

Front.   Back.

Cupid Wreath.

23012 A beautiful little clock. Silver finish; 2-inch dial, an accurate timepiece, with cut steel pinions. Height, 5 inches.
Price............$2.00

23012

Tourist.

Glass sides, Nickel and Gilt finish; 2¼-inch dial. Good, accurate timepiece and a reliable and ornamental alarm clock.

23013 One-day alarm.
Price............$1.85
23014 One-day strike.
Price............$2.00
Height, 7 inches.

23013

Windsor.

23015 A new and handsome novelty alarm clock. Elegant decorated porcelain, with fancy silver dial. As ornamental as it is useful.
Price............$3.75
Height, 8¼ inches.

23015

Dayton.

23016 Antique oak case. Height 23 in., Ansonia movement, 6 in. dial, hour and half-hour strike on wire bell.
Price............$3.00
23017 Same with good bell.
Price............$3.30
Alarm, extra........ .40
Weight, boxed, 17 lbs.

CLOCK DEPARTMENT—Continued.
Fine Mantel Clocks.

"Lisle."

23053 Enameled iron case with gilt trimmings (will not tarnish). Height, 11 inches; 8-day half-hour strike on cathedral gong bell, visible escapement.
Price...$8.30
Same with plain dial...............................7.25
Weight, boxed, 24 lbs.

Danube.

23054 8 Day Half Hour Gong Strike, Star Movement Enameled Iron Case. Bronze columns. Weight, boxed, 49 lbs.; Dial 5¼ inches. Height, 10½ inches, Length 16½ inches. American white dial, Roman or Arabic figures.....................................$10.50
American Gilt dial, Arabic figures...............10.55
Porcelain dial, Roman or Arabic figures..........11.25
Visible escapement additional.......................70

Porcelain B.

25065 Fine porcelain clock, decorated with gold with three colored panels. You cannot imagine the beauty of this clock by looking at the cut, it must be seen to be appreciated. These clocks have formerly been so high priced that we could not use them, but we have made a deal with the makers so that we can offer them to you very reasonable. You should have one of them for your parlor. Price..........................$15.30
Weight, boxed, 28½ lbs.

"Boston Extra."

23056 A very neat, handsome enameled iron case clock with Ansonia works. Height, 11 inches, 8-day half-hour strike on gong bell, visible escapement. Price...$10.00
Plain dial, price......................................8.75
Weight, boxed, 34 lbs.

Berlin.

23057 Clock is enameled iron case, with gold figures, 8-day Ansonia movement, half-hour strike on cathedral gong bell, with visible escapement. Price...........................$7.60
Plain dial, white or gold, price..................5.75
Weight, boxed, 25 lbs.

Rosalind.

23058 One of the handsomest enameled iron case clocks made; is 12¼ inches high, with rich bronze trimmings and gold scroll work; 8-day, half-hour strike on cathedral gong bell, with visible escapement, like cut Price.........................$12.60
With plain dial......................................10.50
Weight, boxed, 32 lbs.

Amiens.

23059 Clock is Ansonia make, with enameled iron case set with gilt trimmings; 8-day, half-hour strike on cathedral gong bell; height, 10¼ in.
Plain dial, white or gold.........................$8.85
Porcelain dial, visible escapement..............10.50

La France.

23060 8-Day enameled iron Ansonia movement, with bronze urn, cathedral gong ½ hhour strike. Bronze trimmings with visible escapement $9.00
23061 Without visible escapement........$7.75

"Alford."

23062 Beautiful onyx, of the best quality, an 8-day Ansonia movement, with porcelain or gilt dial.
Price...$14.40
Weight, boxed, 40 lbs.

Petite.

23063 Marbleized Iron Case, Superior eight-day movement, fancy dial, half-hour strike on gong bell. Height 9¼ inches, weight, boxed, 25 lbs.
Price...$5.50

"Spree."

23064 8-Day, half-hour gong strike, Star movement. Dial 5½ inches, height 11½ inches, length 10 inches. American white dial, Roman or Arabic figures..............$7.00
Porcelain dial, Roman or Arabic figures.........7.60
American gilt dial, Arabic figures...............7.10
Visible escapement additional.....................70

"Ecuador."

23065 This richly enameled iron Boudoir clock, 8-day gong hour strike. Height 9 inches, width 10 inches, dial 4½ inches. Gross w'ght boxed, 30 lbs. Price..$5.75

CLOCK DEPARTMENT—Continued.
Fine Mantel Clocks.

Seth Thomas.

23066 A beautiful Seth Thomas wood Mantel Clock, polished celluloid finish, warranted not to crack or peel; height, 12¾ inches; base, 15 inches; dial, 5 inches; 8-day; strike on cathedral bell.
Price $9.50

"Brennus."

23067 Very handsome Mantel Clock, finished in bronze. Height, 15 inches. New Haven movement; 8-day; half-hour strike on cathedral gong bell.
Price $15.75
Weight, boxed, 53 pounds.

"Magnolia."

23068 Original design, highly artistic, marbleized wood case with gilt ornaments. Supplied with high class 8-day star movement, half-hour strike and deep-toned gong. Dial 5¼ inches, height 13 inches, length 16½ inches.
American white dial, Roman or Arabic figures.....$6.95
American gilt dial, Arabic figures...............6.90
Porcelain or bronzed dial........................7.50
Gross weight, boxed, 24 lbs.

"Tagus."

23069 An original design, richly finished with gilt ornaments and supplied with 8-day Star movement, half-hour strike and deep-toned gong. Dial 5½ inches; height, 11¼ inches; length, 17¾. Can be furnished as follows:
American white dial, Roman or Arabic figures.....$7.00
American gilt dial, Arabic figures...............7.10
Porcelain dial, Roman............................7.50
Gross weight, boxed, 24 lbs.

Seth Thomas.

23070 An elegant marbleized wood Seth Thomas 8-day, half-hour strike, cathedral gong clock; height, 12 inches; base, 15 inches; dial, 5 inches.
Price $8.00

Washington.

23071 Enameled iron, 8-day, half-hour strike, cathedral gong, New Haven movement, gilt trimmings; height, 10½ inches.
Price $7.75

Dexter.
A Clock Ornament.

23072 Handsome bronze ornament for clock like Danube. Height 9 inches.
Price $1.25

Buffalo Bill.
A Clock Ornament.

23073 Handsome Bronze Horse, surmounted by a typical western rider. Splendid piece of work. Height, 10 inches. Weight, 5 lbs.
Price..........$1.35

Music.
A Clock Ornament.

23074 Elegant Bronze Figure for clock ornament. Height 6 inches. Price reduced to $1.10. Weight, 16 ounces.

FINE BRONZE SIDE PIECES AND VASES.

23075 Mars or Minerva. Height, 15 inches.
Each $2.85. Per pair, $5.00

23076 Height, 14 inches.
Price each, $1.50.

23077 Height, 13 inches.
Price each, $1.00.

23078 Warrior. Height, 10½ inches.
Each., $3.25 Per pair, $6.00.

23079 Pitcher. Height, 21 inches.
Price each, $2.90.

OPTICAL GOODS DEPARTMENT.

In this department we include optical goods of all kinds, surveyors', mathematical, meteorological and scientific instruments, drawing instruments and material. We are in a position to furnish nearly everything made in goods of the classes mentioned, whether listed or not. Send us your order and we will make the price right. Write for list of glass eyes for birds and animals.

We have arranged with a leading oculist of this city whereby all orders involving the least question as to the possibility of a perfect fit, will be submitted to him.

Parties ordering spectacles or eyeglasses will please observe the following directions which are required to insure proper glasses:

1st. State if glasses have been used and for what purpose, reading or for more distant objects.

2d. If glasses have not been previously used, state whether vision is defective for near objects, for distant objects, or for both near and distant objects, and if glasses wanted are for reading or walking purposes.

3d. State what the distance is (inches) from the center of one pupil to the center of the other. Measure with a rule or tape across the nose. Is the bridge of the nose prominent or flat?

4th. Give age. 5th. State if glasses wanted are for reading or distant objects.

Type For Testing the Sight.

For Old Sight.

Let the customer state, while holding the page in a good light at 12 to 14 inches distance from the eye, state the finest print that can possibly be read at that distance. The number over the paragraph will be about the number of convex glasses for reading and sewing.

For Near Sight.

Let the customer state the farthest distance from the eyes at which paragraph No. 24 can be *distinctly* seen. The number of lenses so obtained between the card and the eyes will correspond approximately with the number of concave lenses required.

Astigmatism.

If some of the arms in the above figure appear more distinct than others, the presence of astigmatism is indicated. The defect can only be corrected by cylindrical lenses, carefully ground to the oculist's order, or by personal fitting.

No. 48.

The smallest size letter on this card should be read easily at fifteen inches from the eye. If you cannot do so you should wear spectacles. It does not pay to buy cheap spectacles.

No. 36.

They distort the rays of light, disturb the angles of vision, cause pain and discomfort and injure the

No. 30.

eyesight. When it is necessary to hold work or reading matter farther than fifteen

No. 26.

inches from the eyes in order to see distinctly, it is a sure sign of failing vision.

No. 24.

and much annoyance, discomfort and pain will be prevented by

No. 18.

having a pair of glasses fitted.

No. 16.

Buy no other kind.

No. 14.

Crystalline are

No. 10.

the best

Spectacles.

All spectacles costing 50 cents or more are furnished with neat leather case without charge.

Spectacles or Eyeglasses, when sent by mail, allowed 5 cents extra for postage.

All lines of merchandise very generally reduced in price.

Straight Temple Spectacles.

	Per pair.	Per doz
23500— Steel Frame Spectacles, single Single Temple, temples, plano convex lenses, all numbers	$0.10	$1.00

23501 Steel Frame Spectacles, single temples, two screws in joint, well finished, all numbers, plano convex lenses. .25 ... 2.50

23502 Steel Spectacles, single temples, periscopic lenses, good finish ... .50 ... 5.20

23503 Spectacles, highly tempered steel; single temples, extra finish, first quality periscopic convex lenses ... .75 ... 7.65

23504 Singles Temple, solid nickel frame, finest quality periscopic convex lenses. .75 ... 7.65

23505 Alumnico Frames (resembling silver.) *Will not rust.* Fitted with finest quality, periscopic convex, or concave lenses ... 1.10

23506 Coin Silver Spectacles, good weight fitted with first quality lenses ... 1.40 ... 15.00

23507 Steel Spectacles, blue tempered, fitted with finest periscopic Brazilian pebble lenses; retail price, $2.50.
Our price ... 1.75 ... 18.50

The "New Era" Straight Temple Spectacles with patent thumb screw adjustment, which enables you to remove or insert the lenses without danger of breaking or chipping the lenses or breaking the frame; no screw to loose or temple to fall off; recommended for their strength, simplicity and durability.

23508 Spectacles, straight temple, blue finish, highly tempered, first quality lenses.
Price, each ... $0.70 Per doz ... $6.00

23509 Spectacles, nickel plated tempered steel, straight temple frame, first quality lenses.
Price, each ... $0.95 Per doz ... 8.00

23510 Gold Filled, straight temple, round eye wire spectacles of exceptional value.
For those who are partial to gold spectacles, but cannot afford to wear them, these are especially recommended. Finely finished, with periscopic convex lenses, all focal numbers.
Price, each ... $1.25

23511 Bi-Focal Spectacles, double convex, all numbers, upper lens focused for distance, lower lens for reading. Very convenient and popular.
Good steel frame ... $0.50
Finely finished steel frame ... .75
German Silver frame ... .85
Coin Silver frame, genuine ... 1.50
Gold Filled frame, with cemented lenses ... 1.95

Sliding or Extension Temple Spectacles.

Sliding or extension Temples, when closed, have the advantage of taking up less room than the ordinary style. They are often preferred by elderly people.

23512 Sliding Extension Temples, finest periscopic lenses, coin silver mountings ... $2.25

23513 Same as No. 23512, mounted in solid gold frame, 10 karat.
Retail price ... $12.00 Our price ... 8.50

NOTE—All Spectacles and Eye Glasses listed are fitted in focal numbers from 5 to 60, and special focal numbers and prescription lenses fitted to order.

Riding or Hook-Bow Spectacles.

Riding or hook bows are usually recommended for glasses that are worn for distance or for a continued length of time.

23514 Alumnico metal spectacles, resembling silver, well finished hook temples, concave or convex lenses. Each ... $1 25

23515 Bronzed Steel Spectacles, with riding or hook temple bows reaching behind ears, with double or periscopic convex lenses. Each ... $0.75

Riding or Hook Bows.

23516 Bronzed Steel Spectacles, same as above, but fitted with concave or near sighted lenses. Each ... $0.75

23517 Steel Spectacles, with riding or hook bows, fine finish, light weight, nickel plated, convex lenses, each ... 1.25

23518 Same as above, fitted with concave or near sighted lenses. Each ... 1.25

23519 Steel Spectacles, riding bow or hook temples, fine finish with grooved periscopic concave lenses, first quality making the frame almost invisible, for near sighted people ... 1.35

23520 Frameless Spectacles, hook temples, bronzed steel mounted, with periscopic convex lenses, first quality ... .80

23521 Same as 23520, fitted with concave or near sighted lenses. Each ... .85

23522 Gold Filled Spectacles, hook bows, fitted with either periscopic concave or convex lenses. Each ... 1 35

Solid Gold Spectacles, Straight Temples.

Set with Finest Quality Periscopic Lenses.

	Per pair.
23523 Gold Spectacles, round eye wire, flat temples, 8 karat, good medium weight	$3.70
23524 Same as 23523, 10 karat	4.00
23525 Same as 23523, 14 karat	4.90

Frames furnished in flat finish at same price, if preferred.

Solid Gold Spectacles, Riding or Hook Bow Temples.

Set with Finest Quality Periscopic Lenses.

	Per pair.
23526 Solid Gold Spectacles, round eye wire, pair, hook temples, good medium weight, 8 karat	$3.80
23527 Same as 23526, 10 karat	4.20
23528 Same as 23526, 14 karat	5.00

Nos. 23523 to 23528 inclusive, light weight, 25 cents less; heavy weight 25 to 50 cents per pair additional.

23529 Solid Gold Spectacles, hook bows. This is one of the most popular styles, 14 karat.
Retail price $7.00. Our price ... $5.25

23530 Solid Gold Frameless or Skeleton Spectacles, hook bows, made in 14 karat only.
Retail price $6.00. Our price ... 4 75

Half-eye or pulpit pattern spectacles, also side light spectacles, tinted, furnished at low prices.

Colored Lens Spectacles.

Without Focus.

23532—Coquille Spectacles for weak eyes, shell shaped, smoke or blue lenses, straight temples, steel frame, ordinary quality, Price ... $0.20

23533 Coquille Spectacles, blue or smoke lenses, better quality and finish, first quality lenses, straight temples ... .35

23534 Coquille Spectacles, blue or smoke lenses, straight temples, extra fine finish, ground and polished Coquille lenses ... 1.25

23535 Steel Spectacles, riding or hook bows, ordinary quality Coquille lenses blue or smoke. $0.25

23536 Steel Spectacles, riding or hook bows good quality, Coquille lenses, blue or smoke ... $0.50

23537 Steel Spectacles, riding or hook bows, extra finish, with fine quality ground Coquille blue or smoke lenses ... 1 25

23538 Steel Spectacles, riding or hook bows, fitted with *flat lenses*, smoked or blue in light, medium or dark shades, nickel plated frame ... 1.20

When ordering *colored* spectacles, always mention shade of lenses desired.

Eyeglasses.

All eyeglasses costing over 50 cents are furnished with a neat leather case and silk cord without charge.

Each.

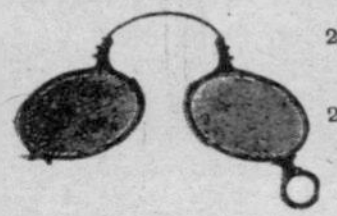

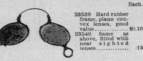

23539 Hard rubber frame, plano convex lenses, good value $0.10
23540 Same as above, fitted with near sighted lenses .... .15

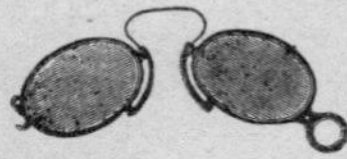

23541 Vulcanized rubber frame good quality, periscopic lenses, steel spring nose piece .... .25

23542 Hard rubber frame, first quality, periscopic lenses, convex or concave, adjustable spring nose guard .... .50
23543 Zylonite (or celluloid) frames; very light weight, highest quality, convex or concave periscopic lenses, with adjustable spring nose piece (see cut of 23546) a fine glass 1.00
23545 Steel frame, fine finish; periscopic convex lenses .... .55

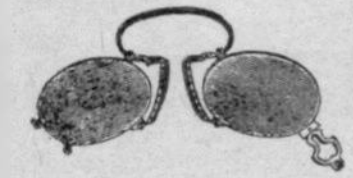

23546 Steel frame good finish periscopic lenses, with patent adjustable spring nose guard, a very comfortable glass, all numbers .... .90

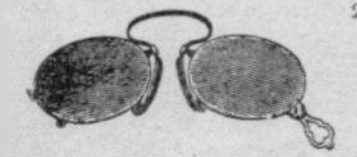

23547 Steel frames grooved periscopic concave lenses, first quality, semi-invisible frames, a beautiful and deservedly popular glass for near-sightedness 1.00
23548 Steel frames, fine finish, double or periscopic convex Brazilian pebble lenses. Nothing better 1.75

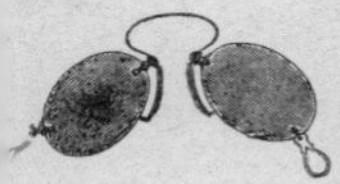

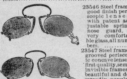

23549 Frameless Eyeglasses, double or periscopic convex or concave lenses, good quality .... .50
23550 Frameless Eyeglasses, same as 23549, extra fine finish, fitted with patent adjustable nose guard .... .75
23551 Alumnico Frame, (resembling silver) periscopic lenses, good quality 1.10
23552 Gold Filled Eyeglasses, seamless gold filled frame with adjustable spring, solid or offset guards. Recommended for those who cannot afford solid gold. Fitted with cork nose pieces, making a light, comfortable, well appearing and popular glass. Has first quality periscopic lenses. 1.25

Gold Eyeglasses.

Assay and Workmanship Guaranteed.

23553 Solid gold frame, first quality periscopic lenses, regular weight, round eye wire.

	8 karat.	10 karat.	14 karat.
Price, each	$3.00	$3.50	$4.50

Each

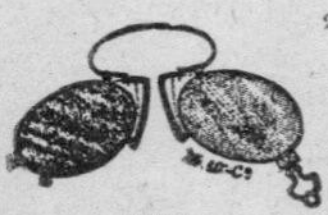

23554.

23554 Solid Gold Frame, with first quality periscopic lenses, medium weight, round eye wire, with self-adjusting spring nose pieces (see cut); a very desirable glass. Retails at $7.00 and $9.00.
Our price—10 karat, $4.75; 14 karat $6.50
23555 Frameless Gold Eyeglasses with periscopic lenses, first quality (see cut of 23549.) Retails at $7.00. Our price, 10 karat 4.25
Cork guards to nose pieces of any eyeglasses to which they can be fitted, 15c. extra.

Colored Lens Eyeglasses.

Nos. 23556 to 23559 are made with either Coquille or flat lenses. Always specify which style you want.

Each.

23556 Rubber Eyeglasses, rubber frames, Coquille or flat lenses, smoke or blue $0.25
23557 Same as 23556, with first quality lenses .. .50
23558 Steel Frames, finest finish, Coquille or flat lenses, smoke or blue .... .50
23559 Same, extra fine finish, with finest ground Coquille or flat lenses 1.25

WALL PAPER? Yes—Any color, any price, any width, border to match—and no drug store prices either. Samples free.

Spectacle and Eyeglass Cases.

Spectacle and eyeglass cases, when sent by mail, allow 2c. extra for postage. Each. Per doz.

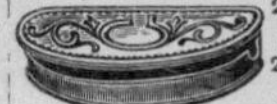

	Each.	Per doz.
23561 Eyeglass Case, nickel, velvet lined	$0 20	$2.00
23562 Spectacle Case, 6 in. hammered, open end, nickel plated	.20	2.00
23563 Spectacle Case, fine planished or japanned tin, side opening with patent snap catch, length 6⅛ inches	.15	1.50
23563½ Riding Bow Spectacle Case, 5 inch, side opening, planished tin	.14	1.40
23564 Spectacle Case, tin, patent open end; length, 6¼ inches	.12	1.10
23565 Spectacle Cases, tin, side opening; length, 7 inches	.10	1.00
23566 Spectacle Cases, leather, open end, common	.05	.50
23567 Spectacle Cases, fine leather, open or closed end	.09	.95

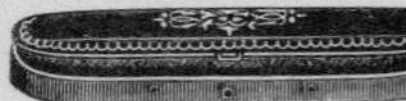

23568 Spectacle Cases, papier mache, inlaid design, closed or open end, or side opening with spring catch, made 6¾ inches for straight temple, and 4¾ for riding bow specs	.25	2.10

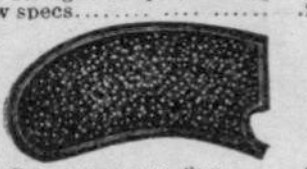

23570 Eyeglass Cases, morocco, fine	.07	.70
23571 Eyeglass Cases, papier mache, metal or pearl, inlaid open or closed end	.25	2.25

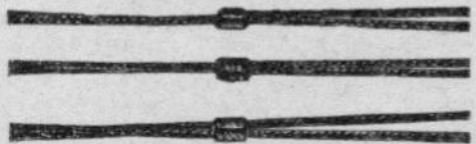

23573 Eyeglass Cords, pure silk, light weight, with bead slide	.05	.50
23574 Eyeglass Cords, pure silk, fast dye, medium weight, with silk covered slide	.08	.75
23575 Eyeglass Cords, pure silk, fast dye, extra heavy weight, with silk covered slide	.10	1.00

Eyeglass Chains and Hooks.

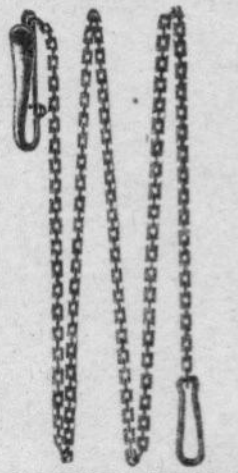

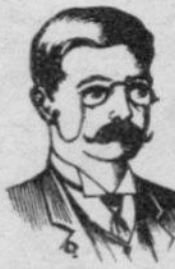

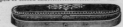

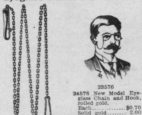

23576

24576 New Model Eyeglass Chain and Hook, rolled gold.
Each $0.70
Solid gold 2.00
23577 Eyeglass Chain, solid gold hook and holder. Each $2.25
23578 Same, 1-10 rolled gold 1.00
23579 Gold Eyeglass Chain, with snap holder and hair pin. Each 2.75

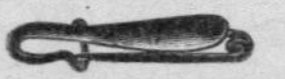

Each.
23580 Eyeglass Hook, solid gold $0.90
23581 Eyeglass Hooks, gold plated, engraved .... .35
23582 Eyeglass Hooks, japanned steel .... .07

Goggles.

When ordering goggles, state color of lenses desired.

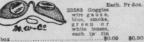

Each. Pr doz.

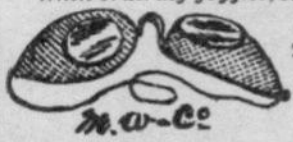

23583 Goggles wire gauze, blue, smoke, green or white lenses, each in tin box $0.09 $0.90
Postage, 5 cents per pair.
23584 Goggles or Eye protectors, good finish, velvet bound edges, in leather case, blue, smoke or white lenses .... .35 3.50
Postage, 5c. per pair.
23585 Railroad or Driving Spectacles, blue or smoke lenses, velvet bound, straight temple bows .... .75 7.50
Postage, 5c. per pair.

Goggles—Continued.

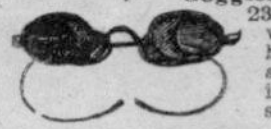

23586 Driving Spectacles, well finished, steel frame, hook temples, fine coquille smoke colored lenses, folding wire gauze protecting shields. Each $1.25
Postage, 5 cents.

Mica Eye Protector.

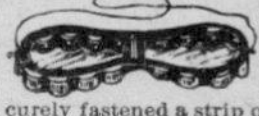

23589 Wholly protects the eye from the entrance of foreign bodies. It consists of a light metal rim, hinged in the middle. Each section of the rim holds a sheet of mica around which is securely fastened a strip of felt, perforated so that perfect ventilation is secured. A silk elastic cord is attached to each, encircling the head of the wearer and holding the protector in place. Made in clear, smoke, or blue. Price $0.45
Postage .... .05

Shooting and Millers' Spectacles.

All shooting spectacles furnished with neat case free of charge.

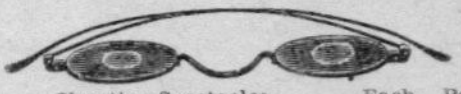

Shooting Spectacles. Each. Per doz.

23590 Shooting Spectacles improve the vision wonderfully when viewing a field or landscape, and prevent the eye becoming affected by strong light. Amber colored shooting lenses $0.25 $2.50
23591 Shooting Spectacles, with fine quality of amber lenses and riding or hook bow frame .... .50 5.50
23592 Millers' or Stonecutters' Spectacles, for protecting the eyes from injury; plain, white lenses, large eyes, turn pin temples .... .20 2.00
Postage on either Shooting or Millers' Spectacles, 5c

Eye Shades.

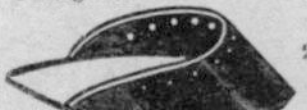

23594 White's Eye Shade, with metal rim and leather bound edge, as illustrated. Each $0.12
Postage .... .03

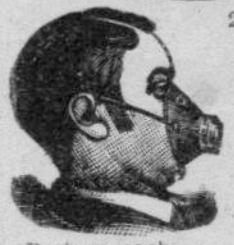

23596 The Patent Dust Protector "An ounce of Prevention is worth a Pound of Cure." Perfect Protection, Perfect Ventilation. Dust protector for protecting the nose and mouth from inhalations of dust of every character. It is constructed of light metal, nickel plated, is handsomely finished, and will last several years.
Price, each $0.90
Price, per dozen 9.00
Postage, each .... .05

Ear Trumpets and Tubes.

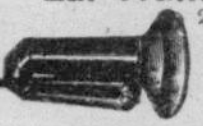

23597 Bugle-Shape Ear Trumpet, japanned metal, made in three sizes, small, medium or large.
Each $2.25

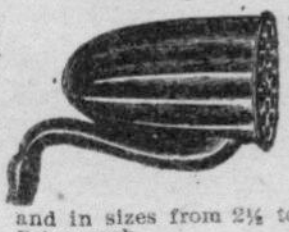

23598 London Hearing Horns, designed for those who are moderately deaf, as they can easily be carried in the pocket and concealed in the hand when in use. Finished in either black or nickel plate and in sizes from 2½ to 4 inches in height.
Price, each 2.63

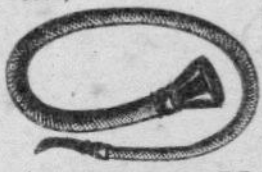

23599 Conversation Tubes, rubber ends, flexible mohair, conical shape tube, 3 feet in length; this tube suits the most obstinate cases of deafness.
Price each 2.75

Field or Marine Glasses.

All have fine achromatic lens; the expression, 24-line or 26-line, gives the diameter of the largest lens in the glass, there being 11 lines to the inch.

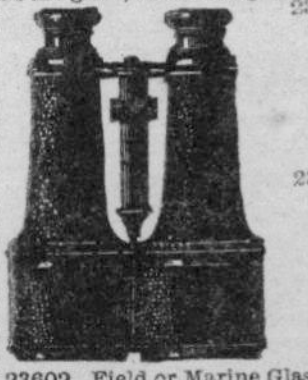

23600 Field or Marine Glasses, extension hood, in neat case with shoulder strap. A good, strong glass for ordinary work.
24-line $8.25
26-line 9.00
Weight, 2¼ lbs.
23601 Field or Marine Glasses, extension hood, in neat case, with shoulder strap. This glass is a little more powerful than the preceding.
24-line 10.25
26-line 10.85
Weight, 2¾ lbs.
23602 Field or Marine Glasses, extension hood, in neat case, with shoulder strap, finest finish, extra quality, high power; weight 2½ pounds.
24-line .... $13.50 26-line 15 25

Boat Compasses—Continued.

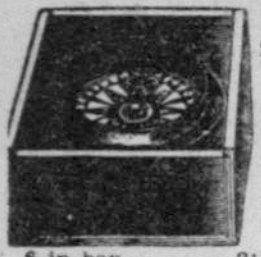

23709 These Boat Compasses have brass bowls and gimbal rings, and are mounted in strong oak box and sliding cover. The cards are jeweled and mounted on hardened pivots. The bowls are heavily weighted to assure steadiness.

6 in. box	3½ in. card	Each $4.50
8 in. box	5 in. card	Each 6.00
10 in. box	7 in. card	Each 8.00

23710 Boat Compasses, same construction as No. 23709, but mounted in dove-tailed mahogany box with sliding cover.

4 in. box	4½ in. card	Each 4.00
6 in. box	3½ in. card	Each 5.00

23711 Yacht Compass, with Singer's jeweled floating card dial, brass bowl casing on gimbals in burnished brass slip cover case.

8¾ in. box ......2¼ in. card ......Each 5.50

Folding Sight Compasses.

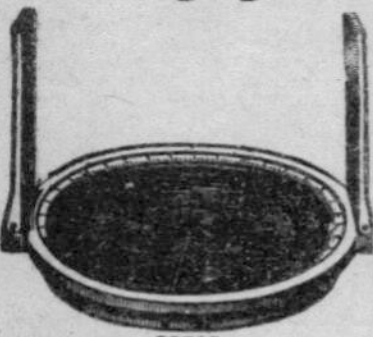

23715

Very serviceable for retracing lines once surveyed. Weight about ten ounces each.

23715 2 in. needle, folding sights in leather case. Each $4.25

23716 2¼ in. needle, folding sights, in leather case. Each...... $5.75

23717 2½ in. needle, folding sights in leather case. Each..$6.00

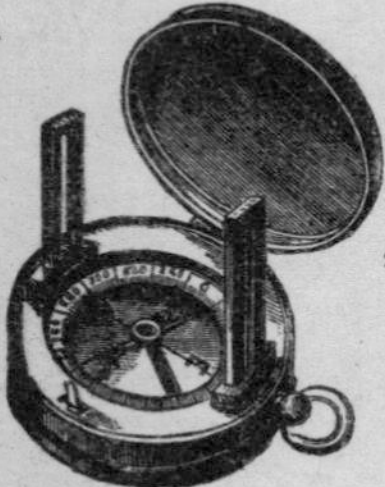

23718-23720

23718 2 inch diameter bar needle hinge cover, nickel plated. folding sights. Each........$4.30

23719 2⅜ inches diameter, bar needle, hinge cover nickel plated. folding sights. Each............$5.00

23720 2¾ inch diameter bar needle, hinge cover nickel plated, folding sights. Each $6.20

Prices on larger size or more expensive compasses furnished upon request. Give description of compass wanted if you can.

Clinometer Compass.

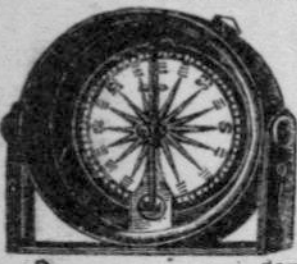

23721 Combined Sight Compass and Clinometer, bronze case, slip cover, silvered dial, graduated to one degree, edge bar needle, with agate center and automatic stop. Pivoted sights, which are turned down to form a base when used as clinometer; can be used for levels or inclinations, in inches, per yard or in degrees. 3 inch diameter. Each, in morocco case....$8.50 Postage................ .15

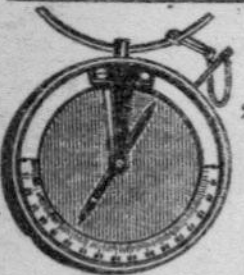

23722 Dip Needle Compass, for prospecting for minerals; a well made and accurate miners' dipping needle compass. Brass rim and nickle plated dial. Each instrument in morocco case. Price, each........$9.75

SURVEYORS' COMPASSES.
Folding Sights.

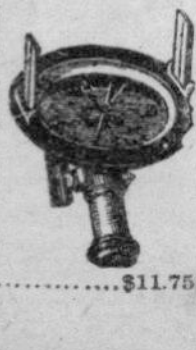

23723 2½ inch needle, folding sights, ball socket, Jacob staff mountings.................. $6.96 Weight, 1 pound.

23724 2¾ inch needle, folding sights, ball socket, Jacob staff mountings........................$8.00 Weight, 1¼ pounds.

23725 3½ inch needle, folding sights, ball sockets, Jacob staff mountings................. $9.00 Weight, 1½ pounds.

23726 3¾ inch needle, folding sights, ball socket, with two levels, Jacob staff mountings. Each...................$11.75 Weight, 2¼ pounds.

Surveyors' Compasses—Continued.

23727 4½ inch needle, folding sight, ball socket, with two levels, Jacob staff mountings. Weight, 2¼ pounds. Each.................. $13.25

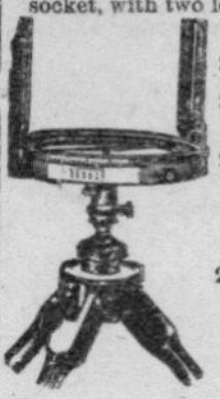

23728 Tripod, with Jacob staff top for compasses. Each..$2.40

23729 Jacob staff with metal shoes. Each............ $0.90 Weight, 2¼ pounds.

23730 Vernier Compass, 3½ inch needle, folding sights, two levels, with tripod. Each.........$19.00 Without tripod .... 15.00 Weight, complete, 7 pounds. Weight, without tripod, 2½ lbs.

23731 Vernier Compass, 4½ inch needle, folding sights, two levels, with tripod. Each........$21.00 Without tripod .... 17.00 Weight, complete, 7½ lbs. Weight, without tripod, 3 lbs.

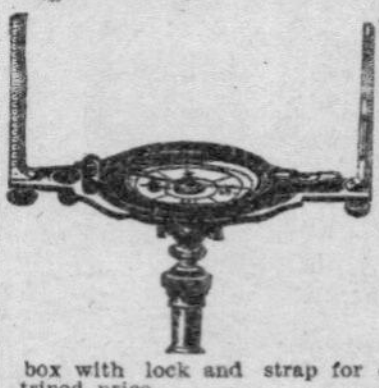

23732 High grade Vernier Compass, 5 inch needle with Vernier inside compass circle, two straight levels, Jacob staff mountings. brass cover, outkeeper, vernier under the glass for adding or subtracting the magnetic variations of the needle, sights graduated for taking angle of elevation and depression; in mahogany box with lock and strap for carrying. Without tripod, price ....$35.00 With tripod, price................................ 40.00

The Vernier Transit or Transit Compass.

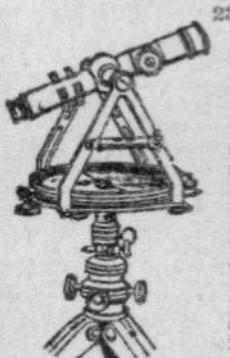

23734 This instrument will be found very convenient for country surveyors who want to do good land surveying and not invest so much money for a regular transit. It is provided with a very substantial leveling arrangement, has 2 straight levels, and in place of the sights it has a strong telescope, 8 inches long, with cross-hairs complete, like the telescope of a transit. The needle is 5¼ inches long, with variation plate inside the circle. The instrument is not heavier than an ordinary compass; weight without tripod, 8lbs., and can easily be carried by passing the arm through between telescope axis and plate. It also has a clamp and tangent screw to center. It is packed in a nice mahogany box containing magnifying glass, adjusting pin and shade. Price. with light tripod..$75.00

Levels and Transit.

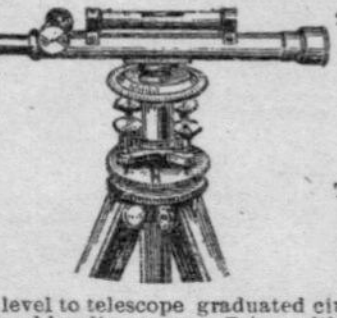

23736 Farmers' and Builders' Drainage and Leveling Instrument, complete with wooden tripod and metal base, for use on walls of buildings in course of erection.

Telescope 11 inches long with rack and pinion adjustment, two-mile range, best achromatic objectives with cross hairs level to telescope graduated circle, with clamp and leveling screws. Price, with carrying case..$35.00 Weight, complete, 3½ pounds.

NOTE.—The addition of a compass, mounted on telescope under the level, furnished, if desired, without extra charge.

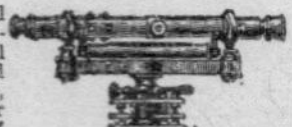

23737 New Improved Leveling Instrument. The principal features of this level are its compactness and lightness. It has a long, stout center of phosphor bronze, and the rings of telescope are of the hardest bell metal. The cross bar is cast hollow, carrying with it, partly inside, the clamp and tangent screw, so they always keep the same relative position to telescope on the right hand side of observer. If desired we provide the inside of wyes with agate bearings at an additional cost of $10.00, as this protects the wyes against wear from the turning of telescope, the cause of frequent adjustment; it is quite an important improvement. The telescope has an adjustable arrangement to keep cross wires in an exact horizontal position, consisting of a projecting pin on the collars. When this pin is brought in contact with this adjustable screw the wire is horizontal. This permits the collars to lay in the wyes without the least strain, and the telescope can be revolved without opening the clasps. Weight of instrument, with 18 inch telescope, 9¼ lbs. Price of 18 in., Y level, each.......................$110.00

Engineering Instruments—Continued.

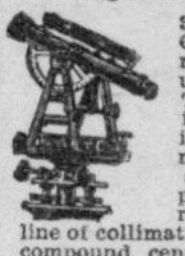

3738 Engineers' Transit, Horizontal Circle, with double Verniers, read to minutes or 30" or 20" if desired, graduations silvered, improved Spring Tangent Screws, shifting center to set instruments exactly over a given point, improved telescope 11 inches long, magnifying 25 times, exactly balanced and reversing on both ends, eye-piece provided with improved screw arrangements to focus cross wires, the line of collimation correct on all distances, long compound centers of phosphor bronze, improved tripod. Weight, 13½ lbs., packed in box containing plumb-bob, screw driver, magnifier and adjusting pins and shade. Price.........$165.00

23739 Same as above, but with level and clamp to telescope...180.00

23740 Same as No. 23739 but with full circle or arc of 3½ inch radius, the arc being fastened with a clamp to the telescope axis, so that instrument can be used as plain transit. Price...200.00

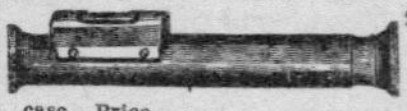

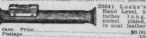

23641 Locke's Hand Level, 5 inches long, nickel plated, in neat leather case. Price...............................$6.00 Postage.. .10

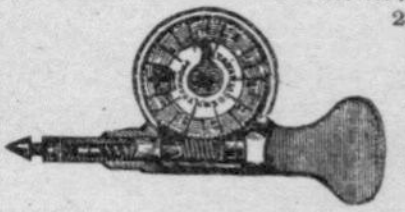

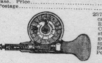

23742 Speed Indicator The Tabor Revolution Counter, with stop motion. A good, simple speed indicator. Each.......$0.90 Postage.... .05

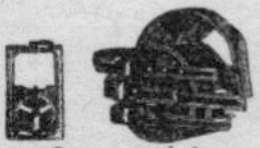

23743 Odometer. Can be attached to any carriage without injury to the wheel and removed at pleasure. The circumference of the wheel being given, the distance is obtained by multiplying it by the number of revolutions recorded upon the dial. Inside dial with leather case and straps. (See cut). Price..$12.75

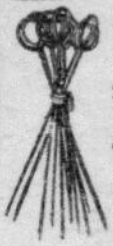

23744 Best Steel Arrows or marking pins, 15-inch, 11 in set. Price, per set. $1.05

23745 Iron Arrows or marking pins, 11 in set, 15-inch......................... .60

Measuring Chains.
Of Steel and Iron.

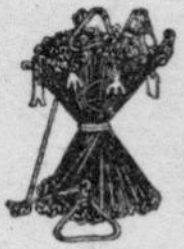

23746 Steel, best grade, brazed links and rings; brass handles.

Feet,	33	50	66	100
Each,	$4.65	$5.70	$8.75	$9.80

23748 Steel, oval Rings, not brazed, brass handles.

Feet,	33	50	66	100
Each,	$3.15	$4.10	$5.75	$6.90

23750 Iron, oval Rings, brass handles.

Feet,	33	50	66	100
Each,	$2.20	$3.10	$3.75	$4.80

Improved Tape Chains.

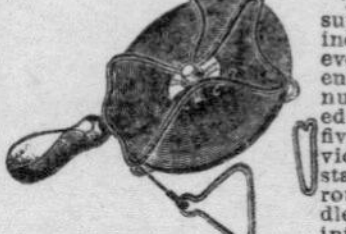

These tapes are made of superior steel, about ¼ inch wide, graduated every foot by a brass rivet, end feet in 10ths and the number of feet are stamped on brass plates every five feet. They are provided with a handy, substantial reel and a pair of round, detachable handles. Thes tapes are not intended to take the place of the finely graduated steel tapes, but are especially designed for convenience and durability to replace the heavy chains in all land surveying, railroad and canal work and town plotting. For country, field and town work these tapes have given excellent satisfaction. They can be dragged through woodland, brush, etc., and if they are nickle-plated, they do not rust and do not require any oiling or cleaning after being used.

23751 50 ft. long, graduated every foot, end feet in 10ths, nickel-plated. Each....................$4.50

23752 50 ft. long, graduated every foot, end feet in 10ths, plain. Each.......................... 3.60

23753 66 ft. long, graduated every link, nickel-plated. Each.......................... 5.40

23754 66 ft. long, graduated every link, plain. Each................................ 4.50

23755 100 feet long, graduated every foot, end feet in 10ths, nickel-plated. Each.............. 5.85

23756 100 feet long, graduated every foot, end feet in 10ths, plain. Each.................... 4.50

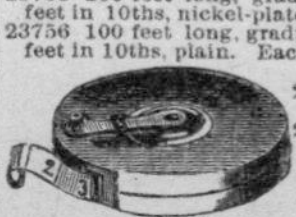

23760

23758 Timber, scribes, medium..........................$0.75

23759 Timber, Scribes, large, extra heavy, with steel gouging blade.......$1.00

Surveyors' and Engineers' Measuring Tapes.

23760 Metallic Measuring Tapes, enameled waterproof linen, wire warp; in leather cases; folding handle; marked feet and 12ths; links on back.

25 ft.	33 ft.	50 ft.	66 ft.	75 ft.	100 ft.
$1.75	$2.00	$2.50	$2.75	$3.00	$4.00

23761 Metallic Tapes, same description, but divided 1-10 foot for engineers' use.

25 ft	33 ft.	50 ft.	66 ft.	75 ft.	100 ft.
$1.75	$2.00	$2.50	$2.75	$3.00	$4.00

23762 Steel Tapes, in leather case, folding flush handle; nickel trimmings; marked feet and inches; links on back.

25 ft.	33 ft.	50 ft.	66 ft.	75 ft.	100 ft.
$3.75	$4.50	$6.00	$7.75	$9.00	$11.00

23763 Steel Tapes, same description, but divided in tenths of foot instead of inches; for engineers' use.

25 ft.	33 ft.	50 ft.	66 ft.	75 ft.	100 ft.
$3.75	$4.50	$6.00	$7.75	$9.00	$11.00

Steel and Linen Pocket Tapes.

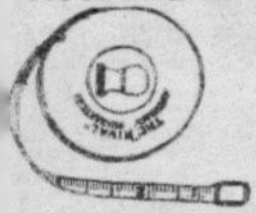

23764 Steel pocket tapes, very light, flush handle, divided 1-12 foot, 25 feet long. Weight, 6 ounces. Each $3.00

23765 Same description as above, 50 feet long. Weight 9 oz. Each $3.65

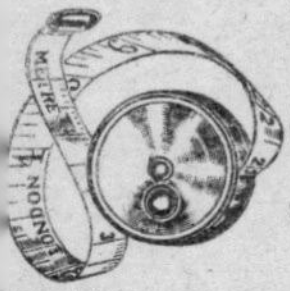

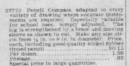

23766 Steel pocket tapes, with spring and stop in German silver cases, divided 1-16 inch.

3 ft.	6 ft.	9 ft.	12 ft.
$0.95	$1.25	$1.75	$2.25

23767 Divided in 1-16 inch and meter.

3 ft.	6 ft.	9 ft.	12 ft.
$1.35	$2.10	$2.70	$3.40

23768 Divided in 1-16 inch on one side and in 1-10 inch on the other side. Length, 6 ft. Each..$1.50

23769 Linen pocket tapes, with spring and stop, in nickel plated cases, divided into inches and meter. Each, 3 ft ...... .40
Each, 5 ft ...... .50

23770 Best water-proof linen spring pocket tapes, in German silver cases, with stop, divided inches and meter. Each, 3 ft ...... .60
Each, 6 ft ...... .85

Other tapes and graduation furnished on short notice.

Mathematical and Drawing Instruments.

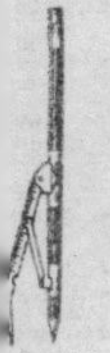

23775 Pencil Compass, adapted to every variety of drawing where accurate instruments are required. Especially valuable for school uses. Simply adjusted. The leg is strengthened by a brace and moving sleeve as shown in cut. Make any size circle from ½ in. to 8 in. in diameter. Price, each, including good quality nickel rubber tipped pencil $0.15
Per dozen 1.50
Postage ...... .02
Special price in large quantities.

Polygraph.

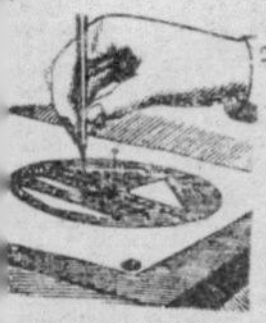

23777 Draws and designs, giving correct curves and degrees. 10,000 mathematical figures can easily be produced. The greatest drawing assistant ever invented. Put up in neat box, with full explanations, directions for use and specimens of drawings.
Nickel plated, each $0.25
Per dozen 2.50
Postage ...... .05

** Always be sure to state the amount of money enclosed with order.

IN OUR

OPTICAL GOODS DEPARTMENT

We include Optical Goods of all kinds; Surveyors', Mathematical, Meteorological and Scientific Instruments, Drawing Instruments and Material. We are in a position to furnish nearly everything made in goods of the classes mentioned.

Drawing Instruments in Cases.

Nickel Plated Drawing instruments, with improved pen and pencil points, in pocket cases with round corners and bar locks.

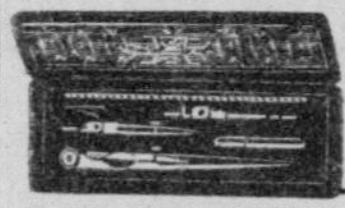

23780 Set with 4¾ inch dividers, with pen and pencil points, rule and leads.
Per set $0.45
Weight, 4 oz.

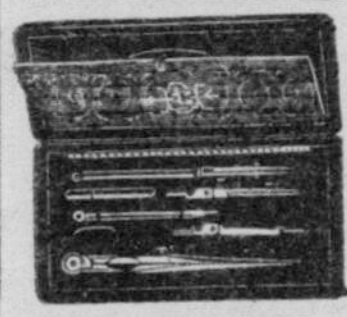

23781 Set with 4¾ inch dividers, with pen and pencil points, lengthening bar and ruling pen, rule and leads and metal protractor.
Per set $0.75
Weight 6 oz.

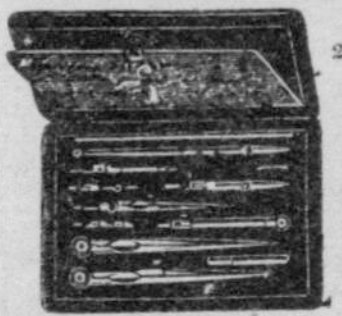

23782 Set with 4¾ inch dividers, with pen and pencil point, lengthening bar, 4¾ inch plain dividers, 3 inch needle point divider with pen and pencil points and improved ruling pen, rule, leads and metal protractor.
Weight, 8 oz.
Per set $1.35

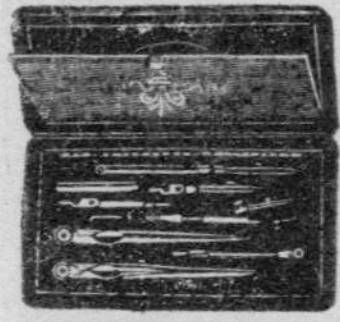

23783 Set with 4¾ inch dividers, pen and pencil points, lengthening bar, 4¾ inch plain dividers, spring bow pen, improved ruling pen, rule, leads and metal protractor.
Weight, 8 oz.
Per set $1.60

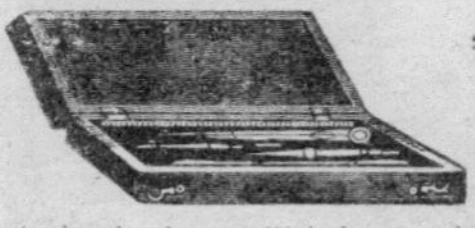

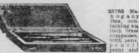

23785 Mahogany Box, containing 4½ inch brass compasses, with pens, pencil point and lengthening bar, drawing pen 4½ inch; crayon holder, horn protractor and divided rule. Weight, 7 oz.
Per set $0.75

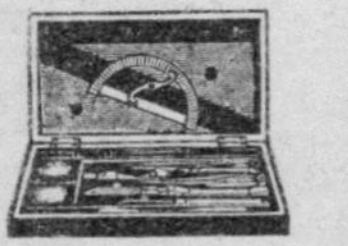

23787 Mahogany Case, brass instruments, 4½ inch compasses with pen, pencil point and lengthening bar, 4½ inch plain dividers, 4½ inch drawing pen, 7 inch scale, 3½ inch protractor, crayon holder, 2 triangles, colors, brushes, etc., very low at the price we ask.
Weight, 15 oz. Per set $1.75

23789 Rosewood Case, with lock and key, brass instruments set in tray, 6½ in. compasses, with pen and pencil points and lengthening bar, 4½ in. plain dividers, 4 in. compass with pen and pencil points, ruling pen, brass and horn protractors, divided rule. Weight, 1¼ pounds.
Per set $3.25

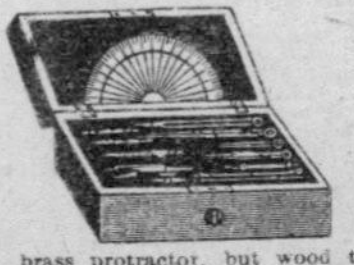

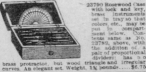

23790 Rosewood Case with lock and key, brass instruments set in tray so that colors, etc., may be put in compartment below. Contents same as No. 23789, above, with the addition of a pair of proportional dividers; has no brass protractor, but wood triangle and irregular curves. An elegant set. Weight, 1¾ pounds......$6.75

BABY'S OUTFIT—Everything complete and SO PRETTY—Cheaper than to make them.

Swiss Drawing Instruments.

Of German silver, steel points and high finish.

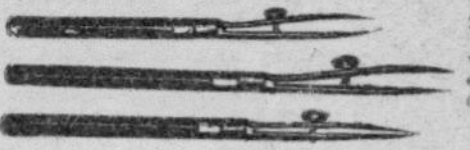

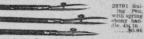

23791 Ruling Pen, with spring ebony handle, 4½ in.. ......$0.85

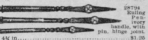

23792 Ruling Pen, with spring, ebony handle, 5 in $0.90

23793 Ruling Pen with spring, ebony handle, 5½ in 1.00

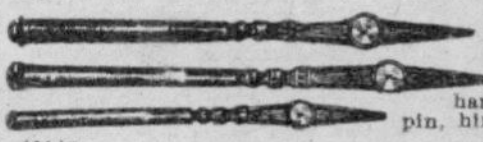

23794 Ruling Pen-ivory handle, with pin, hinge joint. 4¾ in $1.25

23795 Ruling Pen, ivory handle, with pin hinge joint, 5½ in 1.50

23796 Ruling Pen, ivory handle, with pin hinge joint, 6½ in 1.75

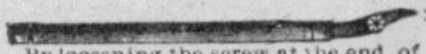

23797 Curved Pen improved

By loosening the screw at the end of handle, the bar running through hollow center acts as a pivot for the pen, which will follow any curve readily without blotting the edges of the curve ruler.

If the upper screw is fastened, it can be used as a drawing pen, and is useful for ruling into corners and for fine work.
Each $1.75

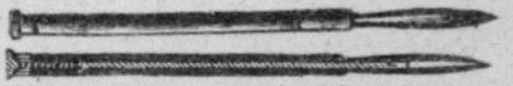

23798 Drawing Pen, improved, without set screw.

The pen opens and closes by turning a thumbscrew at the upper end of handle, making the screw through the blades unnecessary and a displacement of the nibs sideways impossible. As there is no obstruction to the sight in working, this pen is perfect for work.
Each $1.55

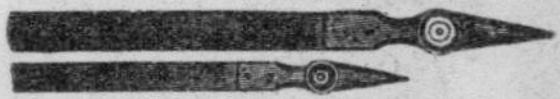

23799 Swedish Style Ruling Pens, for long lines, 5 inches $1.25

23800 Swedish Style Ruling Pens, for long lines. 7 inches 1.50

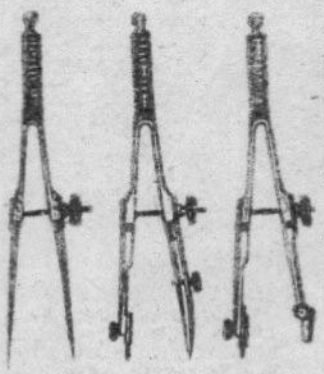

23801 Steel Spring Bow Dividers, 3½ inch metal handle......$1.90

23802 Steel Spring Bow Pencil, 3½ inch metal handle $2.00

23803 Steel Spring Bow Pen, 3½ inch metal handle $2.00

23804 Set of Bows, composed of Nos. 23801-2 and 3 in case......$6.00

23805 Dotting Instrument, with 6 wheels in case $3.65

NOTE.—By throwing back the spring the wheels of different patterns are inserted.

ALTENEDER PATTERN.

All pencil points arranged to hold Faber's leads.

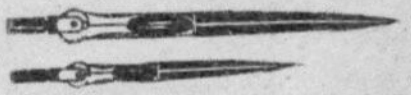

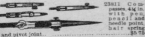

23806 Plain Dividers, 4½ in. pivot joint. Price......$1.75

33806½ Plain Dividers, 6 inch pivot joint......$2.25

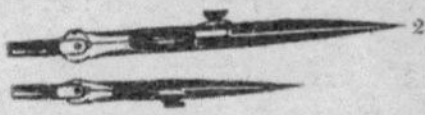

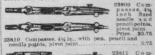

23807 Hair Spring Dividers, 4½ inch joint......$2.50

23808 Hair Spring Dividers, 6 inch pivots, joint.$3.00

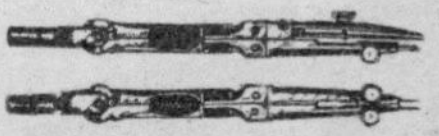

23809 Compasses, 4½ inch fixed needle and pencil-points, pivot joint Price......$3.75

23810 Compasses, 4½ in., with pen, pencil and needle points, pivot joint 3.75

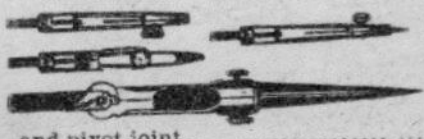

23811 Compasses, 4½ in. with pen, pencil and needle point, hair spring and pivot joint......$5.75

Aneroid Barometers.

(For Farmers, Horticulturists, etc.)

Directions for reading accompany each barometer. Barometers must be carefully handled and adjusted; they are delicate instruments and should not be handled by anyone who does not know how to use them.

24087 Aneroid Barometer, nickel plated case, open face, card dial, diameter 2¼ inches, weight 7 oz. Each $1.75

24088 Aneroid Barometer, nickel plated case, open face, card dial, diameter 4 inches, weight 10 oz. Each $3.25

24089 Universal Aneroid Barometer, closed porcelain dial. Accurate and reliable, nickel plate frame, 5 inch dial, weight, 1 lb. Each $6.00

24090 Aneroid Barometer, polished brass case, 5¼ inch diameter, silvered metal dial with aperture in center exposing working parts of instrument, Fahrenheit thermometer and beveled edge plate glass cover. A beautiful and accurate instrument in velvet-lined case; weight 2 lbs. Price $12.00

24091 Holosteric Aneroid Barometer, same general description as above, but 8 inches in diameter and supplied with two thermometers, Fahrenheit and Centigrade, weight in velvet lined case, 4½ lbs. Price $18.00

24092 "Standard" Aneroid Barometer carved wood frame, 13 in. long, porcelain dial, 8 inches in diameter, opal plate glass thermometer, complete with a perfect thermometer beveled edge, 16 in. long, weight, 10 lbs. Price $20.00

Pocket Aneroid and Altitude Barometers.

24094 Pocket Aneroid Barometer, compensated for temperature and reading to 16,000 feet for altitude. This may be used for measuring height as well as foretelling the weather. Nickel, watch size, 1¾ in. diameter, metal dial, open face, put up in plush-lined morocco case. Weight, 4½ oz. Each $9.50

24096 Pocket Aneroid Barometer, compensated for temperature and reading to 16,000 feet altitude. Brass open face, metal dial, covered with heavy beveled glass, size 1½ in., put in best morocco case, silk lined. Each ... 14.00 Weight, 4 oz.

24096 Pocket Aneroid Barometer, compensated, same general description as preceding, special finish, extra size, 2½ in. diameter, with beveled altitude scale, reading to 16,000 feet. Weight, 7 oz. Each $17.00

24097 Pocket Altitude Aneroid Barometer, watch size, 2 in. diameter, silvered metal dial reading to 16,000 feet, compensated, open face, fitted with heavy beveled glass. The back or reverse side has thermometer reading from 20 to 120 degrees and needle compass, with raised dial; a perfectly made altitude Aneroid Barometer, Thermometer and Compass combined, finish in nickel, put up in best plush and satin lined case. Each .... 20.00 Weight, 6 oz.

Moisture Gauge.

24098 Moisture Gauge or Hygrometer for determining the humidity of the atmosphere or per centage of moisture in the air. Used out of doors or in the house and in incubators. Moisture gauge, with metal back. Each .... $0.90 Postage ...... .05

24099 Moisture Gauge mounted on wooden base. Each .... 1.25 Postage 10

24100 German Hygrometer brass case, card dial. This instrument is guaranteed accurate, measure 3½ in. diameter, weight 4 ounces, suitable to use in connection with our incubator Thermometer. Price each $1.75

24101 German Hygrometer, nickel case card dial, 3½ inch diameter and mounted on 6 inch wood base, making handsome instrument. Weight, 8 ounces. Price, each 2.25

Thermometers.

NOTE.—Thermometers *should not* be shipped by mail. We *cannot* be responsible for breakage.

24105 Thermometer, japanned tin case, white tubes, quicksilver tested. This is the style in ordinary use. Length, 7 inches. One-half dozen in wood box.
Each $0.12
Per dozen 1.20

24106 Length, 10 inches.
Each .... .16
Per dozen 1.65

24107 Length, 12 inches.
Each .... .21
Per dozen 2.00

24108 Thermometers, Standard, with seasoned tubes, tested and graduated with special care as to accuracy. Scale tubes and case extra heavy, mounted with bright metal clasps. No better or more accurate thermometers can be made. Signal service flag stamped on face of each as a guarantee of correctness. Length 10 inches.
Each $0.90

24109 Length, 12 inches.
Each 1.15

24110 Length, 14 inches.
Each 1.50

24111 Standard House Thermometer, with 8 inch metal scale, mounted on solid oak back and graduated in large figures and degrees, reading from 30 to 90 above zero. Magnifying tube filled with red fluid making a most desirable and accurate instrument specially adapted for indoor use.
Price $1.10

24112 Thermometer, same design as above, except has 8 inch metal scale graduated from 20 degrees below to 120 degrees above zero, standard mercury, white back tube, and is practice for either indoor or outdoor use.
Price $0.85

24113 Same style as above with 10 inch scale, graduated from 30 below to 120 degrees above zero.
Price each $1.00

24114 Radial Scale Thermometer, designed to be suspended by an accompanying chain and snap, can be read at a distance from every side of the room. Handsome oxidized metal frame and scale graduated in large figures and degrees, reading from 30 to 100 degrees above zero. Bulb is filled with red fluid and protected on all sides.
Price $1.25

24115 Thermometers, German style, similar to cut black ebonized wood body, graduated on best oak tube, nickeled guard and trimmings. Length 8 inches.
Each $0.25
Per dozen 2.25

24116 Thermometer, high grade 8 inch Germany style, ebonized, oval top, best wood finish, magnifying mercury filled sun glass tube, graduation plain in double degree. Reliable for either indoor or out of door use.
Price, each $0.44

24115 Window Thermometers, 10 inch cylinder glass with porcelain scale, nickel arms, accurate, convenient and good value.
Price, each $0.90

24117 Window Thermometer, heavy plate glass figured, annealed, polished beveled edges with straps support to hold thermometer several inches from the wall or sash. A superb and accurate instrument; 10 inches.
Price, each $1.50

Thermometers—Continued

24118 Metal frame Vestibule Thermometers, filigree pattern, neat finish, Entire length 11 inches. Graduated 8 inch metal scale with brass guard over bulb. Price $0.75

24119 Standard Metal frame Thermometer, filigree design, neat finish. A handsome mantle ornament. Has heavy beveled edge 8 inch metal scale with etched graduation and burnished brass guard over bulb.
Entire length, 11½ in. Price $1.50

Registering Thermometers.

24120 U. S. Signal Service Standard Thermometers, 12 inches long, with brass insulating strap to fasten in position. Degrees etched on metal seal. Each $2.50

24121 Same size and style as above, but minimum self registering thermometer. Each $3.50

24122 Same size and style as 24092, but maximum self-acting thermometer Each $3.50

24123 Minimum Thermometer, very accurate, registers to 50 degrees below zero. Each $1.00

24124 Minimum Thermometer, 10 in. boxwood, self-registering, accurate and good value, scale reading from 40 below to 120 above zero. Each $0.85

Distance Thermometers.

Unequaled for convenience, accuracy and fine appearance. The term Distance Thermometer is applied for the reason that by using large, distinct figures printed in black, gold or silver, and alternating them either side of the scale, the temperature can be read at a glance at a distance of from 12 to 30 feet.

24125 Distance Thermometer ornamented metal, black figures, japan case. Size 2 3 inches. Price $0.23

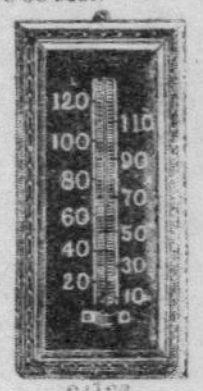

24126 Distance Thermometer standard ornamented white figures, mounted on beveled back of bright polished wood. Size 2½x6 inches. Price $0.95

Chemical and Clinical Thermometers.

24130 Solid Glass Chemical Thermometers, graduation etched on tube or porcelain scale up to 300 degrees and 600 degrees. Each $2.00

24131 Clinical Thermometer, self-registering, 4 inches, in best hard rubber case, straight pattern, with bulb. Very accurate. Each 1.00

24132 Clinical Thermometer, self-registering, 4 inch, in black enameled case with gilt band, safety chain and clasp. Cannot be lost out of pocket. A clinical certificate for accuracy accompanies each thermometer. Each 2.00

Pocket Thermometers.

24133 Pocket Thermometer, accurate and convenient, mounted in imitation cigar.
Price, each $0.25
Per doz. 2.70

Brewers' Confectioners, Evaporating Chemical incubating and angle thermometers furnished at lowest prices.

Incubating Thermometers.

24134 Incubating Thermometer, with graduated metal scale, 6 inches. Very sensitive and accurate. Each .... $0.50 Per dozen 5.50

NOTE.—See quotation of No. 24098-92, Moisture Gauges.

24134

Dairy Thermometers.

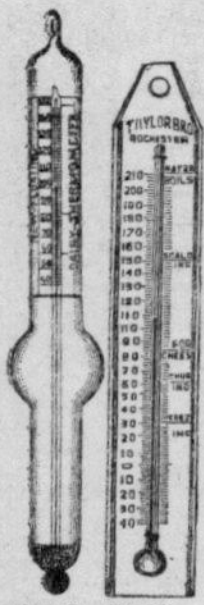

24138. 24136.

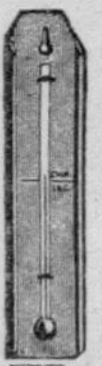

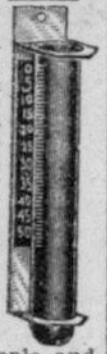

24135 Churn Thermometers, with flanged scale, tested at 62° for churning, and graduated from 30 to 90 degrees.
Each...............$0.15
Per dozen.......... 1.50

24136 Dairy Thermometers, with flange (see cut). For general dairy use; 8-inch.
Each $0.15
Per dozen.......... 1.50
10-inch, each..... .25
Per dozen.......... 2.25

24137 All Glass Thermometers for dairy use, also suitable for bath and weather purposes.
Each..............$0.25
Per dozen.......... 2.00

24138 All Glass Standard Floating Dairy Thermometer, a new and superior instrument; 9 inches long, with swell tube, so that thermometer floats upright
Price, each.........$0.50
Price, per doz...... 5.00

24139 Brown's Improved Cream Tester, simple and practical. Each $0.25
Per dozen............... 2.75

24140 The "Acme" All Glass Milk Tester. Hick's patent.
Price........................$0.50

Instructions for using No. 24140, Hick's Acme Milk Tester: Dip the instrument in the vessel of milk. When nearly full place the forefinger on the top to prevent the milk escaping, lift it out of the vessel and hold it up to the light. If the milk is pure the blue bead will gradually rise to the surface. If it contains water the bead will slowly sink.

NOTE—Thermometers should not be shipped by mail; we cannot be responsible for breakage.

Storm Glass and Thermometers.

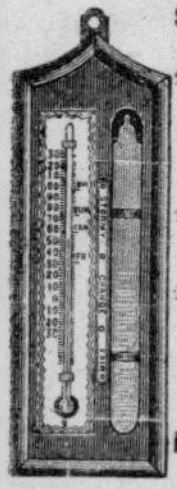

24142 Storm Glass Thermometer and barometer combined: walnut case. Size 3¼x9 inches. See cut. The most popular instrument of the kind ever introduced.
Each..............................$0.20
Per dozen............................ 2.00

24143 Polished Copper Case, Storm Glass and Thermometer, mounted with copper trimmings. Size 9x2¼ inches.
Price, each.......................$0.50

24144 Carved Antique Oak Storm Glass, 6½-inch metal scale thermometer, and 6-inch etched bottle. Size 10x4¾ inches.
Price, each.......................$0.90

Bath and Hot-Bed Thermometer.

24145 Bath Thermometer in square wooden frame 12 inches long, with round handle, enclosed glass cylinder thermometer 8 inches long, with Dr. Forbes specifications of proper temperature, Price each..... $0.48

24146 Hot-Bed Thermometer; a hard wood, round 15 inch frame with handle, box wood scale, red spirit, fitted with sharp-pointed hollow brass ferrule to penetrate the soil. Indispensable to the florist or gardener.
Price each..........................$1.80

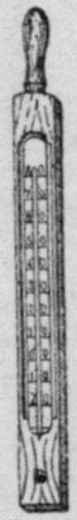

24145

Lactometer.

24150 For testing the quality of milk. Of great value to dairymen and farmers determining the relative value of cows by testing their milk; showing the effects produced by changes in the animal's food—different articles of diet produce milk of different density. Fill a jar with milk, allowing it to cool to the temperature of 60 degrees, immerse the lactometer and notice marks opposite surface of milk. The marks signify as follows:

P—Pure milk.
¾—3 parts milk and one part water.
½—2 parts milk and 2 parts water.
¼—1 part milk and 3 parts water.
W—All water.

Any immediate value can be determined by the decimal scale on the opposite side, zero being water and 100 pure milk.
Each..............$0.35. Per dozen..............$3.75

24151 Urinometers for determining the specific gravity of the urine; is an indicator of the condition of the same, as related to the general health. A circular accompanies each instrument, giving full instructions as to how it should be used. Urinometer, complete with jar, inclosed in round wood box.
Each $0.35

Hydrometers.

24153 Can Furnish hydrometers for any of the following purposes, (give name and number when ordering):

1. Acid.	9. Spirit plain.
2. Alkali.	10. Bark (for tanners).
3. Sugar and Syrup.	11. Liquids heavier than water.
4. Vinegar.	
5. Salt, 0 to 50.	12. Liquids lighter than water.
6. Salinometer, 0 to 100.	13. Sacchrometers.
7. Cider.	14 Ammonia.
8. Shellac.	15. Coal Oil.

Price of any of the above, 50c.

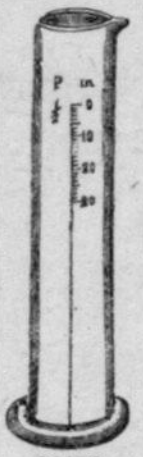

24156

24155 Hydrometer Jars, with foot and pouring spout, plain.
Height, 10 inches; diameter, 1½ inches, each $0 40
Per dozen................................ 4.25
Height, 12 inches; diameter, 2 inches, each............................. .50
Per dozen................................ 5.00
Height, 15 inches; diameter, 2 inches, each............................. .60
Per dozen................................ 6.00
Weight, 6 to 8 ounces.

24156 Hydrometer Jars, with foot and pouring spout; engraved, degrees marked from zero to 30.
Height, 10 inches. diameter, 1½ inches, each .... .60
Per dozen................................ 6.25
Height 12 inches; diameter, 2 inches, each............................. .75
Per dozen................................ 7.50
Height, 15 inches, diameter, 2 inches, each............................. .85
Per dozen................................ 8.50
Weight, from 6 to 8 ounces.

Sand Glasses.

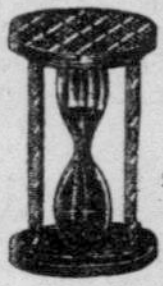

24157 Sand Glasses or Egg Timers. Scotch pattern: size, 2x3¾ inches.
Each $0.25
Prices furnished on application for any size sand glass made.

24159 Signal Service Rain gauge. 3 inches diameter, copper funnel, galvanized iron overflow, measuring stick. Each...........$2.25

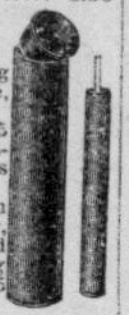

ELECTRICAL GOODS.

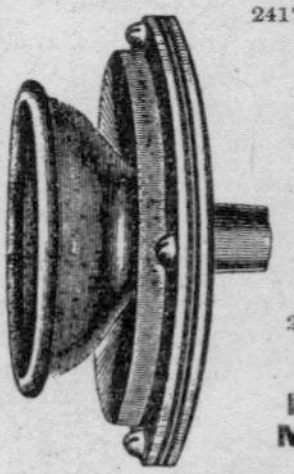

24170 The Elgin Accoustic Telephone, made wholly of metal, nickel plated, self-supporting, not even a screw to hold it in place. The telephone will work on a line ¼ mile long, and is the neatest, most durable and best working mechanical telephone on the market. Telephones, per pair (2), with 200 feet wire, wire for hangers and directions for putting the phone in working order complete.
Weight 3½ lbs.......$5.00

24171 Copper Wire, No. 18, for Elgin Phone, per pound (125 feet).............$0.31

Portable Electro-Medical Batteries.

These magnetic instruments are of undoubted value as the instruments through whose agency physicians effected almost miraculous cures. Our most learned doctors and physicians acknowledge their efficiency in even the worst cases of paralysis, rheumatism, neuralgia, and in fact, all nervous diseases. These machines may be used by all invalids with perfect safety. When doctors fail to effect a cure with drugs and medicines, and electricity is resorted to in the last stage of disease, even then, under such immense disadvantages, electricity often cures.

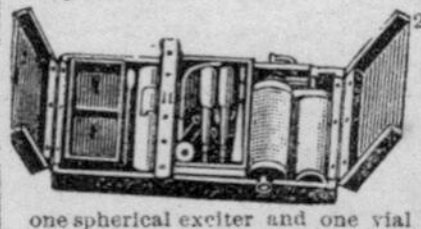

24175 Gaiffe's Battery, three currents, with silk covered conducting cords, two insulated handles, one metallic brush, one olive shaped exciter, one spherical exciter and one vial of bisulphate of mercury. In polished mahogany case, 7½x4x1¼ in. Complete with full directions. Weight, 1¼ lbs.$7.75

24176 Gaiffe's Battery, with same size coil as in preceding, producing two currents instead of three. Mounted in single cover mahogany case, 6¼x4x1¼ inches, containing two insulated handles and one vial bisulphate of mercury.
Weight, 1 lb. Each...............................$6.25

We Sell

The Standard Diaries for 1895.
Send for free price list.

Batteries—Continued.

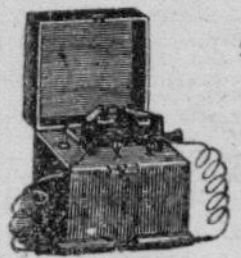

24177 The Crown Family Battery. The merits of this battery will be easily appreciated as possessing neatness of design and simplicity of operating. A pleasant and uniform electric current, both mild and powerful. Three different and distinct currents are produced—the primary, secondary, and both combined in intensity. Mounted in polished cherry case with nickel handles. Size 6x5¼x5¼ inches, with full directions for using. Highly recommended. Weight, 2¼ lbs.
Price complete...........$3.50

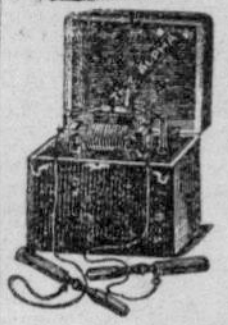

24178 Alpha Faradic Family Medical Battery, constructed upon improved scientific principles and designed for private or professional use. Full description of apparatus, directions for operating and directions for making solution furnished with each instrument. Weight 3½ lbs.
Each $5.00

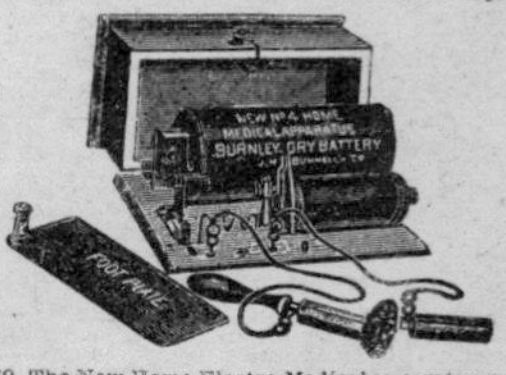

24179 The New Home Electro-Medical apparatus, with dry battery. This battery is the most convenient and reliable of any hundreds of forms ever introduced. It is reliable, because with its dry battery so much less care is necessary to avoid getting it out of order than is required with any other known form. The entire absence of acids, liquors or salts will be appreciated by any one who has ever had occasion to use a medical battery. The appliance furnished with the apparatus consists of foot-plate, sponge, cords and handles (electrodes). The electrode having a wooden handle is used as a sponge-holder when required. The size of the apparatus is 3½x5x8¼ in. Weight, 4 pounds.
Price, complete.....$7.00 Extra battery, per cell $0.75
Extra Sponge Holder .50 Extra Handles, pair.. .75
Extra Metallic Hair Brush, electrode.............. 1.25
Extra Cords, 4 feet, per pair........................ .50

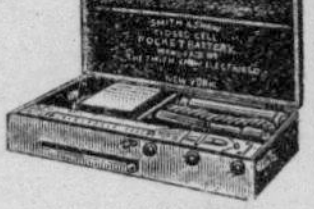

24180 The Genuine Smith & Shaw Portable Pocket Battery. Powerful current. The most practicable and thorough pocket battery made. Cells cannot spill contents.
Price, with two cells (weight 1½ lb).....$8.50
Price with three cells (weight 2 lbs.....$10.00

Magnetic Electro Battery.

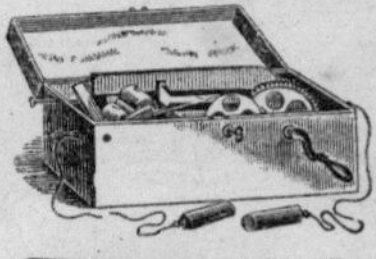

24182 Davis & Kidder's Genuine Magneto-Electric Machines.
Price each..$7.25
Weight 6½ lbs.

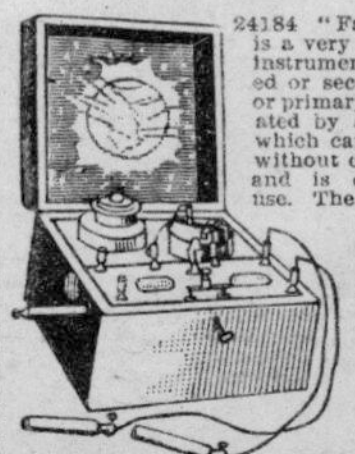

24184 "Family" Battery. This is a very effective and portable instrument, produces the induced or secondary, and the direct or primary current, and is operated by an open battery which can be used for months without changing the solution and is constantly ready for use. The power may be increased by gradually withdrawing the tube from the helix. In polished black walnut case with cords and handles; weight, 8 lbs.
Each.......... $10.00

*** Always be sure to state the amount of money enclosed with order.

Medical Battery Parts.

Order No. 24185 and be sure to specify what Battery the parts are for.

	Each.
Zines for the Crown Family Battery	$0.20
Carbons for same	.25
Glass Jars for same	.25
Tops complete for same, zinc and carbon attached	.65
Zincs for the Alpha Battery	.25
Carbons for same. Each	.25
Glass Jars for same	.25
Zinc for family battery. Per pair	.50
Postage on pair zincs	.18
Platinas for same	1.00
Clamps for same	.25
Cords for same. Per pair	.50
Glass Jars for same	.25
Metal Springs for Magnetic Battery	.10
Cord belt for same	.05
Bisulphate Mercury for use with batteries Nos. 24175, 24176 and 24180 per ounce	.10
Price per ¼ lb. bottle	.75
Price per 1 lb. bottle	1.25
Bichromate Potassium for use with batteries, Nos. 24177 and 24178. Per lb	35.

Medical Induction Coil, Without Battery.

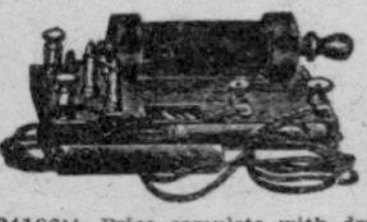

24186 Induction Coil, mounted on neat wooden stand with pair of hand electrodes and sponge holder of best quality. Can be operated with any acid battery. Price without battery.......... $3.50

24186½ Price complete with dry battery cell, ready for use. Weight 3¼ pounds........ 4.00

24187 Medical Induction Coils, small size, producing primary current which can be increased at will of operator. Complete with battery...... 1.00

Electric Motors.

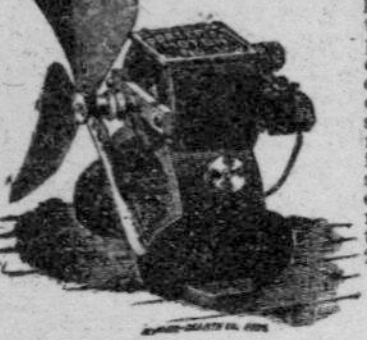

The Porter Electric Motor, a practical machine for a little money. An entirely novel principle underlies the construction both electrically and mechanically, insuring simplicity, low cost, reduced size, diminished weight, higher speed and wonderful economy in power required to operate them.

24190 The No 1. Motor, although a very small one in size, is highly efficient. With one cell of acid battery it will operate a small dental lathe, a fan, a revolving window stand, an egg beater, a music-box, etc. It is no toy. Its electrical efficiency is about $\frac{1}{32}$ horse power, or from 35 to 40 watts on a continuous run. No better Motor can be furnished to meet the wishes of young students engaged in the study of experimental physics. Its efficiency will surprise the user. Weight 1¾ pounds. Price each..........$2.90

24191 The No. 2 Motor, same construction as above, but larger size, weighing 3 pounds and capacity of $\frac{1}{16}$ horse power. Price.............. 4.75

24192 The Porter Electric Motor No. 3. Size, 5½ in. long x 4½ in. high x 4¾ in. wide. The No. 3 Motor will suffice to run a sewing machine nicely; a cooling and ventilating fan; a lathe, buffer or grinding machine, such as are used in jewelers' and dentists' work, etc. It requires about 20 amperes of current under pressure of 6 to 10 volts. At normal speed of 2,200 revolutions per minute using four cells of battery it will yield an efficiency of about $\frac{1}{8}$ horse power; four cells will answer to operate any household sewing machine. For its size and power, this Motor (No. 3) is equal to any domestic electric motor sold to-day, and costs from one-third to one-half less money. Weighs 6 pounds. Price each.......... 9.00

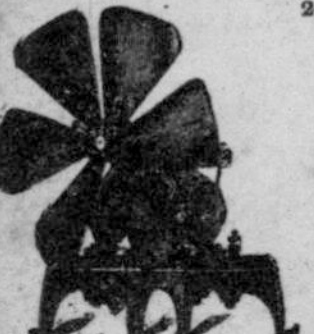

24193 The Porter Electric Motor No. 3 with stands, same size, description and capacity as the No. 24192, but provided with iron stand so that motor is sufficiently elevated to allow the use of a 10 in. 6 blade ventilating fan. Both the No. 24192 and No. 24193 are furnished with switch for instantly starting and stopping the machine. Total weight 7½ lbs. Price..........$11.00

BARB WIRE.

Send for our latest price list of Barb Wire and you will see that our prices are low. Worth your while to write us before buying elsewhere.

Battery Outfit for No. 3 Porter Motor.

24194 For operating sewing machine or doing other work requiring same power as sewing machine.

4 Cells, 6x8, Battery	@	$2.50	$10.00
2 lbs. Battery Powder (4 chges.)	@	.50	1.00
			$11.00

NOTE.—When doing work requiring less power than a sewing machine, or when using the No. 1 or No. 2 Motors, use a less number of cells of battery than four. We will furnish one or more cells at above prices. When purchasing battery outfit for the No. 1 or No. 2 Motors, order a one point switch at 25 cents, as these sizes are not provided with switch.

Fans for Motors.

Order No. 24195.

4 Inch	3 Blades.	Each $0.25
5 "	3 "	" 85
6 "	4 "	" 40
8 "	4 "	" 75
10 "	6 "	" 1.25

Switches.

Order No. 24197.

Round, hardwood base.

1 Point	2 Point	3 Point
25 cts.	30 cts.	35 cts.

Telegraph Apparatus.

High Grade Brass Telegraph Instruments.

NOTE. Instruments wound to but 5 ohms are designed for local lines, practice use, etc. Those wound to 20 ohms resistance are practical, working instruments for all short lines up to 10 or 15 miles in length.

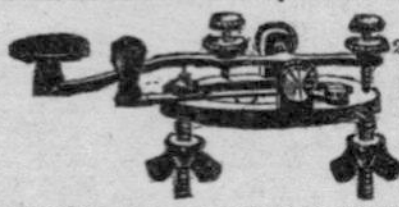

24200 Steel Lever Solid Trunnion Leg Key. This key is more durable and in every respect better than any other for rapid and perfect Morse sending. The lever is only one-half the weight of the ordinary brass lever, as generally made. The entire lever and trunnions together being made of but one piece of fine wrought steel, the common defect of loose trunnions is avoided, the strength of a heavy brass lever is obtained with much less weight of metal, and by the perfect bearing which the solid trunnion gives, together with the use of the hardened platina points, sticking is absolutely prevented. The size and proportions are such as to make it the most perfect operating key possible to obtain, either for the hand of the skilled and rapid expert, or the beginner. Price each, $1.50. Postage..........$0.10

24201 Steel Lever, Solid Trunnion Desk Key. Exactly the same in construction as No. 24200, except that it is made without legs. A beautiful and perfect instrument, suitable for use on fine desks, or wherever a legless key is preferable. Price each.....$2.00. Postage.......... .10

24202 The Giant Sounder is now recognized throughout America as the best standard of excellence in Sounders. It gives a loud, clear sound with just half the amount of local battery required for other forms of sounders. Wound with fine wire to 20 ohms resistance for main line use (without relay), on lines up to 15 miles in length. Each, $2.50. Postage .... .20

24203. Giant Sounder, same as above, but wound to 5 ohms resistance. Each, $2.00. Postage.... .20

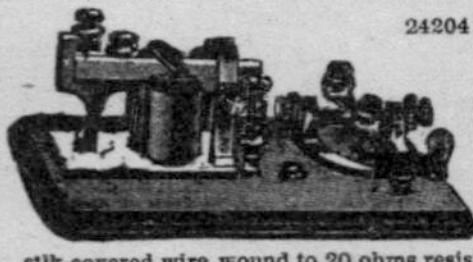

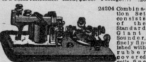

24204 Combination Set consists of the Standard Giant Sounder, finely finished with rubber covered coils, fine silk-covered wire wound to 20 ohms resistance, mounted on polished mahogany base, with a Steel Lever Key. The handsomest and most perfect set of Short Line instruments ever produced. Each..........$4.00 Postage..........$0.35

24205 Same as 24204, but wound to 5 ohms. Each..........$3.50 Postage.......... .35

Learner's Telegraph Instruments.

THE AJAX LEARNERS' SET.

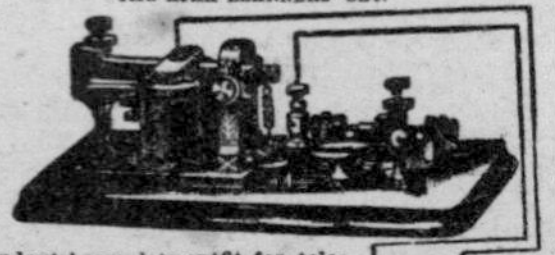

Students' complete outfit for telegraphing, comprising full size key and sounder; mounted on polished mahogany base. Battery, chemicals, wire, book of instruction, everything necessary for operating, for private practice or on short service line.

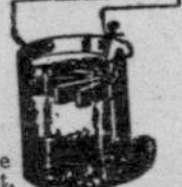

24208 Ajax (student) outfit, complete packed in light wood box, weight, 10½ lbs..........$3.50

Telegraph Instruments—Continued.

24209 Instruments only, mounted on base; weight, 2 lbs..........$2.80

24210 Instrument only (3), mounted on base, sounder wound for long distance. This instrument should be used on lines of half mile or more, as it will give better results. Weight. 2 lbs.......... 3.50

24211 Extra 5 ohms sounder; weight 1¼ lb..... 1.60

24212 Extra Keys; weight, ¼ lb.......... 1.20

24213 Battery cells, extra, complete; weight, 5 lbs. 5x7 size.......... .65

24214 Battery Jars, 1¾ lbs.......... .25

24215 Zinc, complete; weight, 1¾ lbs.......... .30

24216 Copper; weight, 5 oz.......... .20

24217 Blue Vitrol. Per lb.......... .09

Estimate for Half Mile Private Line.

24218 Two No. 24208 instruments, wound with fine wire, at $3.50	$7.00
½ mile No. 12 B B Galvanized Iron Wire, 85 lbs. at 9c	7.65
14 Pony Glass Insulators, at 5c	.70
15 Oak Brackets, at 3c	.45
5 Cells Gravity Battery, at 65c	3.25
2 lbs. office wire at 40c	.80
2 lbs, Blue Vitrol, at 9c	1.08
	$20.93

The above estimate is for a practical working line, not a toy.

Quotations given on main line relays, combination sets, sounders, keys, etc., upon application. We can furnish anything used in telegraphy at a discount from usual prices. Electrical supplies of any kind quoted upon request.

Electric Door Bells and Appliances.

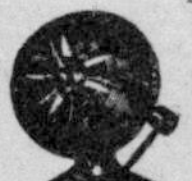

24225 Our "Standard" three inch Electric Bell. The design of bell is new and novel; has perfect adjustment. Price, each..........$0.75 Postage.......... .15

24226 Bell Outfit, consisting of our 3-inch bell, 1 cell, Hayden Battery, 1 bronze push botton, 1 lb. (150 ft.) wire, sal ammonaic and package staples and tape. Price..........$2.50

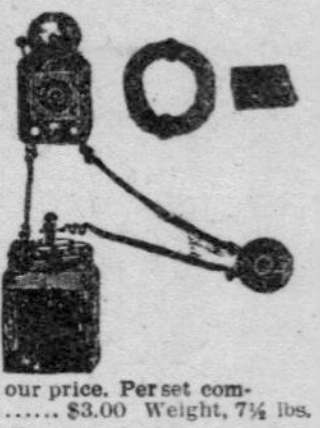

24227—Electric Bell Sets; with walnut push; 3-in electric gong bell; one diamond carbon battery; 100 feet of insulated wire, screws, staples and tape. Packed in wooden box. Weight, 6½ lbs. Per set..........$2 75

24228 Electric Bell Set; same as No. 24227, except has fancy bronze push and 3 inch back walnut box bell. Notice our price. Per set complete..........$3.00 Weight, 7¼ lbs.

Batteries.

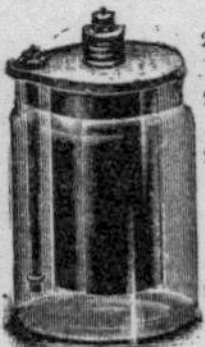

24233

24230 Chicago Carbon Battery, complete; weight 3½ lbs. Each..........$0.70

24231 Leclanche Disque Batteries, complete with box of sal-ammoniac; weight, 4 lbs. Each $0.80

24232 The Imperial Dry Battery; height, 6½ inches; diameter, 2½ inches; ready for use; does not freeze or evaporate. The most compact, practical battery for general use made; weight, 2¼ lbs. Each..........$0.90

24233 The Hayden, a most powerful and enduring open circuit battery; weight, 2½ lbs. Price ....$1.00 Push buttons, sal-ammoniac, wire, etc.

24234 Push Buttons, wood, each..........$0.15

24235 Push Buttons, Fancy Bronze.......... .50

24236 Push Buttons, Floor.......... .40

24237 Sal-ammoniac in paper boxes.
Per box (6 ounces).......... .10
In bulk, per pound.......... .20

24238 Annunciator Wire, for use with electric bells Per lb. (150 feet).......... .85

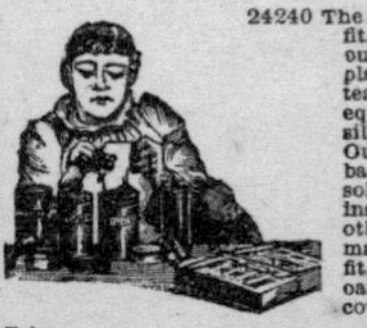

24240 The Amateur Plating Outfit. The best low priced outfit on the market for plating small articles—teaspoons etc. Plates equally well with gold, silver, nickel or copper. Outfit consists of 2 dry batteries, 2 glass tanks, solutions, salts, book of instructions, and all other necessities for making a complete outfit. Packed in strong oak box with hinge cover. Weight 9½ lbs. Price..........$5.00

NOTE.—If you are interested in larger plating outfits send to us for complete catalogue of outfits and material.

Electric Insoles.

24242 Electric Insoles. Sure foot warmers. Recommended by many. State size of shoe worn. Has zinc and copper battery in each insole.

Price per pair..................$0.75
Postage..................... .04

Electric Battery Plasters.

Back and front of the Lion Battery Plaster. 24243 The Lion Electric Battery Plaster has 2 silver disks on face of plaster, connected with a perfect copper and zinc battery on back, which guarantees a current of electricity. This current is diffused throughout the whole system. The battery can be charged with vinegar and used a number of times. Cures all aches and pains instantly. Each...............$0.45 Send for circular of Electric Belts and Specialties.

Surgical Instruments.

NOTE—We are prepared to furnish prices of Human Dental Forceps, Surgical Appliances of all kinds, Deformity Apparatus, Elastic Stockings, Supports, etc.

O·P·C Suspensory.

24245 Automatically adjustable and never fails to fit and give satisfaction. For comfort, security, durability and elegance the best in the world. Order by number. Give size, large, medium or small.
No. 2, lisle..................$0.75
No. 3, silk...................1.25
No. 4, all silk................1.75
No. 5, all silk, fancy colors..2.25

Veterinary Instruments.

In Veterinary goods we illustrate only a few instruments that are commonly used by everyone owning a horse, but we are in a position to supply anything made in this line, and will quote prices upon application.

24246 Universal Wolf Tooth Forceps for extracting Wolf teeth. Length 9 in., weight ¾ lb. Nickel plated.
Each.......................$3.00

24247 Wolf Tooth Forceps, bayonet pattern. Length, 13 in. Nickel plated.
Each.......................$3.00

24248 Wolf Tooth Forceps, curved nickel plated. Length 9 in.
Each.......................$2.50

24249 Small Molar Splinter Forceps, nickel plated. 13 in.
Each.......................$3.00

24250 Straight Incisor Cutter.
Each.......................$3.00

24251 Molar Extracting Forceps. Handles extra.
Each.......................$7.50

24252 Closed Molar Cutters. Handles extra.
Each.......................$7.50

24253 Open Molar Cutters. (Handles extra.)
Each.......................$7.50

24254 Handles for Cutters and extractors
Per pair...................$3.00

24255 Reversible Float, nickel plated, plain. Length, 19 inches. Price..........$1.00

24256 Reversible Float, nickle plated, jointed.
Price.....................1.50

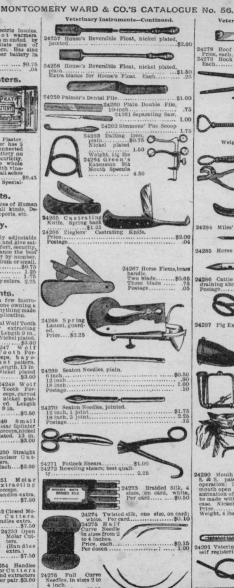

24257 House's Reversible Float, nickel plated, jointed.....................$2.00

24258 House's Reversible Float, nickel plated, plain.....................$1.50
Extra blades for House's Float. Each.......25

24259 Palmer's Dental File.................$1.00

24260 Plain Double File, 10-inch............75
24261 Separating Saw...................1.00

24262 Simmons' Pus Scoop.................1.75

24263 Balling Iron, plain.........$0.75 Nickel plated..................1.50 Weight, 1¼ lbs

24264 Green's Extension Bit Mouth Specula......4.50

24265 Castrating Knife. Spring back........$1.35

24266 Ziegler's Castrating Knife.
Price.....................$2.00
Postage..................04

24267 Horse Flems, brass handle
Two blade............$0.65
Three blade.............75
Postage...............05

24268 Spring Lancet, guarded.
Price......$2.25

24269 Seaton Needles, plain.
6 inch.....................$0.50
12 inch.....................90
18 inch....................1.00
Postage....................10

24270 Seaton Needles, jointed.
12 inch, 1 joint.............$1.75
18 inch, 2 joint.............2.25
Postage...................15

24271 Fetlock Shears.................$1.00
24272 Roweling shears; best quality.......2.25

24273 Braided Silk, 4 sizes, on card, white. Each..................$0.50

24274 Twisted silk, one size, on card; white. Per card............$0.10

24275 Half Curve Needle in sizes from 2 to 4 inches.
Price, each..............$0.15
Per dozen..................1.00

24276 Full Curve Needles, in sizes 2 to 4 inch.
Price, each...........$0.15
Per dozen.............1.00

24277 Straight Needles, sizes, 2 to 4 inch.
Price, each........$0.15. Per dozen........$1.00

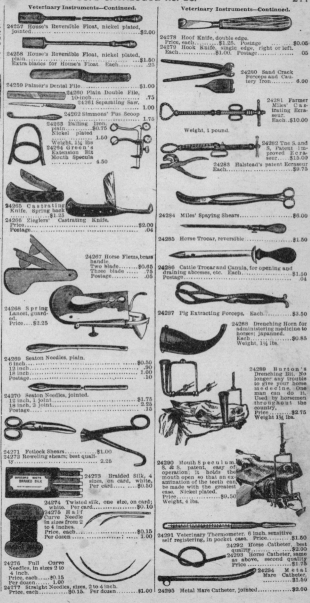

24278 Hoof Knife, double edge.
Price, each........$1.25. Postage...........$0.05
24279 Hook Knife, single edge, right or left.
Each..................$1.00. Postage..........05

24280 Sand Crack Forceps and Cautery Iron.........6.00

24281 Farmer Miles' Castrating Ecraseur.
Each........$10.00

Weight, 1 pound.

24282 Tne S. and S. Patent improved Ecraseur....$15.00

24283 Halstead's patent Ecraseur.
Each..................$9.75

24284 Miles' Spaying Shears.................$6.00

24285 Horse Trocar, reversible.................$1.50

24286 Cattle Trocar and Canula, for opening and draining abscesses, etc. Each..............$1.50 Postage..................04

24287 Pig Extracting Forceps. Each............$3.50

24288 Drenching Horn for administering medicine to horses; japanned.
Each..................$0.85
Weight, 1¼ lbs.

24289 Burton's Drenching Bit. No longer any trouble to give your horse medecine. One man can do it. Used by horsemen throughout the country.
Price..................$2.75
Weight 1¼ lbs.

24290 Mouth Speculum, S. & S. patent, easy of operation; it holds the mouth open so that an examination of the teeth can be made with the greatest ease. Nickel plated.
Price..................$9.50
Weight, 4 lbs.

24291 Veterinary Thermometer, 6 inch. sensitive self registering, in pocket case. Price.........$1.50

24292 Horse Catheter, best quality..................$2.00
24293 Horse Catheter, same as above, second quality
Price..................1.75

24294 Metal Mare Catheter........$1.50

24295 Metal Mare Catheter, jointed..............$2.00

Veterinary Instruments—Continued.

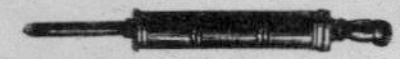

24296 Injection Syringes metal 16 oz.

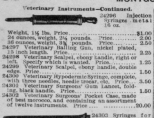

Weight, 1¼ lbs. Price....................$1.00
24 ounces, weight, 2¼ pounds. Price.......... 2.00
36 ounces, weight, 3¼ pounds. Price.......... 2.50
24297 Veterinary Balling Gun, nickel plated, 15 inch length. Price.......... 2.25
24298 Veterinary Scalpel, ebony handle, right or left. Specify which is wanted. Price.......... 1.25
24299 Veterinary Scalpel, ebony handle, double edge. Price.......... 1.50
24300 Veterinary Hypodermic Syringe, complete, with three needles, needle trocar, etc. Price... 3.50
24301 Veterinary Surgeons' Gum Lancet, folding, black handle. Price.......... 1.50
24302 Veterinary Surgeons' Pocket Case, made of best morocco, and containing an assortment of twelve instruments. Price 20.00

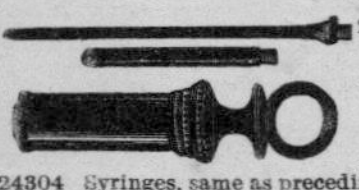

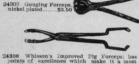

24303 Syringes for administering medicine to horses and other animals. Quittor Hard Rubber, two pipes. Price each.....$1.50

24304 Syringes, same as preceding, but of metal, nickel plated, Quittor, two pipe. Price each.... 2.50
24305 Veterinary Hard Rubber Horse Syringes, capacity, 24 ounces. Each.......... 3.75

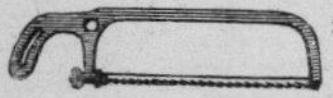

24306 Dehorning Saw, plain finish........$1.50

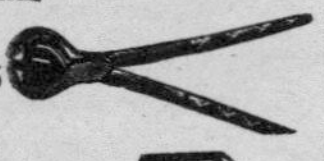

24307 Gouging Forceps, nickel plated......$3.50

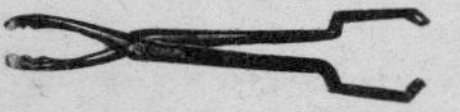

24308 Whisson's Improved Pig Forceps; has points of excellence which make it a most practical instrument, and may be used upon either small or large sows with equal satisfaction. The instrument is made of malleable iron, tinned to prevent rusting. Will not tear the sow or otherwise injure the animal in operation. Price..........$1.00

*** **MRS. HANNAH COBB'S celebrated "Home made Soap," 30 bars in a box (family or trial size). Every bar warranted. We have sold thousands of boxes and all have given entire satisfaction. Try a box and you will see why we praise it. See Grocery List for prices.**

Eureka Cow Milker.

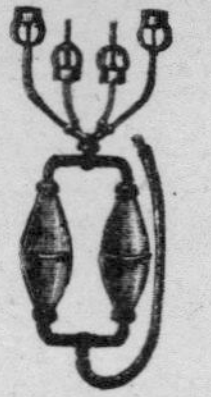

24309 The Eureka Patent Cow Milker weighs only 15 ounces, and is guaranteed not to injure the cow in any way. Perfectly clean; no straining necessary. You can milk a cow perfectly dry in five minutes. A boy or girl 10 years old can adjust and use it, and the cow will not kick. Full directions that are simple and easily understood with each machine. Instrument can be thoroughly cleaned in three minutes; made entirely of soft and vulcanized rubber. Will last for years; and duplicate parts can be had at any time.
Price, each..........$6.00

Coin Silver Milking Tubes, Etc.

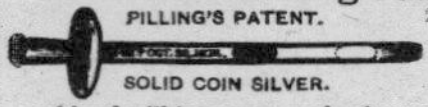

24310 Coin Silver Milking Tubes, for sore and obstructed teats, and hard milking cows; made of pure coin silver and can be used with absolute safety, set of 4 tubes, 1¾ inches long, in neat box, with full directions for use $1.60
Single tubes, each.......... .43

Special length.........	2¼ in.	2¾ in.	3¼ in.	3¾ in.
Each..........	55c.	70c.	80c.	95c.

Postage, 2 cents.

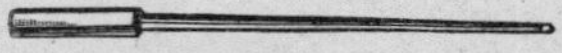

24311 Grooved Director, or instrument for opening cows' teats, with full directions for using.
Each..........$0.60
Per dozen.......... 6.00
Postage, 2 cents.

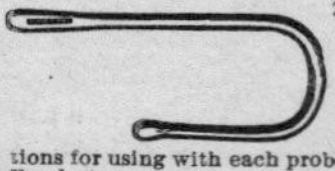

24312 Lead Probes for treatment of stricture and obstructed teats; also for enlarging the opening in cows' teats; made in three sizes, small, medium and large; full directions for using with each probe. Each..........$0.20
Per dozen 2.00
24313 Cow Teat Slitter, best implement, steel, nickeled sheath, 5 inch length. Each.......... 1.25

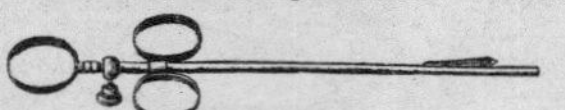

24314 Stricture Cutter, for cows' teats, 7 inch length, made of best implement steel. Each...$2.60

Poultry Instruments.

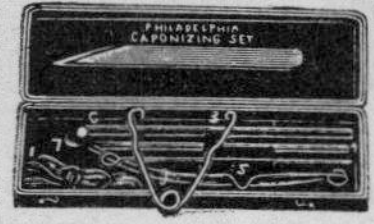

24315 It is well understood that poultrymen can double their profits by caponizing their chicks. The operation is very simple, the instructions being so explicit that any one, after a careful reading, will be able to perform the operation with proper instruments.
The demand for capons far exceeds the supply, even at an advanced price.
The Philadelphia Caponizing Set contains the best instruments on the market; and at the price at which they are offered no one who keeps chickens can afford to neglect the opportunity of increasing their profits.
Price, per set, in velvet lined case (see cut), with book, "Complete Guide for Caponizing"......$2.50
Postage.......... .10

French Poultry Killing Knife.

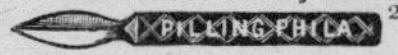

24316 Every poultry raiser should have one. They are made of finely tempered instrument steel, with nickeled handle; will last a life time.
Each..........$0.40. Postage..........$0.05

The Philadelphia Poultry Marker.

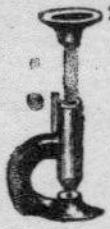

24317 Do you keep a record of chickens? The different breeds, hatches, etc., should be kept. There is no better or quicker way than by this marker, as over 200 different marks can be made by punching web between toes, for instance between first and second toes of right foot can mean Wyandotte or Plymouth Rock; between second and third toes, White Leghorn or Lanshan, so that hundreds of private marks can be made, not only to keep records, but by your private marks you can secure yourself from the chicken thief. They are well made with steel spring and cutter, nicely nickel plated.
Price ....18c. Postage $0.05

Gape Worm Extractor.

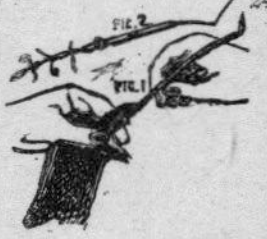

24318 The disease commonly known as Gapes is caused by a small worm in the windpipe of fowls. When the chick seems to gasp frequently it is a sure indication of Gapes, and it should receive attention at once. The only sure cure is to remove the worms by mechanical means. You will save time and money by having on hand a Gape Worm Extractor. The Extractor quickly removes, without injury to the chick, the worms and matter from the windpipe, and effects an instant cure. The instrument is made of brass and will last a lifetime. The cut shows the manner of using the instrument. One chick saved pays price of instrument. Price..........$0.30
Postage.......... .03

PHOTOGRAPHIC GOODS DEPARTMENT.

NOTE.—We do not sell Cameras or outfits on trial, nor can they be returned after having been used. The goods quoted by us are the same as sold by *all* photographic stock houses, and are staple articles of merchandise.

Failure to produce a good negative is in nearly every case the want of carefulness or lack of skill on the part of the operator. While anyone can now learn to take a good photograph at a small outlay of time and money, yet the first few efforts must not be expected to equal the work of one proficient in the art. Do not expect to set up in photography as a means of support with one of our *low priced* outfits. Taking photographs for your own amusement, for the home circle or for your friends, and finishing portraits for a discriminating public are entirely different subjects.

Portrait work requires a high grade lens and camera; while excellent pictures of landscapes can be made with cameras, using a single view lens, of course the picture is much better in detail when a rectilinear lens is used. If you desire any make of camera or lens not found listed in this catalogue, write us for prices, giving name of camera and manufacturer's name. We will cheerfully answer all questions of this nature, and will mail special catalogues of photographic apparatus to those desiring same.

Hand Cameras.

Since the introduction of the Hand Camera, picture making has been so simplified that the possibilities of photography are brought within the reach of all. The Amateur Photographer is now found among persons in nearly every walk of life. The business man finds photography a valuable assistant as well as a pleasant recreation, while for the tourist and pleasure seekers it has many charms. Surely there is no more pleasant souvenir of vacation rambles than photographs, taken by yourself, of the various scenes and incidents connected with your outing. Many recollections are thus preserved, and the history of the pleasant holiday is brought to mind by a glance at the finished picture long afterward.

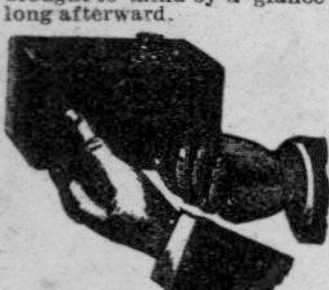

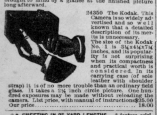

24350 The Kodak. This Camera is so widely advertised and so well known that a detailed description of its merits is unnecessary.
The size of the Kodak No. 1 is 3¼x4¼x7¼ inches, and its popularity is not surprising when its compactness and practical worth is considered. In its carrying case (of sole leather with shoulder strap) it is of no more trouble than an ordinary field glass. It takes a 2½ inch circle picture. One hundred exposures may be made without reloading the camera. List price, with manual of instructions$25.00
Our price.......... 18.00

*** **SHEETING IN 25 YARD LENGTHS. A feature originating with us. See our Domestic Department for information.**

The Bull's Eye Camera.

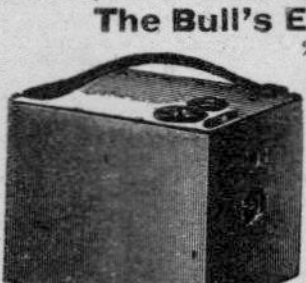

24351 The Bull's Eye (Daylight) Camera. Provided with a roll of film that may be placed in position or removed without the necessity of a dark room. The Film Cartridge is provided at either end with a length of opaque cloth to protect it from the light when being placed in position or removed from the camera in daylight, thus making a *Daylight Camera.* The cartridge is easily adjusted and removed and may be sent by mail to be developed and printed to any photo-goods dealer or photographer if you should not wish to finish the picture yourself. The camera is made in best possible manner and has an achromatic lens, of universal focus, set to take pictures at any distance over 8 feet away. No focussing required, simply aim the camera, push the spring (which is always set) and turn the key when twelve exposures have been made, which uses up the roll of film; the cartridge is removed and a fresh one inserted.
The Bull's Eye takes a picture either square or circle, 3½ inches in diameter. Size, 5¾x4¾x4¾ inches. Weight, about two pounds.
Price, with wood case covered with grain leather $7.50
Price includes 1 film cartridge and book of instructions.
Extra cartridges, for 12 pictures. Each.......... $0.55
24352 Bull's Eye Camera for 4x5 pictures, uses light proof cartridges for 12 exposures, and is a larger and more complete investment than 24351. Size, 5⅛x6½x8¼. Weight, 2½ lbs., covered with grain leather. Price each..........$14.00
Extra Cartridges, for 12 pictures. Each.......... .90

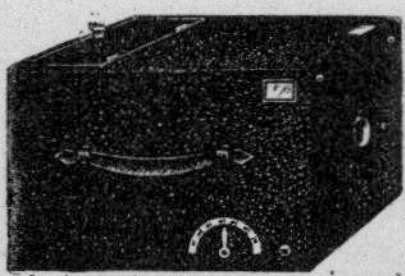

24353 The Night-Hawk, the best *cheap* 4x5 camera ever placed before the public. The Night-Hawk can be focused either with ground glass or focusing dial, and is fitted with a rapid achromatic lens for instantaneous and general work; also an instantaneous safety shutter, with time exposure stop. These cameras are made of the best material, and the workmanship and finish first-class. Can be had either polished antique oak, or in morocco leather covering. Each camera will carry three plate holders.
Price, polished antique oak..........$4.80
Price, morocco leather covering.......... 6.75
Each camera is fitted with one double plate holder and full instructions. Extra double plate holders for Night-Hawk. Each.......... .75

The Kombi.

24353½ This little instrument is a combined Camera and Graphoscope; will take a picture 1⅛ in. square or 1⅛ in. diameter as perfect in detail as a camera many times larger and more expensive. It is made of seamless metal, oxidized finish, is 1⅝ in. square by 2 in. long and is packed in a cloth covered carrying case.
Price, each..........$3.50
1 roll film for 25 exposures.......... .20
1 developing and printing outfit.......... 2.00

Cameras—Continued.

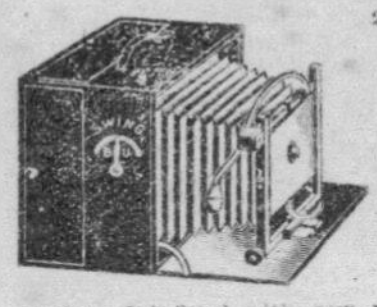

24354 The Folding Night-Hawk. The success with the night-hawk detective camera has induced manufacturers to place on the market a folding camera of superior quality. This camera possesses all the latest improvements known to modern photography. It has reversible back and swing. It is fitted with new regulation time and instantaneous shutter with bulb attachment and rapid rectilinear lens. It can be focused either with ground glass or focusing dial, and is handsomely finished in morocco leather. Each camera carries three double plate holders.

Price, 4x5, with one double plate holder $13.75
Price, 5x7, with one double plate holder 22.50
Price, 4x5, extra double plate holders, each .... .75
Price, 5x7, extra double plate holders, each 1.13

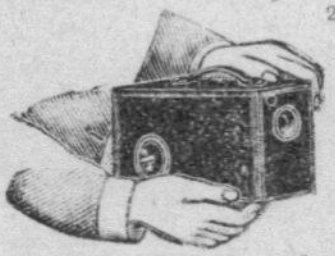

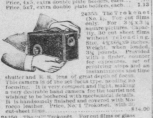

24355 The Trokonet (No. 1). For cut films only. For 3½x3½ square pictures. Capacity, 30 cut sheet films without reloading. Size, 4⅜x6¼x9 inches. Weight, when loaded, 3¼ pounds. Provided with a finder, counter for exposures, set of revolving stops and an instantaneous and time shutter and R. R. lens of great depth of focus. This camera is of the set focus type, needing no focusing. It is very compact and light, making a very desirable hand camera for the tourist not wishing to be bothered with mechanical details. It is handsomely finished and covered with Morocco leather. Price, No. 1 Trokonet, with 30 cut-sheet films $14.00

24356 The "C" Trokonet. For cut films or glass plates. For 4x5 pictures. Capacity, 30 cut-sheet films without reloading. Size, 6¼x7½x11¼ inches. Weight, when loaded, 4⅜ pounds. This Trokonet is provided with a Gundlach double combination rectilinear Trokonet lens, two finders, instantaneous and time shutter, with adjustable speed, focusing rack and pinion with scale for focusing, counter for exposures, and two sockets for tripod screws. The C Trokonet is handsomely finished and covered with Morocco leather. Price of C Trokonet, loaded with 30 cut-sheet films $31.50

24357 The "D" Trokonet. For films or glass plates. The D Trokonet is exactly the same as the C Trokonet, excepting that it has a single, instead of a double, combination lens. This lens is equal to any high grade single combination lens. Price of D Trokonet, loaded, with 25 cut-sheet films $18.75

Trokonet Film.

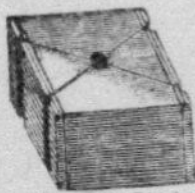

24358 The Trokonet Film makes the Trokonet system possible. The film is sold in packages as here illustrated. Every film is attached to a paper septum, and as the latter costs nothing may be thrown in the waste basket after the films have been developed.

Size, 3½x3½ inches, in packages of 30 .... $1.40
" 4x5 " " " 2.25

24359 Septums for Glass Dry Plates or Films; Size, 4x5 inches. 1 dozen in a package .... .60
Full directions in each package how to use Glass Dry Plates in Trokonets.

The *Premier Camera* is conceded to be one of the best hand cameras on the market, possessing some advantages over all others. They are fitted with the new silent shutter, and either single view or double combination lenses of the well known R. O. Co.'s make. Boxes are well made, covered with grain leather, and are made to carry either four or six double plate holders. Each camera is provided with two view finders and two tripod plates, so that either vertical or horizontal pictures can be made. The back panel is removable, allowing ground glass to be seen for focussing. Glass Plates, cut films or roll films, can be used in the Premier, rendering this, either a detective camera, a view camera, a magazine camera, an instantaneous camera. The 4x5 size for four plate holders measures 6¼x6¾x11 inches, and weighs four pounds. The box for six holders is 1½ inches longer.

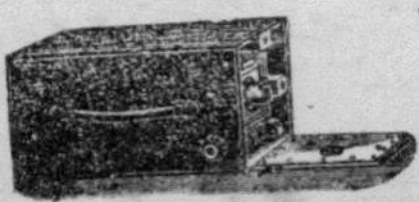

24360 The Premier, for 4x5 or 5x7 pictures, fitted with R. O. Co.'s single view Lens and *one* Perfection Dry Plate Holder.

	4x5	5x7
Price	$13.60	$18.00
Fitted with rapid rectilinear lens	18.90	27.00
Extra dry plate holders	.90	1.12
" facile film "	1.13	1.35
Roll Holders *empty*	7.25	9.00

Cameras—Continued.

24361 The Premier Camera No. 2 is the regular Premier with the addition of swing back and rising and falling front. In other respects the description of the regular Premier applies to the No. 2. The swing back and rising and falling front are used principally when using the camera on a tripod, and are of especial advantage when taking architectural subjects and tall buildings. A hand camera with these improvements possesses all the advantages of a regular tripod camera.

	Size 4x5	Size 5x7
No. 2 Premier with single view lens and 1 plate holder	$16.20	$21.25
No. 4 Premier with rapid rectilinear lens and 1 plate holder	21.50	30.50

The Folding "Premo" Cameras.

The remarks in regard to the regular Premier cameras apply with equal force to the folding Premo camera.

They are extremely simple to open, ready for use. Merely lower the front of camera, which forms a bed, and draw the front with lens forward until the pinion engages in the rack, and the final adjustment is made with the apparatus placed at the front for that purpose.

The appearance of these folding cameras are especially handsome, as the entire front and bed are made of polished mahogany or cherry, which contrasts perfectly with the black leather covering.

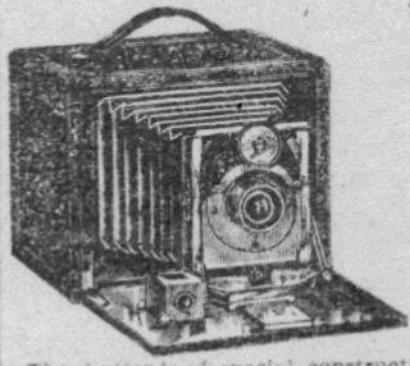

24362 The Folding Premo Camera is a most complete and practical little instrument, possessing all the latest improvements. Has rising and falling front, swing back, reversible view finder and two tripod plates, so that either vertical or horizontal pictures can be taken.

The shutter is of special construction, and the lens is a rapid rectilinear of great power, made specially for this camera. A Roll Holder can be used in this style Premo when desired.

	4x5	5x7	6½x8½
With one dry plate holder. Prices	$27.00	$34.00	$45.00
Extra plate holders	1.15	1.35	1.60
Film holders	1.28	1.45	1.70
Roll holder	7.25	9.00	14.60

24363 Folding Premo Camera "Style B." Almost identical with No. 24362, except that it is fitted with *single view* lens and roll holder cannot be used in it.

	4x5	5x7
Premo B, with one Plate-Holder. Prices	$18.00	$24.25

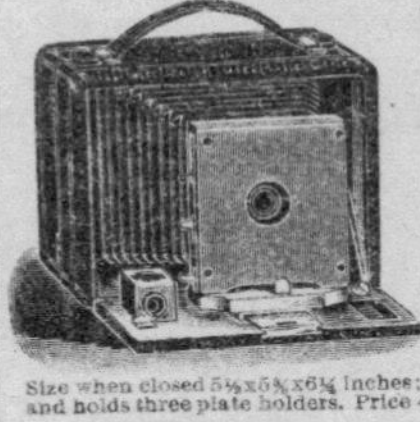

24364 Folding Premo Style D. Cheaper in construction than Nos. 24362 24363 but a thoroughly practical camera. Fitted with single view lens with rigid diaphrams, and new noiseless shutter. Either glass plates or cut films can be used in this style.

Size when closed 5⅛x5⅝x6¼ inches; weight 2 pounds and holds three plate holders. Price 4x5 .... $10.75

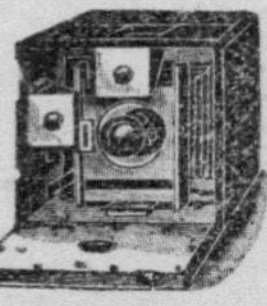

24365 The Rochester for 4x5 pictures one plateholder and fitted with Gundlach Rapid Rectigraphic Lens. $27.00
Rochester Plate Holders, 4x5 .... $0.90
Rochester Roll Holders, 4x5, loaded for 50 exposures $10.75

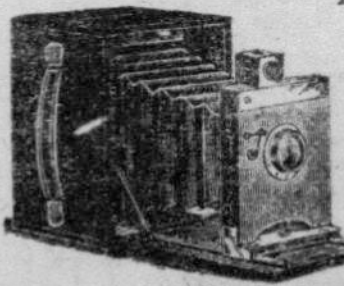

24366 The "Rochester" Folding Camera for 4x5 pictures. This is one of the strongest and most compact of its kind. It measures when closed but 4⅞x5½x7 in. *Glass plates only* can be used in this camera. Fitted with high grade symmetrical lens, with rotating diaphrams Price $22.50

24367 The Rochester Folding Camera for 5x7 pictures, with Rapid Symmetrical Lens $32.50
Rochester Plate Holders, 5x7 .... 1.12
Rochester Roll Holders, 5x7, loaded for 50 exposures 18.50

Cameras—Continued.

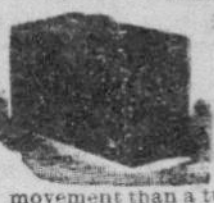

24368 The Heatherington Magazine Camera No. 1, 4x5 size, for glass plates or cut films; is a box of the ordinary hand camera size, strongly and carefully made, that will carry either six or twelve glass plates or cut films always ready for exposure without opening the box and with no other movement than a turn of the wrist.

No. 1, for six plates or cut films, box size 6x6½x9 in., covered with fine black seal grain leather, fitted with rotary shutter that can be set for either time or instantaneous exposure, and fine achromatic lens. $20.00

The Heatherington Magazine Camera No. 2.

24369 For twelve plates or cut films; the best magazine camera on the market. Box measure 6x7½x11 inches, covered with fine seal grain leather, with no projecting points, provided with two view finders of best make. A continuous rotary shutter which requires no attention, and which can be regulated to either slow, medium or rapid speeds. The lens is a Darlot No. 1 Hemispherical of moderate angle with revolving diaphragm working between the lenses. Camera is provided with tally which keeps record of exposures made, and focussing dial. $40.00

NOTE. We are in a position to quote prices of any camera manufactured. Tell your neighbors who contemplate buying a photographic outfit that they can save money by purchasing of us. Correspondence solicited.

The Photoret.

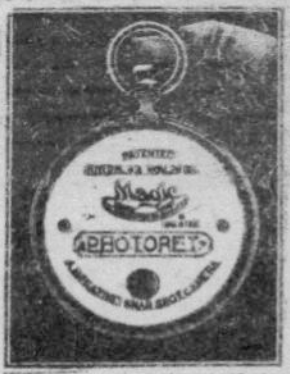

24369½ The Photoret watch size camera is one of the latest results of the inventive mind, and is a remarkable little instrument. It resembles in appearance and size an ordinary hunting-case watch. Takes six pictures without reloading, and may be reloaded outdoors, in daylight, as often as desired. A Photoret booklet, showing specimen pictures sent to any one on application. Outfit complete for 36 pictures. Price $2.50

Detailed descriptions of any of the cameras quoted in this book will be furnished upon request.

View Cameras.

Note reduced prices.

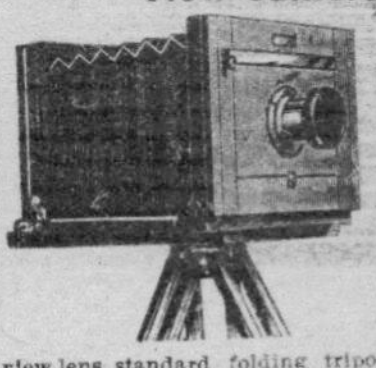

24370 The New Model Camera is well known, having been on the market for years, and is the best low priced camera manufactured. Made of selected cherry, with nickel trimmings, has folding bed, sliding front, and is reversible. With each camera is furnished one R. O. Co. Single view lens, standard folding tripod, one perfection plate holder, and carrying case with handle; *except size 8x10 where neither tripod nor lens are included in price.*

For Pictures.	No Swing.	Single Swing.
3¼x4¼	$7.88	$8.75
4x5	7.90	8.80
4¼x6½	8.70	9.68
5x7	9.65	10.50
5x8	9.70	10.55
6½x8½	11.38	13.23
8x10	11.40	13.25

The New Model Improved.

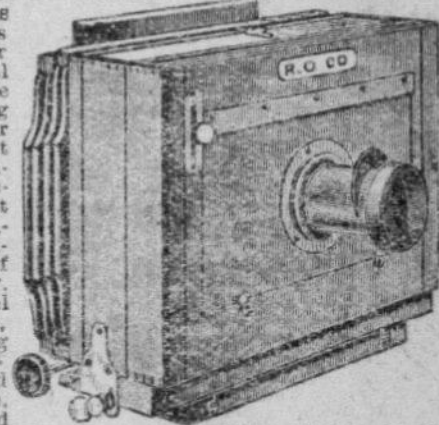

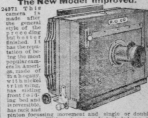

24371 This camera is made after the general style of the preceding but better finished. It has the reputation of being the most popular camera in America, made of mahogany, with nickel trimming, has sliding front folding bed and is reversible, has rack and pinion focussing movement and single or double swing back. With each camera is included one of R. O. Co's, single view lens, Carlton sliding tripod, one perfection plate holder and carrying case, except size 8x10, where price includes neither lens nor tripod.

For Picture.	Single Swing.	Double Swing.
3¼x4¼	$11.37	$13.12
4 x5	12.25	14.00
4¼x6½	14.10	15.75
5 x7	18.80	17.50
5 x8	18.85	17.55
6½x8½	19.25	21.00
8 x10	13 15	14.87

New Model Steroscopic Cameras.

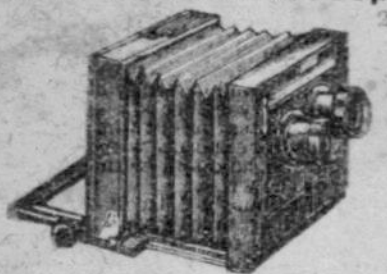

24372 New Model Stereoscopic Camera is patterned closely after the New Model improved, having rack and pinion for focussing, sliding front, folding bed, and is reversible by means of an adjustable reversing clamp. The folding bed is held rigid by a clamp hook, which is the quickest, easiest and best device yet produced for the purpose. The partition and front board are removable so that the camera may be used, if desired, for other than stereoscopic pictures, by the addition of a lens of sufficient size to cover the full plate. Each camera is inclosed in a neat canvas case, with room for two extra Perfection Holders. Price for 5x8, including pair of No. 1 R. O. Co. View Lenses, matched, Carlton Sliding Tripod and one Perfection Holder. Price............$19.25

Use No. 24409 Perfection Plate Holder in New Model, New Model Improved and New Model Stereoscopic Camera.

Victor Camera.

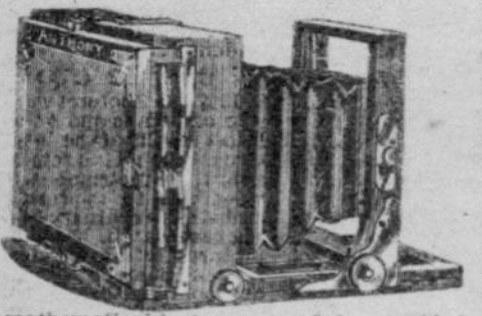

24373— This camera is made of highly polished mahogany, and the metal work has the draw file finish, the same as that used on the finest mathematical instrument. It is provided with rising front and single swing, and is adapted to front focus, having the double rack and pinion movement. The ground glass is fitted with a patent spring actuated movement, which keeps it always attached to the camera, without being in the way of the operator. The camera may be used for making pictures either vertically or horizontally by means of a cap plate on the side. The price includes camera, one eclipse double dry plate holder and canvass carrying case, but no lens or tripod.

Size of View.	Price.	Extra Double Zehper or EclipsePlate Holders. Each.
4 x 5	$ 9.00	$1.12
4¼x 6½	10.35	1.15
5 x 7	10.90	1.20
5 x 8	11.50	1.25
6½x 8½	13.60	1.45
8 x 10	19.12	1.65

Rochester View Camera.

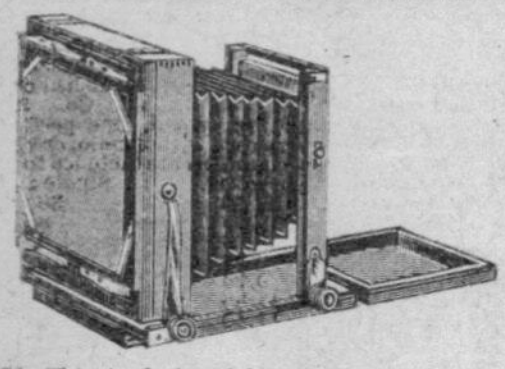

24374 This is designed for a thorough business camera, and can be recommended to both the professional and amateur photographer. It is made of the best selected mahogany, shellac finished, and all the wearing parts are made of brass, draw file finish, and lacquered. It has the reversible back with the latest adjustable spring-actuated ground glass screen, always in position and ready for use. It has front focus, rack and pinion movement. With the reversible back you can change it so as to take a picture vertically or horizontally, without changing the position of the box or altering the focus, and is so arranged that the slide can be drawn from the top, bottom or either side (the change can be made in three seconds). It is made with both vertical and horizontal swing, each swinging at the center. It has a rising and falling front with ratchet movement, cone-shaped bellows, which is attached to the front, allowing it to be raised or lowered with the lens. All its parts are made strong with reference to the work required, thus making the camera a model of lightness and strength. The price includes canvas-carrying case and one double plateholder.

For View.	Price, Single Swing.	Double Swing.	Extra Plate-holder.
5 x7	$17.50	$18.87	$1.13
5 x8	17.75	18.50	1.15
6½x8½	19.25	20.13	1.35
8 x10	21.00	21.38	1.60
10 x12	24.50	26.25	2.50

Upon application we will quote prices upon large sizes (from 11x14 to 20x24). Rochester View Camera.

The Carlton Camera.

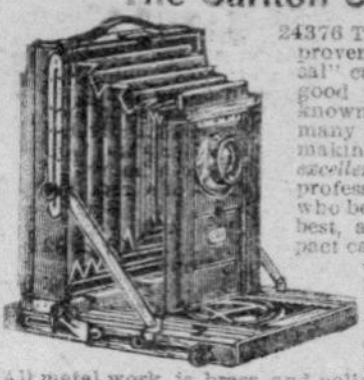

24376 The "Carlton" is an improvement on the "Universal" camera, having all the good points of that well-known box, and in addition many qualities of its own, making it the camera *par excellence* to the amateur or professional photographer who believes in having the best, and is the most compact camera in the market. Owing to the extra length of the bellows, the camera can be used for copying and enlarging, if desired. It has reversible back. All metal work is brass and polished lacquered. The camera box is made of select mahogany, highly polished. The bed carries its own tripod top, adapted to our No. 24451 Combination Tripod. The top is of metal, neatly fitted in the bed, and revolves easily and smoothly, permitting the operator to adjust camera in any direction. A small milled head screw fastens it firmly in position. The Carlton cameras, in sizes to 8x10 inclusive, are furnished with either a long or short canvas case. The former carries the camera and three holders only; the latter will hold the camera, six holders, combination tripod, and in sizes to 6½x8½ inclusive there is a compartment for lenses. In ordering, specify style of case desired.

Size of view.			Price.
Size of view	4 x5	Double swing	$30.62
" "	4¼x6½	" "	31.50
" "	5 x7	" "	35.00
" "	5 x8	" "	36.75
" "	6½x8½	" "	39.37
" "	8 x10	" "	43.75

Horseman's No. 2 "Eclipse" Outfit.

POLISHED CHERRY CAMERA, WITH TRIPOD AND COMPLETE CHEMICAL OUTFIT.

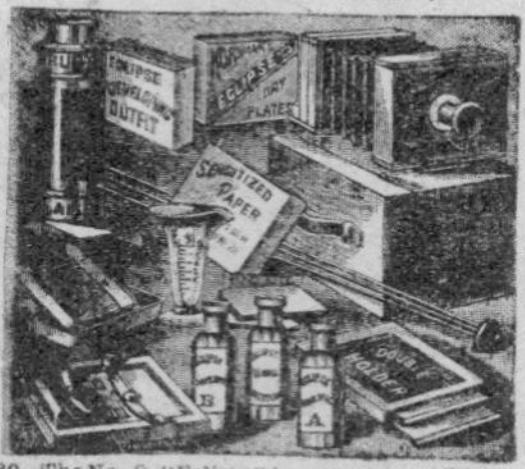

24380 The No. 2 "Eclipse" is gotten up to fill a popular demand. It consists of a Hardwood Camera, for plate size 3¼x4¼ inches, with leatherette bellows, handsomely finished, brass mounted lens, hinged ground glass; double plate holder, tripod and carrying case, weight of above, 2 lbs. The chemical outfit for developing and printing which goes with the above contains: Ruby lamp, ½ dozen dry plates, 2 japanned iron trays, 2 bottles developer, 1 box hyposulphite soda, 12 sheets sensitized paper, 1 printing frame, 1 bottle toning solution, 1 dozen bevel edge card mounts. Weight, complete, 10 lbs. Price for complete outfit..........$4.50

Horseman's No. 3 "Eclipse" Outfit.

24381 The No. 3 Eclipse Camera makes a full size cabinet photograph or view, size 4¼x6½ in. This outfit consists of polished hardwood camera with folding bed and double plate holder, brass mounted lens, with set of stocks, folding tripod, carrying case, printing frame and complete chemical outfit.

Price, for complete outfit............$9.00

Weight, complete, 15 lbs.

SUNDRIES FOR HORSEMAN'S ECLIPSE OUTFITS.

Plate Holders, 3¼x4¼, for No. 2, Each..........$0.45

Plate Holders, 4¼x6½, for No. 3, Each..........90

"A" and "B" Eclipse Developer, per bottle..........10

Eclipse Toning Solution..........10

We do not handle the Ripley Dry Plates. See 24535 and 24536 for quotations on dry plates of standard brands.

View Finder.

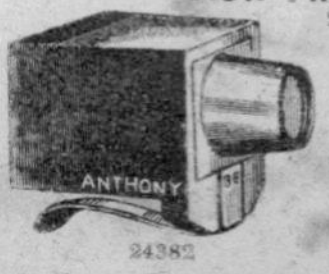

24382

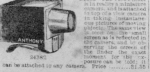

24382 The View Finder is in reality a miniature camera, and is attached to top of a view camera in taking instantaneous pictures of moving objects. The same view is seen on the small screen as is reflected in the camera, and by observing the screen of the finder the exact moment for the exposure can be told; it can be attached to any camera. Price.........$1.35

Lenses.

We aim to keep the lenses quoted below in stock at all times, but it is impossible to always have the higher priced ones on hand, as manufacturers do not always fill our orders promptly. A delay of two to eight days in filling an order wanting a lens may sometimes occur. A lens can always be used to take pictures smaller than its focus; for instance, a 5x8 lens can be used to take 4x5 pictures, but nothing larger than 5x8.

If you want any preferred make or size of lens other than quoted by us, write for net cash price on same. We can furnish nearly anything made.

M. W. & Co. "Crystal" Single Lens.

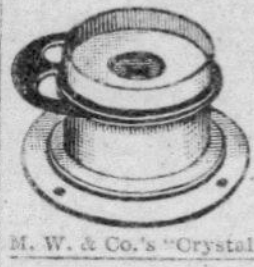

M. W. & Co.'s "Crystal."

24385 M. W. Co.'s Crystal Achromatic Single View Lenses with revolving diaphragm for landscapes; undoubtedly the best Single Achromatic Lens in the market, being much superior to any which usually accompany amateur outfits. They are so constructed as to give pictures of moderate angle with great sharpness and brilliancy.

Size of Plate.	Focus.	Price Complete.
4 x5	6 inch.	$3.85
5 x7	8 inch.	4.50
5 x8	9 inch.	5.00
6½x8½	11½ inch.	6.00
8 x10	12½ inch.	7.25
10 x12	14 inch.	8.50

M. W. & Co.'s Rapid Rectilinear Lens.

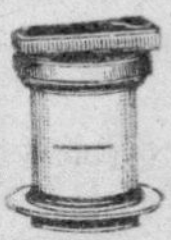

M. W. & Co.'s "Meniscus."

24387 M.W. & Co.'s Rapid Rectilinear *"Meniscus" Double* Achromatic, with set of Waterhouse stops, for portraits, groups, landscapes or instantaneous work. These lenses are not as rapid as our *Extra Rapid Rectilinear "Special"* Lenses, but to those to whom the price of the latter would be an obstacle we can only say that they will meet a long-felt want, as they possess many valuable properties peculiar to themselves.

Visible diam. of Lenses.	Size of Plates.	Back Focus.	Equiv. Focus.	Angle.	Price Complete.
1 inch.	4x5	5¼ in.	2 1/16 in.	75°	$ 8.00
1⅛ inch.	5x7	7½ in.	8¼ in.	75°	9.00
1¼ inch.	5x8	8¼ in.	9⅜ in.	75°	10.00
1⅝ inch.	6½x8½	11⅝ in.	12¾ in.	75°	15.00
2 inch.	8x10	14⅞ in.	16¼ in.	75°	20.00
2⅛ inch.	10x12	16 in.	18¼ in.	75°	25.00

M. W. & Co.'s Extra Rapid Rectilinear Lens.

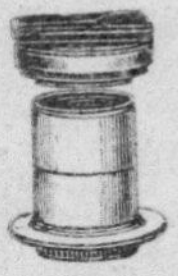

M. W. & Co.'s "Special."

24389 M. W. & Co.'s Extra Rapid Rectilinear, Apalantic Double Achromatic ("Special"). Removable hood; with set of Waterhouse diaphragms, for portraits, groups, landscapes, or instantaneous objects; highest finish and finest quality; each lens guaranteed. Stops cut and working to the standard sizes, with full aperture. These lenses cover plates to the edge, and quality is equal to either of the three popular English lenses, Dallmeyer, Ross and Beck, which are much more expensive.

Visible diam. of Lenses.	Size of Plate.	Back Focus	Equiv. Focus.	Price Complete.	Price with Iris Diaphragm.
1 inch.	4x5	4⅝ in.	5½ in.	$13.50	$16.50
1¼ inch.	5x7	7½ in.	8½ in.	18.00	21.00
1 5/16 inch.	5x8	8¼ in.	8¾ in.	20.00	28.00
1⅝ inch.	6½x8½	10¼ in.	11 in.	26.50	30.00
2 1/32 inch.	8x10	12¾ in.	13⅞ in.	31.00	34.50
2 3/16 inch.	10x12	14 in.	16⅛ in.	40.00	48.00
2 9/16 inch.	12x16	17¾ in.	19 3/16 in.	48.00	60.00
3⅛ inch.	16x20	23¾ in.	25½ in.	65.00	78.00

R. O. & Co.'s Single View Lens.

24394 For Illustration of R. O. Single View Lens, see cut of New Model Improved Camera, No. 24371. For landscape work the single view lens is most used. It gives good results and will even make good interiors and portraits. Brass with *revolving diaphragm*.

Size of Plate.	Length of Focus.	No.	Price.
4 x5	6 inch	1	$2.70
4¼x6½	8 inch	1½	3.15
5 x8	10 inch	2	3.60
6½x8½	11 inch	3	4.50
8 x10	13 inch	4	6.30

Pair No. 1 Lenses matched for Stereoscopic work, mounted on front board.......... 5.50

M. W. & Co.'s Symmetrical Wide Angular Rectilinear Lens.

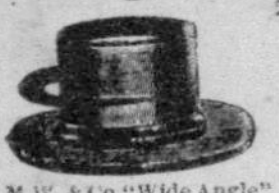

M.W. & Co."Wide Angle" Double Achromatic.

24394 M. W. & Co.'s Symmetrical "Wide Angle." Double Achromatic (Special). For work requiring great width of angle, and extra rectilinear results, such as interiors, architectural or street views, over an angle of 90 or 100 degrees, and have a remarkable depth of focus compared with other wide angle lenses. They are the most rapid wide angle lenses made. They are distinguished by the comparatively large stops with which they give sharp images, a result which is largely due to the great perfection of their polish. Revolving diaphragm. Removable hood.

Diam. of Lenses.	Size of Plate.	Equivalent Focus.	Price Complete.
⅝ inch.	4 x5	4 inch.	$12.50
¾ inch.	5 x8	5 inch.	14.50
⅞ inch.	6½x8½	6 inch.	17.00
1⅛ inch.	8 x10	7 inch.	22.00

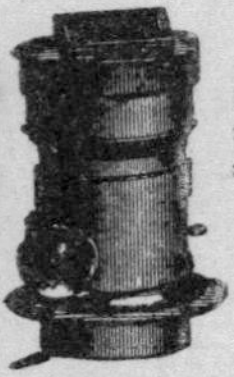

Darlot Portrait Lens.

24395 With Rack and Pinion and Central stops.

Size.	Size of Plate.	Focus.	Price.
¼	3¼x4¼	4½ in.	$8.35
⅓	4x5	5½ in.	13.75
½	5x7	7 in.	16.50
4-4	8x10	10 in.	34.00

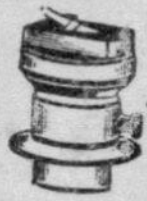

Darlot Rapid Hemispherical Lens.

For Portraits and Views.

24397 60° to 75° Quick Working, perfectly rectilinear, for landscapes and outdoor groups; also for copying maps, engravings, plans, etc.

No.	Back Focus.	Size of Plate.	Price.
1	5¼	4 x5to 5x7	$13.00
2	9	5x7 to 6½x8½	19.00
3	10½	6½x8½ to 8x10	28.50
4	14	8x10 to 10x14	42.50

Drop Shutters.

The Universal Drop Shutters.

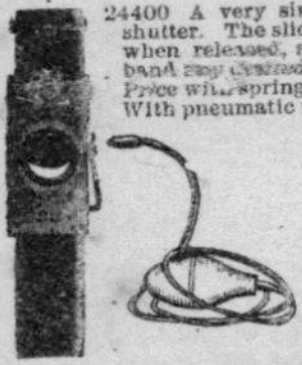

24400 A very simple yet effective form of shutter. The slide falls of its own weight when released, and by the use of rubber band any desired rapidity may be obtained.
Price with spring release $0.90
With pneumatic release, bulb and tube 1.40

The Low Shutter.

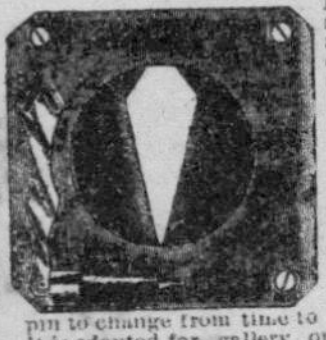

24406 Low Compound Shutter is made with extra large opening in a small shutter, has four wings, and is especially designed for cameras having small front boards; works with pneumatic attachment, self-locking and easily balanced. Is attached to the front board on the inside of the camera, but can be operated entirely from the outside of the camera, and at any distance. It being only necessary to push in or pull out the small brass pin to change from time to instantaneous exposures. It is adapted for gallery or outdoor work. Is made only in four small sizes.

1½ inch opening, 3 in. square $5.00
1¾ inch opening, 3½ in. square 5.00
2 inch opening, 4 in. square 5.50
2¼ inch opening, 4½ in. square 5.50

*** All orders are filled from the latest Catalogue. We shall, whenever possible, on orders from old Catalogues, give the nearest we have, and wish to explain that we change our quotations so as to be able to give the latest styles and better values.

"Marvel Shutter."

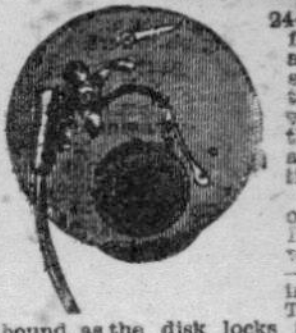

24407 Is made to fit on the front end of the lens tube, and is constructed on the simplest principles and has the following distinct advantages over any other upon the market. It is the easiest and quickest changed from time to instantaneous.

It is less liable to get out of order than any other.

It is steel bronzed over brass, with working parts nickeled—therefore the handsomest in appearance.

There is absolutely no rebound, as the disk locks itself after making the exposure.

It is adjusted to the lens by a velvet-lined flange which is tightened by a screw—therefore avoiding all injury to the tube or making it necessary to cut same.

In ordering, it is only necessary to measure the lens' hood with a strip of paper and forward same to us

Size	4x5	5x8	Larger size,
Prices	$5.00	$5.50	$6.25.

New French Shutter.

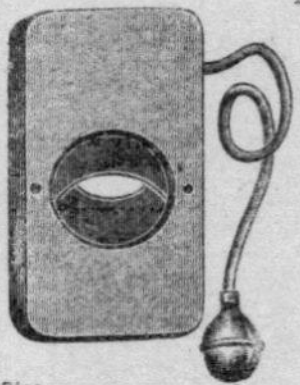

24408 A light, handsome two-wing shutter for both time and instantaneous exposures at a moderate price, handsomely nickeled. The instrument is a tube shutter, and to place same in position unscrew nickel-plated collar from back of frame. Remove the lens hood, slip collar over barrel of lens, and replace hood: fasten shutter and lens together by screwing collar in place. When ordering give diameter of both hood and barrel of lens upon which shutter is intended to be used.

Size.	Price.
1¼ inch opening	$4.00
1⅝ inch opening	4.50
2⅜ inch opening	5.00

Perfection Dry Plate Holders.

24409 The New Model, New Model Improved and New Model Stereoscopic Cameras are the *only* cameras quoted in this catalogue that these holders will fit. We can furnish almost *any* kind of plate holders at less than list price. Where ordering, *be sure to state what camera the holder it is intended to be used in.* The Perfection Double Plate Holder is the simplest and best plate holder ever placed on the market. To load this holde, the end of the plate is rested against the spring-bar at the end of the holder; then by simply pressing the spring bar with the thumb the plate falls into place. Can be loaded and unloaded in absolute darkness, as the plate is held in place by the ends only; the full width of the plate is exposed and but 1-16 inch is cut off from each end.

Size	Each	Size.	Each.
3¼x4¼	$0.90	5 x 8	$1.25
4 x5	.90	6½x 8½	1.45
4¼x6½	1.12	8 x10	1.70
5 x7	1.15		

Inside Kits.

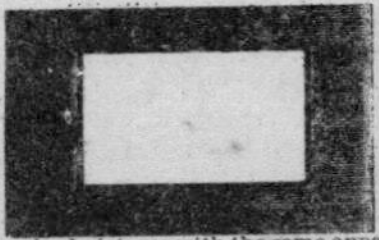

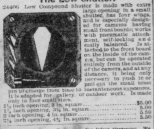

24410 Consists of thin wooden frames, made to fit in the Perfection Plate Holder with openings for smaller plate, with spring for holding plate in place. Enables anyone having a camera to take smaller sized pictures with the same apparatus.

☞ *When ordering, please mention size of plate holder as well as size of plate kits are for.*

Size.		Each.
4 x5	to hold 3¼x4¼ plates	$0.20
4¼x6½	to hold 3¼x4¼ plates	.20
5 x7	to hold 3¼x4¼ or 4x5 plates	.25
5 x8	to hold 3¼x4¼, 4x5 or 4¼x6½ plates	.25
6½x8½	to hold 4x5, 4¼x6½, 5x7 or 5x8 plates	.30
8 x 10	to hold 5x7, 5x8 or 6½x8½ plates	.35
10x12	to hold 5x7, 5x8, 6½x 8½ or 8x10 plates	.45
11x14	to hold 5x8, or 6½x8½, 8x10 or 10x12 plates	.55

Inside kits are made to hold any ONE of the sizes mentioned above, but are not adjustable to all the sizes listed.

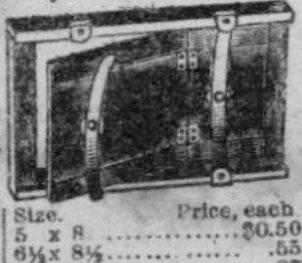

24412 The Favorite Printing Frame, especially desirable for amateurs, on account of its lightness; at the same time being equal in strength and durability to the ordinary flat printing frame.

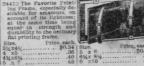

Size.	Price, each.	Size.	Price, each
3¼x4¼	$0.34	5 x 8	$0.50
4 x5	.36	6½x 8½	.55
4¼x6½	.40	8 x10	.67
5 x 7	.45		

Tripods.

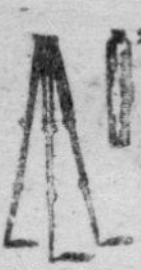

24415 The Columbian Tripod is made adjustable in the length of legs and fold up very compactly. They are perfectly rigid, substantially made, well finished and are provided with screws in the top, which cannot fall out, for clamping the camera. They are strong enough for cameras 6½x8½, or smaller.
No. 3, single fold extension legs. Each $1.75
No. 4. double fold extension legs. Each 2.25

24416 Standard Folding Tripod with iron head. When tripod head is removed, the legs will fold to half length. The screw remains always in the iron top ready for use and not liable to loss. It is light, strong and rigid.
Price, for cameras from 4x5 to 6½x8½ $1.80

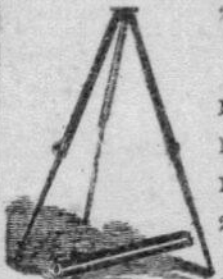

24417 Carlton's Sliding Tripod light, strong and rigid; easy to adjust in rough places, quickly taken down, very compact.

Each.
No. 1, 4x5 and 4¼x6½ cameras $2.25
No. 2, for 5x8 and 6½x8½ camera 2.70
No. 3, for 8x10 and 10x12 camera 3.15

24418 Combination Sliding and Folding Tripod. Length, when closed, only 22 inches; a beauty. No. 1, for cameras 3¼x4¼ to 4¼x6½ 2.75
No. 2, for cameras 5x8 and 6½x8½ 3.15
No. 3, for cameras 8x10 and 11x14 .... 3.60

Developing Trays.

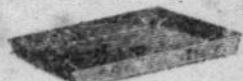

24420 Japanned Tin Developing Trays, made with two small ridges in bottom to prevent plates from adhering.

4x5, each	$0.29	6½x 8½ each	$0.30
5x8, each	.28	8 x10 each	.40
		10 x12 each	.50

24421 Developing Trays, vulcanized rubber.

4x5, each	$0.25	6½x 8½ each	$0.70
5x8, each	.55	8 x10 each	1.00
		10 x12 each	1.50

24422 Amber Glass Trays for developing. Heavy, shallow, for plates.
4¼x6½ size .... $0.25 | 5x8 size $0.35

24423 Papier Mache Trays.

	Each.		Each.
1 size, 3¼x4¼	$0.25	4 size, 7 x 9	$0.70
2 size, 4¼x5½	.30	5 size, 8¼x10¼	.95
3 size, 5½x8¼	.50	6 size, 10¼x12¼	1.40

Quotations given up to size 28x34, when desired.

Funnels.

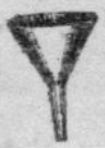

24425 Glass Funnels, for filtering, etc.
½ pint, each $0.15
1 pint, each .... .20
1 quart, each .... .25
2 quarts, each .... .35

24426 Fluted Glass Funnels, for filtering.
½ pint, each .... .15
1 pint .... .20

24427 Hard Rubber Funnels, not easily broken.
¼ pint, each .... .40
½ pint, each .... .45
1 pint, each .... .50
1 quart, each .... .60

Graduated Glasses.

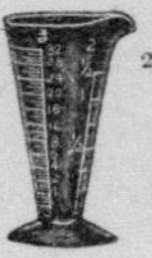

24430 Graduated Glasses for measuring liquids.
1 ounce, each $0.20
2 ounce, each .... .25
4 ounce, each .... .30
8 ounce, each .... .45
12 ounce, each .... .60
16 ounce, each .... .75
24 ounce, each .... .90

Glass Mortars and Pestles.

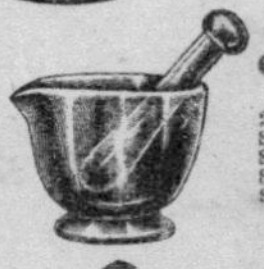

24432—
Size, 2½ inches, each $0.15
Size, 3 inches, each .... .20
Size, 4 inches, each .... .35
Size, 6 inches, each .... .85

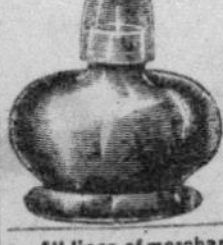

24433 Glass Spirit Lamp ground glass caps.
Size, 2 oz. Each $0.40
" 4 " " .... .50
" 8 " " .... .70

All lines of merchandise very generally reduced in price.

Safes—Continued.

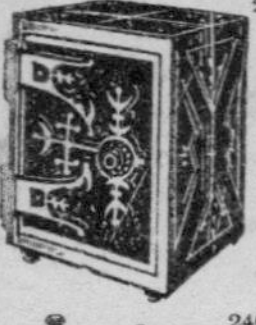

24656 The Boudoir Combination Lock Safe, with two divisions and drawers, handsomely lined with plush and satin; a practical article for every household for the safe keeping of valuables, such as money, jewels, etc., etc. It is strongly made and handsomely ornamented and embossed. Dimensions, 6x6 x8¼ inches, and weighs 13½ lbs. Comes packed in a strong wooden box, making a total weight of 16 lbs.
Price, each............$5.00

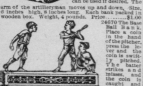

24661 Puzzle locomotive Savings Bank, made entirely of iron, japanned and finely finished. The weight of the money dropped in the slot on top of the cab will, after the bank is full (and not before), loosen the smoke stack, which can then be lifted out and the money poured from the opening. As it is a perfect imitation of a locomotive, and the wheels turn, it is a toy that will please the children.
Weight 1½ lbs.
Each............$0.35

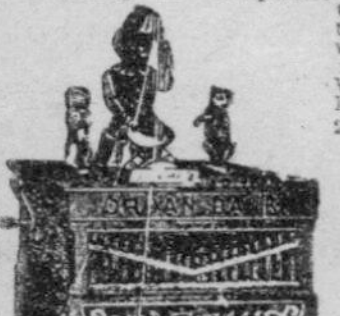

24663 Iron Organ bank (CPO), elegantly finished, large chime of bells, dancing figures revolve when the handle is turned, the monkey deposits the coin in the vault and politely raises his hat: size, 8½ in. high, 5½ in. wide and 3¾ in. deep. Weight, 8¾ lbs. Each ....$0.85 This bank is too heavy to go by mail.

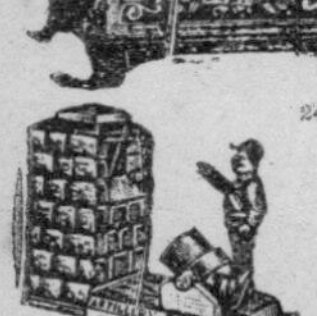

24668 The Artillery Bank, made wholly of iron, highly finished and bronzed throughout. Cannons (or mortar) is brass plated; tower and artilleryman, Japanese bronze. Place the coin in the mortar, push back the hammer and press the thumb piece and the coin is fired into the fort or tower. Paper caps can be used if desired. The arm of the artilleryman moves up and down. Size, 6 inches high, 8 inches long. Each bank packed in wooden box. Weight, 4 pounds. Price.........$1.00

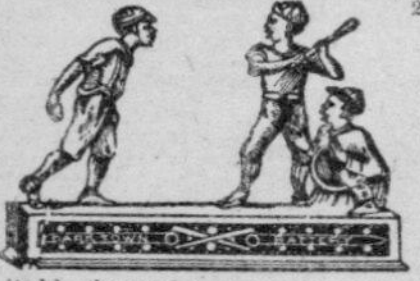

24670 The Base Ball Bank. Place a coin in the hand of the pitcher, press the lever and the coin is swiftly pitched. The batter strikes and misses, and the coin is caught and safely deposited by the catcher. The movements of all the figures are very life-like. Handsomely finished in bright colors. Length, 10 inches; height, 7¼ inches; width 2¼ inches. Packed one in wooden box. Weight 4¼ lbs.
Price..........................$0.90

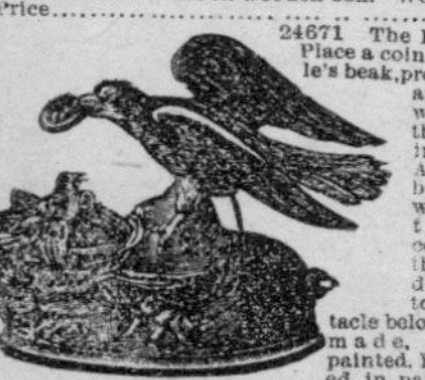

24671 The Eagle Bank. Place a coin in the Eagle's beak, press the lever, and the eagles will rise from the nest crying for food. As the eagle bends forward to feed them, the coin falls into the nest and disappears into the receptacle below. Strongly made, handsomely painted. Eagles painted in natural colors.
Weight, 4 lbs. Price..........................$0.95

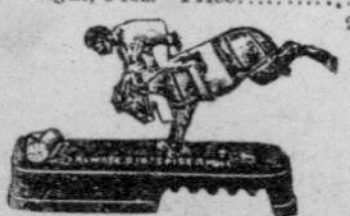

24672 The Kicking Mule Bank. Length 10¼ in. Height, 8in. width, 3 in.; made of iron and nicely finished. The mule and rider being brought into position, a slight touch on a knob at the base causes the mule to kick and throw the rider over his head, when the coin is thrown from the rider's mouth into the receptacle below.
Price..........................$0.88

Safes—Continued.

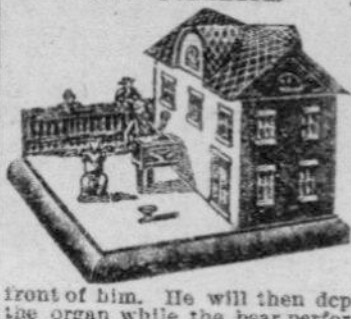

24673 The Dancing Bear Bank, with clock-work mechanism and chimes. Size 6⅞ in. long, 4¾ in. wide, 5½ in. high. This bank represents the front of a country house with an Italian organ-grinder and a bear on the lawn. After winding up the mechanism, place a coin in the slot and push the knob in front of him. He will then deposit the coin and play the organ while the bear performs his part. Handsomely painted. Packed one in a wooden box...$0.98

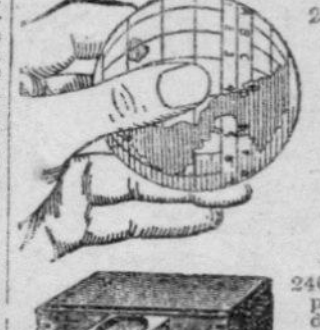

24674 The Columbian Souvenir Pocket Bank, made of nickel, globe shape, 3 inches in diameter, with map of the world engraved upon it. It is opened on the same principle that the Columbus Egg is made to stand on end. Unless the trick is known it is utterly impossible to open it. The best trick bank in the market. Weight, 3 ounces...$0.30

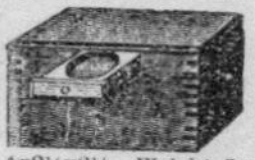

24675 Trick Box Bank. Deposit the coin in the drawer, push the drawer in, and upon opening it again the coin has disappeared; cannot be opened unless you "are on;" made of hardwood; size, 4x2½x2½. Weight, 3 ounces. Price............$0.10

Registering Banks.

We make a specialty of this line.
An examination of the following quotations will convince our customers that we have as good an assortment, at more reasonable prices, than can be found elsewhere.

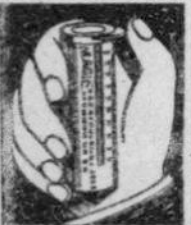

24676 The little Gem Dime Pocket Savings Bank, locks itself and registers the amount deposited; opens automatically when $5.00 in dimes have been deposited without the use of force; is handsomely nickel plated and can be carried in the pocket without inconvenience
Each..............................$0.10
Per dozen........................ 1.00
Postage.......................... .05

24677 The Magic Dime Pocket Savings Bank, same general construction as above, but made of heavier metal. Holds $5.00 in dimes.
Price, each......20 cts. Per dozen.........$2.00

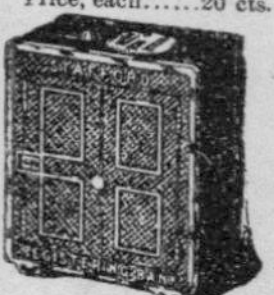

24681 The Stafford Registering Bank, receives and registers correctly nickels, dimes and quarters on one dial. Made of steel and iron, handsomely nickeled and japanned; simply and strongly constructed, and will not get out of order and become a source of annoyance to purchasers. It is the only bank which registers more than one coin on the same dial. Height, 5½ inches. Width, 4½ inches. Weight, 2 lbs. Price................$1.00

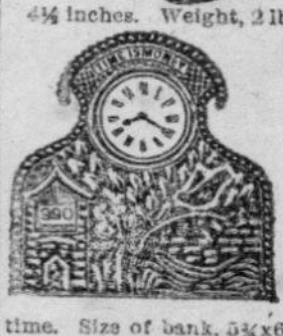

24682 The Ideal Recording Clock Bank, a beautiful ornament for the desk or mantel. Strongly constructed of nickel. The front is handsomely plated with aluminum, giving it the appearance of silver. Deposit a dime in the slot, pull out the lever and the amount contained in the bank will be recorded upon the register. The clock is a first-class "New Haven" timepiece and will keep correct time. Size of bank, 5¾x6x1¾. Weight, 2 lbs....$2.00

Marbles.

24713 Glass figured—		Each	Per doz.
5	weight per dozen 1 lb....	$0.04	$0 35
7	weight per dozen 2¼ lbs....	.05	.50
9	weight per dozen 4 lbs....	.06	.65
11	weight per dozen 7 lbs....	.15	1.75

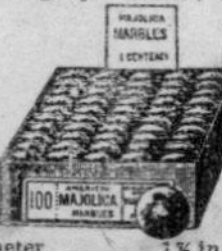

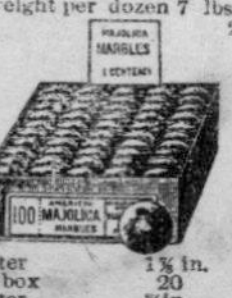

24714 American Majolica Marbles, made in new and fancy colors, and packed each size in a pasteboard box; weight, about 4½ lbs. The only novelty in the marble line that has been introduced for years. Sold only as quoted; we do not break original packages.

Diameter	1⅜ in.	1¼ in.	1 in
No. in box	20	50	100
Diameter	⅞ in.	⅝ in.	⅝ in.
No. in box	200	300	400

Price per box of any size, 70c.
In ordering be sure to mention size desired.

Tops.

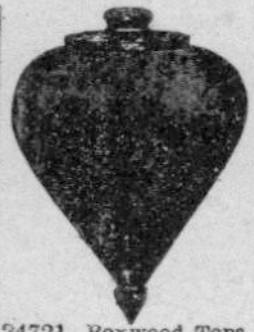

24718 Stained Wood Peg Tops, assorted colors and in four sizes. Price per doz. $0.25
24719 Hardwood Tops, extra quality, peg all the way through; brass button rivet on top. Selected hardwood, malleable iron pegs with hardened points.
Per doz.............$0.35
24720 Boxwood Tops, hardened point pegs, in assorted colors and four sizes.
Per doz.............$0.45
24721 Boxwood Tops, with spear. Extra size and weight; octagon shaped spear, just the thing to split your opponent's top wide open. No. 4 size. Per dozen.................... .70
24722 Lignum Vitae Tops, made of hardest known wood. Assorted sizes. Per doz......... .80

French Choral or Musical Tops.

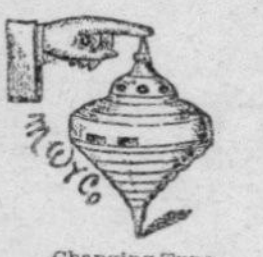

Changing Tune.

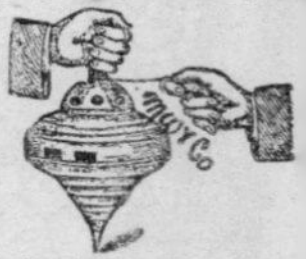

Starting to Spin.

24725 Humming Top, made of tin, striped in bright colors, stands 5 inches high; changeable. Postage 5c. Price each.....................$0.10
Per doz.................................. 1.00
24726 French Musical Top, with handle; produces a beautiful melody while spinning. Striped in bright colors. Height 7 inches; changeable. Postage 7c. Price each..................... .25
Per doz.................................. 2.50
24727 French Choral Changeable Tops (see cut), changes tunes while spinning by touching on top; simple and wonderful. The melody is as finely blended and the chords are as perfect as those of a church organ. Strong and not liable to get out of order. A mammoth toy; height, with handle, 8 inches.
Our price each.............................. .40
Per doz...................................... 4.50
By mail, extra, each 10c.
24728 Our New Globe Gyroscope Top—made of metal; will spin longer than any other, with either end up, in almost any position. A new departure in the Gyroscope variety. Price, ea. .20

Toy Iron Trains.

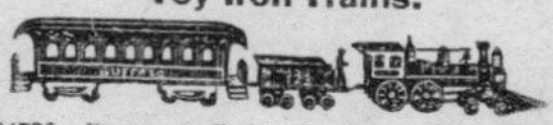

24730 Passenger Train Small size, nickel-plated engine, tender and one coach; length of train 11¼ inches. Packed one in a box. Price..................................$0.25
24731 Passenger Train Same as above except larger; nickel plated. Length of train 19¾ in. Price.............................. .50
24732 Ideal Passenger Train consisting of locomotive, tender and one passenger coach of large size. Made of iron, handsomely nickled jointed connecting rods on drive wheels; all wheels revolve. Length of train, 30 in. Packed one in a box. See cut. Price.................. 1.00

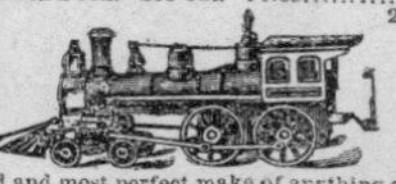

24734 Large size engine and tender; no cars; pull with a string. This engine and tender are the finest finished and most perfect make of anything on the market. Weight, 8 lbs. In box. Each...............$1.50
24737 Freight Train. Small size, engine, tender, and two flat cars. Nickel plated and packed in a box. Length, 15 in. Price..... .23
24738 Freight Train, same as above but larger. Length 25⅞ in. long. Price............. .48
24739 Freight Train consisting of large size locomotive, tender and two flat cars of large size, all nickel plated. Drive wheels on engine are connected with jointed connecting rod, and all wheels revolve. Length of train, 35½ in. Packed in a box. Price.......................... .95

24740 Mechanical Iron Locomotive, new model and finish; guaranteed to work perfectly. Packed one in a box with tender. Length, 10 in. Weight, 2¾ lbs. Price....$1.00

*** Always be sure to state the amount of money enclosed with order.

Steam Toys.

Upright Engines.

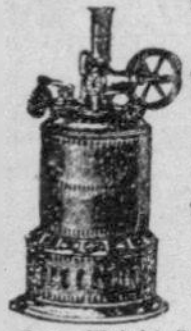

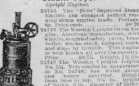

24745 The "Hero" improved Steam Engine, the cheapest perfect running steam engine made. Postage, 8c. Price each.................. $0 20

24746 The Weeden Upright Steam Engine. American manufacture, with whistle, weighted safety valve, brass boiler, smoke stack, exhaust, starts and stops by throttle. This engine is well known all over the country. Price........$0.75. Weight, 1¾ lbs.

24747 The Weeden Upright Engine No. 5½. Very similar in appearance to No. 24748; has water gauge and rotary governor. Height from base to top, 9¼ in., height of boiler, 3 in., diameter of boiler, 2¾ in. Each engine placed in wooden box. Weight, 2¼ lbs. Price......... ....$1.25

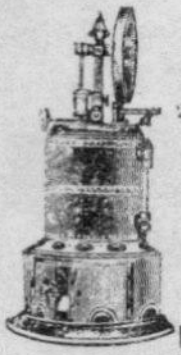

24748 Weeden Upright Engine No. 6. This is a large and attractive upright engine. It is substantially made, and is in every respect strong and durable, and presents a fine appearance when in operation. Has brass boiler, rotary governor, water gauge, etc. Price.......... ....$2.50 Weight, 3½ pounds.

Horizontal Engines.

24750 The "Ajax." Each engine carefully packed in a wood box, complete with lamp, etc. A sensible, practical, instructive toy. Warranted to work perfectly. Absolutely safe. Brass boiler, with copper band, iron stand, etc. Price each.... $0.75
Extra, by mail .16

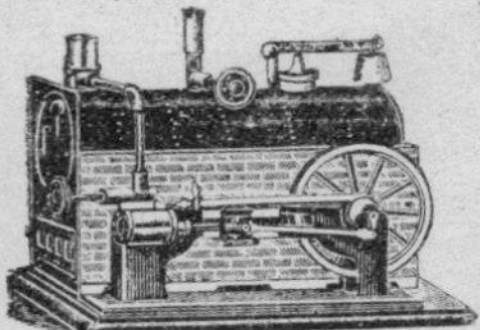

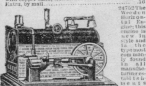

24752 The Weeden Horizontal Engine; this engine is new in style and is the type most commonly found in all manufacturing establishments throughout the country. The boiler bases are of Russia iron, finished in black, gold and red. The other parts are brass and cast metal. Size of base, 4½x5¾ inches; length of boiler, 4¾ inches; diameter, 1½ inches; fly wheel, 1⅞ inches. Packed in wooden box It weighs 24 ozs. Price..$1.50

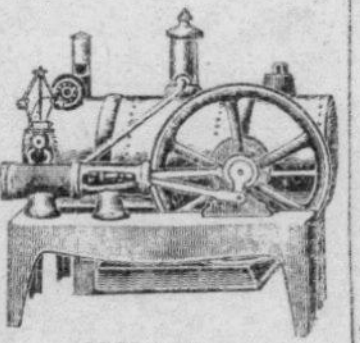

24753 New Horizontal Weeden engine; has large polished brass boiler with stern dome, whistle and safety valve. The frame is cast malleable iron, to which the boiler and engine are firmly attached. The cylinder, steam chest and slide rest are cast in one piece and cannot get out of order. The whole engine is in every way a strong and durable steam toy. Price, each $2.75

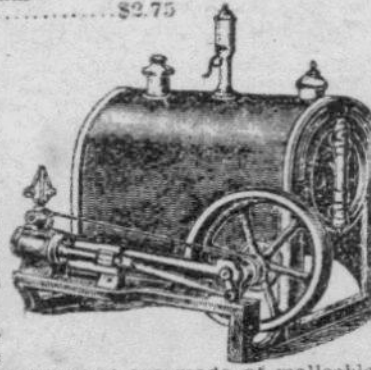

24755 Large Horizontal No. 10; this is the largest and strongest engine we handle. It has a large brass boiler enveloped with a sheet iron jacket to prevent loss of heat. The boiler trimmings are safety valve, whistle, steam dome and water gauge. The boiler frame and engine bed are made of malleable iron, well riveted and pinned together. The cylinder, steam chest and cross head slide rest are made in one piece of solid brass. The piston and rod, the crank and connecting rod, the eccentric and valve rod and slide valve are all made of brass. The balance wheel is made of malleable iron with a polished face. All parts of the engine are securely put together, well finished, and *very durable*. Each engine is carefully tested before packing. Full directions for operating engine will be found in each box, with price list of duplicate parts. Weight, 8½ lbs. Price.........$8.00

Beam and Mill Engines.

24757 The Weeden Beam Engine. This engine is modeled after and has all the essential features of a "Cornish Pumping Engine." The boiler is mounted in imitation of brick setting, including iron stays and working furnace door for management of fires. The top of Boiler is provided with Manhole, Gallows, Frame with Walking Beam, and Filler with Safety Valve. Instead of an oscillating cylinder, it has a device for the introduction of steam into a stationary vertical cylinder, consisting of Rocking Valve with Valve Rod, worked by an eccentric on the main shaft, the inlet of steam to the steam chest being controlled by a screw throttle valve. Size, 6½ in. base, 3½ in. wide, 5½ in. high. Price...........$1.75

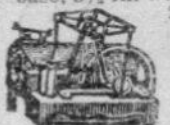

24758 The Walking Beam Engine, 7 in. long, 7 in. high, 4 in. fly wheel, 4½ in. walking beam, heavy riveted brass boiler, with safety valve. Put up, one in a neat paper box complete. Price...$4.50
Weight, 4 pounds.

24759 The Weeden New Double or Mill Engine is modeled after and is almost an exact type of the double engine issue in nearly all the large cotton factories in this country. This is a model engine in every respect, and on that will serve as a valuable lesson to those desiring to study steam engineering as practiced at the present time. Every one is thoroughly tested before being packed for shipment. Finished in bronze scarlet, gilt and black. Size, 10x6¼x3¾. Height to top of chimney, 10 inches. Packed one in a wooden box. Weight, 3 lbs...$3.25

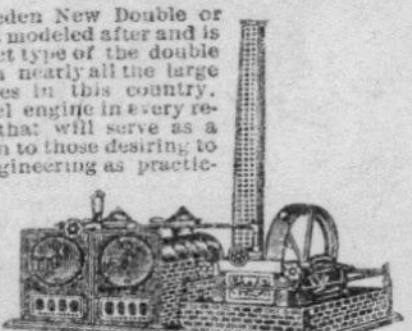

Steam Trains.

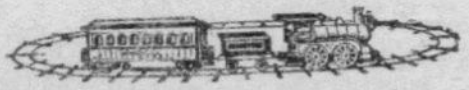

24761 Weeden Steam Locomotive, Tender and Passenger Car, with jointed track on wooden sleepers. Diameter of track, 3½ feet, locomotive, 8 inches long; car and tender in proportion. Put up in wooden box. Weight, 4 lbs. Price for train complete $3.50

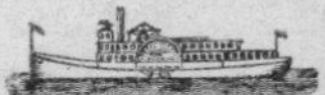

24762 The Weeden New Sidewheel Steamboat. The steamer is new, and is modeled after the modern sidewheel excursion boats; is made of tin and weighs about one pound with ballast. Will steam in a tub or tank of water or on a still water pond. Dimensions; 12 inches long, 3¼ inch beam, 5 in. high. Price, complete, packed in a wooden box, $2.00; total weight 2lbs.

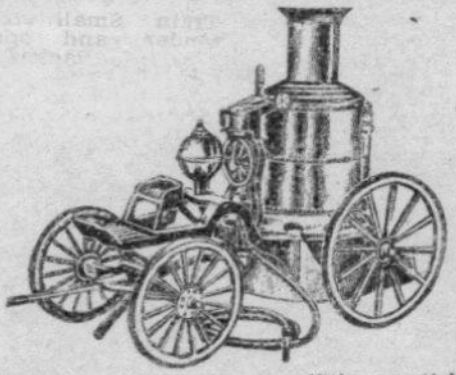

24763 New Steam Fire Engine; has all the essential parts of a modern fire engine. The boiler is polished brass attached firmly to frame and has safety valve, whistle and water gauge. It has two cylinders, pump and hose attachments; is firmly put together, and all its parts are strong and durable. Every engine is thoroughly tested before leaving the factory and fully warranted. Full directions for running the engine inclosed in each box, with price of duplicate parts. Price, each $5.50

Attachments for Steam Engines.

24765 The Village Blacksmith Steam Engine Attachment. Very novel and interesting. Pleases old and young alike. Weight 1½ lbs. Each..........$0.40

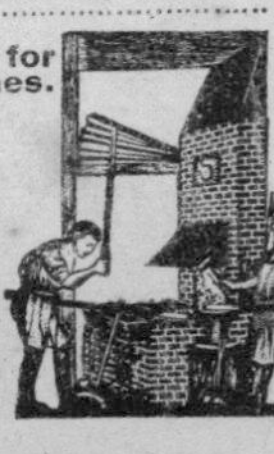

Toy Machinery.

Can be operated by any of our toy steam engines.

24768	Circular Saw and Table	$0.45
24769	Turning Lathe..................................	.55
24770	Grindstone (wood wheel)......................	.35
24771	Cone Pulley to connect with Lathe........	.20
24772	Hangers for shafting...	.10
24773	Pulleys, ½ to 2¼ in, diameter...............	.03

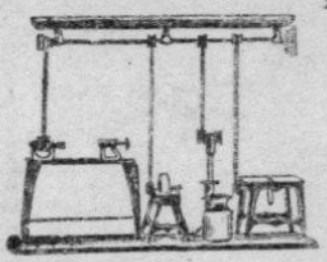

24775 The Model Toy Machine Shop, of five pieces; consists of circular saw and table, turning lathe, anvil press drill and grind, stone mounted on wooden base, with pulleys and overhead shafting. Length, 11 inches. Weight, complete, packed in pasteboard box, 2 lbs.
Price per set....$0.95

Patent Hot Air Toys.

24776 - Hot Air Attachments, single and double figures, made with the patented air wheel.
Each, complete..$0.20

Indestructible Malleable Iron Toys.

24780—Columbus Bell Toy. As the toy is drawn, each revolution of the wheels causes the bell to ring. The design represents an ancient state barge manned by oarsmen, with Columbus standing in the bow. Handsomely painted in bronze and fancy colors. Each one packed in a wood box. Length, 7½ in. Height, 5¼ in. Width, 3¼ inches. Price...$0.50

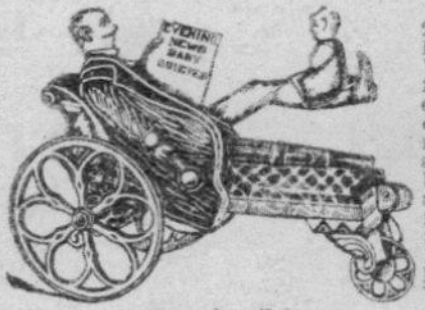

24781 The Baby Quieter Wheel Toy; as it is drawn, each revolution of the wheel rings the bell and jumps the baby. A very amusing toy; finished in fancy colors. Length, 7¼ in. Height, 6 in. Width, 3¼. Weight, 1¾ pounds. Price.......................$0.40

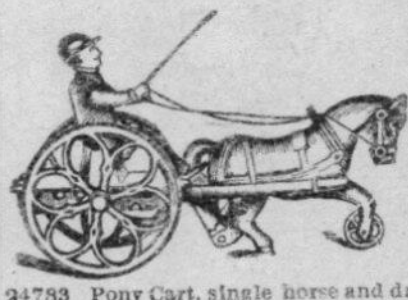

24782 The Pony Wheel Toy, made of malleable iron, handsomely finished in bright colors. Each revolution of the wheel causes the driver to strike the pony with the whip. Length, 9 in. Height, 5½ in. Weight, 1½ lbs. Price......$0.45

24783 Pony Cart, single horse and driver, nickel plated. Length of toy 6¾ in.....................$0.25

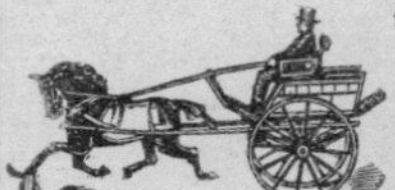

24784 Road Cart A perfect model, made of iron and nickel plated. Single horse and driver. Length of toy, 10¼ in. Price...... $0.50

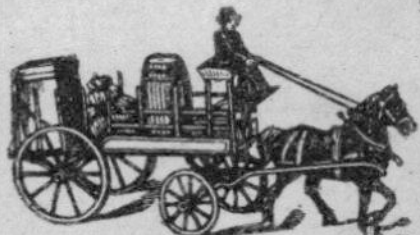

24787 Single Truck (1), with driver and load of merchandise, as represented in cut. Length, 13 in. handsomely painted in colors. Each complete, ...$0.80

Toys—Continued.

24789 Double Truck, with driver and two horses. Load consists of two boxes, two barrels and one sack of merchandise. Horses painted black, harness and running gear of truck painted a bright red, black striped. Packed one in a box; complete. Each......................$1.75

24790 Express Wagon, with driver and two horses. Load consists of two boxes, and one sack. Horses painted cream color, harness black, harness red, collar black, wagon body red, black striped, gilt letters; gear yellow, black striped. Packed one in a box, complete. Each....$2.00

24791 Barouche, with driver in coachman's livery. Cream colored horses, with fancy colored hip blankets, running gear, maroon, gold striped; body black. Both horses trotting when toy is in motion. A particularly handsome article. Packed one in a box. Each.............$1.85

24792 Fire Engine, with driver and engineer in full regulation uniform. When in motion the horses gallop and the gong rings. A complete miniature fire department. Length, 18 inches; with nickel plated boiler and valves. Packed one in a box. Each...................$2.00

24793 Hose cart, (S), with driver and fireman in full uniform, with two Pompier Corps ladders, as shown in cut. Cream colored horses with red running gear to cart and alarm gong, which rings while in motion. Whole finely painted in bright colors. A companion piece to 24792. Length, 18 in. Each..................$2.00

24794 Hook and Ladder Truck, with driver and steersman in full uniform. Four red extension ladders, which can be untied, making a ladder 51 inches in length. Two axles, gaily painted. Length, 24 inches. Too large to illustrate correctly. Must be seen to be appreciated. Each, complete...........................2.00

24795 The above three numbers make a complete miniature fire department. Price per set... 5.50

24796 Engine House, made of malleable iron and wood, handsomely painted in fancy colors, length 26¾ inches; width, 10 inches; height, 18 inches. Has swinging doors, with bell at top. Price, each....................3.25

24797 The "Brave Boy" fireman's complete outfit, consisting of helmet, trumpet and axe. Helmet is made of papier mache and painted black with gilt stripes and is ornamented with a gilt badge fastened to the front. Trumpet is of papier mache and axe of wood. Handsomely painted in bright colors; it is an outfit that will please any boy. Cannot be sent by mail. Price....2.50

24798 Artillery, made of indestructible iron and steel, in a good, substantial manner, as per cut. Horses mismated in color, gun carriage and limber dark green, red stripes. Gun dead black, brass mounted. Men in uniform. Total length of toy, 84 inches. Price...............$4.00

Toys—Continued.

24800 Donkey Cart and stable; a new, complete, well made and finished homes toy, amusing for either boys or girls. Price, each....$1.75

Mechanical Novelties.

24801 Mechanical Walking Horse, made of iron and painted. Size 8½x7 inches. After winding up the correct working of the motor on the horse or any smooth surface, and it will start off at a brisk walk, as natural as life. Weight, packed in pasteboard box, 2 lbs. Each...........................$2.00

24803 Mechanical Monkey; looks as much like a real monkey as it is possible to make it appear. Wind it up and it will vigorously ring a bell. Dressed in bright costume. Packed one in a box. Price....................$2.50

24805 Mechanical Performing Acrobats, representing two gymnasts in various feats of turning on a horizontal bar. A neat and novel toy, interesting to all. Size 8x6x6. Packed one in a heavy pasteboard box. Price..............$2.75
Weight, 3 pounds.

24806 Mechanical Jumping Rabbit, covered with natural skin, white in color; it looks just like a real rabbit. Wind it up and it hops along in a most comical manner. Weight, 4 oz. Price...........................$0.50
Size, 4½x7 in.

24807 Mechanical Dog and Rider, similar in construction to the rabbit and a very amusing toy. Price.................$1.90
Postage.............06

Natural Skin Animals.

24808 Natural Skin Rabbits, with musical attachment. Amusing and interesting for a small child. Price, each.............$0.22

24809 Natural Skin Lamb, mounted on wooden base with wheels; to be drawn with a string. Price, each.............$0.25

24810 Natural Skin Lamb, musical attachment and with rider in fancy colored costume. Mounted on wooden base, with wheels. Price ..1.25

24812 Natural Skin Lambs, with musical attachment, mounted on wooden base, with wheels, 13x5 inches. Length of lamb, 12 inches, height to top of head, 9½ inches. They bleat as natural as life by pressing on the nose. Price...........1.75

24813 Natural Skin Cow, with voice, mounted on wooden base with wheels, 10x4½ inches. By pressing on the nose the cow will low as natural as life. Price, each..$0.95

Toys—Continued.

24814 Toy elephant on platform with wheels, with swinging head and fancy colored blanket. Size of platform 8x3½ in. Length of figure, 8 in. Height, 8 in. Price.........$0.80

24815 Large Size Toy Elephant, with swinging head and fancy trimmed blanket; length of toy, 12 in.; height, 8¼ in. Mounted on rollers concealed in each foot. Each.........................90

24816 Natural Skin Donkey, mounted on wooden base with wheels. Press on his nose and he will bray as earnestly as though alive. Size 12 oz., weight 12 oz. Price..........$0.85

24817 Natural Skin Horse, mounted on wooden base with wheels. Has leather saddle and bridle complete. Length, 8½ in.; height, 7½ in top of head. Price, each.........$0.65

24818 Natural Skin Horse, mounted on wooden base with wheels. Has leather saddle and bridle complete. This is an extra large fine horse, and will please any child. Price............$1.00

24819 Natural Skin Horse and Cart, as shown in cut. Length of toy, 11 inches. Price...$0.75

24820 Natural Skin Horse and Truck. See illustration of No. 24789 for style of wagon. A fine large toy 20 inches in length. Price...........$1.00

24821— Seed Wagon, and Team of natural skin horses Wagonbox 4x8 inches long. Horses 7½ inches high. Price.......$1.25

Animals Mounted on Platforms.

24822 Pressed Paper Horses, patent German process, very light and handsome, small size. Each.........$0.10

24823 Same description, large size. Each.......20

24824 Same Horse as No. 24822, but harnessed to cart. Body of cart is natural wood oiled, wheels of pressed paper. Each....................35

24825 Saddle Horse, made of composition, with handle. Size of horse, 10 inches high, 8 inches long. Price.....................50

24826 Saddle Horse, same as No. 24825, but 12 inches high. 10 inches long and large in proportion. Price....................96

24827 Assorted Animals, small size, on platforms. Assortment consists of tigers, elephants, wildcats, lions, bears and dogs. State kind preferred, and they will be sent if in stock. If not, substitution will be made. Each............25

Plush Animals.

24830 New Plush Dogs, small size, well made. Price.....$0.25

24831 Our New Plush Pug Dog; nice size, and well made. Each.............$0.50
Per dozen...........5.40

24833 Plush Cats, good size, well made and natural as life. Each.........$0.20

Toy Stoves.

24835 The Pastime Toy Heating Stove. A beautiful model of the modern base burner. Has transparent red windows; base top and urn are nickel plated; place a candle in candle stick on inside of stove, and it diffuses a warm, brilliant glow; one joint of pipe with each stove. Size of base 5⅝ inches; total height, 12¼ in; weight, 6 lbs. Price........$0.90

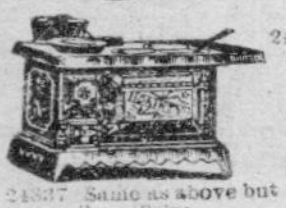

24836 Toy Range, nickel-plated with polished edges and ornamentation. Useful and instructive toys. Size about 4x5x5 inches; packed one in a box with several utensils. Price........$0.50

24837 Same as above but larger and with more utensils. Price........1.00

24838 Large Size Toy Range; a perfect working stove, nickel plated and highly ornamented. Beautiful, useful and instructive. Price includes pipe and half dozen of the most needed utensils. Size about 8¾ inches wide, 8½ inches high, 15½ inches long. Price........2.00

Child's Sad Irons.

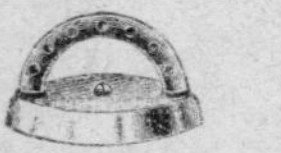

24840 Nickle plated Toy Sad Iron, half pound size, with stand. Each........$0.15

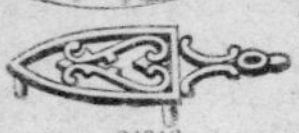

24841 Nickel Plated Toy Sad Iron, one pound size, with stand Each..$0.20

24842 Same as No. 24841, but two pound size. A useful toy. Each..$0.24

24843

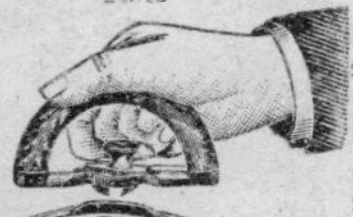

24843 Acme Toy Sad Iron, with solid handle, nickel plated, with stand; small size. Each........$0.10

24844 Mrs. Pott's Toy Sad Iron, with detachable nickle plated and with handle; medium size. Each........$0.25

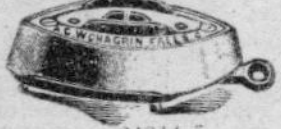

24844-5.

24845 Mrs. Pott's Toy or Polishing Iron, nickel plated, with detachable walnut handle, about two pound size, large enough to be useful. Price with stand, each........$0.35

Toy Scales.

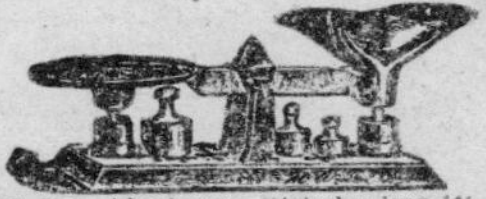

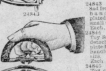

24846 Size, without scoop, 4¼ inches long, 1¾ inches high, 2 inches wide; scoop, 3¼x2 inches. Nicely painted and bronzed, and has three coppered weights. Weight, ½ pound.
Price, each........$0.10
Per dozen........1.00

24847 Toy Scales, 4¾ inches long, 3 inches high, 2¼ inches wide, with a set of weights accompanying each scale. Nicely finished; one in box. Weight, 1¼ pounds. Each........20

Chime Toys.

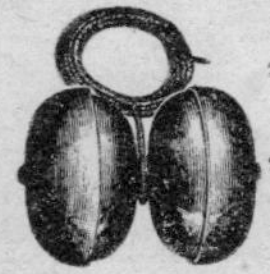

24850 White Metal Revolving bell chime. Gives a very pleasant musical sound.
Small, each........$0.10
Weight, 3 oz. Per doz... 1.00

24851 Same description as above, but larger size.
Weight, 4 oz Each....$0.20
Per dozen........2.25

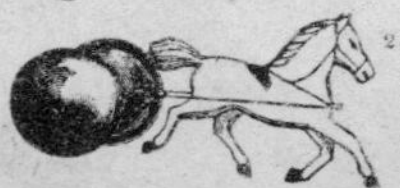

24852 White Metal Revolving bell chime, with horse attached. Weight, 5 oz.
Each........$0.22
Per doz....2.50

All lines of merchandise very generally reduced in price.

The "Sea-Saw" Chimes.

24855 To be drawn with a string. As the wheels revolve, the figures at either end of the "teeter" rise and fall alternately, at same time vigorously ring a chime bell placed between them. Packed in a box. Price........$0.50

24856 The Young America Chime. A large, brightly painted iron chime, with large bell and flag. As toy is drawn the bell revolves and rings. Each........75

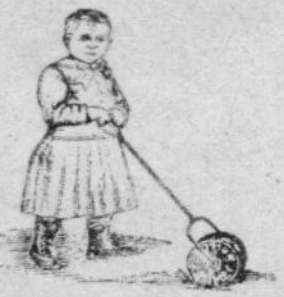

24858 The Roller chime is a handsome lithographed revolving drum with metal handles; as the drum revolves on being drawn over the floor, it produces a succession of musical sound. Weight, 1½ lbs. Each........$0.25

Magnetic and Electrical Toys.

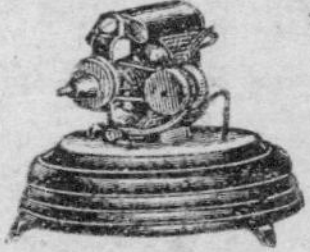

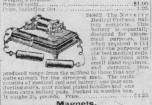

24860 The Boston Motor and Battery Outfit. A new invention. A motor and battery combined. It is right in line with the advancement of the age and enables young people to keep up with the times in the studies of the problems of electricity. Its construction is complete and of the best materials, with all the parts of a large motor, including armature, commutator, magnets, brushes, and a pulley for transmitting power. It is especially adapted for running small mechanical figures, toy machinery, etc., and with a good charge of compound will run a four-inch fan. Packed with full directions in wooden box. Weight, 2 pounds.
Price of outfit........$1.00
Price, including fan........1.25

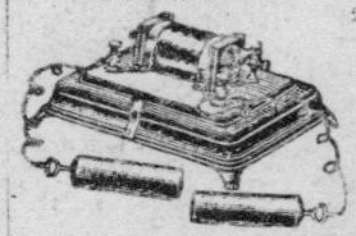

24862 The Novelty Medical Coil and Battery complete. This battery is especially designed for amusement purposes, but when required will serve the purposes of the best medical coils. It is provided with small hand regulator, and currents, thus produced range from the mildest to those that are quite enough for the strongest man. The outfit consists of medical coil and battery, one pair conducting cords, pair nickel plated handles and one dozen extra battery pads. Packed in wooden box. It weighs 2½ pounds. Price........$2.25

Magnets.

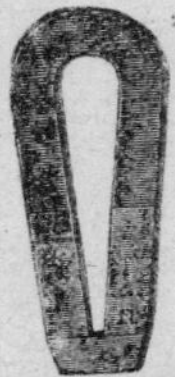

24865 Horseshoe Magnets, superior quality.

Length.	Price Each.	Per doz.
2 inches........	$0.06	$0.60
Postage, each, 2c.		
2½ inches........	.10	.95
Postage, each, 2c.		
3 inches........	.15	1.50
Postage, each, 3c.		
4 inches........	.20	2.10
Weight, each, 5 oz.		
6 inches........	.45	5.00
Weight, each, ¾ lb.		
8 inches........	.85	9.25
Weight, each, 1¼ lbs.		
10 inches........	1.50	16.00
Weight, each, 3¾ lbs.		
12 inches........	2.00	20.00
Weight, each, 4½ lbs.		

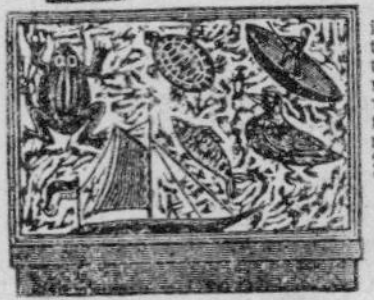

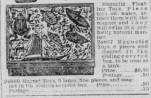

Magnetic Floating Toys. Place toys on water, attract them with the magnet and they will swim in a perfectly natural manner.

24867 Magnetic Toys, 8 pieces and magnet in tin sliding covered box, to be used as a tank.
Price........$0.35
Postage........10

24869 Magnet Toys, 9 large, fine pieces, and magnet in tin sliding covered box. Price........50
Postage........12

It Would be Poor Policy

To misrepresent our goods knowingly, therefore do not hesitate to place confidence in our Buyers' Guide. If goods are not as represented we will cheerfully refund purchase price and pay all transportation charges.

Gray Rubber Toys.

24870 Rubber Mouse, black or white, with whistle. Each........$0.18

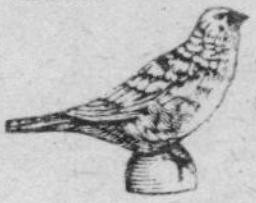

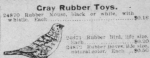

24871 Rubber Bird, life size. Each........$0.20

24872 Rubber Doves, life size, natural color. Each ..$0.50

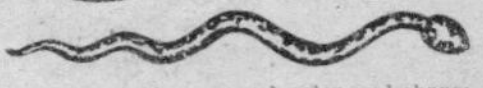

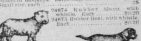

24873 Rubber Snakes, natural color and shape; you can have more fun with them than with a basket of monkeys. Large size, each........$0.40
Small size, each........25

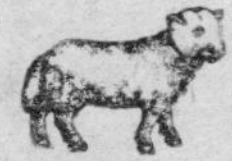

24874 Rubber Sheep, with whistle. Each........$0.20

24875 Rubber Goat, with whistle. Each........$0.20

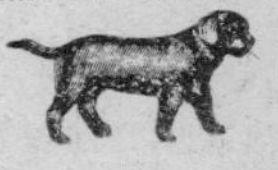

24876 Rubber Dogs, assorted kinds, poodle, mastiff, pointer, etc. Each........$0.20

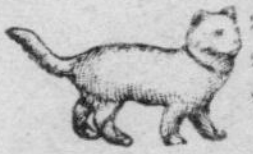

24877 Rubber Cat, with whistle........$0.20

24878 Rubber Horse, with whistle. Each........$0.20

24879 Rubber Donkey, with whistle........$0.20

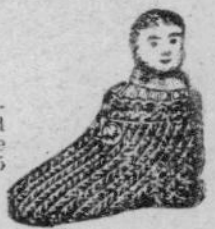

24881 Rubber Old Woman-in-shoe. Only this is not an old woman, but a beautiful little baby. Price........$0.25

Pure White Rubber Toys.

We wish to call special attention to this line of 50 cent toys. All are made of best pure white rubber, and each toy is a perfect model of the animal it represents.

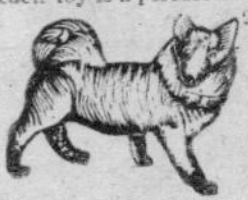

24885 White Rubber Spitz Dog with whistle. Each.....$0.50
Size, 4½x7

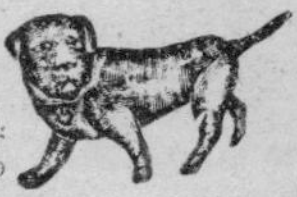

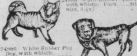

24886 White Rubber Pug Dog, with whistle. Each........$0.50
Size, 4½x7 in.

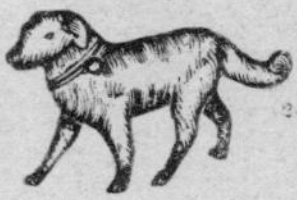

24887 White Rubber Newfoundland Dog, with whistle. Each........$0.50
Size, 4½x7 in.

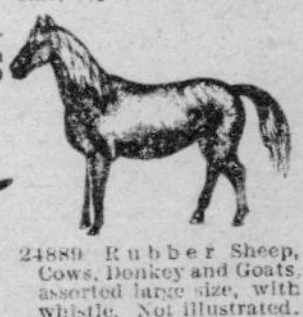

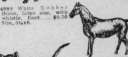

24888 White Rubber Horse, large size, with whistle. Each.....$0.50
Size, 5¼x8.

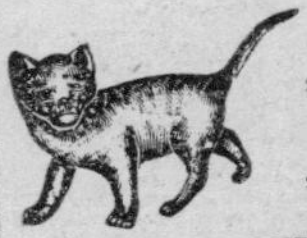

24890

24889 Rubber Sheep, Cows, Donkey and Goats, assorted large size, with whistle. Not illustrated. Each........$0.50

24890 White Rubber Cat, with whistle. Each $0.50
Size, 4½x7 in.

RATTLES.

24895 Globe Bell Tin Rattle, wooden handle, Each........$0.05
Per dozen........50

24896 Globe Iron Rattles, sleigh bell pattern, japanned wood handles. Each........06
Per dozen........65

24897 Same, better quality. Each........09
Per dozen........85

24898 Bone Rattle, with teething ring and 4 metal bells. Each........20

24899 Chime Rattle, 4 chime bells on leather band, enameled handle. Each........10

24900 Rattle and Teething Ring, one bell on enameled handle, rubber ring. Each........12

Willow and Rattan Baby Rattles.

24901 Willow Rattles, natural color, with colored trimmings, straight handle. Each $0.07
Postage .... .02

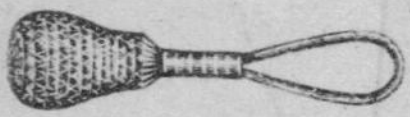

24902 Fancy Rattle, high varnished, hard finished willow and rattan woven; has bent rattan loop handle; handsome, light and durable. Price, each $0.15
Postage .... .02

Rubber Rattles.

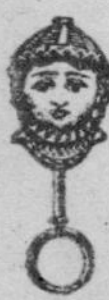
24905

24904 Musical Rattle, with teething ring.
Each $0.10
Per dozen 1.00
Rattle weighs 3 ounces.

24905 Musical Rubber Rattle, with teething ring handle; length, 6 in.; weight, 4 oz.
Each $0.15
Per dozen 1.50

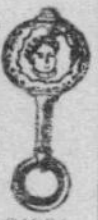
24904

Rubber Balls.

Hollow Balls.

24910—

Size	10	20	30	40
Diameter and inches	1⅜	1⅞	2¼	2½
Each	$0.04	$0.06	$0.08	$0.10
Per dozen	.44	.65	.87	1.08
Weight	2 oz.	3 oz.	3 oz.	4 oz.

Solid Balls.

24911

Size	10	20	30	40
Diameter and inches	1¼	1⅜	2¼	2½
Each	$0.05	$0.07	$0.10	$0.04
Per dozen	.50	.75	1.10	1.60
Weight	3 oz.	4 oz.	4 oz.	4 oz

Light Inflated Balls.

The children's favorite.

24912

Diameter and inches	1⅜	2⅛	2¾	3
Each	$0.07	$0.10	$0.15	$0.20
Per dozen	.77	1.08	1.60	2.15
Postage, each	.02	.03	.03	.04

Stuffed Kid Balls.

24913 Kid House Balls, stuffed with cotton batting and covered with kid, making a desirable house ball for the little people. Large size.
Each $0.20
Postage .... .04

24914 Celluloid balls, assorted colors, small size.
Each $0.10

24915 Celluloid balls, assorted colors, large size.
Each $0.18

MISCELLANEOUS TOYS AND NOVELTIES.

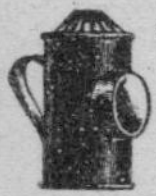

24917 Toy Police Lanterns, 1½ in. bull's-eye, burns candle, changeable light. You should see the boys play policeman with this lantern. Throws strong light. Each $0.10
Per dozen 1.00
Postage, each .... .05

Toy Dinner Bells.

24918 Call Bell, 2¾ inch, japanned iron base, iron hammer, silvered bell, brass push or tongue. The neatest toy bell made. Each $0.15
Per dozen 1.50
Postage, each .... .08

24919 Tea Bells with japanned handle. Each .. .05
Per dozen .... .50

24920 Rubber balloons with trumpet ends. To be inflated by blowing into them. A good loud one. Each $0.04
Per dozen .... .40

Jumping Ropes.

24921 Jute Rope, ¼ in.; length 6½ in: stained handle. Each $0.04
Per dozen .... .40
Postage .... .02

24922 Jute Rope, ¼ inch; length 7 feet, japanned handles. Each .... .06
Per dozen .... .60
Postage .... .03

24923 Jute Rope, ¼ inch; length 8 feet, japanned or polished handles. Each .... .08
Per dozen .... .80
Postage .... .03

Jack Stones.

24924 Nicely coppered, good sizes. Per doz. $0.04
Per gross .... .30
Weight, per dozen, 2 oz.

BABY'S OUTFIT—Everything complete and SO PRETTY—Cheaper than to make them.

The Roaming Toys.

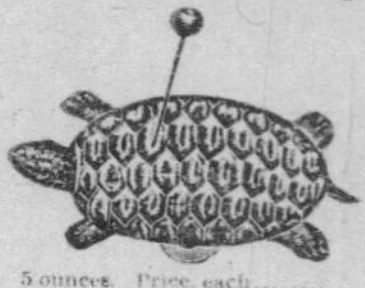

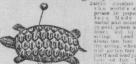

24925 Another of the world's surprises in popular toys. Made of metal and colored in gold, green and blue; led by a string. Lead it about ten feet by the string, when it will go ten feet by itself and lead you. Lots of fun for children. Weight, 5 ounces. Price, each $0.09
Per dozen, assorted .... .75

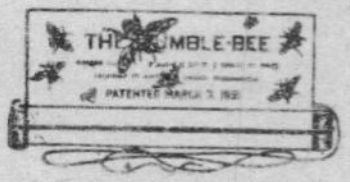

24928 The Bumble Bee, imitates exactly the buzzing of bees, swarming of flies, humming of birds, etc. The very latest novelty, is made in bright colors, and is very amusing, both for young and old. Size, 8¾x3½. Price $0.05
Postage .... .01

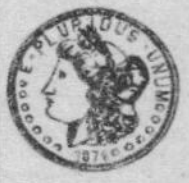

24931 Educational Toy Money. This money consists of disks of very heavy cardboard, on which are imprinted accurate representations of the various coins in common use. This money is interesting as a toy with which children can "play store" and unconsciously learn the act of readily and accurately making change. Each box eight small trays, which are removable. Price per set $0.22
Postage .... .05

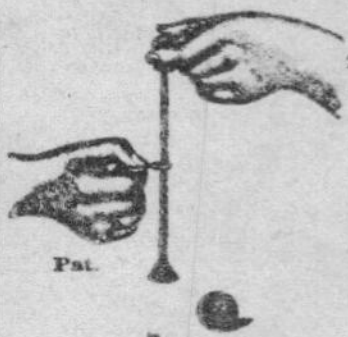

24933 The "Wonderful" Agate Spinner. Simple mechanical action in this toy produces surprising results. Spinner No. 4, threaded glass agate, and directions in neat pasteboard box. Each $0.19
Postage .... .02

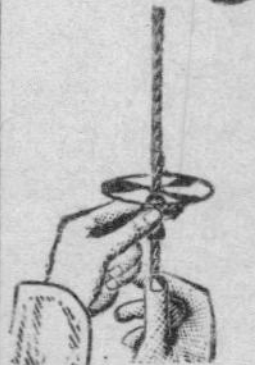

24934 The Air Wheel is one of the greatest toys on earth. The ærial problem solved. Flies high through the air by a simple mechanical movement. It is an amusing and exciting toy. Old and young enjoy it. Put up complete with rod and flyers.
Price $0.10
Postage .... .02

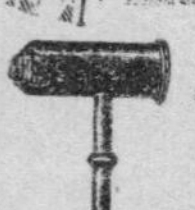

24935 Kaleidoscope. By holding toy to the eye and revolving it, a countless number of beautifully colored figures can be seen. This is a very interesting toy.
Price $0.95

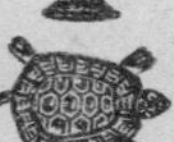

24936 A good imitation of a Tortoise Shell Turtle. Mounted on rollers and to be drawn with a string. As toy is drawn across the floor its head, legs and tail wriggle in most comical manner.
Price $0.10
Postage .... .05

24937 Pewter Fire Department and Cavalry Outfits. These are small pewter metal apparatus, horses and men. Each set put up in pasteboard box. State which set is wanted, if you have a preference, or order both.
Price, each set $0.10
Postage .... .02

Calliope Whistle.

24938 Made of wood, finished in bright colors. All of the notes can be sounded by pulling out the stopper. A good whistle, plenty of fun for boys and girls. Each $0.05
Per doz .... .40
Postage .... .02

***** No one enjoys eating from chipped or cracked dishes—Why not get a new set? Prices low.**

Conjurers' Tricks and Magical Apparatus.

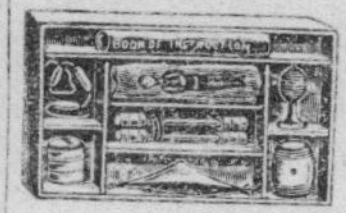

24940 A Box of Magical Wonders. This box of clever tricks will furnish much amusement for the little folks. It contains a variety of amusing tricks, with book of instructions.
Price $0.50

24941 Same general description as above, but containing a greater number of tricks. Sure to please. Price 1.00

24942 Large Size Box of Magical Apparatus, containing apparatus for performing a large number of mystifying tricks, with book of instructions 1.50

Paint Boxes.

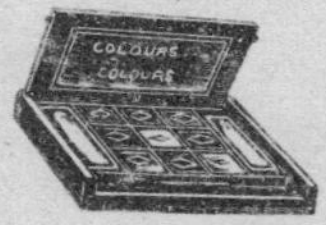

24944 Paint Box, containing 12 pieces water color paints, assorted colors, two dishes and camel's hair brush. Put up in neat box with sliding cover.
Postage, 5c.
Price $0.20

24945 Paint Box, contains 12 large pieces best assorted colors paints, camel's hair brush and two water dishes in polished box with patent hinge cover. Postage .... .10
Price .... .50

Toy Reins.

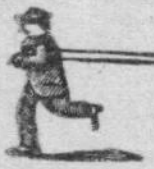

24946 Toy Reins. Made of good weight and red and blue webbing with 1½ web yoke and chime bells.
Per pair $0.10
Postage .... .03

24947 Toy Reins, made of fine red and white 1-inch webbing, crossed leather yoke and five chime bells. Per pair .... .20
Postage .... .04

24948 Toy Rein made of extra heavy red webbing with fancy colored yoke, four brass chime bells on yoke piece. This is an especially good set. Length, 54 inches. Price per set .... .35
Postage .... .08

24949 Toy Reins. Extra heavy red and white webbing, fancy leather yoke and four large nickel chime bells. Price .... .50
Postage .... .10

24950 Toy Reins. Extra heavy red, white and blue webbing, 1 inch snap yoke; yoke and neck piece of white and tan leather. A very handsome set; 7 nickel chime bells. Weight 12 oz.
Price 65

24951 Toy Reins, made of maroon colored leather, fancy stitched. Separate yoke piece made of black enameled leather, trimmed with fancy colored leather and stitching. Has three large silvered metal chime bells, and rings for attaching reins. Two silvered metal bells and snaps on reins. This set can be used for driving a dog or goat, as the reins can be fastened to a bit or collar by means of the snap attachments. Length, 42 inches. Put up one set in pasteboard box. Weight, 12 oz. Price per set .... .85

24952 Toy Reins made of red, white and blue webbing, with large, fancy colored leather yoke; trimmed with 14 silvered metal chime bells. Reins attached to metal rings on yoke. A handsome, showy set for a boy of any age. Length, 48 inches. Price per set 1.25
Postage .... .08

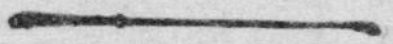

24954 Boys' whip, with loop, fancy. Each .... .05

24955 Boys' whip, 25 inches, wood stock, 22 inches, leather lash. Each .... .08
Per dozen .... .85

24956 With whistle in handle, braided lash, as per cut. Each .... .10
Per dozen 1.00

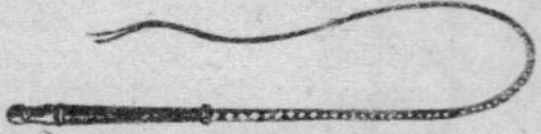

24957 A splendid one, good length, with braided leather lash, fancy colored braided stock, whistle in end of handle. Each $0.15
Per dozen 1.50

Dog Whips.

24958 Ten inch handle with whistle, 28 inch braided leather lash, with whip and cracker; a good article. Each $0.25
Per dozen 2.50

There never was a better year to buy.

Toy Watches.

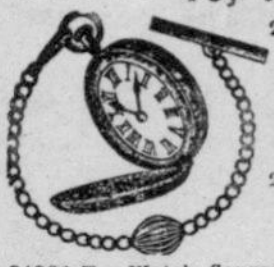

24960 Panoramic watches, open face, gilt chain and charm. As watch is wound the hands revolve and a succession of pictures of birds, animals, etc., are brought into view. Each..... $0.05
Per dozen .... .50
24961 Toy Watch, for girls, open face Swiss style, fancy gilt chain; has long neck chain. Each $0.08
Per dozen .... .90
24963 Toy Watch, figured hunting case, hour and minute hand, stem winder, steel vest chain. Each .... .10
Per dozen 1.00
24964 Toy Watch with bell. Wind watch up and bell will strike. Each .... .15
Per dozen 1.60
24965 Toy Watch, automatic tick movement, stem winding, hands move separately. A good one. Each .... .20
24966 Souvenir Watch, open face, 1½ inch diameter, finely finished, hour and minute hands move separately: has fine neck chain. Each . .25
24967 Grandfather's Clock. A good imitation of the old timepiece. No doll house complete without one. Each .... .25
Postage on toy watches .... .03

Noah's Arks.

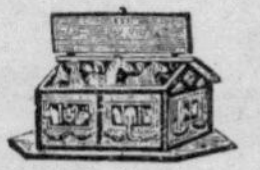

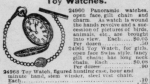

This toy has been a seller ever since the flood, and probably will be as long as the world stands.
24970 Noah's Ark, filled with neatly painted animals, flat ark. Each $0.10
Per dozen 1.00
Weight, ½ lb.
24971 Noah's Ark, same as above, larger. Each, .25
Weight, 1 lb.

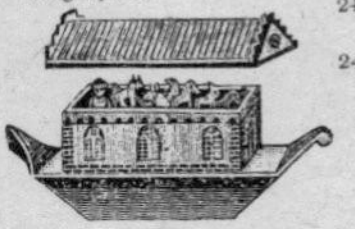

24972 Noah's Ark; boat shape, fancy; weight, 10 oz., 50c.
24973 Noah's Ark., same style as 24972, but larger and better. Each $0.75
Weight, 1¼lb.

Surprise Boxes.

(Jack in the Box.)

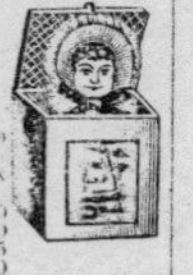

Surprise Boxes ranging from small to large sizes, containing figures of various forms which spring out of the box at will.
24975 Surprise Box. Each $0.10
Per dozen 1.00
24976 Surprise Box. Each .... .25
Per dozen 2.50

WOODEN TOYS.

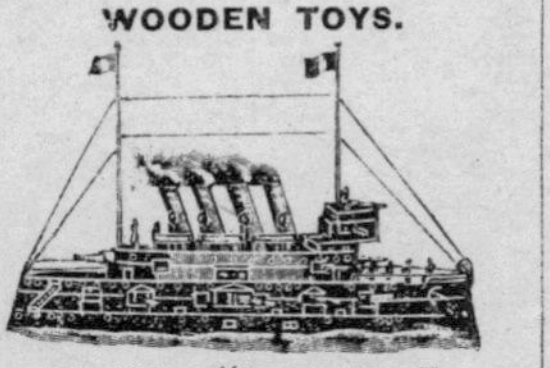

War Ship "Columbia."

24978 A perfect reproduction of this powerful and fast war ship, a model of strength and beauty, and the largest and most complete toy cruiser ever made. A feature is the smoke, giving the cruiser the appearance of being under full steam, and moving at a high rate of speed. It is finely lithographed, thoroughly made, and rigged with two masts; has four smoke stacks, eight ventilators, wire railing, cord, six boats, cannons, etc., and has a crew of twelve officers and sailors. All parts pack inside of boat. Full directions for setting up accompany each boat. Length from stem to stern, 36 inches; 24 inches on top of mast. Price $0.90

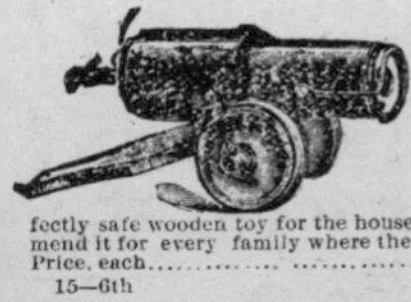

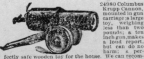

24980 Columbus Krupp Cannon, mounted in gun carriage: a large toy, weighing less than two pounds; a ten inch gun, makes a loud report, but can do no harm; a perfectly safe wooden toy for the house. We can recommend it for every family where there is a small boy. Price, each $0.40

The Royal Guards.

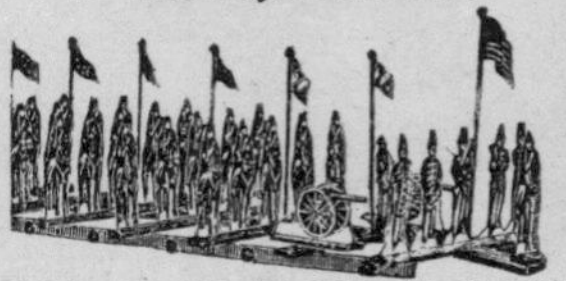

24981 A new and imposing Military Battalion of 33 men, arranged in 5 companies, with band, 2 cannon, 2 gunners, and commander, carrying 8 handsome flags; the whole mounted on wheels. The soldiers are made to march company front, or right and left oblique. The companies can be used separate or together as desired. The soldiers are 7½ inches high, wearing rich, brilliant uniforms. Full length of toy, 42 inches, width 12¾ inches. Very easy to set up. Packed in nice box with elegant label. Price... $0.90

Military Parade.

24982 Same design as No. 24981. Has a force of 28 handsome soldiers arranged in 5 companies, commander and 2 aids, and carries 6 flags; all mounted on wheels. Can be made to march obliquely when desired. Height of soldiers 5¼ inches. Comes packed in nice box 20 inches long, 10 in. wide, with attractive label. Price $0.50

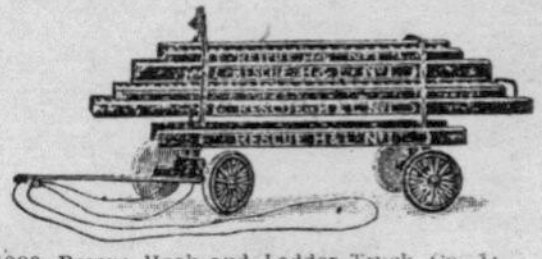

24983 Rescue Hook and Ladder Truck Co. 1; made wholly of wood. Has four handsomely painted ladders, which are so made that they can be joined together, forming one long ladder. An interesting toy for any boy. Price $0.50

Buffalo Bill.

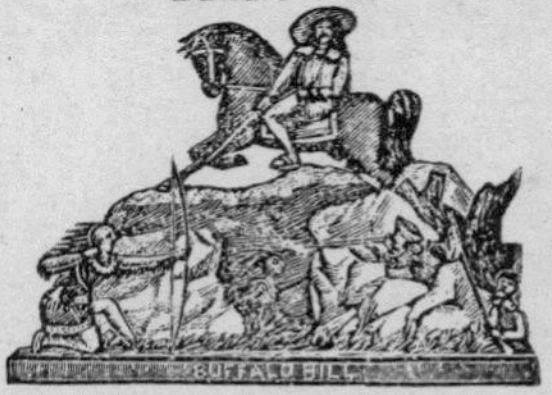

24985 This is a new departure in wooden toys and is decidedly novel in every respect. It illustrates vividly how Buffalo Bill and his scouts overcame a party of ambuscaded Indians. Best thing out. Price $0.75

The Brownie Ladder.

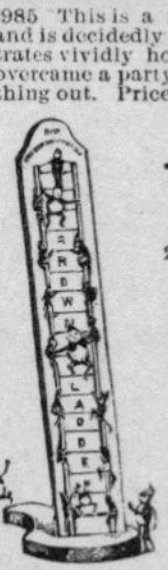

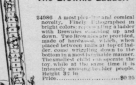

24986 A most pleasing and comical novelty. Finely lithographed in bright colors; representing a ladder with Brownies climbing up and down. Two Brownies are provided, made of hardwood, which, when placed between nails at top of ladder, come wriggling down to the bottom in a most laughable manner. The smallest child can operate the toy, while at the same time it is intensely amusing to older people. Height 32 in. Price $0.25

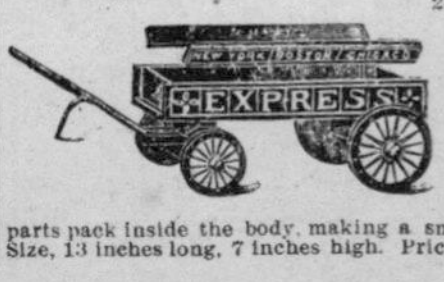

24987 Express Wagon. A new and attractive wagon, neatly ornamented and colored, very strongly made, has two wings and is easily set up. All parts pack inside the body, making a small package. Size, 13 inches long, 7 inches high. Price $0.20

Wooden Soldiers.

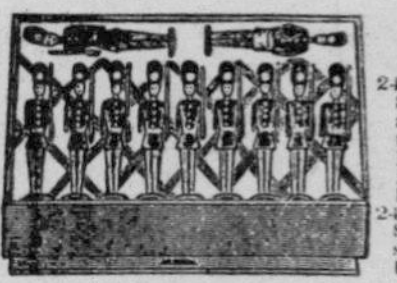

24988 Wooden Soldiers. Movable, each made to stand alone. In box.
Per set $0.20
Per doz. .. 2.10
24989 Wooden Soldiers, large size.
Per set $0.40

Bows and Arrows.

(Unmailable.)

The practice of archery is rapidly coming into style again. To be "in the swim" and to please your boy or girl, get him or her one of our archery sets. We have them in all sizes; for the five year old or for the five year old's big brother.

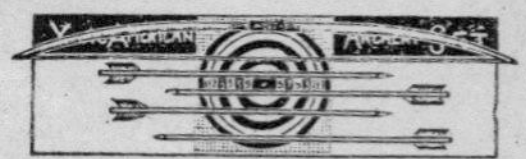

24990 Archery Set: consists of a good, strong bow, 30 inches long, two arrows and target. Bow is nicely finished and arrows striped, feathered and metal tipped. Price $0.19
24991 Archery Set: Contains bow, three arrows and target. The bow is made of polished wood, very strong and pliable, and is 33 inches long. Arrows are handsomely striped, feathered and metal tipped. Price .... .40
24992 Archery Set: This handsome set consists of a strong 39-inch bow, made of very pliable wood, four nicely striped, feathered and metal tipped arrows and a target 9 inches in diameter. With this outfit a boy can become expert in the use of the bow and arrow. Price .... .90

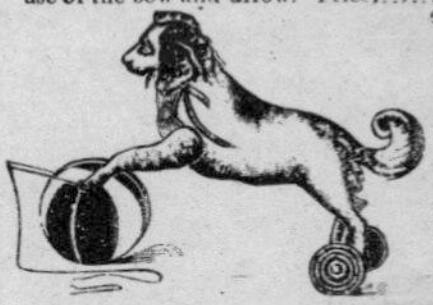

24993 A handsome and pleasing novelty, bright and attractive, representing a dog playing with a ball. By drawing the toy the dog jumps up and down every revolution of the wheel, which is between his paws. Size, 15½ in. long and nine in. high. Each $0.23

Toy Guns and Pistols.

Toy Guns cannot be sent by mail on account of length and liability of breakage.

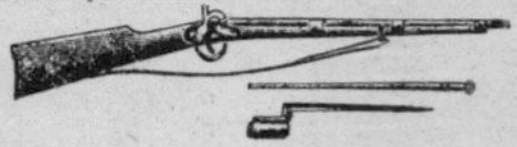

24994 School Drill Gun. The frequent demand for a large size boy's gun for drilling purposes in school or otherwise, has induced us to introduce this gun. It is made of hardwood, well finished, and has the percussion lock to fire off paper caps; it is in size large enough for boys from 12 to 16 years of age. Stock 42 in. long, with bayonet. Each $1.06
24995 Toy Gun, with bayonet and strap, measures 41 inches in length without bayonet; shoots paper cap and stick. Weight, 1¾ lbs. Each.... .90
24996 The "Harmless" Gun. Price .... .85
24998 The Swift and Sure gun. Price .... .25

Vacuum Tipped Arrows, Pistols and Rifles.

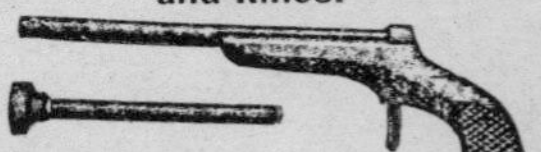

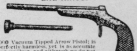

25000 Vacuum Tipped Arrow Pistol; is perfectly harmless, yet is as accurate as a revolver, and although we do not advertise it for children to shoot at each other's eyes, yet we can safely say that should any accident happen it would not harm the most delicate child. It has no equal for parlor amusement or outdoor sport. Made of bronze, with polished barrel; including target. Price $0.50
25001 Same as above in full nickel, with target.. .75
25002 Vacuum Tipped Arrow Rifles, regulation pattern, wood stock and 16 in. bronze barrel. Price includes one arrow. Each .... .95
25003 Same as 25002, but with nickel-plated barrel. Price 1.40
25005 Extra arrows, each .... .15
25006 The Echo Toy Pistol. A harmless, novel and ingenious toy. No caps to endanger the eyes of the little ones, but a loud report to please the boys. It will throw a pea or bean 40 feet with remarkable accuracy. Weight, 4 ounces. Price, each .... .10

Toys—Continued.

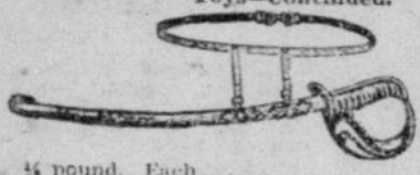

25007 Toy Swords with strap, belt and guarded handle in sheath; length, 25 in.; weight, ½ pound. Each $0.25

Toy Iron Cannon.

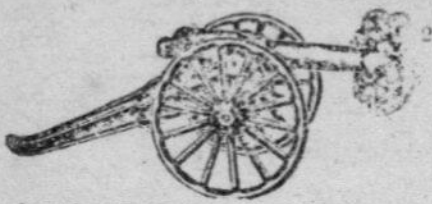

25010 Toy Iron Cannon mounted on wheels, carriage painted red, cannon black; new design, length of barrel, 3½ in.; bore, ¼ in.; weight, ⅜ lbs. Price $0.20

25012 Iron Cannon, same description, but larger; length of barrel 5 in., bore, 5/16 inch, weight, 1⅜ lbs. Price .... .38

25014 Iron Cannon, 7 in. barrel, ⅜ in. bore; weight, 3⅜ lbs. Price .... .85

25016 Iron Cannon 9 in. barrel, ⅜ in. bore, 7½ lbs., 8½ lbs. weight. Price 1.35

25018 Jumbo Iron Cannon, 10 in. barrel, ⅜ in. bore, weight, 12½ lbs. Price 1.90

Brass Cannon.

25020 U. S. Regulation Pattern, solid brass, highly polished, very handsome, strong, and gives loud report, handsomely mounted on malleable iron carriage. Small size; length of barrel 4 in.; weight, 1 lb. Price $0.45

25022 Brass Cannon, same description, but with 5 in. barrel and ⅜ in. bore; weight, 1¾ lbs. Price .... .90

25024 Large Brass Cannon, about same description as No. 25014 but made of brass. Price 1.85

Toy Drums.

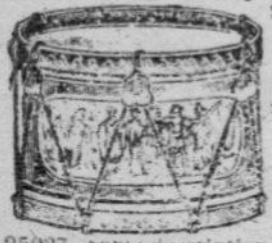

25025 Toy drum, good quality, hammered brass body, corded with sticks, 7 inches in diameter $0.25
Per doz 2.75

25026 Toy drums, good quality, brass body, ornamented with lithographed picture in bright colors, corded 9 inches in diameter.
Price $0.50
Per doz 5.40

25027 Same description as above, but larger size, 12 inches in diameter. Price .... .75
Per dozen 7.75

25028 Toy Drum, flat, imitation mahogany body, calfskin head, corded, enameled sticks, 10 in. diameter. Price 1.00

25029 Same as above with 12 inch head. Price ... 1.50

25030 Same as above with 14 inch head. Price ... 2.00

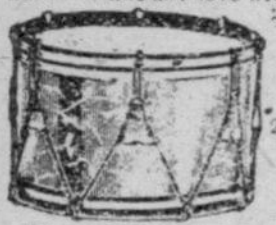

25031 Regulation pattern, high drum, fine 12 in. calf skin head, fancy wood body, corded, with shoulder sling and enameled sticks.
Price $2.25

25032 Same, with 14 inch head.
Price $2.50

Toy Trumpets, Bugles, Trombones, Cornets, Etc.

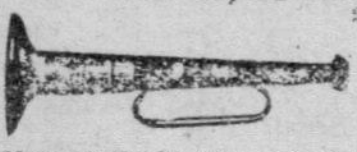

25033 Tin Toy Trumpets, nicely striped and painted, about 9 inches long. Weight, 1 ounce
Each $0.05
Per doz .... .50

25034 Tin Toy Trumpets and rattle, better quality. Weight 2 ounces. Each .... .10
Per dozen 1.25

25035 Horn Toy Bugles about 6 inches long. Weight 1 ounce. Each, $0.05. Per dozen .... .50

25036 Horn Bugles, 8 inches long, with mouth-piece. Each .... .12

25037 Toy Horn Bugles; with horn mouth-piece; length, about 10 inches; extra quality. Weight, 3 ounces. Each .... .20
Per dozen 2.25

25038 Huntsman's Bugle, double note, nickel-plated, large size. Each .... .30

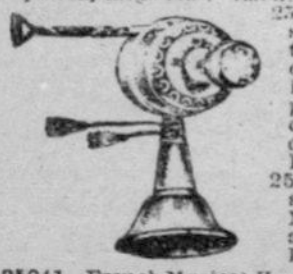

25039 French musical horns, silver finish. By working the lever on the under part of the instrument, and blowing steadily, the horn will play a complete tune. Has cord and tassel, as shown in cut.
Each $0.25

25040 French musical horns, same general description as No. 25039, but much larger and made of better material.
Each $0.40

25041 French Musical Horn, same as above, but with two extra sets of reeds, so that horn can be made to play three tunes. Price 0.50

Toys—Continued.

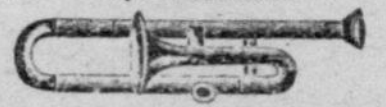

25042 Toy Sliding Trombone, four notes. Length when extended, 15½ inches, when closed, 12 inches. Made of brass with silvered mouthpiece. Each $0.45

Toy Magic Lanterns.

No other toy has been the source of so much wonderment and delight to children as the magic lantern. The line quoted below are high grade toys, and one of them will be the means of providing many hours of entertainment to the little folks.

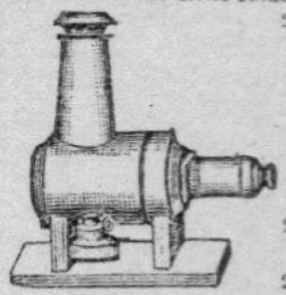

25045 Toy Magic Lantern, neatly ornamented metal body, provided with good condensing and objective lenses, and kerosene lamp, packed in neat box, with 1 dozen slides. Uses 1⅜ inch slides, and magnifies picture to 2½ or 3 feet in diameter.
Price $0.85

25046 Same description, but uses 1½ inch slides.
Price $1.15

25047 Same description, but uses 1¾ inch slides. Price $1.40

25048 Same description, but uses 2 inch slides. Price 1.85

25049 Same description, but uses 2¼ inch slides. Price 2.20

25050 Same description, but uses 2¾ inch slides. Price 2.65

25051 Same description, but uses 3½ inch slides. Price 3.25

The "Gloria" Magic Lanterns.

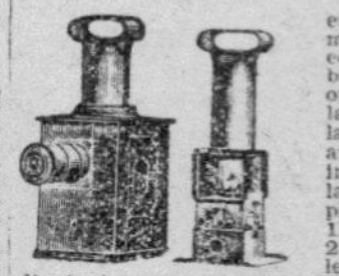

For Parlor and Amateur entertainments. These magic lanterns combine economy and superior brilliant effects over the ordinary juvenile magic lanterns, having a duplex lamp so constructed as to avoid the necessity of using glass chimneys; metal lacquered body, nickel plated chimney and fronts, 1 crown glass condenser, 2 superior crown glass lenses in tubes, dark glass disc in door to avoid blinding vision when regulating flames; includes 12 long covered slides having from four to six subjects on each slide, Chromotrope, 1 comic movable slide, 1 welcome slide, 1 good-night slide. Complete, in neat carrying case with handle. Made in three sizes.

25053 Gloria Lantern, with 2-inch slides, showing 2-foot picture. Price $5.00

25054 Same, 2½-inch slide, showing 3-foot picture. Price 6.75

25055 Same, 2¾-inch slide, showing 3½-foot picture. Price 8.00

The Polyopticon or Wonder Camera.

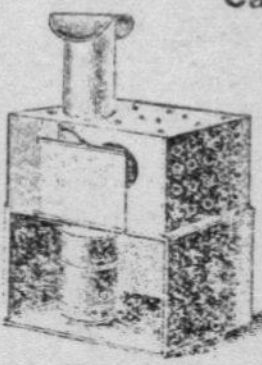

25057 Produces views on screen or wall from cuts from newspapers, magazines, portraits, comic chromo cards, photographs, flowers, comic cuts, etc., in all their colors, enlarged about 400 areas; over a hundred different pictures are given with each Polyopticon, covering almost every conceivable object; with reflector lamp and burner chimney, lens and door, with 3-inch picture window. Weight, 3½ lb.
Price complete $4.40

Toy Magic Lantern Slides.

Note.—We cannot fill orders for any SPECIAL SUBJECTS in toy lantern slides. These slides come to us from the manufacturers put up 1 doz. in a box, and in three to five assortments only.

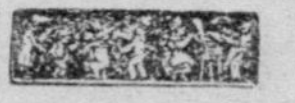

25060 Plain Slides highly colored, for amateurs; nursery tales, Mother Goose Fables, American and German scenery, World's Fair, etc.

Width	Per doz.	Weight per doz.
1⅛ in.	$0.35	7 oz.
1⅜ in.	.45	8 oz.
1½ in.	.50	10 oz.
1¾ in.	.60	15 oz.
2 in.	.90	1¼ lbs.
2⅜ in.	1.00	1½ lbs.
2¾ in.	1.50	2½ lbs.
3½ in.	1.75	3 lbs

Toys—Continued.

25065 Movable Slides, comic colored, for amateurs.

Width	Each	Per doz.	Weight per doz.
1½ in.	10c.	$1.00	1¼ lbs.
1⅞ in.	14c.	1.50	1½ lbs.
2⅜ in.	20c.	1.75	2 lbs.
3⅛ in.	25c.	2.50	3¼ lbs.
4 in.	35c.	4.00	4½ lbs.

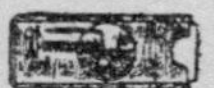

25067 Movable Slides colored landscapes.

Width	Each	Per doz.	Weight per doz.
1¾ in.	20c.	$1.80	1 lb.
2⅜ in.	25c.	2.80	1½ lbs.
3¼ in.	50c.	5.50	2 lbs.
4 in.	75c.	7.20	4½ lbs.

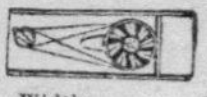

25070 Geometrical Chromotrope slides; consist of two vari-colored wheels, revolving in opposite directions by means of a crank and belt, producing a brilliant effect

Width	1½ in.	2⅜ in.	3½ in.	4 in.
Each	35c.	50c.	75c.	$1.00
Postage	5c.	5c.	5c.	7c.

Magic Lanterns and Sciopticons.

For Sunday Schools, Societies, Army Posts, Home and Public Entertainments.

We carry a full stock of high grade magic lanterns, Sciopticons, slides, screens and accessories, at all times. Special list of these goods sent by mail, free, upon application. We do a large business in this line, and our prices are unusually low for first quality goods.

No 10. Improved Duplex Magic Lantern .... $ 9.50
No 56 Cabinet Magic Lantern 17.00
No. 100. E. A. C. E. Magic Lantern 20.00
No. 300. Triplex Sciopticon 28.00
No 350. Headlight Sciopticon 36.00
No. 400. New York Model Sciopticon 47.00
And many others.

If you are at all interested in the subject of magic lanterns or views, do not neglect to send for our special list of magic lanterns and slides No. G. Free on application.

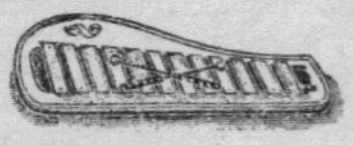

25075 Glockenspiele, or improved Metallophone, eight notes bronze keys, hardwood frame in neat paper box.
Each $0.25
Per dozen 2.70

25076 Glockenspiele, 12 note, bronze keys. Size 7x16 inches. Each .... .50
Per dozen 5.40

25077 Glockenspiele, 18 note, bronze keys. Size, 2x8x23½ inches. Each .... .90
Per dozen 8.00

Toy Harps.

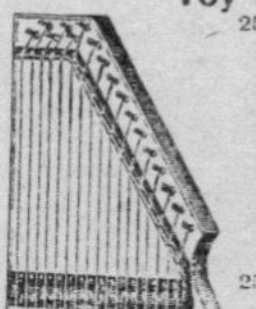

25080 The Phonoharp is not merely a toy, but a musical instrument with 15 strings and having three bars, by the use of which chords are produced to harmonize with sounds obtained by picking the strings as on a common zithern. Five sheets of music with each instrument, which can readily be played by a child.
Price $1.50

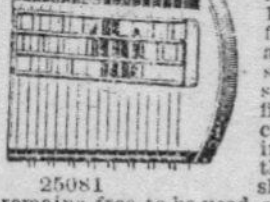

25081

25081 The Phonoharp. This musical novelty consists of a 17 string zithern, on the face of which is fastened a nickel plated three bar shield, which protects certain strings from contact with the finger pick or thumb piece; chords are produced by drawing, pick or thumb piece, in the right hand, across the shields, while the other hand remains free to be used as a damper or to play with as performer may desire. Instrument is made of best materials, only the best piano wire being used, and is handsomely finished in a thoroughly workman-like manner. Price $2.50

25082 Phonoharp, same general description as 25081, but larger and better, with nickel plated parts, 25 strings and 6 bars. Each $4.00

Toy Zithern.

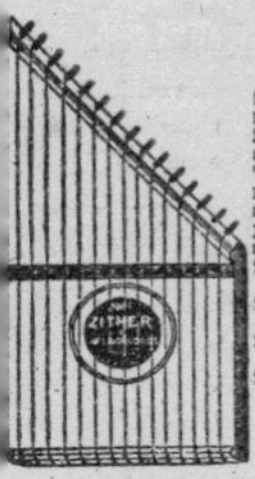

An attractive toy musical instrument, on which the cords may be learned with ease, both instructive and interesting to all. Made plain and harp shape. These goods are handsomely made and finished, and are appreciated and enjoyed by young people of all ages, as they are all tuned to concert pitch.

25084 Plain Shape, 10 strings. Each.....$0.50
25085 Plain Shape, 15 strings. Each.....$0.85
25086 Harp Shape, 15 strings. Each.....$1.00
25087 Harp Shape, 22 strings. Each.....$1.25

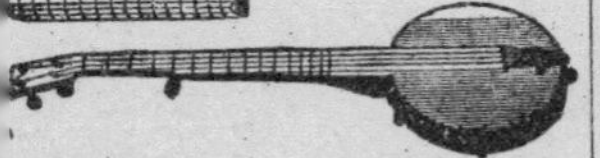

25090 Toy Banjo, 6¼ inch sheep head, ash rim, iron hoop, four brackets. Each.....$0.50
25091 Toy Banjo, 8½ inch calf head, embossed wood rim, brass hoop, six brackets. Each..... .90

Toy Violins.

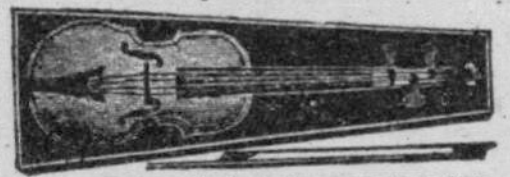

25092 Toy Violin, 16 inch long, one in a box with a bow. Each.....$0.25
Per dozen..... 2.75
25093 Toy Violins, 18 inches long, one in a box, with bow. Each..... .50
Per dozen..... 5.00
25094 Toy Violins, 20 inches long, packed in a box with folding cover and handle for carrying, with bow. Price, each..... .90

Toy Pianos.

(Cannot be sent by mail.)

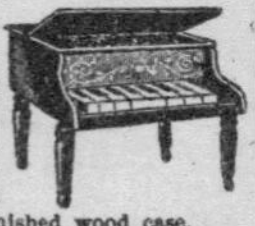

25095 Square Toy Piano, as shown in cut, with high legs and open front, single cover. Size 10x7¼x8¼. Rosewood. Stained and decorated front. One octave. Weight, 2¼ pounds. Price.....$0.40
25096 Square Toy Piano, varnished wood case, open front with folding music rack and 15 keys. Size 6¼x10¼x9. Weight, 5 pounds. Price.....$0.90

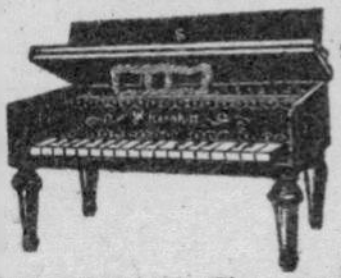

25097 Square Toy Pianos, with high turned legs and full-hinged cover to close. Has 13 keys and folding music rack. Size, 19¼ x 10¼ x 9¼. Weight, 6 lbs. Price.....$1.50

25099 Upright Toy Piano, case varnished, open front and hinged cover, 15 keys. Size 16½x11 x8. Weight, 5 pounds. Price..... 1.25

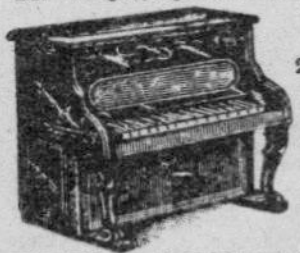

25100 Upright Toy Piano; case handsomely finished, ornamented legs and chandeliers, 15 keys. Packed one in a pasteboard box. Weight, 7¾ pounds. Price.....$2.25

25101 Upright Toy Pianos; same general description as above, but larger size and with 18 keys. Size 18x17½x10 in. Weight, 11 lbs. Price..... 3.50

25102 Upright Toy Piano; extra quality, three octaves, tuned to a perfect concert pitch. Finely carved legs. 23x 24x11. Ornamented and has two gilded chandeliers. Weight, 11 pounds. Price.....$5.00 Each packed in wooden case.

Blocks.

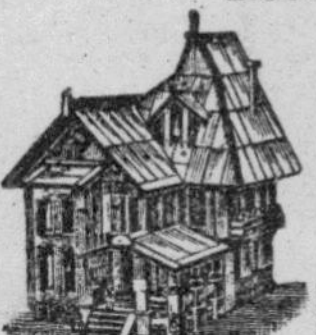

Gilt Edge Building Blocks, made of thoroughly seasoned hardwood, finely finished. The variety and quality of blocks are sufficient to build a large number of pleasing designs.

25105 No. 1 size...$0.20
25106 No. 2 size... .45
25107 No. 3 size... 1.00

25108 Universal Building Blocks, made of hard wood, smooth finished, with ball and joint connecting pins, the best and handsomest plain block on the market. Large size, containing 150 blocks and 206 ball joints. Weight, 11 lbs. Price..... 2.00
25110 Browers' Building Blocks in *colors;* box contains 75 pieces common to all buildings, such as windows, arch door ways, floors, roofs, chimneys, turrets, etc., adaptable to be interchangeably used to form residences, churches, stores, etc. An intensely interesting toy. Price..... .50
25111 Same, but larger size. Box contains 120 pieces. Price..... 1.00

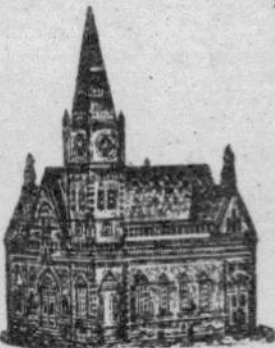

25112 New Cathedral Building Blocks. When put together the blocks form a beautiful cathedral, as shown in cut; 9¾x7¾ in. and 17 inches to top of steeple. It contains a set of blocks beautifully illustrating the story of Noah and the animals entering the ark, with appropriate text of Scripture, a Book of Prayer and one of the Ten Commandments, also the alphabet. Weight, complete, 5 lbs. Each.....$0.75

25113 Wescott's Combination Building and Spelling Blocks with dovetailed edges; a new and novel block. Per set..... .38 Weight, 2½ pounds.

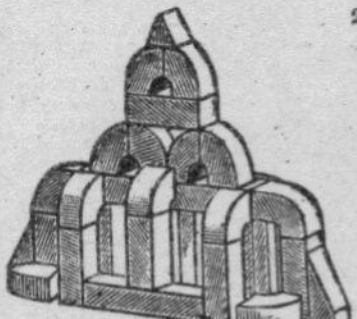

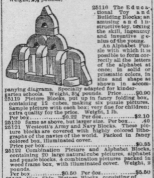

25116 The Educational Toy and Building Blocks; an amusing and instructive toy, taxing the skill, ingenuity and inventive genius of the young.

An Alphabet Puzzle with which it is possible to form correctly all the letters of the alphabet at once; in solid or prismatic colors, in size and shape as shown in accompanying diagrams. Specially adapted for kindergarten schools. Weight, 8¼ pounds. Price.....$0.90
25119 Picture Blocks, put up in fancy folding box, containing 12 cubes, making six puzzle pictures. Sample picture with each box; very fine for children; extra quality for the price. Weight, 1 lb. Per box.....$0.22 Per doz.....$2.10
25120 Same as above, but larger size. Per box... .40
25121 Westcott's Army and Navy Blocks. These picture blocks are covered with highly colored lithographs of the navies of the world. Packed in fancy colored box, illuminated cover. Price per box.....$0.35
25122 Combination Picture and Alphabet Blocks, containing 20 large natural cube pictures, alphabet and puzzle blocks, 4 combination pictures packed in wood frame box, with illuminated cover. Weight, 2 pounds. Per box.....$0.50 Per doz.....$5.50
25123 War Ship Picture Blocks, consisting of twenty-four large size cubes, with which can be made pictures of six of the famous vessels of the White Navy. Pictures are 7¾x20½ inches. Packed in neat box, with pattern pictures. Price..... .90
25124 Capitol Picture Blocks, same description as above, but pictures are those of six prominent buildings at the National Capital. Price..... .90

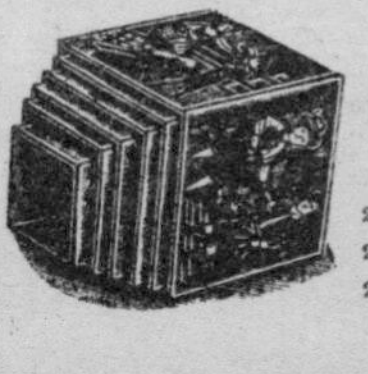

Telescopic Picture Blocks, consisting of hollow cube blocks, covered with fancy lithographed designs. These blocks pack one into another, thus affording endless amusement for the little ones.
25125 Per set of 7 blocks.....$0.25
25126 Per set of 9 blocks.....$0.40
25127 Per set of 12 blocks.....$0.95

Alphabet and Spelling Blocks—Flat.

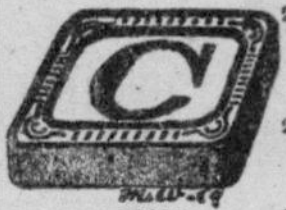

25130

25130 Embossed hardwood blocks, containing letters and numerals. Packed in metal box containing eighteen blocks. Price.....$0.10
25131 Box contains 9 1¾ inch half cubes, natural wood stamped in colors with letters and pictures. Price.....$0.12
25132 Box contains 25 good sized flat blocks, embossed in colors, with letters and numerals..... .18
25133 Handsome box containing 20 2¼ inch half cubes embossed in colors, with numerals, letters and words. Price..... .25
25134 Spelling Blocks. 20 blocks, half cubes, printed in colors, pictures and numerals, packed in wood box, 6x6 inches, slide cover. Price each..... .35

Alphabet Blocks, Cubes.

25139 Mother Goose Cube Blocks, being a combination of letter cubes with the Mother Goose pictures and rhymes oil-painted in a variety of shades and colors. The illustrations are from new and original designs. 12 blocks in a set, packed in a wooden box 7¾x6x2. Weight, 1¼ pounds. Price.....$0.25
25140 Mother Goose Cube Blocks. Better and larger kind; contains 16 blocks, large size, natural wood, printed in bright colors. Packed in paper box with the fine label on cover. Weight, 2¾ pounds..... .45
25141 Mother Goose Cube Blocks, still better and larger. Contains 20 2¼ inch painted and varnished square blocks with letters, illustrations and rhymes; bright colors and superior finish. Price..... .85 Weight, 3¾ lbs.

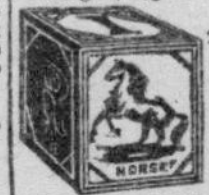

25142 Alphabetical Blocks, 12 illustrated cubes, embossed ends, medium size, with letters and figures, natural wood, printed in bright colors. Per box..... .20
Postage..... .15

25144 Alphabetical Blocks, consists of a set of 35 small size cubes, with embossed ends, containing letters, figures and illustrations of animals, printed in bright colors. Per box..... .34
25145 Alphabet Blocks, 12 medium size cubes, ornamented with letters and figures in bright colors; packed in neat box, Per box..... .20
25146 Alphabet Blocks, 12 large cubes, with illustrations, alphabet and numerals, printed in bright colors; packed in neat box. Per box ..... .25
25147 Alphabet Blocks, 12 large fine cubes, with illustrations, figures and alphabet. The colors are bright and attractive, and workmanship the best. Per box..... .50
25148 Alphabet Blocks. Same as above, but box contains 20 cubes. Per box..... .75
25149 Hill's Alphabet Blocks, contains 24 plain cubes, ornamented with figures and alphabet. Per box..... .40
25151 Hill's Spelling Blocks, full cubes, 30 blocks, printed in colors, pictures, letters, numerals and indicators, wood box, 9¼x11½ inches, hinge cover. Price, per set..... .90

China Toy Tea Sets.

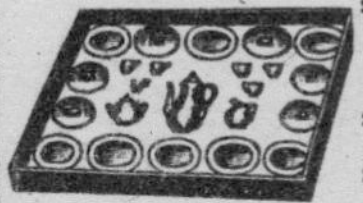

25155

25155 Set consists of cups, saucers, tea pot, sugar bowl and cream; small size; packed in paper box. Price.....$0.10
25156 Same description as above but larger. Price.$0.25
25157 Set consists of decorated plates, cups, saucers, tea pot, creamer, sugar bowl; good sized dishes. Price.....$0.50
25158 Same description but larger. Price..... .75
25159 Same, but larger size and assortment. Price..... 1.00
25163 White Stone China Tea set of 24 pieces, as follows: 6 plates, 6 cups, 6 saucers, 1 sugar bowl and cover, 1 tea pot and cover, 1 creamer, 1 slop bowl. This set is large enough for a miss from 8 to 14 years of age. (Not safe to send by mail.) Weighs 8¼ lbs. Per set.....$1.25
The pieces in this set are larger than usually sold in toy sets; the cups stand 2 inches high, and the plates measure 4¼ inches across.

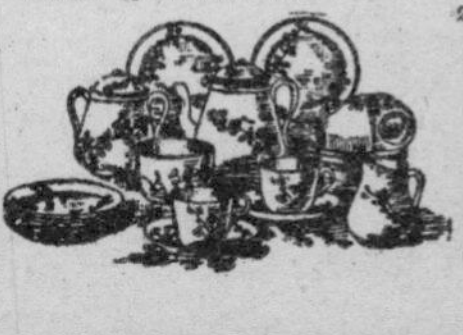

25164—Fancy Decorated Tea Set, same size and assortment as above; elegant patterns. Packed in wooden box, weight 8¼ lbs. Price.$1.75

Decorated China Toy Toilet Sets.

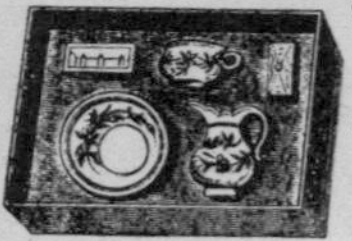

25170 Small Toilet or Wash Set packed in pasteboard box; weight ½ lb.
Per set........$0.20
Per doz. sets.. 2.00

25171 Decorated Toilet or Wash Set, good size, 5 pieces, and 2 perforated covers; weight, 1¼ lbs.
Per set........ $0.35
Per dozen sets........ 3.75

25172 Extra Size Wash or Toilet set, gilt lined and brilliantly decorated; a handsome set. Packed in strong box: weight 3 lbs.
Per set........ .65
Per dozen sets........ 7.00

Britannia Tea Sets.

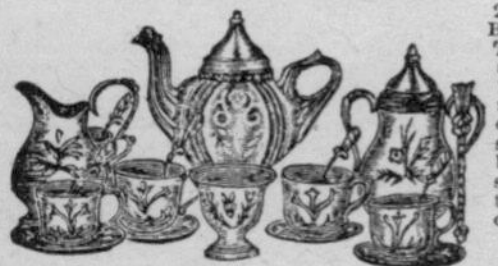

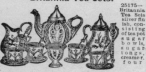

25175—Britannia Tea Sets silver finish, consisting of tea pot sugar bowls, sugar tongs, creamer, four plates and cups. Put up in neat pasteboard box; weight, 5 oz........ $0.09

25176 Britannia Tea Set silver finish, consisting of tea pot, sugar bowl, creamer, six plates, six cups, six spoons and sugar spoons. Embossed decorations; weight, 10 oz.
Price........ .22

25177 Britannia Tea Set, silver finish, consisting of tea pot, sugar bowl, creamer, six plates, six cups and six spoons. A very handsome set; weight, 1¼ lbs........ .45

25178 Britannia Tea Set, silver finish, consisting of tea pot, sugar bowl, creamer, spoon holder, six plates, six cups, six spoons and fancy filigree work sugar tongs. The entire set is handsomely decorated in bas-relief design, making a large showy set; weight, 3½ lbs.
Price........ .85

Superior Quality Toy Tin Kitchen Sets.

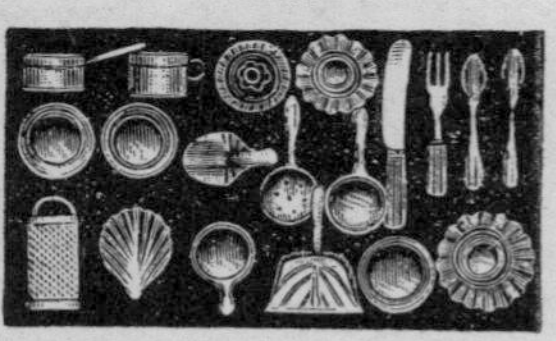

25180 Tin Kitchen Set, small size; consisting of about fifteen pieces tin kitchen utensils. See illustration. Weight, 6 ounces. Price........ $0.10

25181 Tin Kitchen Set, medium size; consisting of 25 or more pieces, tin and wooden utensils. Weight, 12 oz. Price........ .20

25182 Tin Kitchen Set, large size, containing 30 pieces. Weight, 1¼ lbs. Price........ .40

25183 Tin Kitchen Set, Large size. Has 42 or more utensils of good size: some of the pans in Nos. 25181 and 25182 are large enough for baking small loaves, cakes, etc. Weight, 1¾ lbs.
Price........ .65

Superior Quality Embossed Tin Kitchens.

Painted in bright colors and very attractive to the little folks.

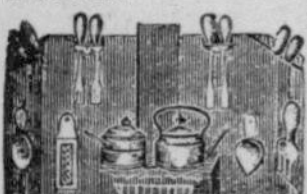

25185 Embossed Tin Kitchen, small size; contains 1-hole range and ten pieces kitchen tinware. Size 6¼ in. high, 11 in. long, 2½ in. deep.
Postage........$0.15
Price........ .25

25186 Embossed Tin Kitchen, medium size. Has in addition a two-hole range, a water cooler and 12 utensils, Size 7x14x4 inches. Weight, 1¾ lbs Price........ $0.45

25187 Embossed Tin Kitchen. One of the largest and best. Two-hole range with warming oven above, water cooler and twenty pieces tin and wooden kitchen utensils of large size. Size 8¼ x19x5 inches. Weight, 2¾ lbs. Price........ .75

All of the above kitchen and kitchen sets are packed in neat boxes

Children's Table Sets.

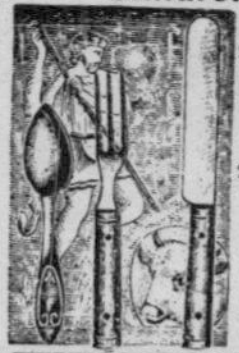

25190 Children's memento sets; knife fork and spoon, on card.
Per set........ $0.10
Per dozen sets........ 1.00
Postage........ .04

25191 Child's Set of three pieces, consisting of knife, fork and spoon, mounted on fancy picture card, 4½x7 inches. This set has cocobola handles, riveted with bolster and cap; blades made of good quality of steel.
Per set........ $0.25

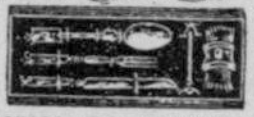

25192 Toy "Britannia" Sets, consisting of knife, fork, spoon, napkin and ring and knife rest in neat box, containing 3 sets.
Per set........ $0.30

25193 Box containing knife, fork, spoon and napkin ring of doll size. Price........ .05

25194 Same, but larger size and provided in addition to above with knife rest.
Price........ .10

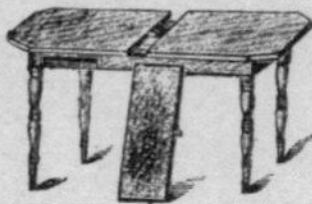

25197 Folding Table, similar to cut. Legs fold under, making it convenient to handle. Nicely made and a new thing in a toy table; size, 21 x 13 x 14½ inches.
Price each........ $0.50

25198 Folding Table, larger than preceding, well made and useful size, 14x24x15½ in.
Price each........ $0.75

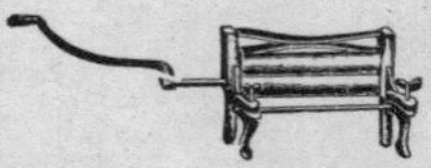

25200 The "Triumph" Toy Wringer; frame made wholly of cast metal, smooth finished, white rubber rolls, ½ inch in diameter and 3 inches long. Can be fastened to side of tub by means of thumb screws. A perfect model of the regular Triumph wringer. Weight, 1 lb. Price, each.. $0.40

Unique Wash Sets.

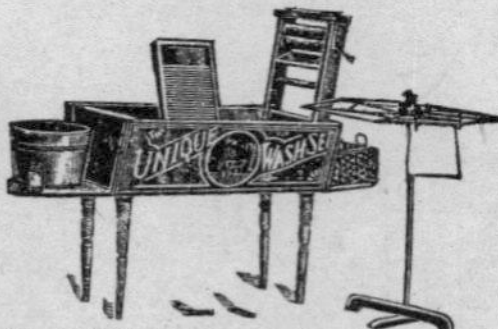

25203 Entirely new and original in design, consisting of latest style Laundry Tub, Wringer, Washboard, Pail, Basket, and double line Clothes Reel with Clothes Pins. All parts pack inside of tub. Compact, attractive and strongly made. Size, 27in. long, 13 in. high, 9 in. wide. Reel 16 in. high. Price........ $0.90

25204 Similar in design to above. Consists of new style Laundry Tub, Wringer, Washboard, Basket, Clothes Reel and Pins. All parts pack inside of tub. Size, 18 in. long, 7 in. wide, 9½ in. high. Reel 11 in. high. Price........ .50

23205 Toy Washing Machine. A complete practical toy for washing dolls' clothes. Modeled after pattern of a large washer. Is 6¼ inches wide, 12¼ inches long, stands 7¼ inches high, and is nicely painted in bright colors.
Price each........ .95

Kitchen and Wash Sets.

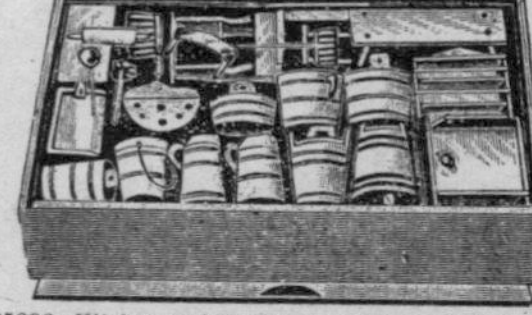

25206 Kitchen and Wash Sets, nicely packed in wooden box, about 22 utensils, all neatly made, such as tubs, pails, ladles, spoons, roller, masher, washboard, stand, churn, and many other articles. Per box........ $0.95
Per dozen boxes........ 10.25

Doll Beadsteads.

The Silver Queen Dolls' Wire Bedstead with mattress and pillows. A most perfect dolls' bed; made in three sizes.

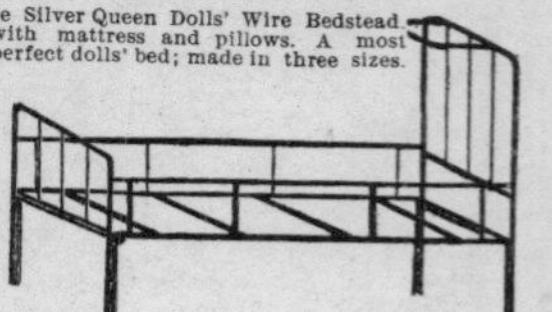

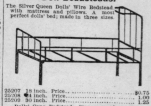

25207 18 inch. Price........ $0.75
25208 24 inch. Price........ 1.00
25209 30 inch. Price........ 1.25

Dolls' Cane Bedstead. Strong wood frame, wrapped in fancy patterns with split cane. Has turned wood head and foot posts, and ordinary slat mattress. Made in two sizes.

25210 Small size, 10x 6 x 11 in.
Each........ $0.70
25211 Large size 12x10x12 inch. headboard. Each........ $0.90

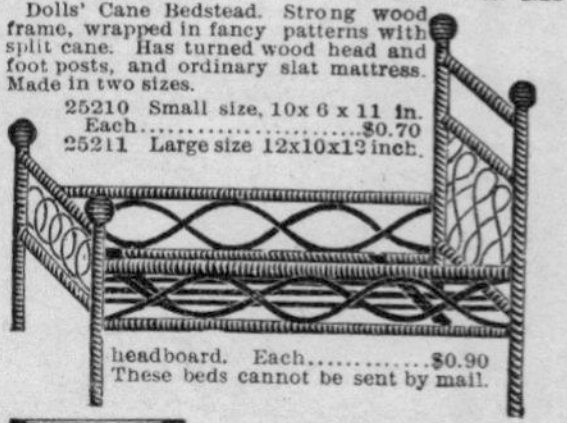

These beds cannot be sent by mail.

Doll Swings.

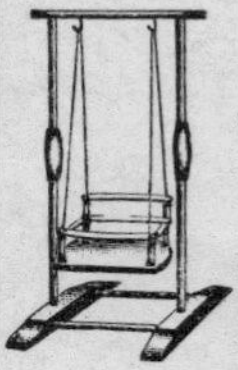

25212 Dolls' swing; stands 20 inches high. Measures 12x12 inches at the base; the seat of the swing 7 inches across; knocks down flat. Each swing wrapped and tied in packages, 2x5x13.
Price, each........ $0.15

25213 A Doll's Swing, not illustrated. Different construction from the one quoted above, but a good swing.
Price........ $0.20

Doll Hammocks.

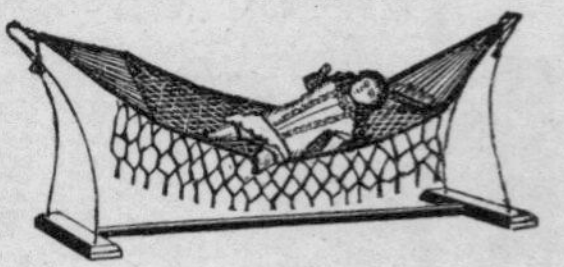

25162

25214 Toy Doll Hammocks. Made of fancy colored seine twine, hand woven, strong and durable. Metal rings in each end for suspending hammock. Length, 40 inches. Each........ $0.15
Postage........ .02
Stands for same. 2 ft., 6 in. long. Each........ .25

25215 Toy Doll Hammocks. Fancy colors, with spreaders. Length, 50 inches. Designed to be used with a rack stand as illustrated.
Price of hammock........ .25
Stands for same, each........ .25

25216 Toy Doll Hammocks. Fancy colors with pillow and spreaders Corded edge of extra heavy braided twine, with variegated tassels. A very superior article. Price, each........ .50

25217 Stands for same, each........ .25

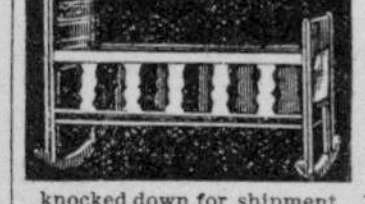

25219 Doll's Cradle, made of chestnut wood, with foot and head board paneled and painted in handsome design. Will hold a 20-inch doll. Extreme length, 22 inches; height, 16 inches; width, 11 inches. Packed knocked down for shipment. Weight, 3 lbs.
Price........ $0.75

25220 Doll's Cradle, same style finish and wood as above, but designed to accommodate a 16-inch doll. Extreme length, 18 inches; width, 9 inches; height, 12 inches; weight, 2 lbs.
Price........ .45

25221 Doll's Cradle, same general construction, but smaller, extreme length being 15 inches; height, 8 inches; width, 7 inches; weight, 1 lb. Price........ .25

Toys—Continued.

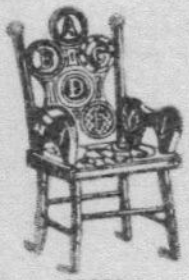

25221

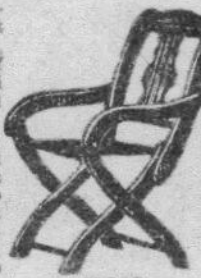

25223

25222 Alphabet Chair. Made of hard wood and covered with handsomely illuminated letters. This chair is so made that it can be taken apart and set up in a few moments, affording amusement and instruction to any child. Height to top of back of chair, 11 inches; to seat, 5 inches; width, 5 inches; weight packed, knocked down, ½ pound. Price....................$0.19

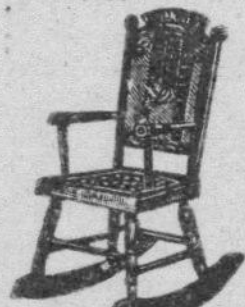

25223 Doll's Folding Chair Made of hardwood with fancy cloth seat; height, 11½ in. Price....................$0.20

25224 Doll's Spelling Rocker. A new feature for chairs. A large selection of words for children to learn to spell, together with a pleasing design in bright colors. Height, 14 inches.
Price....................$0.22

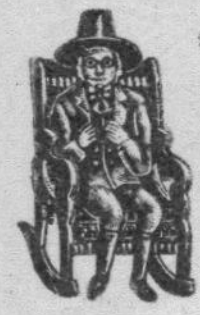

25225 Grandpa Rocker. An original and pleasing feature in rockers, consisting of handsomely designed chair represented as being occupied by grandpa, and having a very life-like appearance. Size, 13 inches high, 6 inches wide.
Price....................$0.25

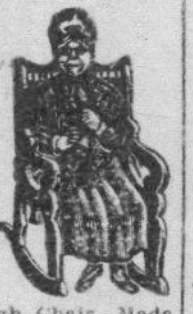

25225½ Same, but chair is occupied by grandma.
Price....................$0.25

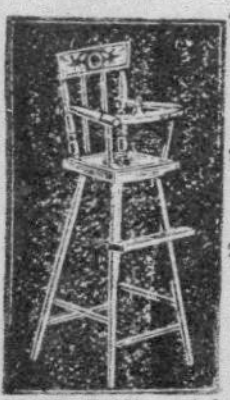

25226 Doll's High Chair. Made of hardwood, smooth finish and handsomely ornamented to represent cane work. Each packed in neat pasteboard box. Height, 8 inches.
Price....................$0.24

25227 Doll's High Chair, same construction and size as above, but has lap board with wooden dishes attached.
Price....................$0.28

25228 Doll's Alphabet High Chair. One of the latest patterns and an exceedingly handsome chair. On the back, seat and step are lithographed the full alphabet, figures and pictures. Height, 22 in. Packed in neat box. Price........$0.30

25229 Folding Alphabet Table, lithographed in bright colors, circular in shape. Ornamented with letters of the alphabet, 10 inches in diameter; 8¼ inches high.
Price....................$0.25

Toy Furniture.

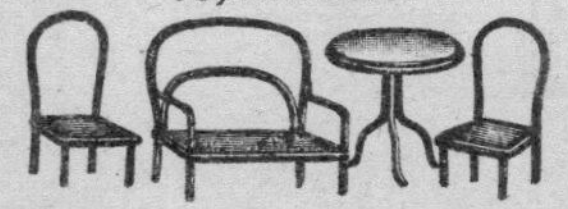

25230 Toy Furniture Set, consisting of sofa, two chairs and center table, made of bent rattan, put together and varnished. The seats and table top made of solid wood covered with leather. The set complete weighs less than 3 oz. Dimensions of sofa or settee, 1¾ in. wide by 4 in. long, or 3¼ in. to top of back. Table stands 3 in. high and measures 2x3 in. on top.
Price, per set....... $0.20 Postage............$0.05

25231 Toy Furniture Set, same description as preceding, but larger, sofa being 5¼ inches long, 2½ inches wide and 6 inches to top of back; chairs 2¼ inches high, or 5¼ in. to top of back, with heavy arms and padded cushions.
Price, per set........$0.35 Postage............ .10

Toys—Continued.

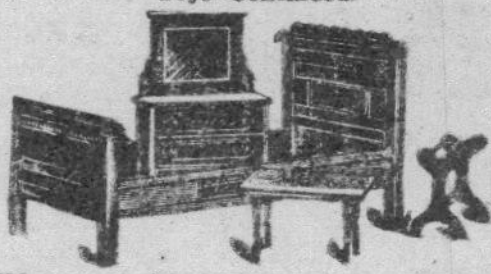

25233 A new, and decidedly the richest and most elaborate Dolls' Chamber Suite manufactured, representing nice carved work and handsome grained panels. The suit is composed of bedstead, dressing case, rocker, table and towel rack, all of latest patterns and well made. Comes nearly set up, nicely packed in a box. Size of bed, 18x10½ inches; dressing case, 7x9 inches; chair, 9 inches high; table 6x4 inches. Price....$1.00

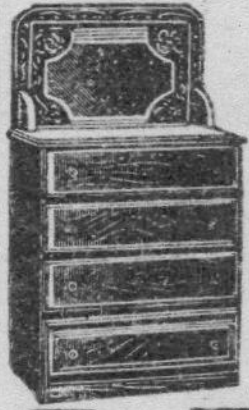

25234 Imperial Chiffonnier, a very fine and handsome piece of furniture. The drawer fronts and extension top are lithographed in perfect imitation of rich burl panels and carved work. Has 4 drawers with polished metal knob fronts. It is strongly made and finely finished, and is exceedingly attractive. Size, 9 inches long, 18 inches high.
Price....................$0.95

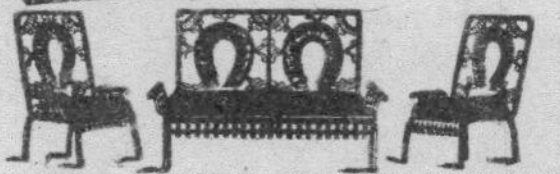

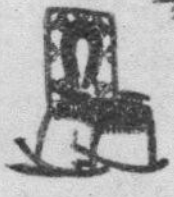

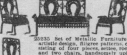

25235 Set of Metallic Furniture of artistic design, filigree patterns, consisting of four pieces, settee, rocker and two chairs, handsomely upholstered in velvet. Size of settee, 5 in. long, 4 in. high; chairs, 2 in long; rocker, 2¼ in. wide, 3¼ in. high.
Price....................$0.35
Postage.................... .10

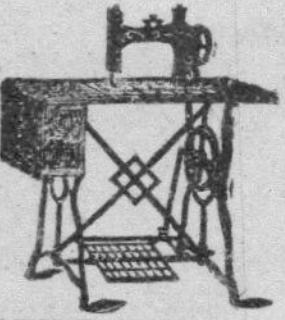

25236 The Fairy Sewing Machine, an ingeniously contrived toy. The belt runs, wheels turn, and treadle works. Stands about 4½ inches high. Something that every child will appreciate.
Each....................$0.25

CHILD'S FURNITURE.

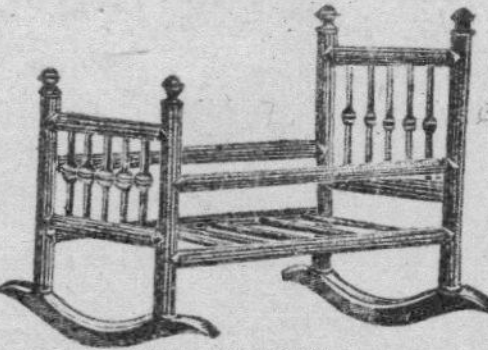

Order No. 25238.

A description and the illustration of crib does not do justice to this line of goods. The pieces are imitation enamel, corrugated, finished in white and gold, and are large enough to be of practical value.

Beds.

18 inch.	Price, eace....................	$1.00
21 inch.	Price, each....................	1.25
24 inch.	Price, each....................	1.50

Cribs.

18 inch,	Price, each....................	1.25
21 inch.	Price, each....................	1.50
24 inch.	Price, each....................	1.88
Child's Rocker.	Price, each....................	1.50
Child's Chair.	Price, each....................	1.35
Child's Settee.	Price, each....................	2.50
Dolls' Chair.	Price, each....................	.38
Child's Chair.	Price, each....................	.75
Child's Table.	Price, each....................	1.13
Child's Table.	Price, each....................	.75

Black Boards.

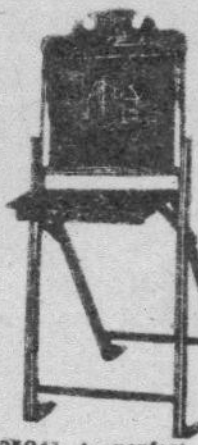

25240 One of the finest and most complete blackboards made. A well arranged combination of easel and desk, having a movable sawed extension, with designs for drawing on either side. The board is made of new material of best quality, smooth and warranted not to check. The desk is provided with an extra large drawer with ornamented front. The board drops forward to form the desk, showing additional designs for drawing. It is made in a substantial manner and folds very closely for shipping. Height, 48 in. Size of board, 16x19 in.
Price....................$1.00

25241 A perfect Blackboard and Easel; no cut. Has fluted standards. Complete alphabet on the the frame of the board. A movable extension having designs for drawing on both sides. The back support can be easily removed so as to make a very thin package: height, 41 inches. Size of board, 18½x12½ inches.
Price....................$0.45

Dolls! Dolls!! Dolls!!!

All kinds and sizes. Do not delay ordering Christmas dolls until December, as by sending us your order early you may be reasonably certain of receiving exactly what you select and avoid receiving a substitute. We handle only such dolls as are quoted below and on the following pages.

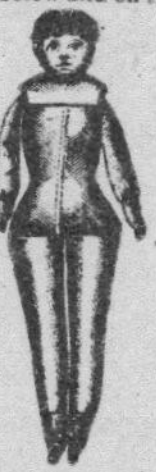

25244 China Limb Dolls, stitched nankeen bodies, not dressed. Length 13¼ inches.
Each....................$0.10
Per dozen.................... 1.00

25245 China Limb Dolls, stitched nankeen bodies, not dressed. Length 14¾ inches.
Each.................... .15
Per dozen.................... 1.60

25246 China Limb Dolls, stitched nankeen bodies, not dressed. Length 17½ inches.
Each.................... .25
Per dozen.................... 2.60

25247 Same as No. 25246 but 21 inches long.
Price.................... .35

Jointed Dolls, Bisque Heads, with Chemise.

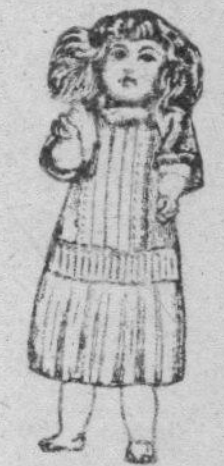

25248 Jointed Dolls, with bisque heads, flowing hair and long chemise. Length, 14 inches.
Price....................$0.25

25249 Jointed Dolls, bisque heads, flowing hair, teeth, and long plaited chemise. Length, 15½ inches.
Price.................... .50

25250 Jointed Dolls, with bisque heads, flowing hair, teeth and long chemise. Length, 19 inches.
Price.................... .90

25251 Jointed Dolls, extra large and fine, with flowing hair, teeth and long chemise, bisque heads. Length, 25 inches.
Price.................... 1.90

Kid Body Dolls, Not Dressed, Jointed.

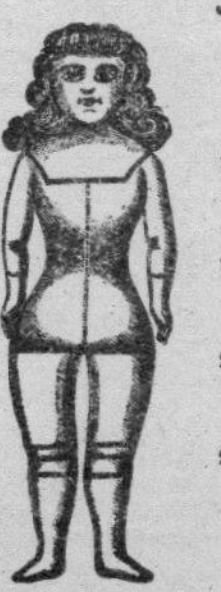

25252 Kid Body Dolls with bisque heads, flowing hair and teeth, solid eyes. Length, 12 inches.
Price....................$0.25

25253 Kid Body Dolls with bisque heads, woven wig, flowing hair, teeth and solid eyes. Length 15 in.
Price.................... .50

25254 Kid Body Dolls, bisque heads, woven wig, flowing hair and teeth. Length, 17 inches.
Price.................... .75

25255 Kid Body Dolls, with bisque heads, flowing hair woven wig, teeth and solid eyes. Length, 21 inches.
Price.................... 1.25

25256 Kid Body Dolls, bisque heads, woven wig, flowing hair, teeth and solid eyes. An extra large superfine doll. Length, 25 inches. Price.......... 1.75

Kid Body Dolls, Ne Plus Ultra Patent Joints, Closing Eyes.

Will sit erect without support.

25257 Kid Body Doll, patent hip joint, jointed arms, fine bisque head, flowing hair on full woven wig, teeth, closing eyes, openwork stockings and shoes. Length, 12 inches.
Price.........................$0.85

25257½ Same description, 14½ inches long............ 1.00

25258 Same description, 17½ inches long............ 1.35

25259 Same description, 21 inches long............ 1.85

25260 Same description, 25 inches long............ 2.45

NOTE.—Above dolls are the finest we could buy, and anyone desiring a first-class doll with closing eyes will obtain it by purchasing one of this line.

Patent Indestructible Dolls; worthy of the name, as they cannot be broken, as they cannot be broken to the rough usage to which a doll is usually subjected. Imitation bisque heads, flowing hair, solid eyes, teeth, stuffed cloth body, shoes, stockings, and chemise.

25262 12½-inch. Price.....$0.45

25263 14½-inch. Price... .75

25264 18½-inch. Price.. 1.10

25265 22½-inch. Price. 1.70

Dressed Dolls, Patent Indestructible Heads.

25266 Indestructible Head. Dressed Doll, cloth body, painted hair. Length 13 in. Price.....................$0.20

25267 Indestructible Head. Dressed Doll, cloth body, hair stuffed, painted hair, cloth shoes. Length, 17 inches. Price.....................$0.40

25268 Indestructible Head. Dressed Doll. Same as above. 20 inches long. Price.... $0.60

25269 Indestructible Head. Dressed Doll, largest size, 24 in. long. Price.............$0.80

Dressed Dolls, American Bisque Heads.

25271 Dressed Dolls, American bisque heads, cloth body, painted hair. Length 10½ in. Price.....................$0.15

25272 Dressed Dolls, American bisque heads, same as above. Length, 14½ in. Price.... $0.25

25273 Dressed Dolls, American bisque heads, hair stuffed, cloth body, painted hair, cloth shoes. Length, 15 in. Price.......$0.35

25274 Dressed Dolls, same description as No. 25273 but 18 in. in length. Price...........$0.50

Our claim that this Catalogue opens the large markets to you is no idle boast. Where else can you find so much? As a genuine guide to prices it has no equal.

Dressed Dolls, Cloth Bodies, with Kid Joints.

25275 Dressed Dolls, with kid joints, bisque heads and arms, teeth and flowing hair. Dressed in handsome costume; length, 13 inches.
Price.....................$0.50

25276 Dressed Dolls, cloth body, kid joints, bisque heads and arms, flowing hair, teeth, shoes, stockings. Dressed in costume of handsome design and good material; length, 14½ inches.
Price.....................$0.85

25277 Dressed Dolls, cloth body, kid joints, bisque head and arms, flowing hair, teeth, solid eyes, shoes and stockings; dress is of the best materials, in fashionable colors and well made; length, 17 inches. Price.... 1.00

25278 Dressed Dolls, cloth body, kid joints, bisque heads, flowing hair, teeth, solid eyes, shoes and stockings, dressed in an elaborate costume of satin, with large turned-up hat, length, 20 inches. Price.............. 2.00

Dressed Baby Dolls, Jointed.

25280 Full Jointed Dolls, finest bisque head, flowing hair, solid eyes; long baby dress of woolen stuff and silk, neatly trimmed. See cut. Price..........$1.00

25281 Same description but larger size, and more elaborate dress. Price...$1.45

25282 Superior quality, superfine dolls; jointed, with bisque heads, flowing hair, teeth, shoes and stockings. Dressed in "Baby" costume of nun's veiling, with cap to match. Length, 12 inches.
Each.....................$0.65

25283 Same description as above but larger. Each...........$0.90

25284 Large size "Baby" doll. Length, 16 inches. Price.. $1.50

Jointed Dolls, Dressed.

25285 Finest bisque heads, solid eyes, flowing hair, teeth, shoes and stockings. Superior quality dolls. Dress made of cotton stuff, trimmed, silk bonnet. Price.....................$0.50

25286 Same description; dress of changeable silk, embroideries, straw hat. Price...... .75

25287 Same description; dress of muslin and lace, bonnet trimmed with ribbon. Price.... 1.00

25288 Same description; dress and bonnet of changeable silk trimmed with ribbon. Price.. 1.15

25289 Same description; dress, finest muslin, woven through with ribbons. Full silk bonnet with silk strings and balls. Price......... 1.25

25290 Same description; dress of fine woolen goods, trimmed with silk ribbons or embroidered. Some hair lace hats, some bonnets. Price........................ 2.00

25291 Same description; dress, fine cashmire trimmed with silk and lace. Full silk bonnet, lace trimmed. Price.............. 2.25

25292 Same description; dress, full winter costume of fine woolen goods, trimmed with plush and ribbons. Bonnet to match. Price........ 3.50

Columbus Dolls.

These are the most beautifully dressed dolls now on the market. Each one in a full costume of a Spanish Cavalier of the XVth Century, consisting of "doublet and hose," cape, tunic, cap, and buckled shoes.

The costumes are works of art, made of the finest silk velvet and satin, in contrasting colors. Each Cavalier wears at his side a tiny sword. The broad cap is surmounted with an ostrich plume, while the inscription "1493C. Columbus 1893" is emblazoned upon its front.

25293 Columbus Doll, jointed, bisque head, flowing hair, teeth, solid eyes. Length, 15 inches. Price.....................$1.80

25294 Columbus Doll, same description as above. Length. 18 inches. Price...........$2.50

25295 Columbus Doll, large size. Length. 21 inches. Price.............$3.25

Indestructible Wool Dolls.

25296 Worsted, dressed girl dolls, assorted, similar to cut. 10 inches long.
Price.....................$0.20

25297 Worsted, dressed dolls, 12½ inches long. Price.....................$0.35

25298 Worsted, dolls dressed to represent a clown. In full costume, cap and balls. Length, 12½ inches. Price.....................$0.50

25299 Worsted Dolls, large size, with fine knitted wool dresses. Length, 15 inches. Price.....................$0.85

25300 Rubber Doll, musical, with knitted worsted hat and dress. Length, 7½ in. Price.....................$0.25

25301 Rubber Doll, musical, with worsted hat and dress. Length, 9 in. Price.............. .35

25302 Rubber Doll, musical, worsted hat and dress. Length about 11 in. Price.............. .50

25303 Rubber Jointed Boy Doll, musical. Will turn his head from side to side and raise his hands at will. Dressed in school costume. Length, 7 inches. Price...........$0.25

25304 Same style as above, 9 in. length. Price.............. .40

Clapping Figures.

25305 Various styles and costumes, bisque heads. We formerly catalogued these figures at from 25 to 75 cts. each, but to dispose of stock we offer them at the uniform price of each.............$0.25

25306 Indestructible soldiers, dressed in oilcloth suits in combination colors. Length, 10½ in.
Each.............$0.10
Per doz.............. 1.00

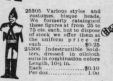

25307 Whistling Doll Figures, consists of a doll securely fastened upon a stick. The toy, upon being shaken produces a succession of shrill whistles.
Each.....................$0.22

25308 Same as above, except that figure is that of a rabbit, covered with natural skin. Price.....................$0.20

25309 The Musical Doll Figure is a doll head fastened upon a circular music box, secured to a stick handle. Upon being revolved, beautiful music is produced. Price.....................$0.40

25310 The Bird Musical Figure is the same style as above, but the figure is that of a bird, represented as standing over its nest. The music box is under the nest. See cut. Price.............$0.45

Paper Dolls.

25311 Our Pets Dressing Series. A new idea in paper dolls consists of finely lithographed dolls 9¾ inches long, on heavy cardboard, cut out with easel back. Each doll has three dresses of different colors and styles with hats to match, packed in neat box. The costumes all modern styles; six different designs.
Price, each $0.20
Postage .... .04

25312 Our Pets Paper Dolls, reduced size, same description as above but smaller.
Price, each $0.12
Postage .... .03

25313

25313 Princess and Princesses Paper Dolls, same size and description as No. 25311 but each doll is provided with four Regel costumes.
Price, each $0.23
Postage .... .04

25314 Paper Dolls, made of heavy cardboard, printed in colors, showing both front and back, furnished with four complete costumes with bonnets to match, all fashionable styles. Three designs each in separate envelopes, 4x7 inches.
Price each $0.05
Per dozen assorted, 3 kinds .... .50
Same, size 6x10 inches, each .. .10
Per dozen, assorted, 3 kinds $1.00
Postage on paper dolls, each .... .02

Paper Doll House.

25315 Doll houses made of extra heavy card board, printed in bright colors. Can easily be put together by any child. Comes knocked down, and packs into small space for shipping. Each $0.35

25316 Paper Toy Furniture for children to cut out. Three styles—*Parlor*, *Dining-room*, and *Bed-room*. Each sheet contains a full set of beautiful new style furniture, lithographed in eleven colors, printed on fine card board, and elegantly embossed. Sheets are 15x17 inches. Any child can cut them out. When cut they have only to be bent, no fitting or mucilaging of parts together. When ordering specify what style is wanted. Price per set .... .10
Per set of 3 (Parlor, Dining-Room, Bed-Room) .. .25

Doll Heads.

NOTE.—The measurements on China and Bisque Doll Heads are from shoulder to shoulder and from front to back.

25317 China Heads, painted hair and eyes.

No.		Size		Price	
No. 2	Size	3x2	Price	10	cents.
" 4	"	3½x2¼	"	15	"
" 6	"	4x2½	"	20	"
" 8	"	4½x3	"	25	"
" 10	"	5x3½	"	35	"

25318 Bisque Doll Heads: none better. Woven wig, flowing hair, teeth, and solid eyes.

No.	Size	Price
No. 5	Size 3¾x2	Price $0.60
7 "	4½x2¾ "	.80
9 "	5½x3 "	1.00
11 "	6¼x3¼ "	1.25

25319 Bisque Doll Heads, same kind as No. 25318 but with closing eyes.

No.	Size	Price
No. 4	Size. 3¼x1¾	Price $0.50
6	" 4¼x2¼	" .65
8	" 4¾x2¾	" .85
10	" 6x3	" 1.10

Muslin Doll Bodies.

(NO HEAD.)

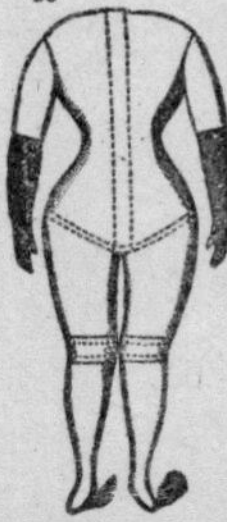

25320 Doll Bodies (no head); made of white muslin, with seat, white kid arms, and removable corsets.

Length.	Each.	Per doz.
10½ in.	$0.15	$1.60
13 in.	.20	2.15
17 in.	.30	3.00
19 in.	.40	4.00

Fine Silesia Doll Bodies.

(NO HEAD.)

25321 Fine Doll Bodies (no heads): made of extra heavy silesia, flesh colored, wool stuffed. Bisque or kid arms and bands, shoes and stockings. This body, used in conjunction with our Genuine Bisque Heads will make a superfine doll.

Length		Price
Length	15 inches.	Price, $0.45
"	16 "	" .60
"	18 "	" .75
"	20 "	" .90
"	22 "	" 1.00

Dolls—Continued.

25322 Adjustable Doll Stand, made of polished steel, nickel plated: any child can easily apply it and the doll will be held firmly. This article has become a necessary part of a doll outfit. Enables the child to have doll parties, receptions, promenades, etc., and have each doll supported in any position desired.

Size and prices as follows:

		Each	Doz.
No. 1	For Dolls, 3½ to 6 inches long	$0.10	$0.85
No. 2	For Dolls, 6½ to 11 inches long	.20	1.70
No. 3S	For Dolls, 12 to 20 inches long	.35	3.80
No. 3	For Dolls, 16 to 24 inches long	.50	4.25
No. 4	For Dolls, 24 to 36 inches long	1.25	12.75

Doll Sundries.

25323 Doll Shoes, assorted sizes. Per pair $0.10
25324 Doll Stockings, assorted sizes. Per pair $0.10
25325 Doll Corsets, assorted sizes. Per pair $0.10
25326 Doll Caps, made of fine lace or embroidery, with full lace ruches. Assorted styles and sizes. Each $0.20

25326 25327½

25327 Doll Hats, made of Mull or Cambric, on wire frame. Strings to match, assorted sizes and colors. Each $0.30

25327¼ Dolls' Silk Embroidered caps, lace trimmed, ribbon strings, assorted styles and sizes. Each $0.50

25327½ Dolls' Silk Caps, plush and lace trimmed, assorted sizes and colors. Each $0.40

25329

25327¾ Dolls' Plush Caps, lace trimmed and Plush, Tam O'-Shanter shape with ornament. Each $0.35

25328 Doll "Tam O' Shanter" Cap and Hood, made of fine zephyr. Assorted colors. Each .... .20

25329 Doll Shetland Floss Sacques, made in combinations of two colors. Each .... .25

25330 Doll Shetland Floss Sacques, finer quality than above, trimmed with silk embroidery. Each .... .40

25331 Dolls' Superfine Saxony Sacques, (15) double knit of fine Saxony wool. Handsomely embroidered with triple row of silk floss, and finished with a row of narrow satin ribbon Each. .60

25332 Doll's Cloak, made of fine white flannel, silk embroidered. Wide collar and mutton leg sleeves, assorted sizes. Price .... .50

25333 Doll's Cloak, made of fine Bedford cord. Trimmed with double row of silk embroidery, satin ribbons, divided collar and mutton leg sleeves. The handsomest doll's cloak on the market. Each .... .75

25334 Doll's Saxony Bootees crocheted of fine Saxony wool, in combinations of two colors. Per pair .... .15

25335 Doll's Bootees same style as above, but tops embroidered with silk floss, and supplied with silk ties and tassels. Per pair .... .20

GAMES.

In this department we catalogue what we confidently believe to be the best assortment of amusements for the home circle that can be found anywhere.

Folding Board Games.

Note our line of 85c games. Every game in this list from No. 25340 to 25351 retails at $1.00 and $1.25 each. Our price, 85c each.

25340 The new and exciting game Columbia. Is bound in durable dark green paper (imitation Morocco), 22 inches square folds in center, with fancy label, printed in best gold bronze, mounted on heavy cloth board; best quality. The game is lithographed, in colors—red, blue, gold, brown, gray, black, white and yellow: containing the portraits of all the presidents, large size, in life colors, giving the date of their birth, death and inauguration, and term of years. On the four corners are historical pictures in brilliant colors—the landing of Columbus; signing the Declaration of Independence; surrender of Cornwallis, and surrender of General Lee, with their dates. A box containing 30 disks—15 red ones and 15 blue ones; also rules for playing, with an explanation of the historical and geographical features of the game. Price each $0.85

Games—Continued.

25341 The Presidential Election Game. The game is both simple and practical. It is elegant in appearance, it gives information concerning the electoral vote, and is played in such a manner as to combine instruction with lots of fun. Weight, 2 lbs. Price $0.85

25342 The Electoral College Game. The game played by either two or four persons, and during its progress shows the methods used in electing a President of the United States. The game is played upon a beautifully lithographed board, containing the portrait of all the presidents, the date and place of meeting of the different National Conventions, the Electoral Vote of all the States, and many more statistics of national interest. Size of board, 18x18 inches. Weight, 3¼ lbs. Price .... .85

25343 The Military Game. Toy soldiers in connection with a game; every wide-awake boy will want it: handsomely lithographed box containing two armies with their commanders-in-chiefs and other officers, and toy pistols for artillery, Pistols make loud reports and discharge projectiles. Full directions for playing game in two ways, packed in box. Weight, 3½ lbs. Price .85

25344 The Games at the Old Homestead Combined; consists of a backgammon board 12¼x14¼, checker and chess board 12½x14¼, enameled finished, and the grand race game, size, 27x14½ inches, the whole folding into a book 14½x6¾x¼ in., and packing into a fancy pasteboard box, with lithographed cover, size, 17x9½x2 inches, containing a set of stained wood chessmen, set of checkers, two plain wood dice boxes, two dice and six colored cardboard racehorses and riders mounted on wooden stands, with directions for playing the various games. Weight, complete, 2¾ lbs. Each $0.85

The Yale-Harvard Games.

A High Class Game for Thoughtful Players.

25345 A new game of skill of rare merit for two players. The basis of the game is foot-ball, the idea of each side being to carry the ball into the opposite goal. The pieces used are numbered, and can be moved as many spaces as their numbers indicate. New style of drawer game board. Price $0.85

The Limited Mail and Express Games.

25346 The new, popular board game, elegantly produced and played upon a map of the United States with Miniature Railroad Trains, etc. The trains carry cotton from the South, tobacco from Virginia, corn from Iowa, live-stock from Texas, etc., as well as mail matter from all parts of the country. It is extremely amusing. Played on new style Drawer Game Board (14x21 inches). Price $0.85

The Soldier Boy Games.

25347 A very large, showy, folding board, almost two feet square. Especially captivating for boys. With the game come four metal soldiers and spinning indicator for playing. The game relates the stirring story of the battlefield, and illustrates the promotion gained by ability, bravery and emotions. The winner of the game is the player who first attains the position of "Commander-in-Chief." Price $0.85

The Game of "Hopity."

25348 This is a game of skill, which can be played by two, three or four persons of any age. The principal feature of the game is the popular jumping move, pieces being allowed to jump over friend and foe alike to reach the opposite side of the board. The game is beautifully issued on a board seventeen inches square. Price $0.85

25349 Innocence Abroad represents the journey of a party of people, who travel by various routes toward the same destination, and who meet with curious experiences and occurrences. A handsomely lithographed folding board 10x19 inches, shows roads running through a very picturesque country, past farms forests, mountains and across rivers whose course can be traced from their source to the ocean. Packed complete with directions in pasteboard box, 10½x10½x1½ inches. Weight, 2½ pounds. Price $0.85

The Game of Travel.

25350 A handsome and instructive game, representing a journey through Europe. Metal steamships and railroad trains of different colors are used for pieces. The game is played with route tickets. The idea of the game is to make a tour to Europe as far as Constantinople, then returning to America. Played on new style patent game-board, with drawer for pieces (14x21 inches). Price $0.85

All lines of merchandise very generally reduced in price.

Games—Continued.

25351 Chessinda is founded upon an ancient legend wherein four rulers combine their armies to besiege a fortress containing an immense treasure. There were four approaches to this citadel, and the one who first gained share of the wealth it contained. The game has been designed to represent, with its King and Knights, the march of the four armies in their attack upon the fortress. It has been called "the best of all home games," and it will interest all ages. The game is mounted upon a substantial board 18 inches square. The design of which carries out the spirit of the story. There are four sets of implements, with which two distinct games can be played, contained in a separate box. Weight, 1½ lbs. Price $0.85

The Game of Electors and Presidential Puzzle.

35353 Popular edition of a good game, played on handsome lithographed board with colored implements. New and exciting. Packed in box with directions for playing both games....$0.25

25356 Solitaire; consists of a board 8x8, on one side of which is a lithograph of the well-known game of solitaire, and on the reverse a Checker Board; 33 cards accompany each game, all of which comes in a neat box and weighs 12 oz. Price $0.25

25357 Knuckle Billiards. A peculiar new game and a very interesting one. It is simple and makes a great deal of fun. Packed complete in neat box with directions. Weight 10 oz. Price...$0.40

25358 The Grand Race Game, consists of a substantially cloth bound, folding board, 26x14 in. in size; printed in colors to represent a race track, including fences, etc. Has six colored cardboard horses and riders, mounted on wooden stands, two wooden dice cups and two dice. Full directions for playing accompany each game. Weight, complete, 1½ lbs. Price..........$0.45
25359 Extra fine edition, price...........................60

25360 Royal Game of Parchesi complete. This is an entertaining game for the family circle. It can be played by either two, three or four persons. Besides greatly interesting the lookers-on. Full instructions accompany each game. Best grade, including a book, muslin bound folding board, embossed and stamped in gold, with box containing 8 dice, 4 dice cups and 16 counters. A nicely gotten up set. Weight, 1½ pounds. Price, complete $1.35

25361 Across the Continent is the most elaborate board game ever issued. The large folding board upon which the game is played is a bird's eye view of the United States, showing the principal cities, railway lines, etc. It is an instructive and handsome picture. In course of the game players make a trip across the Continent and back, follow the route taken on their tickets, and pay traveling expenses. Railway tickets, toy money, fine celluloid pieces, enameled cups, and full directions with each game. It has use-ple for six players, but any number can play. It is an exciting and educational amusement. Size of board, 21x42 inches. Weight, 3½ pounds. Price................$2.75

25362 Around the Circle game, a new and attractive board game for two or more up to six players. Extremely interesting; finished in high colors, with implements and instructions packed in an attractive box. Price.......................96

25363 "Jaclu," a new, interesting and instructive method of playing two games. Figures and letters. Either two or four persons may play, and as mathematics enter largely into the game it is a most entertaining one for thoughtful players. The game is played upon a handsomely finished hardwood board 8x18 inches in size. Price, each..........................50

Miscellaneous Games.

25365 Disco, the Great Carom Game. The object of the game is to deposit the disk in the opponent's pocket. Each such score counts one, and a total of nine wins the game. The cues are 8 inches long, made of hardwood, and are to be held in the hand like a pencil. The disk of steel, hollow in the center and tired with rubber. The combinations by which the pockets may be gained are innumerable. Sure to become as popular as crokinole. Size of board, 16x28 inches $2.25

25366 Crokinole, a new and intensely interesting game for everybody, with no objectionable features. There is no game where the element of chance is smaller, as the winning of the game depends wholly upon the skill of the player. The engraving shows the board placed in position on a table, also the position of the hand in the act of playing. Size, octagon shape, 32 in. across. Made of polished oak. Each..............$3.50
25367 Made of cherry or oak, covered with fine quality of flannel $4.50
25368 Parlor Tennis. This new and fascinating game is arranged for parlor or lawn use and is played with 12 light rubber balls. Can be played individually or by sides. Weight, 3 lbs. Packed, each game complete, in pasteboard box. Price..............$1.75

25369 Parlor Quoits. Another pleasant and interesting game for either parlor or lawn; consists of two turned posts, firmly set in nicely finished brass, 8 inches in diameter, and four quoits five inches in diameter, made of wood, and firmly wound with heavy, fancy colored webbing. Packed in neat box with fine lithographed label on cover. Price..............$0.90

25373 Bean Bag Game. A game of skill, is always popular. Consists of board, 9x12 inches, elevated at the end by two turned standards to give it the proper angle. Has three openings, and furnished with five wooden disks. Directions on cover of box in which the game is packed. Price..............$0.25

25375 The Jolly Marble Game. Handsomely lithographed, nicely made and easily set up. It is intensely fascinating to watch the figures as they pass a marble from one to the other in a very natural manner until it rolls on the board and is counted. Size, when set up, 19½ in. long, 8½ in. wide, 21 in. high. Each game inclosed in a box. Price..............$0.70

25377 Magic Hoops; has nine beautifully plated rattan hoops, and a post in two sections. Full directions for playing accompany each game. Weight, 2¾ lbs. Price..............$0.70

25378 Pitch-a-ring consists of a highly polished chestnut wood box and 5 posts nicely painted and varnished. The 8 rings are plated rattan in fancy colors. A most novel and interesting game. Weight, complete, 3 lbs. Price..$0.65
25379 The New Race game. This fascinating novelty is the only perfect imitation ever devised of a genuine horse

race upon the turf or track. Put up in a fine strong wood case, neatly finished. The horses and uprights are all finely made of the lat. Size 12x12 inches, 7 in. deep. Weight, four pounds. Price $1.00
25380 Marble Arch, a new game for boys. Played with marbles. It will please the little folks. Price $0.25

Games—Continued.

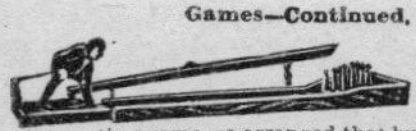

25382 The Automatic Bowling Alley. Another new and interesting game, so arranged that by pressing a knob at the end of the board the man's arm is drawn back and held by a spring; then the marble is allowed to roll down the track and strike a wire coil, releasing the arm which rolls the marble at the ten pins in a very life-like manner. Size of board 6½x36 inches. Height of man, 6½. Packed in box. Price..................$0.75
Weight, 4½ pounds.

25383 Parlor Pool. A miniature pool table, 7¾x29 in. with hardwood cue and three colored balls, on which can be played a number of interesting games. Price....................$0.85

25385 The old Oaken Bucket consists of a hard wood platform on which is fastened the well-sweep and bucket. Also thirty card buckets with a line of the poem on each, embracing the entire poem; 15 duplicate buckets, 4 fish, 4 lizards, 4 turtles, 3 frogs, 1 McGinty, and a card with complete poem. Made in three different grades. Each game packed in a pasteboard box with full directions for playing. Weight of each game 3¾ lbs. Finely finished polished oak size of platform 24x8¼ in. An elegant outfit....................$0.95
25386 Same, hardwood, stained and varnished size platform 21x8½ in.................... .74
25387 Same, hardwood, smooth finish (1), size platform 20x7 in. Price.................... .58
25388 Ding Dong Bell Game. Same size and styles of construction as the Old Oaken Bucket, game but a practical elucidation of the nursery rhyme Ding, Dong Bell. Can be played by any number up to twenty. Packed each game in a pasteboard box; weight, 3¾ lbs. Finely finished oak Price.................... .95
Same, hardwood, stained and varnished (2). Price.................... .74
25389 Same, hardwood, smooth finish (1)........ .58

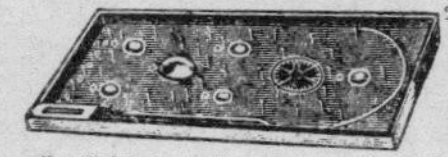

25390 Bagatelle Boards, imported edition, well made, with spring cue. Length, 16 in; weight, 1 lb. Price....................$0.25
25391 Bagatelle Boards, American edition, 18 in. length; made in best possible manner, with spring cue, indicator, bell and pins. Price..............$0.45
25392 Bagatelle Boards, American edition, covered with oil cloth, has spring cue, brass indicator, chime bell and pins; length, 24 in.; weight, 1¾ lbs. Price....................$0.85
25393 Bagatelle Boards, American edition, covered with oil cloth, has spring cue, brass indicator, silvered metal bell, and metal lined pitfalls, strongly made with dovetailed corners; length, 30 in.; weight, 3¼ lbs. Price....................$1.50

25394 Table Croquet with arches 6 balls and mallets complete; smooth finish and painted. Per set.................$0.50 Weight 2¼ lbs.
25395 Table Croquet, complete as above, but larger, with 8 balls and mallets, elegantly striped. Per set....................$0.80
Weight, 2¾ lbs.
25396 Parlor Croquet, suitable for playing on the floor, finely varnished and painted. Price per set, complete..............$0.85 Weight, 6 lbs.

Hardwood Ten Pins.

Polished and striped complete with balls. In strong wood boxes. Well made and finished.

No.	Size.	Weight.	Per set.	Per doz.
25397	7 in.	2¼ lbs.	25c.	$2.50
25398	9 in.	4 lbs.	40c.	4.00
25399	12in.	10 lbs.	70c.	7.25

Games—Continued.

25400 Brownie Band Ten Pins. The latest style of Brownie ten pins, consisting of ten musicians with instruments, showing comical expressions and occupying laughable attitudes, each standing 8 inches high, together with 3 polished balls. Packed in a handsome labeled box.
Price..............$0.45

25401 Ouija, or Egyptian Luck Board. The Ouija is without a doubt a most interesting, remarkable and mysterious production. Its operations are always interesting and sometimes invaluable, answering as it does questions concerning the past, present and future. Directions for operating the Ouija accompany each board. Packed each one in a pasteboard box.
Each....................$1.00
Cannot be sent by mail.

25403 The scientific Planchette Board, made on the same principle as the old and popular planchette boards of 1860. Style (No. 2,) fine polished boards, cherry finish, nickel plated casters, with swivel joint, boxwood wheels, lead tip pencil with rubber. Put up in paper box with full directions and full account of its workings. Each....................$0.95
Postage.................... .10
25404 Planchette No. 3, hardwood board, varnished, brass casters, maple wheels and pencil. Put up in neat paper box with full directions,
Each.................... .50
Postage.................... .10

Miscellaneous Parlor Games, Small.

Tiddledy Winks may be played by any number of people on any small table with a thick cloth on. Each player is provided with four to six counters of the same color, and one larger one, the use of the larger one being to press to the edge of the smaller one and in that way cause it to jump into the cup, which is in the center of the table. The player who first gets all his counters into the cup wins the game.
25410 Popular edition, for four players..........$0.20
Postage.................... .05
25411 Popular edition, for six players.................... .40
Postage.................... .08
25412 Hop Scotch Tiddledy Winks, a novel method of playing this popular game. Full directions with each game.
Price.................... 45
25413 Tiddledy Winks Ten Pins, a new and entertaining combination of Tiddledy Winks and Ten Pins.
Price per set.................... .50
25414 Tiddledy Winks Tennis, a good combination of Tennis and Tiddledy Winks.
Price.................... .85
25415 Game Box, consisting of jumping rope, shuttlecock, cup and two balls. Finely finished in white and gold enamel. A fine present for a girl. Weight, 1 pound. Each.................... .75
25416 The Cuckoo Game. The latest society craze; consists of six handsomely printed cards 4½x4¼ inches, divided into 9 fancy colored squares, 54 colored counters, one wooden dice box and one cube enameled in colors corresponding with the squares on the cards. Put up in fancy lithographed covered paper box. Size, 6½x5x1¾; weight, 8 oz. Price.................... .20
25417 Cuckoo Game, with 10 cards, 2 dice cups and colored cubes, and 90 counters complete in box size, 12x5¼x1¼, weight 14 oz. Price..... .35
25418 Cuckoo Game, with 16 cards, 4 fancy colored cups, 4 colored cubes, and 144 colored counters packed in separate box, all packed in a varnished wood box with sliding cover, size 13x5½x2¼, weight 1¾ lbs. Price.................... .60
Full and complete directions for playing accompany each game.

⁎ **Read pages 1 and 2 before ordering goods. You obtain a discount by sending money with order. Send money by Express, Draft on Chicago or New York, Post Office Money Order, or Registered Mail.**

Jack Straws.

25420 This is an old-fashioned game, but its popularity increases yearly.
Price per box with directions....................$0.08
Per doz.................... .80
By mail, extra.................... .02
25421 Jack Straws, consisting of carved wooden implements, such as rakes, hoes, forks, poles, hooks, etc., put up in a neat box. The latest forms and the most difficult game; all made of carved wood. Per box.................... .10
Per doz.................... 1.00
By mail, extra.................... .02
25422 Magnetic Jack Straws, differing from the ordinary game in consisting of metal straws of various shapes and a magnet to be used in picking up the straws, instead of the usual hook.
Postage.................... .05
Price.................... .25

Lotto.

This famous German game has become very popular in America. It is very easily learned, and may be played by the youngest children and grown up people. Directions in each box.

	Each.	Per doz.
25425 In slide box, 3¾x6, 13 cards, ordinary quality..........	$0.09	$0.95
25426 Wood box, 5½x9, 18 large cards, numbers in bag inside box with glasses and counters..........	.50	5.50
25427 Wood box, 7½x12, hinge, cover, 36 large cards, numbers in boy, 2 inside boxes, with glasses and counters, soay box wrapped separately..........	.75	8.00

Card Games.

Ten Cent Series.

25428 Authors. This interesting little game, giving titles and works of the best authors, contains classified and lettered books, and is interesting to old and young alike. Directions in each box.
Plain cards. Price....................$0.10
25429 Hidden Authors, different from above in manner of playing. Price.................... .10
25430 Old Maid, a new edition of this popular game. Price.................... .10
25431 Snap, an old game in a new dress; everything in the game has to do with the word snap. Price.................... .10
25432 Anagrams, the game of letters under a new name. Letters in plenty for playing both games. New and attractive. Price.................... .10
25433 Peter Coddle; our 10c. edition of this popular card game is complete, and equal in every respect to the usual 25c. series. Price.... .10

Card Games.

Nineteen Cent Series.

Every game in this series retails at 25 and 30 cents. Our price 19c. Postage from 4c to 10c.

25434 Capitol Cities. A new Card Game very similar to the popular "Authors." Books are made up in the same manner as in authors, but the names of the United States are used, instead of the names of writers and their books. The game is interesting and instructive. Price....................$0.19

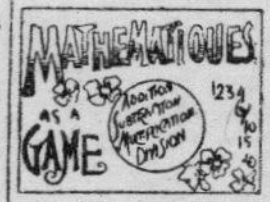

25435 Mathematiques. Another of the Educational Series. Games are won on the lines of addition, subtraction, multiplication and division. An instructive and intensely fascinating game. Packed in neat box with full directions. Price..........$0.19
25436 Authors popular edition vignetted.
Price.................... .19
25437 Proverbs. The old standard game revised, consisting of 100 cards containing the best proverbs, with directions for playing game seven different ways. Price.................... .19
25438 Letters. An entertaining and popular game. Greatly improved and containing nearly 300 letters and directions for playing both Letters and Anagrams. Price.................... .19
25439 Roses. Containing 36 cards on which are printed roses, nine each of red, yellow, pink and blue. The object of the game is to avoid taking any of the blue roses. Price.................... .19

STOVES OF ALL KINDS.

We have them, and guarantee each and every one. Ours are not the cheapest, but they are the best. See Index for quotations.

Games—Continued.

25440 The World's Revelator, an educational game, containing 10 cards, 25 questions and answers on each card. Important points on all known subjects presented in pleasing forms. Price........ $0.19

25441 The Corner Grocery enables children to gratify their desire to "play store" and is highly exciting and entirely novel. Buying and paying for groceries is the purpose of the game. Price........ $0.19

25442 **Peter Coddle.** This humorous game consists of about 200 cards, containing amusing sentences, together with a 16-page book describing in a spicy manner the adventures of Peter Coddle in New York. Parts of the story are omitted and blanks left to be supplied by the cards. One of the most amusing and comical games published. Directions in each box. Price........ .19

26443 **Timothy Tattle**, a new reading game giving an account of a visit to the World's Fair by a young man from the Tuttle family. Timothy tells what he saw and what he thinks of the many curious things he found in the great Exposition. Price........ .19

26444 **Fortune Telling Card Game.** It would be unwise to rely on the predictions contained in it, but young people will find it very entertaining. Price........ .19

25445 **Mother Goose Old Maid.** Best quality, full assorted, superior finish cards. Price........ .19

25446 **The County Fair** is another popular trading game. Cards bearing names of articles usually exhibited at "cattle shows" with tickets of admission, money for premiums and various expenses constitute the game. Price $0.19

25447 **Husking.** The cards of this game are printed in several colors, and represent the features of an old fashioned husking party. The good and poor ears represent, respectively, the red ear and the smutty ear corn. Price........ .19

25448 **Wang** combines in its methods originality, simplicity and novelty. It is put up in very attractive form, containing 72 cards, divided into two sets, each of a different color, and one hundred metal counters called shekels. The game will never become old, as the variations are unlimited. Price........ $0.19

Card Games.

40 Cent Series.

The games in this series are those that usually sell at 50 cts., 60 cts., and 75 cents.
Our price, each........ $0.40
Postage, from 6 to 12 cents.

25450 The Wild Flower Game. A beautiful game, consisting of more than 60 cards, lithographed with pictures of wild flowers. The game follows a course in botany, and is recommended to students.
Price........ $0.40

25452 Logomachy, or War of Words. The new premium games. One of the best new parlor card games published. Full directions accompany each game; put up in handsome box, 6x8¼x1 inch.
Each........ $0.40

25453 Negomi. A new game containing forty beautifully lithographed cards and implements for counters, packed in neat box with full directions for playing. Price........ .40

25455 American History, an educational game, consists of sixty enameled cards on which are printed questions relating to the various headings, these questions being selected for their general interest and importance. Price........ .40

When ordering goods shipped by mail, be sure to allow money for postage. If you send too much we will refund balance.

Games—Continued.

25456 American Cities. A beautiful and instructive game. Fifty-two cards printed in many colors, giving views of fifty-two different cities. Each card bears the population of the city, and a small amount of descriptive matter. In good sized boxes, 7x9 inches, with handsome label. Price........ $0.40

25457 The Bible Game, arranged in form of questions from the Old and New Testaments. Prepared with the greatest care. It is the best game upon the subject so far issued. Price........ .40

25458 Authors, finest edition published, in neat cloth covered box with sliding cover.
Price........ .40

Puzzles.

Mystic Square.

TAKE THE FIVE SMALL SQUARES, (TEN PIECES) AND WITH THEM FORM ONE PERFECT SQUARE.

25463 Follow the directions on the engraving and you will be entertained for an entire evening. Each..$0.14 Per dozen..$1.25 Postage..$0.02

25468 The Mystoscope. The Wonder of How Columbus Discovered America. The latest and best puzzle on the market. Directions with each.
Each........ $0.22 Postage........ $0.05

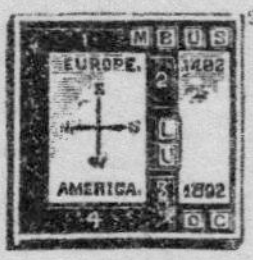

25470 The Columbus Puzzle is a block puzzle of much interest. The problem is to transfer the blocks, which are in order, and spell the word "Columbus" across the top of the board to the bottom of the board and have them spell the same word.
Packed in neat box.
Each........ $0.18
Postage........ .05

25472 The Ferris Wheel Puzzle consists of a neatly made box with a glass top. Inside is a perfect miniature Ferris Wheel revolved by a button underneath. The puzzle is to place a passenger (ball) into each vacant car. Can you do it?
Price each........ $0.20
Price, per doz........ 2.10
Postage, 5c.

25474 Three Blind Mice. See how they run. In the center of the 7x7 inch pasteboard box is a representation of an ordinary three-spring mouse trap. Catch all three mice in this trap in the puzzle or trick; and it is a teaser.
Price, each........ $0.19
Price, per dozen........ 2.00
Postage, 4c.

25476 Columbus Egg. The trick with this egg is to make it lie flat on its side. *It can be done.* A most amusing toy, or it can be used as a novel paper weight.
Price, each........ $0.09
Per dozen........ .75

25478 Columbus Egg Puzzle. One of the cutest and most ingenious little tricks ever devised; made of brass, handsomely nickeled, showing the bust of the great navigator (stamped in the head of each egg). Put up one in a box, with full directions how to make the egg stand on end.
Price, each........ $0.18
Per doz........ 2.00
Postage on either of above eggs, 2 cents each.

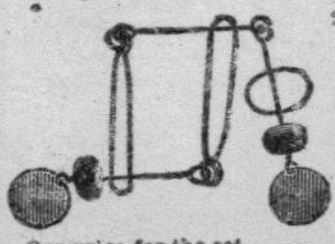

25479 Wire Puzzle. A collection of eight puzzles that are every one good, and from simple to complicated designs. This set with instructions for working is the most complete and in every way the best collection of wire puzzles ever offered.
Our price for the set........ $0.60

All lines of merchandise very generally reduced in price.

Cut-Up Puzzles.

25480 Cut-Up Jumbo Puzzles, consisting of a large colored picture of the celebrated elephant "Jumbo," 12x15 inches, mounted on heavy board and cut up into irregular pieces, put up in a handsome box. Each box contains a complete picture, showing how pieces look when put together.
Each........ $0.15
Per dozen........ 1.50
Postage........ .05

25481 Blown-Up Steamboat Puzzle, same as 25480, only the picture is that of a steamboat.
Each........ .16
Per dozen........ 1.60
Postage........ .05

25482 Bird Slips, or puzzle picture game for the little folks, put up in fancy colored box.
Each........ .18
Postage........ .05

25484 A Sectional Picture Toy of the American Fire Department, lithographed in brilliant colors on heavy cardboard and cut up, making one of the most entertaining sectional puzzle games in the market, forming when put together a complete fire department of five pieces. Packed in wood box, with lithographic label. Weight, 20 oz. Price........ .50

25485 Dissected Map of the United States. This map is engraved in outline, with only the more prominent features and localities, thereby presenting to the child no more than can be easily remembered. On the back are illustrations of the prominent industries, products and animals of the country, thus combining with the map an interesting dissected picture, the whole forming a complete object lesson of the geography and natural history of the United States. Size, when put together, 22x15. Packed in pasteboard box. Weight, 1½ lbs. Price........ .45

25486 Dissected Map of the United States, same size as preceding, but mounted on wood and dissected in entire states, allowing a practical comparison of the different states. Packed in wooden box. Weight, 1½ lbs. Price........ .75

Occupations.

25494 Spelling Boards. These boards are 13¼ in. long by 9 in. wide, and have 56 lettered hardwood blocks, neatly made and highly ornamented. Instructive and amusing; letters cannot come out or be placed in position upside down. Weight, 1¾ pounds. Price, each $0.75

25496 Picture sewing. This game or occupation consists of a box containing a collection of cards, having traced on them outlines of various objects, which are to be sewed in colored threads. Just the thing for little girls. Box contains cards of colored threads, a perforating needle, pad, pictures, etc. Sure to Please. Price........ $0.25

25498 Children's World's Fair Instructor, put up in handsome lithographed envelope, and consisting of a folding board 12x19 inches, showing a handsomely painted diagram of outline of Exposition grounds, with over 100 slots cut and numbered to receive the embossed, ivory finished pieces, representing the buildings, etc., also numbered, and to be placed in their correct positions, repoducing, in miniature, the entire Columbian Exposition in a comprehensive form. Price, $0.20. Price per dozen, $1.75. Extra by mail........ .15

25499 Drawing Teacher. A neat box containing 20 different designs; perforated on heavy paper with full instructions. Each........ $0.25
Postage........ .06

Our claim that this Catalogue opens the large markets to you is no idle boast. Where else can you find so much? As a genuine guide to prices it has no equal.

ORGANS AND PIANOS.

We Ship on Trial to Any Part of the United States. Read Our Offer.

ORGANS.

Our Windsor Organs are made in one of the largest and best equipped factories in this country, and we guarantee them to be equal in every way to the very best. Thousands have been sold, and with one or two exceptions every instrument has given perfect satisfaction. The actions are perfect. The cases are made of solid black walnut or oak, finely finished, and handsome in design. Our prices are lower than offered by any other house in the world for instruments of equal value. The reason why we can afford to make such low prices is because we do a strictly cash business and employ no agents. We deal directly with the consumers, and they get the benefit of the agent's profits. We warrant our Organs and Pianos for five years; also allow every purchaser the privilege of giving them a thorough trial, so there is no chance whatever for deception. This is our offer:

How We Ship Organs and Pianos on Trial.

We will ship any Windsor Organ or Piano on trial to any railroad shipping point in the United States, subject to the following conditions. Upon receipt of order we will ship the instrument to our own address, send a sight draft with bill of lading attached, to your bankers. When the shipment arrives at destination the purchaser will be required to deposit with the bank the price of the instrument, but with the understanding that the money is to be held fifteen (15) days. During this time the instrument may be given a thorough trial at your home, freight charges one way to be paid by purchaser. If you find that it is not in every way satisfactory you can return it to station agent at any time before the expiration of time specified and by obtaining bill of lading showing that the instrument has been returned to us in good order, and presenting same at bank, the entire amount deposited will be refunded.

We advise all purchasers, however, to send in full amount of money with order. By so doing you not only avoid all unnecessary trouble, but get the benefit of our cash discounts, (pianos excepted) which otherwise we do not allow (see rule 4, page 2); besides, when cash accompanies order we allow a trial of 30 days, and if not satisfactory, may be returned at our expense and money will be refunded.

Description of the Windsor Organs.

We use but one style of works, having adopted the standard 6 ten stop double coupler actions. They have two full sets of reeds with double riveted tongues, the celebrated Wilcox divided coupler (the best in the world) operated by two stops, heavy mouse proof bellows, two swells, "knee" and "grand organ." They have ten stops, viz: Diapason, melodia, dulcet, echo, principal forte, celeste, cremona, piano bass coupler and treble coupler. The tone is smooth, clear and powerful and cannot be excelled at any price. This organ will last just as long and produce equally as good music as any $200 organ; in fact our manufacturers state that they cannot make us anything better as far as works are concerned. We shall handle the Windsor Organ in nine styles, as shown and described below. Every instrument guaranteed exactly as represented or may be returned at our expense. We box them and put on board of cars free of charge.

Solid Black Walnut Case, entirely new and modern in design, hand rubbed and finished in oil. Symmetrically proportioned top, with elaborately carved turnings, large French Plate bevel edged mirror in centre, adjustable music desk, with pocket underneath, fancy carved brackets and scroll work throughout. Knee swell and grand organ, pedals covered with brussels carpet. Five octaves compass, divided as follows; two octaves diapason, three melodia, three octaves celeste, two octaves principal. Dimensions: height; 6 feet 9 inches; length, 4 feet 3½ inches; depth, 2 feet. This is one of the most elaborate and finely finished cases ever put on the market.

25500 Windsor Organ, 5 octaves (Style 1) as described above, including stool and instruction book; boxed for shipping. Each...........$60.00

The Windsor Organ. Style 2 and 3.
5 octaves, $56.00; 6 octaves, $63.00.

Solid black Walnut, hand rubbed, finest oil finish, extended curtain top, elaborately carved richly ornamented scroll and pressed work, highly polished, lower part of center panel is of red silk plush, upper part contains a French bevel plate mirror and adjustable music rack, beaded front and end panels, lamp stands, handles, two swells, "knee" and "full organ," keyboard five octaves compass divided as follows: Two octaves diapason, three octaves melodia, two octaves principal, three octaves celeste reeds. Height,6½ feet; depth, 2 feet; length, 4 feet. Pedals covered with Brussels carpet, brass heel plates. This is an entirely new case, solid in construction, elegant in design and finish; in fact nothing is wanting to make it perfect in every respect.

25501 Windsor Organ, Style 2, as described above, including instructor and stool (No.26038) boxed for shipping..........$56.00 Weight,boxed, about 400 pounds.

25502 Windsor Organ, Style 3, same style and finish as 25501, with 6 octaves. Weight, boxed, about 450 pounds. Price, including stool and instruction book, each.............$63.00

The Windsor Organ, Style 6.

This case (style 6) is entirely new in design, handsome in appearance and though moderate in price, is one of our best styles. They are made of solid black walnut; height 61 inches, length 48 inches, depth 23 inches, hand rubbed, extension top, scroll work of fancy design, elaborately carved panels at top and sides; large plate glass mirror in center panel; adjustable music desk, lamp stands, castors, nickel plated pedal frames, best brussels carpet on pedals. The keyboard is five octaves; compass two full set reeds, divided as follows: two octaves diapason, three melodia, two principal, three celeste.

25504 Windsor Organ (style 6), as described above, including stool and instruction book, boxed for shipping. Each..........$45.00 Weight boxed,about 400 lbs.

25504½ Windsor Organ, same style as 25504, made of oak, including stool and instruction book, boxed for shipping. Each..............$47.00

25505 Windsor Organ, same style case as 25504 Walnut woodwork, with six octaves, including Stool and Instruction Book, boxed. Each...........$55.00 Weight, boxed, about 450 lbs.

25505½ Windsor Organ, same style as 25504 Oak woodwork, with six octaves, including Stool and Instruction Book, boxed. Each.............$57.00 Weight, boxed, about 450 lbs.

The Windsor Organ, Chapel, Style 7.

Description of Style 7.
Solid black walnut case; hand rubbed, oil finished, height 4 feet 8 inches, length 3 feet 9 inches, depth 21 inches; double end tops, lamp stands, handles, two swells, knee and full organ, pedals covered with Brussels carpet, keyboard, five octaves compass divided as follows: Two octaves diapason, three octaves melodia, two octaves principal, three octaves celeste. This case is intended more particularly for church and school purposes, the back being finished so that it can be turned toward an audience. It will prove a very acceptable and low priced case for any and all uses.

25506 Windsor Organ: style 7, as described above, including instruction book and stool (26038), boxed for shipping. Each..........$37.00 Weight, boxed, about 300 pounds.

Concertinas—Continued.

25570 Concertina; fine rosewood case with elaborate German silver inlayings, leather bound bellows, 20 keys, broad reeds, heavy tone, finely finished. Wt. boxed, 8 lbs
Price, each.. $6.00

English Concertinas.

25576 Anglo-German pattern, made of mahogany 20 keys, leather bound bellows, 5 folds, in wood case.
Each $10.00
Weight, boxed, 8 lbs.

25578 Anglo-German pattern, mahogany, steel reeds, 30 keys, leather bound bellows, 5 folds, in wood case
Each $12.00
Weight boxed, 7 lbs.

HARMONICAS.
Our "Windsor."

25585 Our improved Windsor Harmonicas are made expressly for us by one of the first makers of Europe, under our own name and brand, and after giving them a thorough trial, we feel justified in pronouncing them the best Richters ever put on the market. They have ten single holes, 20 reeds, extra heavy nickel plated reed plates, extension ends, nickel covers. Especial attention has been given to tuning and we guarantee every one to be absolutely perfect. Each is stamped with firm name. Each.. $0.20
Per dozen 2.15
Weight, each, 3 oz.
25585½ Set of four of our celebrated Windsor Harmonicas. No. 25585 in neat cloth covered pocket case (see cut). We send assorted keys unless otherwise instructed. Per set....$0.95

25586. The "Golden Lark" Richter Harmonicas, 10 single holes, 20 reeds, nickel plated reed plates, gold gilt, covers, satin finished, perfectly tuned. Each in satin lined plush case. Weight, 4 ounces.
Price, each..$0.40

Per dozen 4.30

25588 The "Golden Lark" Concert Harmonicas, 10 double holes, 40 reeds, nickel plated reed plates, extension ends,gold gilt covers, satin finish, tuned in octaves and absolutely perfect. Each in satin lined plush case.
Price each......... $0.75
Per dozen 8.10
Weight, 5 ounces.

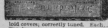

25592 Richter Harmonica, fine quality 10 single holes 20 reeds brass reed plates, celluloid covers; correctly tuned. Each.. $0.35
Per doz....................... 3.75
25593 Concert Harmonica, 10 double holes, 40 reeds, brass reed plates, celluloid covers, absolutely perfect in tone. Each... $0.55 Per doz. 6.00
The seamless celluloid shell into which the harmonica slides, acts as a resonator as well as cover for the instrument, and avoids putting the lips in contact with the brass plates.

Genuine Hohners.

Our prices on this famous line of Harmonicas are lower on a single instrument than your local dealer CAN BUY THEM in gross lots.

25596 Hohner, 10 single holes on one edge. Brass reed plates, nickel covers.
Each......... $0.12
Weight, 3 oz.

25597 10 double holes on one edge double reeds, nickel plated covers.
Each .... $0.29. Weight, 5 ounces.

25598 10 double holes on each edge, double reeds, nickel covers.
Each.............. $0.90
Weight, 7 ounces.

Carl Essbach's.

25600 Carl Essbach's Richter Harmonica, good quality, 10 single holes, 20 reeds, brass reed plates, nickel cover. Each....... $0.10
Per dozen......................... 1.00
Weight, 3 ounces.

25601 Carl Essbach's New French Harp, extra fine quality, pure tone, perfectly tuned; ten single holes, 20 German silver reeds, brass reed plates nickled, nickel covers, extension ends.
Each............ $0.15
Per dozen......................... 1.60
Weight, 3 ounces.

25604— Essbach's Miniature concert harmonica. 10 double holes, 40 reeds, brass reed plate, nickel covers. This harmonica "fills a long felt want," it being a full "concert," but of small size, therefore the tones are easily produced, besides, it can be covered with the hands, same as the Richters
Each............ $0.35
Per dozen......................... 3.75
Weight, 4 ounces.

Koch.

We now carry in stock the celebrated Andreas Koch Harmonicas, and can recommend them for either professionals or amateurs. They are perfectly tuned and easy to blow.

25605— Koch Richter 10 single holes, 20 reeds, brass plates extension ends, nickel covers all keys.
Each............ $0.15
Per dozen......................... 1.60
Weight, 3 ounces.

25606 Koch Double Richter, 10 single holes on each edge, 40 reeds brass plates, extension ends, assorted keys. Price each....... $0.20
Per dozen......................... 2.25
Weight, 6 ounces.

Harmonicas—Continued.

25607 Koch Professional Richter, Organ tone, 16 double holes, 32 reeds tuned in octaves, brass plates, nickel covers, excellent tone; every player should have one.
Each......... $0.35
Per doz. 3.75
Weight, 5 ounces.

25609 Koch Concert Harmonica, top double holes, 40 reeds, brass plates, nickel covers, extension ends, every one a gem. Price, each....... $0.40
Per doz. 4.35
Weight, 6 ounces.

25610 Koch Double Concert Harmonica, ten double holes on each edge 80 reeds, brass plates, nickel covers.
Price, each............. $0.80

Ludwig's.

25611 The Genuine Gebr. Ludwig Harmonica, Richter pattern, 10 single holes, brass, reed plates, nickeled single holes, nickel covers. extension ends, assorted keys. Weight, 3 ounces. Each.........$0.12
Per doz......................... 1 30

Miscellaneous Makes.

25617 "Jim Dandy" Richter Harmonica, 10 single holes, brass plates, 20 reeds, nickel covers, best harmonica in the market for the money.
Each.........$0.05. Per dozen $0.50
Weight 3 ounces.

25618 Original "Emmet" Richter, good quality, 10 single holes, 20 reeds, nickel covers, bone mouthpiece, extension ends, assorted keys. Each. $0.15
Weight, 3 ounces   Per dozen.................. 1.60

25619 Meinel's Concert Richter, 10 double holes, 20 reeds full concert size, brass plates, extension ends, loud tone. Each, $0.20. Per dozen...... $2.70
Weight, 4 ounces.

25620 Meinel's double concert Richter, 10 double holes on each edge, 40 reeds, nickel covers, assorted keys. Each........$0 30. Per dozen...$3.25
Weight, 6 ounces.

Harmonicas——Continued.

25622 The Philharmonic Concert Harmonica, excellent quality, rich tone, 10 double holes on each edge, 80 reeds, brass plates one side is tuned in octave, the other side in duet, perfectly tuned. Each $0.75
Weight, 6 ounces.

25623 One set of four "This" Harmonicas in pocket case. Each has 10 single holes on one edge, brass reed plates, German silver covers, each in different key. Per set $0.75
Weight, 12 ounces.

25624 The Philharmonic Duet Set of Harmonicas, concert size, each has 10 double holes, 40 reeds, nickel covers, one is tuned in octave, one in duet, perfectly tuned both in same key, produces excellent music when played together.
Price per set $0.80
Weight, 7 ounces.

Bell Harmonicas.

25626—Bell Harmonica, Richter, German silver, 10 holes, 1 bell. Each $0.35
Weight, 4 oz.

25628 Bell Harmonica, Richter, German silver, 10 holes, 2 bells ..$0.58
Weight, 5 ounces.

25629 Bell Harmonica, Concert, German silver, 10 holes, double, 1 bell $0.65
Weight, 6 ounces.

25631 Bell Harmonica, Concert, German silver, 10 holes, double, 2 bells $0.85
Weight, 7 ounces.

HARMONICA POCKET CASES.

25632 Pocket Case for Richter Harmonicas, made of kid, nickel plated frame at top, with clasp.
Each $0.10
25633 Pocket Case for Concert Harmonica, same style as 25632.
Price, each $0.15

Harmonica Holders.

25635 Excelsior Harmonica Holders (see cut) are constructed on an entirely new principle, and are giving excellent satisfaction. They consist of a wood breast-plate, to which are attached heavy spring wire shoulder pieces. Harmonica of any size is held firmly in proper position for playing by two springs, thus leaving the hands free to play accompaniment on any other instrument. They are quickly and easily adjusted. Price each $0.50. Weight, 8 ounces.
25636 Harmonica Holder, consists of heavy metal tube, painted and varnished, with opening at top for either Richter or Concert harmonicas; also opening at one end, and is used to regulate the tone and produce "tremolo" vibrations.
Each ...$0.10. Per dozen ...$1.00. Weight, 6 ounces.

Violin Cases, "C.S.B."

25640 Wood, black, half lined with flannel, remainder with paper. Each $1.00
Weight, boxed, 8 pounds.
25641 Wood, black, with lock, half lined with flannel, remainder with paper. Each 1.25
Weight, boxed, 8 pounds.
25642 Wood, black, with lock and clasps, lined throughout with felt or flannel. Each 2.00
Weight, boxed, 8 pounds.
25643 Papier Mache, French, violin shape, lined with baize, lock, handle and clasps. Each ...2.50
Weight, boxed, 10 pounds.
25645 Genuine leather covered, black, finely finished, lined throughout with velvet, leather handles, nickel clasps. Each 4.50
Weight, boxed, 8 ̄ ̄

Flutes.

(Instruction book free with each flute.)

No music dealer will warrant flutes, clarinets, piccolos or fifes not to check or crack. This often happens by change of temperature. Great care should be exercised in use of such instruments, not to suddenly expose to heat when they have been in cold air. They are always examined and leave in perfect shape. We will not be responsible for them after they arrive at destination.

25657

25650 D, 1 key, with tuning slide, German silver trimmed, in paper case $1.75
Weight, 12 ounces.
25651 D, 4 keyed, Grenadillo, German silver rings and slide, in paper case 3.00
Weight, 13 ounces.
25652 D, 6 keyed, Grenadillo, German silver rings and slide, cork joints, paper case 4.00
Weight, 14 ounces.
25654 D, 8 keyed, Grenadillo, German silver rings and slide, cork joints, in leather case 7.00
Weight, 26 ounces.
25655 D, made of Grenadillo with 10 German silver keys and trimmings, slide cork joints, each in fine morocco case. Price 10.00
Weight, 26 ounces.
25657 D, 10 keyed, Grenadillo, ivory head, with slide, in fine case, like illustration 17.75
Weight, 25 ounces.

Piccolos.

Each in Paper Case.
(Instruction Book 45c.)
Weight, 6 to 8 ounces.

25662 Each.

25660 E flat or D, 1 key, cocoa, German silver tipped $0.60
25661 E flat or D, 4 keys, cocoa, German silver tipped and tuning slides. 1.00
25662 E flat or D, 4 keys, cocoa, German silver tipped and tuning slide. 2.00
25663 E flat or D, 6 keys, cocoa, German silver tipped and tuning slides 2.50

25665

25665 E flat or D, 6 keys, Grenadillo, ivory head, tuning slide, cork joints, German silver tipped ..$5.00

Flageolets.

EACH IN PASTEBOARD BOX.

25671

25667 Flageolet, Key of D, made of Grenadillo wood, German silver trimmed, one key. Each ..$1.75
25668 Flageolet, Key of Bb, Grenadillo wood, German silver trimmed, one key. Each 2.10
Weight, 10 ounces.
25669 Flageolet, Key of D, Grenadillo wood, 4 keys, German silver trimmings. Each 2.50
Weight, 10 ounces.
25671 Flageolet, Key of D, Grenadillo wood, German silver trimmings, 6 keys. Each 2.75
Weight, 10 ounces.

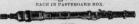

25675 Nightingale Flageolets (see cut), made of brass, nickel plated, finely finished, correctly tuned, made in following keys: Bb, C, D, Eb, F and G. Price, each, any key......................$0.25
Weight, 6 ounces.

Piccolo Flageolets.

This combination consists of a Piccolo with an extra Flageolet head and can be used as either instrument.

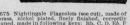

25678 Piccolo Flageolet, key of D, made of boxwood, German silver trimmed, 1 key.
Price, each $2.00
25679 Piccolo Flageolet, key of D, made of Grenadillo wood, German silver trimmed, 6 keys.
Each 3.00
Weight, 12 oz.

Flute and Piccolo Cases.

25681-85.

25681 Flute Case, Morocco covered, velvet lined, for 4 or 6 keyed flute. Each $2.00
Weight, 16 oz.
25685 Flute Case. Morocco covered, velvet lined, for 8 to 10 key flute. Each 2.50
Weight, 16 oz.
25695 Piccolo Cases. Morocco covered, velvet lined, for Eb or D Piccolo. Each 1.40
Weight, 10 oz.

Fifes.

(Instruction Book, 15c.)
Fifes are made in key of Bb and C only.

25687

25687 Fifes made of Maple, brass tipped. Each ..$0.20
Weight, 6 ounces.
25688 Fifes made of Cocoa, German silver tipped. Each 40
Weight, 6 ounces.
25689 Fifes made of Ebony, German silver ferrules. Each 60
Weight, 8 ounces.
25690 Fifes (Crosby) made of Ebony or Cocoa, long model, U.S. Regulation pattern, long German silver ferrules. Each 85
Weight, 8 ounces.
25691 Fifes made of German silver, raised holes. Each $1.25
Weight, 10 ounces.

Flute, Fife and Piccolo Mouthpieces.

25693-95

25693 Mouthpieces for Flute, composition, with adjustable screws $0.20
25694 Mouthpieces for Fife 12
25695 Mouthpieces for Piccolo $0.12
Weight, 3 ounces.

Clarionets.

Clarionets are made in the following keys only; A, Bb, C, D, and Eb. We give an instruction book free with instrument. Always mention what key is desired.

25705 Clarionet made of Grenadillo wood, black, with 13 German silver keys, German silver trimmings, any key.
Price, each $13.00
Weight, 20 oz.
25707 Clarionet, Grenadillo wood, black, Albert system, with 13 German silver keys, 2 patent rings, German silver trimmings in any key. Price, each $15.00
Weight, 22 oz.
25709 Clarionet, Grenadillo, black, Albert system, with 13 German silver keys (extra Bb and C sharp, two rings, German silver trimmings, any key.
Price, each $18.00
Weight, 21 oz.
25710 Clarionet, Albert system, made by Buffet, Crampon & Co., Paris, Grenadillo wood, 13 German silver keys, 2 rings with trill keys, each has 2 mouthpieces. Price, each $35.00

25705 25707 25709
Weight, each, 1 ounce.
Give key of clarionet for which reed is wanted.
25711 "Martin" Brand, good quality, any key. Each, $0.05. Per dozen $0.50
25712 "Le Fin" Brand superfine quality, any key. Each, $0.10. Per dozen 1.00
25713 "Artists" Brand, the best brand in the market, made expressly for soloists. Each 15
Per doz. 1.50

Clarionet Reeds.

Clarionet Reed Trimmers.

25713½ Flach's patent. Clarionet Reed Trimmer and Regulator (see cut) is a new invention, and clarionet players will see at once that it is not only useful, but economical. By its use the annoyance of broken and imperfect reeds is avoided; besides, a reed can be made to last a long time. They are made entirely of metal, fitted with knife of best quality; also has the steel file on back; can be carried in vest pocket. Price, in neat case, each..$1.75
Weight, 3 ounces.

Clarionet Reed Case.

25714 Clarionet Pocket Reed Case, leather covered, holds six reeds. Each........................$1.00
Weight, 5 ounces.

Clarionet Cases.

25716

25715 Leather case, lined, with handle strap. Give key of clarionet.
Each........................$2.00
Weight, 9 oz.
25716 Clarionet Case (see cut), leather covered lined with flannel, handle, hooks and lock; for set of three clarionets.
Each........................$3.50
Weight, 4 lbs.

Clarionet Music Racks.

25718

Always state key of instrument for which rack is wanted.
25718 German Silver, with adjustable ring.
Each........................$1.00
Weight, 4 oz.

Clarionet Mouthpieces.

Weight, 4 ounces. Give key of Clarionet.

Each.
25720 Cocoa or Ebony, without reed holder, any key........................$0.45
25721 Cocoa or Ebony, with German Silver reed holder, any key........................ .70

Clarionet Mouthpiece Caps.

Weight, each, 3 ounces.
25726 Clarionet Mouthpiece Cap or Protector, made of cocoa. Each........................$0.35
25727 Clarionet Mouthpiece Cap, nickel plated. Each........................ .45
Give key of Clarionet.

Music Boxes.

Cannot send through the mail, neither will we send them C. O. D. subject to examination, as they are delicately constructed, and we cannot afford to take the responsibility of having inexperienced parties handle them.

We now import our entire line of music boxes, buying of the leading manufacturers of Switzerland, and a careful inspection of description and prices given below will convince the most skeptical that we are headquarters for this line of goods.

25730.

25731.

25730 Round Nickel Case, 2¾ inches in diameter, decorated top and bottom, 18 notes, one air, operated by turning small crank on top. Weight 10 ounces.
Price, each $0.50
25731 Square Wood Case, size, 4x3½ inches, decorated top, 18 teeth, operated with crank, plays two airs. Weight, 16 ounces.
Price, each $0.80

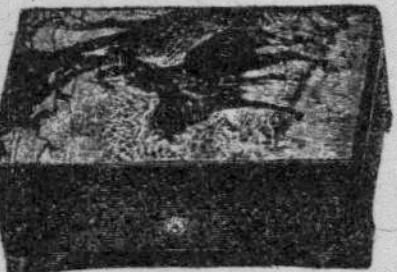

25732 Highly Polished Mahogany Case, size, 4¾x3½x2⅜, inteior glass cover to protect works, covers decorated with pretty chromos, self-acting cylinder, 2½ inches long with mainspring, winds like a watch, with attached key, has 36 notes, plays 2 airs. Weight, 16 ounces.
Each........................$3.00

25736 Imitation Rosewood case, highly polished, size, 12x6½x4½, covers richly decorated, bevel edges and white lines inlaid in top, also on front of box, interior glass cover; spring lever movement, starting and "change" levers, 3⅜ in. cylinder, plays 6 airs
Weight, boxed, 8 lbs.
Price........................$9.25

Music Boxes—Continued.

25740 Imitation rosewood Case, size, 18x8½x5½ in. 7½ in. cylinder, cylinder tune indicator, zither attachment, Plays 10 airs. Weight, boxed, 25 lbs.
Each..$18.00

25741 Imitation Rosewood, same style as 25740, size, 20½x9x5⅝, with 9¼ inch cylinder tune indicater, zither attachment; plays 12 airs. Weight, boxed, 30 lbs. Each........................27.00
25742 Imitation Rosewood, same style as 25740, 23¼x9½x9, 13 inch cylinder, plays 10 airs, has zither attachment, speed regulator, tune indicator; a very fine instrument. Each........................31.50

Mandolins.

Weight, boxed, 8 pounds.

This instrument is becoming very popular, our sales having more than doubled during the last year. We would state for the benefit of those desirous of learning to play the mandolin, that they are "tuned" same as the violin, and fingering is the same, so that one who can play a violin may easily learn to manage the mandolin. Instruction book free with each instrument.

Each.
25745 Mandolin, American, full size, maple and oak ribs. Highly polished plain front, rosewood finger board, brass patent head, correct scale, finely finished, warranted for one year not to split or warp. *The best mandolin ever put on the market for the money.* Price........................$5.50
25746 Our Conservatory Mandolin, full size, American made, mahogany and maple ribs, rosewood band, all French polished orange front, ebony finger board, position dots, inlaid striking piece, rosewood tipped, fully warranted. Nickel plated patent head. Price........................ 9.00
25747 Our Professional Concert Mandolin, American manufacture, rosewood and mahogany ribs, white inlaid edges, rosewood bound inlaid soundhole, ebony or rosewood finger board, position dots, full French polished, Italian patent head, warranted not to split or warp........................13.00
25748 The Joseph Bohmann American Mandolin, full concert size, 19 maple ribs, highly polished, rosewood finger board, pearl position dots, patent tail piece, inlaying around sound hole, patent head, scale guaranteed absolutely perfect. Warranted one year. Each........................15.00
25748½ Our "Windsor" Mandolin, American made, full size, rosewood, 26 ribs, white inlaid stripes between ribs, highly polished, orange front, edge finely inlaid with white and colored woods, tortoise shell striking piece, cedar neck, full plate patent heads, inlaid ebony finger board. A beautiful and excellent toned instrument.
Each........................25.00

Mandolin Pick.

25749 Mandolin Picks, made of celluloid imitation tortoise shell, oval pattern, *very best quality.*
Each............$0.04
Per dozen........ .40

Mandolin Cases.

25750 Mandolin Case, made of brown canvas, leather bound, flannel lined strap fastenings.
Each..............$1.50
25751 Mandolin Case, wood, black, lined with flannel, lock, handle and spring clasps.
Each........................$2.25
25752 Mandolin Case, leather covered, russet or black color, hand sewed, flannel lined, fine quality. Each........................ 5.50
25754 Mandolin Bags, made of green cloth, Each........................ .75
25755 Mandolin Bags, canvas, fleece lined patent fasteners. Each........................ .90
25756 Mandolin Bags, made of silk plush, extra fine quality. Each........................ 4.50

Violoncellos.

Instruction book and bow free with each Violoncello. Each one in case ready for shipping. Weight, boxed, 43 pounds.
25763 Violoncello, German make, reddish brown color, fair quality, *peg head.* Each........................$8.50
25764 Violoncello, better quality, dark red, good model, with *patent head.* Each........................$10.00
25766 Violoncello, light red color, polished, fine model, good tone, inlaid edges, brass plates, patent heads. Each........................$12.50
25769 Stradivarius model, dark brown color, inlaid edges, patent head, fine quality, excellent tone.
Each........................$18.00

Violoncello Patent Heads.

Weight, per set, 11 ounces.
25775 Iron plates and screws, maple pegs with pearl dot inlaid in head........................$1.75
25776 Brass plates, iron screws, maple pegs with pearl dot inlaid in head........................ 2.00

Double Bass Viols--Patent Heads.

Instruction book and bow free with each. Weight, boxed, about 125 pounds.
25779 Double Bass, half size, dark red, shaded and polished, 3 strings, good quality. Each ..$19.50
25780 Double Bass, same size and style as No. 25779, with 4 strings. Each........................21.00
25781 Double Bass, three-quarter size, 3 strings, dark red shaded and polished, good quality. Each 22.00
25782 Double Bass, same size and style as No. 25781, with 4 strings. Each........................24.00
25783 Double Bass, half size, 3 strings, dark red, polished, inlaid edges, fine quality. Each.... 30.00
25784 Double Bass, three-quarter size, 4 strings, dark red, polished, inlaid edges, fine quality. Each........................35.00
25785 Double Bass, three-quarter size, 4 strings, dark red, polished, inlaid edges, swelled back, extra fine quality. Each........................45.00

Double Bass Bows.

25787 Maple, red painted, light wood frog.
Each........................$1.35
Weight, 10 ounces.
25788 Red wood, natural color, ebony frog, good quality. Each........................ 2.50
Weight, 12 ounces.
25789 Pernambuco wood, natural color, ebony frog, German silver lined, inlaid eye (professional model). Each........................ 4.75
Weight, 12 ounces.

Double Bass Bridges.

25795 Maple, plain scroll, good quality, for half size bass. Weight, 3 ounces. Each............$0.45
25796 Maple, plain scroll, good quality, for three-quarter size bass. Weight, 4 oz. Each.......... .55
Instruction book free with each guitar.

GUITARS.

We handle American made Guitars exclusively, and select the instruments carefully, with the view of selling only those that we can thoroughly recommend. Guitars that are "hawked" about the country at ridiculously low prices are made simply to sell cheap, without any care being given to their musical properties. We guarantee every Guitar in our stock to be absolutely perfect in scale and to have a smooth, musical tone. They are made in the largest factories in this country, the workmanship is the very best, and we warrant each instrument regardless of price (for one year), not to crack or warp. We recommend gut and silk wound strings under all circumstances. If steel strings are to be used, however, we suggest that a tailpiece be put on the instrument, otherwise the sounding board is liable to "spring" at the bridge and in time injure the guitar.

25800 OUR LEADER, American made Guitar, standard size, back and sides made of maple and handsomely finished in imitation of either rosewood, mahogany or oak, all highly polished, yellow top, imitation ebony finger board, position dots; patent head, raised frets, *warranted for one year.* Weight, boxed, about 15 lbs.
Price........................$4.50
25801 OUR KENWOOD, American made, standard size, back and sides made of "quarter-sawed", oak, highly polished, finely finished cedar sounding board, cedar neck, raised frets, patent head, excellent tone and warranted not to split or warp. Weight, boxed, 15 lbs.
Price, each........................ 6.00
25803 OUR COLUMBIAN, STANDARD American made guitar, standard size, solid MAHOGANY back and sides, edges inlaid with white celluloid, highly polished rosewood finger board, correctly fretted, cedar neck, patent heads, manufactured expressly for us and warranted not to split or warp. Weight, boxed, about 15 lbs.
Price, each........................ 9.00

Guitars—Continued.

25804 Our Columbian "CONCERT" American Guitar, same style and description as No 25803. Concert size, rich tone. Weight, boxed, about 18 lbs. Price, each.............................$11.00

25804½ Our Columbian GRAND CONCERT American Guitar, same style as 25803. GRAND CONCERT size. A superb instrument. Weight, boxed, about 20 lbs. Price, each...........13.00

25805 Our "WINDSOR" American made, Conservatory Guitar, solid rosewood back and sides, yellow cedar top, cedar neck, ebony finger board, inlaid stripe in back, standard size, finely polished, and *fully warranted in every respect.* Weight, boxed, 15 lbs. Each...................12.00

25806 Our WINDSOR CONCERT Guitar, American made, same description as 25805, only they are the large or concert size, each is absolutely perfect in every respect, and warranted not to split or warp. Weight, boxed, 15 lbs. Price each....14.00 NOTE.—The "Windsor" Guitars are manufactured expressly for us in one of the very best factories in the country, and we can safely say they are *the best* instrument ever offered for the money. The name Montgomery Ward & Co.'s "Windsor" is burned on inside of each.

25807 WASHBURN American Guitar, solid rosewood body, mahogany or cedar neck, patent head, ebony finger board, warranted not to split or warp, standard size. Weight, boxed, 15 lbs. Each........................$22.00

25808 WASHBURN American Guitar, of solid rosewood body, mahogany or cedar neck, ebony finger board, warranted not to warp or split. Concert size. Weight, boxed, 15 lbs. Each...26.00

Capo D'Astros.

NOTE.—The Capo D'Astro is used to clamp on guitar finger board at first fret to facilitate playing in flat keys.

25809

25809 Capo D'Astro, nickel plated, cork lined, with adjusting screw, fit any guitar. Each.....$0.20 Weight, 3 ounces.

25809½ The Patent "Lightning" Capo D'Astro, metal frame, nickel plated, cork lined cap, heavy spring quickly adjusted. Weight, 3 ounces. Each............$0.35

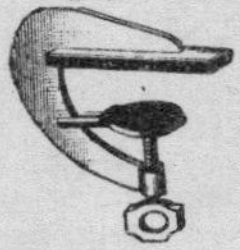

25810 Capo D'Astros, brass with cork lined string cap and adjusting screw, like cut. Weight, 3 oz. Each............$0.40

25811 Capo D'Astros, same as above, nickel plated. Weight, 3 oz. Each............$0.50

Guitar Tail Pieces.

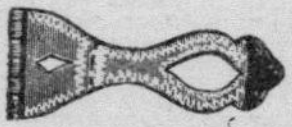

25813 Guitar Tail Pieces, made of Celluloid. Each............$0.50

25814 Guitar Tail Pieces, made of brass, nickel plated (see cut). Weight, 5 oz. Each............$0.75

NOTE.—If steel strings are to be used on a guitar it is essential to the tone and durability of the instrument that they should be attached to a tail piece.

Guitar Cases.

Each.

25815 Brown canvas, leather bound, with opening in end for standard size guitar. Weight 5½ lbs.............$1.75

25816 Brown canvas, same as above, for concert size guitar. Weight, 5¼ lbs...............2.00

25817 Wood, half lined, with handle and hooks, for standard size guitar. Weight, boxed, 18 lbs...1.90

25818 Wood, half lined, with lock, handle and hooks, for standard size guitar. Weight, boxed, 18 lbs.............2.00

25819 Wood, full lined, with handle and spring clasp, for concert size guitar. Weight, boxed, 20 lbs.............2.85

25822 Leather, russet color, hand sewed, finely embossed, full lined, opening in end for standard size. Weight, boxed, 20 lbs. Each......5.25

25823 Leather, russet color, same style as No. 25822, for concert size. Guitars, each.......5.75

Guitar Bags.

25824 Green Felt, for either standard or concert size guitars. Weight, 9 oz...............1.00 *Give size of guitar.*

Guitar and Banjo Frets.

25826 Guitar or Banjo Frets, brass, per set of 18.$0.20 **25827** Guitar or Banjo Frets, German silver, per set of 18...............30 Weight, per set, 3 oz. NOTE.—We do not break sets. 16—6th

Banjos.

(Weight of banjos boxed, 18 lbs.) Instruction book free with banjo.

25828 Maple Shell, 10 inch, imitation cherry, sheepskin head, four brass brackets, marked frets. Each............$1.75

25829 Nickel shell, 10 inches in diameter, wood lined, imitation cherry neck, marked frets, calfskin head, 7 brass brackets. Each............$2.75

25831 Nickel shell, 11 inches in diameter, wood lined, highly polished birch neck, imitation ebony finger board, raised frets, inlaid positions dots, celluloid pegs, 21 nickel brackets, calfskin head. Each............$4.50

25832 Nickel shell, 11 inches in diameter, wood lined grooved hoop, 24 nickel brackets, French polished birch neck, imitation ebony finger board, inlaid position dots, wired edge, celluloid pegs, patent tail piece, calfskin head. Each............$5.50

25834 German silver shell, 11 inches in diameter, wood lined, both edges wired, grooved hoop, 24 nickel brackets, French polished birch neck, ebony veneered finger board, fancy inlaid position dots, handsome scroll, elaborately inlaid with pearl, patent pegs No. 26212, an extra fine instrument. Each............9.00

25836 German silvered shell, 11 inches in diameter, wood lined, both edges wired, corrugated hoop, 26 nickel brackets, French polished neck, full ebony finger board, extending over scroll highly polished, fancy pearl inlaid position dots, patent pegs No. 26212, excellent tone, fine calfskin head, a perfect banjo every way. Each............12.00

25837 Professional banjo, Steward model, 12 inches in diameter, nickel plated German silver shell, both edges wired, wood lined, finely polished birch neck, extra heavy strainer hoop, ebony finger board, raised frets, 29 nickel brackets, neck ornamented with pearl, calfskin head. Each............13.00

25841 Our Windsor Professional Banjo, 11 inches in diameter, polished German silver shell, 30 nickel brackets, wood lined, both edges wired, grooved corrugated hoop, patent tail piece, raised frets, French polished walnut neck, full ebony finger board extending over head piece, elaborately inlaid with pearl, back of head piece covered with ebony, German silver name plate, patent pegs, calfskin head; this banjo is a new model made expressly for us, and is one of the most beautiful as well as perfect instruments ever put on the market. Banjos of no better quality are sold daily at double our price. Each............$18.00

Banjo Thimbles.

25846 Banjo Thimbles of German silver. Price, each 5c; per dozen 50c. Weight, each, 1 ounce.

Banjo Cases.

25847 Pasteboard, marbled; weight, boxed, 12 pounds. Each............$0.45

25848 Wood, black, varnished, flannel lined, with lock, handle and hooks, for 11 inch banjo; weight, boxed, 17 lbs.............2.00

25851 Brown canvas, leather bound, with opening in end for 9, 11 or 12 inch banjo; weight, 6 lbs.............1.75

25852 Banjo Case, made of solid leather, flannel lined, hand sewed, fine quality, with opening at end for 11 inch banjo; weight, 7 lbs.............4.50

Banjo Bags.

25854 Green felt, for 9, 10 or 11 inch banjo; weight, 7 ounces............$0.90

25855 Gossamer rubber, for 9, 10 or 11 inch banjo; weight, 9 ounces............1.35

25857 Banjo Wrenches for Brackets, etc., brass. Each.10c **25858** Banjo Wrenches, nickel plated. Weight 2 ounces. Each............$0.20

Zithers.

(Weight, boxed, 12 lbs.)

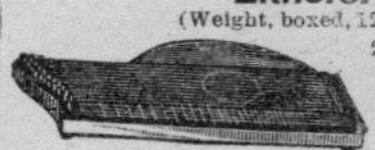

25860-61

25860 Imitation rosewood, full strung, plain head, neatly inlaid, good quality and finish, in paper box............$4.00

25861 Rosewood, full strung, neatly inlaid, plain head finely finished, in paper box.....$7.00

25863 Rosewood, polished, inlaid sound holes and edges, with patent head, in pasteboard case. Each............11.00

Zither Rings.

25865 German Silver, plain, each............$0.03 **25866** Horn, plain, each............05

Zither Strings.

25868 Steel and brass for finger board. Each....$0.05 **25869** Accompaniment and bass, wound on steel wire. Each............07 **25870** Full set, wound on steel wire, weight, per set, 6 oz............1.75 NOTE.—When ordering strings for zither be sure and give number and letter of string wanted.

Zither Cases.

(Weight, boxed, 10 lbs.)

25873 Wood, black varnished, flannel lined, with lock, handle and hooks. Each............$2.00 **25874** Wood, black varnished, velvet lined, with lock, handle and spring clasp............6.50

Zither Tuning Pins.

25875 Steel blued, per dozen............$0.10 **25876** Nickel plated, per dozen............30 Weight, per dozen, 4 ounces.

Columbia Zither.

25878 Columbia Zither, is a new musical instrument similar in style and has the same quality of tone as the ordinary Zither, but by a peculiar system of tuning, and, as it requires no fingering, it is in other words a *simplified Zither.* The bass strings are arranged in groups of four, which produce the necessary chords (played with left hand), and the air is played with right hand on the seventeen treble strings. Directly underneath the strings is a white celluloid scale, giving the letter of each string; also a section of the staff showing the position of different notes. It has in all 34 strings, and is easily learned. Full instructions accompany each; also a collection of good music arranged by letters and figures, so you can play without any knowledge of reading music. They are made in imitation of rosewood, finely finished. Size, 17¾x13 inches. Price, including wrench and picks. Each............$5.00 Weight, boxed, 10 lbs.

Dulcimers.

25879 Dulcimers, American made, imitation rosewood, neatly decorated body, finely finished, chromatic, can be perfectly tuned in all keys; in short, it is the most complete and carefully made instrument of the kind produced. Price, each............$16.00

25880 Dulcimer Beaters, flexible handles, felt covered heads. Per pair............35 Weight, 4 ounces.

Dulcimer or Zither Wire.

25881 English steel, best quality, in ¼ pound coils, per lb............$1.20 **25882** Brass, best quality, on ¼ lb. spool, per lb...1.00 **25894** English steel on spools, 2 yards each, per dozen spools............45 **25885** Brass on spools, 2 yards each, per dozen spools............45 Weight per dozen spools, 5 oz.

Dulcimer Tuning Pins.

25887 Steel blued, with square or oblong heads. Per dozen............$0.12 Weight, per dozen, 6 oz.

Blank Music Books.

26382   6 Staves, 40 pages, cloth back, marbled paper covers, oblong; size 7½x9½ in. Each $0.15
   Weight 7 oz.

26384   8 Staves, 64 pages, same size and style as No. 26382. Each .... .20
   Weight 10 oz.

26385   12 Staves, 84 pages, same size and style as No. 26382. Each .... .30
   Weight 6 oz.

26386   10 Staves, 52 pages, cloth back and sides, full gilt; size 7½x9½ in. Each .... .40
   Weight, 12 oz.

26387   12 Staves, 80 pages, leather back and corners, cloth sides; size 9x11½ in. Each .... .60
   Weight, 22 oz.

26388   14 Staves, 80 pages, leather back and corners, cloth sides; size 10½x13¾ in. Each ... .75

Roller Organ.

The Roller Organs are new and very popular mechanical musical instruments, and our prices are so low that our sales are already very large. The music is produced from reeds (regular organ size) 20 in number, which are perfectly tuned and covered with steel valves. The latter are operated by the music roller which is supplied with pins similar to those on an ordinary music box. The roller is made to revolve with gearing, which also drives the bellows. All the working parts are made of solid metal, easily accessible, and on the whole so well made and durable. They have a tone of good volume. Any child can play them, and we can furnish all kinds of music.

26400   THE GEM ROLLER Organ as described above, in imitation black walnut case, length 16 inches, width, 14 inches, height 9 inches. Price complete, including three rollers.........$4.50

Weight, boxed, 15 pounds.

26401   THE CONCERT ROLLER Organ, larger in size, hence greater volume of tone, handsome black walnut case, glass top finely finished. Length, 19 inches, width, 16 inches, height, 14 inches. Price, complete, including five rollers...$9.00
   Weight, boxed, 30 pounds.

26401

We can furnish extra rollers for above at 23c. each; per dozen, $2.50. Extra by mail, each 7cts. Each roller plays one tune. Music list furnished on application.

Band Instruments.

The German Piston Valve Instruments are made expressly for us by a reliable manufacturer in Germany, and we can recommend them as being equal to any German Piston line on the market. We have also taken the exclusive agency for the celebrated French Piston Valve Instruments manufactured by Jules De Vere & Co., of Paris, which are now being largely used by French military bands. While we do not claim these instruments to be "the best in the world," we can safely say they are equal to the better grades that other dealers are selling at from 20 to 50 per cent. higher than our prices. The fact that we buy direct from manufacturers, and that we are always willing to give our customers all benefits possible, enables us to make prices lower than ever offered before.

On orders of 5 or more band instruments we will be pleased to quote special prices on application.

German Piston Valves.

Water key, music rack and German silver mouthpiece with each instrument.

26410-11

26410   E♭ Cornet, brass. Each........$6.25
26411   B♭ Cornet, nickel plated. Each........$7.75
   Weight, boxed, 6 pounds.

26412   B♭ Cornet, brass, same style as No. 26410. $7.10
26413   B♭ Cornet, nickel plated. Each........ $8.50
   Weight, 7 pounds.

26414   E♭ Alto Valve Trombone, brass.......$8.50
26415   E♭ Alto Valve Trombone, nickel plated. Each........$11.30
   Weight, boxed, 8 pounds.

26414-15—E♭ Alto.

26416   B♭ Tenor Valve Trombone, same style as 26414, brass.......$11.15
26417   B♭ Tenor Valve Trombone, same style as 26414, nickel plated.......13.90
   Weight, boxed, 9 pounds.

Band Instruments—Continued.

26420-21

26420   E♭ Alto, Bell up, brass...............$8.50
26421   E♭ Alto, Bell up, nickel plated........$11.30
   Weight, boxed, 8 pounds.
26422   B♭ Tenor, Bell up, Same style as 26420. Brass.....$11.15

26423   B♭ Tenor, Bell up, same style as 26420, nickel plated...............$13.90
   Weight, boxed, 9 pounds.
26424   B♭ Baritone, Bell up, same style as 26420, brass........$12.90
26425   B♭ Baritone, Bell up, same style as 26420, nickel plated.......$16.50
   Weight, boxed, 10 pounds.
26426   B♭ Bass, Bell up, same style as 26420, brass........$14.60
26427   B♭ Bass, Bell up, same style as 26420, nickel plated........$19.25
   Weight, boxed, 15 pounds.

E♭ Basses.

26428   E♭ Bass, Bell up, brass........$20.25
26429   E♭ Bass, Bell up, nickel plated........ 25.75
   Weight, boxed, 18 pounds.

Improved French Piston Instruments.

With genuine light action valves, manufactured by Jules DeVere & Co., Paris. Water key, music rack and German silver mouthpiece with each instrument.

26431   E♭ Cornet.

26431   E♭ Cornet, brass. Each........$8.00
26432   E♭ Cornet, nickel plated........$9.40
   Weight, boxed, 6 pounds.

26433-34

26433   B♭ Cornet, brass. Each........$8.75
26434   B♭ Cornet, nickel plated. Each........$10.55
   Weight, boxed, 7 lbs.

26435   E♭ Solo Alto, bell front, brass. Each........$11.80
26436   E♭ Solo Alto, bell front, nickel plated. Each........$14.60

26437-38

26437   E♭ Alto, Valve Trombone, bell front. Each........$11.80
26438   E♭ Alto Valve Trombone, bell front, nickel plated. Each........$14.60
   Weight, boxed, 9 pounds.

                                                     Each.
26439   B♭ Tenor Valve Trombone, same style as No. 26437. Brass........$14.00
26440   B♭ Tenor Valve Trombone, same style as No. 26437. Nickel plated........16.80
   Weight, boxed, 10 pounds.
26441   B♭ Baritone Valve Trombone, same style as No. 26437. Brass........16.00
26442   B♭ Baritone Valve Trombone, same style as 26437. Nickel plated........19.80
   Weight, boxed, 11 pounds.

26443 and 26444

26443   B♭ Tenor Slide Trombone, Brass........$9.25
26444   B♭ Tenor Slide Trombone. Weight, boxed, 8 pounds.
Nickel plated........$12.00

26445 and 26446

26445   E♭ Alto, Bell up Brass...............$11.80
26446   E♭ Alto bell up, nickel plated........$14.60
   Weight, boxed, 8 lbs.
26447   B♭ Tenor, bell up. Same style as No. 26445. Brass........$14.00

26448   B♭ Tenor, bell up, same style as No. 26445. Nickel plated........$16.80
   Weight, boxed, 10 pounds.
26449   B♭ Baritone, bell up, same style as No. 26445. Brass...............16.00
26450   B♭ Baritone, bell up, same style as No. 26445. Nickel plated........19.80
   Weight, boxed, 10 pounds.
26451   B♭ Bass, bell up, same style as No. 26445. Brass........18.10
26452   B♭ Bass, bell up, same style as No. 26445. Nickel plated........22.90
   Weight, boxed, 16 pounds.

E♭ Basses.

26453   E♭ Bass, bell up. Brass........$26.40
26454   E♭ Bass, bell up. Nickel plated........ 32.00
   Weight, boxed, 25 pounds.

Solo B♭ Cornets.

26455   B♭ Cornet Brass, long model German silver, light action, French piston valves, water key, German silver mouthpiece, "A" set piece, a superb instrument.
   Price........$9.75
   Weight, boxed, 7 pounds.
26456   B♭ Cornet. Same as above. Nickel plated........$11.50

26458   B♭ Cornet, light action, improved model, French manufacture, extra quality, richly mounted with figured metal. German silver pistons and mouthpiece, with double water keys and "A" set piece. Brass........$20.50
   Weight, boxed, 8 pounds.
26460   B♭ Cornet, same style as No. 26458. Nickel plated. Each........$22.50
26462   B♭ Cornet, same style as No. 26458. Silver plated. Each........$28.50

Solo "C" Cornets.

26463   "C" Cornets, brass, improved model, French manufacture, light action, German silver piston valves, with water key, extra B♭ crook. Each..$9.75
26464   "C" Cornet, same style as No. 26463. Nickel plated. Each........ 11.50

NOTE.—We guarantee our band instruments to be in perfect condition, as each one is thoroughly examined by an experienced workman before being shipped. They also have the name of Montgomery Ward & Co. stamped in the metal.

Cornet Mutes.

26465   Cornet Mutes, nickel plated, used to place in the bell of the instrument to soften the tone for practising, or to produce the "Echo." Each..$1.25
   Weight, 12 ounces.

Band Instrument Mouthpieces.

26466   German silver for E♭ or B♭ Cornets. Each........$0.40
   Weight, 2 ounces.
26467   German silver for altos and tenors. Each...............65
   Weight 2 ounces.
26468   German silver for B♭ baritones, or E♭ basses. Each........ 1.00
   Weight, 3 ounces.
26469   "Professional" silver plated and burnished "Higham" or "Austin" models, for E♭ or B♭ cornets. Each........ .70
   Weight, 2 ounces.
26471   "Professional," same as No. 26469, for altos or tenors. Weight, 3 ounces. Each.. 1.00
26472   Professional, same as No. 26469, for baritone. Weight, 3 ounces. Each........ 1.40
26474   Professional, same as No. 26469, for B♭ or E♭ bass. Each........ 1.65
   Weight, 5 ounces.

Band Instrument Music Racks.

26475

26475   Music Rack, improved pattern, 3 prongs for band instrument, brass. Each...............$0.50
26476   Music Rack, same as number 26475, nickel plated. Each........$0.75
26477   Music Racks for slide Trombones, brass, 75 cents each; nickel plated, each $1.00

Bugles.

Weight, boxed, 6 lbs.

26478   Cavalry Bugles, key of F, brass. Each........$2.25
   Nickel plated. Each........$3.00

26480   Infantry Bugles, key of C, with B♭ crook, brass. Each........$3.00
   Nickel plated. Each........$4.00

26481   Artillery Bugles, key of G, brass. Each........$3.25
   Nickel plated. Each........$4.25

26482   Hunting Horns, brass, one turn. Each........$1.00
26483   Hunting Horns, brass, three turns. Each........$1.50

26483

Cornet Cases.

26484 Wood, black varnished, lined; lock, handle and hooks. Each.......... $1.25

26486 Brown canvas satchel form, leather bound, flannel lined, with shoulder strap. Each.......... $1.50 Weight, 22 ounces.

26488

26488 Pebbled Leather, black satchel form, flannel lined, nickel plated trimmings, with shoulder strap (see cut).......... $1.60 Weight, 25 ounces.

26489 Leather, russet color, satchel form, flannel lined, nickel plated trimmings, with shoulder strap. Weight, 25 ounces.......... 1.75

Vocal and Instrumental Musical Collections.

The most popular musical collections on the market to-day are what are known as "50 cent Folios" and as the demand is almost entirely for this style many of the best copyrights are published in this form. These books are full sheet music size printed from excellent plates on good paper with neat and attractive covers and AT OUR PRICE you can get a collection of from twenty to sixty pieces of good music at the cost of a single piece at retail. We quote below a complete list of the best publications up to date, and as the music ranges from the easiest to the most difficult grades every taste can be supplied. As our space is limited we can give only a brief description of each, but every number will be found a "gem" of its kind and sure to please. If you order these books by mail, allow 12 cents each, extra for postage.

Vocal Music.

26495 American Ballad Collection, 54 modern ballads. Each.......... $0.40

26496 American Song and Chorus Collection, 68 popular copyright songs. Each.......... .40

26497 Artists' Song Folio, a selection of classic concert songs. Each.......... .40

26498 Choice Baritone, and Bass Songs, an excellent collection for low voices. Each.......... .40

26499 Choice English Songs, by modern composers. Each.......... .40

26501 Empress of Song, a good collection of songs of the day. Each.......... .40

26502 Excelsior, baritone and bass folio, late songs by well-known composers. Each.......... .40

26503 Excelsior Song Folio, popular songs and ballads. Each.......... .40

26504 Excelsior Vocal Folio; a collection of standard songs. Each.......... .40

26505 Famous Songs, a superior collection by famous writers. Each.......... .40

26506 Floral Offering, a superior collection of concert and parlor music. Each.......... .40

26507 Folio of Standard Songs, 144 pages of vocal favorites. Each.......... .40

26508 Galaxy of Song, a compilation of standard popular songs. Each.......... .40

26509 German Songs, a late collection of standard songs by the best authors. Each.......... .40

26510 Ideal Folio, 2 vols., collection of songs in the popular style. Each.......... .40

26511 Ideal Gems of English Song, choice English songs and ballads. Each.......... .40

26512 International Song Folio, a volume of popular songs. Each.......... .40

26513 Italian Song Classics, selected from popular modern writers. Each.......... .40

26514 Musical Chatterbox, 2 volumes, new and popular songs and pieces for piano or organ for young folks. Each.......... .40

26515 Magnet, new and standard songs, duets and quartettes. Each.......... .40

26516 Millard's Songs contains many of Harrison Millard's best compositions. Each.......... .40

26517 Monarch of Song, a superb collection of popular music. Each.......... .40

26517½ The "Maywood" Folio, a new collection of popular songs and instrumental music by George Schleiforth, 111 pages, every piece new and good. Price.......... .40

26518 National Classic Song Folio, high-grade standard songs. Each.......... .40

26519 National Song Folio, 4 vols. classic and popular songs of every grade. Each.......... .40

26520 National Waltz-Song Folio, standard waltz-songs, by the best composers. Each.......... .40

26521 Ne Plus Ultra Song and Chorus Collection, 49 well selected songs with choruses. Each. .40

26522 New and Old Favorites, popular compositions in the folk song style. Each.......... .40

26523 Old Homestead Songs. "The dear old songs our mothers' sang." Each.......... .40

26524 Operatic Song Folio, gems from the popular operas. Each.......... .40

26525 Palace Folio, royal songs by popular composers. Each.......... .40

26526 Pearls of Vocal Music, polished gems by popular writers. Each.......... .40

26527 Popular Song Classics, 2 vols. Each.......... .40

26528 Prima Donna Album, brilliant and classic music for a high voice. Each.......... .40

26529 Royal Vocal Folio, a collection of standard medium grade songs. Each.......... .40

26530 Royal Collection of Ballads, contains the latest and best ballads of the day. Each.......... .40

Vocal Music—Continued.

26531 Royal Collection of Songs with Choruses, popular copyrights by famous American composers. Each.......... $0.40

26532 Royal Collection of Songs, standard songs by eminent hands. Each.......... .40

26533 Selected Songs, the Cream of the American and English ballads. Each.......... .40

26534 Singer's Portfolio, 2 vols., selected songs new and very good. Each.......... .40

26535 Song Bouquet, new and popular vocal music. Each.......... .40

26537 Song Casket (Whitney's), selected popular vocal gems. Each.......... .40

26538 Song Diamonds, a collection of charming songs and ballads. Each.......... .40

26539 Song Folio, 4 vols., the best vocal music by American and foreign composers. Each.......... .40

26540 Song Offering, choice songs, ballads and duets. Each.......... .40

26541 Songs of Ireland, melodious echoes from the Green Isle. Each.......... .40

26542 Songs of Scotland (Hitchcock's), gems of Caledonia in song and ballad. Each.......... .40

26543 Songs of Scotland (W. S. & Co.), 78 beautiful songs, popular with all. Each.......... .40

26545 Song Souvenir, a collection of popular vocal gems. Each.......... .40

26546 Song Treasures, charming songs and ballads in the popular vein. Each.......... .40

26548 Standard Song Album, world-famous songs by the most renowned composers. Each.......... .40

26549 Standard Vocal Album, a magnificent collection of popular songs, ballads and duets. Each .40

26551 Superb Songs, the best creations of master song writers. Each.......... .40

26552 Superior Song Collection, choice and new vocal compositions. Each.......... .40

26553 Vocal Casket, excellent songs by excellent writers. Each.......... .40

26555 Vocal Folio, 2 vols., new and standard vocal favorites. Each.......... .40

26556 World's Exposition Vocal Repertoire, a collection worthy the Columbiad. Each.......... .40

Sacred Song Folio.

26558 Album of Sacred Music, popular solos and quartets for church and home. Each.......... $0.40

26559 Excelsior Sacred Folio, new sacred music by the best authors. Each.......... .40

26560 Folio of Sacred Songs, contains standard music for all voices. Each.......... .40

Vocal Duet Folios.

26562 Brainard's Vocal Duet Folio, a fine collection of popular duets. Each.......... $0.40

26563 Excelsior Vocal Duet Folio, selected gems from the best composers. Each.......... .40

26564 Standard Vocal Duets, choice and melodious numbers by popular writers. Each.......... .40

26565 Thirty-two Vocal Duets, a collection of popular duets by the best authors. Each.......... .40

26566 Vocal Duet Folio, 2 vols., well-known compositions, popular in the best sense. Each.......... .40

Comic, Minstrel, College and Topical Songs.

26568 Album of Comic Songs, a collection of popular comic songs. Each.......... $0.40

26569 Bouquet of Comic Songs, made famous by dialect artists at home and abroad. Each.......... .40

26571 Comical, Topical and Motto Songs, contains a large variety of the best songs of the day. Each.......... .40

26572 Comic Casket, collection of late comic songs. Each.......... .40

26573 College Songs (octavo form), 200,000 copies sold. Best book of its kind ever issued. Each .40

26575 Comic Songs, Old and New, including some good sentimental songs with choruses. Each.......... .40

26576 Famous Comic Songs of England and America, popular on the stage and in the parlor. Each .40

26578 Harvest of Minstrel Songs, standard "burnt cork" favorites. Each.......... .40

26579 Minstrel Folio, 2 vols. footlight flashes, witty, sentimental and serio-comic. Each.......... .40

26581 National Minstrel Folio, a superior collection of new and old favorites. Each.......... .40

26582 New Album Comique, famous songs by popular composers. Each.......... .40

26583 Songs for Harvard, Yale and Princeton Students, and everyone else who likes lively music. Each.......... .40

26585 Songs of the Past and Present, comic and sentimental songs, old and new. Each.......... .40

26586 Songs of the Period, the best "hits" of recent times. Each.......... .40

26587 They're After Me, Folio, a good album of favorite comic songs. Each.......... .40

Miscellaneous Vocal Collections.

26589 Grand Army War Songs. A valuable collection of war and camp songs, to which is added a selection of memorial songs and hymns for Decoration Day, etc.; choruses all arranged for male voices, organ or piano accompaniment; 100 pages, heavy paper covers. Price.......... $0.45 Extra by mail.......... .05

26590 *The Treasury of Song.* A mammoth collection of the very best vocal gems, both sacred and secular, selected from the works of the best composers. Every piece a favorite. A book of 550 pages; size, 10x7, handsomely bound in cloth. The largest collection ever put on the market. Regular price, $2.50. Our price.......... 1.25 Extra by mail.......... .24

26592 Minstrel Songs, old and new, book of 214 pages, board covers, containing a collection of over 100 of the famous minstrel and plantation songs, including the most popular of the celebrated Foster melodies; arranged with piano or organ accompaniment.......... 1.25 Extra by mail.......... .18

Vocal Music—Continued.

26593 Male Quartette and Chorus Book by J. Herbert. A new collection of music for male voices designed for use in glee club, concert, college or home; contains 108 pieces. Board covers; Price, $0.55. Extra by mail.......... $0.08

26595 "Recent Gems of Song," containing some of the most popular songs of the day. Price.......... .10

26596 The Celebrated Dockstader Songster, containing 50 minstrel and variety songs, with words and music. Price, $0.08, Postage.......... .02

26597 The Gem Songster. A fine collection of 200 pieces, including comic and patriotic songs, popular ballads and favorite negro melodies. Price, paper covers. (Postage, 5c).......... .15

Gospel Hymns.

26600 Consolidated, Nos. 1, 2, 3, 4. Large type words and music. 400 pages.

Each.......... $0.75
Per dozen.......... 7.72
Postage.......... .10

26601 Same as 26600, bound in ½ leather, red edges, words and music. Each.......... $1.50
Per doz.......... 15.40
Postage each.......... .10

26602 Words only. Nos. 1, 2, 3, 4. Each.......... $0.20
Per doz.......... 2.15
Postage.......... .04

	Each.	Per doz.
26603 Gospel Hymns, No. 5, with words and music. Board covers..........	$0.30	$3.10
Postage..........	.06	
26604 Same as No. 26603, bound in limp cloth, very handsome..........	.50	5.40
Postage..........	.06	
26605 Gospel Hymns, No 6, bound in boards..........	.30	3.10
Postage..........	.06	
26606 Gospel Hymns No 6, *Christian Endeavor* Edition, bound in boards. Each	.35	3.60
Postage..........	.06	
26607 Same as No. 26606, bound in limp cloth, very handsome..........	.50	5.40
26608 Just out. Nos. 5 and 6, combined. Words and music..........	.60	7.00
Postage..........	.08	
26609 Same as 26608. Words only..........	.22	2.30
Postage..........	.04	
26610 Gospel Choir, by Ira D. Sankey and James McGranahan; 128 pages, board covers. (Postage, 10c)..........	.40	4.00

Cornet Edition.

26612 Melodies of the Gospel Hymns, Nos. 1, 2, 3, 4 consolidated. Arranged for the cornet by Hayslip, for use in Sabbath schools, Gospel meetings, etc. A piano or organ played from the regular edition will agree perfectly with the cornet played from this. Price, paper covers.. $1.00 Extra by mail.......... .08

26613 Gospel Hymns No. 5, arranged for the cornet, containing the melodies and altos of all the members. Price, paper covers.......... .80 Postage, 5c extra.

26614 Gospel Hymns, No. 6, arranged for the cornet, paper covers. Each.......... .80 Postage, 5c. extra.

INSTRUMENTAL MUSIC.

Piano Folios.—Medium and Difficult Grades.

Postage, each 12 cts extra.

26620 American Artists' Edition Album, 2 vols., music of the higher grades. Each.......... $0.40

26622 American Piano Collection, 50 pieces of choice piano music. Each.......... .40

26623 *Chicago Collection of Standard Piano Music. Each.......... .40

26624 *Columbian Collection of Piano Music, popular and high grade music. Each.......... .40

26625 *Famous Favorites, a collection of classic piano music. Each.......... .40

26626 *Folio of Marches, selected from the works of celebrated composers. Each.......... .40

26627 *Golden Hours, an album of marches, waltzes, etc. Each.......... .40

26628 *Kinkel's Folio, 2 vols., bright and sparkling music of easy and medium grades. Each.. .40

26630 *Liszt's Best Compositions. Each.......... .40

26631 *Operatic Folio, 2 vols., gems from the latest operas. Each.......... .40

26632 Paderewski's Concert Album. Each.......... .40

Reed Organ Folios.

26635 *Excelsior Organ Folio, an album of popular music. Each.......... $0.40

26636 *Folio Gems, popular and standard music. Each.......... .40

26637 *Folio Leaves, an excellent collection of medium grade music. Each.......... .40

26637½ Gems of Strauss containing 100 pieces by this great composer. Each.......... .40

26638 *Golden Folio, music of easy and medium grades. Each.......... .40

26639 *Hitchcock's New Organ Book, a folio of popular pieces in light style. Each.......... .40

26640 *National Organ Folio, a selection of standard pieces for organ. Each.......... .40

26641 Organ Pearls, easy and medium grade music. Each.......... .40

26643 *Parlor and Cabinet Organ Selections, vocal and instrumental music. Each.......... .40

26645 Parlor Bouquet, medium grade music for piano or organ. Each.......... .40

26646 *Parlor Organ Folio, music of the medium and higher grades. Each.......... .40

26647 Reed Organ Companion (Brainard's), easy pieces for organ suitable for beginners. Each.. .40

Manicure Sets.

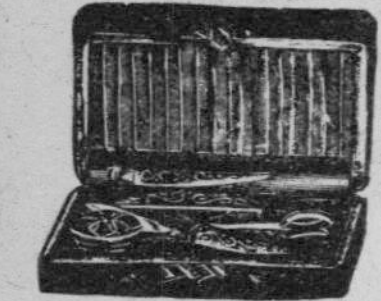

27720 Manicure Set, Size, 6x3¾, made of silk plush, lined with satin; contains scissors, knife, powder box and nail polisher. Each.........$0.75 Weight, 12 ounces.

27722 Manicure Set. Size, 7½x5, made of silk plush satin lined; contains 6 pieces Manicure fittings. Price, each..$1.00 Weight, 12 ounces.

27726 Manicure Set. Size, 8¼x6; made of celluloid lined with fine satin; case is handsomely ornamented with silver and contains 7 pieces silver fittings. Each..........$3.00 Weight, 24 ounces.

27727 Manicure Case, fancy shape, size, 11x8, made of the finest plush and satin; finely embossed top, contains, celluloid fittings, gold plated tips and ornaments; knife, scraper, polisher, tweezers, scissors, button hook, two powder boxes. Price, each..$3.50 Weight, 46 ounces.

27728 Jewel Case, covered with imitation seal leather gold plated trimmings, lined with the finest satin, beaded mirror on inside of cover; size, 8¾x6½; contains 8 large celluloid fittings, same as number 27727. Price, each.....$4.25 Weight, 40 ounces.

Work Boxes.

27730 Work Box made of plush, satin lined, silver ornament on top; size, 5x6½. Contains 4 pieces fittings, Each.$0.50 Weight, 10 ounces.

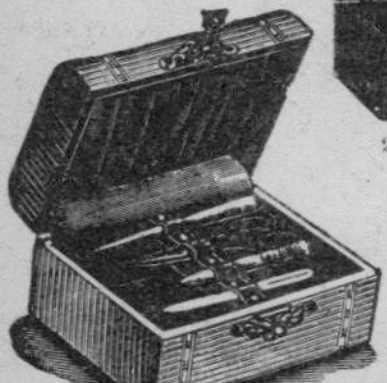

27731 Work Box; size, 4¾x3¼, made of celluloid, embossed satin lining, contains four work fittings. Each........$0.60 Weight, 8 ounces.

27732 Work Bax, silk, 5½x7¼, made of fine silk plush, silver ornaments, lined with satin, mirror on inside of cover, contains five pieces work fittings. Each....$0.75 Weight, 14 oz.

Work Boxes—Continued.

27733 Work Box: size, 8x5¾x3¼ made of celluloid, ribbed end, embossed front, handsome raised spray of colored flowers on top. Each..............$1.00

27736 Work Box; size, 9½ x 7¾, fancy shape, lined with the finest satin, silver ornaments on top; contains six pieces of fittings. Price, each..$1.50 Weight 26 ounces

27738 Work Box; size, 9¼x5x4; made of silk plush, fancy shape large celluloid panel on top; handsomely embossed with colored flowers and leaves, satin lining, bevel mirror on inside of cover, contains 7 pieces white work fittings. Each.......$1.90 Weight, 27 ounces.

27742 Work Box, fancy shape: size, 10x8. Made of fine silk plush and satin lining, silver ornaments, large bevel mirror in cover, contains large fittings, as follows: Two crochet hooks, two button hooks, tape needle, stiletto and scissors. Price, each.....$2.75 Weight, 45 ounces

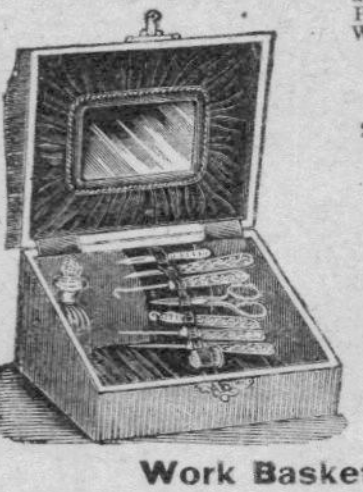

27744 Work Box, fancy shape; size, 8x6½x5, made of celluloid, ribbed sides and front, embossed top, satin lined, bevel mirror inside of cover, contains seven carved bone fittings, good scissors and odor bottle. Each...$3.00 Weight, 42 ounces.

Work Baskets.

27751 Fancy Work Basket, satchel shape; made of heavy braided straw, ribbed sides; size, 10x6¾x5; nickel handle and clasps, lined with fine padded satin, pockets at sides. Each...........................$3 50 Weight, 30 oz.

Perfumery Stands.

27756 Large Odor Stand made of two large horns highly polished, large bevel mirror; size, 4½x6½, with plush frame, plush lined socket, 4 oz. cut glass bottle. Price, each.........$2.00 Weight, 52 ounces.

Toilet Mirrors.

27760 Plate Glass Mirror, bevel edge, with easel back, either for hand or used with back for shelf. The edges of plush in assorted colors; size, 4x6 inches. Price, each.$0.25 Per dozen........... 2.75 Weight, 8 ounces.

27762 Tourists' Patent Mirror, 5¼ in. diameter, silk plush back and sides, nickel sides, nickel and plush standard. This mirror can be adjusted to any angle, also fold together to avoid breaking. Price, each.......$0.75 Per dozen......... 8.10 Weight, 15 ounces.

Hand Mirrors.

27774

27774—Florence Hand Mirror, entirely new shape, handsomely decorated back. French plate glass; size, 5x9½ inches; color black Weight, 11 ounces. Each $0.75 Per dozen 8.10

27779-82

27779 Oval Hand Mirror, rubber back, bevel plate glass; length, 9 inches; colors black or brown; weight, 7 ounces. Each..........................$0.25

27782 Oval Hand Mirror, Florence, rubber back; 9⅜ inch glass; weight, 9 ounces. Each......... .45

27788

27788 Hand Mirror, oval bevel plate with silver plated frame, engraved back, white metal handle; size, 4x1¼. Price, each.......................... .65 Weight 14 ounces.

27790

27790 Novel Hand Mirror, in shape of heart, size 5½x11, with silver plated frame, engraved back, white metal handle. Price each...$0.85 Weight 16 ounces.

27792 Pocket or Hand Mirror; size, 4¼x3, fancy nickel sides, easel back. Each........................$0.10 Per dozen...................1.00 Weight, 5 ounces.

Open. 27794-02

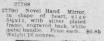

27794 Round Mirror, 3 inches in diameter with nickel frame and folding handle. Each.$0.05 Per dozen .... .50

27795 Round Mirror, same as 27794, 5 inches in diameter. Each.....................$0.10 Per dozen..................1.00

27801 Round Zinc Folding Mirror, No. 1, 2½ inches in diameter. Weight, 5 ounces....$0.03 Per dozen.................. .33

27802 Same, 3 inches in diameter. 3 ounces. Each......$0.04 Per dozen.................. .43 Weight, 6 ounces.

Triplicate Mirrors.

27805 Triplicate Mirror, made of three mirrors that fold to the center; back of frame covered with leatherette, sides and front with silk and plush; assorted colors; chain attached for hanging. Size of frame 5x7½. Mirrors of beveled plate glass; size, 4x6 in.
Each $1.10
Postage .... .23

27806 Triplicate Mirror (369) with three heavy bevel plates, size 6x6, with fancy nickel plated frames, with fancy ornament, flowered front.
Price $2.00
Weight, 35 oz.
27807 Triplicate Mirrors, same description as 27806, with plates; size, 5x8.
Each $3.75

27806

27808

27808 Triplicate Mirror in fancy carved and polished wood frame, with plush front,patent hinged, bevel plate glasses. Sizes, 8 x 8. New and stylish.
Price $4.00
Weight, 45 ounces.

27809 Triplicate Mirror of extra fine quality, oval plates, size, 7x9, fancy gold plated frames, decorated celluloid front panels,metal standard chain to hang.
Each $6.00
Weight, 53 ounces.

Whisk Broom Holders.

27811 Whisk Broom Holder, with Torchon back, celluloid front, hand painted. Size 6½x6½.
Each .... 30 cts.

27813

27813 Whisk Broom Holder made of silk plush. Size, 5½ x5 Imitation silver broom socket, fitted with broom.
Each $0.35
Weight, 10 oz.
27815 Whisk Broom; size, 4x6½, made of translucent celluloid, hand painted decorations,ribbons to hang; fitted with broom.
Each $0.50
Weight 12, ounces.

27815

27818

27818 Whisk Broom Holder, size, 13x5 in. Shape of snow shoe, with heavy cord lac ings, broom socket made of plush and celluloid, with handsome decorated fan embossed on front, fitted with good broom.
Each $0.65
Weight, 15 ounces.
27819 Whisk Broom Holder. Shape of toboggan. Size 10x3½ in. Made of wood trimmed with satin ribbon. Broom socket made of celluloid, silk plush and satin, metal band, fitted with good broom.
Each $0.85

27819

Ladies' and Men's Toilet and Traveling Cases.

We quote nearly all of Men's Traveling and Shaving Cases without razor, as every gentleman either possesses a good razor or wishes to make his own selections. When razors are desired please make selections from our regular line quoted in this catalogue, adding cost to regular price of case.

27827 Men's Toilet Set, in leather case, russet color; size 8½x2¼, containing hair, tooth and nail brushes, comb and whisk broom. Weight, 8 oz.
Price $0.70
Per dozen 8.15

27829 Toilet Set in sole leather case, russet color, contains solid back hair brush, nickel soap box, comb, tooth and nail brushes.
Each $1.00
Weight, 14 ounces.

27829

27831 Men's Traveling Case; made of sole leather, russet color. Size, closed, 3x3¾,hand stitched Contains nickel plated leather brush and soap box, button hook, nail file, comb, solid back hair brush, tooth and nail brushes.
Each $2.25
Weight, 20 ounces.

27831

27833 Ladies' Folding Traveling Case. Size, 8½x4½. Made of fine imitation seal. Leather lining contains solid back hair brush, comb,nickel soap box, perfume bottle, scissors, nail file and button hook.
Each $2.50
Weight, 20 ounces.

27833

27835 Men's Traveling Case. Made of sole leather; nickel clasps. Size, closed, 9x3½x2½; contains Torrey razor, strop, comb, solid back hair brush, nickel lather brush and soap box,tooth and nail brushes in glass bottle.
Each $2.75
Weight, 24 ounces.

27836 Ladies' Traveling Case, made of Alligator leather, lined with rubber cloth,fancy clasp; contains solid back hair brush, comb, perfume bottle, nickel soap box, tooth and nail brushes and button hook.
Each $3.50
Weight, 20 ounces.

27836

27837 Ladies' Traveling Case, made of embossed leather; lined throughout with leather; contains plate mirror, 6x3,solid back hair brush, tooth and nail brushes, cut glass perfume bottle, celluloid soap box, comb, scissors, button hook and scraper, also pocket for towel; weight, 38 ounces.
Each $4.50

Shaving Cases.

Nearly every gentleman possesses a razor, or at least wishes to make his own selection. For this reason we quote our Shaving Cases without razors. If you wish to order razor, please make selections for our line quoted in this catalogue and add cost to price of case.

27839 Shaving Case, size, 7x5, made of silk plush, satin lined, silver ornament on top; contains partition, mug and lather brush.
Price each $1.25
Weight 28 ounces.

27840 Shaving Case, round pattern, size 7x4, made of celluloid, ivory finish, fancy ribbed sides, embossed panel on top, satin lined; contains fancy mug, lather brush and detachable bevel mirror. Each $1.85
Weight, 26 ounces.

27840

27841 Shaving Case, made of celluloid, imitation of carved ivory, lined with fine satin; size, 7x6; containing fancy decorated mug, good lather brush.
Price $2.00
Weight. 30 ounces.

27842 Shaving Case. Size,11x6x4½, fancy shape, made of celluloid, ivory finish, ribbed sides, large spray of beautiful colored flowers embossed on top, lined with satin; contains fancy partition,mug, comb, lather brush.
Each $3.25
Weight, 39 ounces.

27843 Shaving Case,fancy shape made of silk plush satin lined silver ornaments on top, contains fancy mug,brush and adjustable plate mirror;size of case, 9x6½x 5½.
Price,each $3.00
Weight, 48 oz.

No razor furnished with this case.

27845 Shaving Case. Size, 12x6¾x1½, made of celluloid imitation, carved sides, bevel edge, cover, top finely embossed with spray of flowers, lined with satin; contains bevel mirror, fancy mug, lather brush, comb and scissors.
Weight, 50 ounces.   Each $3.15

Atomizers.

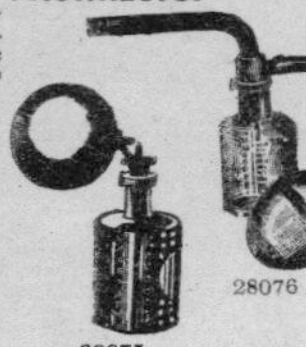

28076

28075

28075 Daisy Atomizer, similar to cut, bottle unfilled. Price with or without the bottle the same.
Each......$0.20
Per doz.... 2.16
Weight, 12 oz.

28076 Throat and Toilet Atomizer No. 1, with bulb and tube of extra quality, hard rubber nozzle; bottle holds 2 ounces; continuous spray, perfect and durable.
Each...............................$0.40
Weight, 8 oz.

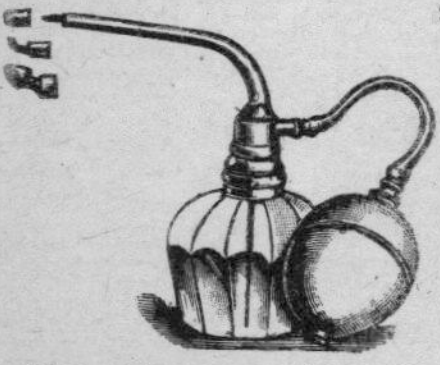

28077 Throat and Nasal Atomizer of fine quality, large bulb continuous spray, three hard rubber screw tips; long straight tube for throat or general applications downward; tube for larynx; also Nasal tip.
Each...$0.75

Hair Oil and Brilliantine.

28085 Bay Rum Hair Oil, an excellent dressing, made from the very best oils and bay rum, put up in 4 oz. fancy bottles.
Per bottle......$0.18 Per dozen.....$1.95
Weight, 16 oz.

28087 White Rose Hair Oil, extra fine quality, scented with White Rose, 4 ounce fancy bottles. Per bottle............$0.20
Per dozen............................. 2.15
Weight, 16 oz.

Brilliantine.

28090 A preparation for the moustache, giving a glossy appearance; is also used for the hair: perfectly harmless, 1 ounce bottles. weight 4 ounces. Price............$0.20
Per dozen............................. 2.15

Perfumery and oils can be sent by mail.

Bandoline, Sea Foam, Etc.

28092 Bandoline. A preparation for the hair (not a dressing) to be applied after combing to keep it in place. Put up in 1½ oz. bottles.
Each..............................$0.10
Per dozen.......................... 1.00
Extra by mail........................ .07

28095 Shampoo Powder or "Seafoam," for cleansing the scalp, put up in bottles. Each bottle contains enough powder to make one quart of the mixture. Full directions with each bottle.
Price per bottle..................$0.25
Per dozen.......................... 2.70
Weight, 5 oz.

Sachet Powders.

28110 Sachet Powder in 1 oz. glass jars, four colors, viz: White Rose, Heliotrope, Jockey Club and violet. Each.....................$0.20
Weight, 6 oz. Per dozen................ 2.15

28114 Sachet Powder, packet of smaller size, containing about ¼ oz. of powder in assorted colors. Each...........................$0.10
Per dozen.............................. 1.08
Weight, 2 oz.

Montgomery Ward & Co.'s Cough Syrup.

D5600 This is an old and well known preparation for relieving and curing all forms of colds. Useful in bronchial, throat and lung diseases. The formula is published on every bottle and you know just what you are taking. Your physician will tell you that this is one of the best combinations of the pharmacopoeia for coughs and colds. Try a bottle and be convinced.
Price per bottle.....................$0.30
Per dozen.............................. 3.00

D5601 Montgomery Ward & Co.'s Beef, Wine and Iron. Each fluid ounce contains the nutritive portion of two ounces of lean beef, 4 grains of citrate of iron, dissolved in pure sherry wine. Price per pint bottle............$0.35
Price per dozen pints.................. 3.50

***** Write your name and Address on package returned to us if you want it to have attention; send letter of instructions by mail; do not put it in package.**

Compound Cathartic Pills.

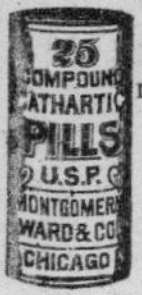

D5602 Montgomery Ward & Co.'s Compound Cathartic Pills, sugar coated, 25 pills in neat wooden box. Compound after U. S. Pharmaceutical recipe.
Per box.................................$0.11
Per dozen boxes.......................... .75
Weight, 2 oz.

Vegetable Liver Pills.

D5604 Montgomery Ward & Co.'s Vegetable Liver Pills, sugar coated, formula printed on outside of wrapper; put up 25 in a box.
Per box..................................$0.12
Per dozen boxes........................... .75

Quinine Pills.

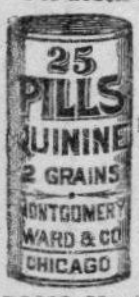

D5608 Montgomery Ward & Co.'s Sulphate Quinine Pills, 2 grains, gelatine coated, made of absolutely pure quinine.
Per bottle, 100 pills....................$0.24
Per dozen bottles........................ 2.40
Weight, 3 oz.

D5610 Montgomery Ward & Co.'s Insect Powder, warranted to be of the very best quality. "Sure death" to insects. Put up in 1 lb. packages.
Price, each................................ .35
Per dozen.................................. 4.00

Borax.

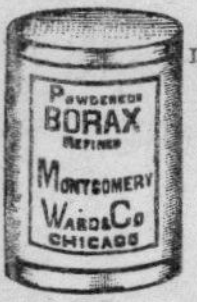

D5614 Borax, refined, powdered, put up in our own factory, and guaranteed perfect. Makes a handy and cleanly package for household use.
1 lb. package, each.................$0.17
Per dozen............................ 1.80

Epsom Salts.

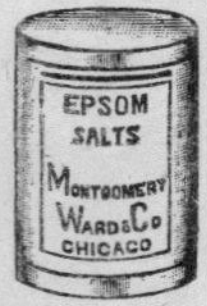

D5616 Epsom Salts. These salts should not be purchased in bulk, as they lose their strength upon exposure to the air. We pack this in our own factory, using only fresh and selected stock. 1 lb. pkg
Each.................................$0.06
Per dozen.............................. .65

Rochelle Salts.

D5618 Montgomery Ward & Co.'s Rochelle Salts of the very best quality, put up strictly for medical purposes. Not at all disagreeable to the taste.
¼-lb. pkg., each.......................$0.30
Per dozen................................ 3.25
1-lb pkg., each........................... .50
Per dozen................................ 5.00

Sulphur.

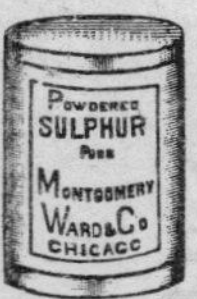

D5620 Sulphur, powdered, refined; packed in our own factory, from the brightest and cleanest stock we can buy. 1 lb. package.
Each $0.07
Per dozen............................. .80

Ammonia.

D5622 Ammonia, household, extra quality, pint bottles. Put up expressly for Montgomery Ward & Co. Per bottle..........................$0.12
Per dozen................................ 1.25
Weight, 24 oz.

Spirits of Camphor.

D5624 Montgomery Ward & Co.'s Spirits of Camphor, put up in 4 oz. bottles, and guaranteed to be chemically pure. Each.................$0.25
Per dozen................................ 2.50
Weight, 10 oz.

Glycerine.

D5628 Montgomery Ward & Co.'s Glycerine, warranted absolutely pure.

	Each.	Per doz.
2 oz. bottles	$0.10	$1.00
4 oz. bottles	.15	1.50

Paregoric.

D5630 Montgomery Ward & Co.'s Paregoric, carefully compounded, 2 oz. bottles.

2 oz. bottles	$0.15	$1.50
4 oz. bottles	.25	2.50

Weight, 5 and 8 oz.

Peppermint.

D5632 Montgomery Ward & Co.'s Tincture of Peppermint, best quality

	Each.	Per doz.
2 oz. bottles	$0.15	$1.50
4 oz. bottles	.25	2.50

Court Plaster.

	Per Envelope.	Per doz.
D5634 Court Plaster, about 2x3 in. on silk; black, white or pink; 1 sheet in envelope	$0.04	$0.30
D5636 Court Plaster, about 1¼x2½ in., 3 sheets in envelope, assorted 3 colors, on muslin	.03	.25

Spirits Nitre.

D5638 Montgomery Ward & Co.'s Sweet Spirits Nitre, U. S. P. Absolutely pure.

	Each.	Per doz.
2 oz. bottles	$0.15	$1.50
4 oz. bottles	.25	2.50

Tincture of Arnica.

D5644 Tincture of Arnica, standard quality, U. S. P., made expressly for us, and quality and strength guaranteed.

4 oz. bottles (¼ pints)	$0.20	$2.10
8 oz. bottles (½ pints)	.35	3.50

Extract Hamamelis.

D5646 Extract of Hamamelis (or Witch Hazel). Guaranteed exactly same as Pond's Extract. Everywhere recognized as an universal all healing remedy. Undoubtedly the most valuable medicine to have in every house. Nothing equals it for sore throat, hemorrhage, sprains, bruises, wounds, sore eyes, stiff joints, in fact, is useful in nearly every accident that one can have. Bottled expressly for us and warranted pure.
½ pint bottle ($0.50 size). Each....$0.22
Per dozen................................ 2.30
Weight, 12 oz.
1 pint bottle ($1.00 size), each.................. .33
Per dozen 4.10
Weight, 24 oz.
1 quart bottle ($1.50 size), each................. .60
Per dozen... 6.50
Weight, 45 oz.

Cook's Witch Hazel Toilet Lotion.

D5648 An elegant preparation for chapped hands, face and lips; one of the finest lotions to use after shaving in the market; our employes use it in preference to any other.
Per bottle, 4 oz. size.......................$0.18
Per dozen bottles............................ 2.00

Cook's Bay Rum.

Distilled expressly for Montgomery Ward & Co. by Dr. John G. Cook, and is equal to the finest imported.
D5654 Bay Rum, quart bottle. Each...........$1.00
Per dozen...................................10.50
D5656 Bay Rum, pint bottle. Each.............. .60
Per dozen..................................... 6.00
Weight, packed, per bottle, 30 ounces.
D5658 Bay Rum ½ pint bottles. Each............ .35
Per dozen..................................... 3.50
Weight, packed, per bottle, 16 ounces.
D5660 Bay Rum, ¼ pint bottle.................. .19
Per dozen..................................... 2.00
Weight, packed, 12 ounces.

Petroleum Pomade (Perfumed).

Guaranteed exactly similar to cosmoline or vaseline, and at a much lower price.
D5666 Purified Petroleum Pomade or Vaseline, scented, for chapped or rough skin, blotches, pimples, sores, lip salve for toilet purposes. Nothing equals it as a hair dressing in place of the old style hair oil. Put up expressly for us, and purity guaranteed; 4 oz. bottles.
Per bottle........................ $0.15
Per dozen......................... 1.50
Extra, by mail.................... .21

Petroleum (Like Cosmoline).

D5668 This is a preparation made from purified petroleum oil, is similar to cosmoline and vaseline, and is the best remedy known for healing cuts, bruises, burns, etc. Plain, not perfumed.

	Each.	Per doz.
2 oz	$0.06	$0.50
4 oz	.10	1.00
1 lb. cans	.25	2.50

D5670 Carbolized Petroleum; same as No. D5668 with the addition of carbolic acid; 2-ounce bottles. Each.. .15
Per dozen.. 1.50

Ink Powder.

D5672 Ink Powder, put up in ½-oz screw cap vials containing powder sufficient for one pint best quality of ink; colors, green, red, black or violet.
Each..$0.12
Per dozen.................................... 1.25
Per gross....................................13.50
Weight, 1 ounce each.

There never was a better year to buy.

Cook's Cough Cure.

D5676 Low Price, yet as efficacious as any made from an old fashioned recipe. Put up expressly for M. W. & Co. Per bottle................$0.20
Per dozen........................ 2.00
Weight, 3 oz.
D5678 Cook's large size. ½ pint cough cure. Per bottle.................. .75
Per dozen bottles................ 7.50

Flake Tar Camphor.

D5686 Flake Tar Camphor, a chemically pure product of coal tar for the preservation of furs, clothing, feathers, etc., etc. from moths. It is free from oil or alkali and will not injure the most delicate fabrics. Put up in 1-lb. packages.
Price per pkg................... $0.25
Per doz........................ 2.25
Weight, 18 oz.

Cook's Eye Water.

                                    Each. Per doz.
D5688 A remedy of 25 years' standing. Absolutely harmless to the youngest infant. For weakness or inflamation of the eyes it has no equal. Moisten the eyes and drop a little inside three or four times a day.
In 2 oz. bottles............... $0.15 $1.40
In 4 oz. size, with eye cup and dropper......................... .35   3.25

Catarrh Snuff.

D5690 Dr. Cook's Catarrh Snuff, for nasal catarrh, hay fever, cold in the head, etc. This is a recently discovered compound; is indorsed by all the leading practitioners of this country, does not stain and affords immediate relief without causing irritation or sneezing. Put up in handy screw top bottles. Each......$0.17
Per doz......................... 1.90

Seidlitz Powders.

D5696 Seidlitz Powders, pure, good strength; in tin boxes, 10 powders in a box. Per box......$0.20
Per doz......................... 2.00
Weight, 8 oz.

Condition Powders.

D5698 Dr. Cook's Condition Powders, for horses and cattle. This is made after one of the best known formulas in existence, and will prove to be a thoroughly reliable remedy. We are just introducing it, and offer it at a popular price. 1 lb. pkg. (25c. size).
Each............................ $0.18
Per doz......................... 2.00
50c pkg., each.................. .35
Per doz......................... 3.75

Cook's Neutralizing Cordial.

D5700 Put up in 4 oz. bottles. This medicine is a pleasant, anti-(acid) and laxative preparation; very useful in piles, habitual costiveness, diarrhœa, sour stomach, indigestion, summer complaint of children, etc., etc. Per bottle........$0.28
Per dozen bottles............... 2.75
Weight, 12 oz.
D5702 Blizzard Insect Powder Gun, holds 2 oz. of Powder.
Each............................ $0.06
Per dozen....................... .50
Extra, by mail, each about 5c.

The Great Russian Corn and Bunion Exterminator.

D5704 The manufacturers claim that if directions, which accompany each bottle, are followed, a cure is certain, and as we have investigated this assertion we are satisfied that no person suffering from corns and bunions should fail to give the Russian Exterminator a trial. It requires from two to four vials to effect a cure in a bad case.
Two bottles..................... $0.35
Four bottles.................... .64
Per dozen bottles............... 1.68
Postage, 5 cents on two bottles.

Insect Powder Guns.

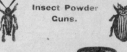

D5706 This is the best Insect Powder Gun in the market for destroying roaches, black beetles, insects on plants, animals and all vermin in house or garden. Each...................... $0.06
Per dozen....................... .50
Extra, by mail, each, about..... .05

KEEP YOUR EYE ON OUR BOOK DEPARTMENT AND YOU WON'T PAY AGENTS FANCY PRICES.

Insect Powder Guns—Continued.

D5708 "Jumbo" Insect Powder Guns, same general style as above, made to meet a demand for as large a gun as can be held in the hand, 4 inches in diameter, holds ½ pound of powder, bottom and spout screws off, large opening for filling. Each.......................... $0.18
Per dozen....................... 2.00
D5710 Dr. Cook's Insect Powder, strictly pure and guaranteed equal to anything in the market. Per package................... .10
Per dozen....................... 1.10
Extra by mail, about............ .05

Handy Pocket Goods.

(In metal screw top air-tight glass vials.)
Postage on handy pocket goods, 3 cents.

                                    Each. Per doz.
D5714 Aromatic Cachou Lozenges, for perfuming the breath; makes a very delicious confection; in 1 oz. vials. See cut................... $0.08 $0.85
D5716 Cachous Diamond, for perfuming the breath; in 4 oz. vials; vest pocket size..................... .08   .85
D5718 Chlorate Potash Tablets, five grains each; for sore throat, hoarseness, etc. In ½-oz. vials..... .08   .85
D5720 Licorice Pellets, druggists' pure, 1 oz. vials, same as 2340.... .08   .85
D5722 Soda Mint Tablets, for sour stomach, colic, flatulency, etc. 4-oz. vials, pocket style............ .08   .85
D5724 Cook's Bronchial Troches, exactly similar to Brown's cough troches, in ¾ oz. vials, as above... .08   .85
D5726 Muriate Ammonia Tablets, 3 grains each, in 1 oz. vials, as above... .08   .85
D5728 Borax Tablets, 5 grains each, in ½-oz. vials, as above.......... .08   .85
D5730 Cook's Paregoric Tablets; each Tablet represents 15 drops paregoric. Dose, 1 to 4, according to age; 50 tablets in each vial.......... .08   .85

*** All orders are filled from the latest Catalogue. We shall, whenever possible, on orders from old Catalogues, give the nearest we have, and wish to explain that we change our quotations so as to be able to give the latest styles and better values.

SEWING MACHINES.
Our High Arm "Drop Cabinet" Sewing Machine.

High Arm Drop Cabinet. (Open.)   High Arm Drop Cabinet. (Closed.)

28145 Drop Cabinets. The above cuts represent our popular High Arm Sewing Machines in the new Automatic Drop Cabinet Cases that "Agents" throughout the country sell at from $50.00 to $75.00 each. They are supplied with the latest improved "drop," are easily handled, and will last a life time. The cases are finished in either walnut or oak, highly polished top, polished panels in back and sides, beaded panel doors in front, and when closed they make a handsome piece of furniture which may be used either as a writing desk or table. The dimensions, closed, are as follows: Length, 25 inches; width, 22 inches; height, 30 inches. Please bear in mind that the machine head and attachments are the same as on our regular "High Arm," described on following page. Price, each, boxed............$28.00
Weight, boxed, 200 pounds.

Montgomery Ward & Co.'s

High Arm Sewing Machine.

THIS CUT IS AN EXACT REPRESENTATION OF THE MONTGOMERY WARD & CO. HIGH ARM SEWING MACHINE.

Prices.

No. 5—Four Drawers, as shown, walnut woodwork, **$19.50.**

No. 5½—Four drawers, as shown in cut. Oak woodwork, very popular; price, **$19.70.**

No. 6—Six drawers, three on each side, walnut woodwork; price, **$20.50.**

No. 6½—Six drawers, three on each side, oak woodwork; price, **$20.80.**

High Arm Machines Crated weigh about 120 lbs.

We allow every purchaser the privilege of a thorough trial before final acceptance.

We give with each High Arm Machine a complete set of the best steel attachments free of charge.

Every M. W. & Co. High Arm Machine is accompanied by a warranty certificate for five years.

To the best of our knowledge and belief we are the only house in the country that gives such a warrant.

A machine similar to the Domestic and White, with extra improvements, which add to the machine and simplify its use. The Montgomery Ward & Co. New Improved High Arm Machine combines to a great degree all the elements of the latest improved high arm machines, being simple in its managements and possessing strength and simplicity in its machinery. The head is "let in" to the table, swings on patent hinges, can also be held firmly down by the thumb screw. Having few bearings, the machine is easily oiled and kept clean. These bearings are made of the best steel and are all hardened and adjustable. The shuttle is cylindrical in form, self threading, very simple, uses a large bobbin and moves in a circular course. The shuttle carriers are lined with steel, making them almost noiseless when running. The feed is a double four motion drop feed, and has no springs. The machine will make either a long or short stitch, the length being regulated by a thumb screw on the upright portion of the arm. The needle is self-setting, and the stitch is a double thread lock stitch. Each machine is also supplied with the patent tension liberator for releasing the work at the end of the seam. It has its new automatic spooler for winding bobbin without removing the work. By a peculiar arrangement of the levers a still and light running machine is secured. There is a large space under the arm, affording room for handling bulky goods, as dresses, cloaks, etc. The fly wheel, plates, screws and *all the working parts are nickel plated.*

The design of the cabinet work is the very latest, as we are now using the oval covers, drop leaf and skeleton drawer frames, also full-length center drawer with velvet lined compartments for the attachments. The materials used are either oak or walnut highly polished, and finished throughout in the best possible manner. The stand is made of the very best material; the balance wheel is on the inside of castings and is adjusted on *two centers,* the object of which is to give a more steady motion, also to facilitate the "light running" qualities.

The Attachments.

The most important features in connection with a Sewing Machine are the "attachments," and until quite recently there were none made that could always be relied upon to do perfect work. We wish, however, to inform the public that all difficulties in this direction are at an end, as we have *the best* and most *perfect* set of Sewing Machine Attachments ever put on the market. They are made of heavy *cold rolled steel,* highly polished and nickel plated. Every piece is guaranteed absolutely perfect, and being of steel, cannot get out of order. Each Montgomery Ward & Co. High Arm Sewing Machine will be supplied FREE OR CHARGE, with complete set of new steel attachments as follows: 1 ruffler and gatherer, 1 tucker, 1 braider, 1 binder, 1 quilter, 4 hemmers (⅛ to 1 inch); also the following accessories—1 thread cutter, 12 needles, 6 bobbins, 1 gauge and screw, 1 wrench 7 screw drivers, 1 oil can, 1 instruction book. We make no charge for crating machines or cartage. N. B. Instruction books for our sewing machine are printed in English only.

Read This.

To show our confidence in our sewing machines we make the following offer: We will ship one machine by express on 20 days' trial, to any express office on a railroad within 500 miles of Chicago, under the following conditions: When a machine arrives at the express office the person ordering it deposits with the express agent the price of the machine together with transportation charges and the return charges on the money. The express agent is instructed on each C. O. D. bill to hold the money 20 days. If by the expiration of 20 days the machine is not returned to him, the express agent sends us the money, but if returned, he pays back every cent of the money deposited to the person who deposits it, and sends us the machine at our expense both ways. If you want the machine shipped on these terms, please be particular to say so in your order.

Please note that we do not ship machines by express upon these terms to any point more than 500 miles from Chicago, as the charges would be too high, and it would be much better to ship by freight.

Machines ordered by freight and paid for may be returned if unsatisfactory, after 30 days' trial, at our expense both ways, and money will be refunded.

We also ship our sewing machines on trial by freight, under the same conditions as organs and pianos. For full particulars we refer you to page 235.

We have made some new improvements in our High Arm Sewing Machine since our last issue, the more noticeable ones being the new style wood work which is not only the very latest pattern with oval covers and skeleton drawer frames, but it is highly polished and handsomely carved. We have also added a new patent tension liberator, which by a single touch releases the work at the end of the seam, thus doing away with the annoyance of pulling the thread with fingers. As a matter of fact we are constantly on the lookout for new improvements, and purchasers may be assured that our High Arm will always be at the head of the procession and that in every case they will get a sewing machine with all modern improvements and "up to the times in every particular." We wish it understood that we guarantee our High Arm Machines to be in every way equal to the very best, and are anxious whenever it is possible to have their merits judged in competition with the Domestic, New Home, Genuine Singers, Wheeler & Wilson, White, or any other style in the market. We have a special catalogue of our sewing machines, with large lithographed cuts, showing the machines and wood work in *their natural color.* A copy will be mailed free upon application.

FOR THE LADIES.—Our new Dressmaking Department will be glad to send you a Catalogue showing styles and prices of dresses made to measure. Order Catalogue E. Mailed free.

Montgomery Ward & Co.'s Improved Automatic Sewing Machine.
Price, $27.00.

The above cut is an exact representation of Montgomery Ward & Co.'s Improved Automatic Sewing Machine No. 3, price $27.00.

With this issue of our catalogue we quote for the first time our new Automatic Sewing Machine. They are exactly the same style as the celebrated Wilcox & Gibbs, with all the latest improvements, and we guarantee them to be *fully equal in every respect*. With this valuable addition, our Sewing Machine Department is complete. We can now supply every want in a Family Machine. The introduction of the Automatic might not, and *must not*, cause any one to overlook the excellent qualities of our Improved "High Arms" quoted on proceeding page, as the latter represents a different style, being a "lock stitch" machine and belongs to the same class as the Domestic, New Singer, New Home, White, &c., and *stands at the head*. The Automatic, however, possesses many superior features that recommend it for certain conditions and grades of work, which is impossible to produce with any other machine. One great advantage claimed is that it is the lightest running machine made, easiest to operate, and no lady however delicate need fear to use it. The only reason why they are not more generally used is because they have been sold heretofore at such enormous prices (from $65.00 to $150.00 each) and it is due only to persistent efforts on our part that we can now offer them at a reasonable figure. No other house in this country can sell the same machine at our prices. Another important feature is the tension (which is the ordinary machine is the source of considerable annoyance) is strictly and positively automatic, on all kinds of goods and with any kind or size of thread or silk, it being regulated by the size of thread used, and requires no adjustment whatever on the part of the operator. It uses neither shuttle or bobbin. The strands of thread are interwoven and twisted together from a single spool, which is placed on spool pin in such a manner that it does not revolve, thus taking away considerable friction, and through the action of the automatic tension device a perfect stitch is formed; while it really makes what is called a "chain" stitch, it will not rip under any circumstances unless deliberately unlocked. It can then be taken out easily without injury to the fabric. The feed is accurate and positive in its action, prevents the thread from gathering on hook by carrying along without assistance light or heavy work; passing over thick seams, and working equally well on very thin or thick material. The needle is short, straight and self setting. The machine has a rotary motion, enabling it to be run at a high rate of speed, is *noiseless* and on account of its simplicity is not easily gotten out of order. All bright parts are nickel plated. It also has an automatic device which prevents at all times the wheel from running backwards, so the thread is never broken. The attachments are simple and easy to operate. We give with each machine the following *set free of charge*: Ruffler, tucker, narrow hemmer, wide hemmer, hemmer nut, quilter, gauge and screw, 12 needles, oil can, bottle of oil and instruction book. The woodwork is either oak or walnut and finely finished. The stand is made of the very best materials. We warrant each machine for FIVE YEARS, also ship them on trial under same conditions as our other styles. (See page 260.)

2147 Automatic Sewing Machine, as described above, (style 2) with plain table, with cover and one drawer, oak or walnut woodwork, each $25.00. Weight, crated, about 100 lbs.

28148 Automatic Sewing Machine, as described above, (style 3) with drop leaf, cover, center drawer, two drawers on end (see cut), oak or walnut woodwork, each $27.00. Weight, crated, about 110 lbs.

Montgomery Ward & Co.'s New Improved Singer Model Sewing Machine, With High Arm.

Price $13.50.

28150 The above cut shows an exact representation of our new improved Singer Model Sewing Machine *with high arm*. We handle one style only, No. 3, walnut drop leaf, box cover, and two drawers. Packed, crated for shipment. Each...........$13.50

Description of Singer Model Sewing Machine.

The New Improved Singer Model Sewing Machine is easily managed, has a high arm, uses a self threading shuttle, automatic bobbin winder, a straight self setting needle, makes a double thread lock stitch. It will hem, fell, bind, braid, seam, quilt, tuck, ruffle, hemstitch, or gather, and is adapted to every variety of family sewing.

The materials used in its construction are steel and iron of the best quality. Every wearing point is thoroughly hardened and smoothly finished. Case, table and drawers are finished in black walnut in the most complete and substantial manner. Every machine is warranted perfect, and if any part fails from imperfection, it will be supplied free of cost, upon return of the defective piece. The warranty does not apply to needles or shuttles, or the breakage by careless handling.

The following outfit accompanies each machine without extra charge: One dozen needles, assorted sizes; 6 bobbins, 1 gauge and screw, 1 extra check spring, 1 tucker, 1 ruffler, 1 set four widths of hemmers, 1 hemmer (used also for felling), 1 wrench, 1 screw driver, 1 oil can, 1 instruction book.

There will always be a demand for a low-priced sewing machine; for this reason we shall continue the Singer Model. We wish it understood, however, that we advise every purchaser to order our regular improved High Arm Sewing Machine, quoted on preceding page, as they are in *every way superior* to the Singer Model, and the difference in price is comparatively small.

Sewing Machine Needles and Attachments.

We can furnish duplicate parts for nearly every sewing machine now in use. In ordering sewing machine goods be sure and give name of machine, and *always* send sample of parts wanted, if possible. Weight of sewing machine needles: per doz., ½ oz.

28151 Machine Needles, Singer, the short one with plain shank used for our High Arm Sewing Machine & Co.'s old style Singer Model, Singer N. F. (new and old), also Home (old) and Blees.
Per doz.............$0.12

28153 Machine Needles, Singer, medium; the long, straight and plain shank needle.
Per doz.............12

28155 Machine Needles, Oscillating Singer for the machine having round shuttle, either flat or round shank. (Be sure and state which kind or send sample.)
Per doz.............18

28156 Machine Needles, Singer, latest improved vibrating shuttle, flat shank.
Per doz.............20

Sewing Machine Needles—Continued.

28158 Sewing Machine Needles, Montgomery Ward & Co.'s High Arm. There are three kinds. (Always send sample)........................$0.26

No. 11.

No. 12.

No. 13.

Above cuts show the different styles of our High Arm needles.

28159 Machine Needles for Montgomery Ward & Co.'s new Singer Model, No. 28150.
Per doz................$0.20

28160 Machine Needles round shank, American (plain), Davis (old). Domestic (plain), Grover & Baker (curved or straight), Household, Home-Shuttle, E. Howe, Remington (plain), St. John, Weed, Wilson, Wheeler & Wilson (curved or straight), and Wilson oscillating; White, three kinds (round shank, flat and automatic). If not certain of the kind send a sample...........18

28162 Machine Needles (flat shank), American self-setting, Crown, New Davis, Dauntless, Diamond, Ætna Improved, Florence, Howe, Guarantee, New Home, New Stewart, Remington (flat shank), Royal St. John, Domestic (flat shank), Domestic with shoulders shank, Eldredge, Victor, Whitney, Jennie June, Leader, White (flat shank), Whitehill, Springfield. Send sample in every case...........26

28164 Machine Needles, Wilcox & Gibbs.........26

28166 Goodrich Tuckers. Always give name of machine for which they are wanted. Each..........35

28168 One set 4 widths of hemmers, ⅜ to 1 in. in width, with good dress binder, all nickel plated and easily managed...........16

28175 Rufflers for Singer Machine...........18

28176 Johnson Rufflers for other machines (be sure and give name. Each..........5

Sewing Machine Shuttles.

There have been so many changes made in the running parts of different machines within the last few years that now nearly every machine in the market uses from one to three different styles of shuttles, and some few as many as five. It is absolutely necessary to send the old shuttles for a sample when a new shuttle is required. We give below the prices of a few of the most popular shuttles.

	Each.
28220 American, old style.........	$0.75
28221 American, No 7.........	.75
28222 Blees.........	.60
28224 Crown, old style.........	.75
28225 Crown, cylinder.........	1.25
28227 Dauntless Oscil.........	1.25
28228 Davis, 3 styles.........	.80
28230 Domestic, 4 styles.........	.75
28232 Eldredge, 4 styles.........	.75
28234 Florence , 2 styles.........	1.25
28236 Grover and Baker.........	1.25
28238 Howe, old.........	.75
28239 Howe, "B" and "G".........	1.25
28241 Hartford.........	1.25
28242 Household.........	.75
28243 Helpmate.........	.75
28245 Jennie June.........	.75
28246 Leader, substitute.........	1.25
28248 Montgomery Ward & Co.'s Singer Model, low arm.........	.75
28249 Montgomery Ward & Co.'s Singer Model, high arm.........	.75
28250 Montgomery Ward & Co.'s Singer, high arm, old style.........	.65
28251 Montgomery Ward & Co.'s, New Improved high arm.........	.75
28253 New Home.........	.75
28254 Remington, No. 1.........	.40
28255 Remington, No. 3.........	1.00
28256 Remington, No. 5.........	1.25
28257 Royal St. John, 2 styles.........	1.00
28258 St. John.........	1.00
28259 Springfield.........	.75
28261 Singer, N. F. and medium.........	.92
28262 Singer, V. S. high arm.........	1.00
28263 Singer, Oscillating.........	1.15
28265 Union.........	1.00
28266 Victor, old style.........	.90
28267 Victor, latest.........	1.00
28268 Weed, old style.........	.65
28269 Weed, cylinder.........	1.25
28270 White, 2 styles.........	.75
28271 Whitehill.........	1.25
28272 Wilson, old style.........	.60
28273 Wilson, Oscillating.........	1.25

Note.—We will be pleased to quote prices on shuttles not named in this list.

28282 1 Check Spring for Singer Machine......$0.03

28283 Spool Holder, weight 1 ounce.........20

28284 1 Spooler Rubber for Singer Machine.........05

Per dozen, weight 1 ounce..........35

28286 1 Bobbin for Singer Machine..........03

Per dozen, weight 1 ounce..........25

28288 1 Thumbscrew for Singer Machine.........08

Per dozen, weight 1 ounce.

28290 Sewing Machine Belts, round, each..........10

28291 Sewing Machine Belts, flat, each..........25

Weight, 3 ounces.

Magic Needle Threader.

See Index for Sewing Machine Oil.

28292 Magic Needle Threader to be used with any machine; a very useful and convenient article. Full directions with every threader.
Each..........$0.06

Per dozen..........85

262   MONTGOMERY WARD & CO.'S CATALOGUE No. 56.
CLOTHING DEPARTMENT.
For description of rules for self-measurement see opposite page.

Style No. 1.

Style No. 2.

Style No. 3.

Style No. 5.

Style No. 6.

Style No. 7.

Style No. 10.

Style No. 8.

Style No. 10. Open

Style No. 12.

Style No. 12.

Style No. 13.

Style No. 16.

Good Clothes Open All Doors.

Danish Proverb.

Our Clothing Department, one of the leading departments of our house, has grown to such proportion through giving our customers exceptionally good values in the past, that we are now placed in a position practically beyond all competition. This Fall and Winter we will offer special inducements to all our patrons, as well as those who are skeptical about buying away from home, by sending samples of some of our special drives to convince you of the merits of our clothing. We would gladly send samples of all our clothing, but manufacturers are constantly changing their styles, and in many cases we could not match the particular pattern you would want, but we never send an inferior *quality*. Our suits, single pants and overcoats embrace the following styles of cloth: Jeans, Cotton Worsteds, Satinets, Union Cassimeres, all wool, and Wool Cassimeres, Silk and Fancy Mixed Cassimeres, Blue Cloths and Flannels, Corduroys, Black and Fancy Cheviots, Black Diagonal Worsteds and Corkscrew Imported and Domestic Fancy Worsteds, Clay Worsteds, Broadcloths, Beavers, Meltons, Kerseys, Frieze Cloths, Chinchilla Beavers, Plushes, Waterproof Duck, Leather and Fur Coats. In fact, anything in Cheap, Medium and Good Clothing, our line was never so complete, especially in medium grades and prices, which is our stronghold and is demanded by the masses. A trial order almost invariably makes a permanent customer in our Mammoth Clothing Department. We call particular attention to our $3.00 Pants, $10.00 Suits and $10.00 Overcoats.

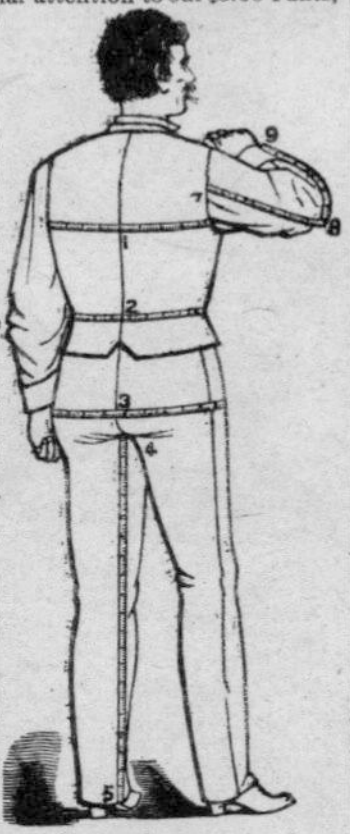

FOR COAT—Measurement to be taken over vest. Chest measure, adjust tape measure at figure 1 in cut, giving number of inches *around body*. Length of sleeve to elbow, from 7 to 8 per cut; from elbow to hand, 8 to 9 per cut.

FOR VEST—Measurement to be taken over vest and should be same as for coat.

FOR PANTS—Measurement around the body *under* vest for waist measure as figure 2, per cut; at figure 3 for hip measure, per cut; and for measure of inside seam, from 4 to 5 per cut.

FOR OVERCOAT—Same as for coat.

REMARKS—Give your height, weight and age. State whether you have stooping or square shoulders.

Average waist measurement for pants to correspond with coat and vest chest measure:

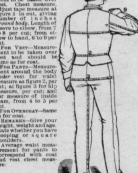

Coat and Vest Measures.	Pants Waist Measures.	Coat and Vest Measures.	Pants Waist Measures.
34	30 and 31	38	34 and 35
35	31 and 32	39	35 and 36
36	32 and 33	40	36 and 37
37	33 and 34	42	37 and 38

N. B.--The Illustrated figures on page 262 show cut and shape of clothing, as follows:

Style No. 1 represents Single Breasted Sack Suit.
Style No. 2 represents Single Breasted Square Cut Suit.
Style No. 3 represents Double Breasted Sack Suit.
Style No. 5 represents Three Button Cutaway Walking or Dress Suit.
Style No. 6 represents Single Breasted Prince Albert Dress Coat.
Style No. 7 represents Double Breasted Prince Albert Dress Coat.
Style No. 8 represents Full Dress Evening Suit.
Style No. 10 represents Single Breasted Fly Front Sack Overcoat.
Style No. 12 represents Double Breasted Storm Ulster, extra long.
Style No. 13 represents Single Breasted Prince Charles or Storm Coat, extra long.
Style No. 14 represents Double Breasted Loop Overcoat.
Style No. 16 represents Double Breasted Sack Overcoat.
Style No. 17 represents Double Breasted Pea Jacket.
Style No. 26 represents Children's Knee Pants Suits, corded.
Style No. 27 represents Children's Knee Pants Suits, pleated.
Style No. 28 represents Children's Knee Pants Suits, with double breasted coat.
Style No. 29 represents Children's Jersey Cloth Suits.
Style No. 30 represents Boys' and School Long Pant Suits, single breasted.
Style No. 31 represents Boys' and School Long Pant double breasted.
Style No. 33 represents Children's Cape Overcoats.
Style No. 34 represents Boys' Double Breasted Ulster Overcoats.
Style No. 35 represents Boy's Suit, Coat, Vest and Knee Pants; ages 10 to 15.

Men's Black and Blue Worsted Suits.

A Black Suit of Clothes is Never out of Fashion.

Our line is complete. A trial order will convince you how cheap we sell them.

We charge you less for a suit of black clothes made first-class than is usually charged for inferior makes by your merchants. Sizes 34 to 42 chest measure. Pant size 30 to 40 inch waist measure, and 30 to 35 inside seam measure. Half sizes are not made in ready made clothing.

N. B.—We do not sample any ready made clothing, except where stated in quotation.

Clay worsted suits weigh from 4 to 4½ lbs. according to size and quality.

Black Corkscrew Suits weigh from 4½ to 5 lbs. according to size and quality.

Black Worsted Suits weigh from 4½ to 5 lbs. according to size and quality.

30000 Black Diagonal Worsted Suits, Corkscrew weave. A suit to suit the times; good but cheap. Sample sent on application. Style 1, each ... $5.00
30001 Black Diagonal Worsted Corkscrew Weave. Style 1, each ... 6.75

30002 Black Diagonal Worsted Corkscrew weave. Style 5, each ... $7.25
30003 Blue Worsted, fancy weave and pattern. Style 2 ... $9.75

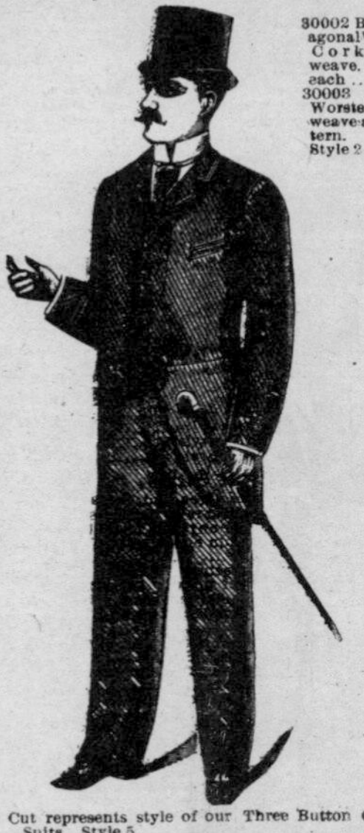

Cut represents style of our Three Button Cutaway Suits. Style 5.

Black Clay Worsteds have come to stay, the pattern is neat and desirable, and is dressy on all occasions; the effect is rich, its wearing qualities are unsurpassed. They are made in all grades and weights, both Foreign and Domestic. The domestic goods are now on the market, and are being sold as imported goods. It requires an expert to distinguish the difference before the goods are worn, and unless you are a competent judge of woolens, you are liable to buy the domestic fabric and regret your purchase when it is too late. We handle only the Genuine Imported Clay Worsteds, from the lowest to the best grades. We sell more Clay Worsteds and at cheaper prices than any other firm in this country, thus making us the headquarters for these goods. We request that you send for samples of Montgomery Ward & Co.'s guaranteed Clay Worsteds for comparison; the particular grade is made from 15 ounce goods, a weight suitable for winter or summer. Sack, single breasted, square front, or three button Cutaway styles, stitched edges.

30004 Black Suit, style 1 ... $10.00
30005 Black Suit, style 2 ... 10.00
30006 Black Suit, style 5 ... 10.00
30007 Black Diagonal Worsted, Corkscrew weave, style 1 ... 12.00
30008 Black Diagonal Worsted, Corkscrew weave. Style 5 ... 12.50
30009 Darkest Navy Blue Worsted, fancy plaid, Style 1 ... 12.00
30010 Black Diagonal Imported Clay Worsted suits, coat and vest bound. Style 1 ... 12.00
30011 Black Diagonal Imported Clay Worsted suits, coat and vest bound. Style 5 ... 12.75
30012 Black Diagonal Imported Clay Worsted suits. Style 1 ... 12.50
30013 Darkest Navy Blue Imported Diagonal Clay Worsted suits. Style 1 ... 12.50

Suits—Continued.

30014 Black Diagonal Imported Clay Worsted suits. Style 2 ... $12.75
30575 Darkest Navy Blue Imported Diagonal Clay Worsted suits. Style 2 ... 12.75
30576 Black Diagonal Imported Clay Worsted suits. Style 5 ... 13.00
30577 Darkest Navy Blue Imported Diagonal Clay Worsted Suits. Style 5 ... 13.00

Numbers 30012 to 30577 are made from an extra heavy weight of clay worsted.

30578 Black Worsted, fancy patterns and weaves. Style 1 ... 13.00
30579 Black Diagonal Imported Clay Worsted. Style 1 ... 14.00
30580 Black Diagonal Imported Clay Worsted, Style 2 ... 14.00
30581 Black Diagonal Imported Clay Worsted. Style 5 ... 14.50
30582 Darkest Navy Blue Diagonal Imported Clay Worsted. Style 2 ... 10.00
30583 Black Diagonal Imported Clay Worsted Suits. Coat and Vest bound. Style 1 ... 15.00
30584 Black Diagonal Imported Clay Worsted Suits. Coat and vest bound. Style 5 ... 15.50
30585 Black Imported Worsted, small neat seed pattern Style 1 ... 15.00
30586 Black Imported Worsted, small neat seed pattern. Style 2 ... 15.00
30587 Black Imported Worsted, small neat seed pattern. Style 5 ... 15.50
30588 Darkest Navy Blue Imported Worsted, small neat seed pattern. Style 1 ... 15.00
30589 Darkest Navy Blue Imported Worsted, small neat seed pattern. Style 2 ... 15.00
30590 Darkest Navy Blue Imported Worsted, small neat seed pattern. Style 5 ... 15.50
30591 Black Worsted, neat fancy check and fancy weave. Style 1 ... 15.50
30592 Black Diagonal Imported Clay Worsted, stitched edges. Style 1 ... 16.00
30593 Black Diagonal Imported Clay Worsted, stitched edges. Style 5 ... 16.50
30594 Black Diagonal Imported Clay Worsted Suits, "Regents," extra long cut coat, stitched edges. Style 5 ... 17.00
30595 Black Diogonal Imported Clay Worsted, stitched edges. Style 1 ... 17.50
30596 Black Diagonal Imported Clay Worsted, stitched edges. Style 5 ... 18.00
30597 Black Diagonal Imported Clay Worsted Suits, coat and vest bound. Style 1 ... 20.50
30598 Black Diagonal Imported Clay Worsted Suits, coat and vest bound. Style 5 ... 21.00
30599 Black Diagonal Imported Clay Worsted Suits, double breasted coat and double breasted vest, stitched edges. Style 3 ... 20.00
30600 Black Diagonal Imported Clay Worsted Suits, stitched edges. Style 7 ... 18.00
30601 Black Diagonal Imported Clay Worsted Suits, coat and vest bound. Style 7 ... 19.00
30602 Black Diagonal Imported Clay Worsted Suits. stitched edges. Style 6 ... 21.00
30603 Black Diagonal Imported Clay Worsted Suits, stitched edges. Style 7 ... 22.00
30604 Black Diagonal Imported Clay Worsted Suits, coat and vest bound. Style 7 ... 23.00
30605 Black Diagonal Imported German Worsted Suits. Style 7 ... 25.00
30606 Black Diagonal Imported Clay Worsted Suits, silk faced coat, coat and vest bound. Style 7 ... 27.00

Broadcloth Suits.

BROADCLOTH SUITS, STYLES 6, 7 AND 8.

Sizes, 35 to 42. Per Suit

30607 Black Broadcloth. Style 6 ... $23.06
30608 Black Broadcloth. Style 7 ... 24.00
30609 Men's Black Broadcloth, imported goods, full dress suit. Style 8 ... 86.00
30610 Men's Black Broadcloth, imported goods, extra fine quality, satin lined. Style 8 ... 40.00

Men's Suits.

The quotations under this heading are for a full suit; coat, vest and pants together. All men's sizes.

Before ordering suits, read instructions for measurement and remarks under same. Be sure and make your figures plain and correct. We cannot exchange single coats for another if size is wrong. Return full suit. Half sizes are not made in ready made clothing.

Sizes 34 to 42 only. Larger than 42 chest measure comes under the head of extra sizes. Waist measure for pants under this heading smallest, 30 inches; largest, 40 inches.

NOTE.—We take pleasure in announcing to our customers, that we will offer the most complete line of suits, from the lowest (well made) to the best grade in ready made clothing. All made from the best standard materials, and are absolutely correct in style, shape and finish. A great many people who are not thoroughly posted on clothing imagine that if a suit is not all wool it will not wear well. Such was the case years ago, but owing to the improved machinery and skilled workmen at the present time, we are able to manufacture some of the finest grades which have a fine cotton warp in the back, which adds weight, strength and durability, and cheapens the cost of production, while the face of the fabric is strictly all wool or sometimes silk mixed; will wear equally as well as any all wool suit. We never misrepresent our clothing, and late in the season we are sometimes obliged to substitute, using our best judgment, always to your advantage.

30613 Black and Old Gold Mixed diagonal cotton worsted. Style 1 ... 3.50
30614 Black and Gray Mixed satinet suitings. Style 1 ... 4.75

Caps—Continued.

31673 Men's Blue Cloth Conductor's Caps, with patent wire cloth frame; will always keep its shape. Without badge.
Each.............$1.50
Per doz........16.20

Frame Covered.

Uncovered.

Badges.

31676 Black Silk Gros Grain Ribbon Badges, printed in gold letters. We carry in stock the following: Messenger, Conductor, Brakeman, Porter, News Agent, Station Agent, Steward, Captain, Agent, Drayman, Hackman, Bellman, City Hotel, Omnibus Transfer and City Expressman, Each................$0.25
Printed badges with other lettering than above will have to be made to order, require five days to make, and cost 75 cents each.
31677 "News Agent," embroidered in gold wire block letters........$1.00
31678 "Brakeman," embroidered in gold wire block letters.........1.00
31679 "Conductor," embroidered in gold wire block letters, with double band of gold.
Each.............$1.50
Embroidered badges with over nine letters will cost 10c. for each additional letter.

INITIALS

31680 Gilt or silvered initials, two attached pins on each letter for fasteners. Cut represents ⅓ the size of letters. Each.$0.04
Per doz.............40

Boys' Winter Caps.

Sizes 6¼ to 7.
31689 Boys' Navy Blue All Wool Tricot Cloth Caps, pull-down black satin khan band, satin lined, silk embroidered top.
Each...........$0.75
Per doz..........8.10

31690 Boys' Double Knit Wool Caps, derby ribbed, seamless pull-down band, gray mixed or blue black.
Each..........$0.25
Per doz...........2.70

31691 Boys' Chinchilla Mask, felt lined; protects face ears and neck when drawn down, also can be worn as plain turban.
Each.............$0.40
Per doz..........4.32
31692 Boys' Blue Black Beaver Mask Caps. Same style as above.
Each.............$0.60
Per doz..........6.48

31691-31692.

31693 Boys' Dark Navy Blue Cloth Caps, winter yachting with pull down band, lined.
Each.............$0.45
Per doz..........4.86
31694 Boys' Brighton Caps, dark navy blue cloth, with pull-down band, lined.
Each.............$0.40
Per doz..........4.32

"Brighton."

31697 Boys' Windsor Caps, dark broken plaids and fancy mixtures, lined.
Each.............$0.30
Per doz...........3.24
31698 Boys' Windsor Caps, heavy weight, medium colors, broken plaid beaver, lined.
Each.............$0.50
Per doz...........5.40
31700 Boys' Windsor Caps, dark gray Scotch knit cloth, square crown, lined.
Each.........$0.40 Per doz....$4.32

Windsor.

Caps—Continued.

31703 Boys' Dark Mixed Mottled Turbans, extra heavy double knit Scotch wool, pull-down band.
Each.............$0.50
Per doz...........5.40

31704 Boys' Academy Caps, medium dark fancy plaid cassimeres, pull down band; lined.
Each.............$0.50
Per doz...........5.40
"Academy" 31704

31705 Boys' Black Silk Plush Turbans, pieced; silk lined, pull down band.
Each.............$0.50
Per doz...........5.40

31705

31706 Boys' Black Silk Plush Turbans; square crown, pull down band; lined.
Each.............$0.65
Per doz...........7.00
31707 Boys' Black Silk Plush Turbans. Very fine; satin lined, square crown, pull down band.
Each..............85
Per doz..........9.18

31709 Boys' Black Silk Plush Winter Yachting Caps, with pull down band; neat ornament in front; lined.
Each.............$0.75
Per doz...........8.10

Men's Cold Weather Caps.
Sizes 6¾ to 7½.

31710 Men's Genuine Gray Mixed Scotch Caps; lined, full shape.
Each.............$0.30
Per doz...........3.24
31711 Men's Genuine Scotch Caps; dark navy blue, lined; full shape.
Each.............$0.30
Per doz...........3.24

31713 Men's Genuine Scotch Caps; dark navy blue, lined. Extra heavy, full shape.
Each...............45
Per doz...........4.86
31714 Men's Improved Genuine Scotch Caps, dark heather mixed, with inside adjustable band which pulls down and protects forehead, neck and ears. Each...........50
Per doz...........5.40
31715 Men's Improved Genuine Scotch Caps; dark navy blue, same style as above. Each....$0.50
Per doz...........5.40
31718 Men's Chinchilla Mask Caps; felt lined, protects face, ears and neck when drawn down; also can be worn as plain Turban.
Each.............$0.50
Per doz...........5.40
31719 Men's Blue Black Beaver Mask Caps; same style as above.
Each.............$1.00
Per doz..........10.80

31727 Men's Brighton Caps. Assorted, dark and medium plaids. Mixed Cassimeres, lined. Pull down band.
Each.............$0.25
Per dozen..........2.70

"Brighton."

31728 Men's Brighton Caps. Dark Navy Blue Cassimere, lined, pull down band.
Each.............$0.45
Per dozen..........4.86

The Brighton Cap.

31729 Men's Brighton Caps. Dark Oxford Mixed Frieze Cloth, satin lined, pull down band.
Each.............$0.60
Per dozen..........6.48
31730 Men's Brighton Caps, made of black astrakhan plush, satin lined, pull down band.
Each.............$1.00
Per dozen..........10.80

Caps—Continued.

31731 Men's Black, Oil Tanned Leather Caps, quilted lining; large pull down band. "The Viking." Each..$0.75
Per doz...........8.10
"The Viking."

31732 Men's Windsor Caps, Dark, Broken Plaid Cassimere, lined.
Each.............$0.25
Per dozen..........2.70
31733 Men's Windsor Caps, medium dark cassimere, assorted, medium and dark colors, lined.
Each.............$0.50
Per dozen..........5.40
Windsor.

31734 Men's Genuine Scotch Windsor Caps. Dark Navy Blue, lined. Each..$0.45
Per dozen..........4.86
31735 Men's Windsor Caps, extra heavy, smooth finish, blue black beaver, satin lined. Each....$1.00
Per dozen..........8.10
Windsor.

31736 Men's Storm King Caps, made of Chinchilla, felt lined, large sliding band.
Each.............$0.50
Per doz...........5 40
"Storm King."

31737 Men's Blue Black Beaver, smooth finish. Storm King Caps, felt lined, large sliding band.
Each.............$0.75
Per doz. 8.10

"Winter Tourist."

31743 Men's latest style Winter Tourists' Cap, dark gray mixed cassimere, lined, telescope top to pull down over ears. Each...........50
Per doz...........5.40

Men's Plush Caps.

Silk Plush Caps, strictly high grade, unsurpassed for style finish and durability. We guarantee all caps to be exactly as represented. Note the great reduction in prices. Fur caps we do not handle, as they give very poor satisfaction, but can quote price of styles that are in market if desired.

31744 Men's Black Silk Plush Turbans, one piece, square crown, double roll band, lined.
Each.............$0.75
Per doz..........8.10

31745 Men's Black Silk Plush Turbans, round crown, double roll band, satin lined.
Each.............$1.00
Per doz..........10.80

31746 Men's Black Silk Plush Windsor Caps, one piece top, double roll band, satin lined.
Each.............$0.75
Per doz..........8.10

Plush Windsor.
31747 Men's Black Silk Plush Windsor Caps, six piece top, double roll band, satin lined
Each..............1.00
Per doz..........10.80
31755 Men's Black Silk Plush Windsor Caps, six piece top, double roll band, satin lined.
Each..............1.25
Per doz..........13.50
31757 Men's Black Silk Plush Windsor Caps, six piece top, double roll band, extra satin lined.
Each..............1.50
Per doz..........16.20
31759 Men's Black Silk Plush Windsor Caps, one piece, block top, double roll band, extra satin lined. Each..............1.75
Per doz..........18.90

There never was a better year to buy.

Caps—Continued.

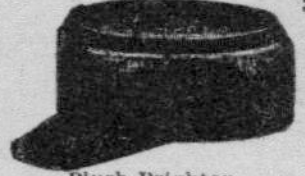

31760 Men's Black Silk Plush Brighton Caps, one piece top; lined; pull down band. Each.................$0.75 Per doz............... 8.10

Plush Brighton.

31763 Men's Black Silk Plush Brighton Caps, one piece top; satin lined; pull down band. Each............................$ 1.00 Per doz.............................. 10.80

31764 Men's Black Silk Plush Brighton Caps, one piece top; extra satin lined; pull down band. Each ....$1.50. Per doz..........16.20

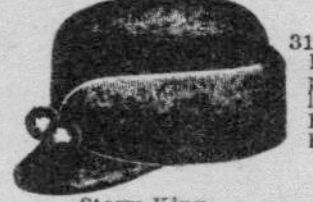

31768 Men's Black Silk Plush Storm King Caps; pull down band; satin lined. Each..................$ 1.50 Per doz............. 16.20

Storm King.

31769 Men's Black Silk Plush Yachting Caps, telescope top; pull down band; satin lined. Each...$ 1.00 Per doz..........10.80

31769-31770

31770 Men's Black Silk Plush Yachting Caps, telescope top; pull down band; satin lined. Each .... $1.25 Per doz 13.50

N. B.—Price governs quality on all plush caps.

Ladies' Silk Plush Caps.

Sizes 6¾ to 7⅛

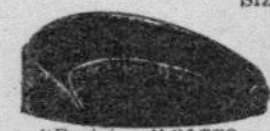

31772 Ladies' Black Silk Plush Caps, Parisian style, double roll band and adjustable visor, extra satin lined. Each..$1.25 Per doz............ 13.50

"Parisian," 31772

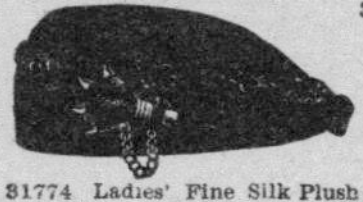

31773 Ladies' Fine Plush Caps, "The Persian." Trimmed with astrakhan fur, roll band, with ornament on side. Each........$1.75 Per doz........18.90

31774 Ladies' Fine Silk Plush Caps, "The Persian." Trimmed with mink fur, roll band, with ornament on side. Each .... 1.50 Per doz...16.20

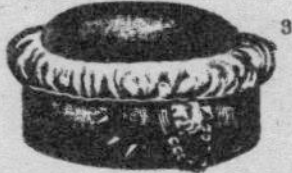

31775 Ladies' Fine Black Silk Plush Turbans, "The Arctic," roll band, trimmed with white Grebe breast feathers, ornament on side. Each.....................$2.00 Per doz...................21.60

Children's Caps.

Sizes, 6¼ to 6¾.

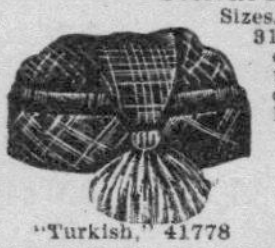

31778 Child's Turkish Caps, cardinal and navy broken plaid flannel, roll band, silk tassel on side, lined. Each....$0.45 Per doz.......................... 4.86

"Turkish," 41778

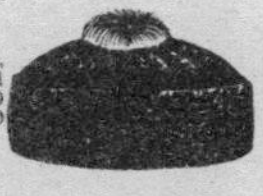

31779 Child's Caps, navy blue, soft nap chinchilla, roll band turban. Each..........$0.50 Per doz..................... 5.40

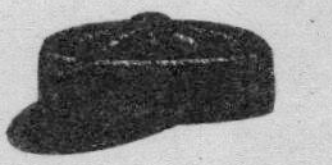

31780 Child's Velvet Caps, turn-down band, gathered top. Colors: wine, navy or seal. Each..................$0.50 Per doz.......................... 5.40

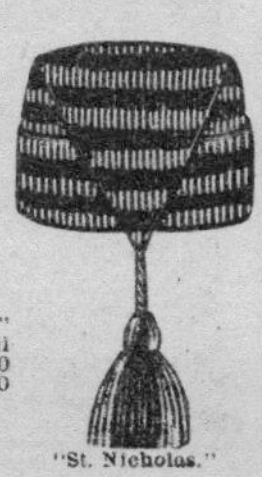

31781 Child's "St. Nicholas" Cap, double knit wool, roll band. Each...............$0.50 Per dozen.................... 5.40

"St. Nicholas."

Caps—Continued.

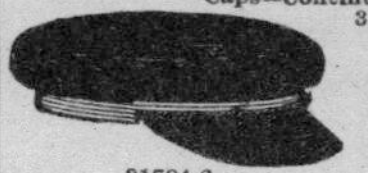

31784 Child's Velvet Caps, double gilt cord band in front, lined. Colors: dark brown, wine or cardinal. Each...........$0.50 Per dozen....... 5.40

31784-6

31786 Child's Silk Plush Caps, gold tinsel braid in front, satin lined, with ear muffs to match. Colors: reseda, royal blue, golden brown or heliotrope. Each.. .75 Per dozen.. 8.10

Medium Weight Caps.

Children's, 6¼ to 6⅞.

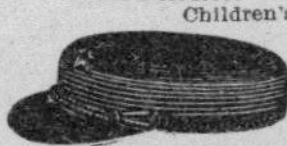

31788 "Little Puck" child's navy blue cloth caps, trimmed with black hercules braid and silk cord; star ornament in front. Weight, 2 oz. Each..$0.50 Per doz..................... 5.40

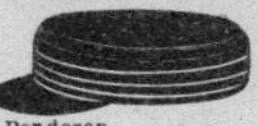

31791 "The Junior" child's navy blue cloth jockey caps, trimmed with 3 rows silver tinsel braid, very neat and dressy.. Weight, 2 oz. Each ....$0.40 Per dozen.................................... 4.32

Yacht Caps.

ALL THE RAGE.

Children's and Misses', sizes 6¼ to 7.

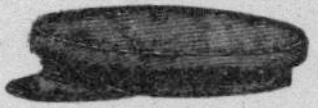

31793 "The Ferris Wheel" children's or misses' yacht caps made of plain flannel, good quality, lined, narrow gilt band in front, gilt buttons. Colors: navy, fawn, cardinal or gray. Weight, 2 oz. Each..................................$0.37 Per dozen.. 4.00

31795 "The Altoona" Misses' and Children's yacht caps, navy blue flannel, cord band, fancy lining; sizes, 6¼ to 7; weight, 2 oz. Each........ .40 Per doz.. 4.32

31802 "The Grassmere." Men's Fine Cassimere Yacht Cap. Small mixed plaid patterns, medium and light colors; an ideal summer cap; mention size. Each.. .50 Per dozen.. 5.40

31804 "The Portsmouth." Men's dark blue yacht caps, lined, trimmed with double black silk cord band, made of fine broadcloth; mention size. Each.. .50 Per dozen.. 5.40

31806 "The Lakeside." Men's yacht caps, made of fine quality blue black corkscrew worsted cloth, trimmed with heavy double black silk cord band, ½ inch black silk ribbon and buttons to match, leather sweat bands, fancy lining. Each.. .60 Per dozen.. 6.40

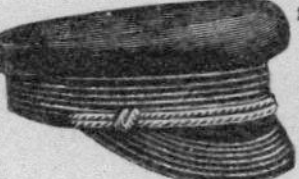

31808 "The Palatka." Men's navy blue broadcloth yacht caps, lined, 1 inch black hercules braid and double black silk cord trimming, ½ inch hercules braid on visor; mention size. Each.$0.65 Per dozen............ 7.00

Ladies' Caps.

Sizes, 6½ to 7¼; average weight, 2 oz.

31809 "The Puritan." Ladies' yacht caps, made of fine quality flannel, silk cord band, fancy lining. Colors: Navy blue, white, cardinal and fawn. Mention color and size. Each..........$0.50 Per doz.. 5.40

31810 "The Regatta." Ladies' Extra Fine Quality Broadcloth Yacht Caps, satin lined, trimmed with one inch hercules braid, silk cord band, a beautiful cap; colors: tan or marine blue; sizes, 6½ to 7¼. Each......$1.00 Per dozen.........10.80

Boys' Caps.

Sizes, 6½ to 7. Average weight, 2 oz.

31811 "The Topeka." Boys' Light Colored Fancy Plaid Cloth Yacht Caps, gray mixtures, 1 inch fancy hercules braid trimming, double silk cord band; sizes, 6½ to 7. Each, 45c Per dozen.....$4.86

31812 "The Admiral." Boys' Dark Navy Blue Broadcloth Yacht Caps, trimmed with 1 inch black hercules braid, double black silk cord and buttons to match, very dressy; sizes, 6½ to 7. Each.................. $0.55 Per dozen........... 6.00

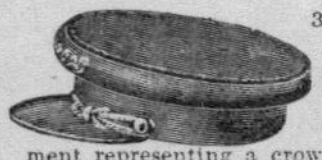

31813 "The Commodore." Boys' extra fine quality navy blue broadcloth Yacht Caps, satin lined, heavy braided double gold cords and buttons to match. Beautiful ornament representing a crown, embroidered in gold, silver and scarlet tinsel wire on front of cap. Handsomest yacht cap in the market; sizes, 6½ to 7. Each ....$0.75 Per dozen.. 8.10

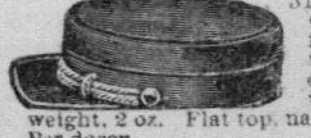

31814 Boys' University Caps, made of good quality navy blue flannel, lined; trimmed with double gilt cord and buttons; leather visor; sizes, 6½ to 7; weight, 2 oz. Flat top, navy style. Each ....$0 35 Per dozen.. 3.80

Caps—Continued.

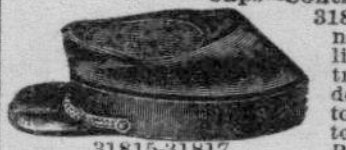

31815 Boys' Soldier Caps, navy blue broadcloth, lined, heavy leather visor, trimmed with heavy double gold cord and buttons to match; sizes, 6½ to 7. Each ....$0.50 Per dozen............. 5.40

31815-31817

31816 Boys' Soldier Caps, same as above, with ornament of two-crossed guns; sizes, 6½ to 7, blue or gray. Each.... ...$0.55. Per dozen.........$6.00

Special attention will be given to orders from schools, clubs and boys' military organizations for the above caps.

Men's Caps.

Sizes 6⅞ to 7⅝. Average weight, 3 ounces.

31817 Mens' Soldier Caps, same shape as 31815, made of fine quality broadcloth, trimmed with ½ inch black patent leather band and brass buttons. Extra heavy leather visor, leather sweat band. Colors: Navy blue or cadet gray; mention color and size. Each....$0.75. Per dozen.... $8.10

Yacht Caps.

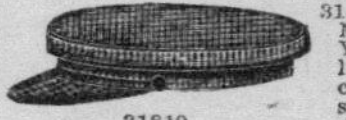

31818 "The Florida." Men's navy blue flannel Yacht Caps, full top, lined, double black silk cord band, medium-shaped visor. Mention size. Each.......$0.37 Per dozen 4.00

31819

31819 "The Gordon." Men's plain navy blue Yacht Cap lined, 1 inch black hercules, braid trimming and double black silk cord band, medium shape. Mention size Each.....$0.45. Per dozen..........4.86

SHIRTS.

Men's Negligee Overshirts.

WORKING, BOATING, TENNIS, CYCLISTS', TOURISTS' FIREMEN'S AND BLUE FLANNEL SHIRTS.

Weight of men's overshirts average as follows: Light summer weight, 7 to 10 ounces; medium weights, 10 to 15 ounces; heavy weights, 18 to 25 ounces. Sizes, 14½ to 17 only. Always give neck measure.

N. B.—We do not sample overshirts.

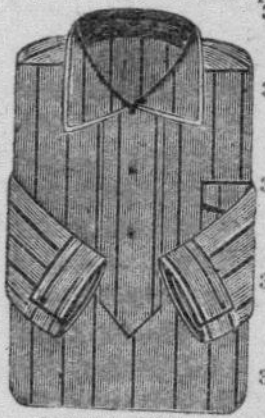

32281 Men's Overshirts, fancy stripe cotton, medium colors, no pocket. Each.......$0.25 Per doz..................... 2.70

32283 Men's Overshirts, neat stripes, heavy twilled cotton working shirt, handkerchief pocket. Each...........$0.42 Per doz....................... 4.54

32284 Men's Overshirts, neat stripes, domette flannel, medium colors, handkerchief pocket. Each...........$0.50 Per doz 5.40

32286 Men's Overshirts, striped moleskin, medium dark colors, handkerchief pocket. Each ....$0.50 Per doz......................... 5.40

32281 to 32302.

32288 Men's Overshirts, heavy twilled cotton buckskin cloth with nap on the inside, yoke back, handkerchief pocket, pearl buttons. Each, $0.75 Per doz.............$8.10

32290 Men's Overshirts, striped cassimere shirting, medium colors, yoke back, handkerchief pocket, pearl buttons. Each, $0.75. Per doz.... 8.10

32292 Men's Overshirts, neat stripe heavy moleskin, yoke back, handkerchief pocket, pearl buttons. Each...........$0.75 Per doz............. 8.10

32294 Men's Overshirts, fancy stripe, wool mixed, twilled cassimere, dark colors, handkerchief pocket. Each..$0.80 Per doz............. 8.64

32296 Men's Overshirts, fancy stripe, twilled union cassimere, yoke back, handkerchief pocket, pearl buttons. Each, $0.85. Per doz.... 9.18

32298 Men's Overshirts, heavy wool cassimere, with fine cotton warp to keep from shrinking, handkerchief pocket, pearl buttons, neat stripes medium colors. Each, $1.50. Per doz.........16.20

32300 Men's Overshirts, extra fine wool flannel, in neat stripes, good weight, yoke back, handkerchief pockets. Each......$2.00 Per doz...$21.60

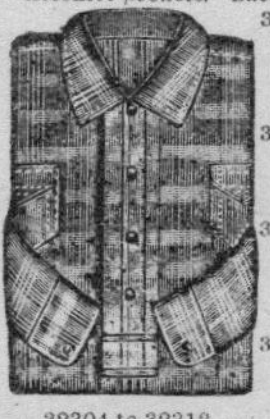

32302 Men's Overshirts, pure silk, neat stripes, beautiful colorings, French yoke back, watch and handkerchief pockets, pearl buttons. Each.............................$3.50

32304 Men's Overshirts, plaid domette flannel, medium dark colors, handkerchief pocket. Each..........$0.40 Per doz. 4.32

32306 Men's Overshirts, neat plaids, heavy twilled cotton buckskin cloth, with nap on inside, yoke back, handkerchief pockets, pearl buttons Each. $0.75 Per doz..$8.10

32308 Men's Overshirts, fancy plaid twilled union flannel, handkerchief pocket, medium colors. Each...$0.75 Per doz 8.10

32304 to 32312

32310 Men's Overshirts, neat broken plaids, twilled cassimere, yoke back, handkerchief pocket, pearl buttons. Each..$1.00 Per doz..10.80

32312 Men's Overshirts, fancy silk mixed plaid, twilled union cassimere, yoke back, handkerchief pockets, pearl buttons. Each.....................$1.25 Per doz....................13.50

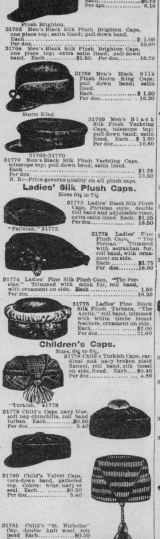

Children's Cambric Dresses.

Children's Dresses average 3 ounces in weight.

33082

33080 Child's White Cambric Dress, three plaits down front, flounce on neck and sleeves, hemmed at bottom of skirt; No. 3, 3 years. Each..........$0.40

33082 Child's White Cambric Dress, solid Hamburg yoke, hemmed at bottom. No. 1, 1 year; No. 2, 2 years; No. 3, 3 years. Each.............60

33084

33084 Child's White Cambric Dress, tucked yoke, Hamburg trimming on neck and sleeves, tucked and hemmed at bottom. No. 1, 1 year; No. 2, 2 years; No. 3, 3 years. Each..........$0.75

33086 Child's White Cambric Dress, elegantly trimmed with Hamburg on neck, sleeves and down front, Hamburg ruffle 6 inches deep at bottom. No. 1, 1 year; No. 2, 2 years; No. 3, 3 years. Each.............1.15

Infants' Cambric and Flannel Skirts.

Children's skirts average six ounces in weight.

33089 Infant's Long White Cambric Skirt, four tucks and four-inch ruffle at bottom. Each..........$0.50 Per dozen....5.40

33091 Infant's Long White Cambric Skirt, with waist, tucked and trimmed with Hamburg at bottom....$0.75 Per doz............8.10

33093 Infant's Long White Cambric Skirt with 9½ inch hamburg at bottom. Each............$ 1.00 Per dozen......... 10.80

Flannel Skirt.

33095 Infant's All Wool Long Flannel Skirt, scalloped and embroidered with silk at bottom one inch deep......$1.25 Per dozen........13.50

33097 Infant's All Wool Long Flannel Skirts scalloped and embroidered with silk at bottom 2½ inches deep........$1.50 Per dozen.........16.20 Cut represents style only, not pattern of embroidery.

33099 Infant's All Wool Long Flannel Skirt, scalloped and embroidered with silk at bottom 3 inches deep. Each......$1.75. Per dozen....$21.60

Infants' Embroidered Flannel Shawls or Blankets.

33100 Infant's Cream White All Wool Flannel Shawl or Blanket; silk stitched scalloped edges and silk embroidered on corner; size, 24x24 inches.
Each............$0.70
Per doz.............7.56

33102 Infant's Cream White All Wool Flannel Shawl or Blanket, silk stitched scalloped edges, with cluster of silk embroidered flowers on corner. Size, 27x27 inches.
Each..........$1.00
Per doz...........10.80

33104 Infant's Cream White All Wool Flannel Shawl or Blanket; embroidered edge with one inch fancy silk all around, large silk embroidered flower on corner; size, 29x29 inches.
Each............$1.25
Per doz..............13.50

Flannel Shawl.

33104½ Infant's Cream White All Wool Flannel Shawl or Blanket; silk stitched, scalloped edges, silk embroidered vines, flowers and butterflies on one corner and flower design on diagonal corner. All embroidered in light blue. Size, 33x33 inches.
Each...............2.00
Per doz.............21.60

Infants' Outfits.

33105 Cambric Robe, Hamburg inserting and edging down front and on sleeves.......$1.06
1 White Flannel Blanket, scalloped in silk embroidered silk flower on corner...........70
1 Cambric Night Slip.............35
1 Cambric Day Slip...............75
1 Cambric Skirt, with waist...............82
1 Cambric Shirt, lace trimmed..............22
2 Saxony Wool Shirts, 30..............90
2 Pair Wool Bootees, 15..............30
1 Flannel Band, hemstitched, herring bone silk stitched..........20
1 Flannel Pinning Skirt, or Barrie Coat, 33 inches long..........60
1 Long Flannel Skirt, 32 inches long........1.10
13 pieces, price per outfit...............$6.70
The above articles are sold separately if desired. Weight, 26 ounces.

33165 1 Cambric Robe, elegantly trimmed with tucking and inserting from neck to bottom......$1.75
1 Flannel Blanket, scalloped in silk embroidered silk flower on corner............1.25
1 Cambric Night Slip...............47
1 Cambric Day Slip...............92
1 Cambric Skirt, with waist...............97
1 Cambric Shirt, lace trimmed..............31
2 Saxony Wool Shirts, 30..............60
2 Pair Wool Bootees, 20..............40
1 Bib..............06
1 Flannel Band, hemstitched, herring-bone silk stitched............20
1 Flannel Pinning Skirt, or Barrie Coat, herring-bone, silk stitched..............75
1 Long Flannel Skirt, herring-bone, silk hemstitched............1.25
14 pieces, price per outfit...............$8.83
The above articles are sold separately if desired. Weight, 40 ounces.

33107 Fine Muslin Robe handsomely trimmed with inserting and fine tucking all over front, Hamburg edge around bottom.........$2.62
1 Flannel Blanket, scalloped in silk, very large silk embroidered flower on corner........1.75
1 Cambric Night Slip...............47
1 Cambric Day Slip, trimmed down front with inserting, Hamburg flounce..............1.80
1 White Skirt, with waist, Hamburg flounce......1.12
1 Cambric Shirt, lace trimmed..............53
2 Saxony Wool Shirts, 30..............60
2 Pair Wool Bootees, 20..............40
2 Bibs, laced trimmed, 11..............22
1 Short Dress, embroidery, fine tucked yoke, skirt falling from yoke..............2.25
1 Flannel Band, herring-bone silk, hemstitched....20
1 Flannel Pinning Skirt, or Barrie Coat, herring-bone, silk stitched..............75
1 Long Flannel Skirt, with 3 clusters of 3 tucks each..............1.50
16 pieces, price per outfit...............$14.27
The above articles are sold separately if desired. Weight, 46 ounces.

Ladies' Summer Skirts.

Weight, 9 to 16 ounces.

33110 Ladies' Skirts, blue and white striped wash poplin, knife and box plaits at bottom. Per doz.. $0.50
5.40

Skirts—Continued.

33113 Ladies' Skirts, blue gray mixed wash poplin, heading of same with deep knife plaits, with four rows of white braid or plaits. Weight, 12 ounces.
Each..........$1.00
Per doz.........10.80

33114 Ladies' Skirts, extra fine silk finish, mohair, silver gray box plaits.
Each..........$2.00
Per dozen........21.60

33116 Ladies' Black Sateen Skirts, with 3½-inch ruffle at bottom. Each.............$0.65
Per dozen.............7.00

33118 Ladies' Fast Black Sateen Skirts, 3-inch ruffle trimmed with 2-inch black yak lace. Each...$1.00 Per doz.10.80

Ladies' Flannel, Melton Mackinaw and Sateen Skirts.

Prices govern quality on all Melton skirts. Weight from 12 to 24 ounces.

33121 Ladies Mackinaw Skirts, made of gray mottled heavy napped cotton skirting, with five-inch quilting at bottom. Each..........$0.60 Per dozen 6.48

33123 Ladies Dark Gray Mixed Melton Skirts 1¼-inch piped heading and 2-inch ruffle. Each...$0.60 Per doz.....6.48

33125 Ladies Dark Gray Mixed Melton Skirts, black sateen heading, embroidered 3¾ in. ruffle at bottom. Each...$0.75 Per doz........8.10

33127 Ladies' Dark Gray Mixed Melton Skirts, very large, 1 in. head-ing, 3¾ in. ruffle. Each.....$0.85 Per doz.......9.18

Skirts—Continued.

33129 Ladies' Gray Mixed Melton Skirts, two rows of black velvet with silk, embroidered designs and 5½ in. ruffle at bottom.
Each.......$1.00
Per doz....10.80

33129

33131 Ladies' Oxford Mixed Melton Skirts, 5½ in. ruffle, elegantly embroidered with silk floss.
Each.....$1.25
Per doz....13.50

33131

33133 Ladies' Blue Gray Mixed Melton Skirts, 7 in. ruffle, with silk embroidered scalloped and neat design at bottom.
Each.....$1.50
Per doz....16.20

33133

33135 to 33139

33137 Ladies' Fast Black Sateen Skirts, lined with striped domette flannel; 15 inch heavy quilting at bottom. Each.......$1.00
Per doz.............10.80

33139 Ladies' Fast Black Sateen Skirts, lined with domette flannel, 14 inch heavy quilting, bound at bottom with velvet. Each.......1.25
Per doz.............13.50

33141 Ladies' Fast Black Sateen Skirts, lined with fast black cotton, knife pleats 4 inches deep. Each.......1.35
Per doz.............14.58

33143 Ladies' Fast Black Sateen Skirts, lined with fast black cotton, 6 inch ruffle, scalloped and embroidered in silk. Each.......1.50
Per doz.............16.20

33153 Ladies' Knit Skirts, 30 inches long; made of Egyptian cotton. Colors: Sanitary brown, mixed or plain black.
Each..............$0.50
Per doz.............. 5.40

33155 Ladies' Improved Knit All Wool Skirts, crochet stitch. Will not shrink, ravel or sag when worn. French yoke band. Length, 38 inches; weight, 16 ounces. Colors: Black, navy blue or sanitary brown, mixed.
Each.............. $ 1.50
Per doz.............16.20

33153

33157 Children's and Misses' Improved Knit All Wool Skirts, crochet stitch. Will not shrink, ravel or sag. Colors: Cardinal, navy blue or sanitary brown, mixed.
Size, 18 inch. Each....$0.60
Per doz...............6.48
Size, 22 inch. Each......90
Per doz................9.72
Size, 28 inch. Each....1.20
Per doz...............12.96

33159 Ladies' Divided Skirts, all wool, crochet stitch; cardinal only, 24 or 27 inch. To close, until sold.......$1.00

33159

Tights—Continued.

33161 Ladies' Equestrienne Tights, made of fast black combed Egyptian cotton; small, medium and large sizes.
Per pair..........$ 1.00
Per doz...........10.80

33162 Ladies Equestrienne Tights, made of black worsted; small, medium and large sizes.
Per pair...........$ 1.35
Per doz............14.58

33164 Ladies' Equestrienne Tights, made of fine imported Saxony yarn; small, medium and large sizes.
Per pair............$ 1.60
Per doz.............17.28

33166 Ladies' Equestrienne Tights, made of extra heavy, fine imported Saxony yarn; small, medium and large sizes.
Per pair..........$ 2.00
Per doz...........21.60

GLOVES AND MITTS.

Infants' Misses' and Ladies' Mitts, Wool, Worsted and Silk.

Weight of children's and ladies' mitts, 1 to 3 ounces; men's 4 to 7 ounces.

33300 Infants' Cashmere Wool Mitts, fancy silk stitched wrists. Colors: Cardinal, light blue, black or white.
Per pair.............$0.23
Per dozen.............2.50

33301 Infants' Saxony Wool Mitts, fancy wrists; Colors: Cardinal, light blue, black or white.
Per pair............$0.10 Per dozen.......1.08

33304 Infants' Saxony Wool Mitts, silk woven in on outside. Colors: Black or white. Per pair......35
Per dozen...........3.78

33306 Children's Plain Wool Mitts, colors, black and white.
Size 2, per pair...........09
Per dozen...............90
Size 4, per pair...........10
Per dozen..............1.00
Size 5, per pair...........11
Per dozen..............1.18

33307 Children's Plain Wool Mitts. Colors: Navy blue, seal brown.
Until sold per pair.........05

33308 Children's and Misses' Cashmere Wool Mitts. Black only. Sizes 3, 4 and 5.
Per pair.............$0.12 Per dozen.............1.30

33309 Children's and Misses' Cashmere Wool Mitts. Colors: Seal brown, wine, navy blue.
Until sold per pair.........07

33310 Misses and Children's Double Knit Wool Mitts. Made of fine saxony wool, black only.
Per pair...........$0.25 Per dozen............2.70

33311 Misses and Children's Double Knit Wool Mitts. Made of fine saxony. Colors: Wine or seal brown.
Until sold per pair.........18

33312 Misses' and Children's Double Knit Wool Mitts, fancy back, made of fine Saxony yarn. Black only. Assorted sizes. Per pair......30
Per dozen.............3.24

33313 Misses' and Children's Double Knit Wool Mitts, fancy, made of fine Saxony yarn. Wine, seal brown. Assorted sizes. Per pair......30

33314 Ladies' Plain Wool Knit Mitts, derby ribbed wrists. Black only. Per pair......$0.10
Per doz................1.08

33315 Ladies' Cashmere Wool, Knit Mitts, fancy knit wrist. Black only. Per pair.........25
Per doz................2.70

33317 Ladies' Cashmere Wool Knit Mitts, plain and fancy wrist; colors: Wine, navy blue, or seal brown. Until sold. Per pair.......15

33319 Ladies' fine Saxony Wool Knit Mitts, fancy open work back. Black only. Per pair.......28
Per dozen..............3.02

33320 Ladies' Double Knit Saxony Wool Mitts. With derby ribbed wrist. Black only. Per pair......25
Per dozen..............2.70

33323 Ladies' fine Saxony Wool Mitts, Double Knit, with neat satin bow on back. Black only.
Per pair............$0.38 Per doz.............4.10

33324 Ladies' Double Knit Mitts, made of fine coral Saxony yarn, fancy open work back.
Per pair................40
Per dozen..............4.32

33325 Ladies' Double Knit Mitts. Made of fine Saxony yarn, fancy open work back. Colors: Wine, seal brown or navy blue. Until sold.
Per pair................25

33326 Ladies' Double Knit Mitts. Made of fine Saxony yarn, fancy open work stitch on back and cuff. Black only. Per pair......50
Per dozen..............5.40

33328 Ladies' Double Knit Mitts, very fine Saxony on outside, with Angora wool lining, very warm; black only. Per pair..........60
Per dozen..............6.48

Ladies' Silk Mitts.

33326 Ladies' Plain Silk Mitts, derby ribbed wrist. Black only. Per pair.....$0.45 Per dozen $4.86

33330 Ladies' Plain Silk Mitts, derby ribbed wrists. Colors: Wine, seal brown or navy blue. Until sold, per pair......55

33331 Ladies' Spun Silk Mitts, knit double, silk on outside and cashmere wool on inside. Black only. Per pair............$0.60. Per dozen....6.48

33332 Ladies' Spun Silk Mitts, knit double, silk on outside and cashmere wool on inside. Colors: Wine, seal brown or navy blue. Until sold, per pair.....50

33333 Ladies' Silk Mitts, knit double, cashmere wool lined, fancy open work stitch on back. Black only. Per pair......$1.00. Per dozen...10.80

33334 Ladies' Silk Mitts, knit double, cashmere wool lined, fancy open work stitch on back. Colors: Wine, seal brown or navy blue. Until sold, per pair.........75

33335 Ladies' Double Silk Mitts, fancy open work stitch on back and wrist, with neat silk cord and belt ornament on back. Black only.
Per pair............$1.50 Per dozen..........$16.20

33336 Ladies' Double Silk Mitts, finest grade, fancy open work stitch on back and wrist, with neat satin bow on back. Black only.
Per pair............$2.00 Per dozen..........21.60

33337 Ladies' Double Silk Mitts, fancy open work stitch on back and wrist, with neat satin bow to match on back. Colors: Wine, navy blue or seal brown. Until sold, per pair.......1.25

N. B.—Ladies' Silk Mitts make a very acceptable and useful present or Christmas gift. Numbers 33307, 33309, 33301, 33313, 33317, 33325, 33330, 33334 and 33337 are special bargains. The prices are below manufacturers' cost. Give first and second choice of colors.

Boys' Mitts.

33341 Boys' All Wool Heather Mixed Double Knit Mitts, for rough wear. Per pair........$0.18
Per dozen.............1.95

33342 Boys' Double Knit All Wool Mitts, wine, seal brown, navy blue or black. Per pair.......18
Per dozen.............1.95

33344 Boys' Double Knit Wool Mitts, large size, colors as above. Per pair....$0.20. Per dozen....2.16

33346 Youth's Double Knit Wool Mitts, same colors as above. Per pair..............22
Per dozen.............2.38

33348 Boys' and Youths' Fulled Mackinaw Mitts, heavy weight. Per pair.....$0.15. Per dozen....1.62

33349 Boys' Scotch Wool Gloves, assorted styles and sizes. Per pair.....$0.25. Per dozen....2.75

Men's Knit Wool Mitts.

33350 Men's Double Knit Mitts; colors: Black, seal or navy. Per pair....$0.25 Per dozen....$2.70

33352 Men's Double Knit Saxony Wool Mitts; Colors: Seal, brown black or wine. Per pair.......40
Per dozen.............4.32

33353 Men's Double Knit Silk Mitts, lined with fine wool; black only. Per pair.............1.25
Per dozen.............13.50

33355 Men's Extra Heavy Genuine Australian Kangaroo Hair Mitts, fulled, sanitary brown color; very warm and strong. Per pair.......25
Per dozen.............2.70

33356 Men's Kangaroo Hair Mitts, same as above, made double. Per pair....$0.40 Per dozen....4.32

Men's Mittens.

Weight of Men's Mitts and gloves 4 to 9 ounces per pair.

33361 Men's fulled Mackinaw Mitts, grained leather palms. Per pair.$0.35
Per doz...3.78

33361-33362

33362 Men's fulled Mackinaw Mitts genuine oil tanned calf palm and welted seams. Per pair.....$0.45 Per dozen....$4.77

33363 Men's extra heavy knit wool mitts, tufted wool lining, back and palm covered with genuine oil tanned calf, welted seams. Per pair....$0.50
Per dozen...5.59

33363-33379

33368 Men's extra heavy Esquimax Mitts, camels hair and wool mixed, plush lined, back and palm covered with genuine oil tanned calf, welted seams, warmest mitt made..........75
Per dozen................8.10

33374 Men's extra heavy knit wool mitts, tufted fleece lining, back and palm covered with genuine oil tanned calf, welted seams. Per pair....85
Per dozen................9.18

Hoods—Continued.

33765

33765   Misses' Tab Hoods, made of Shetland yarn, teaseled lining, tufted top; colors, black, white, seal or navy blue. Each........$0.50
Per dozen..........5.40

33767   Ladies' or Misses' Tab Hoods, hand made, of Shetland floss, covered with silk floss, tufted top, edged with silk; colors, black or white. Each...........80
Per dozen..........8.64

33769   Ladies' or Misses' Tab Hoods, hand made, of Shetland floss, completely covered with waves of floss; top, back and top trimmed with satin ribbon to match; colors, black, white or pink. Each......$1.00
Per dozen..........10.80

33771   Ladies' or Misses' Tab Hoods, hand made, of Spanish floss, beaded all over with bugle beads, tufted top; colors, black, white, wine, light blue or pink. Each..........$1.00
Per dozen..........10.80

33771

33773-75

33773   Ladies' Tab Hoods, large full sizes, hand made of Shetland floss, edged with bugle beads, tufted top trimmed with beads; colors, black or white. Each..........$0.80
Per dozen..........8.64

33775   Ladies' or Misses' Tab Hoods, hand made, of fine imported Saxony yarn, covered with silk floss, edged with bugle beads, tufted top, trimmed with beads; colors, black or white. Each..........$1.25
Per dozen..........13.50

33779

33779   Ladies' Tab Hood Fascinator, hand made of Shetland yarn and Berlin wool, covered with silk floss, trimmed with swan's down, ribbon bow on top; colors, black, white, pink or wine. Each..........$1.75
Per doz..........18.90

Hoods—Continued.

33781   **33783**

33781   Ladies' hand-made hoods, double knit of Shetland floss, ruche top; colors, black, white, seal or navy blue. Each..........$0.50
Per doz..........5.40

33783   Misses' Hoods, made of worsted floss, 3 inch cape; colors, black, white, navy blue or seal brown. Each...........40
Per doz..........4.32

33785   **33787**

33785   Ladies' or Misses Hoods, double knit, hand made, of Shetland floss, ruche front and top, 3 inch cape; colors, black or white. Each..........$0.75
Per doz..........8.10

33787   Ladies' Hand-Made Hoods, fine Shetland yarn, lined with teaseled yarn, three rows of shell work on front, back and top and six rows on a 6-inch cape, all edged with silk satin ribbon, bows on top and back; colors, black or white. Each..........$1.00
Per doz..........10.80

33789   Ladies' Hand-Made Hoods, made of imported Saxony yarn, lined with Germantown yarn, heavy satin ribbon on sides and back, large satin bows on top and back front, sides and back edged with silk; colors, black, white, seal brown or wine. Each..........$1.75
Per doz..........18.90

33791   Ladies' or Misses' Toboggan Caps with large silk trimmed pompon; colors, black white, wine or pink. Original price, 80c.
Each, until sold.........$0.25

Infants' Knit Sacques.

33789

33793   Infants' Knit Sacques, made of Shetland floss; colors: Main body, light blue; also white trimmed with light blue, cardinal or pink. Each..........$0.25
Per doz..........2.70

33795   Infants' Knit Sacques, made of Shetland floss, trimmed all around with ribbon to match, same colors as above. Each...........50
Per doz..........5.40

Men's and Boys' Knit Jackets.

Weight of boys' jackets average ¾ pound, men's jackets, 1¼ to 1¾ pounds.

33800   Boys' Knit Cardigan Jackets, fancy front, for ages 6 to 10. Each..........$0.75
Per dozen..........8.10

33802   Boys' Knit Cardigan Jackets, fancy front, for ages 4 to 10. Each..........$1.00
Per dozen..........10.80

33804   Men's Knit Cardigan Jackets, medium size, black or brown. Each..........$0.75
Per dozen..........8.10

33806   Men's Knit Cardigan Jackets, medium size; black or brown. Each..........$1.00
Per dozen..........10.80

33808   Men's Knit Wool Cardigan Jackets, full size; black or brown. Each..........$1.25   Per doz..........$13.50

33810   Men's Knit Worsted Cardigan Jackets, large size, colors, black or brown. Each..........$1.50   Per dozen..........16.20

33812   Men's Knit Worsted Cardigan Jackets, extra large sizes, colors black or brown. Each..........$1.75   Per dozen..........18.90

33814   Men's Knit Wool Cardigan Jackets, full sizes, double breasted, colors, black or brown. Each..........$2.00   Per dozen..........21.60

33816   Men's Knit Worsted Cardigan Jackets, full sizes, black or brown. Each..........$2.50   Per dozen..........27.00

33818   Men's Knit Worsted Cardigan Jackets, full sizes, colors; navy blue or wine. Each..........$2.50   Per dozen..........27.00

33820   Men's Knit Worsted Cardigan Jackets, large full sizes, double breasted; colors, black or brown. Each..........$2.75   Per dozen..........

33822   Men's Knit Worsted Cardigan Jackets, extra fine, full sizes; colors, black or brown. Each..........$3.00   Per dozen..........32.40

33824   Men's Jersey Jacket, fleeced back, heavy weight, very dressy, double breasted; black. Each..........$4.00   Per dozen..........43.20

33826   Men's Jersey Knit Jackets for office wear very neat, comfortable and dressy, fleeced back, single breasted. Colors: Tan or fawn. Each..........$4.50   Per dozen..........48.60

Colored and White Saxony, Shetland and Knitting Worsteds.

33840   Knitting Yarns, western made, long wool, solid colors, cardinal, scarlet, seal brown, navy blue, medium blue or black.
Per pound..........$0.65
In packages of 5 lbs., solid colors..........3.00

33842   Knitting Yarns, same as above, in sheep's gray or black mixed. Per pound...........65
In packages of 5 lbs., solid colors..........3.00

33843   Knitting Yarns, best Ohio wool, selected stock. Colors: Navy, cardinal, golden brown, black or purple. Per pound..........1.00
In packages of 5 lbs., solid colors..........4.50

33844   Spanish Knitting Worsted, colors: black, white, seal brown or navy blue. Per pound...

33846   Superfine German Worsted Worsted Knitting Yarns, 4 skeins to the pound, come in the following solid colors: medium blue, navy blue, blue, light blue, royal blue, medium brown, seal brown, gold brown, medium shade pink, scarlet cardinal, claret, wine, slate, drab, sheep's gray or black mixed. Per pound..........1.00
When sold in packages of 5 lbs., one color..........4.50
Black or white. Per pound...........90

33847   German Worsted Knitting Yarns, 4 skeins to the lb., same colors as 33846. Per pound...........80
Black or white. Per pound...........70

33848   Saxony Wool, best imported. Colors: scarlet, garnet, cardinal, claret, wine, pink, baby blue or light blue, medium blue, navy blue, seal brown, gold brown; 16 ounces to box. Per pound..........1.35
Black or white. Per pound..........1.25

33849   Fairy Floss or Crinkled Yarn, for fancy knitting, black or white only. Per pound..........1.00

33850   Shetland Wool, best imported. Colors: scarlet, garnet, cardinal, claret, pink, wine, baby blue or light blue, medium blue, navy blue, seal brown, gold brown; 8 skeins to pound, 12 ounces to package, sold as 1 pound. Per package..........1.20
Black or white. Per pound..........1.10

All yarns sold at manufacturer's weight.

OUR GROCERY PRICE LIST

Germantown Yarn.

33852 Germantown Yarn, plain white or plain black. Per pound $1.25

33854 Germantown Yarn in the following plain shades: Seal brown, scarlet, pink, green, cardinal, wine, light blue, medium blue, navy blue, yellow, green, salmon, ashes of roses, slate, drab or purple. Per pound 1.35

Germantown yarn comes put up in 10 and 12 skeins to the pound, manufacturer's weight. We do not sell less than one skein of any shade or color.

When ordering goods shipped by mail, be sure to allow money for postage. If you send too much we will refund balance.

Yarn—Continued.

33856 Imported Ice Wool, cream white, Per ball $0.03
Per Box of 8 balls .... .17

33858 Imported Ice Wool, black, per ball .... .03
Per box of 8 balls .... .17

33860 Best Quality Imported Angora Wool, put up in one-quarter-pound boxes, 16 balls to the box. Colors: Brown, gray, black or white.
Per ball .... .20
Per box 2.25

☞ It will be a favor to us (and perhaps to your friends) if you will place, where they will do the most good, any duplicate Catalogues or advertising matter which you may receive from us.

Yarn—Continued.

33868 Imported Berlin Zephyr Worsted, single or 4-fold colors: Scarlet, pink, cardinal, garnet, wine, baby blue, medium blue, dark blue, navy blue, light, medium and dark green, tan, brown, drab, olive, orange, canary, purple, black or white; 40 laps to the pound, manufacturer's weight. Per pound $1.75
Per lap .... .05

Wool Yarn.

		Per lb.
33870	Wool Yarn, white, scoured, No. C	$0.60
33872	Wool Yarn, white Shaker, No. EE	.80
33874	Wool Yarn, blue mixed, No. A	.60
33876	Wool Yarn, blue mixed scoured long wool No. 1	.80
33878	Wool Yarn, blue mixed, best Ohio wool, long staple selected stock. Per pound	1.00

CLOAK DEPARTMENT.

All Garments guaranteed exactly as represented.

Ladies' garments are made in sizes 32, 34, 36, 38, 40 and 42 only.

In our Cloak Department, which has been greatly enlarged to better supply the wants of our customers on short notice, will be found the leading styles and newest materials in Children's Misses' and Ladies' Jackets, Reefers, Capes, in all the new effects. We know our customers want full value for their money, so we have advanced another step in the right direction by giving you a higher grade of material at prices lower than ever before, and a more complete line to select from.

☞ Be sure to send bust and waist measure for cloak. (Measure over bust close under arms.) All cloaks larger than 42 inches will have to be made to order, and cost extra in proportion to size and style desired. If you require extra sized garment, send us a full description of garment wanted, being sure to state bust, length, and waist measure. We will then forward measurement blank and quote exact price for having garment made to order. *N. B. We do not sample cloaks.*

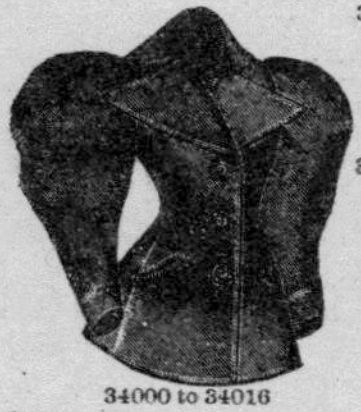

34000 to 34016

34000 Ladies' Jacket, 30 inches long, plain black melton, pleat back, pompadour sleeves, coat collar and large lapels. Each $3.00

Weight, 3 to 3¼ lbs.

34002 Ladies' Jacket, 32 inches long, plain black heavy melton beaver, large pleated pompadour sleeves, long pointed lapels, pleated umbrella back, curved side pockets and coat collar. Weight, 3½ to 3¾ lbs. Each $5.00

34004 Ladies' Jackets, same style and material as above in dark navy blue. Each 5.00

34006 Ladie's Jacket, same style and material as 34002, in a tan brown mixture. Each 5.00

34008 Ladie's Jacket, 30 inches long, dark Royal Blue Milton cloth, large pleated pompadour sleeves, square lapel pockets, coat collar, long pointed lapels, fancy stitched seams, six large pearl buttons, double breasted; weight, 3¼ to 3½ lbs. Each 6.00

34010 Ladies' Jacket, 32 inches long, medium gray Covert cloth, fine diagonal wool twill, large pleated pompadour sleeves, large pointed lapels, coat collar, curved pockets, pleated umbrella back, large buttons; weight 3¼ to 3¾ lbs. Each 8.00

34012 Ladies' Jacket, 32 inches long, medium light brown, mixed diagonal cheviot cloaking, half tight fitting, roll pleat umbrella back, six large fancy horn buttons, pleated pompadour sleeves, curved pockets, fancy stitched seams in back, coat collar, large pointed lapels; weight, 3 to 3¼ lbs. Each 9.00

34014 Ladies' Jacket: 34 inches long, medium dark fawn beaver, beautiful shade; large pleated pompadour sleeves, large pointed lapels, coat collar, large genuine fancy horn buttons. Pleated umbrella back, curved pockets. Weight, 3¾ to 4 pounds. Each 10.50

34016 Ladies' Jacket, same style and material as above, in black beaver. Each 10.50

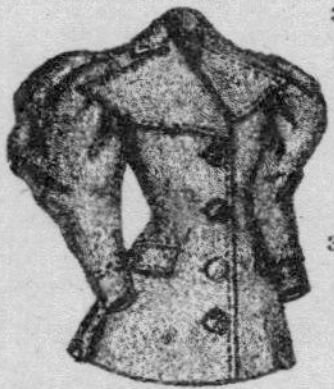

34018–34038

34018 Ladies' Jacket; 32 inches long; Oxford gray, mixed melton cloaking, pleated pompadour sleeves, full umbrella back, large pointed lapels, large horn buttons, coat collar; welt seams in back, square lapel pockets. Weight, 3¼ to 3½ lbs. Each $4.00

34020 Ladies' Jacket: 30 inches long; neat mixture of gray, brown and tan cloaking, pleated pompadour sleeves, large pointed lapels, large horn buttons, coat collar, welt seams in back, square lapel pockets, full umbrella back; weight, 3¼ to 3¾ lbs. Each $4.00

34022 Ladies' Jacket: 32 inches long; plain black melton cheviot, large pleated pompadour sleeves, full umbrella back, welt seams in back, large pointed lapels, square lapel pockets, large fancy horn buttons, round corner collar; weight, 3¼ to 3½ pounds. Each 5.00

34024 Ladies' Jacket, same style and material as 34022, in dark navy blue. Each $5.00

34026 Ladies' Jacket, same style and material as 34022, in Havana brown. Each 5.00

34028 Ladies' Jacket; 30 inches long; large pleated pompadour sleeves, large pointed lapels, large buttons, curved pockets, coat collar, full umbrella back; dark navy blue beaver; weight, 3¼ to 3¾ pounds. Each 6.50

34030 Ladies' Jacket, same style and material as above, in Havana brown. Each 6.50

34032 Ladies' Jacket; 32 inches long; navy blue worsted serge cloaking, large pleated pompadour sleeves, large pointed lapels, coat collar, large buttons, welted seams, square lapel pockets, full umbrella back; weight, 3¼ to 3½ pounds. Each 7.50

34034 Ladies' Jacket; 32 inches long; light, tan and Spanish olive mixture, fine twill covert cloth, large pleated pompadour sleeves, large pointed lapels, square lapel pockets, large fancy horn buttons, coat collar, full umbrella roll back, welted seams. A very stylish garment; weight, 3¾ to 4 pounds. Each 9.00

34036 Ladies' Jacket; 32 inches long; beautiful shade of Havana brown Kersey cloaking, large pleated pompadour sleeves, full umbrella back, welt seams in back, square lapel pockets, large pointed lapels, coat collar, large fancy horn buttons; weight, 3 to 3¼ pounds. Each 9.50

34038 Ladies' Jacket, same style and material as above, in Plain black kersey. Each 9.50

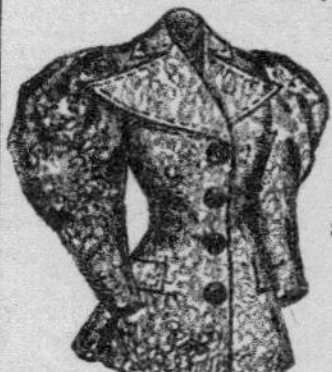

34040-34048

34040 Ladies' Jacket, 32 inches long, short nap, blue chinchilla beaver, large pompadour sleeves, large pointed lapels, square lapel pockets, large fancy buttons, full umbrell roll back, coat collar. Weight 3¾ to 4 pounds. Each $5.25

34042 Ladies' Jacket, 32 inches long, large pompadour sleeves, large pointed lapels, square lapel pockets, large fancy pearl buttons, full roll umbrella back, heavy navy blue chinchilla beaver, long nap, coat collar. Weight 4 to 4¼ pounds. Each $10.00

34044 Ladies' Jacket, same style and material as above in black. Each 10.00

34046 Ladies' Jacket, 34 inches long, fine and heavy long nap, black chinchilla beaver, large pompadour sleeves, large pointed lapels, satin side lining, coat collar, full roll umbrella back, square lapel pockets, large fancy pearl buttons, very stylish. Weight, 4¼ to 4½ pounds. Each 17.00

34048 Ladies' Jacket, same style and material as above in dark navy blue. Each 17.00

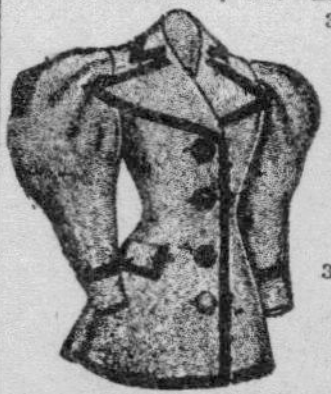

34050-34058

34050 Ladies' Jacket, 32 inches long. Oxford gray mixed cloaking, pleated pompadour sleeves, large pointed lapels, coat collar; square lapel pockets, trimmed with one inch hercules braid, full umbrella back, large buttons, square lapel pockets. Weight; 3¼ to 3½ pounds. Each $4.50

34052 Ladies' Jacket, 34 inches long. Tan brown mixed cloaking, small neat pattern, large pleated pompadour sleeves, full umbrella back, pointed lapels, coat collar, square lapel pockets all trimmed with one inch wide black hercules braid, large buttons to match. Weight 4 to 4¼ pounds. Each $5.75

34054 Ladies' Jacket, 32 inches long, smooth finish black beaver, large pleated pompadour sleeves, full umbrella back pointed lapels, square lapel pockets, all trimmed with one inch mohair braid, large buttons. Weight, 3½ to 3¾ pounds. Each $6.50

34056 Ladies' Jacket, same style and material as above in dark navy blue. Each 6.50

34058 Ladies' Jacket, same style and material as 34054, in Havana brown. Each 6.50

34060 Ladies' Jackets, 34 inches long. Black Berlin wool, twilled beaver, large pleated pompadour sleeves, pointed lapels, coat collar, curved pockets, full Umbrella back, all trimmed with narrow mohair braid, large buttons. Weight, 3¾ to 4 lbs. Each 7.50

34062 Ladies' Jacket, 32 inches long, navy blue worsted serge cloaking, cheviot effect, large sleeves, pointed lapels, coat collar, square lapel pockets; all trimmed with black mohair braid, full umbrella back. Weight, 3½ to 3¾ lbs. Each 8.00

34064 Ladies' Jacket, 32 inches long, medium dark gray cheviot cloaking, small neat pattern, pleated pompadour sleeves, pointed lapels, coat collar, square lapel pockets; all trimmed with wide black Hercules braid, full umbrella back, welt seams. Weight, 3¼ to 3½ lbs. Each 8.50

34066 Ladies' Jacket, 32 inches long, smooth finish black beaver cloaking, large pleated pompadour sleeves, pointed lapels, square lapel pockets, All trimmed with wide black Hercules braid, full umbrella back, welt seams; weight, 3¾ to 4 lbs. Each 10.50

34068 Ladies' Jackets, same in style and material as above in navy blue. Each 10.50

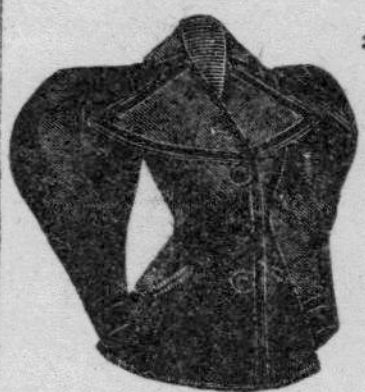

34070-34078

34070 Ladies' Jacket, 34 inches long, gray and brown mixed, fancy pattern, heavy cloaking, large pleated sleeves, pointed lapels, coat collar, all trimmed with one row of wide and two rows of narrow mohair braid, pleat umbrella coat back, stitched diagonal pocket, large fancy buttons. Weight, 4 to 4¼ lbs. Each $5.50

34072 Ladies' Jacket, 34 inches long, heavy black melton beaver, large pleated pompadour sleeves, roll umbrella back, pointed lapels and coat collar trimmed with three rows of narrow worsted braid. Weight, 4 to 4¼ lbs. Each 6.00

34074 Ladies' Jacket, same style and material as above, in dark navy blue. Each 6.00

34076 Ladies' Jacket, same style and material as 34072 in Havana brown. Each 6.00

34078 Ladies' Jacket, 34 inches long, black Berlin wool, twilled beaver, coat collar, pointed lapels and cuffs trimmed with four rows of narrow worsted braid, edged all around with wide mohair braid, pleated umbrella coat back, fancy curved pockets, silk serge side lining, large balloon sleeves. Weight, 4¼ to 4½ lbs. Each 11.00

BABY'S OUTFIT—Everything complete and SO PRETTY—Cheaper than to make them.

Our Medical, Scientific and Electrical Books are the best practical editions.

Have you noticed our quotations on Scientific Books?

Furs—Continued.

34340 Child's Muff and Stole, white coney fur. Per set, $0.85
34342 Child's Muff and Stole, white Llama fur. Per set, $1.50
34344 Child's Muff and Stole, white Angora fur. Per set, $1.75
34346 Child's Muff and Stole, steel or tan color. Per set $2.00
34348 Child's Muff and Stole, white Thibet fur. Per set 3.00
34350 Child's Muff and Stole, Thibet fur. Colors: Tan, steel, light blue or salmon. Each 3.00
34352 Misses' Muff and Stole, white Angora fur. Each ....
34354 Misses' Muff and Stole, Angora fur. Colors: Salmon, light blue or tan. Each 5.00

Infants' Cloaks.

New goods, latest designs, lowest prices.

N. B.—The average weight of infants' long cashmere cloaks is 16 ounces each. Short cashmere walking jackets, 12 oz. When ordered separately by mail or special prepaid express, allow one cent per ounce extra for charges.

34360 Infants' long union cashmere cloaks, fleece lining, pleated collar; 7 in. cape and bottom of cloak embroidered with silk to match. Length of cloak, 36 inches; colors: tan, cream and cardinal. Each $1.00
Per doz. 10.80
34363 Infants' fine union cashmere cloaks, 36 inches long, sateen lining, yoke collar, 8-inch cape and bottom of cloak embroidered with silk to match. Mother Hubbard waist, full sleeves; colors: Tan, garnet, cream. Each $1.65
Per doz. 17.82

34360–34364

34364 Infants' fine wool cashmere cloaks, 36 inches long, fine twilled sateen lining padded with wadding, fancy collar. Mother Hubbard waist, plain skirt, large full sleeves with fancy silk embroidered scalloped cuffs; 7-inch double cape handsomely embroidered in silk. Colors: Cream, white and tan only. Each $2.75
Per dozen 29.70

Walking Jackets.

FOR CHILDREN FROM 1 TO 3 YEARS.

34366 Infants' Mother Hubbard cashmere walking jacket or short cloak, 7 inch cape and bottom of cloak embroidered in silk to match. Silesia lining, full sleeves, length 22, 24, 26 and 28 inches. Colors: Cream, white, tan and garnet. Each $1.25
34368 Infants' fine cashmere walking jacket, with cape, Mother Hubbard waist, full sleeves, sateen lining, padded with wadding, richly embroidered on skirt and cape with silk. Length 22, 24, 26 and 28 inches. Colors: cream, white, tan and garnet. Weight, 12 ounces. Each $2.25

Walking Jacket.

SAMPLES OF DRESS GOODS.

We make no charge for samples, and for that reason we request you, when writing for them to be very explicit in stating exactly what is wanted, giving Catalogue number when possible; if not, the width, price, quality, color, etc., so that we can send you just what you need, instead of a great lot of samples that are of no use to you and cost us considerable money.

Latest Novelties.

The following garments do not have fur trimming unless so stated in the quotation. Average weight is 16 ounces each.

34370 Infants' Elder-down Cloaks, Mother Hubbard waist, large full sleeves with cuffs, fleece lining; roll collar, small neat pin head check pattern, black and gray or tan and gray. Lengths 22, 24, 26 and 28 inches.
Each $0.90
Per doz. .... .72
34372 Infants' Elder-down Cloaks, Mother Hubbard waist, full sleeves with cuffs, fleece lining, collar trimmed with 6 inch white Angora fur, Colors Steel blue and silver gray mixed. Weight 16 ounces, 1 to 4 years.
Each $1.00
Per doz. 10.80
34374 Elder-down Cloaks, Mother Hubbard waist, pointed collar, large full sleeves, with cuffs made plain without trimming. A very neat and serviceable garment, fine fleece lining. Colors: Cream, light blue, pink, tan, cardinal, 1 to 4 years. Lengths 22, 24, 26 and 28 inches. Each $1.50
Complete with muff and hood to match. Per set 2.50

34370–34378

34376 Fancy Elder-down Cloaks, Mother Hubbard waist, large full sleeves with cuffs, fancy pointed collar and cuffs trimmed with 6 inch white Angora fur. These garments are made in fancy broken stripe mixture of tan, browns, grays and ecrus; we can furnish background colors in tan, light blue, pink or cream with beautiful contrasting stripes. Lengths 22, 24, 26 and 28 inches. Weight, 20 ounces, 1 to 4 years. Each 2.25
Complete with muff and hood to match. Per set 3.75
34378 Fancy Mother Hubbard Elder-down Cloak, large sleeves, fancy silk braided cuffs, pointed collar and down front, trimmed with Angora fur 6 inches long. Design and colors same as 34376. Lengths 22, 24, 26 and 28 inches, 1 to 4 years. Each 3.00
Complete with muff and hood to match. Per set. 4.50

34380   34382

34380 Elder-down Cloaks, extra selected goods, Mother Hubbard waist, large pleated pompadour sleeves with cuffs, fine quality sateen lining; neck, sleeves and cuffs trimmed with gathered satin ribbon, large satin bow and ribbons in back; lengths, 22, 24, 26 and 28 inches; weight, 24 oz.; 1 to 4 yrs.; colors, gray, ecru, cream, with stripes in beautiful contrasting shades. Light colors only. Each $3.75
Complete, with muff and hood to match. 5.85
34382 Elder-down Cloaks, extra fine quality, Mother Hubbard waist, large sleeves, with 3-inch silk cuffs to match, fancy pointed silk collar and wide silk epaulets, trimmed with elder-down; hook and eye fastenings in front, covered with three fine silk bows; a very handsome and stylish cloak; colors, pink, cream, steel gray or tan, intermingled with fancy designs of contrasting colors; lengths, 22, 24, 26 and 28 inches; weight, 24 oz.; 1 to 4 yrs. Each 4.00
Complete, with muff and hood to match. 6.50

A New Idea—Russian Combination Sets.

34384

34384   Extra fine white camel's hair set, consisting of three pieces, viz., cloak, hood and muff all to match. Cloak has Mother Hubbard waist, large pompadour sleeves, with cuffs, large pointed collar of solid ermine fur, the muff, hood and cuffs of the set are all trimmed with white ermine fur, studded with black; sizes, 22, 24, 26 and 28 inches; 1 to 4 years; sold in full sets only, weigh 2¼ lbs. Per set complete. $7.50

Ladies' Gossamer and Mackintosh Coats.

In taking measures for Ladies' Gossamers, measure from collar down the back to length desired; sizes 54 to 62 inches long. No odd sizes; weight of gossamers, put up in small box, 1½ to 2½ lbs., according to size and quality.

34400-01   34402

34400 Ladies' Silver Gray Gossamer Circulars.
Each $1.00
34401 Ladies' Silver Gray Pin Stripe Circular with hood. Each $1.35
34402 Ladies' Silver Gray Stripe Common Sense Gossamer, with large cape. $1.75

N. B.—Single texture means a printed or woven fabric on outside, with heavy rubber coating on inside. Double texture means a printed or woven fabric on both sides with gum rubber between.

34404 Ladies' single texture Inverness Circular, with large military cape; black and gray pin stripes.
Each $2.00
34406 Ladies' single texture Mackintosh, with large military cape, black diagonal or narrow wale pattern.
Each $2.50
34408 Ladies' single texture Mackintosh, with large military cape, black and white hair line stripe.
Each $3.00
34410 Ladies' single texture Mackintosh, with large military cape, wide wale diagonal pattern, black.
Each $3.50
34412 Ladies' single texture Mackintosh, with large military cape, half lined, black or blue chevron diagonal. Each $4.75

Ladies' Mackintosh.

34414 Ladies' single texture Mackintosh, with large military cape, all wool navy blue tricot.
Each 6.00
34416 Ladies' double texture Mackintosh, with large military cape, black or blue cashmere, with fancy lining. Each 6.00
34418 Ladies' double texture Mackintosh, with large military cape, all wool black or navy blue tricot, with black lining Each 9.00

34420 Ladies' single texture Mackintosh, with triple cape, gray mixed print. Each $3.50
34422 Ladies' single texture Mackintosh, with triple cape, black diagonal narrow wale. Each $4.50
34424 Ladies' Mackintosh, same as above, in navy blue. Each $4.50
34426 Ladies' double texture Mackintosh, with triple cape, black or navy blue cashmere, with fancy lining. Each. $8.00

Men's Mackintosh.   Triple Cape Mackintosh.

Men's Mackintosh Coats.

Sizes 34, 36, 38, 40, 42, 44, 46, 48. Chest measure to be taken over the coat it is to be worn over.

34430 Men's double texture Mackintosh, with detachable cape, wide wale diagonal, fancy lining, black or blue. Each $4.00
34431 Men's double texture Mackintosh, with detachable cape, gray mixed plaids or stripes. Each $4.00

Mackintosh Coats—Continued.

34432 Men's Double Texture Mackintosh Coat, with Detachable Cape. Black diagonal clay pattern, fancy plaid lining; can be worn without cape in place of light weight overcoat. Can furnish samples of this coat if desired. Each...$4.50
34434 Men's Mackintosh Coat, same as above, in dark navy blue. Each ... 4.50
34436 Men's Double Texture Mackintosh Coat, with Detachable Cape. Black or navy blue cashmere, with fancy plaid linings. Each...... 6.00
34438 Men's Double Texture Mackintosh Coat, with Large Detachable Cape. All wool black or navy blue tricot, with fancy plaid lining. Each 7.50
34440 Men's Double Texture Mackintosh Coat, with Large Detachable Cape. Brown mixed double and twist cassimere, with fancy plaid lining. Each... 8.00
34442 Men's Double Texture Mackintosh Coat, with Large Detachable Cape. All wool black tricot, lined with fine black cashmere twill. Can be worn without cape in place of light weight overcoat. Most serviceable coat made. Can furnish samples if desired. Each ... 9.00
34444 Men's Mackintosh Coat, same as above, in dark navy blue. Each... 9.00
34446 Men's Double Texture Mackintosh Coat, with Large Detachable Cape. All wool black and gray, small broken check, with fancy plaid lining. Each...12.00
34448 Men's Double Texture Mackintosh Coat, with Large Detachable Cape. All wool black cheviot, with woven lining. Suitable for an overcoat. Each...15.00

Medium and Heavy Weight Rubber Clothing.

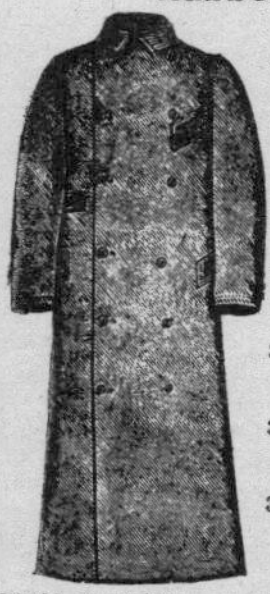

N. B.—We do not sample rubber or mackintosh coats, except where so stated.

34454 Men's Medium Weight Fine Black Rubber Coats, fancy plaid back: 50 inches long, double breasted...$2.15
34456 Men's Medium Weight Coats, wine color, velvet collar, fancy plaid back, double breasted...$2.50
34458 Men's Medium Heavy Black Rubber Coats, fancy plaid back, double breasted...$2.75
34460 Men's Medium Weight Black Rubber Coats, fancy plaid back, double breasted...$3.00
34462 Men's Medium Heavy Black Rubber Coats, fancy plaid back, double breasted...$3.25
34464 Men's Medium Weight Black Rubber Coats, patent ventilate epaulet shoulders, fancy plaid back, double breasted...$3.50
34466 Men's Heavy Black Rubber Coats, fancy striped twilled back, double breasted...$3.50
34468 Men's Medium Heavy Black Rubber Coats, double back, fancy sateen back, double breasted, velvet collar... 3.60
34470 Men's Heavy Weight Black Rubber Coats, double back, buff colored twilled drill back, double breasted... 3.75
34472 Men's Medium Weight Black Rubber Coats, extra long double back, fancy striped back, double breasted... 4.00
34474 Firemen's Regulation Rubber Coats, double coated, extra wide fly front, with snaps and rings, straps and buckles on sleeves and neck... 4.00
34476 Policeman's Regulation Rubber Coats, fancy plaid back, double back, patent ventilated shoulders, patent ball and socket buttons, straps on sleeves, pocket for billy and shield for star... 5.00
34478 Boys' Rubber Coats, on heavy sheeting, black, luster finish. Sizes, 24 to 34 chest measure... 1.50
34480 Boys' Rubber Coats, on heavy sheeting, black, dull finish. Sizes, 24 to 34 chest measure. 1.85
34482 Boys' Medium Wine Colored Rubber Coats, velvet collar, fancy plaid back, double breasted... 2.25
34484 Misses' Silver Gray Gossamer Circular, with hood. Sizes. 34 to 48 inches long ... .90
34485 Misses' Silver Gray-Stripe Gossamer, with large cape and hood ... 1.65

Men's Heavy Rubber Clothing.

Weight of Rubber Clothing. 3½ to 5½ pounds, according to size and quality.

Sizes on men's clothing are as follows:

Size,	3	4	5	6	7
Chest,	36	38	40	42	44

We do not guarantee our rubber clothing, but sell only the best made.

34486 Rubber Coats, on heavy sheeting, black luster finish, officers' length...$1.60
34488 Rubber Coats, on heavy sheeting, dull finish, officers' length... 2.00
34490 Rubber Coats, on heavy sheeting, dull finish. mountaineers' length, extra long... 2.75
34492 Rubber Coats, on heavy drill, dull finish, officers' length... 2.25
34494 Rubber Coats, on heavy drill, dull finish, mountaineers' length, extra long, can be buttoned around legs and made a riding coat if desired... 3.00

Men's Rubber Leggings, Hats and Blankets.

Each.

34496 Rubber Camp Blankets, on heavy sheeting, with ball and socket fastener. Size, 54x72 inches. Weight, 3½ pounds...$1.25
34498 Rubber U. S. A. Poncho Blankets, on heavy sheeting. Size, 45x72 inches. Weight, 3 pounds... 1.50

Per pair.

34500 Rubber Leggings, long, black luster...$0.78
34502 Rubber Leggings, long, black, dull finish. .90
34503 Rubber Leggings, on drill, long, black luster finish... .83
34504 Rubber Leggings, on drilling, long, black dull finish... 1.00
Postage on rubber leggings, 18 to 20 c. per pair.

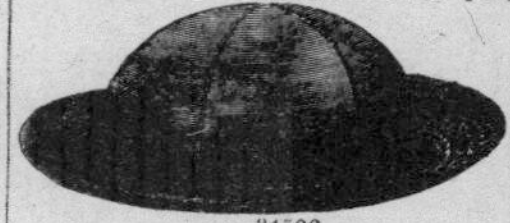

34506

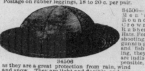

34506—Men's Round Crown Rubber Hats. For shooting, gunning and fishing, they are indispensible, as they are a great protection from rain, wind and snow. They are light and flexible, and can be carried in the trousers' pocket. Each $0.25

Each.

34508 Rubber Caps, with capes, black luster...$0.50
34509 Ladies' Gossamer Rubber sleeves, 16 inches long Per pair... .35
34510 Gossamer Hat Covers, for stiff hats... .20

Rubber Gloves and Mittens.

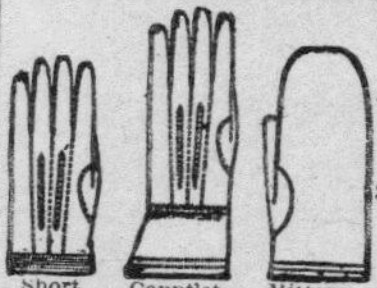

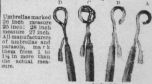

Short. Gauntlet. Mittens.

Postage on Rubber mitts and gloves, 6 to 9 cents per pair.

34512 Ladies' Rubber Gloves, gauntlet, black or tan, sizes, 6, 7, 8 and 9. See cut. $1.20
34513 Ladies' Rubber Gloves, short, black or tan, sizes, 6, 7, 8 and 9, See cut...$1.00
34514 Men's Rubber Gloves, heavy, short; sizes, 10 to 15. See cut. Black or tan. 1.15
34516 Men's Rubber Gloves, gauntlet, black or tan; sizes, 10 to 15. See cut... 1.50
34518 Men's Extra Heavy Rubber Mittens. See cut... 1.15
34520 Men's Wool Lined Rubber Mittens; black 1.35
34522 Ladies' White Rubber Aprons, with bib, medium size... .85
34524 Ladies' White Rubber Aprons, with bib, large size... 1.10
34526 Pure Gum or Rubber Tissue, used by tailors for bottom of pants. Ladies' Arm Shields, rents or tares in Ladies' dress fabrics can be mended without sewing, by placing a small piece of tissue under the cloth and press with a hot iron. Used for all kinds of invisible patching; 36 inches wide, about 7¼ yards to the pound. Per pound...$2.25. Per yard... .33
34527 Gossamer Rubber Cloth, black only, 36 inches wide. Per yard... .35
34528 Double texture Mackintosh cloth, all wool, black Tricot with fancy plaid lining, 36 inches wide; for making coats, cloaks and Mackintoshes. Per yard... 1.25

Extra Quality, Yellow Oil Clothing, double made.

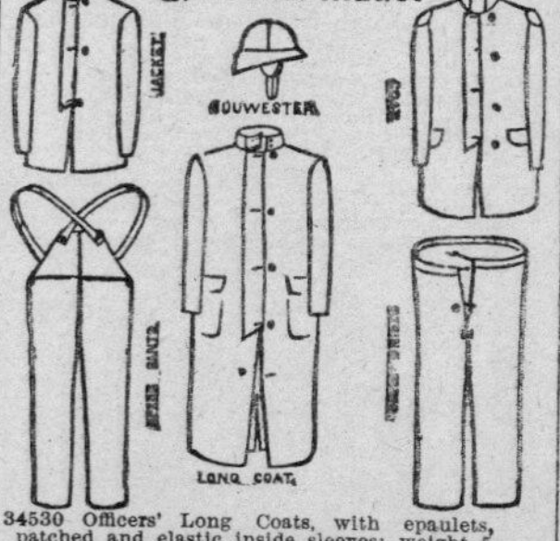

34530 Officers' Long Coats, with epaulets, patched and elastic inside sleeves; weight, 5 lbs...$2.00
34531 Frock or Half Coats, with epaulets patched and elastic inside sleeves; weight, 3¾ lbs... 1.40
34532 Jackets. short and plain, weight, 3 lbs... 1.00
34533 String Pants; weight 2¼ lbs... .90
34534 Apron Pants; weight 2¼ lbs... 1.00
34535 Squam Sou'wester, yellow; weight, 7 oz... .25
34536 Cape Ann Sou' wester; weight, 8oz... .50

Extra Quality, Black Oil Clothing.

34537 Officers' Long Coats, with epaulets. patched and elastic inside sleeves; weight, 3¾ lbs....$2.10
34538 Jackets, short and plain; weight 3 lbs.... 1.10
34539 String Pants; weight, 2¼ lbs... 1.00
34540 Apron Pants; weight, 2¾ lbs... 1.10
34541 Squam Sou'wester, black; weight, 7 oz... .30
34542 Cape Ann Sou'wester, black; weight, 8 oz. .60
34543 Waterproof Dressing, or prepared oil. A superior dressing for oiled clothing; keeps the goods soft and waterproof. Put up in pint cans, black. Per pint... .80
34544 Yellow Oil Dressing. Per pint... .60
34545 Pommel Slicker, stockman's long coat, riding or walking; weight, 6¼ lbs. Yellow duck brand... 2.40
34546 Black Pommel Slicker, same as above.... 2.50

UMBRELLA DEPARTMENT.

NEW GOODS, LATEST DESIGNS.

LADIES' AND GENTLEMEN'S UMBRELLAS.

Weight of umbrellas 1 to 1¾ lbs. The illustrations of umbrella handles below do not always represent the exact pattern of those quoted, but simply give an outline style of handles. Weight on Gingham Umbrellas 1¼ to 1¾ lbs., silk umbrellas 1 to 1¼ lbs.

Umbrellas marked 26 inch measure 25 inch; 28 inch measure 27 inch. All manufacturers of umbrellas and parasols, mark them from 1 to 1½ in more than the actual measure.

D C B A

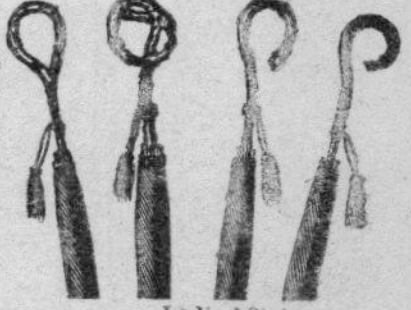

Ladies' Styles.

34575 Ladies' good quality black cotton Gloria Umbrellas; plain handles, 8-rib steel frame; size, 26 inches. Each...$0.70
34577 Ladies' Black Gloria Cotton Umbrellas, silver trimmed, fancy handles, 8-rib steel frames. Size, 26 inches. Each... .60
34579 Ladies' Black Silk Gloria Umbrellas; plain natural wood handles, style G; 8-rib paragon frame; size, 26 inches Each.... .95
34580 Ladies' Black Silk Gloria Umbrellas; assorted metal handles, style A & D; 8-rib paragon frames; size, 26 inches. Each... 1.15
34581 Ladies' Black Silk Gloria Umbrellas; natural wood twisted handles, assorted designs; style C; 8-rib paragon frame; size 26 inches. Each... 1.00

H G F E

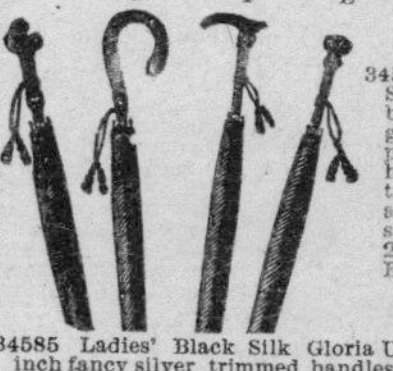

34583 Ladies' Black Silk Gloria Umbrellas; 8-rib paragon frame. Imported Acacia wood handles, silver trimmed; very neat and stylish handle; style F & H; size, 26 inches. Each ...$1.50

34585 Ladies' Black Silk Gloria Umbrellas; 8-inch fancy silver trimmed handles, 8-rib paragon frame, handles assorted; size, 26 inches. Each... 1.50
34586 Ladies' Silk Black Gloria Umbrellas; 8-rib paragon frames, combination silver and celluloid handles; beautiful designs; style E; size, 26 inches. Each... 1.65
34588 Ladies' Umbrellas, finest quality black Gloria silk; 8-inch French horn handles; style H or E; 8-rib paragon frames, stylish and durable; size, 26 inches. Price, each... 1.75
34589 Ladies' Silk Umbrellas, finest quality black Gloria silk, 8-rib paragon frames, handsome celluloid hook handles, similar to style B; size 26 inches. Price, each... 1.75
34590 Ladies' Umbrellas, union twilled black Gloria silk, fine quality, silk cover to match, 8 rib paragon frames, superior gold knob handles; style E, size 26 inches. Price each... 1.78
34592 Ladies' extra quality black silk and linen mixed umbrellas, in silk cases, fine gold knob handles similar to style E, 8-rib paragon frame, size 26 inches. Price each... 2.00
34594 Ladies' extra quality black silk and linen twilled umbrellas, 8-rib paragon frames, beautiful engraved aluminum ball handles, all new and handsome designs; size 26 inches. Price each... 2.00
34596 Ladies' Umbrellas, extra quality black silk and linen twilled goods, will wear better than pure silk and has the same appearance. These umbrellas have 8-inch pearl octogan handles and 8-rib paragon frame. They ordinarily retail at $3.25. Size 26 inches. Our price, each ... 2.50

Men's Hose—Continued.

36385 Men's Super Stout Merino Half Hose, assorted tans, seamless, double heels and toes.
Per pair.............................$0.19
Per doz.............................2.00

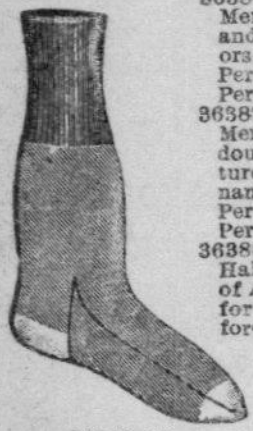

36385-88

36386 Men's Extra Stout Seamless Merino Half Hose, double heels and toes, regular made, tan colors, or fast black,
Per pair.......................$0.25
Per doz.......................2.80

36387 Men's Superfine Seamless Merino Half Hose, ribbed tops, double heels and toes, English mixtures in olive, gold, brown or cinnamon.
Per pair.......................$0.20
Per doz.......................2.25

36388 Men's Extra Fine Merino Half Hose, made of extra quality of Australian worsted, warranted for durability and comfort, Oxford mixed or tans.
Per pair.......................$0.35
Per doz.......................3.85

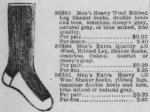

Men's Ribbed All Wool Shaker Socks.

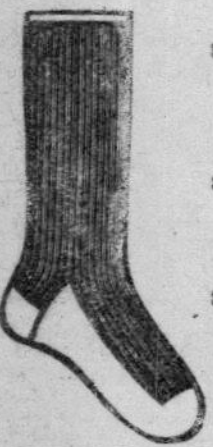

36389 Men's Heavy Wool Ribbed Leg Shaker Socks, double heels and toes, seamless, sheep's gray, natural gray, or blue mixed, fine quality.
Per pair.......................$0.22
Per dozen.......................2.40

36390 Men's Extra Quality All Wool, Ribbed Leg, Shaker Socks, seamless. Colors: Scarlet or sheep's gray.
Per pair.......................$0.29
Per doz.......................3.25

36391 Men's Extra Heavy All Wool Shaker Socks, ribbed legs, seamless double heels and toes, blue mixed or natural gray.
Per pair.......................$0.25
Per doz.......................2.85

36392 Men's Extra Heavy Ribbed Leg Shaker Socks, fine quality lamb's wool, double heels and toes. Colors: Scarlet, gray or indigo blue.
Per pair.......................38
Per doz.......................4.00

Men's Cashmere Half Hose.

NOTE.—(Cashmere ½ hose are made of medium or light weight fine yarn, all wool.)
(Average weight, 32 oz. to a dozen.)

36395 Men's Super Stout, All Wool Cashmere Half Hose, seamless double merino heels and toes Colors: Sanitary gray, light or dark olive or slate. Per pair.......................$0.20
Per dozen.......................2.25

36396 Men's Medium Weight Wool Cashmere Half Hose, double heels and toes, full seamless. Colors: tan, slate, Scotch gray or black.
Per pair.......................19
Per dozen.......................2.00

36397 Men's Super Stout Scotch Wool Half Hose, cashmere finish, medium weight. Colors: Sanitary or natural gray or camel's hair brown or black. Per pair.......................22
Per doz.......................2.40

36399 Men's Heavy Cashmere Half Hose, seamless, double heels and toes. Colors: Cardinal, navy blue, seal brown or black. Per pair.......24
Per dozen.......................2.75

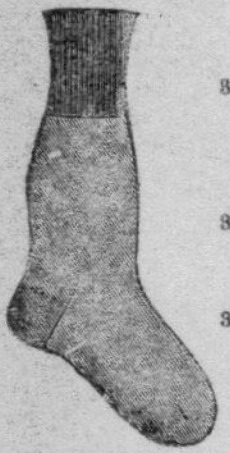

36395 to 36402

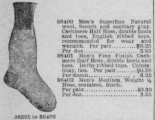

36400 Men's Superfine Natural wool, Scotch and sanitary gray. Cashmere Half Hose, double heels and toes, English ribbed tops. recommended for wear and warmth. Per pair...........$0.25
Per doz.......................2.85

36401 Men's Fine Finish Cashmere Half Hose, double heels and toes. Derby ribbed tops. Colors: Gray, tan. Per pair...........$0.29
Per dozen.......................3.25

36402 Men's Medium Weight ½ Hose, seamless, black.
Per pair.......................$0.30
Per doz.......................3.25

Men's Hose—Continued.

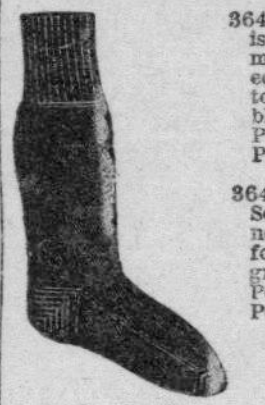

Extra fine 36403-7

36403 Men's Extra Fine Silk Finished English Worsted, ½ hose made of 3-ply yarn, full fashioned, seamless, double heels and toes. Colors: Sanitary gray, black, modes, tans.
Per pair.......................$0.45
Per dozen.......................5.00

36405 Men's Extra Fine All Wool Seamless Cashmere Half Hose; no better sock for wear and comfort. Colors: Black or sanitary gray.
Per pair.......................$0.35
Per dozen.......................3.85

36406 Men's Extra Fine All Wool Seamless Cashmere ½ Hose, Worsted finish, made of fine Australian wool, fine and durable. English mixtures in tan, cinnamon, olive. Per pair..........$0.35
Per dozen.......................3.85

36407 Men's Extra Fine Imported Cashmere Half Hose; full regular made. Black or sanitary gray.
Per pair.......................45
Per dozen.......................5.00

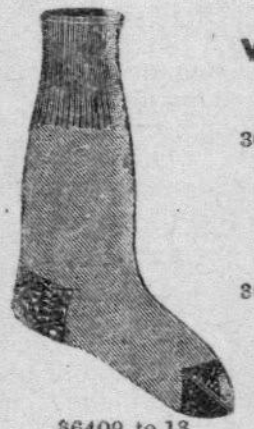

36409 to 13

Men's Medium Weight Lamb and Scotch Wool Half Hose.

36409 Men's Medium Weight Fine All Wool Half Hose, seamless, double heels and toes, ribbed tops. Color: Scotch gray, scarlet, sheeps gray, blue mixed. Weight, 2¾ lbs.
Per pair.......................$0.25
Per dozen.......................2.85

36410 Men's Medium Heavy All Wool Socks, Derby ribbed tops; double heels and toes, seamless. Colors: Scarlet, blue mixed, sheep's gray or Scotch gray; weight, per dozen, 48 ounces. Per pair..........$0.30
Per dozen.......................3.25

36411 Men's Scotch Wool Seamless Half Hose, double heels and toes, super stout, ribbed tops. Shetland gray or natural wool.
Per pair.......................35
Per dozen.......................3.85

36413 Men's Extra Quality Scotch Wool Socks, extra super stout, ribbed tops, double heels and toes, full fashioned. Colors: Sanitary gray, natural wool or black; weight, per dozen, 32 ounces. Per pair.......................40
Per dozen.......................4.50

Men's Heavy Weight English Merino Socks.

36415 Men's Super Stout Seamless Merino Socks, double heels and toes, English mixtures of tan, or brown mixed. Very durable and perfect fitting. Per pair.......................$0.25
Per dozen.......................2.85

36416 Men's Extra Fine English Merino Socks, seamless, double heels and toes, English mixtures in natural gray, pink, or gold. Very comfortable and durable. Per pair.......................35
Per dozen.......................3.85

Men's Heavy Knit Seamless All Wool Socks, Double Heels and Toes.

36420 Men's Heavy Knit Wool Mixed Socks; weight, per dozen, 32 ounces. Per pair..........$0.14
Per dozen.......................1.50

36421 Men's Heavy Knit All Wool Socks. Colors: Gray or blue mixed. Per pair.......................19
Per dozen.......................2.00

36422 Men's Heavy Knit All Wool Socks; ribbed tops, scarlets, blue mixed, sheep's gray; weight, per dozen, about 40 ounces. Per pair.......................20
Per dozen.......................2.25

36426 Men's Heavy All Wool Socks; ribbed tops, homespun. Colors: Blue mixed or Scotch gray.
Per pair.......................22
Per dozen.......................2.40

36427 Men's Heavy All Wool Socks; ribbed tops, fancy colors. Per pair.......................20
Per dozen.......................2.25

36428 Men's Extra Heavy All Wool Socks; ribbed tops, home-spun. Colors in Scotch gray, blue gray, or sheep's gray; 3½ lbs. to a dozen.
Per pair.......................25
Per doz.......................2.85

36429 Men's Medium Heavy All Wool Socks; ribbed tops. Blue gray, Scotch gray or scarlet.
Per pair.......................27
Per dozen.......................3.00

36430 Men's Heavy Fancy Mixed All Wool Socks; ribbed tops Colors: Blue and white, or red and white mottled. Per pair.......................25
Per dozen.......................2.85

Our prices are reasonable; orders filled promptly and carefully.

Men's Extra Heavy Knit All Wool Seamless Socks.

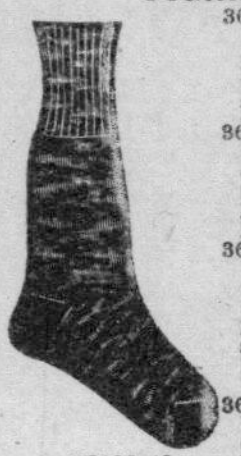

36439-40

36439 Men's Heavy All Wool Mottled Seamless Socks, made out of pure 2-ply yarn, double heels and toes.
Per pair.......................$0.25
Per dozen.......................2.85

36440 Extra Heavy All Wool Mottled Half Hose, ribbed tops, double heels and toes, fancy mottled shades. 3 lbs. to a dozen.
Per pair.......................$0.30
Per doz.......................3.25

36441 Men's Extra Heavy All Wool Seamless Half Hose, ribbed tops, plain legs, double heels and toes. Colors: Canada blue, scarlet or white. Weight 3½ lbs. to a dozen.
Per pair.......................$0.30
Per doz.......................3.25

36444 Men's Extra Heavy All Wool Ribbed Leg Half Hose, double heels and toes. Colors: Canada gray, Scotch gray or red.
Per pair.......................$0.30
Per doz.......................3.25

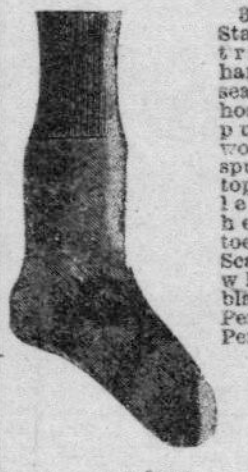

36446

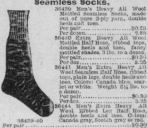

36446 Our Standard extra heavy hand finished seamless half hose, made of pure fleece wool; double spun, ribbed tops, plain legs, 4-ply heels and toes. Colors: Scarlet, gray, white or black.
Per pr..$0.37
Per dz.. 4.00

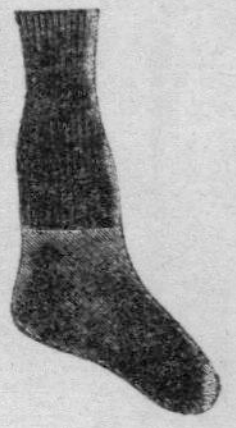

36444-8

36447 Our Esquimaux Extra Heavy all wool seamless socks, double ribbed legs, double heels and toes, scarlet sheeps gray or Canada gray. 4 lbs to a dozen. Per pair.......................$0.33
Per dozen.......................3.60

36448 Our Arctic extra heavy hand finished socks, made of a fine quality of pure fleece wool; double ribbed legs. Heavy, warm and durable; colors: Cardinal sheep's gray or white. Weight 4 lbs. Per pair.......................40
Per dozen.......................4.50

36450 Our Inverness sock. Made of pure home spun, 4-ply all wool yarn. Ribbed tops, plain legs. Hand finished in scarlet, gary or white; weight, 4¼ pounds to the dozen. Per pair.......45
Per dozen.......................5.00

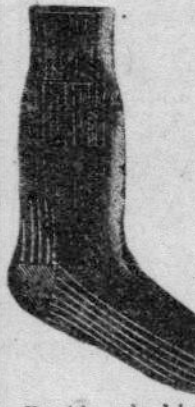

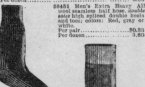

Double sole, high spliced heel.

36451 Men's Extra Heavy All wool seamless half hose, *double soles* high spliced double heels and toes; colors: Red, gray or white.
Per pair.......................$0.33
Per dozen.......................3.60

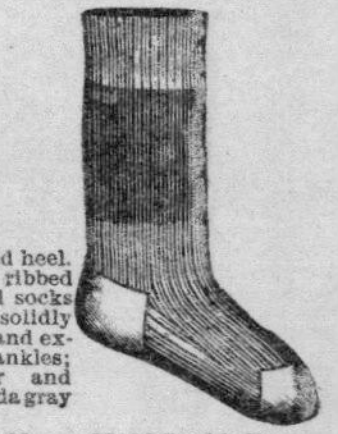

36452 Double Foot.

36452 Our Extra heavy ribbed leg all wool re-enforced socks have a double lining, solidly knitted into the feet and extending above the ankles; unsurpassed for wear and warmth; colors: Canada gray and brown mixed.
Per pair $0.33
Per dozen 3.60

36453 Men's Extra Heavy *Double Knit*, all wool fleece lined Socks; very warm and durable, full seamless; equal in thickness to a fulled sock. Colors: Gray or white. Per pair.......................$0.40
Per dozen.......................4.50

If any of our goods are found to be not as represented, we take them back and exchange for other goods, or refund the money paid for them, at the option of the purchaser.

Men's Extra Length Bicycle and Athletic Hose.

For all sorts of athletic sports, games, etc. Weight about 42 to 50 ounces to a dozen.

36458 Men's Heavy All Wool Ribbed Cashmere Hose, double heels and toes; color: black.
Per pair...........$0.50
Per doz...........5.50

36459 Men's Bicycle Hose, made of extra stout double thread worsted, very durable, extra length, Derby ribbed. Seamless; colors: navy blue, seal brown, black or gray.
Per pair..........$0.75
Per doz...........8.00

36460 Men's Heavy Ribbed Bicycle Hose, cotton, seamless, double heels and toes, fast black.
Per pair....................25
Per doz...................2.85

36461 Men's Bicycle Cotton Stockings, extra heavy, ribbed, seamless. Fast black.
Per pair....................35
Per doz...................3.85

36462 Men's Extra stout ribbed All Wool Bicycle Stockings, the most durable stockings made; black only.
Per pair.................$1.25
Per doz..................12.00

Men's Hunting Stockings.

36470 Men's Extra Heavy Hunting Stockings, all pure wool and lined with warm knitting to above the ankle. Ribbed top, plain boot; black, gray or red, 24 in. leg. Per pair.........$1.10
Per dozen.................12.00

36471 Men's Extra Heavy Hunting Stockings, all pure wool, ribbed legs with gray and black stripe, plain black boot, all wool, tufted to above the ankle, length 24 in.
Per pair..................$1.20
Per dozen................13.50

36470-71

36473 Men's Royal Norway Hunting Stockings, made of extra fine all wool 6-ply yarn, in handsomely variegated mixtures of black, brown and gray; black, blue and gray; or black, red and gray. Double feet, fleece lined, length, the inch leg. No finer snow stocking. Per pair..$1.25
Per dozen................14.00

Royal Norway.

Heavy Lined All Wool German Socks.

We guarantee every pair of our German socks, should any prove unsatisfactory after a fair trial return them, and we will refund your money or give you a new pair in exchange. Straps and buckles with every pair.

36478 Our New Patent German Socks or Blizzard Boots, made of a good quality of wool; are put through a special process of fulling and lined all through with wool, solidly spliced into the sock. We guarantee them to be unequaled for wear and warmth. Color: Sheep's gray or brown striped. Length, 18 inch leg, weight 24 ozs. to a pair. Per pair.....$1.10
Per dozen................12.00

36479 The Waukesha All Knit All Wool Sock. Guaranteed to outwear anything of its kind in the market. Heavy, warm and durable. Color: Sheep gray only. Per pair...$1.10 Per dozen....$12.00

Socks—Continued.

36480-81
(Guaranteed.)

36480 Our Extra Heavy all knit German Socks, made of strictly all pure wool, warm tufted lining to above the ankle; black only; length, 18 inches.
Per pair............$1.00
Per dozen...........11.50

36481 Same as 36480, with tufted lining all through. Very warm and durable, black only. Per pair..$1.10
Per dozen...........12.00

36486 Men's Extra Heavy All Wool German Socks; all wool tuft lined feet and ankles, extra patented square heels; black only. For 2, 15 inches.
Per pair...........$0.75
Per dozen..........8.00
No. 3, 18 inches.
Per pair.................85
Per dozen............9.50

36488 Men's Tufted German Socks, extra heavy; black; lined at the heels with leather, to strengthen and make them more durable. Length, 18 inches.
Per pair...........$0.95
Per dozen..........10.50

Leather Lined Heels.

36489 Our Extra Quality German Socks, made of pure warm Wisconsin wool, tuft lined feet and ankles, hand finished tops; we guarantee every pair or money refunded. Length 18 inches, color, black only.
M. W. & Co's. Prize Stock.
Per pair...........$1.20
Per dozen..........13.50

36494

AGRICULTURAL IMPLEMENTS.—We have a special catalogue of these goods, in which we quote everything necessary for practical farming of all kinds, and a great many other things also. Postage 4 cents. Don't you want one?

Men's Extra Long All Wool Hose.

Weight to a pair, 36490-8oz., 37491-12 oz., 36492-7 oz., 36494-15 oz.

36490 Men's Polar Long Hunting Stockings, extra heavy all wool, ribbed, gartered tops; colors: Scarlet, gray or black. See cut.
Per pr..$0.49
Per dz...5.50

36491 Extra Heavy, all wool, Lumberman's Socks, hand tuft lined feet and ankles, loop lined up to the top; gray and brown, or black and red stripes. Length of leg, 18 inches.
Per pair..........$0.50 Per dozen.......5.50

36492

36492 Boys' Extra Heavy Long Polar Stockings; all wool ribbed legs; very warm; 23-in. legs; Colors: Black, gray or red. Per pair....$0.45
Per dozen...................5.00

36493 Boys' half lined all wool German socks, heavy and warm. Colors: Black, scarlet or red.
Per pair..................$0.70
Per dozen..................7.50

36494 Men's Extra Heavy and Extra Long Hunting Stockings. Made of pure Wisconsin wool, all wool tuft lining. Very warm and durable. Colors: Red, black or sheep gray; length of leg, 24 inches.
Per pair................$1.10
Per dozen...............12.00

Boys' Cotton Half Hose.

Weight, per dozen, 23 ozs.
36495 Boys' Blue or Brown Mixed Seamless Cotton Half Hose, plain tops.
Per pair.................$0.06
Per dozen pairs............69

36496 Boys' Cotton Half Hose, blue or brown mixed. Extra heavy 9 in. Rockford.
Per pair.................$0.09
Per dozen pairs............90

Boys' All Wool Half Hose.

36497 Boys' All Wool Half Hose, seamless; Colors: blue, mixed or gray; sizes, 9 inches. Per pair $0.17
Per dozen...............1.89

36498 Boys' Extra Fine Cashmere Socks; 8½ and 9½ in. seamless double heels and toes; assorted colors. Per pair.................20
Per dozen...............2.25

CHILDREN'S CAPS AND BONNETS.

For Fall and Winter Wear, all lined and wadded, for ages 1 to 5 years.

36500 Child's Hood, made of Bengaline Silk Lace Ruche, sateen strings and pompom. Color, Cardinal, navy, brown, tan and cream; sizes 14 to 17 inches.
Each.............$0.25
Per dozen.........2.85

36500

36501 Child's Hood, made of fine corded eider-down, ruche strings and pompoms made of Cashmere, assorted mixed colors; sizes 14 to 16.
Each................$0.25
Per dozen.............2.85

36502 Child's Hood, made of all wool eider-down, sateen strings and pompom, cream white; sizes 14 to 16. Each....$0.25
Per dozen.............2.85

36503 Child's Hood, made of silk faced plush, pompom and strings of cashmere, lace roche; sizes 14 to 16. Colors: cardinal, navy blue, or brown. Each.........$0.50
Per dozen..................5.50

36502-36503

36504 Infants' Lambs' Wool Hood, full lace Ruche, Cashmere pompon and strings; sizes 14 to 16. Cream white.
Each.................$0.47
Per dozen.............4.50

36505 Child's Bonnet, made of heavy Bengaline silk, extra deep cape, fur trimming strings of Bengaline silk, very neat pompon; colors: cardinal, navy blue, brown or tan. Sizes 15 to 17.
Each...................$0.85
Per doz.................9.00

36505

36506

36506 Child's Hood, made of fine Bengaline silk and facings made of fine watered silk, large Pompons, wide strings; colors: navy blue, gold brown, tan or cardinal. Sizes 15 to 17. Each.......$0.85
Per dozen..................9.00

Corsets—Continued.

M. W. & Co.'s French Strip, Corset, No. 831.

Please give your size.

36831 M. W. & Co.'s French Strip Corset, No. 831, made expressly for us. This corset is equal in fit, material and durability to any French corset now in the market at double its price. $2,800,000 one. Colors; drab, ecru or fast black.
Each .... $ 0.99
Per doz. 10.50

36832 M. W. & Co.'s High Bust Dress Form Health Corset; has an extra long waist. The bust pads are flexible but always retain the shape. White or drab. Sizes 18 to 30.
Each .... $ 0.99
Per dozen 10.50
Absolutely fast black.
Each .... $ 1.19
Per dozen 12.00
Extra Quality, all English Sateen and French Staying, white, black or drab. Sizes 18 to 30.
Each .... $ 1.35
Per dozen 15.00

High bust, extra long waist.

36833 M.W.&Co.'s Nursing Corset, (No. 833), made expressly for us, is the most convenient ever introduced. The bust pieces have patent clasp fasteners and can be removed or replaced without any trouble, the front is nicely corded and the back is regular French strip style, Colors; Fast black or drab only.
Each ....$ 1.25
Per doz.... 13.75

M. W. & Co.'s Nursing style 833.

36834 M. W. & Co.'s Corset No. 834 is the longest waist corset made; suitable only for tall slim figures. It is made to measure. It has a 14½ inch unbreakable steel, is made of the best English sateen elaborately flossed; comes in black, white or drab; the same sold everywhere for $3.50. Our price.
Each ....$ 2.19
Per doz.... 24.00

36835 M. W. & Co.'s 6 Hook Columbia Corset No. 835 (same Style as 36834). Made of fine jeans with Sateen covered strips. Colors, drab only.
Sizes, 18 to 30. Each $1.00
Per dozen 11.00
Black is all sateen. Each 1.39
Per dozen 15.00

Madam Foy's Improved Corset.

Madam Foy Corset.

36836 These are the only skirt supporting corsets with shoulder brace and side lacing and are without exception the best of their kind in the market. White or drab only. Sizes 18 to 30. Improved, per doz. $12.00. Each, including extra sizes.............. $1.25

Nursing.

36837 Is a Perfect French form and nursing corset thoroughly boned; soft and pliable busts, made of fine corset jean, with French sateen covered strips, white or drab, sizes, 18 to 30.
Each $0.89
Per doz............. 9.50

36838-39-40

36838 Ladies' Summer Corset, made of open work material, very light and cool. White only; sizes 18 to 30. Each ....$0.40 Per dozen....$4.50

36839 Our M. W. & Co.'s Guaranteed Summer Corset, made of extra quality open work material. Guaranteed not to rip or tear, or money refunded. White only; sizes 18 to 30. Each........ .50
Per dozen........ 5.50
Extra sizes 31 to 36. Each............. .75

36840 French Form long waist ventilating summer corset. Made of extra fine open work material, thoroughly boned and stayed; guaranteed not to rip or tear or money refunded. White only. Sizes 18 to 30.
Each $0.95
Per dozen ... 10.50
Extra sizes 31 to 36. each...........$1.25

36841 Our "Jersey" Corset, made of good serviceable jean. The best in the market at the price. White or drab. Sizes 18 to 30. Each........$0.35
Per dozen 3.75

36842 Corset is perfect fitting French Strip Corset. Colors; White, drab, ecru. Each $0.45
Per dozen 5.00

Note.—We cannot ship corsets if you neglect to give your size.

Special Catalogue O.—Blacksmiths' and Wagonmakers' material. Very complete and prices low. Sent free upon request.

Corsets—Continued.

36843 This finely finished 5-hook corset is made of good sateen, double steel. It has a double section lined with two series of bones, giving extra strength where it is most needed. White, drab or black. Sizes 18 to 30.
Each $0.50
Per dozen 5.00

36843

36844 Corset, made of extra heavy coutille, long waist, double side steels, guaranteed to outwear any corset in the market at the price, or money refunded. Sizes 18 to 30. Colors, white or gray. Each $0.99
Per dozen 10.50

36844

Bortree's Duplex Corset.

36847 Bortree's a perfect fitting duplex corset, double bone, double seam, warranted not to rip. It can be adjusted to any form by means of the adjusting straps; sizes 18 to 30.
Each $0.85
Per dozen 9.00
Extra sizes, 31 to 36.
Each 1.15
Colors, white or drab.

Dr. Warner's Abdominal Corsets.

36849 Dr. Warner's Abdominal Corset, with extension front, boned with coraline, made with a 13-inch steel, the corset extending below the steel in front from 2 to 3 inches. On each side a silk elastic gore is inserted. Ladies who cannot wear the ordinary abdominal corset can wear this one with ease. White or drab; sizes, 20 to 30.
Per dozen $16.50
Extra sizes, 31 to 36
Per dozen 21.00

Black, sizes 20 to 30. Per dozen..............$18.00
Black, sizes 32 to 36. Per dozen.............. 22.00

36850   36851

36850 Dr. Warner's Coraline Corset, made of French cloth, 96 coraline stays, which are superior to bone or whalebone. Side steels removable, double front steels, a fine shaped bust; white, drab or black; sizes 18 to 30.
Per doz. $9.00
Extra sizes, 31 to 36. Per dozen............ 12.00
36851 Dr. Warner's Health Corset, boned with Coraline flexible coraline bust; sizes 18 to 30.
Per dozen, white or drab.......................$12.00
Extra sizes, 31 to 36, each...................... 1.50
Black, sizes 18 to 30, per dozen............ 16.50

Misses' Corsets.

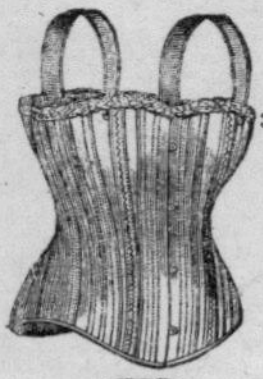

36854 Misses' Corsets, ages 12 to 15 years. Can also be worn to advantage by *ladies* having short waists and small bust development; white or drab; sizes, 18 to 27.
Each........................$0.60
Per dozen................. 6.00

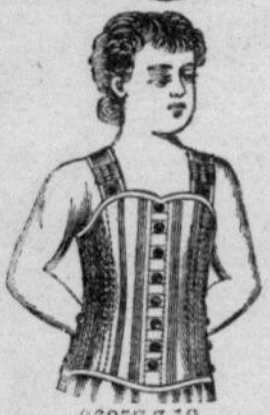

36857-7-12.

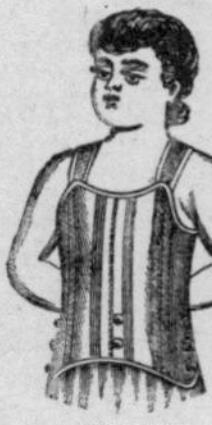

36858-3-7

36857 Our Misses' Waist, ages 7 to 12, made of finest washing silesia, white or drab, sizes 19 to 26. Each..........$0.70. Per dozen.......$7.50
36858 Our Childs' Waist, ages 3 to 7 years, finest washing silesia. Each .... .50
Per dozen.............................. 5.65

Ferris' Good Sense Corset Waists.

FOR CHILDREN, MISSES, YOUNG LADIES AND LADIES.

Always give the size. Age does not determine waist measure correctly.

36860 Ferris Waist, white or drab; No. 247 baby's style 1 to 4 years. No. 248,child's, 4 to 8 years.
Each..$0.25
Per dozen.. 2.50

36861 Ferris Waist, white or drab; style 209, for ages 1 to 4 years; style 204,ages 4 to 6 years,boy or girl.
Each.. .50
Per dozen... 5.00

Corset Waists—Continued.

36864 Style 215 Misses' waists, ages 7 to 12 years. White or drab.; sizes, 20 to 28. Each............$0.75
Per dozen.. 7.50
36865 Misses' styles 223; ages, 12 to 17 years; white or drab; sizes 20 to 28. Each............ 1.00
Per dozen.. 0.50
36866 Ladies' Good Sense Waist; style 262; fast black; medium form; fine satin jeans; sizes, 20 to 30. Each..........$1.25 Per dozen..........12.00

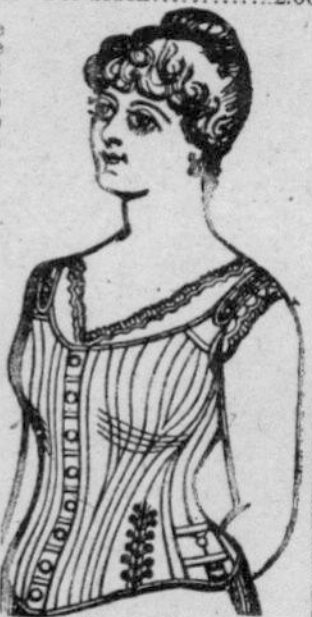

36867 Ladies' Good Sense Waist. Style 220, white or drab; sizes, 20 to 30; button front, lace back.
Each $1.00
Per dozen.... ...10.00
36868 Ladies' Good Sense Waist. Style, 230; medium form, long waist, side lacing, white or drab, buttoned front, laced back. Sizes, 20 to 30. Each..........$1.25
Per dozen..........12.00
Extra sizes 31 to 33. Each.......... 1.50
Per dozen..........16.50
36869 Ladies' Good Sense Waist. Style 219, medium form, long waist, buttoned front, laced back and sides, extra fine pearl buttons, superfine material, white or drab.
Each...............$1.50
Per dozen..........15.50
36870 Same as above. Style 264; fast black, horn buttons; sizes 20 to 30. Each........$1.75
Per dozen..........18.50
36871 "The Florence," children's double stitched corded waists with adjustable shoulder straps, fine sateen, white or gray. Sizes, 21 to 28. Ages, 2 to 8 years. Each $0.25
Per dozen... 2.85

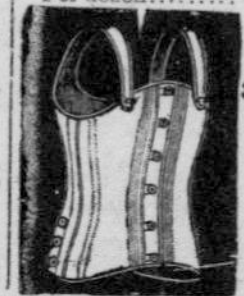

36873 Child's Waist, made of extra quality washing material, tape fastened horn buttons. Ages 2 to 10 years. Sizes 20 to 23. White or gray.
Each..........................$0.40
Per dozen........................ 4.50

Child's Ribbed Seamless Waists.

Healthful, Durable, Economical.

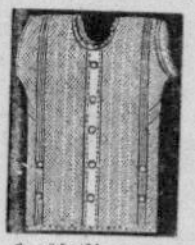

36874 Child's Seamless Knit Ribbed Waist is a shirt and waist combined. Can be worn with or without undershirt; has shoulder straps; tape stays support all the buttons, two rows of waist buttons for underclothes. A complete comfort and health garment. Ages 1 to 12 years. Age represents size. Price quoted is for all or any size.

No. 1. Medium weight, with metal buttons, guaranteed not to rust. Each $0.15
Per dozen... 1.50
No 2. Heavy weight, linen buttons. Each.... .19
Per dozen... 2.00
No. 3. Extra heavy weight, horn buttons. Ea.. .22
Per dozen... 2.35

Tampico Dress Form.

(Weight 2 to 3 ounces each.)

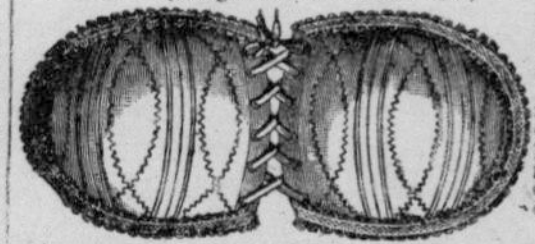

36875 These Dress Forms are made of tampico grass cloth, cover'd with sateen or ventilated; they are light, soft and flexible and yet so elastic that they will retain their shape; separable or inseparable; cut shows the separable.
No. 1 Each..........$0.25 No. 2 Each..........$0.35

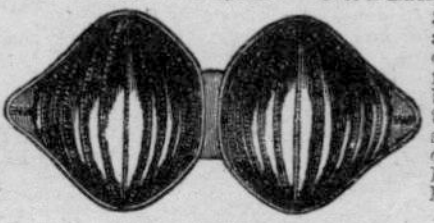

36876 New and adjustable dress form, ribs of featherbone. Two extra reenforcing strips with each form.
Each.....$0.30
Per doz.. 3.00

Bustles.

Weight, 3 ounces.

36880 Solid Comfort Coil Wire Bustle; until sold, each..$0.01

All lines of merchandise very generally reduced in price.

HARNESS DEPARTMENT.

Single Pony Harness.

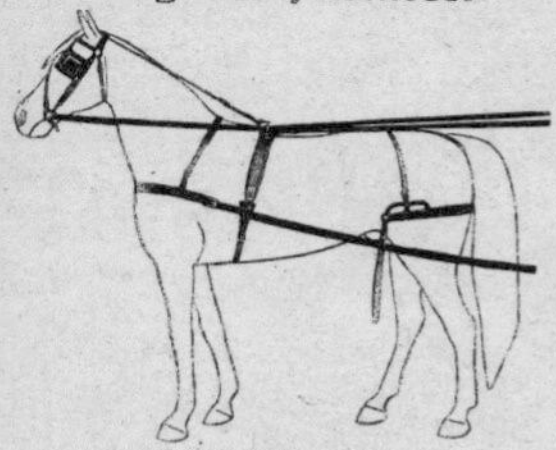

Russet Leather Only.

This harness is made of Fair Russet Leather of the best oak tanned skirting.

It can be adjusted to fit a pony weighing 500 lbs. or a small horse weighing 900 lbs. It is not suitable for anything larger or smaller than we mention.

We make it in *one style only*, and we insure satisfaction to every purchaser.

It is well made and well finished; is complete in every respect, and is decidedly nobby in appearance.

37000 Single pony harness, all fair russet leather; breast collar, 1¾ inch wide, folded with layer, box loops for traces; traces 1 inch, double and stitched, to buckle to breast collar; blind bridle with overcheck and round winker stays; breeching, 1¾ inches wide, folded with layer; saddle, 3¼ with leather pad and leather covered seat; round dock, flat back and hip straps; folded bellyband with Griffith's patent buckles; flat lines; full nickel mountings. Per set.........$13.50
Weight, per set, packed in box, 19 pounds.

We Sell

The Standard Diaries for 1895.

Send for free price list.

37002 Single Russet Pony Harness, single strap; Imitation Hand sewed; Bridle, ½ inch, box loops, round winker stay, layer on crown; Breast Collar, 1¼ inch; Traces, 1 inch, stitched to breast collar; Breeching, 1⅜ inch; side straps, ⅝ inch; Hip Strap, ½ inch; Turnback, ⅝ inch; scolloped, round crupper; Saddle, 2½ in.; "Strap," leather jockey, skirts and bottom, leather covered seat; Bellyband, "Griffith." Lines, ⅞ inch to loop in, 1 inch hand parts; No hitch strap; Full nickel mounting. Per set...$10.00
Weight, per set, wrapped in paper, 11 lbs.

Single Buggy Harness.

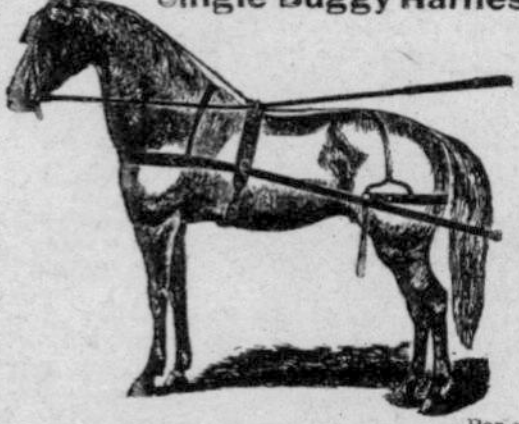

Per set.

37004 Single Buggy, Breast Collar Harness, mountings; bridle, ⅝ inch overcheck, flat winker stay; breast collar, folded; traces, 1 inch, doubled and stitched to breast collar; turn-back ⅝ inch, folded crupper; saddle,2½ inch, enamel cloth lined; lines, ¾ inch; hip straps, ½ inch. We cannot furnish above harness in any other style than as described..............................$3.98
Weight, per set, wrapped in paper, 10 pounds.
37006 Single buggy harness, breast collar, double stitched layer, 1 inch double traces, sewed to breast collar, ⅝ inch blind bridle, flat cheeks and flat side or overcheck, ¾ inch flat lines, 2½ inch gig saddle, folded breeching with layer, ¾ inch side straps, ⅝ inch hip straps, folded crupper, no martingale. XC plated mountings.. 4.75
Weight, per set, wrapped in paper, 11 lbs.
We do not furnish hitch straps with single harness at quoted prices.

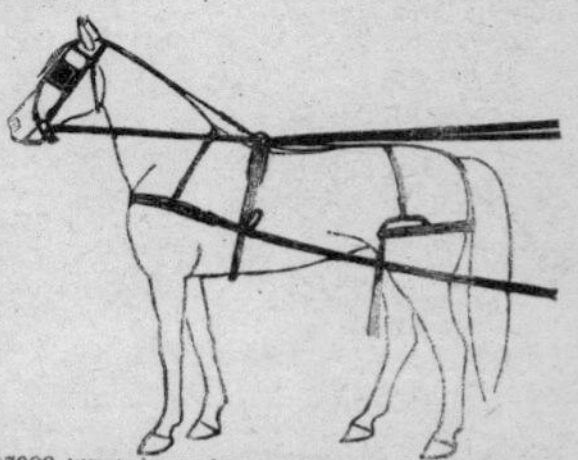

37008 Single buggy harness, breast collar, folded with layer and box loops, traces, 1 inch, double and stitched to buckle to breast collar, 2½ inch saddle, breeching folded with layer; belly-bands folded Griffith's style, bridle ⅝ in., box loops, patent leather winkers, flat side or over check, turnback, plain, with round crupper, hip strap ⅝ in., lines ¾ in., white mounting. Per set.....$6.00
Hames and collar in place of breast collar, extra 1.25
Round lines in place of flat........................ .90
37008 Harness with breast collar weighs 12 lbs.; wrapped in paper and with hames and collar, about 16 lbs.
37010 Single Buggy Harness, Saddle, 2½ inch japanned jockey patent leather skirts, enamel cloth lined. Bridle ⅝ with box loops, patent leather winkers, round winker braces, overdraw or round side checks. Traces 1 inch, doubled, raised and stitched to buckle to breast collar; lines, ⅞ inch flat, to loop in bit. Breast collar folded with layer and box loops; breeching, folded with layer; belly-bands, folded Griffith's style; side straps, ⅝ inch; turn back, plain with round crupper; hip straps, ⅝ inch; no martingales; all black mountings..............................$7.00
37011 Same in XC mounting.............................. 7.25
37012 Same with half nickel mountings.............. 7.50
Hames and collar in place of breast collar,extra. 1.50
Round lines in place of flat, extra.................. .90
When ordering single buggy harness, mention whether side or over check bridle is wanted.
37010-1-2 Breast Collar Harness, wrapped in paper, weighs 12¼ lbs. per set; with hames and collar, 17 lbs.

Leather Plow Back Bands.

37369 Leather back bands, with patent hooks to fasten in trace chains for horse or ox plow harness.

ness.	3 in.	3½ in.	4 in.
Each	50c.	56c.	62c.

Weight, each, 20 to 26 ounces.

Cotton Back Bands.

37370 Cotton back bands, with patent hooks to fasten in trace chains for horse or ox plow harness.

ness.	3 in.	3½ in.	4 in.
Each	25c.	28c.	33c.

Weight, each, 10 to 14 oz.

Chain Piping.

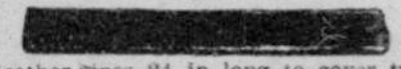

37372 Leather pipes 24 in. long, to cover trace chains for plow harness. Per set of four for two horses....$1.35

Side Straps.

37374 Side straps for breeching on double team harness, length 6 feet.

	⅞ in.	1 in.	1¼ in.
Per pair	55c.	70c.	85c.
Weight per pair	14 oz.	16 oz.	22 oz.

37375 Side straps for single buggy harness 4 feet long, either nickel or imitation rubber buckles.

	¾ in.	⅞ in.	1 in.
Per pair	40c.	50c.	60c.
Weight, per pair	8 oz.	10 oz.	12 oz.

Harness Leather, Etc.

37377 Hemlock Tanned Black Harness Leather; common or "B" grade, whole sides only. Sides weigh from 15 to 20 pounds. Per pound....$0.28

37379 Oak Tanned Black Harness Leather; common or "B" grade; whole sides only. Sides weigh from 15 to 22 pounds. Per pound.... .31

37381 No. 1 Hemlock Tanned Harness Leather, black; weight, per side, from 15 to 20 pounds. Per pound, in full sides.... .30

37383 No. 1 Oak Tanned Harness Leather, black; weight, per side, from 15 to 22 pounds. Per pound, in full sides.... .34

37385 No. 1 Rawhide Lace or Whang Leather oiled and tanned, side measures from 7 to 18 square feet. Per square foot.... .25
Weight, per foot, 4 oz.

37387 Belt Lacings or Saddle Strings, cut from No. 1 oil tanned rawhide or whang leather: put up in bunches of 50 feet.

Width	⅜ in.	½ in.	⅝ in.
Per bunch	$0.50	$0.65	$0.80

37389 Russet Leather Sheepskin, good medium size. Each....$0.70
Weight, each, 16 oz.

37390 Russet Leather sheepskins, good large size for blacksmiths and lumbermen's aprons, etc. Each....$1.00
Weight, each, 24 oz.

37391 Sheepskins, tanned with wool on, used for lining saddles and harness, large size. Each.... .99
Weight, each, about 2 pounds.
Prices of leather subject to market change without notice.

37393 Deer Skins dressed with the hair on, guaranteed to be No. 1 in quality. These skins are used for carriage or floor rugs, for binding harness, facing horse collars and making collar pads, but are especially valuable for use by bedridden invalids, being placed under the sheets to prevent or cure bed sores, and are frequently ordered by physicians for that purpose. They are graded very closely as regards size on account of their value. Price is governed by the size. Each from....$2.00 to $4.00

Buggy or Carriage Whips.

37395 Straight rattan, well finished. The best value ever offered for the money. Length 6 feet. Each....$0.10
Per dozen.... 1.00

37396 Black, platted through, Japan Cap, one 1½-inch beaded nickel ferrule, loop snap; made with Overin's Patent Lining, strongest and best. Superior to any other whip made for the money. Practically unbreakable; a first-class livery whip; length, 6 feet.
Each.... .18
Per dozen.... 2.00

37398 Black straight rattan, platted through, linen lined, smooth finish, 1½ inch beaded nickel head and 1½ inch beaded nickel ferrule, Philadelphia snap.

Length	5½ ft.	6 ft.
Each	$0.20	$0.25
Per dozen	2.15	$2.70

37399 Black, straight rattan, terra cotta painted handle, metal and linen lined, textile head button, two 2¼ inch beaded C gilt ferrules and one 1½-inch center ferrule, English snap; length, 6 feet. Each....$0.40
Per dozen.... 4.50

37400 Stocked Java Whip, black platted through, smooth finish, metal and buck lined, 1¾ inch, chased nickel head, and one 1½ inch nickel ferrule, English snap; length, 6 feet.
Each....$0.50
Per dozen.... 5.50

37401 Full Buck Top, smooth finish, wove handles, metal lined, two English textile buttons, English snap.

Length	6 ft.	6½ ft.
Each	$0.55	$0.60
Per dozen	6.00	6.50

Whips—Continued.

37403 Patent Solid Rawhide center, one-half length, water proof lined, smooth finish platted through double cover, rubber cap, six stitch head, and 30-ring patent buttons, English snap.

Length	5½ ft.	6 ft.	6½ ft.
Each	$0.60	$0.70	$0.80
Per dozen	6.48	7.56	8.64

37405 Stocked Java Whips, buck and metallic lined, smooth finish, black, platted through, seven ½ inch plain nickel ferrules between two 3¼ inch chased nickel ferrules, English snap; length, 6½ feet. Each....$0.75
Per dozen.... 8.10

37406 One-half Whalebone, metal and buck lined, smooth black finish, platted through, English textile head and button. English half silk snap. Length, 6 ft.
Each....$0.85
Per dozen....10.00

37409 Full Whalebone. No. 1 bone right through to spike, smooth black finish, platted through, metal and buck lined, rubber cap, three English buttons, English silk snap.

Length,	6 ft.	6½ ft.	7 ft.
Each	$1.25	$1.37	$1.50
Per dozen	13.50	14.85	16.20

37410 Cart or Sulky Whip, solid rawhide, double covered, one long butt button. Length, 4 feet. Each.... .50
Per dozen.... 5.75

37412 Ladies' Riding Whips, 25 cents, 50 cents, 75 cents, $1, $1.25, and $1.50 each, according to style and quality.

Riding Crops.

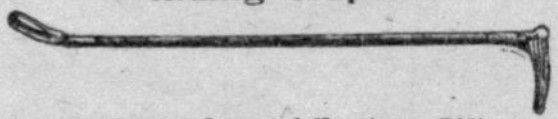

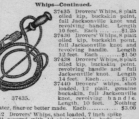

37416 Gentlemen's Imported Hunting or Riding Crops. Made of Malacca with English buckhorn hooks and elkskin loops. Each....$2.00

37417 Ladies' Imported Hunting or Riding Crops, Malacca stocks with English buckhorn hooks and elkskin loops. Each.... 1.60

Express Whips.

37419 Express Whips; Java stock handle, black thread cover, one nickel ferrule: white horse-hide braided drop top. Length 6 ft.
Each.... .40
Per dozen.... 4.50

Solid Leather Team Whips.

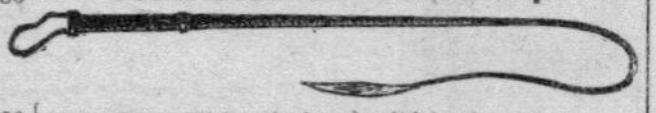

37420 Team Whips, body of solid leather, cover of oil tanned leather, thong stitched, snake style (XX). Length, 5 feet. Each....$0.65

37421 Team Whips, body of solid leather, cover of oil tanned leather, thong stitched, snake style (XX). Length, 5½ feet. Each.... .75

37422 Team Whips, body of solid leather, cover of oil tanned leather, thong stitched, snake style (XX.) Length, 6 feet. Each.... .85

Colorado Team Whips, Shot Loaded.

37424 Colorado Team Whips, made of oil tan kip, double covered, sewed with buckskin, one-half kip and one-half 8-plait buckskin, shot loaded, 6½ feet long. Each....$1.50
Weight, each, 28 oz.

37425 Colorado Team Whips, made of oil tan kip, double covered, sewed with buckskin, one-half kip and one-half 8-plait buckskin, shot loaded, 7 feet long. Each.... 1.70
Weight, each, 32 oz.

Mule or Hog Whips.

37427 12 plait calf, shot loaded, 5 feet, revolving handle. Each....$0.95
Weight, 18 ounces.

37428 Mule or Stallion whip; 4 plait braided whip leather, colored handle wired, buck cracker. Length, 4½ feet. Each.... .35
Per doz.... 3.90

Drover's Whips.

We are headquarters for drovers whips, and sell more than all other dealers combined. All hand made and well finished.

Each.

Weight, 10 to 25 ounces.

37430 Boys' Drovers' Whips, 6 plait, kip lash, 6 feet long, wired on 9-inch revolving handle, California style....$0.40

37431 Boys' Drovers' Whips, 6 plait, 7 feet long, 9-inch handle. California style, lash fastened securely.... .50

37432 Boys' Drovers' Whips, 8 feet long, 9-inch revolving handle, 6 plait, lash firmly attached to handle.... .65

37433 Drovers' Whips, revolving handle, Jacksonville knot, 8 plait kip, buck point, length, 9 feet.... .90

37434 Drovers' Whips, 10-inch revolving handle, lace fastener, 6 plait kip buck point; length, 10 feet.... 1.00

Whips—Continued.

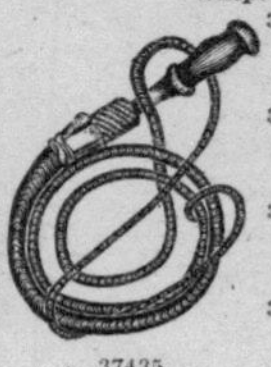

37435.

37435 Drovers' Whips, 8 plait oiled kip, buckskin point, full Jacksonville knot and revolving handle. Length 10 feet. Each....$1.25

37436 Drovers' Whips, 8 plait oiled kip, buckskin point, full Jacksonville knot and revolving handle. Length 12 feet. Each....$1.50

37438 Drovers' Whips, 8 plait oiled kip, buckskin point, revolving handle and full Jacksonville knot. Length 14 feet. Each....$1.75

37440 Drovers' whips, shot loaded, 12 plait, genuine buckskin, full Jacksonville knot, revolving handle. Length, 10 feet. Nothing neater, finer or better made. Each....$3.00

37442 Drovers' Whips, shot loaded, 7 inch spike butt, covered with 12 plait rawhide, body of whip is 12 plait oiled calfskin with buckskin point, no wooden handles. This is as servicable a whip as can be made. Length, 10 ft. Each.... 2.00

37443 Drovers' Whips, shot loaded, 7 inch spike butt covered with 12 plait rawhide; body of whip is 12 plait oil calfskin with buckskin point. Length, 12 feet. Each.... 2.50

37445 Drovers' Whips, shot loaded, 8 plait oiled calfskin with buckskin point, revolving handle, full Jacksonville knot. Length 10 feet. Each.. 1.75

37446 Drovers' Whips, shot loaded, 12 plait oiled calf lace leather with long buckskin point, full Jacksonville knot and revolving handle. Length, 10 feet. Each.... 2.25

Quirts.

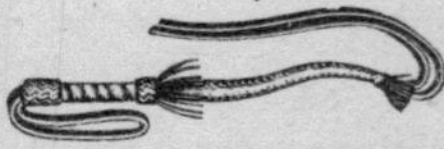

37448

37447 Braided rawhide, shot loaded, 12-plait, no tassel. Each. $1.50

37448 Braided Buckskin, shot loaded, with three tassels, 12 plait.... 1.25

37449 Braided Calf Strand, shot loaded, 12 plait. 1.00

37450 All leather covered, buckskin stitched, shot loaded, three tassels. Weight, each, 16 oz.. .50

37451 Oiled leather cover, buckskin stitched, two tassels, not loaded. Weight each, 8 ounces. Each.... 0.35

Whip Lashes.

Weight, 3 to 6 ounces.

37453 Six plait Genuine Buck Lashes.

Length	5 ft.	6 ft.	7 ft.	8 ft.	9 ft.	10 ft
Per doz.	$4.30	$5.10	$5.85	$6.70	$8.30	$9.75
Each	.40	.45	.50	.60	.75	.87

37454 Four-plait Genuine Buck Lash.

Length	5 ft.	6 ft.	7ft.
Per doz	$3.64	$4.20	$4.90
Each	.32	.36	.44

37456 Eight-plait California Stage Lashes, genuine buck.

Length	10 ft.	12 ft.	14 ft.	16 ft.
Per doz	$12.36	$14.95	$17.00	$19.50
Each	1.10	1.35	1.55	1.75

37457 Four-plait Imitation Buck Lashes.

Length	4 ft.	5 ft.	6 ft.
Per doz	$1.08	$1.40	$1.70
Each	.10	.13	.16

37459 Six-plait Imitation Buck Lashes.

Length	5 ft.	6 ft.	7 ft.	8 ft.
Per doz	$2.00	$2.50	$2.85	$3.60
Each	.18	.22	.25	.32

37460 White Hickory Whip Stocks.

Length	3½ ft.	4 ft.	4½ ft	5ft.
Per doz	$1.30	$1.50	$1.70	$1.90
Each	.12	.14	.16	.18

37461 Whalebone Whipstocks, with 5 nickel ferrules, 4 feet long. Each....$0.90

37462 Whalebone Whipstocks with 5 nickel ferrules, 4½ feet long. Each.... 1.10
Weight, 8 to 10 oz.

37464 Nickel Ferrules for Whipstocks in sets of assorted sizes. Per set of four for one stock.... .14

Whip Crackers.

We do not break dozens.

37466 Cotton Whip Crackers, 7 inches long. Per dozen....$0.10

37467 Whip Crackers, half silk and half cotton, 7 inches long. Per dozen.... .25

37468 Whip Crackers, all silk, best quality, 7 inches long. Per dozen.... .40

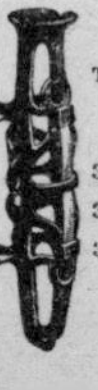

Patent Whip Sockets.

These sockets will admit any ordinary sized whip. They have nickel plated steel spring on side. The top half opens at the entrance of the whip, then closes tightly, always holding the whip in position.

37470 Sockets for Wood Dash. Each....$0.20

37471 Sockets for Leather Dash Each.... .25

37472 Whip Socket and Rein Holder combined. This device for holding the whip and reins is a convenience and a necessity. For wood dash, each....$0.28

37473 For leather dash, each.... .29

Waterproof Horse Covers.

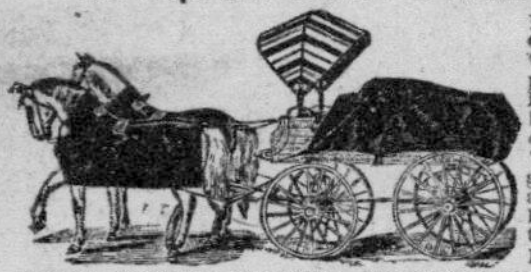

Black Oiled Waterproof Hame horse covers. These goods, as we have them prepared, are absolutely rainproof. The coating applied to the canvas contains nothing that will in any way injure the fabric, but is rather a preservative. Our covers extend on the neck twelve inches in front of the collar and can be used over either single or double harness. They are made with hame leathers, trace straps, and straps across the breast.

37476 Made of black oiled 8 oz. duck in sizes from 5 feet to 5 feet 6 inches from collar to tail. Each $2.00
Weight, each, about 8 lbs.

37477 Made of black oiled drill in sizes from 4 feet, 8 inches, to 5 feet 4 inches, from collar to tail. Each 1.75
Weight, each, about 5 lbs.

37478 Made of black oiled sheeting, medium or large sizes. Weight, each, about 4 pounds. Each 1.50

Rubber Horse Blankets.

37480 "Pure Gum" Rubber Horse covers or blankets. Dull finish, all seams both gummed and stitched, to neck only. The best made, small, medium or large sizes. Weight, 4 to 5 lbs. Each $3.25

37481 Luster Sheeting Rubber Horse covers or blankets, to collar only. Small, medium or large. Weight, 3 to 4 lbs. Each 2.50

37482 Long Luster Sheeting covers to head. Made in one piece, with holes for ears. Strapped for holding securely in place, small, medium or large. Each 3.50
Weight, about five pounds each.

Fly Nets.

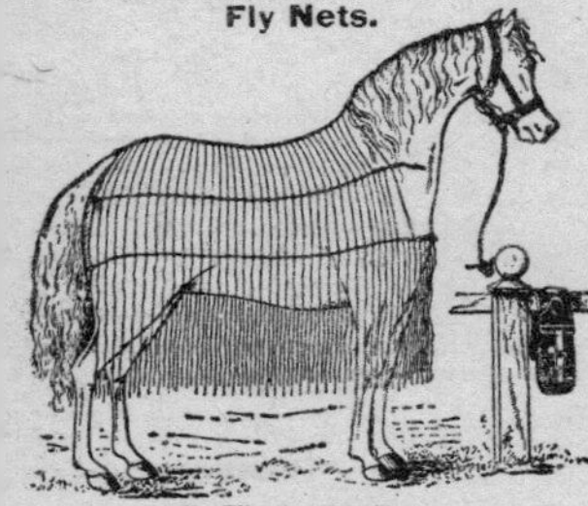

No Flies on This Horse.

Cut shows styles of nets quoted as "Body and Breast" nets.

NOTE.—Our quotations for fly nets are not by the pair, but for one single net for one horse.

37490 Upper Leather Team Nets, to head, standard weight, 5 bars, 84 lashes, body and neck. Weight, each net, 3¼ lbs. Each $1.90

37492 Heavy Upper Leather Team Nets, to head, 5 bars body and neck, with heavy hame bars.

No. of strings	60	72	84	100
Price each	$1.75	1.95	2.25	2.60
Weight, each	3½ lbs.	4 lbs.	4½ lbs.	5 lbs.

37494 Heavy Upper Leather Team Nets, body and breast, 5 bars with 60 lashes in body. Each $2.10
Weight, each net, 3½ lbs.

37496 Oiled Russet Leather Team Nets, 5 bars, 50 lashes in body, and breast piece. Bars are ¾ inch wide, lashes are very heavy, cut 5 to an inch and 7 feet long. Each 2.15
Weight, each net, 3¼ lbs.

37500 5 Bar, 40 Lash Team Nets to breast; blacked and polished. Bars are ¾ inch wide, lashes are extra heavy and 7 feet long. Each 1.50
Weight, each, 3½ lbs.

RUSSET LEATHER FLY NET, HEAVY.

37504 5 Bar, 60 strings, all leather team nets, with metallic fasteners on bars; the cheapest all leather net in the market, made in body, neck and breast, 5 bar, 60 strings, not counting breast strings. Each ..... $1.10 Per doz. 12.50
Weight, each, 53 oz.

37505 Russet leather team nets, body and breast; with metallic fasteners on bars. 5 bars, 42 lashes in the body and breast piece. Each 1.00
Per doz. 10.80
Weight, each, 44 oz.

FINE ROUND BLACK LEATHER FLY NETS.

For Buggy or Carriage use. The quality is the very best.

37510 5 Bar, body and breast, braided ends.

No. strings	50	60	75	90
Each	$1.55	$1.80	$2.25	$2.75
Weight, each net	24 oz.	26 oz.	30 oz.	35 oz.

Fly Nets—Continued.

37512 5 Bar, 72 strings to head, fine leather nets, extra quality. Each ..... $2.00 Per doz. $23.50
Weight, each net, 35 oz.

37514 Fine Calfskin Flank Nets, for carriage use. 5 bars, braided ends.

No. strings	40	50	60
Each	$1.55	$1.80	$2.05

Weight, each net, 16 oz. to 20 oz.

COMBINATION NETS.

37518 Indestructible Nets, body and head, leather tops, extra large bottoms, heavy cotton cord meshed; color: Black with canary bottoms. Each ..... $1.20 Per doz. $13.00

37519 Triumph Team Nets, body and head, 5 heavy cotton bars, 72 all leather lashes, russet in color. Each 1.12
Per doz. 12.75

37520 Non-Tangler Team Nets, 5 bar, 72 strings, body, neck and breast, web bars, with leather strings hanging from lower bar, thus preventing the tangling of strings. Each ..... .90
Per doz. 9.72
Weight, each net, 42 oz

Cotton Mesh Nets.

37524 White cotton mesh nets, body, neck and ear tips. Common or standard grade. Each $0.60
Per doz. 6.60

37525 Cotton mesh nets, body, neck and ear tips; all new combinations of fancy colors. Common or standard grade. Each ..... .65
Per doz. 7.00

37527 Heavy cotton mesh fly nets, white, with with colored trimmings, body, neck and ear tips. Exceptional value. Each ..... .70
Per doz. 7.75

37528 Heavy cotton mesh fly nets. All fancy colors with contrasting colored trimmings, body, neck and ear tips. All mesh nets hand made. Each ..... .80
Per doz. 8.75

37530 Extra heavy cotton mesh nets to head, body, neck and ear tips. Colors: Steel, ecru and black. The heaviest mesh net in the market. Each 1.00
Per doz. 10.80

37531 Improved Clipper Nets, to head; have gold brown meshed bottoms, which cannot tangle, and lashes at the top which will not catch in the harness. Each ..... .90
Per doz. 10.25

37533 White Shaft Nets to head, 1 inch meshes, white with blue trimmings. Longer and deeper than ordinary shaft nets. Each ..... .87
Per dozen 9.85

37534 Fancy Shaft Nets to head, all solid colors, Extra size. The most popular grade of shaft nets. Each 1.00
Per dozen 10.80

37536 Fancy Shaft Nets to head, woven back bands, all one pattern, a combination of drab and ecru colored cord with ecru trimmings. Each 1.10
Per dozen 12.00
Weight, each on shaft nets, 18 ounces.

37537 Shaft Nets to head, 1 inch meshes, woven back-bands; a combination of black and canary color cord, canary tassels. Entirely new and very handsome. Each 1.10
Per doz. 12.00

Horse Covers.

All made with hame holes, so as to be used over harness.

	Each.
37540 Striped Burlap	$0.50
37542 Linen Covers, E. Dublin in fancy plaid colors	.60
37543 Hercules, with strengthening bands	.80

Weight on covers from 20 to 28 ounces.

Horse Sheets.

Horse sheets, used in the stable, keep horses smooth and clean and ready for driving. They are strongly sewed down the back, stayed in the neck and have straps securely fastened.

	Each.
37546 Striped Burlap Sheets	$0.42
37547 Plaid Cotton Sheets	.58
37548 Brown Stable Sheets, hemmed fig., 4 stay	.70
37549 Improved Exhibition Sheets, linen finish, fast colors	.90
37550 Excelsior Duck Stable Sheets, fawn ground, fancy patterns	1.20
37551 "Ironside" Sheets, 40 in. deep, woven in Baker plaid, sewed straps, leather pockets, round corners; nothing better made	1.50

Weight of sheets, from 28 to 36 ounces.

Afghans or Baby Carriage Robes.

37555 Baby Carriage Robes Pink, elder-down, with diamond shaped blue embroidered center piece, pinked edge; size, 27x32 inches Each $0.40

37556 Baby Carriage Robes Tan wool elder-down, with fancy flower scroll, embroidered center piece, pinked edge; size, 27x32 inches. Each ..... .50

37557 Baby Carriage Robes. White wool eider-down, flower spray embroidered in center in blue and old gold colors, pinked edge; size, 27x32 inches. Each ..... .75

37558 Baby Carriage Robes. Fine white wool eider-down with the word "Baby" embroidered diagonally across the center in light blue and tinsel cord, intermixed with flower buds, pinked edges: size, 27x32 inches. Each.. 1.00

Carriage Robes—Continued.

37559 Extra fine white wool eider-down, lined with cambric, cluster of stalks of grain embroidered with light blue silk, the stalks being tied with blue silk ribbon, light blue herringbone stitch border; size, 27x32 inches $1.50
Weight, each, from 5 to 8 ozs., according to number

37560 White China Goat Baby Carriage Robes, with plain white wool eider-down lining and felt border. Each 2.75
With embroidered eiderdown lining 3.00
Size, 27x32 inches.

37561 White Angora Sheep Baby Carriage Robes, with plain white wool eider-down lining and felt border. Each 3.50
With embroidered eider-down lining. Each 3.75
Size, 27x32 inches; weight, each, 2 to 3 pounds.

Momie Lap Robes.

We have them in a large variety of new and beautiful designs. We cannot always duplicate patterns, as manufacturers are constantly producing new designs. We sell this style of goods very close.

37566 Fancy Dusters. In a variety of handsome and fancy plaids, not embroidered. Each $0.42

37568 Fancy Dusters, heavy novelty cloth, knotted fringe, double border, not embroidered. Weight 20 ozs. Each ..... .60

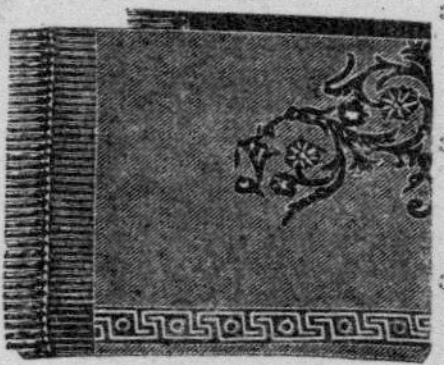

One design among many.
Price governs quality.

37570 Momie Lap Robes, with embroidered center piece designs. Each .. $0.40

37572 Momie Lap Robes, with embroidered center piece designs. Each. $0.50

37574 Momie Lap Robes, with embroidered center piece designs. Each $0.60

37576 Embroidered Dusters, novelty momie cloth with handsome patterns of new designs embroidered in center. Each ..... .75

37578 Embroidered Dusters, novelty momie cloth, assorted colors, 21 inch designs, all new patterns, knotted fringe. Each ..... .90

37580 Momie Lap Robes with embroidered center and fancy border, all new goods and new patterns 1.00

37582 Momie Lap Robes with embroidered center and fancy border, all beauties in this lot. . 1.25

37584 Elberon Lap Robes, mottled grounds with white plaids; worsted finish; three rows of stitching; not embroidered; superior value. Each 1.60

37586 Carriage Lap Robes, with jacquered borders and knotted fringes and embroidered center 1.50

37588 Embroidered Dusters, heavy, 18 ounce, novelty cloth, assorted fancy colors, knotted fringe, large, 32 inch, peacock design, in colors as natural as life. Each 2.00

37590 Imported Lap Robes, dark brown ground with light brown stripes from end to end, close and firm, knotted fringe. Weight, each, 16 ounces. Each 1.10

37592 Imported Lap Robes, light brown ground with dark brown stripes, knotted fringe. Size, 48x62 inches. Weight, each, 16 ounces. Each. 1.15

37594 Imported Lap Robes, light or slate color grounds, woven in a herringbone pattern, with a narrow stripe of another color every 2 inches. Size, 48x62 inches. Weight, 16 ounces. Each 1.20

Green Cloth Summer Lap Robes.

This class of goods is becoming very fashionable.
Each.

37596 Single Face Fabric Cloth, plain green, all wool, light weight, hemmed; sizes, 44x60 in; weight, 9 oz. $1.30

37598 Green Fabric Cloth, all wool, fine quality, pinked edge, and colored herringbone, stitch inlay, fancy embroidered center piece in contrasting colors; size, 46x60 in.; weight 11 oz. Price 1.75

37601 Green Beaver Lap Robes, fine quality heavy beaver cloth, with an overlay border 1 in. wide; size 52x60 in.; weight, 50 oz. 3.90

37602 Green Beaver, extra heavy quality of fine grade beaver cloth, with wide worsted braid binding; has a colored silk braid inlay 3 in. from edge, with fancy corners of the same; size 56x62 in.; weight, 58 oz. 6.35

Linen Lap Robes.

We have received a large consignment of Linen Lap Robes direct from the manufacturers in Belgium. We can offer you better value than ever in these goods for this year.
Each.

37606 Linen Lap Robes; ground is of natural linen color, with fancy stripes, plain fringe $0.45

37607 Linen Lap Dusters, medium grade; ground is of natural linen color, with fancy stripes and checks, fringe on each end ..... .60

37609 Linen Lap Robes, extra quality, fancy checks and stripes, with border and fringe; size, 48x60 in.; weight, about 12 oz. ..... .75

37610 Linen Lap Robes, all plain, momie style, very heavy for this kind of goods, heavy knotted fringe; size, 52x62 in.; weight, about 16 oz. 1.00

37612 Linen Lap Robes, plain body, with cluster of fern leaves embroidered in center; weight, 16 oz. 1.25

Turf Goods—Continued.

37846 Ankle Boots, can be used on either front or hind ankles. Heavy leather shield, kersey lining and wrap, chamois bound, two straps.
Per pair..........................$1.00
Weight, per pair, 7 ozs.

37848 Front Leg Shin and Ankle Boots kersey wrap, chamois bound, three straps; length, 6½ ins. Weight, per pair, 9 ozs.
Price, per pair..................$1.20
37850 Hind Leg Shin and Ankle Boots, kersey lined, chamois bound, leather cap, three straps; length, 11½ inches. Weight, per pair, 13 ozs.
Price, per pair..................$1.50

37848-50

37852 Straight Shin Boots front or hind, kersey wrap, chamois bound, leather cap, three straps; length, 8½ inches. Weight, per pair, 10 ozs.
Price per pair..................$1.50

37854 Front Shin and Ankle Boots, wool kersey wrap and wide elastic, chamois bound, 3 straps; length, 10 inches. Weight, per pair, 13 ozs.
37854 per pair, $1.50

Quarter Boots.

37856 Close Fitting Quarter Boots, solid leather quarters and heels, blue felt body, three straps, extra valve, small, medium and large sizes.
Weight, per pair, 10 ozs.
Price, per pair..................$2.00

37858 Close Fitting Quarter Boots, elkskin lined, solid leather quarters and heels, three straps. The most serviceable boot in the market, small, medium and large. Weight, per pair, 11 ozs.
Price, per pair..................$3.00

37860 Hinged Quarter Boot, side action, elkskin lined California style, hand made, small, medium or large.
Price, per pair..................$3.75

37862 Quarter Boots, solid leather body and quarters, elkskin lined, chamois bound, two straps.
Weight, per pair, 12 ozs.
Price, per pair..................$2.35

37864 Bell Quarter Boots, solid black leather body, wool lined, with wool roll around the top; small, medium and large sizes. Weight, per pair, 14 ozs.
Price, per pair..................$2.40

Swabs or Soaking Boots.

37866 Soaking Boots, to buckle over horses hoofs to keep them soft. Made of six thicknesses of Baker Kersey with four rows of stitching. Soak well with water and apply in the evening. They will keep wet all night. Per pair $1.00

37868 Imported Swabs or Soaking Boots, made of best English white all wool felt, one inch thick. A pair of these applied wet to a horse's hoofs at night, after a hard day's driving, will remove all fever, and preserve the hoof.
Weight, 22 ozs. Per pair..................3.25

Knee Boots.

37870 Knee Boots, made of solid black leather, chamois lined all through, strong and substantial, sure protection for horses that knock their knees.
Per pair..................$2.40
Weight, per pair, 12 oz.

Scalping Boots.

37872 Plain Scalping Boots, made with steel spurs, padded at top on the inside, solid russet leather, small medium or large sizes.
Price, per pair..................$1.50
Weight, per pair, 10 oz.

37873

37874 High Scalping Boots, made with best extensions and steel spurs. Top padded inside, solid russet leather, small, medium or large sizes.
Price, per pair..................$1.85
Weight, per pair, 11 oz.

Toe Weights.

37876 The Stick Fast Toe Weight, the best in the market. These weights have an improvement which consists of a small spur resting on the shoe. The weight and spur being one piece prevents jar on the hoof and relieves the screws of all strain. Weight, 2, 3, 4, 6, 8 and 10 oz. each. When ordering give weight wanted.
Price, per pair..................$1.25

37878 Fenton's Security Toe Weights, with detachable spurs. The best known weights and the most popular, with all horsemen. Weight 2, 3, 4, 5, 6, 8 and 10 ounces each.
Price, per pair..................$1.25
Be sure and mention weight desired.

Rubbing Cloths.

37880 Genuine imported Ashton salt sacks for rubbing cloths; full size, best quality.
Each..................$0.40. Per dozen..................$4.50

Interfering Device.

37882 This device has been in use for some time, and has never failed to stop the most obstinate case of interfering, and in most cases can be dispensed with after using from 10 days to three weeks. They will spread the colt's gait and make him a wide traveler. Every horseman will understand the merits of them when seen.
Price, per pair..................$1.25
Each..................65
Weight, per pair, 12 oz.

Derby Bandages, Cotton.

Full length, 6 feet, with strings.
37884 White Bandages, 4 to the set, per set..................$0.40
37885 Brown Bandages, 4 to the set, per set..................45
Weight, per set, 14 oz.
37886 Fine Wool Derby Bandages, fawn colored, per set of 4..................1.45
Weight, per set, 12 oz.

Trotting Balls.

37888 Rubber Trotting Balls
Per string..................$0.16
Per doz. strings..................1.75
Weight, per string, 7 oz.

Whip Spurs.

37890 Whip Spurs. To be used on a whip to rub on a horse's hips when speeding.
Each..................$0.90
Postage..................03

Horse Tooth Rasps.

37892 House's Patent Horse Tooth Rasps with handles (handle not shown in cut), fine polished, complete and ready for use.
Each..................$1.20
Weight, each, 24 oz.
37893 Extra Shoe Files, 3½ inches long, for horse tooth rasps. Each..................20
Weight, each, 4 oz.

Horse Tail Holder.

37895 For clasping and holding to gather the hair of the horse's tail, protecting it from the mud.
Each..................$0.1
Per doz..................2.0

Common Sense Horse Tail Clasp.

37896 This is a simple device for holding the hair of a horse's tail. It is made of one piece of spring brass without buckles or other contrivances.
Each..................$0.1
Per doz..................1.5
Weight, each, 2 oz.

Hoof Picks.

37898 Hoof Pick and Corkscrew combined.
Each..................$0.35
37899 Hoof Pick, plain Instrument.
Each..................$0.25
Weight, each, 4 oz.

37902 English Clipping Shears, with leather covered bows, 7½ inches long.
Each..................$1.1

37903 German Silver Mane Combs, 7¼ inches long. Weight, each, 2 oz. Each..................

37905 Heavy Sweat Scrapers, 1½ inches wide, 19 inches long, with wood handles on each end.
Each..................$0.45
Per doz..................5.50

37907 With leather handles on each end.
Each..................$0.55 Per doz..................6.00
Weight, each, 12 oz.

Wood Sweat Scraper.

37908 Wood Sweat Scrapers
Each..................$0.1
Weight, each, 4 oz.

Horse Blanket Pins.

37910 Blanket Pins, protected points; size, 3¼ in.
Per doz..................$0.40
Weight per doz., 8 oz.

Stallion Support.

For track or road use.

37912 This support is manufactured from the purest quality of rubber, made, and has met with universal success with all horsemen and stallion owners.
Weight, each, 10 oz.
Each..................$2.00

DIRECTIONS.
When not in use keep in a cool, dark place. When applying wring out mouth in water. When ordering state size, small, medium or large.

The Perfection Stallion Guard.

37914 Perfection Stallion Guard. Patented in U. S., Canada and all the leading countries in Europe. 3,000 sold in first season. A molded rubber medial or right material no black torture or chafing; no irritation or danger. They are flexible, simple, humane, clean and safe. Interferes with none of nature's functions. Fits like a glove, and buckle attaches or detaches, puts off or on in thirty seconds, weighs less than two pounds complete. The Perfection is guaranteed to be all and do all that is claimed or money refunded. No stallion owner should be without it. Price, each..................$3.30

Cribbing Muzzles.

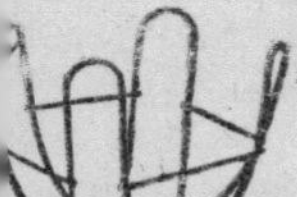

37916 Wire Cribbing Muzzle, complete with headstall. Each..$1.25
Weight, each, 30 oz.

Horse Muzzles.

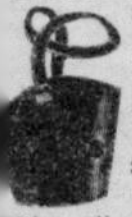

37918 Leather Horse Muzzle, made of No. 1 russet leather, having 1¼ inch halter attachment and ⅝ inch throat latch.
Each........$1.50
Weight, each, 25 oz.

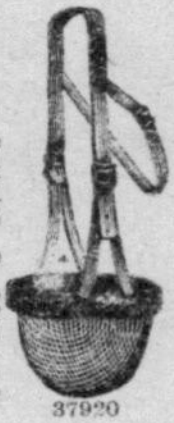

37920

37920 Wire Horse Muzzle. Is made of woven wire, and bound vith woolly sheepskin, having 1¼ in. alter attachment, and ⅝ inch hroat latch. Each............$1.65
Veight, each, 36 oz.

Horse Clippers.

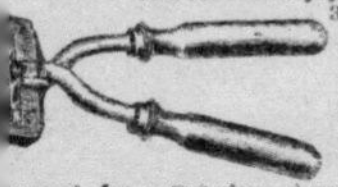

37922 The "Chicago" Horse Clipper. This is the perfection of the hand horse clipper. It combines simplicity of construction and durability of action. It is intended to meet the emand for a first-class, durable clipper, and s such is warranted to give perfect satisfaction.
ach.......................................$2.25
Veight, per pair in box, 18 ounces. Extra top lates, each, $0.80 Extra bottom plates each.. 1.00
ostage on extra plates, 4 cents.

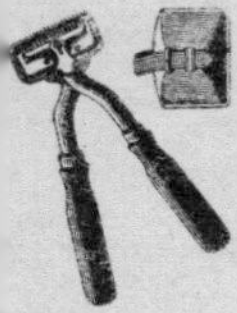

37924 The Newmarket pattern Horse Clippers, the most poupiar in the market; cutting plates of best refined steel.
Each....................$2.00
Weight per pair, 18 oz.
Extra top plates, each .75
Extra bottom plates, each....................$1.05
Postage on extra plates, 4c.

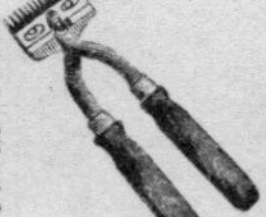

926 French Horse Clippers. ese are imported goods, ich we can sell for about the ce of a single cutting plate. ey have self-adjusting set ews. We positively cannot nish any extra parts. ngth, 10½ in.; weight, 14 nces. Each............$1.25
Index for Toilet Hair Clip-s.

Hand Power Machine.

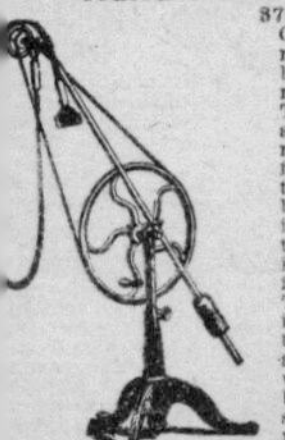

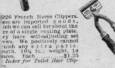

37928 This Hand Power Clipping Machine is the most substantial, powerful, light running, noiseless machine on the market. The base is of such design and proportion that the machine stands perfectly firm at all times, whether the floor is even or not. The balance wheel is 24 inches in diameter and runs on a turned steel shaft. All bearings are of steel, perfectly fitted and interchangeable. The connection for conveying power from head to cutting knives is by means of an improved flexible shaft, which can be curved and bent in any direction, insuring perfect freedom of motion and extensive range. The knives are of the finest steel, and tempered by an improved process. Every one is tested before leaving the manufacturers and is warranted to be in perfect cutting condition. Full directions for setting up and operating sent with each machine. Weight, boxed ready for shipment, 100 pounds. Price of machine complete..........$32.50
Extra handles, each, $3.00 Extra knives, per set, 4.00

Singeing Lamps.

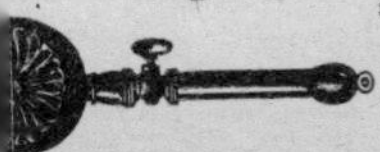

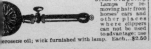

37930 Singeing Lamps for removing hair from horses' ears and other places where clippers can not be used to advantage; use erosene oil; wick furnished with lamp. Each...$2.50

Horse Standards.

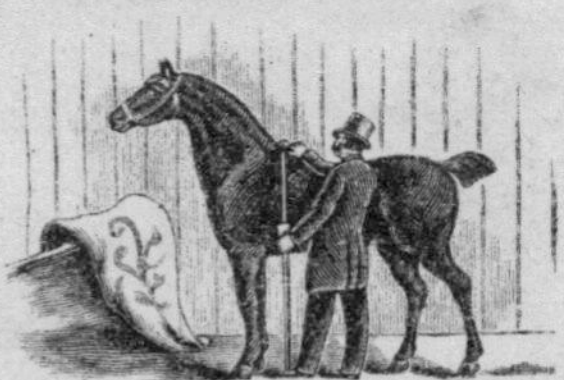

37932 Horse Standard measuring canes. They are regular gentlemen's walking canes, made of bamboo, metal tipped, with boxwood rule in side marked in inches and standards, which pulls up straight with the handle. Arranged to measure from 10 to 16¾ standard. A valuable article to breeders, dealers in horses, liverymen, etc. When carried in the hand has the appearance of being a cane only.
Style No. 1, with plain bamboo knob top. Each..$2.75
Style No. 2, Bamboo knob top, studded, with silver headed nails. Each........................ 3.50
Style No. 3, with English buck horn hook handles. Each...................................... 5.50
Style No. 4, with 2-inch engraved silver knob top. Each.. 5.75

Feed Bags.

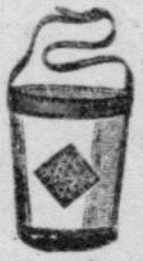

	Each	Per doz.
37934 Cotton Duck body, soft leather bottom, leather ventilator; weight, each 12 oz..................	$0.55	$6.00
37936 Extra heavy cotton duck body, heavy sole leather bottom, leather ventilator on side and leather bound top................	.75	8.25

Curry Combs.

We do not break dozens at dozen prices on curry combs.

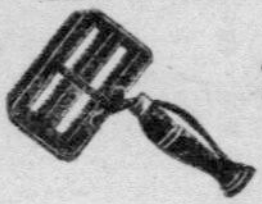

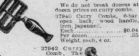

37940 Curry Combs, 6-bar open back, wood handle, iron, japanned.
Each......................$0.04
Per dozen........................ .35
Weight, each, 4 oz.

37942

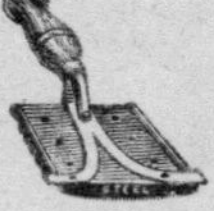

37944

37942 Curry Comb. The standard 7-bar open back, extra refined, well riveted best malleable iron frames, heavy knockers, hardwood handle.
Each...............$0.09 Per dozen..........$0.90
Weight, each, 10 oz.

37944 Curry Comb, 8-bar, heavy iron, closed back, heavy wrought iron shank; brace runs through handle and riveted, heavy iron knockers, all well riveted, black enameled. Each.... .13
Per dozen.................................... 1.35
Weight, each, 13 oz.

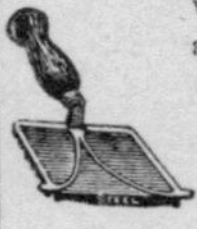

37946 Curry Comb, Climax 8-bars fine steel, closed back, japanned, malleable iron, tinned frame, iron knockers, all well riveted, black enameled handle.
Each................................$0.15
Per dozen.......................... 1.55
Weight, each, 10 ounces.

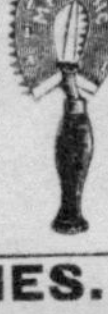

37948 The "Magnetic" Curry Comb. This comb, as its name implies, is made of a magnetic metal; it will not cut the hide or skin of the animal; is a positive self-cleaner; will not rust, and is absolutely unbreakable. Each $0.25
Per dozen 2 70
Weight, each, about 13 ounces.

Curry Combs—Continued.

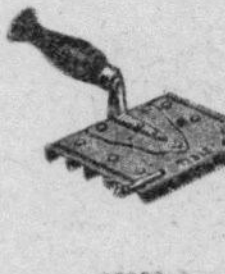

37952

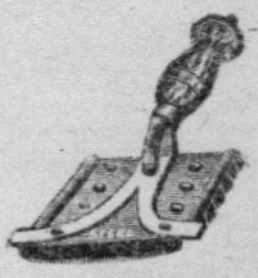

37954

37952 Curry Comb, warranted steel, 8-bar, extra heavy steel, blued, black enameled handle pinned to wrought iron shank.
Each..$0.20
Weight, each, 15 oz. Per dozen 2.10

37954 Curry Comb, the Climax, all steel 8-bar, closed back, extra heavy steel shank passing through handle and riveted; steel knockers. ☞ We call your special attention to this comb. It is undoubtedly the best for the money in this market. Each.. $0.25 Per dozen..........$2.65
Weight, each, 15 oz.

Combination Mane and Curry Comb.

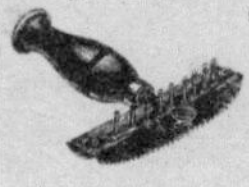

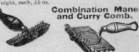

37956

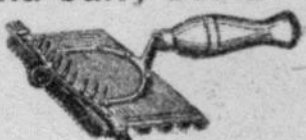

37958

37956 closed back, 2-bar, japanned iron.
Each..............$0.05 Per dozen.........$0.50
Weight, each, 6 oz.

37958 Mane and Curry Comb, combined, closed back, 6-bar, tinned iron. Each.......... .10
Per dozen.. 1.00
Weight, each, 10 oz.

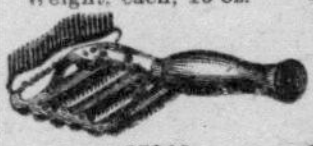

37960

37960 Mane and Curry Comb combined, new pattern, extra heavy 6 bar, tinned iron.
Each...............$0.15
Per doz................ 1.62
Weight, each, 12 oz.

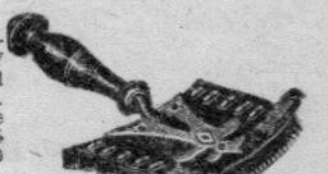

37962 Imported English Curry Combs, 7 rounding bars, closed back, strong and durable. The finest comb in the country. Each.....$0.45
Per doz.................. 5.00
Weight, each, 10 oz.

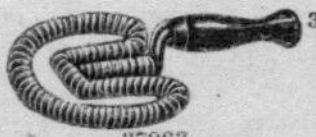

37963

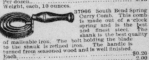

37963 The "Humane" Curry Comb. This is the only comb fit to use on horses' legs or on clipped or short haired horses. It is impossible to hurt a horse with it. It is also the best thing ever produced for a cattle cleaner. Each........$0.18 Per dozen..............$1.95
Weight, each, 8 ounces.

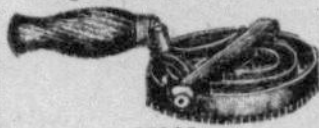

37965

37965 Circular Steel Spring Curry Combs. Three complete circles of steel working independent of each other, attached to an iron back by a hinged joint, wood handles. A good solid comb. Each...............$0.21
Per dozen.. 2.15
Weight, each, 10 ounces.

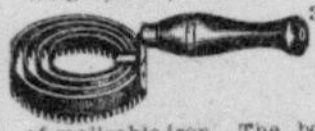

37966 South Bend Spring Curry Comb. This comb is made out of a clock spring and is the best and finest steel. The shank is the best quality of malleable iron. The bolt holding the blade to the shank is refined iron. The handle is turned from seasoned wood and is well finished.
Each...$0.20
Per dozen.. 2.00
Weight, each, 8 ounces.

Horse Curry Cards.

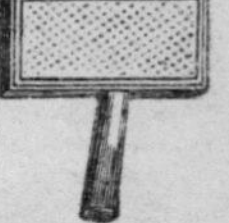

37968 Large, 3¼x8¼ inch, first quality. Each...............$0.09
Per doz.......................... .95
37969 Small 3¼x5½ inch,
Each........................... .08
Per dozen....................... .85
Weight, each, 8 ounces.

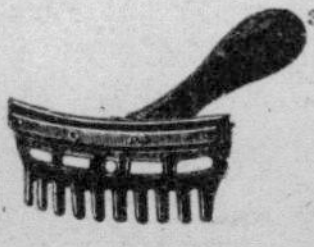

37970 Mane Comb, shedder and sweat scraper combined. A good, strong iron mane comb, with a rubber shedder or sweat scraper, 5½ inches long on the back. Far superior to a wooden sweat scraper. Each.....$0.15
Per dozen.......... 1.62
Weight, each, 8 ozs.

DAIRY SUPPLIES.

We carry a large line. Compare our prices with those asked by other houses and you will notice a big difference. See Index for quotations.

Trace Splicers.

38180 Malleable Iron Trace Splicers for mending traces, simple, quick, cheap and durable. They can be used for buggy, express or farm harness.

Price, per dozen $0.40
Weight, per dozen, 16 oz.

Whip Racks.

38184 Hall's Whip Racks, japanned sheet iron, 6 inches long; two nails or screws will hold one in position, and each rack will hold a dozen whips. Weight 2 oz. Each $0.08
Per dozen .... .85

Harness Snaps.

By size of snap we mean the width of strap that can be used.

38186 German Harness Snaps, bronzed finish. We handle only the heaviest and best snaps of this style made.

Size	⅝ in.	1 in.	1¼ in.	1½ in.	1¾ in.	2 in.
Per doz.	$0.13	$0.20	$0.32	$0.42	$0.54	$0.60
Weight per doz.	13 oz.	18 oz.	26 oz.	32 oz.	48 oz.	50 oz.

38188 Coverts' Banner Bolt Snaps. The principle feature of this snap lies in the spring being entirely covered, shutting out all foreign substance.

Size	⅝ in.	1 in.	1¼ in.	1½ in.	1¾ in.	2 in.
Per dozen	$0.24	$0.26	$0.40	$0.44	$0.48	$0.52

38190 Bristol's Patent Snaps, strictly first quality. Every snap is throughly tested in the factory before being packed.

Size	⅝ in.	1 in.	1¼ in.	1½ in.	1¾ in.	2 in.
Per doz.	$0.38	$0.40	$0.48	$0.56	$0.65	$0.78

38192 The American wrought steel harness snaps are strong competitors for public favor. All made with swivel strap eye.

38192.

Size	⅞ in.	1 in.	1¼ in.	1½ in.	1¾ in.
Per doz	$0.35	$0.37	$0.45	$0.52	$0.60

38194 The American wrought steel snap for rope halters or cow ties the strongest made.
Each .... $0.04 Per dozen $0.45

38196. Bristol's Patent Round Eye Snaps for rope, tinned finished. Polished on the loop and milled at the nose of the hook. Every snap is thoroughly tested.

38196

Size	⅝ in.	¾ in.
Per dozen	$0.45	$0.50
Weight, per dozen	15 oz.	25 oz.

38198 Bag Snaps, nickel plated bag or baby snaps. Will take strap ½ inch.
Per doz $0.25

38200 Buffalo Patent Snap, 2 in. long, japanned; can be used for halter bridle and bit. Weight per dozen, 14 ounces.
Each .... $0.05 Per dozen $0.50

California Belt Buckles.

	Each.	Per doz.
38202 California Nickel Plated Belt Buckles, 1¼ inch	$0.07	$0.75

Weight per dozen, 12 oz.

Trace Buckles.

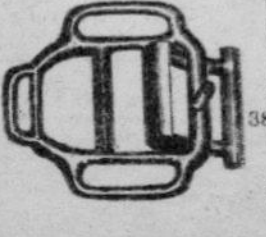

38204 Three-Loop Champion Trace Buckle, made of best malleable iron, japanned finish.

	Each.	Per doz.
1½ in.	$0.06	$0.65
1¾ in.	.07	.75

38205 Three Loop Champion Trace Buckles XC plate.

	Each.	Per doz.
1½ in.	$0.06	$0.65
1¾ in.	.07	.75

Harness Buckles.

(Black.)

38210 Japanned Iron Center Bar Harness and Halter Buckles for straps.

Size	½ in.	⅝ in.	¾ in.	⅞ in.	1 in.	1¼ in.	1½ in.
Per doz.	6c	8c	10c	12c	14c	18c	25c
Wt. pr. dz.	2 oz.	4 oz.	6 oz.	9 oz.	12 oz.	16 oz.	22 oz.

38211 "XC" plated (white) Iron Center Bar Harness and Halter Buckles for straps.

Size	½ in.	⅝ in.	¾ in.	⅞ in.	1 in.	1¼ in.	1½ in.
Per doz.	6c	8c	10c	12c	14c	18c	25c
Wt. per doz.	2 oz.	4 oz.	6 oz.	9 oz.	12 oz.	16 oz.	22 oz.

38214 Japanned (Black) Iron Barrel Roller Buckles.

Size, inches	½	⅝	¾	⅞	1	1¼	1½	1¾	2
Per dozen	4c	6c	8c	10c	12c	14c	16c	18c	20c
Weight per doz., in oz.	3	5	6	8	10	12	15	18	22

38215 "XC" plated (white) Iron Barrel Roller Buckles.

Size, inches	½	⅝	¾	⅞	1	1¼	1½	1¾	2
Per dozen	4c	6c	8c	10c	12c	14c	16c	18c	20c
Weight per doz. in oz.	3	5	6	8	10	12	15	18	22

Harness Rings.

38218 Breeching and Halter Rings, japanned iron, black finish.

Diameter, inches	½	⅝	¾	⅞	1	1⅛	1¼
Per dozen	4c	4c	5c	5c	6c	8c	10c
Weight per doz., in oz.	3	4	5	6	7	8	10
Diameter, inches	1½	1¾	2	2¼	2½	3	
Per dozen	12c	14c	20c	24c	30c	35c	
Weight per doz., in oz.	16	18	22	32	35	37	

38219 "XC" plated (white) Iron Breeching and Halter Rings.

Diameter, inches	½	⅝	¾	⅞	1	1⅛	1¼
Per dozen	4c	4c	5c	5c	6c	8c	10c
Weight per doz. in oz.	3	4	5	6	7	8	10
Diameter, inches	1½	1¾	2	2¼	2½	3	
Per dozen	12c	14c	20c	24c	30c	35c	
Weight per doz. in oz.	16	18	22	32	36	37	

38221 Halter Squares. Japanned malleable iron.

Sizes	1x1¼ in.	1¼x1½ in.	1½x1¾ in.
Pr doz.	10c	12c	15c
Wt. pr. doz.	10 oz.	14 oz.	18 oz.

38222 Halter Dees, japanned malleable iron.

Sizes	1¼ in.	1½ in.	1¾ in.
Per doz.	10c.	15c.	20c.
Weight per doz.	10 oz.	14 oz.	18 oz.

38223 Halter Bolts, japanned iron

Sizes	1 in.	1¼ in.	1½ in.
Per doz.	6c.	8c.	10c.
Weight per doz.	5 oz.	7 oz.	9 oz.

Martingale Rings.

These are inside measurements.

Per doz.

38225 Genuine Black Rubber Rings, plain, light in weight but strong $0.50
38226 Genuine Black Rubber Rings, imitation stitched edge, light but strong, diam., 1½ in.; weight, per doz., 7 oz. .... .65
38228 Red Duranoid Rings, 1⅝ inches .... .30
38229 White Duranoid Rings, 1⅝ inches .... .30
38230 Blue Duranoid Rings, 1⅝ inches .... .30
Weight, per doz., 14 oz.
38234 Bone Rings, red, 1 inch in diameter .... .40
38235 Bone Rings, white, 1 inch in diameter .... .40
38236 Bone Rings, blue, 1 inch in diameter .... .40
Weight, per doz., 3 oz.

38238 Celluloid Spreaders, composed of 3 solid celluloid rings in assorted fancy colors.
Per string $0.60
Per doz. strings 6.75
Weight, each, about 4 oz.

Celluloid Rings.

Red, white or blue.
Unless color is mentioned we invariably send white.

Diameter, inches. 38240	1¼	1⅜	1½	1⅝	1¾	2	2¼
Each	$0.10	$0.13	$0.16	$0.19	$0.22	$0.25	$0.28
Per doz.	1.00	1.40	1.75	2.15	2.50	2.80	3.15

White Zylonite Rings.

Diameter, inches. 38242	1¼	1⅜	1½	1⅝	1¾	2	2¼
Each	$0.09	$0.11	$0.13	$0.16	$0.19	$0.22	$0.25
Per doz.	.90	1.15	1.45	1.75	2.10	2.40	2.65

Weight on celluloid and zylonite rings, 5 to 17 oz., Per doz., according to size.

Celluloid Loops.

38244 Celluloid Loops, red, Diameter ⅝ in. ¾ [illegible]
Per doz. .... $0.33 $0[illegible]
38245 Celluloid Loops, white, diameter. ⅝ ¾
Per doz .... .33 [illegible]
38246 Celluloid Loops, blue, diameter. ⅝ ¾
Per doz .... .33 [illegible]
Weight per doz., 2 oz.
The above loops are used for connecting any s[illegible] rings for making spreader straps.

Morsman's Buckle Shields.

Buckle Shields are very ornamental on harness a[illegible] protect the horses' tail from being pulled out on t[illegible] buckle tongues.

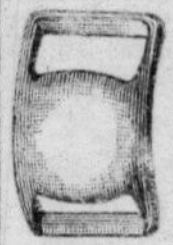

38248 Brass.

Size	½ in.	⅝ in.	¾ [illegible]
Per doz.	$0.70	$0.80	$0.[illegible]

Size	⅞ in.	1 in.	1⅛ in.	1¼ [illegible]
Per doz	$1.00	$1.10	$1.45	$1.[illegible]

38250 Same, in nickel.

Size	½ in.	⅝ in.	¾ [illegible]
Per doz.	$0.75	$0.85	$0.[illegible]

Size	⅞ in.	1 in.	1⅛ in.	1¼ [illegible]
Per doz	$1.05	$1.15	$1.30	$1.[illegible]

Weight, per doz., 6, 8, 10, 12, 14, 1[illegible] 18 oz.

Bridle Plumes.

Bridle Plumes. Curled Horse Ha[illegible] Plumes, or Tassels for team harne[illegible]
38254 Bridle Plumes, colors red [illegible] yellow, 9 inches long.
Per pair .... $0.[illegible]
38256 Bridle Plumes, colors red [illegible] blue, 11 inches long.
Per pair .... $0.[illegible]
38258 Bridle Plumes, colors red [illegible] green, 13 inches long.
Per pair .... $0.[illegible]
Mention color wanted. Weight, p[illegible] pair, 3, 4, 5 ounces.

Carriage Top Dressing.

38260 Frank Miller's Dressing for buggy and carriage tops. Gives an elastic, durable, jet black, waterproof gloss. Can be safely used on the finest stock. Directions on each can.
Pint cans. Each .... $0.60 Per doz .... $6.[illegible]

Harness Dressing.

38262 Frank Miller's Harness Dressing; for harness, saddles, fly nets, etc. Gives a beautiful finish, does not lose its luster. Directions for use on every package.
Pint cans, each .... $0.[illegible]
Quart .... [illegible]

Waterproof Blacking.

38264 Frank Miller's Leather Preservative and Waterproof Oil Blacking. This blacking is designed to render leather soft, pliable, waterproof and durable.
Directions on each package.

	Small size.	Large siz[e]
Each	$0.09	$0.[illegible]
Per doz.	1.00	1.[illegible]

Harness Soap.

38266 Frank Miller's Harness Soap. This is without question the best harness soap made. By using it your harness will wear longer and look better. Per cake .... $0.[illegible]
Weight, per cake, 12 oz.
38268 Crown Soap. The Chiswick pure English crown soap. Pint jars. Each ....[illegible]
Quart jars .... [illegible]

Harness Oil.

38270 Jumbo Harness Oil. The product of the Atlantic Oil Co. Put up in handsome lithographed cans, with screw tops.
Pint cans, each .... $0.[illegible]
Per doz. .... 2.[illegible]
Quart cans, each ....[illegible]
Per doz .... 3.0[illegible]

Axle Oil.

38272 Jumbo Axle Oil, manufactured and put up by the Atlantic Oil Co., in handsome lithographed cans with spout top.
For other oils see Index.

	Each.	Per do[z.]
Pint cans	$0.17	$1.[illegible]
Quart cans	.26	2.9[illegible]

Horse Foot Remedy.

38274 The Horse Foot Remedy. This remedy is a sure cure for all ailments of horses' feet; and for healing cuts, wounds, galls, soreness over the kidneys, etc., it can not be excelled. It is specially effective in healing barb wire scratches. Thrush or Foot Rot cured in three applications. It is easily applied, and does the work quickly and surely. Full directions on each package.

	Each.	Per do[z.]
Quart cans	$0.55	$6.0[illegible]
Half gallon cans	.85	9.2[illegible]
Gallon cans	1.60	17.2[illegible]
Five gallon cans	7.15	77.2[illegible]
38276 Neatsfoot Oil, quart cans	.35	4.0[illegible]

38278 Gladding's Hoof Dressing, quart cans, with brushes. Each .... .5[illegible]
38280 Continental Hoof Ointment, ¼ lb. cans.
Each .... .1[illegible]
Per dozen .... 2.0[illegible]
For other oils, see Index.

SADDLE DEPARTMENT.

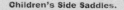

Children's Side Saddles.

38300 Two-Horn Child's Side Saddle, made on a Somerset side tree, full covered bars, with good pad. Good carpet seat, russet leather skirts, 3 inch super cotton girth, to buckle on both sides, metal shoe stirrup. Suitable for girls from 5 to 12 years of age. Each...........$3.00
Weight, each, 7½ lbs.

38310 Two-Horn Side Saddle, made on the Ruwart Tree; bright cherry red leather skirts; dished seat covered with velvet carpet; padded bars covered with white duck; 3 inch cotton corded girth; metal shoe stirrup. A very showy saddle, which we sell at a low price for the quality. Weight about 13 lbs.
Price.........$6.00

38318 Three-Horn Side Saddle, made on the improved Ruwart side tree. Genuine buckskin quilted seat, round russet leather skirts; bars covered with leather and padded. Double cinche rig to tie; 4 inch hair cinches; 2 inch leather surcingle; metal shoe stirrup; weight about 15 lbs. Each.........$9.50

38302 Three-Horn Child's Side Saddle, made on patent Morgan tree, buckskin seat, English slipper stirrup tie la igoos and hair cinche. This saddle is especially adapted for pony use for girls from 5 to 12 years of age. Weight 10 pounds. Price....$6.50

38312 Made on Morgan Tree, plush seat; bars are covered with leather and padded; ½ in. stirrup strap, with XC iron shoe stirrup, double cinche rigged, heap ping horn, two 4-inch hair cinches; weight, 14 pounds. This is the lowest priced double cinche rigged saddle ever sold. It is of much finer quality than one would expect at the price. Price... $6.50

38320 Side Saddle, made on the patent Ruwart side tree, fine quilted leather seat and roll, leaping horn, raised ornamental flower work on skirt, cotton surcingle, ¾ in. stirrup straps and slipper stirrup, double cinche rigged, one 4-inch and one 5-inch hair cinche; weight, 16 lbs. Price each.... $10.00

Ladies' Saddles.

38306 Two-Horn Somerset Side Saddle, made on somerset tree fancy carpet seat, creased border, stuffed pad under bars, cotton corded surcingle to draw and buckle on off side, metal shoe stirrup. Weight about 10 lbs. Price...........$3.75

38314 Side Saddle, made on Morgan Tree, quilted leather seat with leaping horn; bars are covered with leather and padded; russet leather skirt, with raised flower ornamentation; double cinche rigged with two 4 in. common hair cinches, ¾ in. leather stirrup strap with XC plate, patent shoe stirrup; weight, 15¾ pounds. Price.....$8.00
For slipper stirrup in place of shoe stirrup, add 75 cents.

38322— Three-Horn Side Saddle, made on the Ruwart side tree, seat is covered with imitation buckskin and quilted; bars are covered with brussels carpet; large russet leather skirts, double cinche rig. tie halter es; 13-cord cotton girths; metal shoe stirrup. Weight, about 16 lbs. Price...........$11.00

38308 Two-Horn Somerset Side Saddle, made on an extra large Somerset tree with round skirts of imitation enameled leather, fancy carpet seat, seamed horn, extra heavy pad under bars, cotton buckle girth and inside surcingle, metal shoe stirrup. Weight about 10 pounds. Price $4.80

38316 Three-Horn English Style Side Saddle, made on somerset tree; genuine hogskin seat; large russet leather skirts and jockeys; leap horn covered with buckskin and seamed, full stuffed pad, making it comfortable for both horse and rider, best white cotton girth and surcingle, ¾ in. stirrup strap, metal shoe stirrup, weight 14 lbs. Price.........$8.50

38324 "Park" Three-Horn Side Saddle, made on Somerset Tree-quilted buckskin seat and forepiece, russet leather skirts and jockeys with hogskin impression, slipper stirrup, skirt surcingle, two girths, full pad, buckskin faced. A very superior style which we sell at a very moderate price. Weight about 18 lbs. Each.........$11.50

Saddles—Continued.

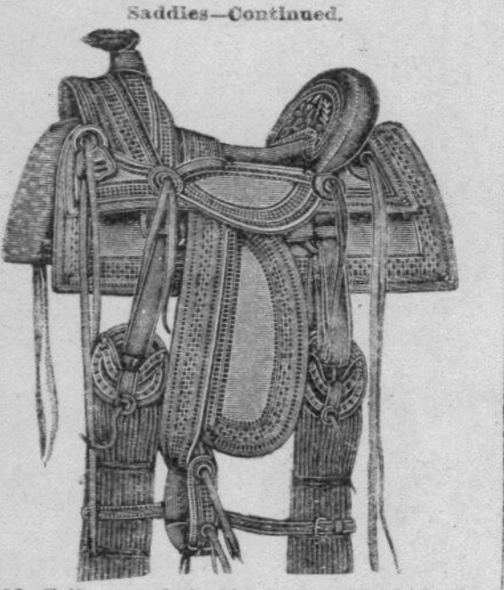

38482 Full covered, double cinche rigged Cowboy Saddle, made on a 16-inch hide-covered steel fork, long Friesecke tree. Leather used is best oiled skirting. Skirts are 30in. long and well wool lined. Stirrup leather, 3-inches wide, double at bottom, and have large fenders attached. Large jockeys on each side over stirrup leathers. Seat has steel seat plate. Tie-straps, 1¾ inches wide, 6½ feet long; on off side 2 in. to buckle. Cinches, California strand white hard hair, with wool-lined chafes and connecting straps. Stirrups, 1¼ inch steel, leather covered, fine extended roll cantle, leather covered rings, fine raised stamped border and seat. *Weight, about 40 lbs.* Price. $35.00
We will make this saddle to order, with single cinche rig, for $33.75.

Our New "Pride of the West."

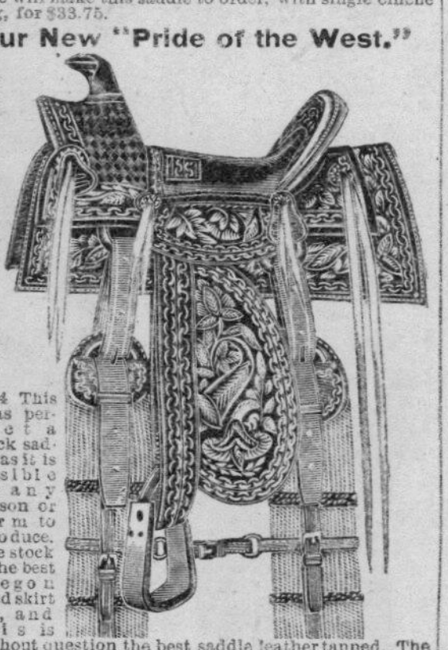

38484 This is as perfect a stock saddle as it is possible for any person or firm to produce. The stock is the best Oregon oiled skirting, and this is without question the best saddle leather tanned. The sewing, stamping and carving is all done by hand by men who are artists as well as the most expert saddle makers. We absolutely guarantee these saddles to be made on the best and strongest trees, to be made of the very best saddle leather by skilled workmen, and that there is nothing better to be obtained. Tree 16 inches, "Steel Fork," genuine Visalia, rawhide, covered; skirts, 30 inches long, wool lined extending well back of cantle, all hand stamped "T" rail border; seat made concave or dished, loop in front, steel seat plate, solid jockeys, fine, hand sewed roll cantle; stirrup straps, 3 inches wide to fasten with whangs, large fenders attached; "T" rail border, hand stamped; stirrups, 2½ inch heavy wood, brass bound, 3-inch roller bars; double cinche rig to buckle; Covered rings two-inch latigoes; two 20 strand white, hard hair cinches, with wool-lined leather chafes, connecting strap and martingale brace from ring to ring. Weight, as described, 40 lbs.
Price as described $37.25
Price without stirrups. 36.00

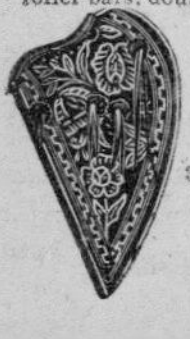

38486 23 inch Eagle Bill Tapideros, put on 2½ inch brass bound stirrups, hand stamped and made to exactly match our "Pride of the West" saddles. Per pair. $9.00
Without stirrups. 7.75
Weight per pair, complete, 6½ lbs.

Cantanas.

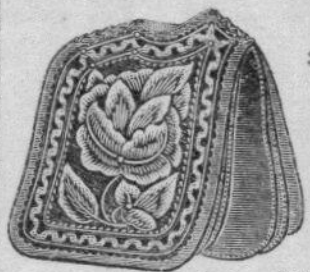

38487 Cantanas to match our "Pride of the West" saddle. To be hung on horn. Outside size, 10x13 inches on each side; size of bags, 9½ in. each way. Weight, per pair, 2¼ lbs.
Per pair. $5.40

Saddle Bags.

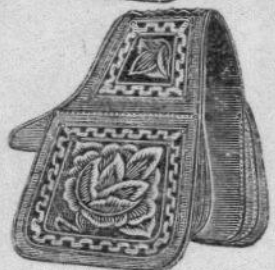

38488 Saddle Bags to match our "Pride of the West" saddle. To be fastened to skirts of saddle behind cantle; length from center to bottom, 15 inches; width of flaps, 9½ inches, size of bags 9 ins. wide, 7 ins. deep. Weight, per pair, 2¼ lbs.
Per pair. $4.60
We will attach any of these parts to any saddle for quoted prices. No charge for extra labor.

Saddle Trees.

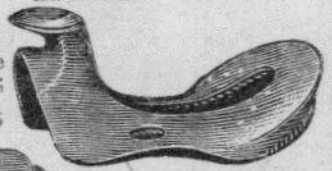

38492 Morgan Saddle Tree, rawhide covered; weight, 3¼ lbs.
Each. $1.25

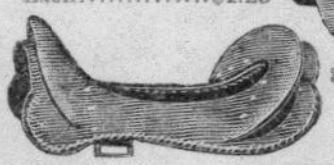

38493 McClellan Saddle Tree, iron arches, rawhide covered. Weight, 4¼ lbs.
Each. $1.50

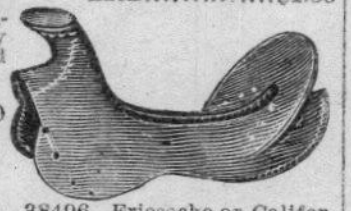

38495 Friesecke or California Tree, heavy rawhide covered, "solid fork."
Weight 6¼ lbs.,
Each. $3.00

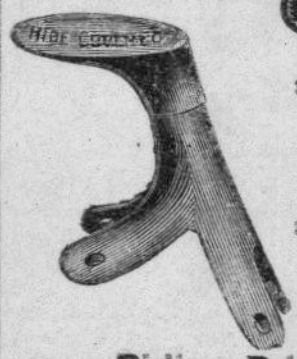

38496 Friesecke or California tree, "steelfork" rawhide covered. Weight, 9 pounds.
Each $4.00

Repair Forks.

38498 Best Malleable Steel Forks for repairing saddles with broken or damaged horns. Can be fitted to any tree.
Each. $0.80
Postage. 20

Riding Bridles, Cowboy's or Stockman's Bridles.

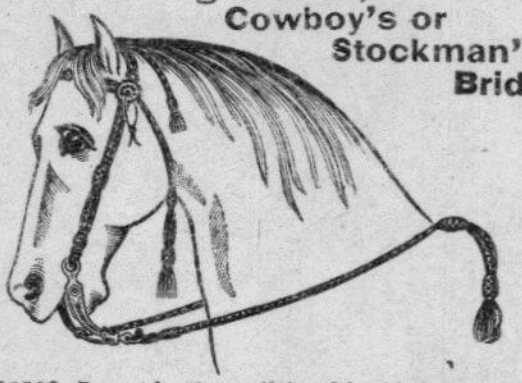

38500 Russet leather, all hand braided, made of 8-plait braided calfskin, fine, all round, with double cheeks and head piece; single reins, made with fancy braided loops and slides, in place of buckles, with leather tassel and curb strap; no martingales; without bit. Each $5.25

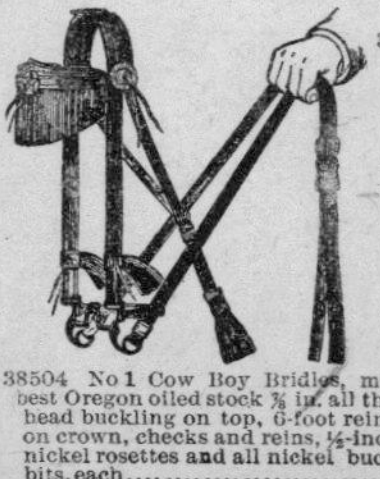

38502 Double Headstall Bridle, made of oiled stock russet leather only; heavy fringed front, one inch cheeks; fringed slide loops on cheeks, throat and reins; 1 inch 6½ feet quirt reins; nickel buckles, port bit.
Each. $2.25
Without bit. . 2.15
Weight, each, 38 ounces.

38504 No 1 Cow Boy Bridles, made from the best Oregon oiled stock ⅞ in. all through. Double head buckling on top, 6-foot reins. Box loops on crown, checks and reins, ½-inch curb straps, nickel rosettes and all nickel buckles. Without bits, each. 1.80

Bridles—Continued.

38506 Made of oiled russet California leather. Headstall cut in one piece, one inch wide with one buckle on top of bridle, reins, ⅞ inch to buckle in bit; are six feet long, laced together on end with buckskin strand; curb straps ⅝ inch wide, nickel rosettes, XC plated port bit.
Each. . . . . . .$1.40 Without bit. $1.30
Weight, each, 32 oz. Martingale, extra. Each .50

38508 (No. A.) Cowboys' Bridles, made of the same stock as No. 38506, with ¾ inch head-stall cut in one piece to buckle on top; ¾ inch reins 6 feet long to loop in bit, laced together on end with buckskin, ⅝ in. curb strap, with XC plated port bit, nickel rosettes. Each. 1.15
Without bit. 1.05
Weight, each, 26 ozs. Martingale, each, extra. .50

38510 Cowboys' Bridles, of oiled California black leather; headstall cut in one piece one inch wide with one buckle on top of bridle; ⅞ inch reins 6 feet long, laced together on end with buckskin to buckle on bit; curb strap ⅝ in.; nickel rosettes and XC plated port bit. Each. . 1.40
Without bit. 1.30
Weight, each, 32 ozs. Martingale, extra, each. .50

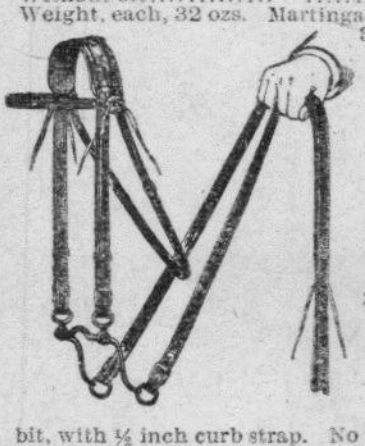

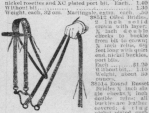

38512 Oiled Bridles, 2 inch solid crown with layer; ⅞ inch double cheeks to buckle from bit to crown; ⅞ inch reins, 6½ feet long with quirt end, nickel buckles, port bits.
Each $1.20
Without bit. . . . 1.10
Weight, about 30 ounces.

38514 Round Russet Bridles ⅝ inch single cheeks, ⅝ inch double reins; all buckles are leather covered; 4 ring nickel plated curb bit, with ½ inch curb strap. No martingale. $3.00
Weight, each, 26 ozs.
Martingale to match, with round forks and neck strap, and leather covered rings. 1.00

38516 Round Bridles, ¾ inch single cheek, and ⅝ inch single reins, leather covered buckles, 2 ring nickel plated curb bit with ½ inch curb strap. No martingale. 2.25
Martingale to match above. 1.00

38517 Round Bridle, ¾ inch single cheeks and ¾ inch single reins, imitation covered buckles, 2-rings nickel plated curb bit with ½ inch curb strap. No martingale. 1.80
Weight, each, 24 ozs.
Martingale to match above. 75

38519 Flat Bridles, ¾ inch single cheek, and ¾ inch double reins, 4 ring, XC plated curb bit and buckles, ½ inch curb strap. No martingale 1.50
Weight, about 30 ounces each.
Martingale to match above. 50

38520 Flat Bridle, ⅞ inch single checks. ⅞ inch double reins, XC center bar buckles, 4 ring XC plated curb bit with ½ inch curb strap. 1.65
Weight, about 32 ounces each.
Martingale to match above. 50

38522 Flat Bridles, ⅝ inch single cheeks, ⅝ inch single reins, full cheek, XC plated snaffle bit and buckles. Each. 1.00
Weight, about 19 ounces each.
Martingale to match above. 50

38523 Round Bridles, round cheeks, fronts and reins, solid crown, ¾ inch nickel buckles, curb strap, XC bit. Each. 1.25
Weight, about 22 ounces each.

38526 Flat Bridles, ⅝ inch cheek, ⅝ inch single rein, full cheek XC, plated snaffle bit and buckles; all riveted. 70
Weight, about 18 ounces each.
Martingales to match above. 38

38527 Flat bridles, ⅝ inch cheeks, ⅝ inch reins, cheeks and reins sewed in XC, jointed ring bit. . .55
Weight, about 16 ounces each.
Martingale to match above. 35

38528 Rawhide Bridles. These bridles are all made of the best oil tanned rawhide, ⅞ inch cheeks, ⅞ inch reins, 5 feet long, with curb bit; no martingales. 1.35
Weight, about 26 ounces each.

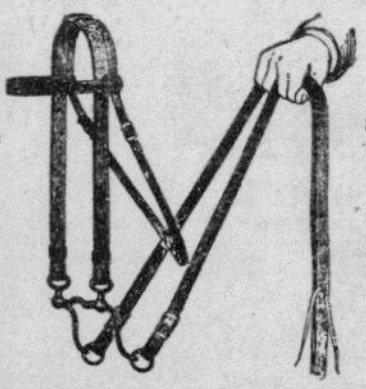

38530 Double Head Stall Bridles, made of oiled stock; ¾ in. double checks to buckle on top; ¾ inch reins, 5 feet long with quirt end; XC buckles; port bit. Each.
With bit. $0.75
Without bit. 65
Weight, about 24 ounces.

38532 Genuine Imported English "Weymouth" Riding Bridles. Made in England of English russet leather. Double head and double reins; one head has two-ring English nickel bit with curb chain, the other head has nickel snaffle ring bit. All hand sewed. Each. $4.25
Weight, each, 2¼ lbs.

Bridles—Continued.

38533 Genuine Imported English "Pelham" Riding Bridle. Hand made. Best English russet leather. Single head and double reins: four ring English short port, nickel plated bit. Each. $3.25
Weight, each 1¾ lbs.

38535 Black Web Riding Bridles, adjustable for any size horse or pony, 1¼ inch head piece, ⅝ inch reins, 5 feet long, with bit and curb strap. Not sold without bit. Each .60
Per dozen 6.48

38536 Fawn Web Riding Bridles, adjustable for any size horse or pony, 1¼ inch head piece, ⅝ inch reins, five feet long, with bit and curb strap. Not sold without bit. Each .60
Per dozen 6.48
Weight, each, 22 ounces.

Saddle Girths.

38540 Super Cotton Web, 3 inches wide, 3½ feet long, with 1¼ inch buckle on each end. Each. $0.20

38541 Extra Fancy Union Web, 3¼ inches wide, 3½ feet long, with 1¼ in. buckle on each end. Each .30
Weight, each, 7 ounces.

Cotton Webb Cinches.

38544 Heavy Cotton Web Cinches, 3½ in. wide, with leather chafes on each end. Each $0.30
Weight, each, 10 ounces.

38546 Heavy Cotton Web Cinches, 3½ in. wide, with leather chafes and connecting strap. Per pair .70
Weight, per pair, 21 ounces.

Hair Cinches.

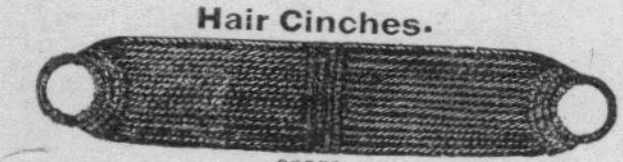

38551

	Each.
38548 Hair Cinches, 4 inch, plain gray	$0.25
38549 Hair Cinches, 5 inch, plain gray	.30
38550 Hair Cinches, 6 inch, plain gray	.35
38551 Hair Cinches, Mexican string, 6 inch	.40
38552 Hair Cinches, Mexican string, 9 inch	.60

Weight, each, 12 oz. to 24 oz.

Cotton String Cinches.

38555 4-inch Cotton String Cinche, colored $0.20
38556 5-inch Cotton String Cinche, colored .25
38557 6-inch Cotton String Cinche, colored .30
For tongues on any of the above cotton cinches, add 3c. to each. Weight, each, 10 oz. to 12 oz.

California Cinches.

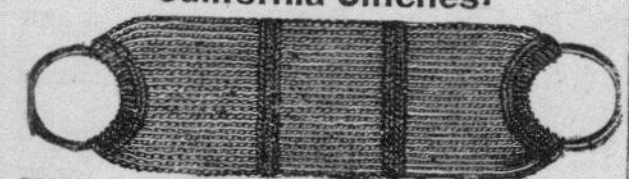

38560 32 strand, 6 cord, 2 bar, white hair, weight each, 20 ounces $1.25

38562 24 strand, 8 cord, diamond center, white hair; weight, each, 30 ounces 1.45

38564 20 strand, 6 cord, 2 bar fancy white and black hair; weight, each, 10 ounces. Each .60

38566 Connected Cinches, two 6-inch California white hair cinches, 20 strand, 2 bar, with leather chafes, tongues and connecting strap. Weight per pair, 3 lbs Per pair 2.00

38568 Connected Cinches, 4 inch cotton back band, front cinche, 6 inch Mexican string back cinche, with leather chafes, tongues and connecting strap. Weight, per pair, 2¾ lbs. Per pair 1.40

Ladies' Saddle Blankets.

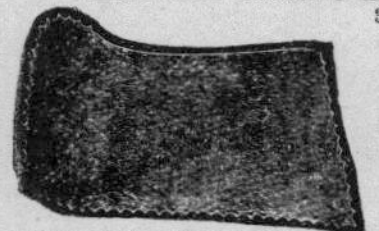

38574 Side Saddle Blankets, of heavy brown felt, long on one side; has wide fancy waved binding, with braid inlay. Figure of crossed whip and stirrup worked in corners. Weight, 16 oz. Each $1.25

38576 Side Saddle Blankets, same style as above, but made of blue felt. Weight, 16 oz. Each 1.25

38578 Side Saddle Blankets, same style as 38574; color is green. Each 1.25

Men's Saddle Blankets.

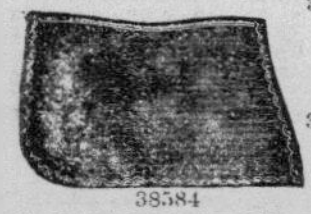

38584

38580 Men's Saddle Blankets, made of dark felt, light in weight, but good value. Each $0.40
Weight, each, 15 oz.

38582 Men's Felt Cloth Saddle Blankets, medium grade, have fancy colored braid border. Weight about 10 oz. Each $0.60

38584 Men's Saddle Blankets, good weight, felt, in dark colors, fancy borders and bound all around: extra quality. Each $0.90
Weight, each, 12 ounces.

Graduated Saddle Blankets.

Thickest in parts where the hardest wear comes.

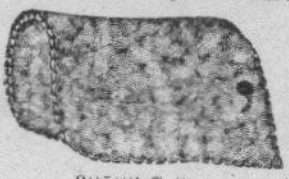

38586-7-8

38586 Blue Heavy Graduated felt, scolloped and pinked edge. Each $1.10

38587 Yellow Heavy Graduated Felt, scolloped edge. Each $1.15

38588 Red Heavy Graduated Felt, scolloped and pinked edge. Each 1.20

38590 Spencer's Graduated Felt, plain gray, plain edge. Each 1.25

38592 Spencer's Graduated Felt, plain gray, medium weight. Each 1.65

38594 Spencer's Graduated Felt, plain gray, extra heavy. Each 2.00
Weight, from 1½ to 2½ lbs.

Woven Hair Saddle Blankets.

38596 Woven Hair Saddle Blankets, 25x36 in., web bound; weight, 3 lbs. Each $1.35

Stirrup Straps.

38600 Stirrup straps, 4 ft. 6 in long, with buckle either black or russet leather.

Width	1 in.	1¼ in.
Per pair	$0.50	$0.65
Weight	14 oz.	17 oz.

38602 California Style Stirrup Straps, cut from the best Oregon oiled skirting leather, 5 ft. 6 in long, with lace strings.

Width	2 in.	2¼ in	2½ in.	2¾ in.	3 in.
Per pair	$1.25	$1.40	$1.65	$2.30	$2.80
Weight	28 oz.	32 oz.	36 oz.	40 oz.	44 oz.

Latigoes.

38604 Latigo Straps, 2 inches wide, for buckle cinche rig, cut from the best Oregon oiled skirting, with lace strings to fasten.
Length for draw side, 5 ft. 6 in., per pair $1.25
Length for off side, 2 ft. 8 in., per pair .65
Weight, per pair, 24 oz., 12 oz.

38606 Latigoes for tie cinche rig, with lace strings to fasten to saddle rings.
1¼ in. 5 ft. long, per pair $0.75
1½ in. 5 ft. long, per pair .90
Weight, per pair, 12 oz., 15 oz.

Stirrups.

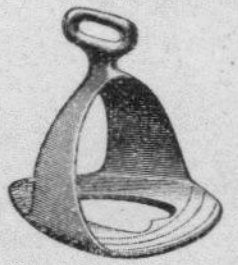

38610 Metal Shoe Stirrups for side saddles, "XC" plated. Each, $0.15. Per dozen, $1.62
Weight, each 6 ounces.

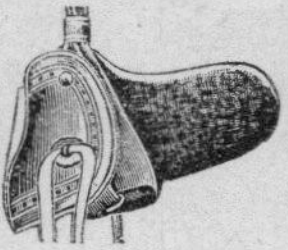

38611

38611 Tapidero Stirrups for ladies' saddles, made of russet leather with long wool lined chafe, and attached to 2 inch wood stirrup, leathered on bottom. Each $0.60
Weight, each, about 12 oz.

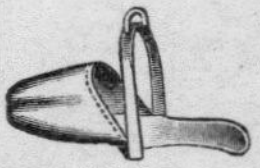

38612

38612 Slipper Stirrups, for side saddles; sole or shank is of steel, covered with leather stitched on, heavy hogskin vamp, strong iron swing, comfort and security combined. Each $0.90
Weight, 14 ounces.

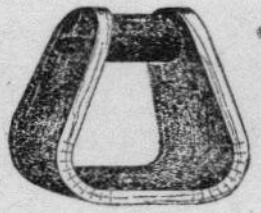

38616 Texas Bolted Wood Stirrups, 5 inch bottoms. Bars are 2 inches long and suitable for stirrup leathers from 1½ to 2 inches wide.
Per pair $0.17
Per single dozen .95
Weight, per pair, 1¾ lb.

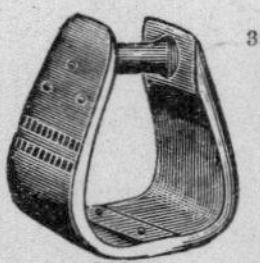

38618

38618 2¼ inch brass bound heavy bolted wood stirrups, with 3 inch rollers.
Per pair $1.00
Per single dozen 5.50
Weight, per pair 2¼ lbs.

38620 Ox Bow Stirrups, 1¼ inch wood stirrups, ox-bow shape, 2¾ inch bar bolted through.
Per pair $0.35
Per single dozen 2.00
Weight, per pair, 1¾ lbs.

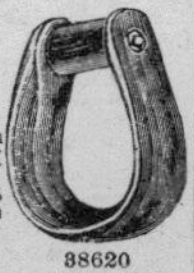

38620

Stirrups—Continued.

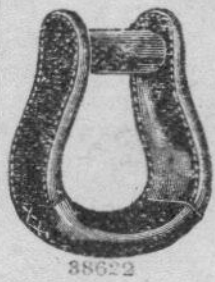

38622

38622 Two-inch Steel Stirrups, covered with oiled California leather, California pattern; bars will admit 3-inch California stirrup strap. Per pair $1.50
Weight, per pair, 2½ lbs.

38624 Three-inch Wood Stirrups, long California pattern, with one bolt. Per pr 30c. Per dozen single stirrups $1.65
Weight, per pair, 21 ounces.

38625 Cuban Stirrup, made of heavy forged steel, blued finish; will take 1¼ inch straps. Per pair $1.25

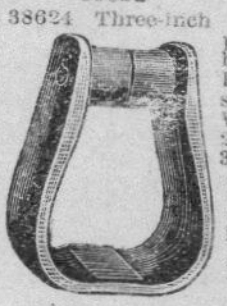

38624

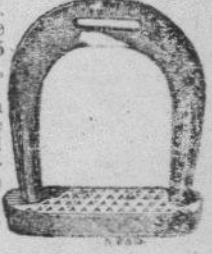

38625

Tapideros or Covered Stirrups.

Taps or covers are made of Oregon oiled skirting; are put over good wood stirrups with bars suitable for stirrup straps from 1¼ to 2½ inches wide.

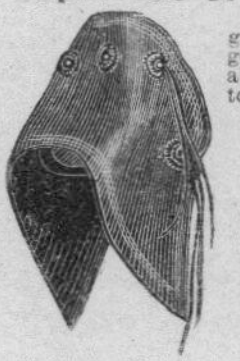

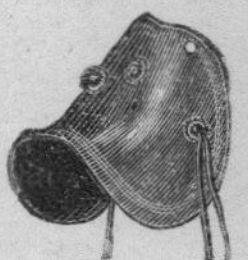

38627 $2.00 per pair. Weight, per pair, 4 lb.

38628 $1.65 per pair. Weight, per pair, 2¾ lbs.

Cow Boy Stirrups, California Pattern, Regulation Size.

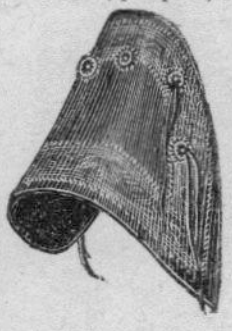

38629

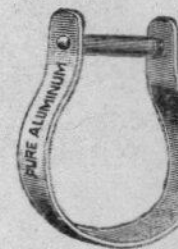

38630

38629 $1.80 per pair. Weight, per pair, 3 lbs.

38630 Made of solid aluminum, strong as steel, light as a feather, weight only 8 oz. each. Only made with 3-inch stirrup bars.
Per pair $1.75

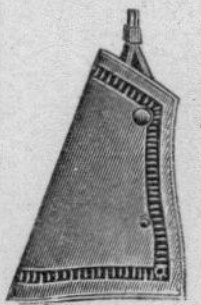

38632 Covered Stirrups, light wood stirrup, fair leather cover, embossed border. Will take stirrup straps from ⅝ to 1¾ in. wide.
Per pair $0.65

Cowboys' Saddle Bags.

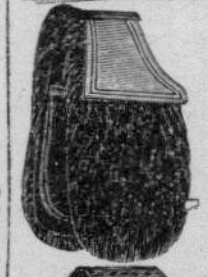

38636 Large Size "Cow Boys" Saddle Bags; pockets on each side. Size, 7¼x8 inches. Outside flaps are covered with long black Angora fur; length, from center to lower edge of fur, from 26 to 28 inches. Per pair $3.25
Weight, per pair, 3½ lbs.

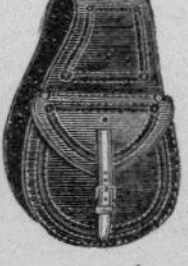

38638 Cowboys' Saddle Bags, to be tied on back of cantle. Pockets 7¼x8 inches, made of Oregon oiled skirting leather. Postage, 30 to 35 cents. Per pair $2.60

38639 Cowboys' Saddle Bags, extra large size, made of best oiled skirting. Size of pockets, 10x14 inches on each side.
Per pair $4.50
Weight, per pair, 4 lbs.

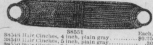

Leather Cantanas.

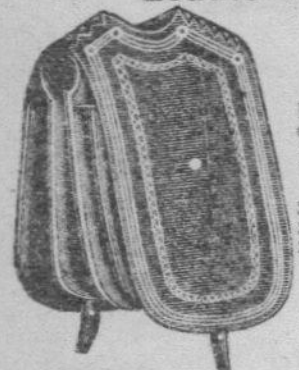

This bag is to be hung on horn of saddle; size of pockets, 9x14 inches on each side. Made of Oregon oiled skirting. Weight, each, 3 lbs.

	Each.
38642 Plain cover	$3.75
38643 Stamped cover	4.20
38644 Angora goat cover	5.00

Chaparejos.

Cowboys' Riding Pants.

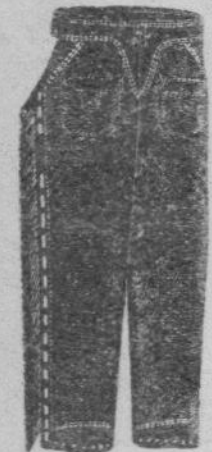

38646 Chaps, or Cowboys' Riding Pants, made of oiled chaparejos leather, stock being specially prepared for this purpose; solid leather waistband, laced together, fringe on outside of each leg, two pockets; made for service. Sizes, 28 to 34 inches in length of leg. Waist measurement not necessary. Per pair $8.50
Weight per pair, 5½ to 6½ lbs., according to length.

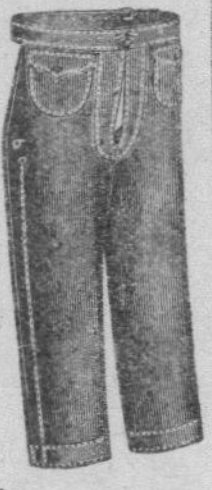

38648 Chaps or Cow-Boys' Riding Pants, made of a flexible grained russet leather. Pockets on each side; waist band is both lined and faced, making three ply of leather. Sizes from 28 to 34 ins. inside seam.
Plain legs, per pair $4.75
Fringed legs, per pair 5.75
Average weight, per pair, 4 lbs.

Horse Hobbles.

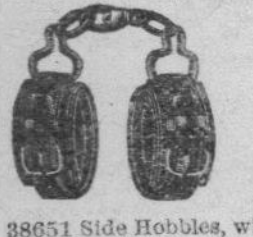

38650 Front Hobbles, two leather anklets connected by short swivel chain. To be attached to the two fore legs of a horse to prevent running or straying away when loose.
Per pair $0.60
Per dozen pairs 6.50
Weight per pair, 1½ lbs.

38651 Side Hobbles, with chain and snap. To be attached from one fore leg to one hind leg.
Per pair $0.70
Per dozen pairs 7.60
Weight, per pair, 2¼ lbs

Lariats.

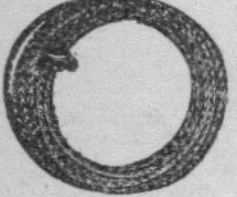

38653 Rawhide Lariats, four plait, best quality of oil tanned rawhide, cable cord center, all hand plaited and whole strands from end to end without splicing. Rawhide Hondas.

Length	40 ft.	43 ft.	45 ft.
Each	$6.25	$6.75	$7.25
Weight	2¼ lbs.	2½ lbs.	3 lbs.

38655 Cotton Lariats, extra quality braided cotton rope, ½ inch in diameter; honda of the same, securely fastened.

Length	35 ft.	50 ft.
Each	$1.50	$2.00
Weight	3 lbs.	4½ lbs.

38656 Linen Lariats, extra quality braided linen rope, ¾ inch in diameter, with rawhide honda. Have been boiled in oil, which keeps them soft and pliable and renders them waterproof; will not kink or snarl and will hold anything that runs on hoof. Ends are patent grip fastened. Length, 40 feet; weight, 2¼ pounds.
Each $2.50
50 ft. long; weight, about 3 lbs. Each 3.00

Lariat Hondas.

38658 Hondas for lariats; firmly pressed rawhide. Each, 20c. Per dozen, $2.00.

Bit Burnishers.

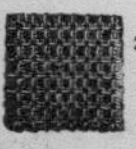

38659 Steel Chain Bit Burnishers, with buckskin back, 4x4 inches. Used for cleaning bits, spurs and buckles.
Each $0.40
Per dozen 4.75
Weight, each, 6 ounces.

Bridle Bits.

We always carry a large stock of bits on hand, as we do probably the largest business in bits, spurs, saddles, etc., of any house in America selling direct to the consumer.

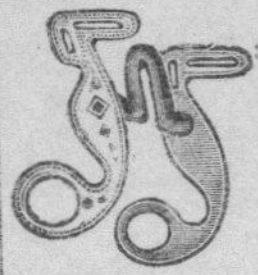

38670 Fine Blued Mexican Curb Bits, with short port on mouth bar.
Each $0.18
Per dozen 1.95
Weight, each, 11 oz.

38671 Fine nickel Plated Texas Port Bits, small copper roller on port bar. Large rings for bridle straps. Each $0.30
Per doz 3.35
Weight, each, 9 oz.

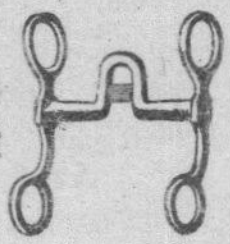

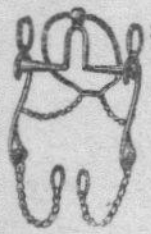

38673

38673 Fine Dead Smooth Filed Mexican Curb Bit, with large ring and rein chains; weight, 19 ounces.
Each $0.75
Per dozen.. 8.10

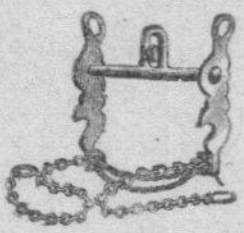

38674

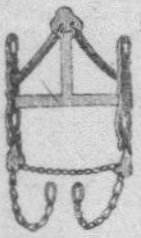

38674 XC Plated Cowboys' Curb Bits, with roller and rein chains; weight, 24 ounces. Each $0.50
Per dozen 5.50

38676 Fine Dead Smooth Filed and Chased California Spoon Curb Bits, with rollers and rein chains. Weight, 18 ounces. Each $0.75
Per dozen 8.10

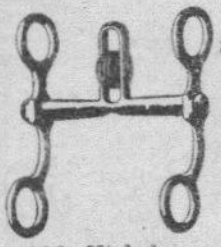

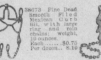

38678 Fine nickel plated Colorado port bit, plain finish. Heavy mouth bar, 2 inch port with large copper roller. Large rings
Each $0.80
Per doz 9.00
Weight, each, 7 oz.

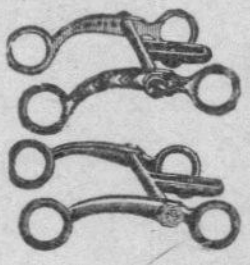

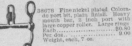

38680 Nickel and Chased Patent Long Port Mouth, with roller; weight, 15 ounces.
Each $1.00

38681 Same as above, hand forged steel, not chased. Weight, 15 ounces.
Each $2.50

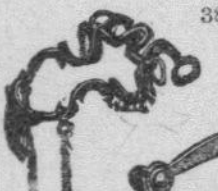

38682 Mexican Curb Bits. Patent filed and chased with trinkets, rein chains and roller. Weight, 18 ounces. Each $1.75
Per dozen 19.50

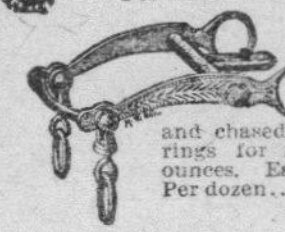

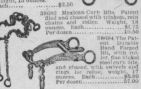

38684 The Patent Durable Hand Forged Bit, with roller, fine nickel steel curb bits, and chased, with swivels and rings for reins; weight, 17 ounces. Each $5.00
Per dozen 57.00

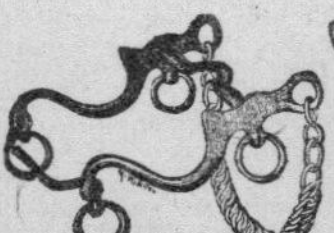

38686

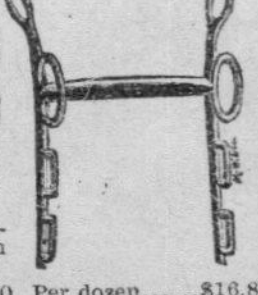

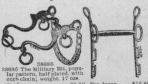

38686 The Military Bit, popular pattern, half plated, with curb chain; weight, 17 ozs.
Each .... $1.50 Per dozen $16.80

38687 Hanoverein Fine Nickel Plated Curb Bit, with wrought mouth and stiff cheeks. This bit is used largely in fine carriage, coach or double buggy harness; weight, 15 oz. Each .... .75
Per dozen 8.00

Bits—Continued.

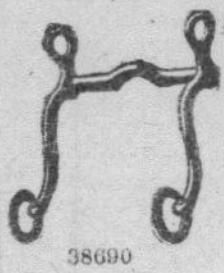

38690

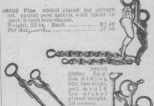

38690 XC plated Kentucky Short Cheek Racking Bits, with short port on mouth bar.
Each $0.10
Per dozen 1.08
Weight, each, 8 ounces.

38691 Two Ring XC plated riding bits with straight round cheeks and short port. Each .... .11
Per dozen 1.20
Weight each, 8 ounces.

38693 Fine nickel plated leg pattern bit, patent port mouth, with roller in port, 9-inch rein chains.
Weight, 22 oz. Each $2.40
Per doz 27.50

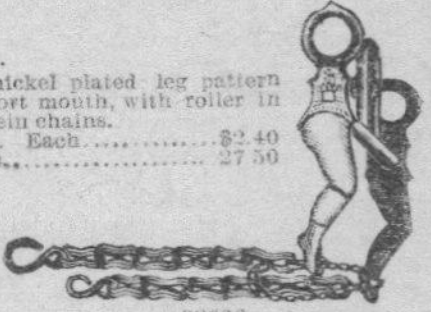

38693

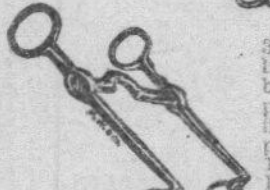

38695

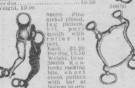

38695 English Riding bits, two rings, port mouth fine nickel plated; weight, 10 ounces.
Each $0.75
Per doz. 7.50

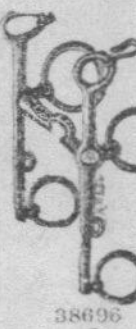

38696

38696 English Riding Bits, 4 rings, port mouth, fine nickel plated.
Each $1.25
Per doz 13.50
Weight, 12 oz.

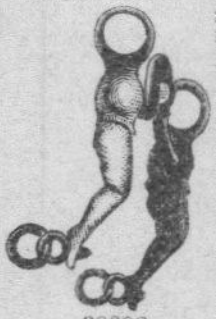

38698

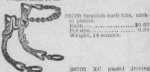

38698 Fine nickel plated, leg pattern, bit, port mouth with roller in port.
Each .. $1.25
Per doz, 13.50
Weight, 16 oz.

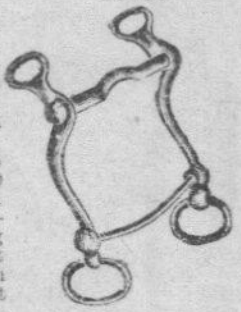

38699

38699 Kentucky racking bits, short cheek pattern with bar at bottom to prevent cheeks from spreading.
Each .... $0.50 Per doz $5.25
Weight, each, 10 oz.

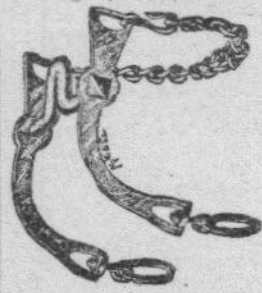

38700 Spanish curb bits, nickel plated.
Each $0.60
Per doz 6.30
Weight, 14 ounces.

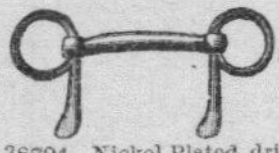

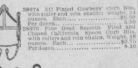

38702 XC plated driving bits, stiff mouth.
Each $0.10
Per dozen 1.08

38703 All black driving bits, stiff mouth.
Each $0.10
Per dozen 1.08
Each 1.08

38704 Nickel Plated driving bits.
Each .... $0.18 Per dozen 2.00

38706 Par silver or solid nickel driving bits, half cheek snaffles, very strong and are non corrosive. Absolutely will not soil or tarnish. Mention whether stiff mouth or jointed mouth is wanted.
Each $1.50

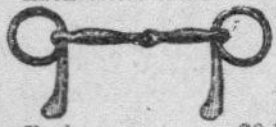

38708 All black driving bits, jointed mouth.
Each $0.10
Per dozen 1.08

38709 XC plated driving bits, jointed mouth.
Each .... $0.10 Per dozen $1.08

38710 Nickel plated driving bits, jointed mouth.
Each .... $0.18 Per dozen 2.00
Weight, 10 ounces.

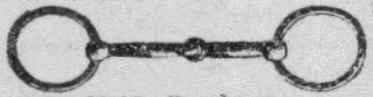

38712 Bridle bits for team bridles; heavy, for work harness, 2¾ inch rings, XC plated.
Each $0.08 Per dozen $0.85
Weight, each, 8 ounces.

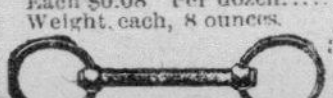

38713 Bridle Bits with stiff mouth for use in bridles of work harness, 2¾ inch rings, XC plated. Each ..$0.08 Per dozen $0.85
Weight, each, 8 ounces.

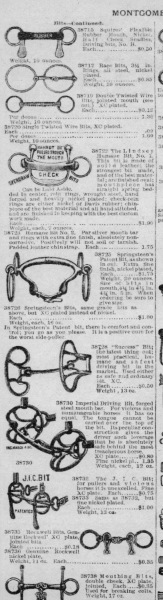

Bits—Continued.

38715 Squires' Flexible Rubber Mouth, Nickel, Half Cheek Snaffles, Driving bits, No. H. Each.... ....$0.50
Weight, 16 ounces.

38717 Race Bits, 3½ in. Rings, all steel, nickel plated. Each..............$0.85
Weight, 10 ounces.

38719 Double Twisted Wire Bits, jointed mouth (see cut.) XC plated. Each....................$0.12
Per dozen...... .... 1.30
Weight, 10 ounces.

38720 Single Twisted Wire Bits, XC plated.
Each .... .09
Per dozen 1.00
Weight, 10 ounces.

Can be Laid Aside.

38722 The Lindsey Humane Bit, No. 1. This bit is made of solid leather; the strongest bit made, and of the best material; are finished oval; mouthpiece has straight spring bedded in center, rein rings, wrought steel, hand forged and heavily nickel plated; check-rein rings are either nickel or Davis rubber; chinpiece of the best material and all hand stitched, and are finished in keeping with the best custom work made.
Each.......... ....$1.90
Weight, each, 7 ounces.

38723 Humane Bit No. 2. Par silver mouth bar and rings with extra fine finish, absolutely noncorrosive. Positively will not soil or tarnish. Padded leather chin strap. Each.................. 1.75

38725 Springsteen's Patent Bit, as shown in cut. Extra fine finish, nickel plated. Each..........$1.75
Weight, 20 ounces. Size of bits in mouth, 4¼ in 4½ in. 4¾ in. 5 in. When ordering be sure to give size.

38726 Springsteen's Bits, same grade bits as above, but XC plated instead of nickel.
Each $1.00
Weight, each, 16 oz.

In Springsteen's Patent bit, there is comfort and control; you go as you please. It is a positive cure for the worst side-puller.

38728 "Success" Bit; the latest thing out; most practical, humane and safest driving bit in the market. Used either as safe and ordinary bit. XC.
Each $0.50
Weight, 13 oz.

38730

38730 Imperial Driving Bit, forged steel mouth bar. For vicious and unmanageable horses it has no equal. The tongue cannot be carried over the top of the bit. Its peculiar construction gives the driver such leverage that he is absolutely safe behind the most treacherous horse.
XC plate...........$0.80
Fine nickel pl.. 1.35
Weight, each, 12 oz.

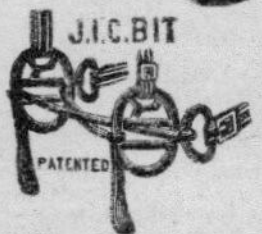

38732 The J. I. C. Bit; for pullers and vicious horses it is unexcelled. Fine XC plate. Each...........$0.75
38733 Same as 38732, but fine nickel plated.
Each........................$1.00
Weight, 13 oz.

38735 Rockwell Bits. Genuine Rockwell XC plate, jointed bits.
Each $0.18
38736 Genuine Rockwell nickel plate.
Weight, 11 oz. Each........................$0.35

38738 Mouthing Bits, double cheek, XC plate, jointed. Each $0.35
Used for breaking colts.
Weight, 17 oz.

Bits—Continued.

38740 Overcheck bits; to be used as a separate bit on overdraw check reins, XC plate. Each ....$0.05. Per doz..............$0.40
38741 Over-check bits, finely nickel plated.
Each ....$0.08. Per doz............ .75
Weight, each, 2 ounces.

38743 Loose Ring Tongue or Lolling Bit. XC plated. Each $0.40
Weight, 15 ounces.

Used to break horses of the habit of hanging the tongue out of the side of the mouth.

Safety Bridle Rein Chains.

Weight, 6 ounces to 10 ounces.

38750 Safety Bridle Rein Chain, nickel plated, with snaps, 11 in. Per pair....................$0.90
38751 Regular Bridle Rein Chain, nickel plated, with snaps, 10 in. Per pair.................... .50
38752 Regular Bridle Rein Chain, polished, with snaps, 10 in. Per pair .... .35
38753 Covert's Bridle Rein Chain, XC plated, with snaps, 11 in. Per pair .... .25

Stallion Lead Chains.

38756 English Steel Lead Chains, 3-16 wire, 18 inches long, polished, with snap and swivel.
Each..................$0.55. Postage..............$0.12
38757 American Company Steel Stallion Lead Chain, steel snap, swivel and "D" ring.
Each..................$0.25. Weight 7 oz.

Spurs.

Spurs are quoted by the dozen (12 spurs to the dozen) and by the pair (2 spurs to the pair). Make no mistake. Single spurs will cost just one-half the price given per pair.

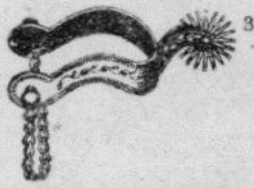

38760 Fine Steel Spurs, nickel and chased, 1⅝ inch malleable rowels, without straps. Per pair.........$0.45
Per single dozen......... 2.50
Weight, per pair, 6 oz.

38761

38761 "OK" Spurs, fine blued finish; heavy heel band, one button and chain; 1¼ inch steel plate rowels, without straps. Per pair......$0.55
Per single dozen......... 3.00
Weight, per pair, 12 oz

38763

38763 Fine steel spurs, polished and chased, one button and chain, 2-inch malleable rowels; a very popular spur, without straps. Per pair.....$0.40
Per single dozen......... 2.20
Weight, per pair, 4 oz.

38765

38765 New Patent Steel Spurs with chains, burnished and engraved, solid, medium weight, heel band 1⅝ in. rowel, very rapid sellers, without straps. Per pair.$1.00
Per single doz... 5.50
Weight, per pair 13 oz.

38767

38767 Eureka Spurs, wide steel heel band, nickel plated, 1¼ inch malleable rowels. Two buttons, without straps. Per pair..................$0.30
Per single dozen................. 1.65
Weight, per pair, 5 oz.

38769

38769 Stock Spurs, modern style, good weight band, imperial finish, one button, and chain, 1⅜ inch steel rowels, without straps. Per pair.............................$0.50
Per single doz........... 2.75
Weight, per pair, 11 oz.

38770 Excelsior Steel Spurs, nickel plated and engraved, very finely finished. Extra wide, fancy shaped heel band, 1½ inch malleable rowel, one button and chain, without straps.
Per pair.......................................$1.40
Per single dozen.................................. 7.75
Weight, per pair, 10 oz.

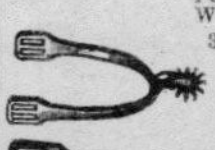

38772 Solid Brass Spurs, (No. 9), medium weight, ¾ inch steel plate rowels, without straps.
Per pair..................................$0.20
Per single doz................................ 1.10

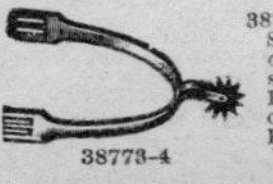

38773-4

38773 Extra Heavy Solid Brass Spurs. (No. 11): Heavy oval heel band, 1⅜ in. rowel shank, ⅞ inch steel plate rowel. Regular military style, without straps. Per pair.....$0.50
Per single dozen.......... 2.75
Weight, per pair, 8 oz.

Spurs—Continued.

38774 Extra heavy malleable spurs, No. 11, XC plate; see cut 38773. Heavy oval heel band, ⅞ inch steel plate rowels. Without straps.
Per pair...$0.30
Per single dozen.. 1.65
Weight per pair, 7 oz.

38776 Fine Imported English Park Spurs, nickel plated, light oval band, ⅝ inch steel rowel. One button and strap buckle, with over and under straps.
Per pair........$1.00 Per single dozen..........$5.60
Weight, per pair, 5 oz.

38778

38778 Paragon Spurs, wide steel heel band, plain nickel plated finish, two buttons, 1⅜ inch blued steel plate rowels, without straps.
Per pair.......... ....$0.50
Per single dozen......... 2.70
Weight, per pair, 8 oz.

38780 Thompson's Pocket Spurs, made of best material and nickel plated. Can be attached or detached in a moment and can be carried in a vest pocket when not in use. No straps required. Per pair..$1.25
Weight, per pair, 2 oz.

38782 California Spurs, hand forged steel, nickel and chased leather lined, 1¾ inch rowel, without strap, 1 button and chain.
Per doz $14.00
Per pair............. 2.50
Weight, per pair, 16 oz.

38783 California Spur, hand forged steel, nickel and chased, leather lined 2⅜ inch rowel, without strap; 1 button and chain.
Per doz............$16.80
Per pair 3.00
Weight per pair, 18 oz.

38785 California Spurs, hand forged steel, silver inlaid, blued finish, medium weight heel band, 1 button and chain, 2¾ inch rowel with steel bells or danglers, without straps. Per pair.......... ..$3.00
Per doz...18.00
Weight, per pair, 16 oz.

38786 California Spurs, hand forged steel, silver inlaid, blued finish, extra heavy heel band, 1 button and chain, 2¾ inch rowel, with steel bells or danglers, without straps.
Per pair...$5.00
Per doz.......................... ....30.00
Weight, per pair, 24 oz.

38792 Spur Straps, Texas pattern, made of oiled California stock, with nickel ornaments on sides and nickel buckles. These spur straps are for spurs with 1 button and chain.
Per dozen, single straps.............................$4.05
Per pair.. .75
Weight, per pair, 7 oz.

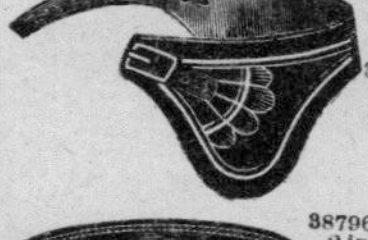

38794 Eureka Straps for spurs with 2 buttons.
Per pair.......$0.25

38796

38796 Mexican Spur Straps, 2 in. wide, 12 in. long, for spurs with 1 button.
Per pair.........................$0.15

38797 Spur Straps, ¼ in. wide, 17 in. long, for spurs without buttons. Per pair.............. .07

38798 Texas Spur Straps made of oiled skirting, stamped border and outside. Four button holes on inside end. For spurs with one button.
Per pair $0.50
Weight, per pair, 4 oz.

For Guns and Sporting Goods, we are headquarters. Remember this.

We Sell

The Standard Diaries for 1895. Send for free price list.

Linoleums.

Linoleum is but another name for an oil cloth of superior quality, and is made of ground cork and oil. Patterns are the same as in oil cloth. Linoleums are made in three widths only, other widths cannot be furnished.

	1 yard wide.	2 yards wide.	4 yards wide.
39427 Linoleum	$0.55	$1.10	......
39429 Linoleum, better	.70	1.40	......
39431 Linoleum, best grade	1.80	3.60	......

Carriage Oil Cloths.

Made for floor of carriages. Background is black and patterns are all small designs in light and dark colors.

39441 Width, 22½   27 in.   32 in.   36 in.
Price per yd. 20c.   24c.   29c.   31c.

Oil Cloth Stove Squares.

Made of good material. Assorted designs.

Notice reduced prices.
39443 Sizes, 1¼x1¼ yds. 1½x1½ yds. 2x2 yds. square
Price, each, 49c.   71c. $1.26
BEST GRADE.
39445 Sizes, 1¼x1¼ yds. 1½x1½ yds. 2x2 yds. square
Price, each, 71c. $1.00 $1.75

Metallic Oil Cloth Binding.

39447 Metallic Oil Cloth Binding for fastening down the edges of the oil cloth; per set of following number of yards, with corners and tacks complete.

	Zinc.	Brass.
4 yards, per set	$0.09	$0.15
5 yards, per set	.13	.19
6 yards, per set	.16	.22
8 yards, per set	.21	.27

Oil Cloth Mats.

39449 Printed in bright designs. "Dog's Head," etc. They are printed in bright colors on good oil cloth, nicely bordered with design in center. Size, 22½x36 inches. Each........................$0.40

Cocoa and Cane Mats.

39451 Cane Mats rough, and harsh for outside use.
Sizes...... 14x25   16x27   18x30
Price...... 40c.   52c.   64c.

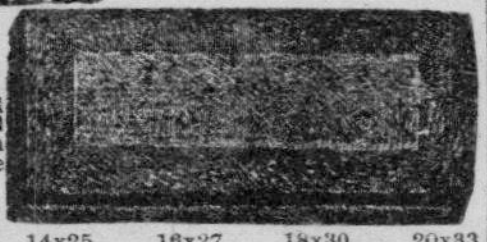

39453 Red Bordered Cocoa Mats (like cut).

Sizes	14x25	16x27	18x30	20x33
Price each	33c.	40c.	54c.	78c.

39455 Mats finer and softer than above; very durable; all sizes, plain.

Sizes	14x25	16x27	18x30	20x33	22x36
Price each	38c.	50c.	63c.	75c.	94c.

39457 Cocoa Mats, better grades.

Sizes	14x26	16x27	18x30	20x32	22x36
Price each	56c.	68c.	87c.	$1.06	$1.31

Motto Mats.

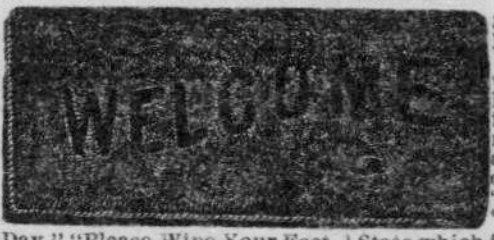

39459—Improved Cocoa with red lettering in center, mottoes are: "Welcome," "Use Me." "Good Day," "Please Wipe Your Feet." State which is wanted.

Size—   16x27   18x30   20x33
Price, each.... 80c. $1.06 $1.25

National Wire Mats.

39461— These mats are made of steel wire, are thin enough to permit any door having a threshold to pass over them; are always clean, catch the dirt but do not clog.

Rigid Pattern.

Size	16x24	18x30	22x36	26x48
Price	$0.75	$1.00	$1.50	$2.50

Rubber Door Mats.

Notice Our Reduced Prices.

These mats wear well, look neat, don't retain dirt, easily cleaned, etc.

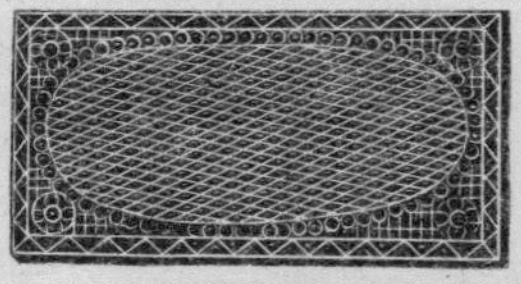

OVAL MATS
39465 Size, 17x31. Price each............$1.36

OBLONG MATS.
39467 Size—17x31   18x36   20x40   15x30
Price each—$1.47 $1.75 $2.40 $1.34
The $1.75 and the $2.40 oblong mats have no fancy border. The $1.34 and $1.47 grades are similar to first cut.

RUGS.

This is an age of rugs. It has become the fashion and because of slow growth will stay. In many homes carpets have been abandoned and rugs substituted. The effect is rich. A partly worn carpet can be made to look very presentable with rugs. A new carpet can be saved by them. They are made all sizes, all colors, all designs. We have them all.
Rugs make splendid Birthday, Wedding or Christmas presents, as they are elegant and useful.

Reversible Madras Rugs.

39501

39501 A handsome pattern on both sides. Fringed on both ends and colors bright and pleasing. They are the most serviceable and practical Rug we have ever offered.
Think of a Rug like the above, size 30x60 inches, at this price.........................$0.69

• Always be sure to state the amount of money enclosed with order.

Aubusson Rugs.
A New Thing In Rugs.

39503

Known as the Aubusson Art Rug. These rugs are in appearance on the order of an ingrain carpet, but the designs are especially suited for rugs designed with a bordered edge in keeping with a figured center with a fringe on each end. Colors are cream, old gold and brown, ecru and wine, olive and crimson, etc.
The point most interesting to the customer is the price.
39503 Size.........26x54   30x60   48x84
Price.........$0.45   .80   1.40

Chenille Rugs.

39505 Mottled Chenille Rugs, made same as curtains of same name, but much heavier. Size 35x62 inches, fringed on both ends, colors are mixed and are light or medium dark as preferred. They are soft and pliable, wear well, and the price is used as a means of introducing you to our growing carpet department, rather than to make any profit. Price each.................$1.00

Smyrna Rugs.

39507 Smyrna rugs are similar in appearance to velvet carpet, but are much more durable. They are reversible and fringed on both ends. The colors are soft and subdued, or bright and attractive, as desired. Sizes given do not include fringe.

Victoria Smyrna Rugs.

Notice our reduced prices.

39507 These Rugs we recommend with confidence, knowing that they are the best Smyrna Rug ever offered for the price. The patterns are all new in floral geometrical and animal designs.

18x36	Dog, Lion, Peacock, Floral	$0.81
21x45	Dog, Lion, Peacock, Floral	1.19
26x54	Lion, Dog, Peacock, Floral	1.69
30x60	Floral, Dog, Peacock, Lion	1.98
36x72	Dog, Lion, Peacock, Floral	2.99
48x84	Floral	4.99

Royal or Imperial Smyrna Rugs.

The best quality of Smyrna rugs, made in the latest colorings and designs, either floral or geometrical. The following grades are the lowest ever offered on this grade of goods.

39509 inches.	inches.	inches.	inches.	inches.
Size...18x36	21x45	26x54	30x60	36x72
Price..$1.44	$2.05	$2.85	$3.45	$5.12
feet.	feet.	feet.	feet.	feet.
Size... 4x7	3x12	3x15	6x9	7½x10½
Price..$8.12	$11.65	$13.81	$18.69	$29.40
Size...	9x15		12x15	12x18
Price..	$52.81		$69.07	$89.40

Low Priced Smyrna Mats.

Good styles, wear everlasting, two styles.
39511 Mottled, fringed reversible, size about 15x28 in.   Each........................$0.31

39513 Fancy like cut, size about 16x34 inch.
Each...$0.75

Harness, Halters and Strap Work—We can save you lots of money on these goods.

Tapestry Rugs.

39517 Same as carpet by that name. These answer where an inexpensive covering is wanted.

Sizes	15x34	23x54	27x61
Price, each	$0.60	$1.30	$1.85

Burmah or Body Brussels Rugs.

These Rugs are made same as the best quality of body Brussels carpet. *Double Faced* (both sides alike) and lay smooth. The colors are light, medium or dark, in elegant effects. One of the most durable rugs on the market. Size does not include the fringe.

39518 Size	27x54	36x63
Price	$3.43	$6.00

Do not pass this rug at the price offered. The quantity is limited.

39519 Moquette Rugs are the acme of perfection from a colorist's standpoint. They are softly blended in colors, toned low and æsthetic, nothing bright or striking. Designs are floral or geometrical, colors mostly light, construction same as carpet bearing same name. No fringe. They are very heavy.

Sizes	18x36	27x60	36x72
Price, each	$1.00	$2.70	$3.75

Loegria Wilton Rugs.

39521 The Loegria Wilton Rug is made in exact imitation of the Royal Wilton and is an elegant rug for the price. Size, 27x54 inches. Price..$1.60

Angora Lamp or Vase Mats.

39523 Wavy Angora Vase or Lamp Mats. Hair is long and silky. Colors delicate and lasting; odorless; Colors: Gold, yellow, orange, cream, white, scarlet, cardinal, nile or sapphire. They are round as cut shows. Different lengths of hair make them vary in size about 12 in. in diameter. Price, each......$0.10

39525 Angora Mats, same as above, but larger. Colors, Old gold, cardinal, gray, lemon, orange, nile, blue, crimson, green or cream. Each ..$0.20

Combination Fur Rugs.
LINED AND ODORLESS.

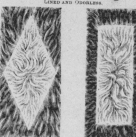

A   B

39526 These are elegant goods and fine enough for any parlor. The combinations are black and white, black and gray, gray and white, gray and grizzly bear, gray and red fox, and gray and blue fox. The designs are like cuts A and B. We also have solid colors in white, black, and gray. Size 28x64 in. Each......$3.75

Cashmere Angora Rugs.

The hair is soft and glossy as silk, very long and of a fine texture. The color are exquisite. Properly plained nothing could be richer. Colors are cream, white, cardinal, black, lemon, orange, light green, dark green, old gold, blue or canary. Lined or unlined as wanted.

39527 Sizes given are measurements of rugs including overlapping hair. Size of skin is always less.

Size, including hair, about	20x32	26x38	24x58	24x62
Price, each	$2.50	$3.50	$7.00	$8.00

Plush Mats, Wool Fringed.

39529 The center is mohair plush, padded cushion like and fringed with bright colored wool that matches or contrasts nicely. Centers are plain or mottled. Colors are yellow, red, orange, black or cream. Size, 15x24 inches.
Price, each......$0.39

Linen Crumb Cloths.

39531 Linen Crumb Cloths, cost little, wear a long time, save a carpet, look well, wash perfectly. Made of dark drab, unbleached linen and woven in square or flowered carpet designs.

Size in inches, about............108x126
Price, each......$3.27

Novelty Art Squares.

39533 Novelty Art Squares, woven the same as cotton ingrain carpets; are fringed on two sides and bordered all around; are woven in one piece and look like bordered carpet, but cost less. No very bright colors.

Sizes	7½x9 feet	9x9	9x10½	9x12
Price, each	$3.40	$4.00	$4.75	$5.40

Liecestershire Art Squares.

Notice reduction in price of Art Squares. Art Squares are large extra super carpets woven in one piece, bordered and fringed, and very popular. All wool. Should you have a room they will fit, or nearly so, you can have an artistic covering at small cost, having great wearing qualities and looking as though it were made for the room that it covers. As crumb cloths under a dining room table, they save the carpet and are easily removed and cleaned. Colors are quiet and subdued; no very bright shades.

39535 Sizes, feet	7½x9	9x9	9x10½	9x12	9x13½
Price, each	$5.50	$6.92	$7.75	$8.85	$9.95
39537 Sizes, feet	9x15	10½x12	12x12	12x13½	12x15
Price, each	$11.05	$10.35	$11.85	$13.40	$15.00

Our claim that this Catalogue opens the large markets to you is no idle boast. Where else can you find so much? As a genuine guide to prices it has no equal.

Jute Art Squares.

A new departure in floor coverings, at less than half the price of the cheapest ingrain carpet. They are made of strong jute, are printed in attractive patterns and colorings, with a 12 in. border, which either contrasts or harmonizes with the color in the center.

The leading colors are red, green, gold and orange, two colors used in the center, three in the border. Red and green are dark shades, the others medium. Please give choice in ordering.

They can be used as crumb cloths, druggets or as rugs to partly cover a worn carpet. It is not necessary to have them fit a room exactly, as the sides are usually taken up with furniture anyway. Think of carpeting a room nicely for this price!

We predict a big sale on these goods. Prices and sizes as follows:

	Each.
39539 6x9 feet, weight, 4 lbs..	$1.20
39541 9x13 feet, weight, 8 lbs..	2.70

39543 Hemp Body Brussels Mats; size, 21x39 inches. Colors are light, medium or dark, and geometrical or floral figures in bright or sober colors, fringed on both ends; splendid for rough wear. Each......$0.25

Weavers' Supplies.

Our Eureka Loom and Reed have given such universal satisfaction and sales have been so great that we still further enlarged our list of weavers' supplies.

39571 Eureka's Eureka Hand Carpet Looms, improved like cut; outfit sent with loom consists of 1 steel reed (state number of dents, splits or spaces wanted to inch or to whole length of reed), 1 set harness, 1 quill wheel 48 spools, 18 shuttles, 1 wrench and hammer combined, 1 tape measure, 1 temple and all the fixtures for putting the warp on the beam and through the harness and reed.
Weight, ready for shipping, 280 pounds.
Price, each, including all attachments........$37.00
Loom with quill wheel separate.............38.50

Instruction Book Free.

Upon request we will send free a 50-page book of instruction regarding carpet looms, spinning wheels, etc.

Warp Measuring Machine.

39577 The Eureka Warp Measuring Machine, measures the warp as it runs from the skein on to the spool; it can be used on any kind of a quill wheel by simply boring an inch hole into the head of the wheel into which to place the post on which the machine hangs. It can also be used with the wheel attached to the loom.

Every weaver who spools his warp needs this machine, no matter what kind of a loom or quill wheel he uses. Price, each......$4.00

Wool Cards.

39579 Wool Cards, No. 30 wire; length, 10 inches; good and strong. Per pair......56

Carpet Reeds.

39581 Steel Carpet Reeds (any length or fineness). Each......$2.25
Reeds longer than 45 inches, finer than 600 spaces, or wider than 4 inches, will cost from 50 cents to $1.50 extra.
Orders for reeds will necessarily be delayed from ten days to two weeks, except those 45 inches long and having either 9, 10, 11, 12 or 13 spaces to the inch. These we have in stock. No reeds sent C.O.D. Carefully state length, and number of spaces wanted.

Write out what you want, enclose the money, tell where to send and we do the rest. Easiest thing in the World

HARDWARE DEPARTMENT.

Bench Planes.

Ohio Tool Co.'s

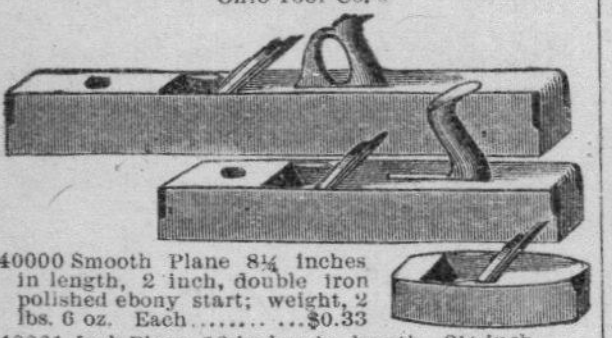

40000 Smooth Plane 8¼ inches in length, 2 inch, double iron polished ebony start; weight, 2 lbs. 6 oz. Each........ ...$0.33

40001 Jack Plane. 16 inches in length, 2¼ inch double iron, polished ebony start. Weight, 4½ lbs.......... $0.35

40002 Fore Plane, 22 inches in length, 2½ inch double iron, polished ebony start. Weight, 6½ lbs.......... .50

40003 Jointer Plane, 26 inches in length, 2½ inch double iron, polished ebony start. Weight, 8 lbs. 14 oz.......... .55

40004 A set of 4 planes. one smooth, one jack, one fore and one jointer. Weight, 22¼ lbs.... 1.65

Barton Planes.

The D. R. Barton Celebrated Bench Planes, made from second growth white beech, thoroughly seasoned. The irons are guaranteed to be the best in the world; every one is fully warranted.

40006 Smooth Planes, Barton's double irons.... $0.56

40007 Jack Planes, Barton's double irons........ .63

40008 Fore Plane, Barton's double irons..... .... .88

40009 Jointer Plane, 30 inch, double irons......... 1.10

40009½ Set of Barton's Bench Planes, Smooth, Jack, Fore and Jointer.......... 3.00

Smooths have irons from	2	to 2¼ in.
Jacks " " "	2	to 2½ in.
Fore " " "	2⅜	to 2½ in.
Jointer " " "	2½	to 2¾ in.

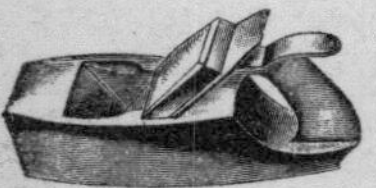

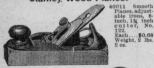

40010 Smooth Planes, Barton's Double Iron Solid Handle. Solid Boxwood........$2.38 Rosewood .. 1.90

Stanley Wood Planes.

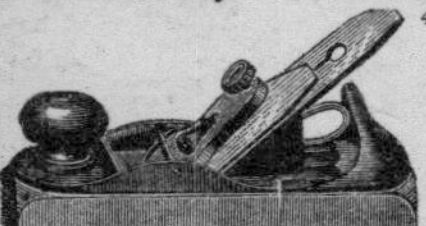

40011 Smooth Planes, adjustable irons, 8-inch, 1¾ inch cutter, No. 122. Each....$0.68 Weight, 2 lbs. 2 oz.

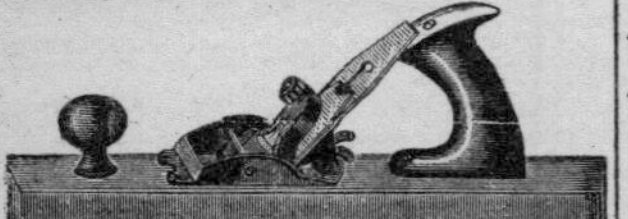

40012

40011½ Handle smooth, adjustable irons, 10 inch, 2⅛ cutter, No. 135. Each.......... $0.90

40012 Jack Planes, adjustable irons, 15 inch 2⅛ inch cutter, No. 127 Weight, 3lbs 8 oz,Each. .90

40013 Fore Planes, adjustable irons, 20 inch, 2⅜ inch cutter, No. 129. Weight, 5 lbs. Each..... 1.05

40014 Jointer Planes, adjustable irons, 26 inch, 2⅜ inch cutter, No. 132. Weight, 6 lbs Each.. 1.15

40015 A set of planes, adjustable irons, consisting of the smooth, jack, fore and jointer, four planes in all, Weight, 14¼ lbs.......... 3.50

40015½ Set of planes with handled smooth plane 10-inch, with 2⅛ inch cutter, instead of 40011, for.......... 3.80

Extra Parts of Stanley Planes.

No	40011	40012	40013	40014
Stocks	$0.36	$0.42	$0.60	$0.75
Top Casting	.40	.40	.40	.40
Levers	.10	.10	.15	.15
Knobs	.15	.15	.15	.15
Irons, double	.30	.35	.39	.42
Irons, single	.17	.20	.22	.24

LOWER PRICES than you ever saw before on Wall Paper, Rugs, Mats, Curtains, etc. See Index for quotations.

The Bailey Pattern Adjustable Wood Planes.

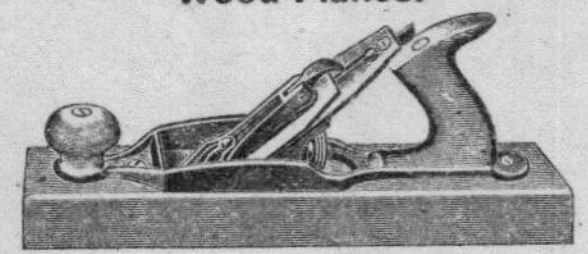

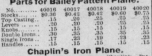

Cut of No. 40020.

Cutters Adjusted by a Lever.

40016 Smooth Plane (adjustable iron), 8 inch in length, 1¾ inch cutter; weight 2½ lbs. Price each.......... $0.80

40017 Handle Smooth Plane (adjustable iron), 10 inches in length, 2⅜ cutter. Price each.......... 1.10

40018 Jack Plane (adjustable iron), 15 inches in length, 2⅛ inch cutter, weight 4⅛ lbs. Price each.......... .98

40019 Fore Plane (adjustable iron), 20 inches in length, 2⅜ inch cutter, weight 5½ lbs. Price each.......... 1.10

40020 Jointer Plane (adjustable iron), 24 inches in length, 2⅜ inch cutter, weight about 5½ lbs. Price each.......... 1.20

40021 Jointer Plane, 26 inches in length, with adjustable iron, 2⅜ inch cutter, weight about 7 lbs. Price each.......... 1.26

40021½ Jointer Plane, 28 inches in length, with adjustable iron, 2⅜ inch cutter, weight 7¾ lbs., Price each.......... 1.26

Parts for Bailey Pattern Plane.

Nó	40016	40017	40018	40019	40020
Stocks	$0.36	$0.42	$0.42	$0.60	$0.75
Top Casting	.15	.20	.25	.25	.25
Levers	.20	.20	.20	.25	.25
Knobs	.15	.15	.15	.15	.15
Double Irons	.30	.35	.35	.35	.35
Single Irons	.17	.23	.19	.23	.23
Handles	.15	.15	.15	.15	.15

Chaplin's Iron Plane.

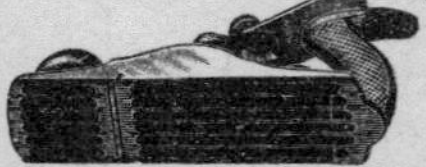

Chaplin's Patent Adjustable Iron Planes with corrugated bottom checkered hard rubber handles nickel finish.

The corrugations in the bottom of these planes are divided by a series of ribs through the bottom, which gives strength without adding weight. The corrugations are air chambers which relieve the suction which is sometimes urged as an objection to planes. Each.

40022 Smooth Plane, 9 inches long, 2 inch cutter $1.89

40023 Jack Plane, 15 inches long, 2⅛ inch cutter 2.30

40024 Fore Plane, 18 inches long, 2⅜ inch cutter 2.70

40025 Jointer Plane, 24 inches long, 2⅝ inch cutter.......... 3.55

40026 A set of Chaplin's Patent Adjustable Iron Planes, consisting of smooth, jack, fore and jointer. Per set.......... 9.95

40027 Plane Irons for Chaplins Plane.

Inch	2	2⅛	2¼	2⅜
Each	30c.	35c.	35c.	40c.

40028 Handles for Chaplin Planes. Each....... .30

Bailey Wood Planes.

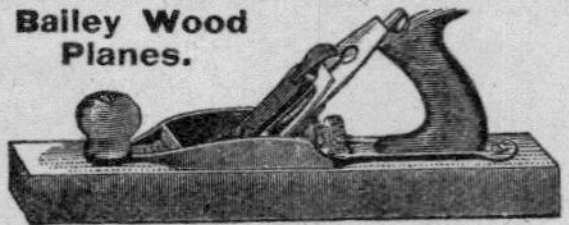

40034

These planes all have the new lateral adjustment, a new method of setting a plane iron side wise to set the cutting edge exactly square with the face of the plane.

40030 Smooth Plane, without handle, adjustable irons, 8 in. in length, 1¾ inch cutter. Weight, 2¾ lbs.......... $0.95

40031 Smooth Plane, 9 in. length, with handle, adjustable irons, 2 inch cutter, No. 35.......... 1.14

40032 Jenny Smooth Plane, 13 inches in length, with handle, adjustable irons, 2⅜ inch cutter. No. 37.......... 1.37

40033 Jack Plane, adjustable irons, 15 in. in length, 2⅛ cutter. Weight, 4 lbs.......... 1.18

40034 Fore Plane, adjustable irons, 20 in. long, 2⅜ inch cutter. Weight 5¾ lbs.......... 1.25

40035 Jointer Plane, adjustable irons, 26 in. in length, 2⅜ inch cutter. Weight, 7¾ lbs........ 1.48

40036 A Set of Adjustable Wood Planes, with No. 40030 smooth jack, fore and jointer, four in all.......... 4.60

40037 A set of adjustable wood planes, with No. 40031 smooth instead of No. 40030. Per set of four.......... 4.80

40038 A set of adjustable Wood Planes, with 40032 smooth instead of No. 40030. Per set of four.......... 5.02

Extra Parts to Bailey Planes.

No.	40030	40031	40032	40033	40025	40034
Stock	$0.36	$0.38	$0.45	$0.42	$0.75	$0.60
Top casting	.15	.25	.25	.20	.25	.25
Levers	.25	.25	.25	.25	.25	.25
Knobs. Beech	.15	.15	.15	.15	.15	.15
Handles. beech	.15	.15	.15	.15	.15	.15
Screw and nut		.15	.15	.15	.15	.25
Irons, double	.30	.33	.42	.36	.42	.39
Iron, single	.17	.18	.24	.19	.24	.23

Bailey Adjustable Iron Planes.

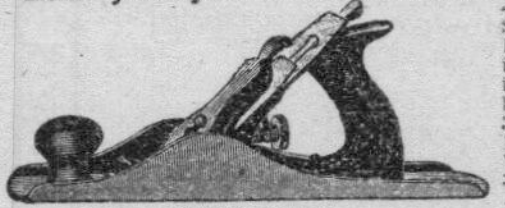

40042½ Smooth Planes, iron, 8 inches long, No 3 cutter, 1¾ in. Weight, 3 lbs 2oz ...$1.37

Cut of 40045.

40043 Smooth Plane (iron) 9 inches long, 2 inch cutter. Weight, 3½ lbs . No. 4. Price, each...$1.50

40044 Smooth Plane (iron), 10 inches long. 2⅜ inch cutter. Weight, 5 lbs., No. 4½. Price, 1.70

40045 Jack Planes, iron, 14 in. long. No. 5, cutter, 2 in. Weight, 4¾ lbs.......... 1.70

40046 Fore Planes, iron, 18 in. long. No. 6. cutter, 2⅜ in. Weight, 7 lbs.......... 2.16

40046½ Jointer Plane (iron), 22 inches long, No. 7 with cutter 2⅜ inch. Weight, 6 lbs. Each 2.40

40047 Jointer Planes, iron, 24 in. long. No. 8, cutter, 2⅝ in. Weight 9¾ lbs.......... 2.96

40048 A Set of Iron Planes, consisting of the 40042½ smooth jack, fore and jointer, four planes in all, Weight, 24 lbs. 6 oz.......... 7.79

Repairs for Bailey Iron Planes.

No.	40042½	40045	40046	40047
Levers	$0.30	$0.30	$0.35	$0.35
Handles, Rosewood	.30	.30	.30	.30
Knobs, Rosewood	.15	.15	.15	.15
Irons, Single	.17	.18	.23	.24
Irons, Double	.30	.33	.39	.42

No.	40043	40044
Levers	$0.30	$0.35
Handles	.30	.39
Knobs	.15	.15
Irons, Single	.18	.23
Irons, Double	.33	.39

Bailey Pattern Adjustable Iron Planes.

Cutters adjusted by a lever. In buying the Bailey Pattern Planes you can depend upon getting a first-class plane.

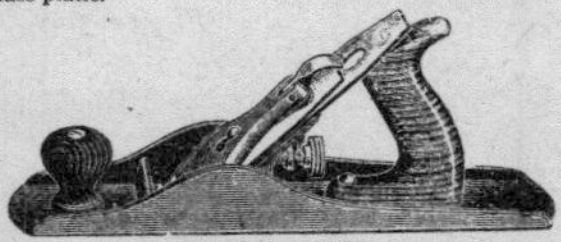

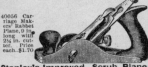

Cut of No. 40052.

40049 Iron Smooth Plane, 8 inches long, 1¾-inch cutter; weight, 3 pounds. No 3. Each $1.15

40050 Iron Smooth Plane, 9 inches long, 2-inch cutter; weight, 3½ pounds. No. 4. Each....... 1.33

40052 Iron Jack Plane, 14 inches long, 2-inch cutter; weight, 4½ pounds. No. 5. Each....... 1.50

40053 Iron Fore Plane, 18 inches long, 2⅜-inch cutter; weight, 6¼ pounds. No. 6. Each....... 1.85

40054 Iron Jointer Plane, 24 inches long, 2⅝-inch cutter; weight, 9¾ pounds. No. 8. Each. 2.50

40055 A set of Iron Planes, consisting of No. 4 smooth, jack, fore and jointer; four planes in all; weight, about 24 pounds. Price, per set.... 6.60

Repairs and irons for the Bailey Pattern Planes cost the same as repairs for Nos. 40042½, 40045, 40046 40047.

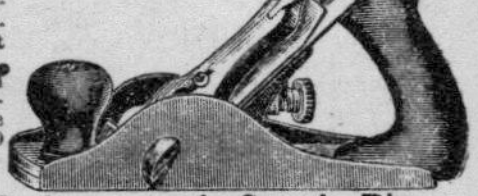

40056 Carriage Makers' Rabbet Plane, 9 in. long with 2⅛ in. cutter. Price each..$1.70

Stanley's Improved Scrub Plane.

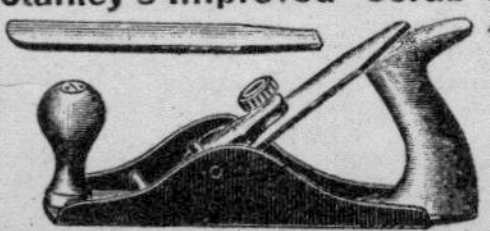

40057 This tool has a single iron with the cutting edge rounded. It is particularly adapted for roughing down work before using a jack or other plane. It has iron stock 9½ inches long with 1¼ inch cutter; made only in this one size. Price, each.......... $0.75

Rabbet Planes.

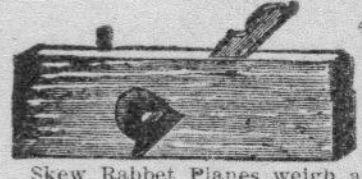

40058 Skew Rabbet Planes, ½, ⅝, ¾, ⅞ or 1 inch Each....$0.30
1¼ inch.. " .... .33
1½ inch.. " .... .35
1¾ inch.. " .... .40
2 inch.... " .... .45

Skew Rabbet Planes weigh as follows; ½ and ⅝, 10 oz. each; ⅞ and 1 inch, 12 oz. each; 1¼ inch, 1 lb. 3 oz.; 1½ inch, 1 lb. 8 oz.; 1¾ inch, 1¾ lbs.; 2 inch, 2 pounds.

40059 Jack Rabbet Planes, 1½ and 2 inch with handles and 2 cutters.......................$0.85

Stanley's Improved Rabbet Planes.

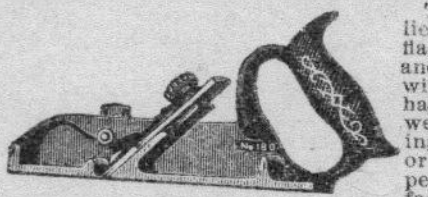

This plane will lie perfectly flat on either side and can be used with right or left hand equally well, while planing into corners or up against perpendicular surfaces.

40060 Rabbet Plane, iron stock, 8 inches in length, 1½ inches wide; weight 3 pounds, 8 oz. Each..........................$0.75

40061 Rabbet Plane; iron stock, 8 inches in length, 1½ inches wide, with spur; weight, 3 pounds 8 oz. Each.................. .80

Extra parts of Stanley Improved Rabbet Planes

Nos	40060	40061
Stocks	55c.	60c.
Cutters	20c.	20c.
Levers	10c.	10c.

Siegley's Patent Combination Plane.

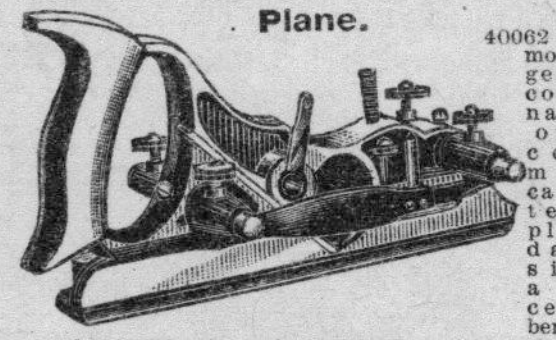

40062 This most ingenious combination of a common carpenter's plow, dado, side and center bead. Nickel plated and handsomely trimmed. Plane, making in all the most serviceable and cheapest tool in the world.

As a Plow, it has advance cutters on each side of the blade, thus saving the work of setting and running a gauge, is very easy to adjust; is more durable and cuts clean in any cross grain wood.

As A Dado, it is adjustable from ⅝ of an inch to any width. The advance cutters are fastened by set screws holding the cutter firmly in its place, and secured to the blades in slanting position, giving a free clearing to the blades.

No. 2 COMBINED PLOW AND DADO includes the following size cutters: 3-16, ¼, 5-16, ⅜, 7-16, ½, ⅝, ¾, and ⅞ inch Match Plane Cutter......$6.10

Also includes the following size Bead Plane Cutters; 3-16, ¼, 5-16, ⅜, 7-16, ½; weight, complete, 6 lbs.

PARTS FOR SIEGLEY'S PATENT.

40063 Single Bits, 26c. each; Cluster Bea Bits, 2 cluster, 30c.; 3 cluster, 35c.; 4 cluster, 40c.; Sash Molding Cutter, working 1¼ to 1½ in., 50c.

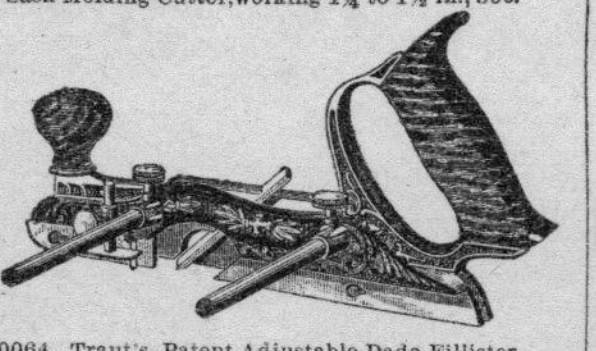

40064 Traut's Patent Adjustable Dado Fillister Plow, etc.......................$4.80

The tool here represented consists of two sections: A main stock with two bars or arms, and a sliding section, having its bottom or face level with that of the main stock.

It can be used as a Dado of any required width by inserting the bit into the main stock, and bridging the sliding section up to the edge of the bit.

The tool is accompanied by eight plow bits, 3-16, ¼, 5-16, ⅜, ½, ⅝, ⅞ and 1¼, a Fillister cutter, a slitting tool and a tonguing tool. These tools, when fastened in stock, are in a *skew*; weight, complete, 5 lbs. 3 oz.

Extra Parts.

Extra Parts of 40064 Traut's Patent Adjustable Fillister Plow, etc. Stock, $2.00; Gates or Fences, $1.50; Guard Plate, $1.25; Spurs and Screws, 5 cts. each; Depth Gauge, Brass, 25c.; Iron, 20c.; Long Arms, 50c. pair; Short Arms, 25c. pair; Cutters, in sets, $1.65; Singly, 3-16, ¼, 10c. each; 5-16, ⅜, ½, ⅝, ⅞, 15c. each; 1¼, 20c; Fillister Cutter, 25c.; Tonguing Tool, 35c.; Slitting Tool, 30c.

Circular Plane.

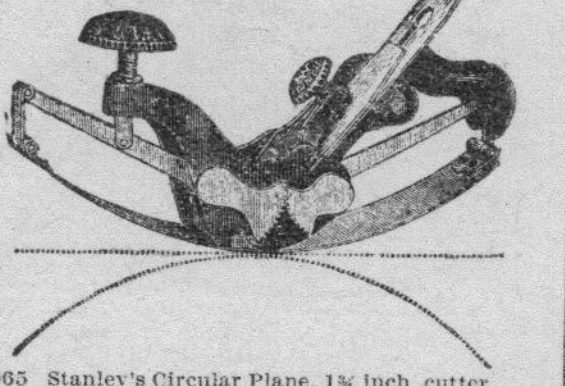

40065 Stanley's Circular Plane, 1¾ inch cutter, concave or convex surfaces; can be worked as easily as straight ones. Weight, 3¾ lbs. Each.$1.80

Traut's Patent Adjustable Beading, Rabbet and Slitting Plane.

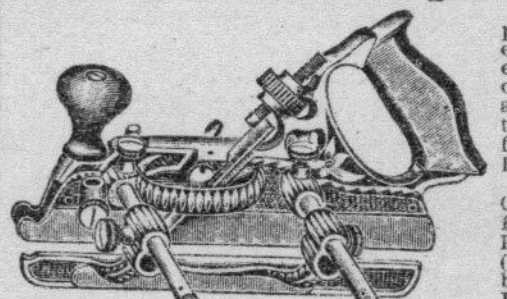

This plane embraces in a compact and practical form, (1) Beading and Center Beading Plane; (2) Rabbet and Fillister, (3) Dado (4) Plow, (5) Matching Plane and (6) a superior Slitting Plane.

For center beading the face may be adjusted to allow of making a bead five inches from the edge of the board if desired.

☞ Each plane is accompanied by seven beading tools (⅛, 3-16, ¼, 5-16, ⅜, 7-16 and ½ inch); nine plow and dado bits (⅛, 3-16, ¼, 5-16, ⅜, 7-16, ½, ⅝ and ⅞ inch), a slitting blade and a tonguing tool. Weight, complete, 6¼ lbs.

40066 Price each...............................$5.25

EXTRA PARTS.

Extra parts of Traut's Patent Adjustable Beading, Rabbet and Slitting Plane.

Stocks, $1.95; Gates or Fences, 75 cents; Sliding Section, $1.50; Spurs or Screws, 5 cents each; Depth Gauges, 20 cents; Slitting Tool, 30 cents; Brass Thumb Screw, 15 cents; Arms, 50 cents; Short Arms, 25 cents per pair. Irons in sets, $2.65; Singly, ⅛, 3-16, ¼, 5-16, 20 cents each; ⅜, 7-16, ½, ⅝, ⅞, 25 cents each; 1, 1⅛, 1¼, 1½, 30 cents each; 1¾, 2, 30 cents each. Beading Irons, ⅛, 3-16, ¼, 16 cents each; 5-16, ⅜, 20 cents each; 7-16, ½, 25 cents each. Reeding Irons, 2 reeds, 20 cents; 3 reeds, 30 cents each.

40067 Nosing Tool, 1¼ inch cutter...................$0.75

Hollows and Rounds.

40068 With Cast Steel Bits to adjust to No. 40066 Plane.

No.	6	8	10	12
Width of Cutter	½	⅝	¾	1 inch.
Works	¾	1	1¼	1½ in. circle
Price, per pair	$0.95	$0.98	$1.00	$1.05

Cutters for Hollow and Round, 20 cents each.

Patent Tonguing and Grooving Plane.

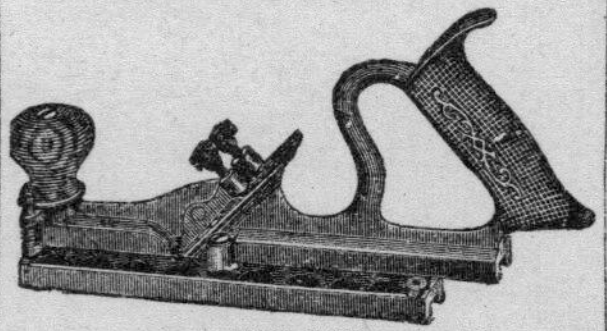

40069-40070.

The stock of this tool is made of metal, and it has two cutters fastened into the stock by thumb screws. The guide or fence, when set as shown in the above engraving, allows both of the cutters to act, and the cutters being placed a suitable distance apart, a perfect tongue plane is made. The guide or fence, which is hung on a pivot at its center, may be easily swung round end for end; thus one of the cutters will be covered and the guide held in a new position, thereby converting the tool into a grooving plane. A groove will be cut to exactly match the tongue which is made by the other adjustment of the tool. Weight, 2¾ lbs.

40069 Iron Stock and Fence for ¾ to 1¼ inch boards. Each.................$1.70

40070 For ⅜ to ¾ inch boards. Each.. ...... 1.75

Extra parts of Nos. 40069 and 40070 Patent Tonguing and Grooving Plane: Stocks, $1.50; cutters, 17 cents; levers, 10 cents; fence, 50 cents.

Hand Beader.

40071 Stanley Universal Hand Beader for beading reeding or fluting straight or irregular surfaces; is invaluable to wood workers. Iron stock with six steel cutter; complete weight, 1 pound, 10 ounces. Price.......................................$0.75

Extra cutters for 40071, each..................... .05

Woodworker's Handy Router Plane.

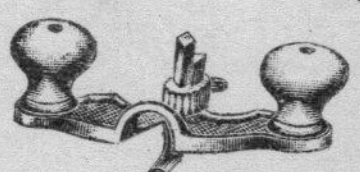

40072 This Tool should be added to the kit of every skilled Carpenter, Cabinet Maker, Stair Builder, Pattern Maker or Wheelwright. It is perfectly adapted to smooth the bottom of grooves, panels or all depressions below the general surface of any woodwork. The bits can also be clamped to the backside of the upright post, and outside of the stock. In this position they will plane into corners, will router out mortises for sash-frame pulleys, or will smooth surfaces not easily reached with any other tool. No. 71. Iron stock, with steel bits (¼ and ½ inch). Price, each.....................$1.00

Adjustable Scraper Plane.

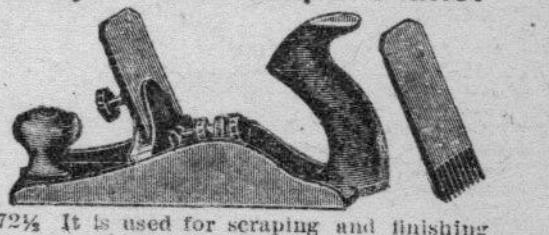

40072½ It is used for scraping and finishing veneers or cabinet work. It can be used equally as well as a tooth plane and will do excellent work in scraping off old paint and glue; 9 inches long, 3-inch cutter. Price, each...........$1.35

Cutter for veneer scraping........................ .15

Cutter for toothing (22, 28, 32 teeth per inch).. .18

Stanley's Adjustable Chamfer Plane.

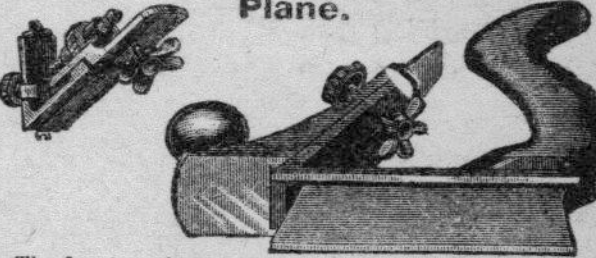

The front section of the plane to which the cutter is attached is movable up and down. It can be firmly secured to the rear section of the plane at any desired point by means of a thumb screw. Without the use of any other tool this plane will do perfect chamfer or stop chamfer work of all ordinary widths.

When the two sections are clamped together so as to form an even base line, the tool can be used as an ordinary bench plane.

40073 Iron Stock, 9 inches in length, 1⅝ inch cutter. Weight, 3 lbs. Price.....................$1.37

40073½ Same as above, with beading and molding attachments.......................... 2.00

Adjustable Beading Plane.

40074 Patent Adjustable Beading Plane. This tool for ordinary beading or for center beading cannot be surpassed. By adjustment of the fence center beading can be done up to 5 ins. from the edge of a board.

Price, including bits, ⅛, 3/16, ¼, 5/16, ⅜, 7/16, ½......$2.73

Duplex Rabbet Plane and Fillister.

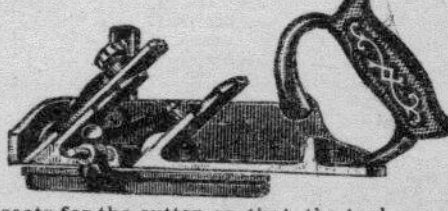

Remove the arm to which the fence is secured, and a handle rabbet plane is had, and with two seats for the cutter so that the tool can be used as a bull nose rabbet if required. The plane will lie perfectly flat on either side, and can be used with either right or left hand equally well while planing into corners or up against perpendicular surfaces.

The arm to which the fence is secured can be screwed into either side of the stock, thus making a superior right or left hand fillister, with adjustable spur and depth gauge.

40075 Iron Stock and Fence (78), 8½ inches long 1½-inch cutter. Weight, 3 lbs. 3 oz. Each....$1.00

Extra parts of No. 40075, Duplex Rabbet Plane and Fillister: Stocks 75c., cutters 20c., levers 10c., fence 25c each.

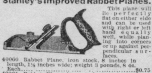

Planes—Continued.

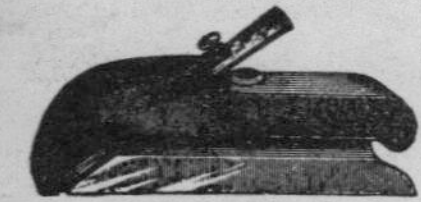

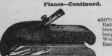

40076 Bull-Nose Rabbet Planes, iron stock, 4 ins. long, 1-in. cutter. Weight, 15 oz. Each $0.23

Iron Block Planes.

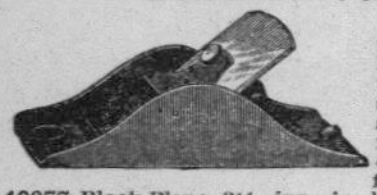

Are valuable to mechanics in all the lighter kinds of wood working, and useful about offices, stores and dwellings for making slight repairs of windows, doors, furniture, etc.

40077 Block Plane, 3½ ins. in length, 1-in. cutter. Weight, 9 oz. Each $0.08

Iron Block Planes.

Cut of No. 40078

40078 Block Plane, 5¼ in. long, 1¼ inch cutter. This plane is not adjustable. Each....$0.17

40079 Block Plane, 5½ inches long, 1¾ inch cutter, *adjustable*, like cut 40080. Each........................$0.25

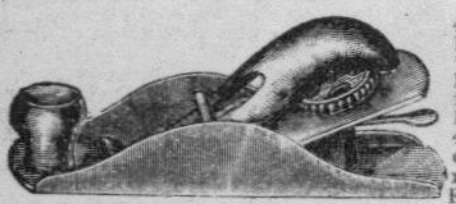

40080—Block plane, 7¼ inches long, 1¾ inch cutter, like cut 40081, without adjustment. Each..$0.25

40081 Block plane, adjustable, 7¼ inches in length, 1¾ inch cutter. Each........................$0.35

Adjustable Block Planes.

These block planes are adjusted by a screw and lever movement, and the mouth can be opened wide or be made close as the nature or the work may require.

Weight of block planes without handle 1¾ lbs., with handle 2¼ lbs.

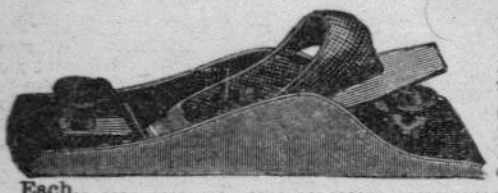

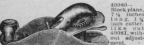

40081½ Block Plane adjustable throat, 6 inches in length 1¾ inch cutter. Each........................$0.65

40082 Block Plane, adjustable throat, 7 inches in length, 1¾ inch cutter. Weight, 1 lb. 14 ounces. Each........................ .68

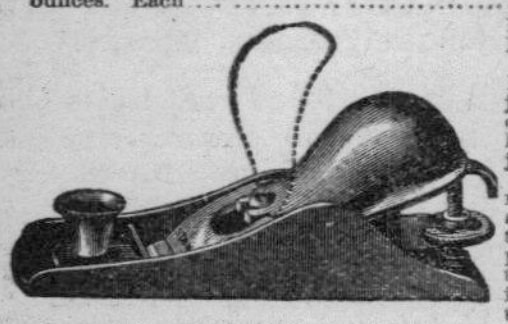

Block Plane, with knuckle joint in cap. The knuckle joint in cap makes it a lever, too, and placing the cap in position will also clamp the cutter securely to its seat.

40083 Knuckle Joint Planes, adjustaole throat, 6 inches in length, 1¾ inch cutter, Stanley's lateral adjustment, nickel plated trimmings. Each........................$0.80

40084 Knuckle Joint Planes, adjustable throat, 7 inches in length, 1¾ inch cutter, Stanley's lateral adjustment, nickel plated trimmings. Each........................ .84

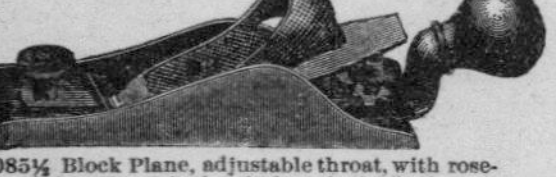

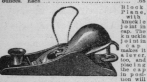

40085½ Block Plane, adjustable throat, with rosewood handle, 6 inches in length, 1¾ inch cutter. Each........................$0.72

40086 Cast Steel Cutters for above planes. Weight, 6 oz. Each........................ .18

Do not send money in a letter by open mail. Many such letters never reach their destination, and we are often blamed for it. See page 2 for information on this point.

Planes—Continued.

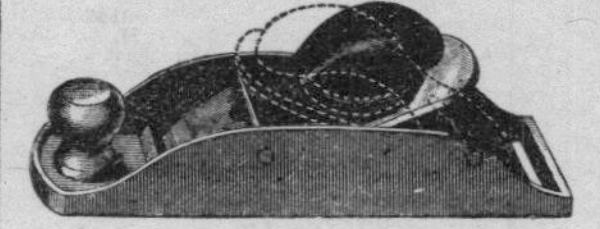

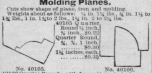

40088 Block Plane (Double Ender), 8 inches in length, 1¾ inch cutter. This plane has two slots and two cutter seats. It can be used as a block plane or by reversing the position of cutter it can be used to plane close up into corners or places difficult to reach with any other plane; not an adjustable mouth plane. Each........ $0.36

Repairs for Block Planes.

No.	40078	40081	40082	40084	40083
Stocks	$0.12	$0.18	$0.60	$0.66	$0.60
Levers	.10	.10	10	.20	.20
Irons	.10	.10	.12	.12	.12
Finger rests			.10		
Adj nut				.10	
Mouth piece					.15

No.	40085½
Stock	$0.60
Levers	.10
Brass adj. nut	....
Irons	.12
Knob	.10

Hollows and Rounds.

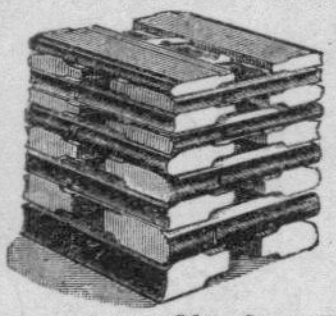

Auburn or Ohio Tool Co. No. 1 2 3 4 5 6
40095 ¼ ⅜ ½ ⅝ ¾ ⅞ inch
Per pair..............$0 35
No. 7 9
40096 1 1¼
Per pair..........$0.40
40096½ No. 11, 1½ in. Per pair.........$0.50
40097 Per set of nine pairs..............$3.20
Weights run from 15 to 32 ozs.

Nosing Plane.

40098 Nosing Plane for steps, two irons, ⅞, 1, 1⅛ and 1¼ inch. Each size........................$0.50
1⅜ and 1½ inch. Each size........................ .54

Bead Plane.

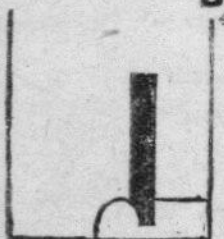

40099 Side beads, single boxed, ⅛, 3/16, ¼, 5/16, ⅜, and ½ inch, each size........................ .22
⅝ and ¾, each size........................ .25
⅞ and 1 inch, each size........................ .32
40100 Center beads, double boxed, ⅛, 3/16, ¼, 5/16, ⅜, ½ in. Each size........................ .27
⅝ and ¾, each size........................ .36
Weights run from 15 to 23 ounces.

Molding Planes.

Cuts show shape of plane, iron and molding.
Weights about as follows: ½ in. 1¼ lbs., ¾ in. 1½ to 1¾ lbs., 1 in. 1¾ to 2 lbs., 1¼ in. 2 to 2¼ lbs.

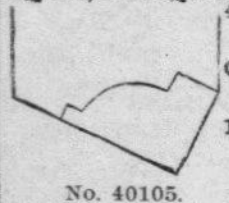

No. 40105.

40105 Quarter Round ½ inch, ⅝ inch..$0.22
Quarter Round, ¾, ⅞, 1 inch. $0.30
1¼ inches, each. $0.35

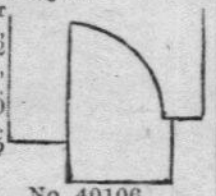

No. 40106.

40106 Quarter Rounds, with fence, ½ to ¾ inch, each........................$0.36
⅞ or 1 inch, each........................ .40
1¼ inch........................ .45

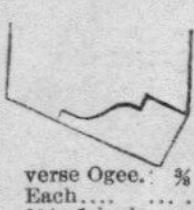

40107 Ogee Plane, ⅜ to 1 inch, each. $0 30
1¼ to 1½ inch. each...........$0.38
1¾ inch........ .45

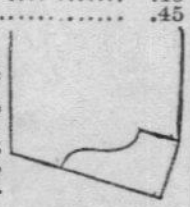

40108 Roman Reverse Ogee. ⅜ to ⅝ inch. Each........................$0.35
¾ to 1 inch, each........................ .38
1¼ inch, each........................ .45
1½ inch, each........................ .53

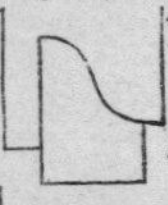

40109 Roman Reverse Ogee, with fence.
½ or ⅝ inch, each......$0.36
¾, ⅞ or 1 inch, each......$0.40

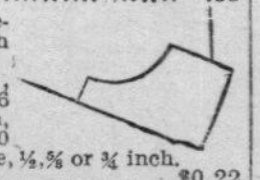

40110 Cove Plane, ½, ⅝ or ¾ inch. Each........................$0.22
Cove plane, ⅞ or 1 inch, each .30

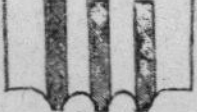

40111 Reeding Plane, ¼, 5-16 or ⅜ inch, two bead. Each........................$0.65

Dados.

40112 With brass side stop, ¼ to 1 inch. Each........................$0.50
40112½ With screw side stop, ¼ to 1 inch. Each........................ .68

Match Planes.

40113 Twins or separate plated, ⅝ to 1 inch. Per pair........................$0.68

Plane Irons.

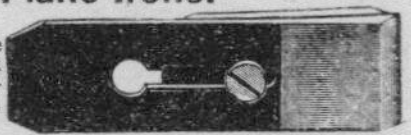

40114 Plane irons, Ohio Tool Company's single or cut irons.

Sizes	1¾	1⅞,	2,	2⅛,	2¼,	2⅜,	2½,	2⅝	2¾ in.
Each	$0.09	.09	.10	.10	.13	.14	.18	.19	.21

40115 Plane irons, Ohio Tool Company's Double irons.

Sizes	1¾,	1⅞,	2,	2⅛,	2¼,	2⅜,	2½,	2⅝,	2¾ in.
Each	$0.24	.24	.25	.25	.27	.28	.32	.33	.35

The D. R. Barton plane irons are guaranteed to be the best made. They are carefully ground and are bright all over. The double plane irons have a cast steel cap.

40116 DOUBLE IRONS.

Size	1½,	1¾,	1⅞,	2,	2⅛,	2¼,	2⅜,	2½,	2⅝,	2¾ in
Each	$0.40	.43	.45	.46	.47	.50	.53	.60	.65	.72

40116½ Plane irons, Barton's single or cut irons.

Size	1½,	1¾,	1⅞,	2,	2⅛,	2¼,	2⅜,	2½,	2⅝,	2¾ in
Each	$0.18	.20	.21	.23	.24	.27	.29	.32	.35	.40

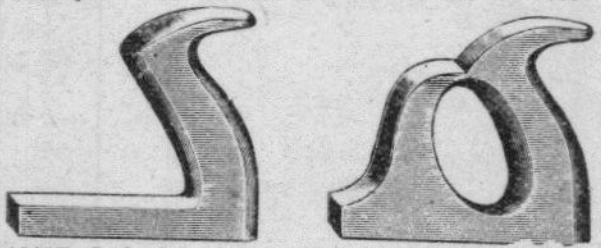

40117 Jack plane handles, beech wood. Each..$0.03
Per doz........................ .33
40118 Fore or jointer plane handles, beechwood. Each..................$0.05 Per dozen........ .54

Jointer Gauge.

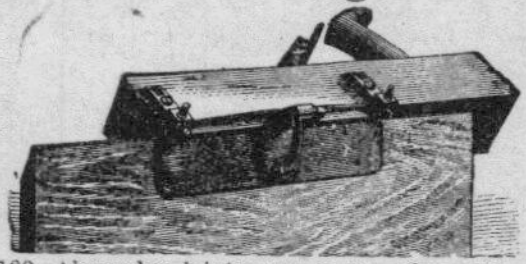

40120 Alexander jointer gauge, no plane, 2¼ pounds. Price, each........................$1.25

Veneer or Cabinet Scrapers.

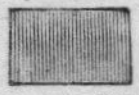

40121 Hand cabinet or veneer scrapers. A very handy article for use where any smooth wood surface is desired. Made of polished saw steel. Assorted sizes up to 6 inches long. Each, any size........$0.06. Per dozen $0.65

New Langdon Improved Miter Box.

Weight, 25 to 32 pounds.

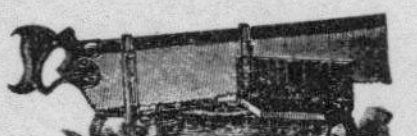

New Langdon Mitre box, improved; ordinary mitre boxes cut from right angles to 45 degrees inclusive.

The New Langdon. Improved cuts by using arms or guides from right angles to 75 degrees on 2¼ inch stuff. The only box adjustable for mitreing circular work in patterns and segments of various kinds.

40124 Langdon New Improved Mitre Box, complete with 22x4 inch saw........................$8.10
40125 Langdon New Improved Mitre box, complete with 28x5 inch saw........................11.25

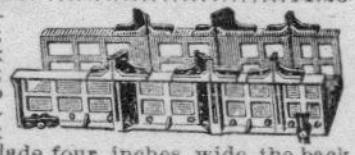

40128 Olmstead's Improved Mitre Box; frame of this box made entirely of iron; a board is secured to the bottom of the inside. When a back saw is used with a blade four inches wide, the back will serve as a stop by striking the top of the adjustable saw guides. Will take work 2½x4 inches. Any kind of a saw may be used. Price, each........$2.75

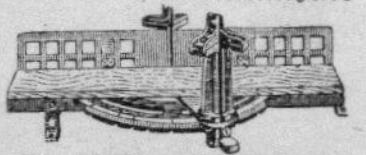

40129 Olmstead's Improved Mitre Box. This box is made entirely of steel and iron; a board is fastened to the bottom. The swinging bar can be placed at any angle desired. By pressing on the lever it can be moved to any of the fixed notches, which are right angle, ⅛, ⅙ and ¼; it can be held at any point between the notches by tightening the screw. The pointed steel springs on the back are used to press into the work to hold it fast while sawing. Any saw can be used. No. 6 will take work 4 inches wide at mitre and 6 inches wide at right angle. Price, each........$4.00

Saws.

Henry Disston & Sons, Wheeler, Madden & Clemsen's and Woodrough & McParlin's Hand, Rip, Cross Cut, Back, Panel, Keyhole, Compass, Butcher, Pit and Circular Saws.

NOTE.—Saws are frequently returned to us which have had teeth broken by prying over on the plate when setting, or which have been cracked by a cold chisel or punch.

We refuse positively to take back a saw injured in any of above ways.

(Saws weigh about 2½ lbs. each)

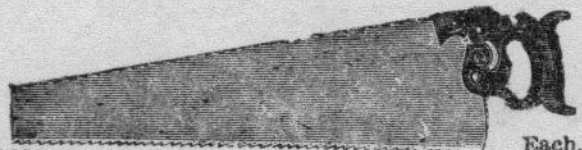

	Each.
40130 Hand Saw, beech handle, polished edge; 3 rivets, 26 inches, 6, 7, 8 points: not warranted.	$0.35
40131 Hand Saw, cast steel, black walnut handles with steel plates; a very handsome and popular saw; 26 inches, 6, 7, 8 points; not warranted..	.55
40132 Rip Saw, 28 inch, same description as No. 40131, 4, 4½ and 5 points; not warranted......	.68
40133 Hand Saw, 26 inch, C. E. Jennings & Co's No. 1½, extra refined London spring steel, skew back, carved apple handles, 5 brass screws, hand smithed and hand filled, set ready for use. This is a very fine saw, fully warranted. 8, 9 and 10 points. Price, each	1.75
40134 Rip Saw, same description as No. 40133, 4 to 6 points	2.00
40135 Rip Saw, 26 inches, 12 teeth to inch, for cabinetmakers' use for ripping where there is a veneered surface, and for all fine work. Price	1 50

40136 Hand Saws, Wheeler, Madden & Clemsen's Skew Back, improved patent handle—

No 24, 16 inch	.70
No. 24, 18 inch	.75
No. 24, 20 inch	.76
No. 24, 22 inch	.80
No. 24, 26 inch, 11, 12 points only	.90
No. 24, 28 inch, rip	1.10

40138 Henry Disston & Sons' Hand Panel and Rip Saws. No. 7. Beech handle; polished edge; grained blade, and etched—

16 inch, panel, 8 to 12 points	87
18 inch, panel, " "	.94
20 inch, panel, " "	1.07
22 inch, panel, " "	1.20
26 inch, hand, 6 to 12 "	1.34
28 inch, rip, 4 to 6 points	1.57

40139 H. Disston & Sons' D. 8 Saw, skew back, apple handle, ground back, 5 improved brass screws with the hand and rip saws. For beauty, finish and utility these saws cannot be excelled.

16 inch, panel, 8 to 12 points	.97
18 inch, panel, " "	1.05
20 inch, panel, " "	1.17
22 inch, panel, " "	1.30
26 inch, hand, 6 to 12 "	1.38
28 inch, rip, 4 to 6 points	1.70

40140 Hand Saw, No. 12. H. Disston & Sons', extra refined London spring steel, carved handle, 4 brass screws. This is one of the best saws in the market and is fully warranted.

16 inch, panel, 8 to 12 points	1 34
18 inch, panel, " "	1.47
20 inch, panel, " "	1.60
22 inch, panel, " "	1.75
26 inch, hand, 6 to 12 "	2.00
28 inch, rip, 4 to 6 points	2.27

40141 H. Disston & Sons', Acme, No. 120 Saw, made of extra London spring steel, polished apple handle, 5 rivets, skew back.

This saw is designed for first class workmen only, runs entirely without set, for use in dry lumber. Do not attempt to set this saw, as the temper is so high that the teeth will break out. We will not take back any of these saws with the teeth broken out.

20 inch, panel, 8 to 12 points	$1.80
22 inch, panel, " "	2.00
24 inch, panel, " "	2.13
26 inch, hand, 6 to 12 "	2.20
28 inch, rip, 4 to 6 points	2.55

Woodrough & McParlin's Warranted Hand and Rip Saws.

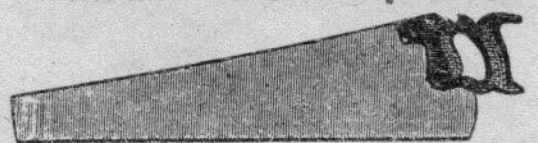

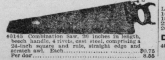

40143 Rip Saw. Woodrough and McParlin No. 12, extra refined London sprung steel blade, carved apple wood handle; 28 inch blade, 4 to 6 points $2.00

40144 Rip Saw, same description as 40143, without carved handle, 28 inch, 4 to 6 points 2.25

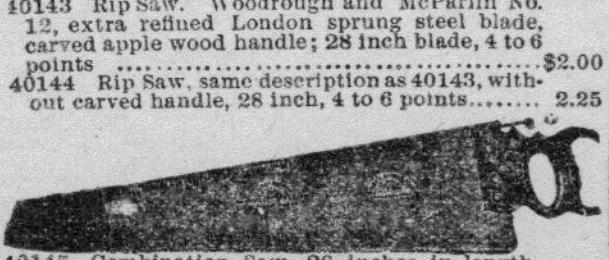

40145 Combination Saw, 26 inches in length, beech handle, 4 rivets, cast steel, comprising a 24-inch square and rule, straight edge and scratch awl. Each $0.75

Per doz 8.55

Back Saws.

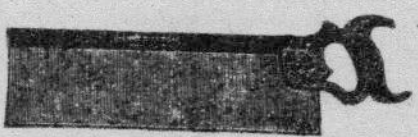

40146 Backsaws H. Disston & Sons' apple handle, 2 rivets, casts steel, polished edges.

Blue black	10 in.	12 in.	14 in.	16 in.
Each	$1.00	$1.10	$1.20	$1.40

Compass Saws.

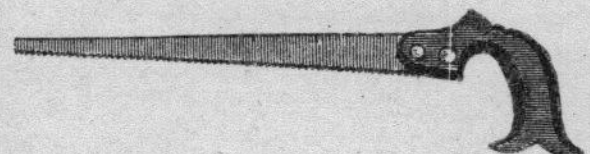

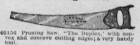

40147 Compass Saw, cast steel.

Size	10 in.	12 in.	14 in.
Each	$0.16	$0.18	$0.20

Nests of Saws.

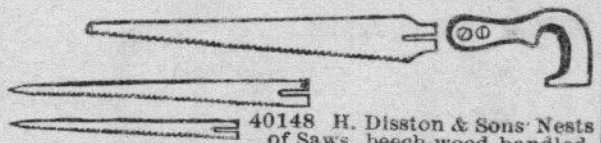

40148 H. Disston & Sons' Nests of Saws, beech-wood handled, with one keyhole saw, one compass saw, and one table or pruning saw. Nest complete $0.95

Pruning Saws.

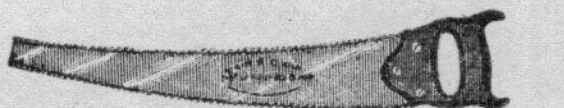

40156 Pruning Saw. "The Duplex," with convex and concave cutting edges; a very handy tool.

18 inches. Each	$0.55
16 inches. Each	.50

Keyhole Saws.

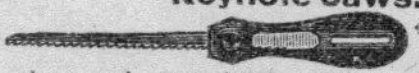

40158 Keyhole Saw, with iron pad. This is a cheap and convenient combination of a keyhole saw, saw pad and screw driver Each $0.20

40159 Extra saw blades for keyhole saw. Each.. .12 Postage, 6c. each.

Kitchen Saws.

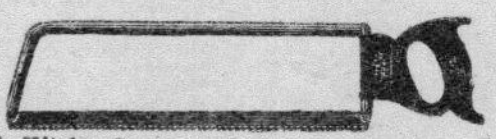

40161 Kitchen Saws, oval back, 12 inches. Each. $0.28

Butchers' Saws.

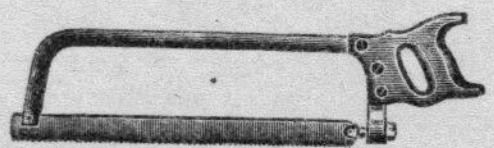

40164 Disston's No. 1, oval back, polished blade.

Size	20 in.	22 in.	24 in.
Each	$1.22	$1.28	$1.35

40165 Disston's No. 7, flat steel back.

24 inches	$1.30
26 inches	1.35

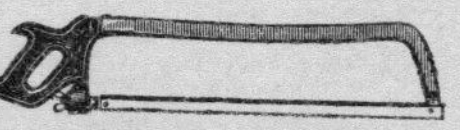

40166 Star Butcher Saw. The blades in these saws are sharpened at the factory and tempered very hard. After cutting bone for six weeks, one of these blades will cut off a ⅛ inch rod of iron twenty times. Saves the butcher much trouble and expense. The backs of the frames are made of crucible steel. Beech handles, with three brass screws.

Length	18 in.	20 in.	22 in.	24 in.	26 in.
Each	$0.90	$0.95	$1.05	$1.15	$1.25

40167 Star Butcher Saw Blades. These blades are sharpened and tempered at the factory where they are made. They cannot be filed. Will last a long time; are so cheap that it would not pay to file them, even if they were soft enough.

Length.	Width.	Teeth to in.	Each.	Per doz.
14 and 16 in.	¾	9½	$0.08	$0.91
18 and 20 in.	¾	9½	.09	1.00
22 and 24 in.	¾	9½	.10	1.12
26 in.	¾	9½	.11	1.22

Disston's Butchers' Saw Blades.

40168 Length.	20	22	24	26 inches.
Each	$0.42	$0.44	$0.46	$0.50
Per doz	4.54	4.66	4.97	5.40

Extension Hack Saw Frame.

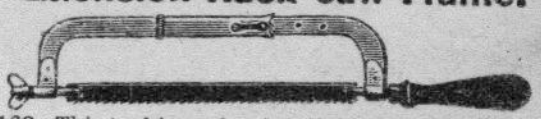

40169 This tool is made of steel, highly finished and so constructed that it can be easily extended from 8 to 12 inches, and when saw is inserted in position, it is as firm as a solid frame. Complete with one blade, as shown in cut.

Price each	$0.8
Price per dozen	9.0

Hack Saws.

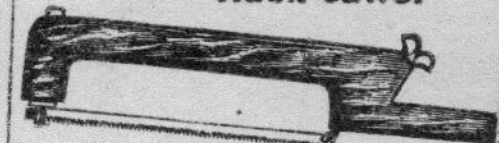

40170 Patent Star Hack Saw, wooden frame made of second growth ash, is strong and substantial and carries a 9 inch blade, facing it only one way. It will do good work and costs but little. Complete with 9 inch blade. Each $0 15

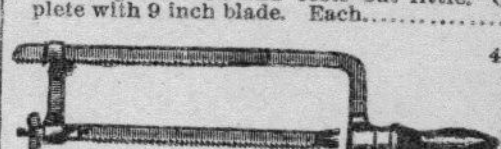

40171 Patent Star, Hack Saw latest improved steel frame, highly polished and nickel plated; will hold blades from 3 to 12 inches. Complete with 9 inch blade. Price, each $0.90

Per doz 9.72

The frame of this saw is made of steel, and as seen in cut is adjustable so as to face the blade in four different directions. The blades are very much harder than a file, and will cut iron or steel as readily as wood. As it cuts everything, farmers and mechanics will find it indispensable.

Double Edge Hack Saw Blades.

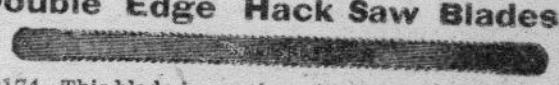

40174 This blade is meeting with a large sale, as it has double the cutting capacity of any other blade on the market; made only in the following sizes:

Length...	8 in.	9 in.	10 in.	11 in.	12 in.
Per doz..	52c.	56c.	67c.	76c.	84c.

Postage, 1c. each. Per dozen, 4 to 10c.

Star Hack Saw Blades.

40175 Length..	6 in.	7 in.	8 in.	9 in.	10 in.	12 in.
Per doz.......	45c.	48c.	54c.	59c.	74c.	89c.

Postage, 1c. each; 4 to 10c. per doz.

Turning Saw.

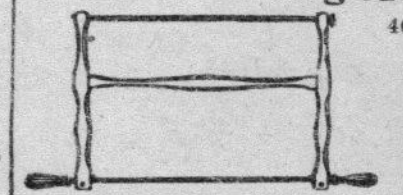

40176 This frame is made of birchwood with ebonized handles. There is an index on each handle to show the operator just how far to turn each. The friction is regulated by screws. It is quite superior to most other kinds in market.

Frame with one blade, each $0.85

40176½ 18 inch blades 15c. each. Per doz 1.69

Felloe Web Saw Blades.

40177 Length.	12	14	16	18	20	22	24 in.
Width..	¼to⅜	¼to⅜	¼to¼	¼to½	¼to⅜	¼to⅜	¼to⅜
Each...	14c.	16c.	18c.	20c.	22c.	25c.	27c.
Doz...	$1.42	$1.62	$1.95	$2.16	$2.38	$2.70	$2.92

Butting and Drag Saws.

40180 Henry Disston & Sons' Warranted Cast Steel Tapered Butting or Drag Saw.

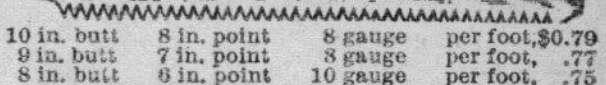

10 in. butt	8 in. point	8 gauge	per foot, $0.79
9 in. butt	7 in. point	8 gauge	per foot, .77
8 in. butt	6 in. point	10 gauge	per foot, .75
7 in. butt	5 in. point	10 gauge	per foot, .72

40181 Drag Saw, equal width, full length of saw, made only to order, and requires from 2 to 5 days.

8 in. wide	10 gauge	per foot,	$0.72
9 in. wide	10 gauge	per foot,	.77
10 in. wide	10 gauge	per foot,	.88
12 in. wide	10 gauge	per foot,	.99

No extra charge for patent or improved teeth. In ordering saws, state whether Mill or Cross-Cut Teeth are wanted. If set and sharpened we charge 9 cents per foot extra.

Mill Saws.

40182 Henry Disston & Sons' Extra Tempered, Patent Ground Mill Saws.

When ordering, give length, width and thickness or gauge of saw, also space from point to point of teeth, and distance from end of saw to point of first tooth.

8 in. wide	No. 5 gauge	Price per foot,	$1.10
8 in. wide	No. 6 gauge	Price per foot,	1.05
8 in. wide	No. 7 gauge	Price per foot,	.97
8 in. wide	No. 8 gauge	Price per foot,	.88
8 in. wide	No. 9 gauge	Price per foot,	.83
8 in. wide	No. 10 gauge	Price per foot,	.80

Pit Saws.

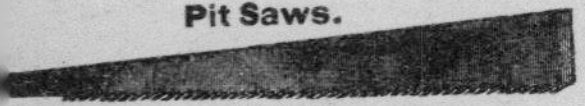

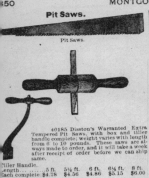

Pit Saws.

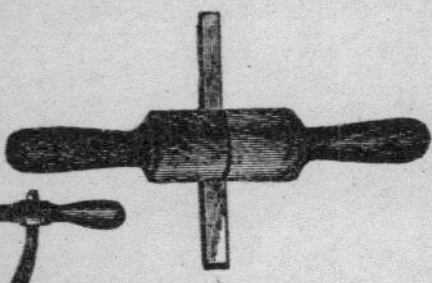

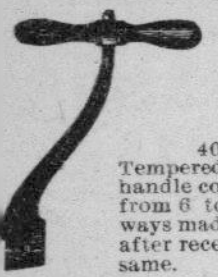

40185 Disston's Warranted Extra Tempered Pit Saws, with box and tiller handle complete; weight varies with length from 6 to 10 pounds. These saws are always made to order, and it will take a week after receipt of order before we can ship same.

Tiller Handle.

Length	5 ft.	5½ ft.	6 ft.	6½ ft.	8 ft.
Each complete	$4.28	$4.56	$4.86	$5.15	$6.00

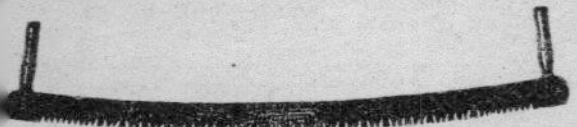

40188 *Disston's Narrow Champion* Two Man Cross Cut Saw with handles.
Length, 5½ feet; weight, 5¼ lbs. $1.45
Length, 6 feet; weight, 5¾ lbs 1.55

40189 *Disston's Plain Tooth No. 2 Cross, Cut Saw,* two men.
Length, 6 feet; weight, 7½ lbs 2.45
Length, 7 feet; weight 9¾ lbs 2.80

40190 *Disston's Champion Tooth,* Two Man Cross Cut Saw with handles
Length, 5 feet; weight, 6 lbs 1.90
Length, 5½ feet; weight, 7 lbs 2.20
Length, 6 feet; weight, 8 lbs 2.35
Length, 6½ feet; weight, 8¾ lbs 2.55
Length, 7 feet; weight, 9 lbs 2.75

40191 *Disston's Diamond Tooth,* Two Man Cross Cut Saw with handles.
Length, 4½ feet; weight, 5 lbs 1.90
Length, 5 feet; weight, 6 lbs 2.10
Length, 5½ feet; weight, 7 lbs 2.25
Length, 6 feet; weight, 8 lbs 2.43

Wheeler, Madden & Clemson's Cross Cut Saws.

40192 Wheeler, Madden & Clemson's Narrow Champion Tooth, two man saws with handle. Length, 5½ feet; weight, 5¾ lbs $1.25

40193 Cross Cut Saw Handles, patent loop. Per pair .... $0.20 Per dozen 1.85

40194 Cross Cut Saw Handles No. 11, reversible. Per pair .... $0.30 Per dozen 3.25

Cross Cut Saws, One and Two Men.

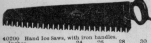

40195 Cross Cut Saw, H. Disston & Sons' beech handle, cast steel champion tooth, one man saw, with supplementary handle
Length, 3 feet; weight, 3¼ pounds. Each $1.41
Length, 3½ feet; weight, 4 pounds. Each 1.56
Length, 4 feet; weight, 4¾ pounds. Each 1.85
Length, 4½ feet; weight, 5¾ pounds. Each 2.00

Ice Saws.

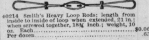

40200 Hand Ice Saws, with iron handles.

Inches	24	26	28	30
Each	$0.78	$0.89	$1.08	$1.12

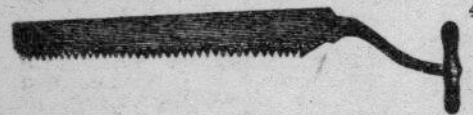

40201—Pond Ice Saws, set and sharpened, tapered from 7 inches to 5 inches at the point; complete with tiller handle, 4 feet long. Each $2.75
4½ feet long. Each 2.95
5 feet long. Each 3.20

All goods sent by mail at purchaser's risk. We can assume no responsibility after goods are deposited in postoffice. We advise insuring everything of value. See page 2.

Bracket Saw Blades.

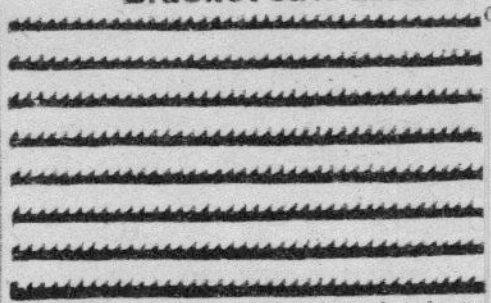

40205 Bracket Saw Blades, 5 inches long. Any number. We do not sell less than a dozen of any one size. Per doz., No. 0 to 6 .... $0.07
Per gross, No. 0 to 6 .... .75
" dozen, No. 7 and 8 .... .08
" gross, " " .... .85
" dozen, 9 10 .... .10
" gross, " " .... .95

Hand Bracket Saw.

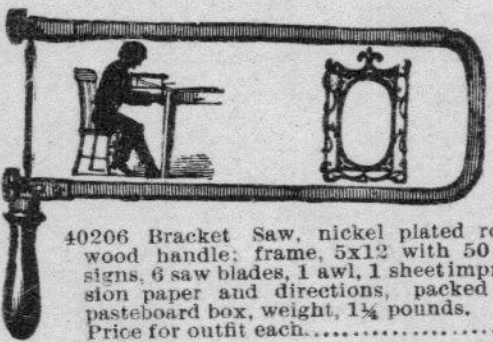

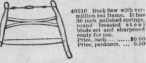

40206 Bracket Saw, nickel plated rosewood handle; frame, 5x12 with 50 designs, 6 saw blades, 1 awl, 1 sheet impression paper and directions, packed in pasteboard box, weight, 1¼ pounds.
Price for outfit each $0.90
Per dozen 10.00

Buck Saws.

The weight of Buck Saws from 3 to 4 pounds.

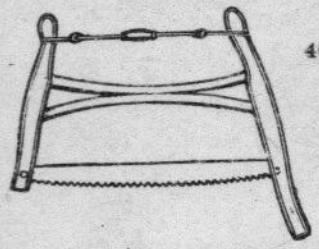

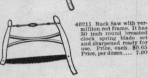

40210 Buck Saw with vermillion red frame. It has 30 inch polished springs, round breasted steel blade set and sharpened ready for use.
Price, each $0.60
Price, perdozen. ... 6.50

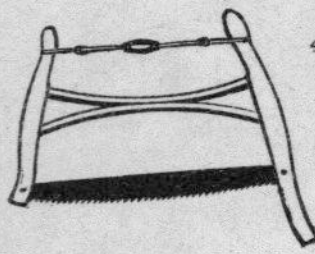

40211 Buck Saw with vermillion red frame. It has 30 inch round breasted clock spring blade set and sharpened ready for use. Price, each .. $0.65
Price, per dozen 7.00

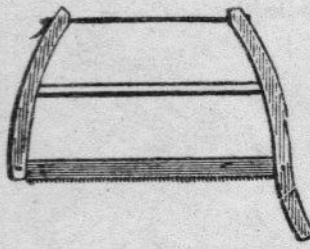

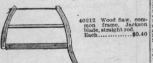

40212 Wood Saw, common frame, Jackson blade, straight rod.
Each $0.40

Wood Saw Blades.

40212½ Wood Saw Blades, Henry Disston & Sons' cast steel, 30 inches, set and sharpened.
Each $0.45

40213 Wood Saw Blades, cast steel, 30 inches, set and sharpened, not warranted. Each ..... .30
Per doz 3.00

Buck Saw Rods.

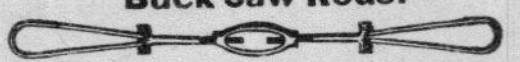

40214 Smith's Heavy Loop Rods; length from inside to inside of loop when extended, 21 in.; when screwed together, 18¾ inch.; weight, 10 oz. Each $0.06
Per dozen .... .65

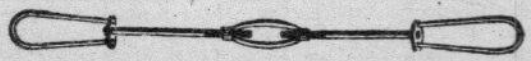

40215 The Clipper Loop Buck Saw Rod, length from inside to inside of loop, when extended, 22 in.; when screwed together 19 in.; weight, 10 oz. Each $0.05
Per dozen .... .54

***** Write your name and Address on package returned to us if you want it to have attention; send letter of instructions by mail; do not put it in package.**

Hand Saw Handles.

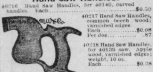

40216 Hand Saw Handles, for 40140, carved handles. Each $0.50

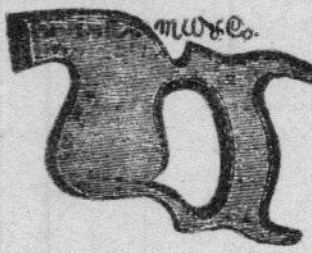

40217 Hand Saw Handles, common beech wood; varnished edges.
Each $0.08
Per doz .... .87

40218 Hand Saw Handles, for 40139 saw. Apple wood, varnished edges; weight, 10 oz.
Each $0.28

	Each.	Per doz.
40219 Back Saw Handles for 40146 back saw, beechwood, varnished edges; weight, 7 oz.	$0.08	$0.87
40220 Disston's One Man Saw Handles, beechwood, varnished edges; weight, 12 oz.	.22	2.38

Circular Saws.

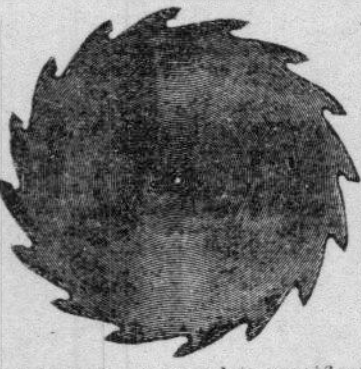

40222 H. Disston & Sons' Patent Ground and Tempered Solid Tooth Circular Cross Cut Saws.

40223 Circular Rip Saws, same price as Cross Cut.

Say whether Cross Cut or Rip Saw is wanted, and give size of hole.

Do not order saws by telegraph. We never have been able in a single instance to fill an order sent us this way, as complete specifications are never given and we never send special or saws made to order C. O. D. Money must accompany the order in all cases.

Diameter.	Thickness.	Size of Hole.	Price, each
4 inches.	19 gauge.	¾ inch.	$0.55
5 inches.	19 gauge.	¾ inch.	.65
6 inches.	18 gauge.	¾ inch.	.77
7 inches.	18 gauge.	¾ inch.	.95
8 inches.	18 gauge.	⅞ inch.	1.10
9 inches.	17 gauge.	⅞ inch.	1.38
10 inches.	16 gauge.	1 inch.	1.65
11 inches.	16 gauge.	1 inch.	1.95
12 inches.	15 gauge.	1 inch.	2.10
14 inches.	15 gauge.	1⅛ inch.	2.47
16 inches.	14 gauge.	1⅛ inch.	3.00
18 inches.	13 gauge.	1¼ inch.	3.85
20 inches.	13 gauge.	1 5/16 inch.	4.68
22 inches.	12 gauge.	1 5/16 inch.	5.50
24 inches.	11 gauge.	1⅜ inch.	6.60
26 inches.	11 gauge.	1⅜ inch.	7.75
28 inches.	10 gauge.	1½ inch.	8.80
30 inches.	10 gauge.	1½ inch.	9.90
36 inches.	9 gauge.	1⅝ inch.	14.00
40 inches.	9 gauge.	2 inch.	19.25
50 inches.	7 gauge.	2 inch.	44.00

Be sure to say whether cross cut or rip saw is wanted; there is no difference in price. Those ordering circular saws will save themselves much trouble by exercising care in making out their orders. We furnish blanks to facilitate this, which can be had on application. An extra charge will be made for saws of heavier gauge than those as listed above. Other sizes of circular saws quoted on application. We charge extra for each additional gauge heavier than those mentioned above. Saws beveled one gauge without extra charge up to 44 inches.

Saws other than sizes and gauges quoted above are not kept in stock. It will take from one week to ten days to make saws to order. Any saw made to order will not be taken back or exchanged.

Circular Saw Mandrels.

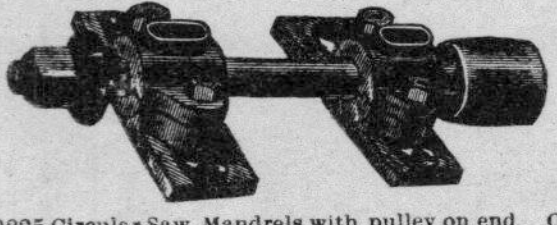

40225 Circular Saw Mandrels with pulley on end. Of the latest and most improved pattern.

Diam, of Pulley.	Face of Pulley.	Diam. of Flange	Length of Shaft.	Diam. of Shaft.	Size of Hole in Saw.	Price of each c'mp'e
2½ in.	3½ in.	2½ in.	16 in.	1 1/16	1 in.	$ 5.95
3 in.	4½ in.	3 in.	19 in.	1 3/16	1⅛ in.	6.80
3¼ in.	4½ in.	3½ in.	20 in.	1 5/16	1¼ in.	7.25
4 in.	5 in.	4 in.	24 in.	1 7/16	1 5/16 in.	8.25
4½ in.	5½ in.	4½ in.	26 in.	1 7/16	1 5/16 in.	9.35
5 in.	6 in.	5 in.	28 in.	1 7/16	1⅜ in.	10.62
5½ in.	6½ in.	5½ in.	30½ in.	1 7/16	1⅜ in.	11.50
6 in.	7 in.	6 in.	32½ in.	1 9/16	1½ in.	13.15
7 in.	8 in.	6 in.	37 in.	1 11/16	1⅝ in.	18.27
8 in.	8 in.	6 in.	41 in.	1 13/16	1⅝ in.	21.88

Band Saws.

HENRY DISSTON & SONS.

40226 In using band saws always keep the correct pitch upon the tooth, so as to give the saw a proper lead into the cut. This will take the friction entirely off the stay-pin. By the use of a round edge file the saw will be kept from galling and breaking. We furnish the saws SET AND FILED at the following prices. We keep in stock up to 1 inch wide; anything wider than 1 inch will have to come from the factory and will require from 10 days' to 2 weeks' time. We cannot allow parties to return the saws if sent as ordered, or countermand after order has gone to the factory from us.

Width.	Gauge.	Extra for joining each saw.	Price. per foot.
¼ in.	21	$0.20	$0.10
⅜ in.	21	.20	.11
½ in.	21	.20	.13
⅝ in.	21	.25	.15
¾ in.	20	.25	.16
⅞ in.	20	.25	.17
1 in.	20	.30	.18

If saws are not filed and set, 4 cents per foot may be deducted from above price. Under no circumstances will we send band saws C. O. D. We can furnish band saws up to 12 inches wide.

CASSELL BROS.' WARRANTED BAND SAWS.

40227 Read (40226) what we say about the use of Band Saws. We cannot allow parties to return saw when sent as ordered, or countermand after order has gone to factory. The price is for saws filed and set but *not brazed or joined*.

Width.	Extra for joining each saw.	Price per foot.
⅛ in.	$0.20	$0.05
3-16	.20	.05
¼	.20	.05
5-16	.20	.06
⅜	.20	.06
½	.20	.06½
⅝	.25	.07
¾	.25	.08
⅞	.25	.09
1	.30	.10

Foot-Power and Power Band Saw.

With Dana's Patent Friction Clutch Attachment.

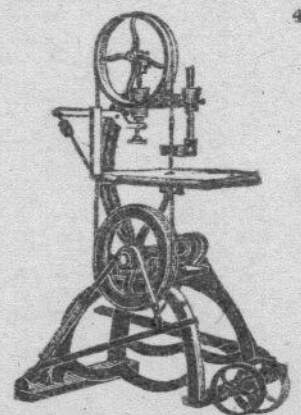

40229 For wagon-makers, carpenters and wood-workers in general. This is a strong, substantial machine, with double treadle, so that two persons can operate it in heavy work. Each treadle is independent of the other. When desired to run by power, we furnish tight and loose pulleys instead of the back treadle. The power pulleys do not interfere with the front treadle. There is no gear, no extra pulleys, and no noise, as the clutches work on the shaft. The wheels are 16 inches in diameter, 1⅛ inch face. The table is 3 feet and 7 inches from the floor. Its size is 21x24 inches. Distance from table to guide, when later is raised its full height, 7 inches. The upper saw pulley can be tilted by means of a band wheel, and can also be raised and lowered with the hand wheel to change tension of saw. Adjustable brass guide for saw, both above and below the table. We furnish two French steel saws with every machine—your choice of widths ⅛, ¼, ⅜, ½, filled and set ready for use. We also furnish brazing clamps, with full directions for brazing saws. This machine meets a long felt want among wagon makers, carpenters, pattern makers, and wood-workers in general. Shipping weight, 350 pounds. Price, with double treadle....................$37.50

40229½ Price with single treadle, with power pulley.................... 37.50

40230 Disston's Patent Self-Feeding Saw Gummer. Showing the Victor in position for work on a 60-inch circular saw. In ordering Gummers state size of cutter wanted.

We make three sizes of cutter shafts for this gummer.

The No. 1 or large shaft is the same diameter as is used in our No. 1 gummer, and is suitable for 1, 1⅛, 1¼, 1⅜ and 1½ inch cutters.

The No. 2 or medium size shaft is same diameter as is used in our No. 2 gummer, and is suitable for cutters ½, ⅝, ¾ and ⅞ inch.

The No. 3 or small shaft is made specially for ⅜ inch cutters. Price, each....................$14.25

***** Read pages 1 and 2 before ordering goods. You obtain a discount by sending money with order. Send money by Express, Draft on Chicago or New York, Post Office Money Order, or Registered Mail.**

Saw Tools and Swages.

40231 Improved Combination Saw Tool for fitting up cross cut saws.

This very handy tool includes a jointer, a side dress, a cleaner, a tooth gauge, a saw set and a set gauge for testing, the amount of set. To properly fit up a cross-cut saw, it is necessary first that the teeth should be uniform in length. To accomplish this, place the file edgeway in the frame and by means of the two screws adjust to the curve of the saw, pass it lightly over the teeth until it touches the shortest cutting tooth, then place the gauge over the cleaner teeth as shown in Cut No. 2 and file them down to the required length.

If the saw requires setting use the saw set on the end of the tool. Give the first tooth the required amount of set, and by adjusting the stop bar under the saw set each tooth will be given the same amount of set.

Price, each....................$0.90

The Conqueror Swage, Jumper or Upset.

Special attention is called to the Conqueror Swages. The Conqueror has given entire satisfaction, and we have the most flattering testimonials of its worth. It is indispensable to any sawyer who uses the spread set. Every swage sold by us is warranted perfect, and to give satisfaction. The sets themselves shall bear their own recommendation.

40232 No. 1. For large circular saws, as per cut. Price each....................$2.50

40233 No. 2. For small circular and mill saws. Price each.................... 2.20

40234 No. 3. For small circular saws. Price each 1.70

Patent Improved Saw Tool.

SIMONDS MFG. CO.
FITCHBURG, MASS
CHICAGO, ILL.

40235 For use in fitting *Cross Cut Saws*. It combines in one tool a perfect *Saw Set, Jointer, Raker Gauge, Set Gauge*, and *Swaging Hammer* in a convenient and compact form. A saw can be fitted up much more quickly and much better with this tool than with any other tools or sets of tools. It takes an 8-inch mill file we do not furnish, except at an additional charge. For price of files see No. 40305. Price, each............$0.60. Per doz............$6.00

No. 3. No. 4.

No. 5. No. 2.

Saw Handle Screws.

40240 Brass.

No.	Each.	Per doz.
2......	$0.02	$0.22
3......	.03	.33
4......	.05	.54
5......	.04	.44

Saw Sets.

40241 Morrill's Perfect Saw Set No. 1, setting all kinds of hand saws; weight, 13 oz.

Hold the saw on any level place, teeth upward. Place the set on the saw, as shown in cut. The anvil, movable up and down, must be regulated to suit the distance the operator desires to set his saw teeth down from their points. The guard when moved forward increases the amount of set, moved backward, decreases it. When made fast to the screw, compress the handles and the plunger goes forward and takes effect on the saw tooth, as shown in cut.

On no account pry over on the saw blade. When the set is properly adjusted simply compressing the handles is all that is necessary. This is for hand saws from 32 to 16 gauge only. Each......$0.65. Per dozen..$7.25

40242 Morrill's Perfect Saw Set No. 3, for single tooth, cross cut and circular saws, from 20 to 14 gauge; weight, 1 lb. 6 oz. Each.................... 1.10

Saw Sets—Continued.

40243 Morrill's Perfect Saw Set No. 4, for Champion or M-tooth cross cut saws, from 22 to 14 gauge; weight, 1¼ lbs. Each....................$1.12

40244 Extra parts for Morill saw sets.

No. 1, Anvils and Plungers, each....................	.10
No. 3, Anvils and Plungers, each....................	.12
No. 4, Anvils and Plungers, each....................	.15

Taintor's Positive Saw Set 93.

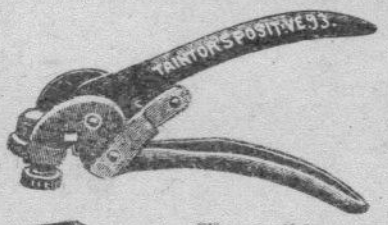
TAINTOR'S POSITIVE 93.

40245 Full directions sent with each Saw Set.

Description—The face of the anvil opposite the punch determines the set of the saw.

The anvil has ten faces, divided into sections marked F, M and C, indicating the faces to be used in setting Fine, Medium and Coarse teeth.

Placing the washer between the anvil and frame divides the difference between two lengths of faces, thus giving two adjustments to a face, or twenty adjustments in all.

All the faces in a division take the same hold of a tooth, but the higher numbers bend the tooth more than the lower ones.

Face No. 4 will set a medium saw about right for general work, and can be used as a trial face.

Price, each....................$0.60
Per doz.................... 7.00

40247 Lever Saw Sets, wood handles; weight, 7 oz. Each....................$0.10
Per dozen.................... 1.00

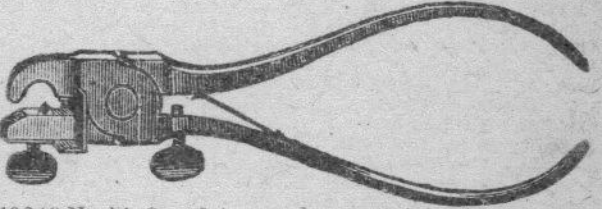

40249 Nash's Saw Sets, new lever; weight, 12 oz. Each....................$0.35
Per dozen.................... 3.85

40250 Nash's Saw Sets, No. 3 for setting cross cut saws. Price each.................... .85

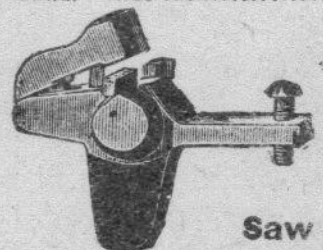

40253 Aiken's Patent Hammer saw sets, made of the highest grade of cast steel and warranted genuine.
Price each........$0.60

Saw Vises.

40260

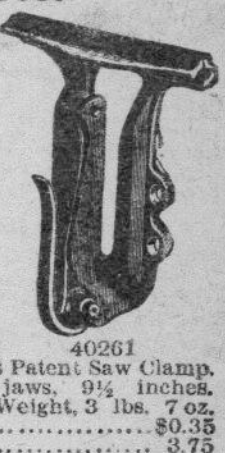

40261

40260 Stearn's Patent Saw Clamp. Length of jaws, 9½ inches. Japanned. Weight, 3 lbs. 7 oz. Each....................$0.35
Per dozen.................... 3.75

40261 Silent Saw Clamp. By one movement of the lever the saw is firmly clamped, after which a third jaw faced with solid rubber is pressed against the saw, preventing all noise of vibration. Weight, 3¾ lbs. Each....................$0.95
Per dozen....................10.60

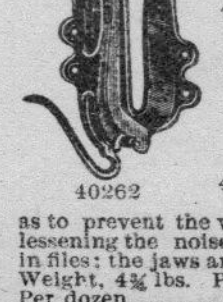

40262

40262 Patent Saw Clamp. The jaws are so constructed as to prevent the vibration of the saw in filing, lessening the noise and causing a great saving in files; the jaws are planed to match precisely. Weight, 4¾ lbs. Price, each....................$0.93
Per dozen....................10.00

Vises—Continued.

40263

40264

40263 Patent saw clamp (3). This vise has a malleable iron screw clamp for attaching it to the work bench, and a lever and cam for holding it in any position. Weight, 5 lbs. Japanned. Each $0.50
Per doz. 5.25

40264 Adjustable ball and socket saw clamp. By the use of this vise a saw can be filed any angle or square as the operator may desire. Weight, 10½ lbs. Price each .... .68
Per doz. 7.50

Saw Clamp and Sharpener.

40266 Elkin's saw clamp and sharpener, for hand, rip, panel, back, wood, band, jig, hack, compass and butcher saws. Any one who can use a saw can sharpen it quickly and accurately with this invention. Weight, 5½ pounds. Each $2.29

Saw Jointer.

40267 The Practical Saw jointer. By its use perfect accuracy is attained in jointing the teeth squarely and to equal lengths. The file can be adjusted in the slot until the surface has been used on both sides.
Each $0.35
Per dozen 3.78

Tanite Emery Wheel.

When ordering emery wheels, give diameter, thickness, size of hole and also be sure to state the nature of your work, kind of metal you intend to use wheel on, etc. This is absolutely necessary in order for us to send you a wheel suitable, as there are about 15,000 different kinds, sizes, classes and shapes of wheels; we haven't the space to quote them all, but will quote prices and furnish any kind or size upon application.
40270 Emery Wheel, flat face.
40271 Emery Wheel, bevel edge, for gumming saws.

Diameter.	40270		THICKNESS.			40271
	¼	⅜	½	⅝	¾	1
	Price Each.					
1½	$0.24	Not made	$0.25	Not made	$0.28	$0.32
2	.27	in	.32	in	.35	.38
2	.40	these	.45	these	.48	.52
3	.43	sizes.	.52	sizes.	.58	.65
4	.60	$0.62	.68	$0.75	.85	1.00
5	.79	.78	.84	.96	1.08	1.32
6	.84	.96	1.02	1.25	1.44	1.84
7	1.10	1.27	1.38	1.80	1.93	2.32
8	1.28	1.42	1.56	1.95	2.63	2.65
10	1.72	1.98	2.23	2.65	3.10	3.95
12	1.80	2.11	2.40	2.90	3.40	4.42

Would be Poor Policy

To misrepresent our goods knowingly, therefore do not hesitate to place confidence in our Buyer's Guide. If goods are not as represented we will cheerfully refund purchase price and pay all transportation charges.

The Eagle Emery Wheel.

In ordering emery wheels the diameter, thickness and size of hole must be given and and the purpose for which they are to be used. *The wheel must be kept very dry in all cases.* Parties must be very particular in this respect to insure perfect satisfaction. Every wheel guaranteed if kept free from dampness.

Wheels less than ½ inch in thickness, same price as ½ inch.
40272 Flat face.
40273 Bevel edge.

diameter.	THICKNESS. ½	⅝	¾	1	1¼	1½	1¾	2
3	$0.30	$0.34	$0 38	$0.44	$0.50	$0.54	$0.58	$0.64
4	.44	.48	.54	.64	.76	.88	1.00	1.10
5	.56	.64	.72	.84	1.04	1.20	1.48	1.52
6	.70	.84	1.00	1.20	1.48	1.72	2.00	2.24
7	.92	1.08	1.26	1.58	2.00	2.24	2.56	2.90
8	1.04	1.24	1.40	1.80	2.28	2.56	3.00	3.32
9	1.24	1.40	1.54	1.96	2.72	3.20	3.68	4.20
10	1.48	1.76	2.04	2.64	3.24	3.80	4.40	4.96
12	1.60	2.00	2.40	2.96	3.60	4.28	5.08	5.60
14	2.48	2.98	3.48	4.28	5.28	6.08	7.00	7.80

Bracket Saw.

Has tilting table drilling attachment and dust blower. Height, of table above floor 32 inches.

Diameter of belt wheel, 12 inches.

Diameter of balance wheel, 5 inches.

Length of arms in the clear, 18 inches.

With each machine we furnish 3 drills, 6 saw blades, wrench, sheet of designs and directions.

Machine, boxed, weighs 36 pounds.

40275 Price of No. 2 Rogers' saw complete $3.60

The new Rogers is altogether superior to any machine offered at the same or less price.
40276 Extra Saw Clamps for new Rogers.
Per pair $0.30
We do not sell designs other than furnished.

Goodell Turning Lathe.

40280 This lathe is provided with a long and short tool rest, five turning tools, wrench and drill points. Swing of lathe five inches, length of bed 24 inches. Distance between center 15½ inches. The large drive wheel has two grooves of varying depths on its face to give it a change of speed: the higher speed is 11 to 1; the lower 7 to 1; the lathe head has a two inch face plate, a spur center, a screw center for turning cups and also a drill chuck to hold from 1-32 to ¼ inch round twist drills for drilling wood or iron. The lathe is thoroughly built and highly finished, the plain and polished parts being nickel plated. Price $8.55
40280½ Goodell Lathe with scroll saw attachments 10.80

Bench Lathe.

The above cut represents our small Bench Lathe, which will be found a most useful tool for light turning, drilling and polishing, and will take the place in many cases of the large and more expensive tools in general use. This lathe is made in two sizes, 24 inch and 36 inch bed: both have 6¼ inch swing. The distance between centers of the 24 inch bed is 14 inches, and the distance of the 36 inch bed between centers is 26 inches. Price each.
40283 Lathe with 24 inch bed $12.00
40284 Lathe with 36 inch bed 14.00

PRICE OF EXTRAS FOR ABOVE LATHE.

40285 Foot Wheels 5.00
40286 Counter Shaft 2.50
40287 Spur Center for Wood 1.00
40288 Crotch Center for Drilling 1.00
40289 Drill Pad for Tail Stock .... .75
40290 Extra Face Plate .... .75
40291 Screw Chuck for Wood 1.00
40292 Drill Chuck fitted to Lathe to hold drills from ⅜ inch down 4.00

Countershafts.

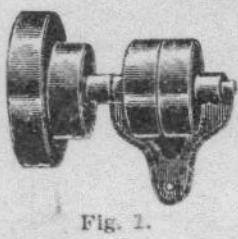

Fig. 1.

Suitable for running the preceding lathes or any other small machinery by power.
40293 Fig. 1 has fast and loose pulleys, 3 inch in diameter, 1⅛ inch face, and flat cone pulley, 5 inch and 3 inch diameter, 1⅛ inch face. Price, each $2.50

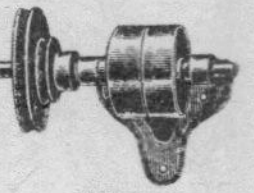

Fig. 2.

40293½ Fig. 2 with fast and loose pulley 3 in. diameter, 1⅛ in. face, and grooved cone pulley, 4 and 2 inches diameter.
Price $2.00

Lathe Head.

40294 Has castiron adjustable bearings and steel spindle; swings 6 inches and is furnished with face plate and arbor.
Price $3.00
40295 Head and tail stock complete. $6.00

Foot Power Emery Wheel Grinding Machine.

Speed, 2,600 to 2,800 Revolutions Per Minute.

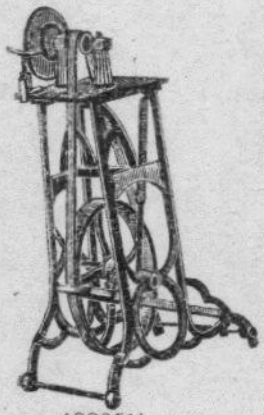

40295½

For price of Emery Wheels, see Nos. 40270, 40271, 40272, 40273. This machine is designed for the use of blacksmiths, carpenters, gunsmiths, and marble granite workers. It will save a blacksmith a great deal of time and many files. It will do three-fourths of all the work he usually does with a file.

For ordinary tool grinding we use an 8x¾-inch Emery wheel, which is furnished with each machine.

A narrow wheel can be used for gumming saws.

This machine will do all kinds of tool grinding in less than one-fourth of the time required on a grindstone, and will do the work much better. It is a light machine, and can be moved around easily.
40295½ Weight, 190 lbs. Price, each $10.50

40296 Emery Grinding Machine, for power. Will run two 6-inch emery wheels, 1 inch thick, has ⅝ inch steel spindle, ½ inch between flanges, pulley 2 inches in diameter, 1⅜ inch face. Weight, 9 lbs.
Price, each $4.00

Polishing Heads.

40298 Stands 6 in. high and has a spindle 9 inches long, one end of which is a taper screw the other end is fitted to hold emery wheels, buffers, polishing wheels, and small circular saws. It is also fitted with chuck for holding drills. We furnish the head only, as shown in the cut. Each $1.20

Polishing Head.

40299 For running emery wheels, circular saws, etc. Has castiron adjustable bearings and steel spindle, and is made to run with round or flat belts: will hold wheels 6 inch in diameter, and 1 inch thick. Price each $3.25

*** MRS. HANNAH COBB'S celebrated "Home made Soap," 30 bars in a box (family or trial size). Every bar warranted. We have sold thousands of boxes and all have given entire satisfaction. Try a box and you will see why we praise it. See Grocery List for prices.

Iron Clamps.

40300 Malleable Iron Clamps, swivel head.

Opens inches.	Weight.	Price, each.
4	1½ lbs.	$0.18
5	1¾ "	.21
6	2 "	.27
7	3 "	.33
8	3¾ "	.38
10	5¼ "	.46

Quilting Frame Clamps.

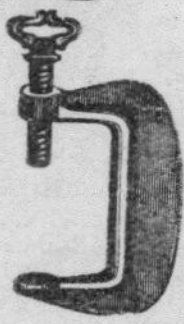

40301 Quilting Frame Clamps, malleable iron, 2¼ inch opening.
Per set of four.................. $0.12

Wood Screw Clamps.

40302 Wood Hand Screws, the Grand Rapids Pattern. This make is unexcelled; the spindles are made of second growth hickory; the jaws are of hard maple or birch thoroughly seasoned; the threads are cut deep enough to prevent stripping.

Diameter of Screw. Inches.	Length of Screw. Inches.	Length of Jaw. Inches.	Size of Jaw. Inches.	Opens Inches.	Price Each.	Price Per doz.
⅝	11	8½	1⅜x1½	5	16c	$1.83
¾	13	10	1⅝x1⅝	6½	20c	2.16
⅞	14	12	1⅞x1⅞	6½	23c	2.50
1⅛	20	16	2¼x2¼	10½	35c	3.78
1¼	22	20	2½x2¾	12	43c	4.65
1¼	24	24	2¾x3	13½	50c	5.40
1¼	26	24	2¾x3	15½	55c	5.95

Iron Clamp Head.

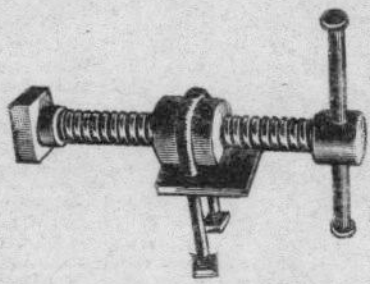

40303 With wrought-iron screw, single nut, iron handle; made only in three sizes.

Dia. of screw each—Inch	1	1⅛	1¼
Price	$0.65	.90	1 00

Stearn's New Door Frame Clamp.

40304 Stearn's new Door Frame Clamp. The jaws are mounted on maple bars, 1¼ x 1½ inches; 4 feet long: the loose jaw is very simply operated, being supported with a spring which holds it at any point required. The stationary jaw has a malleable iron thumb screw with a ball and socket joint, making an adjustable washer. It is unrivaled for ease and rapidity of adjustment, cheapness and strength. Each........$0.45
Per dozen.................. 4.86

Kerney & Foote and Arcade Files.

Our Files are unexcelled for evenness of temper, cutting qualities, durability and general excellence. They are used exclusively by all of the largest machine and railroad shops. This fact alone is worthy of consideration.

40305 Mill Files, no handle:

	Weight.	Each.	Per doz.
6 inch	6 oz.	$0.07	$0.70
8 inch	7 oz.	.10	.90
10 inch	10 oz.	.12	1.20
12 inch	16 oz.	.17	1.70
14 inch	31 ozs.	.25	2.45
16 inch	2 lbs.	.33	3.50
40306 Flat Bastard Files:			
4 inch	2 oz.	.07	.65
5 inch	4 oz.	.07	.70
6 inch	4 oz.	.08	.80
8 inch	7 oz.	.11	1.07
10 inch	12 oz.	.15	1.49
12 inch	1¼ lb.	.21	2.12
14 inch	29 oz.	.30	3 00
16 inch	39 oz.	.40	4.14

23—6th

Files—Continued.

40307 Round Bastard Files:

	Weight.	Each.	Per doz.
4 inch	2 oz.	$0.06	$0.57
5 inch	4 oz.	.07	.63
6 inch	5 oz.	.07	.72
8 inch	6 oz.	.10	.90
10 inch	8 oz.	.12	1.20
12 inch	12 oz.	.17	1.70
40308 Half Round Files, same shape as mill files.			
6 inch	4 oz.	.10	1.08
8 inch	8 oz.	.14	1.36
10 inch	11 oz.	.19	1.84
12 inch	18 oz.	.25	2.43

Taper Files.

40310 Taper or Saw Files, 3 square sides:

	Weight.	Each.	Per doz.
3 inch	2 oz.	$0.04	$0.36
4 inch	3 oz.	.04	.38
5 inch	4 oz.	.06	.54
6 inch	5 oz.	.08	.76
7 inch	6 oz.	.10	.95
8 inch	7 oz.	.12	1.20
40310½ Slim Taper Files:			
3 inch	2 oz	.04	.38
3½ inch	2 oz.	.04	.38
4 inch	3 oz.	.05	.42
4½ inch	3 oz.	.05	.46
5 inch	4 oz.	.06	.54
5½ inch	4 oz.	.06	.61
6 inch	4 oz.	.07	.67
7 inch	4 oz.	.08	.80
8 inch	6 oz	.10	.95

Taper Files.

40311 Stubbs' Taper Files:
An English hand-cut file of superior quality.

	Weight.	Each.	Per doz.
3 inch	3 oz.	$0.12	$1.30
3½ inch	3 oz.	.13	1.35
4 inch	3 oz.	.15	1.50
4½ inch	4 oz.	.19	2.10
5 inch	4 oz.	.22	2.35
6 inch	4 oz.	.25	2.65

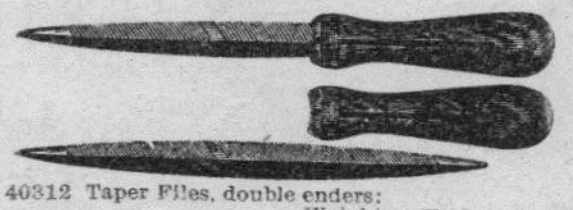

40312 Taper Files, double enders:

	Weight.	Each.	Per doz.
7 inch	2 oz.	$0.08	$0.80
8 inch	2 oz.	.09	.80
9 inch	3 oz.	.10	1.00
10 inch	4 oz.	.12	1.15

40313 Goodell Shoe File, made expressly for family use. It will readily clear any part of the shoe of nails and pegs. The file is made of the best quality of steel finely tempered and so attached to the shank as to make it adjustable to any position, or can be held stationary if desired. Price, each......15 cents Per dozen........$1.50

File Handles.

40314 File Handles, with brass ferrule, assorted sizes, suitable for files quoted above. Weight, 2 oz.
Each........$0.02 Per dozen............$0.22

Horse Rasps.

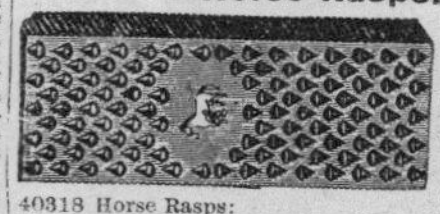

Cut by hand; can furnish either the Arcade, Disston's, or the Kerney & Foote makes at prices quoted, weight, 18 to 42 ounces.

40318 Horse Rasps:

Size	12 in.	14 in.	16 in.
Price, each	28c	40c	56c
Price, per dozen	$3.16	$4.32	$6.18

40319 Heller's Horse Rasps are cut by hand; acknowledged by all blacksmiths to be the best in use

Size	12 in.	14 in.	16 in
Price, each	32c	50c	65c
Price, per dozen	$3.60	$6 25	$7 20

Wood Rasps.

40320 Half Round

Size	6 in.	10 in.	12 in.	14 in.
Price, each	13c	28c	40c	54c
Price, per doz	$1.47	$3 07	$4.32	$5.93

File Cleaners.

40325 Colton's Patent File Cleaner, steel back and frame. This cleaner is the nicest finished and most durable in the market; comes with steel wire picker and without

	Each.	Per doz.
No. 1, without picker	$0.12	$1.30
No. 10, with picker	.15	1.62

File Cleaners—Continued.

40326 File Card and Brush, made for cleaning all kinds of files, rasps, etc.: weight, ½ lb. Each $0.35 Pr doz. $3.78

40327 Syracuse Short Wood Brace Drills, for dowels, casters, tire bolts, sugar bits, etc.; blades from 4 to 10, 2½ inches long, from 11 to 20, 4½ inches long. The numbers indicate the sizes in 32ds of an inch.

Sizes	4	4¼	4½	5	5¼	5½	6	6¼
Each	9c	9c	10c	10c	10c	12c	12c	12c
Sizes	6½	7	7¼	7½	8	8¼	8½	9
Each	15c	15c	15c	18c	18c	18c	20c	20c
Sizes	10	11	12	13	14	16	18	20
Each	20c	24c	24c	27c	27c	30c	33c	36c

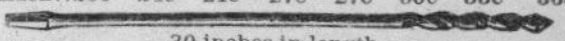

30 inches in length.

40328 Syracuse Long Wood Brace Drills, for bell hangers, telephone and telegraph work; they will go through plaster, nails, and even brick walls, and can be sharpened when dull; are 30 inches in length. The numbers indicate the sizes in 32ds of an inch.

Sizes	6	8	10	12	14	16	18	20	22
Each	65c	65c	72c	72c	78c	83c	89c	90c	95c
Sizes					24	26	28	30	32
Each					$1.00	$1.07	$1.13	$1.18	$1.20

Bit Boxes.

40329 Bartlett's Patent Bit Boxes. The best thing in the market for the purpose. Every mechanic, farmer or any one using auger bits should have one of these; a place for every bit and every bit in its place; made of hardwood, is strong and durable, holds 13 bits.
Price, each..........$0.35
Per doz............... 3.78

Auger Bits.

40330 C. E. Jenning's extra quality double spur auger bits.

Sizes	3-16	¼	5-16	⅜	7-16	½	9-16
Price, each	13c	12c	12c	13c	13c	13c	15c
Sizes	⅝	11-16	¾	13-16	⅞	15-16	1	1⅛
Each	16c	19c	21c	23c	25c	27c	31c	38c

40331 Price, per set of 15 bits.................$2.62
40332 Price, per set of 8 bits, 3-16, ¼, ⅜, ½, ⅝, ¾, ⅞, 1........................ 1.33

40333 Extra Cast Steel Auger Bits, double spur; sold by dealers everywhere as a first-class auger bit.

Sizes	3-16	¼	5-16	⅜	7-16	½	9-16	⅝	11-16
Price each	$0.10	09	.09	.09	09	.10	.11	.12.	.13
Per doz.	$0.95	.81	.81	.88	.98	.95	1.08	1.22	1.35

Sizes	¾	13-16	⅞	15.16	1	1⅛
Price, each	$0.14	$0.15	$0.17	$0.20	$0.21	$0.25
Price, per doz	1.49	1.62	1.76	1.96	2.16	2.70

AUGER BITS IN CANVAS ROLLS.

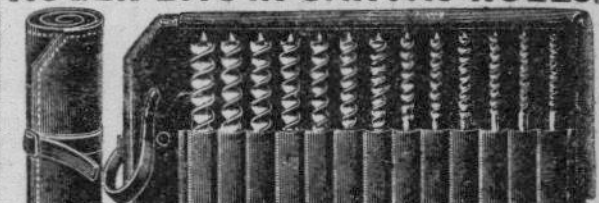

A very convenient method of keeping bits safe from injury, and a handy way for the mechanic to convey them wherever needed. The case is made of dark-colored canvas, nicely lined with canton flannel, having a receptacle for each bit. Shank and points protected by extra canvas. The case rolled up with bits complete, measures 3x11 inches. We positively cannot sell the case without the bits.
40334 With Jennings' patent extension lip bit 1 set of 13 bits (32¼ grs.) 1 each 3/16 to 16/16 inclusive. Price complete with case as shown in cut......$3.95
40335 With 40330 Bits. One set of 13 bits (32¼ grs.) with case.......... 2.80

Russell Jennings Auger Bits.

40337 Genuine Russell Jenning's Auger Bits.

Sizes	3-16	5-16	⅜	7-16	½	9-16	⅝
Each	19c	22c	25c	28c	30c	33c	35c
Sizes	11-16	¾	13-16	⅞	15-16	1 in
Each	40c	42c	45c	50c	55c	58c

40338 Russell Jennings' bits, sets of 7, viz; ¼, ⅜, ½, ⅝, ¾, ⅞, 1 in., complete.................. $2.75
40339 Russell Jennings' bits, full sets of 13, one each of every size. Packed in a patent three-section box 4.69

Bits—Continued.

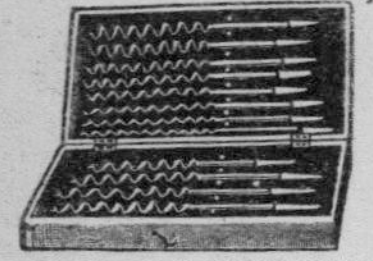

40344 C. E. Jennings' Extra Quality Double Spur Auger Bits, in sets, put up in handsome wood boxes with rack to hold each bit in place. This is a great convenience, as the bits can be put away immediately after using. These boxes alone are worth 50 cents.

The set consists of 13 bits of the following sizes: ¼, 5-16, ⅜, 7-16, ½, 9-16, ⅝, 11-16, ¾, 13-16, ⅞, 15-16 and 1 in. Price per set.................$2.65
Per doz. sets..27.54

40345 The Perfection Bit Set, Russell Jennings' pattern, not made by Russell Jennings but same pattern and considered just as good. Same number and same size as No. 40344 set, in nice wood box. Per set................................ 3.50

Cook's Patent Auger Bits.

40346 Cooks' Genuine Patent Auger Bits, single twist from ¼ to 7-16; double twist from ½ to 1 in.

Sizes..............	¼	5-16	⅜	7-16	½
Price each..........	16c	17c	18c	20c	22c
Sizes..............	9-16	⅝	11-16	¾	13-16
Price each	24c	27c	29c	32c	35c
Sizes..............	⅞	15-16	1		
Price each	40c	40c	43c.		

40347 Per set of 13 Cooks' Bits, without box....$3.24

Handy Home Set.

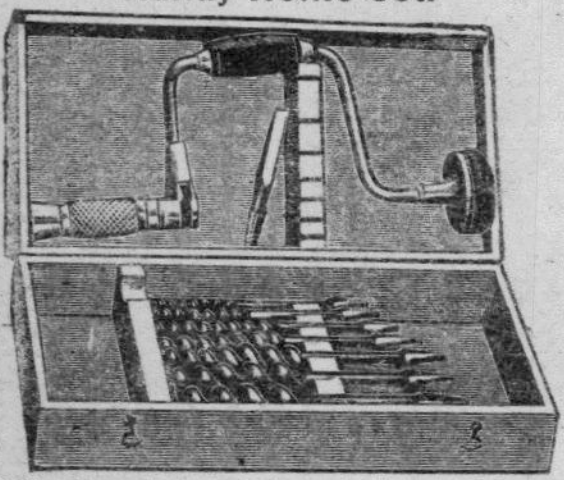

40348 Home Set, containing 1 Peck's 10-inch brace, 1 first quality auger bit of each of the following sizes: ¼, ⅜, ½, ⅝, ¾, ⅞, 1 inch, also 1 brace screw driver bit, put up in a nice wood box like cut. Price, complete, per set.......... $2.60

Ship Auger.

40349 L'Hommedieu Ship Auger Bits. 5 to 6 in twist.

Sizes	4-8 and under.					9-16	⅝
Price, each........	43c.					54c.	54c.
Sizes..........	11-16	¾	13-16	⅞	15-16	1	17-16
Price, each...	65c.	65c.	75c.	75c.	85c.	85c.	97c.
Sizes..........	18-16	19-16	1¼				
Price, each...	97c.	$1.08	$1.08				

40350 Price per set of 32½ quarters, 1 each, from 4 to 16-16ths (13 bits). Price per set...........$8.00

Expansive Bits.

Clark's "Pattern" Expansive Bit. It is made of steel and warranted; complete in three pieces. The spring cap formed by a cut separating, but detaching the face of the stock, secures important advantages. The shank is graduated for depth.

40352 Cuts from ½-inch to 1½-inch weight, 7 ounces Each.............................$1.00
40352½ Cuts from ⅞-inch to 3-inch weight, 12 ounces. Each..................................... 1.35

Expansive Bits have two cutters and can be made to cut any size between the sizes mentioned above by loosening the screw and sliding the bit in or out.

40353 EXTRA CUTTERS FOR BITS No. 40352 The No 1 and 2 are for bit 40352. The No. 3 and 4 are for bit 40352½.

No. 1 cuts from ½ to ⅞-inch. Each.............. .18
No. 2 cuts from ⅞ to 1½-inch. Each.............. .23
No. 3 cuts from ⅞ to 1¾-inch. Each.............. .32
No. 4 cuts from 1¾ to 3-inch. Each.............. .36

Steers' Patent Expansive Bit.

This bit is dropped-forged from selected cast steel, and is finished in a most thorough manner. The cutter is adjusted by means of a micrometer screw, which holds the cutter firmly, preventing any possibility of slipping or creeping.

40354½ No. 1, with 2 cutters, will cut any size from ⅞ to 3 inches. Price, each.................$1.45
40355 No. 2, with 2 cutters, will cut any size from ⅝ to 1¾ inches. Price, each............. 1.00

Bits—Continued.

40355½ Extra Cutters for Steers' Expansive Bits. The Nos. 1 and 2 are for the No. 2 Bit; the Nos. 3, 4, 5 are for the No. 1 Bit.

No. 1 cutter, cutting from ⅝ to 1⅛ in. Each..$0.18
No. 2 cutter, cutting from 1⅛ to 1¾ in. Each.. .23
No. 3 cutter, cutting from ⅞ to 1⅝ in. Each.. .32
No. 4 cutter, cutting from 1⅝ to 3 in. Each .36
No. 5 cutter, cutting from 3 to 4 in. Each.. .75

Center Bits.

40356 Center Bits, cast steel, polished.

Sizes....	⅜	½	⅝	¾	⅞	1	1¼	1½	1¾	2
Each..	5c.	5c.	5c.	5c.	5c.	6c.	8c.	10c.	15c.	19c.

Price, per set, 10 center bits...........................$0.80

Gimlet Bit.

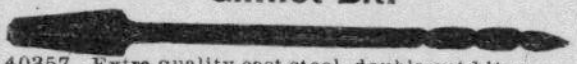

40357 Extra quality cast steel, double cut bits. State size wanted.

Sizes.............	0	1	2	3	4	5	6
Price, each......	3c.	3c.	3c.	3c.	3c.	3c.	3c.

40358 Price, per set of 7 bits, one of each size....$0.20

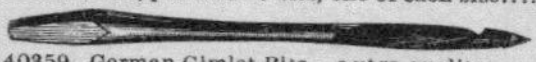

40359 German Gimlet Bits, extra quality.

Sizes.......	2-32	3-32	4-32	5-32	6-32	7-32	8-32	10-32
Price, each..	6c.	6c.	6c.	6c.	6c.	6c.	6c.	7c.
Price, doz.	60c.	60c.	60c.	60c.	60c.	60c.	60c.	70c.

40360 Price, per set of 7 bits, one of each size..$0.38
German Gimlet Bits, up to No. 4, weigh 4 ounces; from No. 5 to 8, 5 ounces; a set weighs 10 ounces. Sizes on German bits are given in 32ds of an inch.

The Forstner Bit.

40362 The Forstner Brace Bit, for smooth round, oval or square boring scroll and twist work.

Unlike other bits, it is guided by its periphery instead of its center. It will bore any arc or circle and can be guided in any direction regardless of grain or knots. Send for circular showing cuts of the work it will do and directions how to operate.

Sizes..........	⅜	7-16	4-8	9.16	⅝	11-16	6-8
Price, each...	40c.	50c.	50c.	62c.	62c.	70c.	72c.
Sizes........	13-16,	⅞,	15-16,	8-8	9-8	10-8,	11-8
Price, each,	80c.	83c.	90c.	95c.	$1.00	$1.04	$1.22

Ship Augur Pattern Car Bits.

40364 Ship Augur Pattern Car Bits, 12 inch twist designed especially for hard wood and rough boring, are very strong; designed for car, boat and bridge building. Same pattern as No. 40349.

Sizes.............	5-16	⅜	7-16	½
Price, each......	60c.	65c.	68c.	72c.
Sizes.............	9-16	⅝	11-16	¾
Price, each......	75c.	80c.	83c.	86c.
Sizes.............	13-16	⅞	15-16	1
Price, each......	90c.	93c.	95c.	$1.05
Sizes.............	17-16	1⅛	19-16	1¼
Price, each......	$1.10	$1.15	$1.22	$1.25

40365 Price per set 16 Ship Augur Pattern Car Bits. 12 inch twist, 1 each of the above size. Weight, 16 lbs.....................................$13.37

40367

Car Bits.

TWELVE INCH TWIST.

40367 C. E. Jennings' Double Spur Pattern Car Bits, 12 inch twist. These are not the poor, cheap articles sold ordinarily by retail dealers, but are extra quality, high grade, good tools.

Sizes,	¼,	5-16,	⅜,	7-16,	½,	9-16,	⅝,	11-16
Each,	26c.	26c.	30c.	36c.	41c.	45c.	51c.	52c.
Sizes,	¾,	13-16,	⅞,	15-16,	1,	17-16,		18-16
Each,	62c.	66c.	71c.	75c.	82c.	96c.		$1.08

40368 Price per set of 15 C. E. Jennings' car bits.. 7.80

Angular Boring Attachment.

40370 Angular Boring Attachment, fits any brace, nickel plated. Weight, 4¾ lbs.
Each...$1.20

Bit Gauge.

40375 This cut shows the gauge in all its parts. It will be seen that one bolt with thumb screw tightens the clamps on the gauge spindle and auger bit at the same time. It will fit any size bit and exactly gauge the depth of hole to be bored. Price, each, no bit.......................$0.25
Per dozen.. 2.70

Extra Quality Warranted Boring Machine Augers.

40376 Sizes.......	1	1¼	1½	2
Prices, each......	$0.40	$0.45	$0.55	$0.75

Carpenters' Augers.

40377 Augers, solid cast steel full polished shank brass nut, price includes handle. These augers are not a cheap grade, but warranted to be first-class tools.

Size..............			⅝ in.	¾ in.	⅞ in.	1 in.
Each..............			$0.25	$0.31	$0.33	$0.36
Size..	1⅛ in.	1¼ in.	1⅜ in.	2 in.	2¼ in.	2½ in
Each..	$0.44	$0.53	$0.65	$0.76	$0.86	$1.20

Adjustable Auger Handles.

40379 Will fit any size auger; very convenient as but one handle is required to a full set of augers. No carpenter's tool chest is complete without one. Weight, about one pound. Price, each.....$0.18 Per dozen.....$1.95

Auger Handles.

Pratt's Ratchet Auger Handle, a new and very convenient tool. Directions: Open the chuck wide enough to admit the auger shank with the nut on it; when the nut sinks into the cavity of the jaws, turn up the sleeves until it is tight.

It ratchets with one handle or both, or may be used without the ratchet; it also answers for a ratchet drill stock for square shank drills, by unscrewing the handle from one side and screwing it into the top. It is not accompanied by three handles, as shown in the cut, but is illustrated this way to show that handles unscrew and how a ratchet drill may be made of it. Carpenters will find this the most useful tool that has yet been invented.

40380 Weight, 3 lbs.
Each..$1.75

Angular Boring Machines.

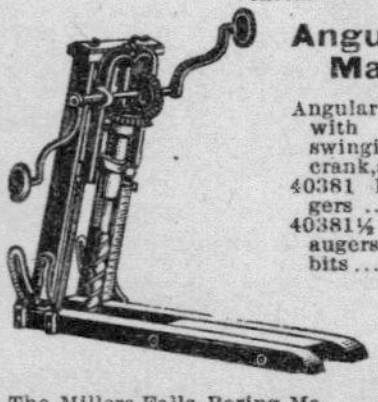

Angular Boring Machines with graduated ways, swinging rack, malleable crank, augers and pointer.
40381 Price without augers $3.00
40381½ Price, with set of augers, 1, 1½ and 2 inch bits....................$4.80

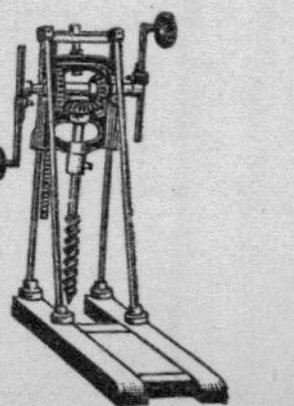

The Millers Falls Boring Machines. This machine has been fully perfected in all its parts and is now sold with full warrant that it will do better work and give better satisfaction than any other kind in use; the frame is made of one-half inch round steel rods; the braces are the same as attached to the rods at the top by a set-screw; when this set-screw is loosened the frame falls over so as to bore at any desired angle.
Weight, 42¼ lbs.

40382 Price, each, without augers......................$6.50
40382½ With 1, 1½, 2-in. augers................... 8.25

Patent Adjustable Hollow Augers.

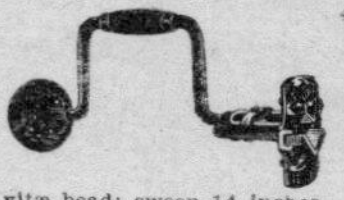

40383 Goodell's Patent Adjustable Hollow Auger. This auger is an improvement on anything hitherto in use, as it has fitted to it a nickel plated bit brace sweep, with rosewood handle and lignum vitæ head; sweep 14 inches. As the brace sweep is fitted to it, it will always work true, which is not the case when the ordinary kind is used in an ordinary bit brace; besides, it often happens that the bit brace on hand is not large enough to drive a spoke auger. The auger is adjustable to cut from ¼ to 1¼ inch.
Price, each, complete with sweep $3.42

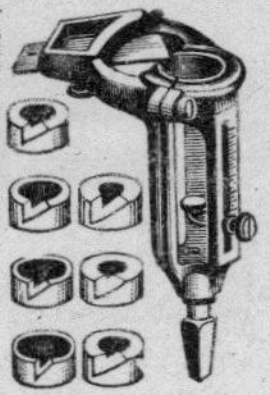

40384 Stearn's Patent Adjustable Hollow Auger, made of maleable iron, and nicely finished. The knife is made of the best tool steel, has adjustable stop, with scale for regulating length of tenon. It cuts eight sizes, as follows: ⅜, 7-16, ½, 9-16, ⅝, ¾, ⅞ and 1 inch. Weight, 1 lb. 9 oz. No. 1, complete $3.00

40385 Made entirely of malleable iron and steel; has adjustable stop and scale with rulings to sixteenths for length, also graduated strap to indicate the diameter of tenon. The jaws or sides are pivoted and are opened and closed by means of a conical nut upon the shank. Cuts any sized tenons, ⅜ to 1 inch and 3 inches in length. Price, each....$3.00

40386 Stearn's Patent Adjustable Hollow Auger No. 3; cuts any size tenon from ¼ to 1¼. The pivoted jaws are provided with a graduated scale by which the size of the tenon is regulated. To secure required length of tenon, a movable stop is operated upon a graduated scale with rulings to sixteenths. This is the finest tool of the kind made.
Each..........................$3.75

40387 Stearn's Patent Hollow Augers, cutting but one size. The only single size of Hollow auger in which the length of tenon is regulated by an adjustable stop and graded scale.

The patent adjustable cap and knife enables the user to overcome any slight variation in size of bits. (No bit furnished.)

Size.	Weight.	Each.	Size.	Weight.	Each.
5-16 in.	12 oz.	$0.52	¾ in.	18 oz.	$0.58
⅜ in.	12 oz.	.52	⅞ in.	18 oz.	.84
7-16 in.	12 oz.	.52	1 in.	18 oz.	.84
½ in.	12 oz.	.52	1⅛ in.	23 oz.	.90
9-16 in.	12 oz.	.58	1¼ in.	23 oz.	.90
⅝ in.	15 oz.	.58	1⅜ in.	23 oz.	1.00
			1½ in.	32 oz.	1.00

Spoke Pointers.

Stearn's Patent Spoke Pointer with graduated adjustable shank. Points 1⅜ inches in diameter.

40388 No. 1, weight, 12 oz. Each..............$0.58
40388½ No. 2, weight, 16 oz. (large). Each.... .97

Drills.

Drills and bits weigh from 5 to 9 ounces, according to size.

40390 Syracuse Twist Drills, for hardwood; will cut through a nail in boring without injuring. The bits are tempered so they will bore iron and stone equally as well as wood.

Sizes	⅛	5/32	3/16	7/32	¼	9/32	5/16	11/32
Each, in cents	10	11	12	15	18	21	22	24
Sizes	⅜	13/32	7/16	15/32	½			
Each, in cents	25	27	28	29	30			

Price per set 13 Drills, 1 each of the above size..........................$2.58

Drills—Continued.

40392 Twist Drills, for Bit Brace. They work in wood or metal.

Sizes	1/16	3/32	⅛	5/32	3/16	7/32	¼	9/32	5/16	11/32
Each	$0.06	6	8	10	12	14	15	18	20	24
Sizes	⅜	13/32	7/16	15/32	½					
Each	$0.27	30	33	36	40					

40393 Set of 15 drills, 1 each of the above......$2.65

ROUND SHANK DRILLS.

40395 Twist Drill, round shank: for drill machine for wood or metal: shank ½ inch in diameter, 2½ inches long.

Sizes	⅛	5/32	3/16	7/32	¼	9/32	5/16	11/32	⅜	13/32
Each	$0.21	22	23	25	27	30	32	34	35	37
Sizes	7/16	15/32	½	17/32	9/16	19/32	⅝	21/32		
Each	$0.38	41	42	44	46	48	50	52		
Sizes	11/16	23/32	¾	25/32	13/16	27/32				
Each	$0.53	54	57	60	65	70				
Sizes	⅞	29/32	15/16	31/32	1 inch.					
Each	$0.73	75	80	85	90					

40396 Straight Fluted Drills, for drill machines, ½ inch round shank; the best drill made for blacksmiths' and brass workers' use; no blacksmith should be without a set of these drills; made of the finest steel.

Diameter.	Length.	Price, each.
⅛ inch.	4⅝ inch.	$0.25
5/32 inch.	4⅞ inch.	.25
3/16 inch.	5⅝ inch.	.25
7/32 inch.	5⅝ inch.	.28
¼ inch.	6 inch.	.30
9/32 inch.	6 inch.	.33
5/16 inch.	6 inch.	.35
11/32 inch.	6 inch.	.38
⅜ inch.	6 inch.	.40
13/32 inch.	6 inch.	.41
7/16 inch.	6 inch.	.42
15/32 inch.	6 inch.	.43
½ inch.	6 inch.	.44
17/32 inch.	6 inch.	.45
9/16 inch.	6 inch.	.46
19/32 inch.	6 inch.	.48
⅝ inch.	6 inch.	.55
21/32 inch.	6 inch.	.58
11/16 inch.	6 inch.	.59
23/32 inch.	6 inch.	.60
¾ inch.	6 inch.	.63
25/32 inch.	6 inch.	.65
13/16 inch.	6 inch.	.68
27/32 inch.	6 inch.	.70
⅞ inch.	6 inch.	.73
29/32 inch.	6 inch.	.75
15/16 inch.	6 inch.	.80
31/32 inch.	6 inch.	.85
1 inch.	6 inch.	.90

The above drills have shanks 2¼ inches long and ½ inch diameter.

Increase Twist Drills for machinists' use. We guarantee our drills to be equal in quality and workmanship with the best made in the world.

Jobbers' Drills.

40397--

JOBBERS' AND MACHINISTS' SETS.

Diameter.	Length.	Price per Dozen.	Price, each.
1/16	2½	$0.50	$0.05
5/64	2⅝	.55	.06
3/32	2¾	.60	.06
7/64	2⅞	.65	.07
⅛	3	.73	.08
9/64	3⅛	.80	.09
5/32	3¼	.90	.10
11/64	3⅜	1.00	.11
3/16	3½	1.10	.12
13/64	3⅝	1.20	.13
7/32	3¾	1.33	.15
15/64	3⅞	1.45	.16
¼	4	1.58	.18
17/64	4⅛	1.70	.19
9/32	4¼	1.83	.20
19/64	4⅜	1.95	21
5/16	4½	2.10	.22
21/64	4⅝	2.25	.23
11/32	4¾	2.40	.25
23/64	4⅞	2.55	.27
⅜	5	2.70	.28
25/64	5⅛	2.85	.30
13/32	5¼	3.00	.32
27/64	5⅜	3.20	.34
7/16	5½	3.40	.36
29/64	5⅝	3.60	.40
15/32	5¾	3.75	.42
31/64	5⅞	3.88	.44
½	6	4.00	.45

*** Our next Catalogue will be sent only to those who send us 15 cents for postage.*

Taper Square Shank Drills Fitting Ratchets.

40400

Price with Shanks ⅝ inch by ⅜ inch and 1½ inches long, and Shanks ¾ inch by ½ inch and 1¾ inches long.

Diameter.	Length.	Price, each.
¼ inch.	5 inch.	$0.65
9/32 inch.	5 inch.	.68
5/16 inch.	5 inch.	.75
11/32 inch.	5 inch.	.78
⅜ inch.	6 inch.	.80
13/32 inch.	6¼ inch.	.83
7/16 inch.	6¼ inch.	.83
15/32 inch.	6¼ inch.	.83
½ inch.	6½ inch.	.87
9/16 inch.	6½ inch.	.90
⅝ inch.	6½ inch.	.95
11/16 inch.	6½ inch.	.97
¾ inch.	6½ inch.	1.00
13/16 inch.	7 inch	1.17
⅞ inch.	7½ inch.	1.37
15/16 inch.	8 inch.	1.53
1 inch.	8½ inch.	1.70
1⅛ inch.	9 inch.	2.10

Improved Drill Chuck.

40401

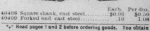

This Chuck has no projections. The jaws and screws are all within the body. The jaws are of the best tool steel carefully hardened.

A guard ring prevents the jaws from being opened so as to take in larger work than is designed for the Chuck. It is very powerful, and guaranteed to hold true and not to injure or shear the finest drill. It holds round or square work, and there is no chuck equal to it for holding wood-boring tools.

The jaws are guided by three strong gibs, which prevent their canting when taking a short bit.

PRICES OF LITTLE GIANT IMPROVED.

Number.	Holding Drills.	Price each.
0	0 to ¼ inch.	$4.00
1	0 to ¾ inch.	5.00
2	0 to 1 inch.	6.50

Machinist Hand Taps.

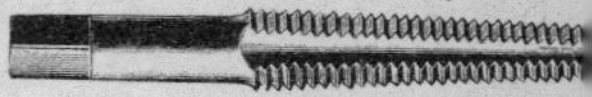

Taper Tap.

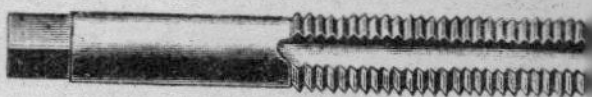

Plug Tap.

40404 Made standard sizes with standard V thread right hand.

Diameter.	Number of Threads to the Inch.	Price each.
¼	16, 18 and 20	$0.22
5/16	16 " 18	.23
⅜	14, 16 " 18	.25
7/16	14 " 16	.26
½	12, 13 " 14	.32
⅝	10, 11 " 12	.42
¾	10 " 12	.55
⅞	9 " 10	.76
1	8	.95

Gimlets.

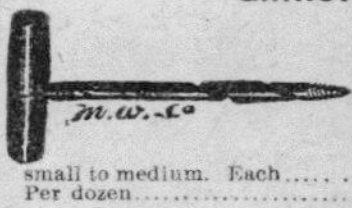

40405 Gimlets, rosewood handles, assorted sizes.
Each..........$0.07
Per dozen...... .78
Weight, 4 oz. each.

40406 Gimlets, cast steel, metal heads, small to medium. Each.....................$0.02
Per dozen.......................... .17

Screw Driver Bits.

	Each.	Per doz.
40408 Square shank, cast steel	$0.06	$0.50
40409 Forked end cast steel	.10	1.08

*** Read pages 1 and 2 before ordering goods. You obtain a discount by sending money with order. Send money by Express, Draft on Chicago or New York, Post Office Money Order, or Registered Mail.*

Reamers.

                Each.   Per doz.

40413 Reamers, square, extra cast steel $0.09 $1.00

40414 Reamers, octagon, extra cast steel .. .12   1.25

40416 The Taper Reamers for wood or iron. These reamers are made of the finest steel and will make true, smooth holes for bit braces.
Sizes, ¼ 5-16 ⅜ 7-16 ½ 9-19 ⅝ 11-13 ¾
Each. 27c. 30c. 33c. 36c. 42c. 48c. 54c. 64c. 72c

Countersinks.

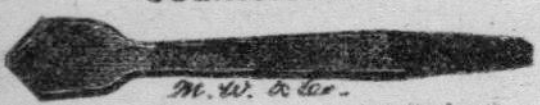

40420 Countersinks, flat, extra cast steel, polished, for metal. Each $0.08
    Per dozen .... .87

40421 Countersinks, extra cast steel. Each $0.08
    Per doz .. .87

40425 Wheeler Countersink, for wood, with gauge.
    Each $0.23
    Per dozen 2.50

40426 Clark's Patent Double-cut Countersink, makes the smoothest work of anything sold; can be kept as sharp as a plane; cuts show it closed for service and open for sharpening. Weight, 5 ounces.
    Each $0.25
    Per dozen 2.70

Prick Punches.

40430 Prick Punches, made of ⅜ octagon steel; weight, 5 ounces. Price, each $0.07
    Per dozen .... .75

Whitney Geared Hand Drill.

40435 Whitney's Geared hand drill for machinists, metal workers, jewelers, and ornamental workers with new tempered improved twist drills.

Six tempered drills, 1-33 to 5-16 in. round size. Each set packed in a hardwood box, with brass hinges and catch, weight, 1¼ lbs. Each $0.75
    Per dozen 8.10

40436 Extra drills, per set of 6 drills .... .12

Hand Drills.

40437 The No. 1 hand drill, single gear, hollow, handle jaws, made of forged steel; complete, with six drill points. Each $1.10
40438 Extra drill per set .... .25

40439 The No. 2 hand drill. The chuck of the drill stock is the same as No. 1. It has cut gears, is heavily nickel plated, and contains six drill points. It is a tool much in demand. Price, each $2.20
40440 Extra drills per set .... .25

with rosewood head and handle. The head is hollow

Hand Drills—Continued.

40441 The No. 4 hand drill stock is 8 inches in length and weighs 8 ounces. It is made of iron with rosewood handle, and chuck for holding the drill points. The chuck is made on a new plan, and it centers and holds the drill perfectly. With each drill stock we send a box containing six superior drill points of various sizes.
    Price, each $0.45
    Per dozen 4.95
40442 Extra drills per set .... .25

Lightning Brace.

Lightning Brace, nickel plated, lignum vitæ and rosewood trimmings, is especially designed for light boring and screw driving; it may be used running the bit back and forward or turn the bit only one way, as it is necessary; the movements are regulated by the head; very rapid in its work; strong and durable.
40445 Like cut $1.40
40446 Small size, principle same as 40445 .... 1.15

Automatic Hand Drills.

40450 Automatic Hand Drill, designed for boring wood, for setting brads, finishing nails, screws, etc. Eight bits or drills, the size of which are indicated by the dots in the above cut, accompanying each tool. Price, each ... $1.15
40451 Extra Points, 8 cents each.

40452 Moodell's Automatic Drills, made of brass, nickel plated, with 8 drill points complete. The drill points are all contained in the handle, the exact location of each is designated by a number on the outside of handle. To remove the drill press slightly upon the pin which fills the hole from which the drill points are taken out; the cap can be taken backwards or forwards until the hole is opposite the desired number, then the point can readily be removed.
    Price, each, complete $1.30
40453 Extra Points, 8 cents each.

Combination Tools.

40458 The handle is cocobolo, a handsome hardwood, resembling rosewood. The tools consist of a chisel, gouge, screw driver, tack puller, gimlet, scratch awl and four brad awls, different sizes, all solid steel, hand forged, of good size, the most practicable and serviceable tool of its kind offered; weight, 9 ounces. Each $0.40
    Per dozen 4.50

Crispin's Awls.

40459 This is a tool for everybody. It is a hollow handle made of hardwood, 5 inches long and weighing 3 ounces. It contains inside, on a spool, 50 feet of best waxed linen shoe thread. The spool is also hollow and contains 3 awls and 3 needles of various shapes and sizes. The thread fits the needles and the awls fit the handle, and are held by a set screw, as seen in the cut. It is for use in the house, stable, field, camp, or on the road, for making immediate repairs, where one use of it will be worth more than its whole cost. Weight, 6 ounces.
    Each $0.22

Our claim that this Catalogue opens the large markets to you is not idle boast. Where else can you find so much? As a genuine guide to prices it has no equal.

Breast Drill.

40460 Breast Drill. This is a very powerful drill; the breast plate is 15 inches long, has very heavy cut gears speeded about two to one and double cranks which are adjustable to any length, the hole in the spindle which receives the drill is ½ inch in diameter; weight, 3½ pounds. See 40395 and 40396 for bits to fit this machine.
    Price $4.25

40461 Geared Breast Drill. *With Peck's Patent Adjustable Chuck.* Nickel plated with cut gears. Rosewood handles and adjustable steel jaws, which will hold equally well; round and square shank boring instruments in every size. Weight, 4 lbs. Price $2.75

40462 Breast Drill. This drill is made of round wrought iron ⅝ of inch in diameter. The handles are rosewood, the head, malleable iron, and the chuck jaws of steel. It has a changeable gear, one even and the other speeded 3 to 1. The change from one to the other can be made in one second. The chuck will hold any shaped shank, round, square or flat, as seen in the cut. It has been improved lately with what is called second grip; after the nut has been screwed down on the bit, as tight as can be done by hand, grasp the nut firmly with the left hand and give the crank a turn from you; this forces the jaws upward, increasing the power of the grip. Weight, 4½ pounds.

☞ These tools are not sold with the drill stock, but are illustrated simply to show the shape of the shank which the chuck will hold.

Drill stock is heavily nickel plated and has cut gear. An extra set of steel jaws goes with each drill stock for holding small round drills. Price $2.50

40463—Drill and Ratchet Brace; combining the regular bit brace and breast drill. Drill detached, nickel plated, 10 in. sweep.
    Price $2.30

Ratchet Bit Braces.

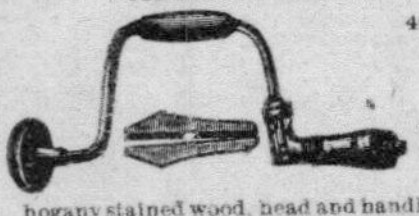

40465 First-class goods in every respect and fully guaranteed to be equal to the very best made; the sweeps, jaws and ratchet are steel. Mahogany stained wood, head and handle; all metal parts are nickel-plated, hard jaws with cam ring to operate the jaws; will take any same bit or bolt shank. 8 inch. Each $1.00
    10 inch 1.10
    12 inch 1.20

40466 *These Ratchet Bit Braces* are the same as No. 40465, except that they are plain polished, and not nickel plated; head and handle black enameled wood, with every part durable and reliable. 8 inch. Each $0.75
    10 inch .... .80
    12 inch .... .85

40467 These Ratchet Braces are not unlike in appearance and finish to No. 40465, but the jaws and socket are not milled. It makes a most excellent brace for farmers to use; made only in 2 sizes. 8 inch sweep. Each $0.60
    9-inch sweep .... .65
    8-inch sweep, nickel plated .... .70
    9-inch sweep, nickel plated .... .75

Bit Braces—Continued.

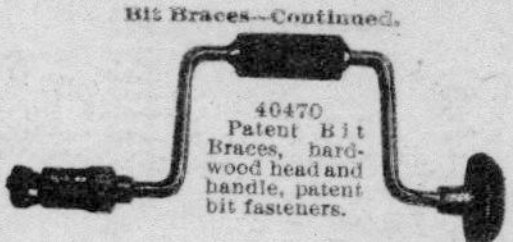

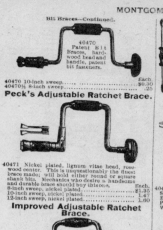

40470 Patent Bit Braces, hardwood head and handle, patent bit fasteners.

	Each.
40470 10-inch sweep	$0.30
40470½ 8-inch sweep	.25

Peck's Adjustable Ratchet Brace.

40471 Nickel plated, lignum vitae head, rosewood center. This is unquestionably the finest brace made; will hold either round or square shank bits. Mechanics who desire a handsome and durable brace should buy this one.

	Each.
8-inch sweep, nickel plated	$1.35
10-inch sweep, nickel plated	1.47
12-inch sweep, nickel plated	1.60

Improved Adjustable Ratchet Brace.

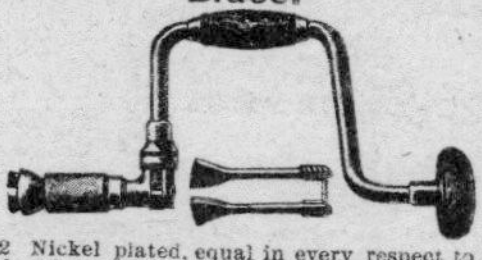

40472 Nickel plated, equal in every respect to the best brace made. It has internal cam ring to operate the pawls. Mechanics who buy this brace will never regret it.

8-inch. Each	$1.20
10-inch. Each	1.30
12-inch. Each	1.45

Barber's Bit Braces.

Barber's Patent Brace, rolled steel sweep, rosewood handle, lignum vitae head; nickel plated. Each.
40473 14-inch sweep $1.25
40474 Bit Brace, not so high priced as Barber's, but a very good brace. Same description as Barber's. 12-inch sweep .... .80

40475 Spafford's Brace, cocobolo wood; head and revolving handle, nickel plated. 10-inch sweep Price, each..$1.25

Rachet Brace, nickel plated and handsomely trimmed; new patent chuck sweep, and jaws are steel.

40476 10 in. sweep $0.90
40477 12 in. sweep 1.00

Nail Sets.

Weight, about 4 ounces.
40480. Nail set, solid cast steel, round common. Each .... $0.04. Per doz $0.38

40481 Cannon's Diamond Point Nail Sets, made of the finest steel and pointed on nail end, which prevents slipping off nail head. Each, 8c. Per dozen $0.87

40482 Hunter's Cup Point Nail Set; will set at any angle, and not split the head. Screws with worn or broken heads easily backed out with this set. Price....$0.06. Per dozen $0.65

Bench Screws.

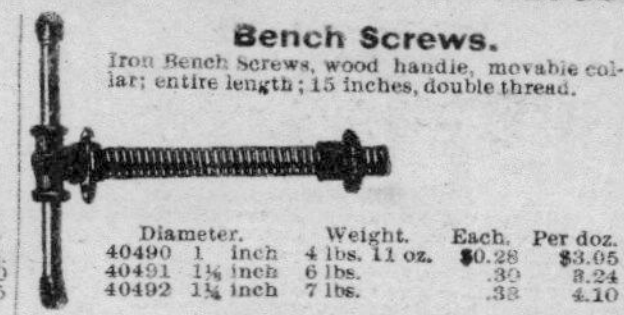

Iron Bench Screws, wood handle, movable collar; entire length; 15 inches, double thread.

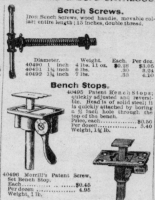

	Diameter.	Weight.	Each.	Per doz.
40490	1 inch	4 lbs. 11 oz.	$0.28	$3.05
40491	1¼ inch	6 lbs.	.30	3.24
40492	1½ inch	7 lbs.	.38	4.10

Bench Stops.

40495 Patent Bench Stops; quickly adjusted and reversible. Head is of solid steel; it is quickly attached by boring a ⅝ inch hole through the top of the bench.
Price, each $0.50
Per dozen 5.40
Weight, 1¼ lb.

40496 Morrill's Patent Screw, Set Bench Stop.
Each $0.45
Per dozen 4.95
Weight, 1 lb.

40497 Bench Stop; reversible double faced cast steel hook
Each $0.32
Weight, 1 lb.

Chiseis.

The weights of chisels graduate from 8 oz. to 39 oz., according to length and width.

40550 Merrill & Wilders' Extra Socket Firmer Chisels; solid cast steel; fully warranted to be perfect, so far as material and workmanship are concerned. Put up in sets in fancy wood box, 12 chisels in a set. ⅛, ¼, ⅜, ½, ⅝, ¾, ⅞, 1, 1¼, 1½, 1¾ and 2 inch, sharpened ready for use. Weight, 8½ pounds. Per set of 12 .... $4.00

40551 Swan's Socket Firmer Chisels, beveled edges, sharpened and honed ready for use; *fully warranted;* put up in hardwood box. 12 chisels to set, from ⅛ to 2 inch. An important feature of this set is the handles, which have an iron ferrule inserted in the end of all except the two smaller sizes; this prevents their splitting and makes them practically indestructible. Price, per set 4.67

40552 Merrill & Wilders' Extra Socket Firmer Chisels, beveled edges, solid cast steel polished, applewood handles, in sets of 12 chisels in wood boxes, same as No. 40550. For a fine tool this chisel is unexcelled, and the bevel edges add greatly to their appearance and cutting qualities 12 chisels: ⅛, ¼, ⅜, ½, ⅝, ¾, ⅞, 1, 1¼, 1½, 1¾ and 2 inch, sharpened ready for use. Weight, 7¾ pounds. Price, per set of 12 .... 4.50

40553 Socket Firmer Chisels (price includes handles). These chisels are of the very best make, and we guarantee them to give satisfaction.

Sizes	¼ in.	⅜ in.	½ in.	⅝ in.	¾ in.	⅞ in.
Price, each	20c	20c	21c	23c	25c	27c
Sizes	1 in.	1¼ in.	1½ in.	1¾ in.	2 in.	
Price, each	30c	33c	35c	38c	40c	

40554 Price per set of 11 socket firmer chisels, one of each size $3.00

***** Freight Rates from Chicago to nearly any railroad point in America will be quoted upon application. If you have any particular class of goods in view mention same when writing. We want you to know what your goods will cost you delivered at your station, as near as possible.**

Beveled Edge Chisels.

40555 Socket Firmer Chisel, beveled edge (price includes handles), These are high grade tools, made in the best manner of the best materials.

Size	⅛	¼	⅜	½	⅝	¾	⅞
Price, each	30c	30c	30c	32c	38c	41c	42c
Size	1	1¼	1½	1¾	2		
Price, each	45c	48c	53c	56c	80c		

40557 Price, per set of 12, Beveled Edge, Socket Firmer Chisels, one of each size. Weight, 5¼ lbs $4.28

Socket Framing Chisels.

40560 Framing Chisels, socket handles (price including handles).

Size, ¼ in.	$0.28	Size, 1 in	$0.36	Size, 1¾ in.	$0.53
Size, ½ in.	.30	Size, 1¼ in.	.40	Size, 2 in.	.55
Size, ¾ in.	.32	Size, 1½ in.	.45		

Corner Chisels.

40561 Corner Chisels, socket handles.

Size	¾ in.	1 in.	1¼ in.
Each	$0.63	$0.75	$0.82

Carpenters' Slick.

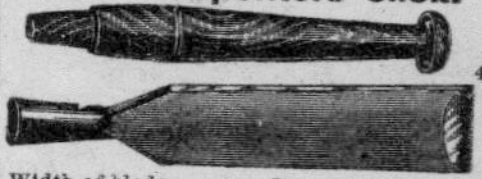

40562—Socket Slicks, best cast steel blade.

Width of blade	2½	3	3½	4
Price each	$0.85	$0.93	$1.10	$1.27

Barton's Chisels and Gouges.

40564 Barton's Millwright Socket Firmer Chisels. 8 in. heavy solid cast steel blades, with hickory handle.

Sizes	¼	⅜	½	⅝	¾
Each	$0.56	$0.62	$0.65	$0.68	$0.72
Sizes	1	1¼	1½	1¾	2
Each	$0.75	$0.85	$0.97	$1.12	$1.32

40565 Price per set of Barton's Millwright Socket Firmer Chisels, from ¼ to 2 in.; 9 chisels, one of each, ¼, ⅜, ½, ⅝, ¾, 1, 1¼, 1½ and 2 in. $7.50

40566 Barton's Millwright Socket Firmer Chisels, with 10 inch heavy cast steel blades, with hickory handles.

Sizes	⅛	¼	⅜	½	⅝	¾
Price, each	$0.68	$0.68	$0.72	$0.75	$.78	$0.82
	⅞	1	1¼	1½	1¾	2
	$0.88	$0.92	$1.00	$1.10	$1.35	$1.57

40567 Price per set of Barton's Millwright Socket Firmer Ghisels, with 10 inch blades. from ⅛ to 2 inch. 12 chisels $11.25

40568 Barton's Millwright Socket Firmer Gouges, 8 in., heavy solid cast steel blades, with hickory handles, inside bevel.

Sizes	¼	⅜	½	⅝	¾
Each	$0.62	$0.65	$0.70	$0.75	$0.80
Sizes	1	1¼	1½	1¾	2
Each	$0.88	$0.95	$1.06	$1.10	$1.50

40569 Price per set of Barton's Millwright Socket Firmer Gouges, from ¼ to 2 in.; 10 Gouges, one of each size $9.34
Weight, 12½ lbs.

Barton's Paring Chisels.

40572 Barton's Long Paring Socket Firmer Chisels, 10 blades, with apple wood handles.

Sizes	⅛	¼	⅜	½	⅝	¾	⅞
Each	$0.58	$0.72	$0.75	$0.80	$0.85	$0.90	$0.98
Sizes	1	1¼	1½	1¾	2		
Price, each	$1.05	$1.13	$1.20	$1.31	$1.42		

40573 Price per set of Barton's Long Paring Socket Firmer Chisels, with 10 inch blades from ⅛ to 2 inches, 12 chisels $11.42

40574 Barton's Socket Firmer Chisels, solid cast steel, 6½ inch blades, apple wood handles, in sets of 12 chisels, in the following sizes; ⅛, ¼, ⅜, ½, ⅝, ¾, ⅞, 1, 1¼, 1½, 1¾ and 2 in.; weight, 11½ lbs. Per set (we do not sell less than a set) $5.13

Buck's Chisels.

40580 Buck's Tanged Firmer Chisels. The 1 in. size is 5½ in. long from bolster to cutting edge; the rest in proportion. *Complete with apple wood handles,* Ground sharp and honed.

Sizes	⅛	3/16	¼	5/16	⅜
Each	$0.17	$0.18	$0.19	$0.20	$0.21
Sizes	½	⅝	¾	⅞	1
Each	$0.22	$0.24	$0.26	$0.29	$0.30
Sizes	1¼	1½	1¾	2	
Each	$0.40	$0.46	$0.57	$0.59	

40581 Price per set of Buck's Tanged Firmer Chisels, complete with handles, ground sharp and honed, 12 chisels, assorted, from ⅛ to 2; by eighths. Price per set $4.00

Chisels—Continued.

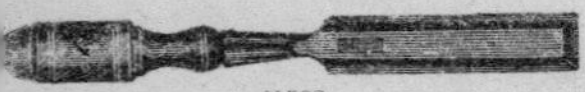

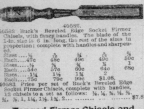

40582.

40582 Buck's Beveled Edge Socket Firmer Chisels, with fancy handles. The blade of the 1-in. size is 6 in. long, the rest of the sizes in proportion; complete with handles and sharpened.

Sizes	⅛	3/16	¼	5/16	⅜
Each	47c	48c	49c	49c	50c
Sizes	½	⅝	¾	⅞	1
Each	54c	57c	60c	64c	68c
Sizes	1¼	1½	1¾	2	
Each	75c	79c	99c	$1.08	

40583 Price per set of Buck's Beveled Edge Socket Firmer Chisels, complete with handles, 12 chisels to a set as follows: ⅛, ¼, ⅜, ½, ⅝, ¾, ⅞, 1, 1¼, 1½, 1¾, 2 .... $7.87

Tanged Firmer Chisels and Gouges.

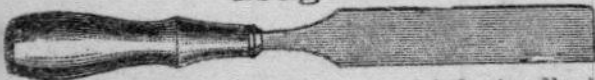

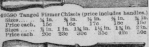

40590 Tanged Firmer Chisels (price includes handles.)

Sizes	¼ in.	⅜ in.	½ in.	⅝ in.	¾ in.	
Price each	15c	16c	17c	18c	19c	
Sizes	⅞ in.	1 in.	1¼ in.	1½ in.	1¾ in.	2 in.
Price each	20c	23c	30c	35c	42c	50c

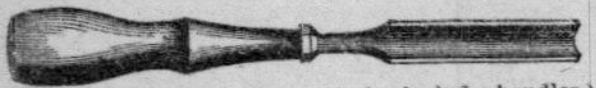

40591 Tanged Firmer Gouges (price includes handles.) Extra quality warranted.

Sizes	¼ in.	⅜ in.	½ in.	⅝ in.	¾ in.	
Price each	18c	19c	20c	21c	22c	
Sizes	⅞ in.	1 in.	1¼ in.	1½	1¾ in.	2 in.
Price each	23c	28c	35c	43c	55c	65c

Turning Chisels and Gouges.

40595 Butchers' Turning Chisels, solid cast steel. Price does not include handle.

Size		¼	⅜	½	⅝	¾
Price, each		15c	15c	18c	21c	23c
Sizes	⅞	1	1¼	1½	1¾	2
Price each	28c	32c	41c	52c	63c	75c

40596 Price, per set of 12 Butcher's Solid Cast Steel Turning Chisels, from ¼ to 2 in., one of each size $3.74

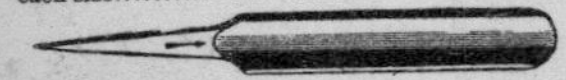

40597 Butcher's Turning Gouges, solid cast steel. Price does not include handles.

Sizes	¼	⅜	½	⅝	¾	⅞
Price each	22c	25c	27c	30c	35c	40c
Sizes	1	1¼	1½	1¾	2	
Price each	45c	58c	75c	88c	$1.08	

40598 Price per set of 11 Butcher's Solid Cast Steel Turning Gouges, from ¼ to 2 inches, one of each size $4.98

Carving Tools.

Order No. 40600.

Addis' Pattern Carving Tools, made of the best English steel and are the equal of any made. These are not amateur tools but are for professional carvers', carpenters' and wood workers' use generally. No carpenter shop should be without this set of tools. We do not furnish handles at this price. For price of Carving Tool Handles, see No. 40601.

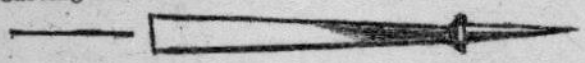

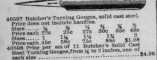

Carving Tool No. 1 Pattern Straight Chisel, ¼ to ½ in. Price each $0.20

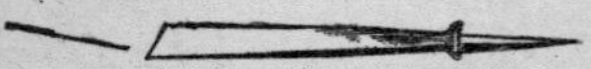

Carving Tool No. 2 Pattern Skew Chisel, ¼ to ½ in. Price each .... $0.2[illegible]

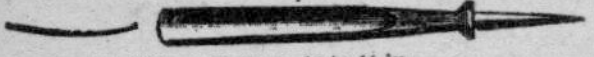

Carving Tool No. 4 Pattern, ¼ to ½ in. Price each .... $0.2[illegible]

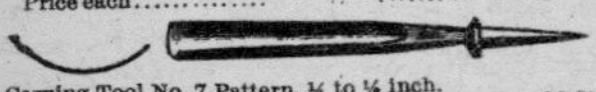

Carving Tool No. 7 Pattern, ¼ to ½ inch. Price each .... $0.2[illegible]

Carving Tool No. 8 Pattern, ¼ to ½ in. Price each $0.25

We supply the best standard books at regular jobbers' prices.

Carving Tools—Continued.

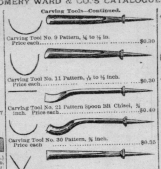

Carving Tool No. 9 Pattern, ¼ to ½ in. Price each $0.30

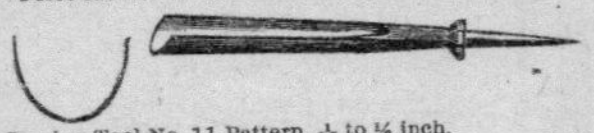

Carving Tool No. 11 Pattern, 1/16 to ⅛ inch. Price each $0.30

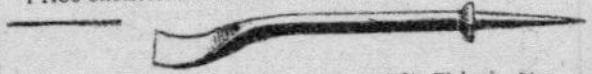

Carving Tool No. 21 Pattern Spoon Bit Chisel, ⅜ inch. Price each $0.40

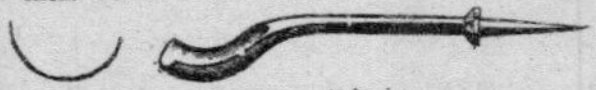

Carving Tool No. 30 Pattern, ⅜ inch. Price each $0.35

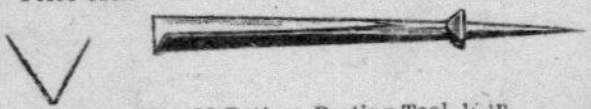

Carving Tool No. 39 Pattern Parting Tool, ¼ in. Price each $0.40

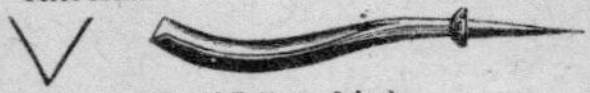

Carving Tool No. 40 Pattern, 3/16 inch. Price each $0.55

40601 Apple Wood Carving Tool handles. Each .08
Per doz .... .75

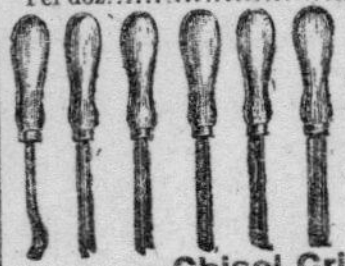

40610 Amateur's Carving Tools, extra cast steel, rosewood handles; weight, 3¼ lbs. Per set of 6 assorted tools in a wood box. Per set $0.85

Chisel Grinder.

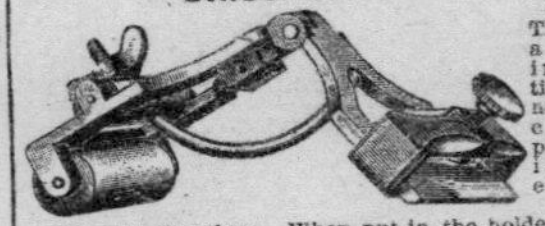

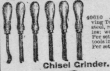

40612 This is a new invention for holding chisels, plane irons, etc., while grinding them. When put in the holder and brought to the right bevel with the adjusting screw, nothing is left to do but to bear it on the stone, and it will grind all right without further care. Price, each $0.64

Chisel Gauge.

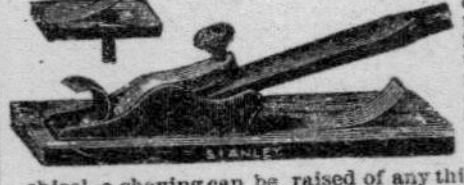

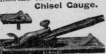

40614 Chisel Gauge for use in finishing work where blind nailing is required. By attaching the gauge to a ¼ inch chisel, a shaving can be raised of any thickness with precision, and when glued down again the shaving will fit its recess perfectly; weight, 3 oz. Made for ¼ inch chisel only. Price, each, no chisel $0.15
Per dozen 1.50

Chisel Handles.

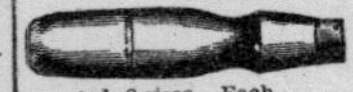

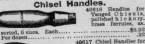

40616 Handles for Tanged Chisels, polished hickory, brass ferrules, assorted, 6 sizes. Each $0.02
Per dozen .... .22

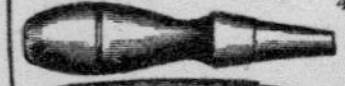

40617 Chisel Handles for Socket Firmer Chisels, polished. Each $0.02
Per dozen .... .18

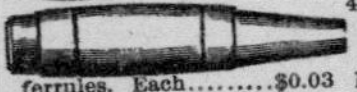

40618 Chisel Handles for socket framing chisels, polished hickory, malleable iron, ferrules. Each .... $0.03 Per dozen $0.25

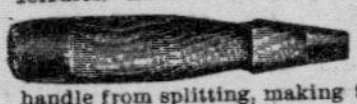

Raw Hide Bound Chisel Handles. The raw hide binding prevents the handle from splitting, making them almost indestructible.
40620 Tanged Firmer Chisel Handles. Each $0.08
Per dozen .... .75
40621 Socket Firmer Chisel Handles. Each .... .07
Per dozen .... .65

Chisel Handles—Continued.

40622 Socket Framing Chisel Handles. Each .. $0.08
Per dozen .... .68
Can furnish raw hide bound handles instead of plain with 40550, 40551, and 40552, set of chisels for .... .50

Screw Drivers.

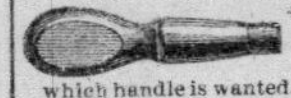

40623 Screw Driver Handles beechwood, polished brass ferrule, assorted. Give length of blade of Screw Driver for which handle is wanted. Each $0.03
Per dozen .... .33

40624 Screw Driver Handles, beechwood, polished brass ferrules large size. Give length of blade of Screw Driver for which handle is wanted. Each .... $0.04 Per dozen .... .38

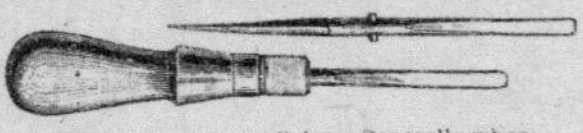

40630 The Duplex Screw Driver. Generally when a screw driver is used some tool is wanted to make a hole for the screw. On the reverse end of the screw driver is a square reamer, better for the purpose than a gimlet; it can be turned around instantly so as to use either end. Made of hand forged steel, nickel plated, with cocobolo handle. Price, each, complete, one bit $0.36
Per dozen 3.90

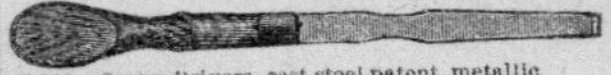

40631 Screw Drivers, cast steel patent metallic fasteners, extra heavy brass ferrules.

Size	3 in.	4 in.	5 in.	6 in.	8 in.
Whole length	7½ in.	9 in.	10½ in.	12½ in.	15 in.
Price, each	6c	8c	9c	10c	14c

40633 Round Forged Blade, warranted, Screw Driver. Highly finished with nickel plated capped ferrule, black handle.

Length of blade	3	4	5	6	8 inch
Price each	8c	10c	12c	13c	16c

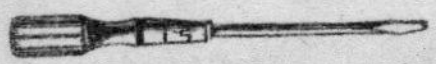

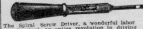

40637 The Champion Screw Driver, undoubtedly the finest made. The blade is forged from the toughest steel, and is fastened securely into a fluted applewood handle; every blade is tested to split a screw head before leaving the factory.

Size	3 in.	4 in.	6 in.	8 in.	10 in.
Price	20c	24c	34c	46c	57c

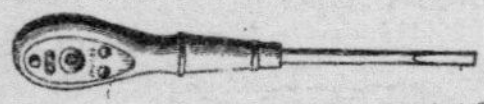

40639 Gay & Parsons' Double Action Ratchet Screw Drivers.

Size	4 in.	5 in.	6 in.	8 in.	10 in.
Price	51c	57c	68c	76c	85c

Spiral Screw Driver.

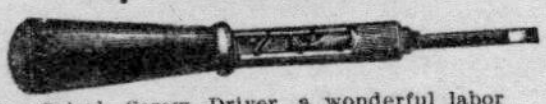

The Spiral Screw Driver, a wonderful labor saving tool, an entire revolution in driving screws; it will drive a screw into wood, soft or hard, in one-third the time of any other method. Pressure on the handle turns the blade and drives the screw. Hand does not turn at all.
40640 No. 1, length extended, 14 inches; closed, 9 inches; blade ¼ inch. Each $0.70
40641 No. 2, length extended, 19 inches; closed, 13 inches; blade, 5/16 inch .... .82

Goodell Brace Screw Driver.

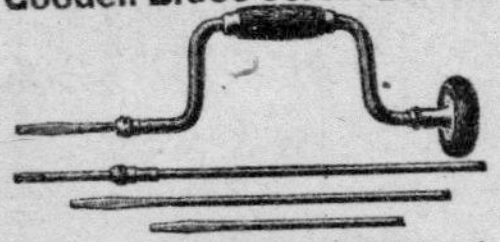

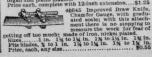

40643 The brace has a nickel plated 6 inch steel sweep, cocobolo head, and handle with patent adjustable collar for taking up the wear. The brace is packed one in a box with four blades, 2-4 inch, 1-8 inch, 1-12 inch, also 1-12 inch extension which gives a variety in lengths of 48 inch, 24-inch, 20-inch, 16-inch and 12-inch. The chuck on this brace is very strong and compact. The tool is designed for carpenters, machinists, electricians, cabinet, carriage, organ and piano makers.
Price each, complete with 12-inch extension $1.25

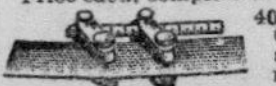

40645 Improved Draw Knife, Chamfer Gauge, with graduated scale; with this attachment there is no stopping to measure the work for fear of getting off too much; made of iron, nickel plated.

Sizes	1 in.	1⅛ to 1¼ in.	1⅜ to 1½ in.	1¾ in.
Fits blades	⅝ to 1 in.	1⅛ to 1¼ in.	1⅜ to 1½ in.	

Price, each, any size $0.55

Drawing Knives.

Weight, 1¼ to 1¾ lbs.

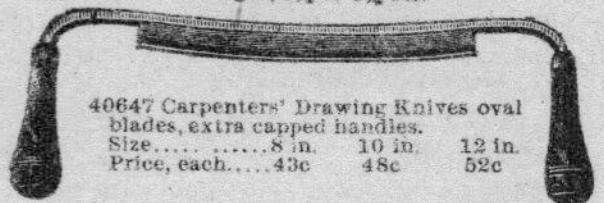

40647 Carpenters' Drawing Knives oval blades, extra capped handles.

Size	8 in.	10 in.	12 in.
Price, each	43c	48c	52c

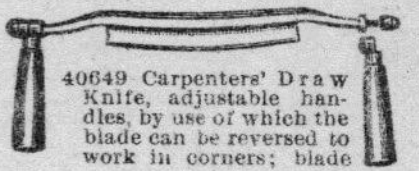

40649 Carpenters' Draw Knife, adjustable handles, by use of which the blade can be reversed to work in corners; blade 1¼ inches wide.

Size	8 in.	9 in.	10 in.
Each	$0.75	$0.87	$0.94

Patent Folding and Adjustable Handle Drawer Knife.

LOCKS AUTOMATIC.

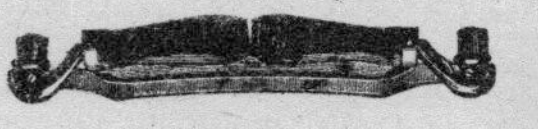

Showing Knife Closed.

40650 Handles can be adjusted for wide, flat surfaces, and can be used where a stiff handle cannot be used. The mechanic will be quick to see the many advantages of a Drawing Knife that can be adjusted, and when not in use can be folded and placed in the kit of tools without danger of injury to the blade.

Every Blade Warranted.

Size	8	9	10 inch
Price, each	$1.25	$1.30	$1.40

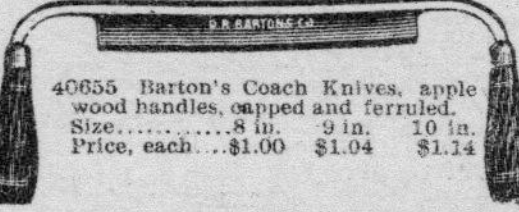

40655 Barton's Coach Knives, apple wood handles, capped and ferruled.

Size	8 in.	9 in.	10 in.
Price, each	$1.00	$1.04	$1.14

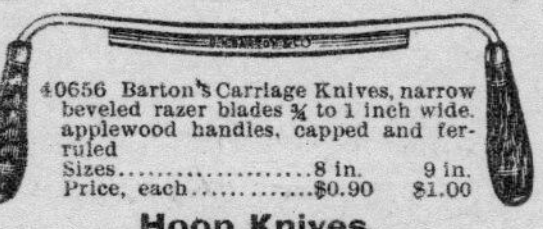

40656 Barton's Carriage Knives, narrow beveled razer blades ¾ to 1 inch wide, applewood handles, capped and ferruled

Sizes	8 in.	9 in.
Price, each	$0.90	$1.00

Hoop Knives.

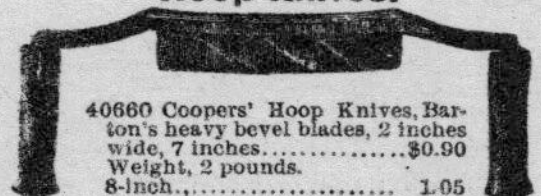

40660 Coopers' Hoop Knives, Barton's heavy bevel blades, 2 inches wide, 7 inches $0.90
Weight, 2 pounds.
8-inch 1.05

Froes.

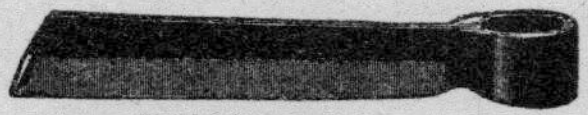

Weight, 2⅛ pounds.

40662 Coopers' Froes, polished steel edge, 12 to 14 inch cut, used by coopers for making staves, and in sections of the country where lumber is scarce for splitting shingles. Each $0.75
Per dozen 8.10

Spoke Shaves.

40663 Spoke Shave, beechwood handle, one 2½ cast steel cutter; weight, 8 oz $0.22

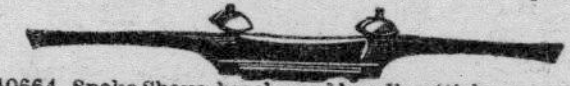

40664 Spoke Shave, beechwood handle with brass set screws, one 3-inch cast steel cutter; weight, 9 oz $0.54

***** It will be a favor to us (and perhaps to your friends) if you will place, where they will do the most good, any duplicate Catalogues or advertising matter which you may receive from us.**

Spoke Shaves—Continued.

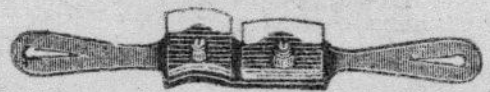

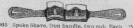

40665 Spoke Shave, iron handle, two cutters, best English cast steel (like cut), weight, 16 oz .... Each $0.20 Per doz. $2.16

Goodell Spoke Shave.

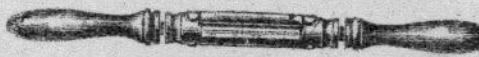

40670 Goodell's Spoke Shave, owing to its circular shape, will work in smaller circle than any other shave. The angle of the knife is such that it cuts instead of scraping the grain of the wood. Either handle can be removed to work in cramped places. Each $0.68
Per doz 7.75

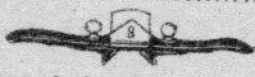

40673 Patent Chamfer Spoke Shave, raised handles, 1¼ in. cast steel cutters, adjusted by means of thumb screw attached to the guides. Will chamfer an edge any width up to 1½ inches; weight, 14 oz.
Each $0.33
Per doz 3.65

Hatchets.

All of our hatchets have handles, but the weights given do not include handles.

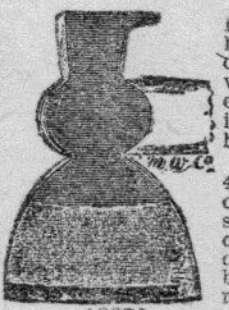

40675

40675 Hatchets, cast steel, with claw (see cut), Y. & P. brand, warranted.

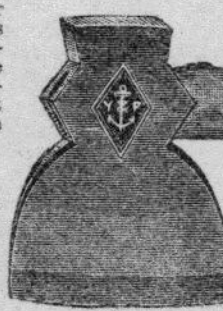

40676

	No. 1.	No. 2.	No. 3.
Weight	1 lb. 3 oz.	1 lb. 9 oz.	1 lb. 15 oz.
Width	3½ in.	4 in.	4½ in.
Each	$0.40	$0.45	$0.50
Per doz.	4.65	4.85	5.40

40676 Broad Hatchets, extra cast steel, wide, heavy and fine quality, bronzed. Y. & P. brand warranted. Weight, 1 lb. 12 oz.; width, 4½ in.
Each $0.54
Per dozen 6.00
Weight, 2 lbs. 2 oz; width, 5 in. Each .... .68
Per dozen 6.85
Weight, 2 lbs. 8 oz.; width, 5½ in. Each .... .75
Per dozen 8.10
Weight, 2 lbs. 14 oz.; width, 6 in. Each .... .82
Per dozen 8.85

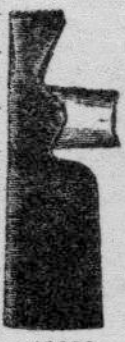

40680

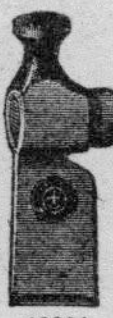

40681

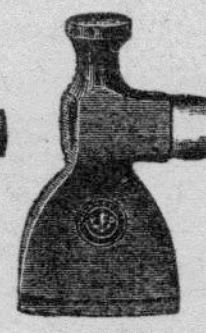

40685

40680—Lathing Hatchet, Underhill Star pattern warranted. Solid cast steel, full polished, extra thin blade, width of blade 2 in.; weight, 1 lb. Each $0.83
Per dozen 8.97

40681 Lathing Hatchet, Yerkes & Plumb's Adz Eye Bell Pole, solid cast steel, thin blade, full polish, cut 2¼ in. Fully warranted. Weight 1 lb. Each .... .80
Per dozen 8.64

40685 Shingling Hatchet, Yerkes & Plumb's Adz Eye Bell Pole, solid cast steel, thin blade, full polished; weight, 1 lb. 4 oz. Full warranted.
Each .... .80
Per dozen 8.64

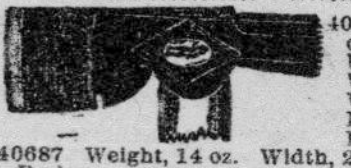

40686 Lathing Hatchet, cast steel, Vulcan brand.
Weight, 10 oz.
Width, 2 in.
Each $0.34
Per doz 3.68

40687 Weight, 14 oz. Width, 2¼ in.
Each .... .38
Per dozen 3.68

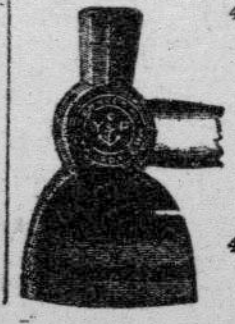

40690 Shingling Hatchet, common pattern, cast steel. Y. & P. brand, warranted.

No.	0	1
Weight,	13 oz.	1 lb., 1 oz.
Width of bit,	3¼ in.	3½ in.
Each,	34c.	38c.
No.	2	3
Weight,	1 lb., 7 oz.	1 lb., 13 oz.
Width of bit,	4 in.	4½ in.
Each,	41c.	43c.

40691 Hatchet Handles $0.05

Adzes.

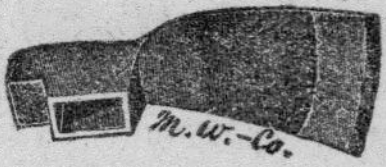

40695 Carpenters' Adze, English cast steel, bronzed 3½ to 4 in. cut; weight 3¾ lbs. Y. & P. brand. Fully warranted.
Each $1.15

40696 Barton's Ship Adze, 4 to 4½ in. cut. Each 2.10
40699 Adze Handles. Each .... .40

Axes.

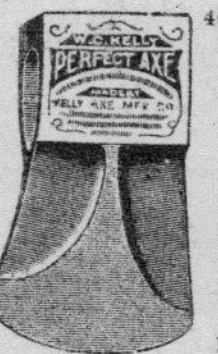

40700 The Celebrated Kelly Perfect Ax. This ax is made of the finest steel and is hand hammered tempered and tested before leaving the shop. The blade is so shaped that it will cut very deep, but will not bind in timber. It will burst the chip, and it will not become stubbed after grinding. It has a taper eye which binds handle. Try one and you will use no other. We can furnish the Western pattern like cut, or Michigan pattern, which has rounded head. Comes assorted weight, from 3½ to 5 lbs each
Each $0.60
Per dozen 6.50

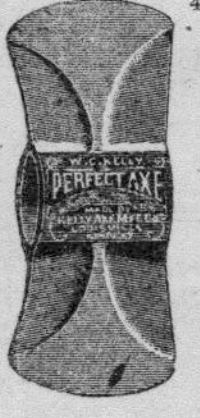

40702 The Celebrated Kelley Perfect double bitted ax, made of the finest steel and hand hammered; will cut deeper than any other ax, and will not bind in timber. Comes in assorted weights, from 3½ to 5½ lbs.
Price, each $1.00
Per doz 11.00

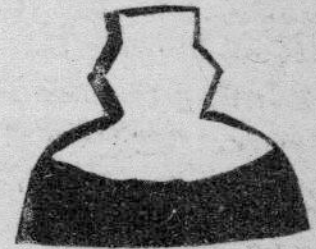

40705 Carpenters' Broad Ax, Western pattern, extra cast steel; weight, 6 to 7½ lbs.; 9 to 11 in. cut. Each $1.50

40706 Broad Ax Handle, extra quality, right or left hand, 26 inches long. Each .... .18
Per doz 1.77

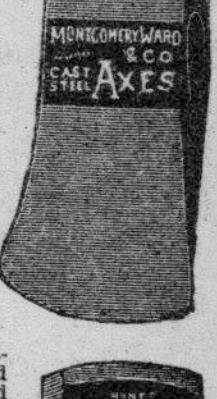

40710 Montgomery Ward & Co.'s Phantom Bevel, solid silver steel, full polished ax. This is a new pattern that promises to give good satisfaction. The peculiar bevel of the bit has the tendency to free it from the wood, besides giving the ax a very neat appearance; weight, 3, 3¾ to 4¾ lbs.
Each $0.69

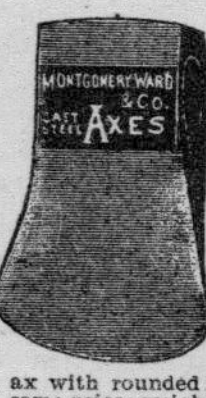

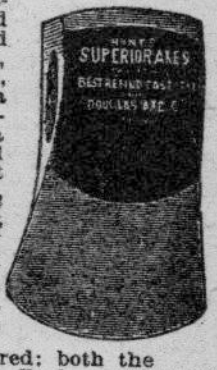

40711 Montgomery Ward & Co's solid silver steel ax, full polished, like cut, a handsome pattern; has a longer and thinner bit than ordinary, is made of best quality of steel, and handsomely finished. We can also furnish the same ax with rounded head, if preferred; both the same price; weight, 3¾ to 4¾ lbs. Each $0.60

40712 Red Warrior Ax, Western pattern, wide bit, heavy poll, inserted steel, manufactured by Wm. Mann, Jr., & Co.; weight, 3¼ to 4¾ lbs; no handles. Each .... .60

40713 Axes, Northwestern pattern; Hunt's narrow bit, heavy poll; inserted steel; weight, 3¼ to 4¾ pounds; no handle. Each .... .65
Per dozen, selected assortment 7.20

40714 Hunters' axes, with handle, extra cast steel, steel poll; weight, 1¾ pounds; this is a very convenient tool; it makes a light ax or a heavy hatchet .... .52

40715 Boys' axes, hickory handle, 27 inches long, highly polished and bronzed .... .65

When ordering goods shipped by mail, be sure to allow money for postage. If you send too much we will refund balance.

Cook's Patent Plumb and Level.

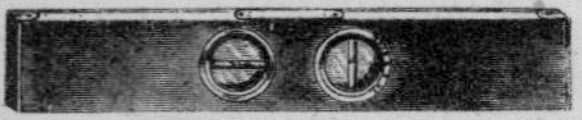

40882 Cook's Patent Level, mahogany, nickel trimmings.......$1.95
40883 Cook's Patent Level, mahogany, made of three pieces glued together, nickel trimmings. 2.20
40884 Cook's Patent Level, cherry, nickel trimmings.......1.65
40885 Cook's Patent Level, cherry, made of three pieces glued together, nickel trimming.......1.95
40886 Cook's Patent Level, cherry, brass trimmings.......1.44
40887 Level Glasses, assorted sizes. Each.......05

Socket Scratch Awls.

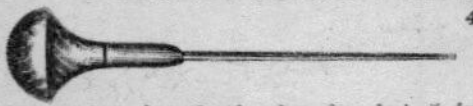

40895 Cast Steel, with cherry handle, Norway iron socket; length of awl and socket, 5 inches. This is a very fine tool. Each.......$0.10
Per dozen.......1.08

Chalk Line Reels.

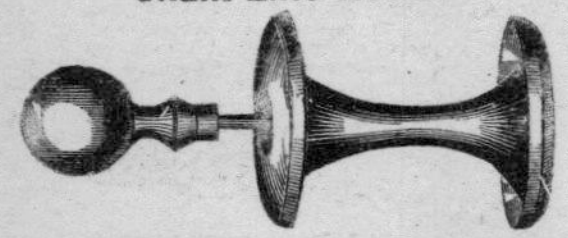

40900 Chalk Line Reels, beechwood, with scratch awls (like cut); weight, 6 oz. Each.......$0.08
40901 Same without scratch awls, 4 oz. Each.......05
40902 Scratch awls only, 5 oz. Each.......05
NOTE.—For Chalk Lines, see Fish Lines in Index.

Shingling Bracket.

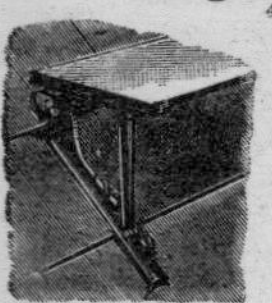

40905 Elmer's Shingling Bracket is adjustable and absolutely safe; made entirely of malleable iron and is very strong; adjustable to any pitch of roof; the more weight the stronger the grip. Directions: In adjusting to roof throw back the top of the bracket as far as it will go, then slide the under jaw under and between two shingles, then rock the can backward and forward according to the pressure required for different thickness of shingles and bring down the top part to the required position and lock the brace with the button. Price, per pair.......$0.48
Per single dozen.......2.82

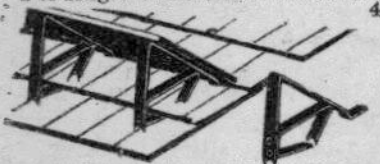

40906 Stanley's Patent Roofing Bracket is an efficient device used in connection with shingling roofs. Every carpenter is employed more or less in doing this kind of work and needs suitable staging for his security. This bracket not only is secure, but may be put in position quicker than any other without the waste of lumber, as in the old way. Each.......$0.25
Per dozen.......2.70

Trammel Points.

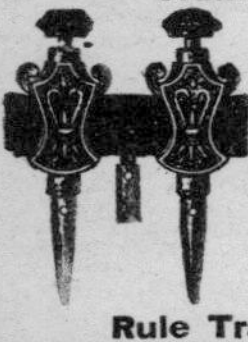

40909 Trammel Points, small, with steel points; weight, 6 oz. Per pair.......$0.70
40910 Trammel Points, medium, with steel points; weight, 6 oz. Per pair.......$0.90

Rule Trammel Point.

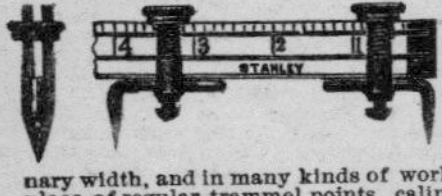

40915 Adapted for convenient use to a carpenter's rule; can be attached to folding rules of any ordinary width, and in many kinds of work will take the place of regular trammel points, calipers or divider. A convenient marking gauge can be made by using the rule for a gauge bar. Complete set consists of two brass-trimmed heads, with movable steel points, and one head with a pencil socket; weight, 3 ounces. Price, each, no rule.......$0.38
Per dozen.......4.10

T Bevels.

Weight, 7 to 9 oz. each.

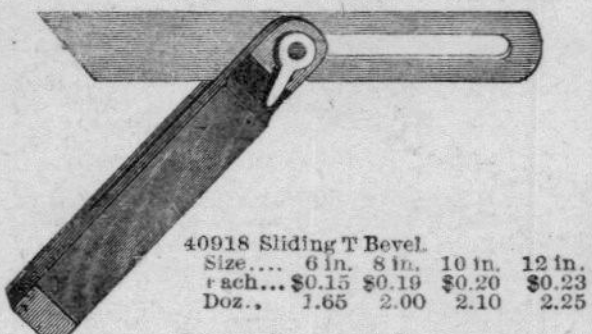

40918 Sliding T Bevel.

Size....	6 in.	8 in.	10 in.	12 in.
Each...	$0.15	$0.19	$0.20	$0.23
Doz..	1.65	2.00	2.10	2.25

Bevels and Squares.

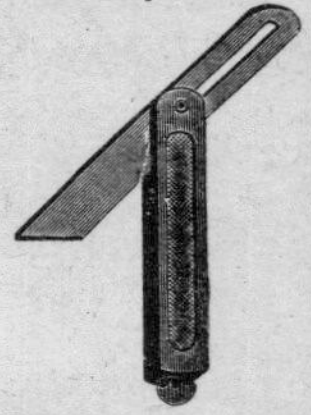

40920 Patent Eureka T Bevels, iron handle, steel blade, with parallel edges. The blade is secured at an angle by turning the thumb screw at the lower end of handle.

Sizes	6 in	8 in.	10 in.
Each	$0.30	$0.33	$0.40
Doz..	3.24	3.42	4.00

Try Square.

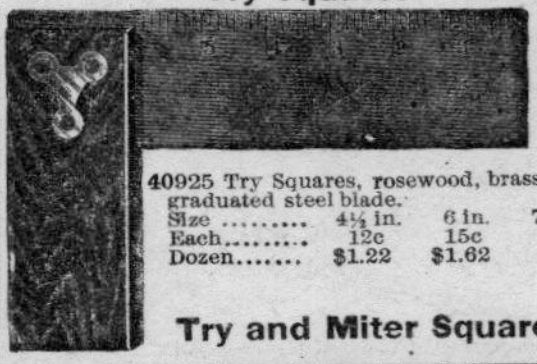

40925 Try Squares, rosewood, brass face, graduated steel blade.

Size.......	4½ in.	6 in.	7½ in.
Each.......	12c	15c	19c
Dozen.......	$1.22	$1.62	$1.87

Try and Miter Square.

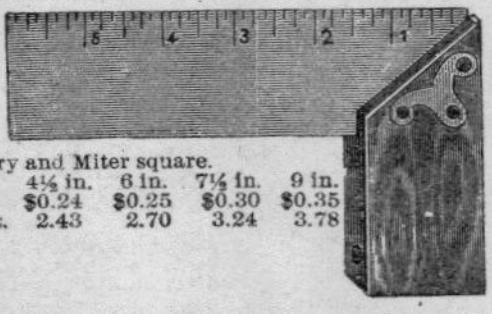

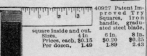

40926 Try and Miter square.

Size	4½ in.	6 in.	7½ in.	9 in.
Each	$0.24	$0.25	$0.30	$0.35
Per doz.	2.43	2.70	3.24	3.78

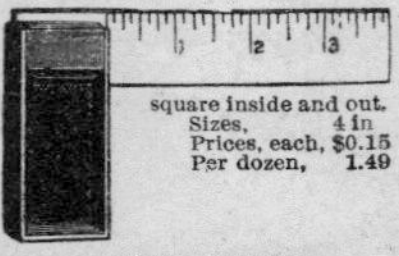

40927 Patent Improved Try Squares, iron handle, graduated steel blade, square inside and out.

Sizes,	4 in	6 in.	8 in.
Prices, each,	$0.15	$0.20	$0.25
Per dozen,	1.49	1.89	2.43

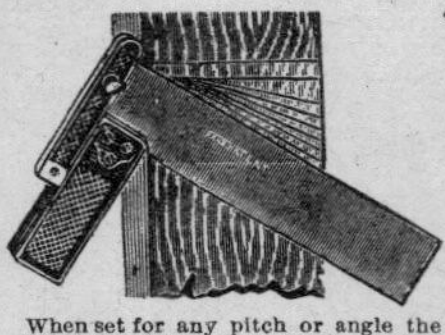

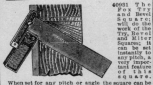

40931 The Fox Try and Bevel Square; will do the work of the Try, Bevel and Miter Squares; it can be set instantly to any pitch, a very important feature of this square. When set for any pitch or angle the square can be used also. The bevel attachment is a sliding bar on the back of the handle. Size, 8 inches each ...$0.75
DIRECTIONS—For pitches of 7 to 16 inches, slide the bar on back of handle to pitch desired; set the mark on the sliding bar exact in line with notch cut in back of square blade; secure when in position by the thumb-screw. For pitches of ix inch and five inch or octagon, place the mark at the top of the slide in line of notch cut in top of blade. By placing the top of slide and rounded corner of handle against the work, the line of the blade will indicate the correct bevel or pitch desired. Weight, 1¼ lbs.

Steel Squares—Continued.

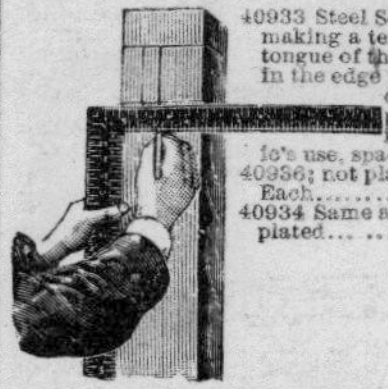

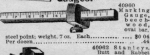

40933 Steel Square calculated for making a tenon or mortise. The tongue of the square has notches in the edge which holds an awl or pencil from slipping; a very convenient tool for mechanic's use, spaced the same as No. 40936; not plated.
Each.......$0.88
40934 Same as No. 40933, nickel plated.......$0.98

Squares.

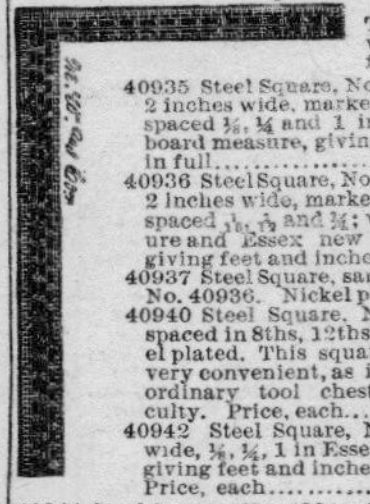

These squares are the very best made and we fully warrant them.

40935 Steel Square, No. 7, extra quality, 2 inches wide, marked on both sides, spaced ⅛, ¼ and 1 inch. Essex new board measure, giving feet and inches in full.......$0.45
40936 Steel Square, No. 3, extra quality, 2 inches wide, marked on both sides, spaced $\frac{1}{16}$, $\frac{1}{12}$ and ¼; with brace measure and Essex new board measure, giving feet and inches in full.......50
40937 Steel Square, same description as No. 40936. Nickel plated.......60
40940 Steel Square, No. 112, one foot spaced in 8ths, 12ths and 16ths, nickel plated. This square will be found very convenient, as it may be put in ordinary tool chest without difficulty. Price, each.......58
40942 Steel Square, No. 14, 2-foot, 2 inches wide, ⅛, ¼, 1 in Essex New Board Measure giving feet and inches in full.
Price, each.......$0.40
40944 Steel Square, No. 100, extra quality, 2 in. wide, marked on both sides, $\frac{1}{32}$, $\frac{1}{16}$, $\frac{1}{12}$, $\frac{1}{10}$, ⅛, with brace measure, 8 square and $\frac{1}{100}$ scale and Essex new board measure, giving feet and inches in full.......90
40945 Same as No. 40944 only nickel plated.
Price, each.......1.00
40947 Iron Square 1¼ inches wide, marked in 8ths on both sides.......18
40950 Iron Square, 2 inches wide, marked in 8ths on both sides.......25

Plumb Bobs.

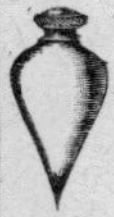

40951 Plumb Bob, iron japanned; weight, 9½ ounces.
Each.......$0.05
Per dozen.......54
40953 Plumb Bob, brass, steel point; weight, 6 ounces.
Each.......25
Per dozen.......2.70
40955 Plumb Bob, brass, steel points, screw caps.
Weight, 1 lb.......85
Weight, 2 lbs.......1 00
Weight, 4 lbs.......1 35

Stanley's Odd Jobs.

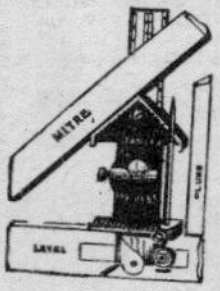

40957 This tool embraces within itself, and when in combination with an ordinary carpenter's rule, a try-square, miter square, T-square, marking gauge, depth gauge, mitre, level, spirit level and plumb, beam, compass, inside square for making boxes and frames; weight, 10 oz.
No. 1, Odd Job, nickel plated with level.
Each.......$0.58

Gauges.

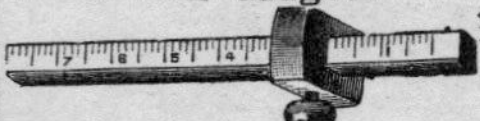

40960 Marking Gauge, beechwood, oval bar, steel point; weight, 7 oz. Each.......$0 04
Per dozen.......44

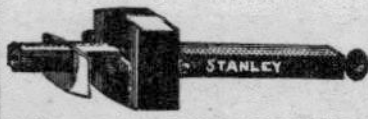

40962 Stanleys, Butt and Rabbet Gauge for hanging doors, mortising, marking, etc. This without question is the most ingenious as well the most convenient tool, for carpenters' use ever invented. No carpenter should be without one. Each.......$1.00

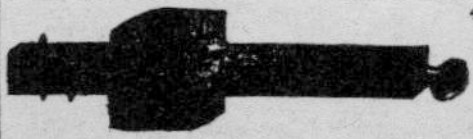

40963 Marking Mortise Gauge, rosewood, plated, head, improved screw slide, brass thumb-screw and shoe, oval bar, marked, steel points; weight, 9 oz. Each.......$0.34
Per dozen.......3.68

Gauges—Continued.

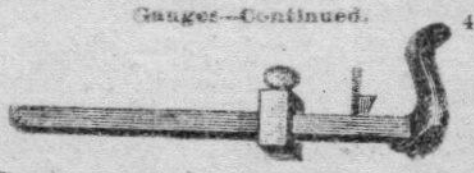

40965 Handle Slitting Gauge, with roller and 17 in. marked bar. Each $0.34
Per dozen 3.68

Barrett's Combination Roller Gauge.

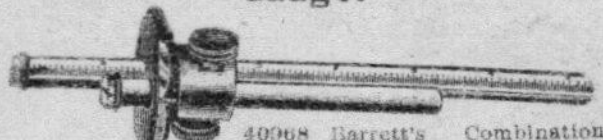

40968 Barrett's Combination Roller Gauge, made expressly for wood workers' use, made entirely of metal; the most perfect tool of the kind ever invented; weight, 15 ounces. Each $0.65

Panel Gauges.

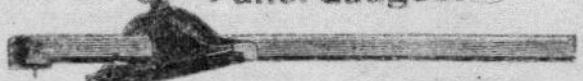

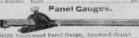

40970 Beechwood Panel Gauge, boxwood thumb screws, 17 inches oval bar. Each $0.15
Per dozen 1.62

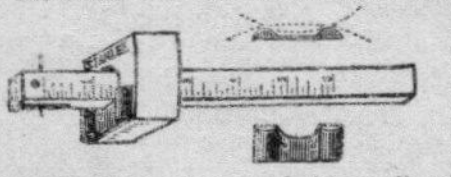

Stanley's Patent Improved Marking Gauges have brass face, with two ribs or projectors attached to one side of the gauge head (see cut); will enable the operator to run a gauge line with perfect steadiness and accuracy around curves of any degree and either concave or convex. The opposite side of the gauge head remains flat and can be used for all ordinary work.
40972 Beechwood, boxwood thumb-screw. Each $0.07
40973 Boxwood, brass thumb-screw and shoe, plated head, adjusting steel point. Each .... .20

Clapboard Marker.

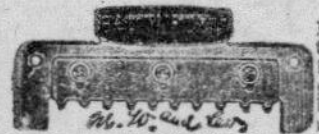

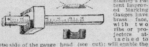

Adjustable Clapboard Marker. This ingenious tool can be used with one hand while the other is employed in keeping a clapboard in position. The marking blade is properly slotted so that the tool can be easily adjusted to any thickness of clapboard. The sharp edge of the teeth on marking board are just parallel with the other edges of the legs when placed against the corner board, and by moving the tool half an inch it will mark a full line across the clapboard exactly over and conforming to the edge of the corner board. There is then no difficulty in sawing for a perfectly close joint.
40978 Adjustable clapboard marker, iron stock, with wooden handles, steel blade. Each $0.40

Clapboard Gauge.

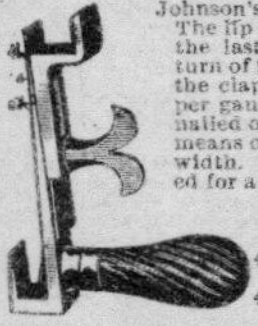

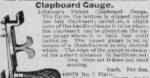

Johnson's Patent Clapboard Gauge. The lip on the bottom is slipped under the last clapboard; nailed on, a slight turn of the handle clamps it to its place; the clapboard can be placed on the upper gauge where it is held fast until nailed on. The upper gauge is set by means of a thumb-screw to any desired width. The edge of the gauge is stamped for a short distance to facilitate setting. Once set it does not need moving.

	Each.	Per doz.
40979 No. 1 Plain, polished	$0.25	$2.92
40980 No. 2 Nickel plated	.35	3.78

Stanley's Clapboard (Sliding) Gauge.

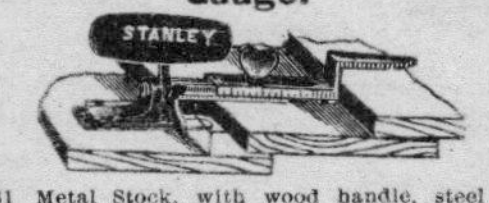

40981 Metal Stock, with wood handle, steel blades. Price, each $0.35

Conductors' Punches.

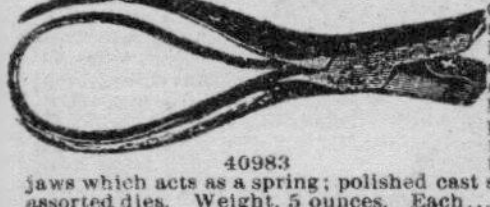

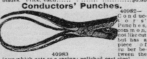

40982—Conductors' Punches, common, not like cut but has a piece of rubber between the jaws which acts as a spring; polished cast steel, assorted dies. Weight, 5 ounces. Each $0.50
40983
Per dozen 5.40
40983 Conductor's Punches, like cut, extra cast steel, nickel plated, assorted fancy dies. Each. 1.00
Per dozen 11.00
40984 Conductors' Punches, nickel plated, with letter die; made only to order.
Weight, 6 oz. Price, each, any letter 2.00

Spring Punches.

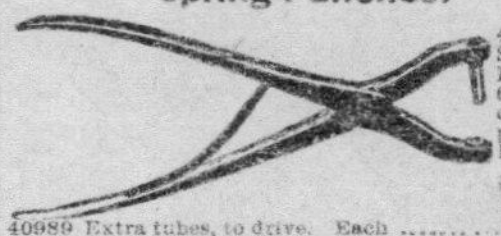

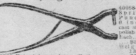

40988—Spring Punch, 6 inch, cast steel polished. Each $0.20
Weight, 13 oz.
40989 Extra tubes, to drive. Each $0.06
Per dozen .... .65
40990 Revolving Spring Punch, extra cast steel, 4 tubes. Each .... .50
Per dozen 5.25
40991 6 tubes. Each .... .60
Weight, 14 ounces. Per dozen 6.25

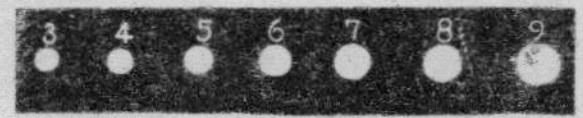

Plate showing size of tubes in 40988 and 40991

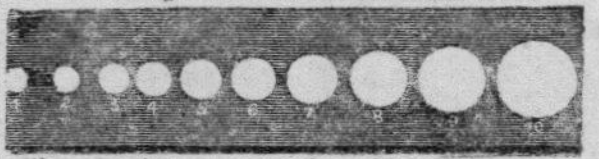

Plate showing size of punches. No. 40992.
40992 Hollow Saddlers' Punches.

Nos.	1, 2, 3, 4, 5.	6, 7, 8, 9.	10.
Price, each	10c.	12c.	15c.

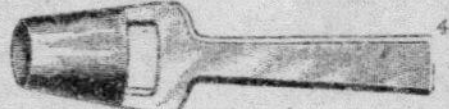

40993 Round Punches, cast steel, hand forged, very fine.

Sizes			⅜	½	⅝
Price, each			45c.	45c.	50c.
Sizes	1⅛	1¼	1⅜	1⅞	2	2⅛
Price, each	75c.	$1.00	1.50	1.50	1.75	1.75
Sizes	2¼	2⅜	2½	2¾	3 in.
Price, each	$2.00	2.25	2.50	3.00	3.50

Pliers.

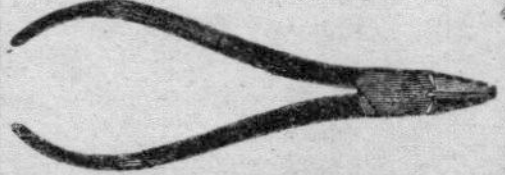

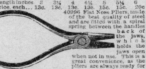

40995—Flat Nose Pliers, made of a fine quality of steel.
Do not buy a small size to do the work that the large sizes are intended for.

Length inches	3	3½	4	4½	5	5½	6
Price, each...	13c.	13c.	13c.	13c.	15c.	15c.	20c

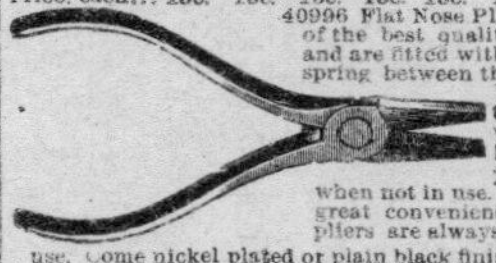

40996 Flat Nose Pliers, made of the best quality of steel and are fitted with a spiral spring between the handles back of the jaws, which holds the jaws open when not in use. This is a great convenience, as the pliers are always ready for use. Come nickel plated or plain black finish.

Length inches	3	3½	4	4½	5	5½	6
Plain, each ..	28c.	29c.	30c.	32c.	33c.	35c.	40c.

40996¼ Round Nose Pliers, polished jaws, 6 in
Each $0.40

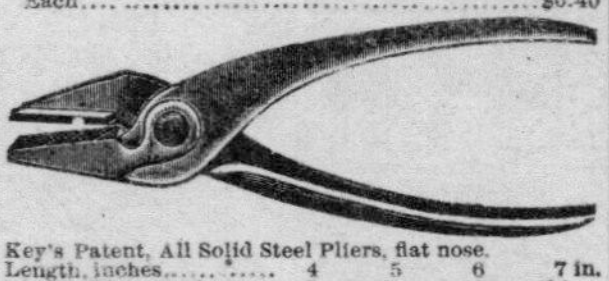

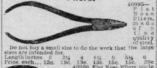

Key's Patent, All Solid Steel Pliers, flat nose.

Length, inches	4	5	6	7 in.
40997 Plain, each	7c.	9c.	12c.	14c.
40997¼ Nickel, each	10c.	12c.	14c.	15c.

Wire Cutters and Pliers.

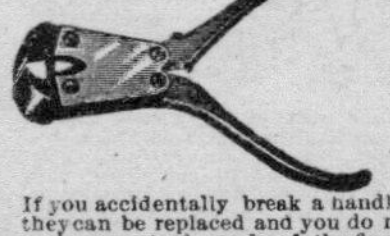

40998 Hall's Patent Compound Lever Nippers. These are without any exception the finest cutting nippers in the market. The most important feature about them is that all the parts are interchangeable. If you accidentally break a handle, jaw, screw, etc., they can be replaced and you do not have to buy an entire new tool; made of the finest quality of steel.

Length, inches	4	5	7	8
Price, each	$0.60	$0.68	$1.00	$1.50.

40999 Extra jaws 1 and 2 22c; 4, 33c; 5, 40c each.
41000 Extra handles, 1 and 2, 22c; 4, 35c; 5, 40c each.
41001 Extra screws 10c. each.
41002 Extra springs, 10c each.

Pliers—Continued.

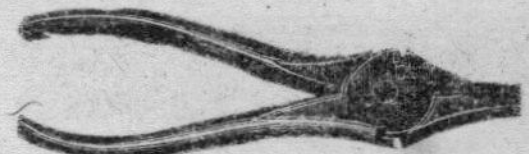

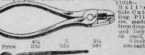

41005 Cronk's Buttons Plier, made of the best quality of tool steel and guaranteed to be the strongest plier in the market. It is better and stronger than the old Buttons Pattern, as the cutting surfaces between the jaws are left out. This was the weak spot in the old make and caused the jaws to break easily.

Size.	Price each.
6 inch	$0.35
8 inch	.45
10 inch	.55

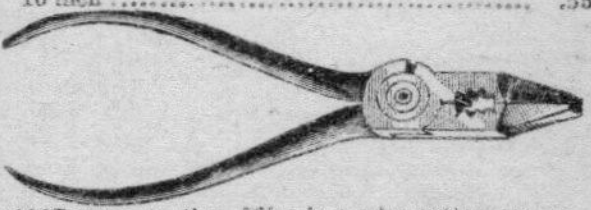

41007 Combination Plier is a wire cutter, gas and flat nose plier in one tool, the most useful article in the market for the money; 5¼ inches in length. Price, each, $0.25 Per doz..... $2.25

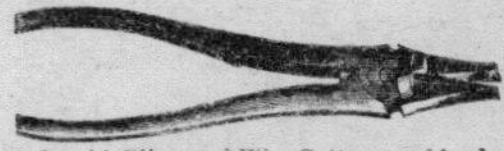

41009 Cronk's Pliers and Wire Cutters combined, the most ingenious and useful tool made for handling wire. A variety of articles may be made with it, such as hog rings and cage springs, wire springs, hooks, etc. Wire may be held in the jaws of pliers, and the wire cut without releasing it. Very handy to have about the house or shop; 8 inch. Weight, 17 ounces. Each, $0.55 Per dozen $6.00

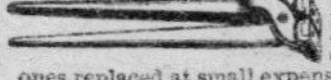

41015 Wire cutting Nippers, the most powerful in use. The cutters can be taken off and ground or new ones replaced at small expense.

Size......	8in.	10in.	11 in.	12in.	13 in.
Each......	70c	80c	90c	$1.00	$1.35

Extra jaws or cutters for Todd's Nippers, any size, 25c per pair. Send sample when ordering.

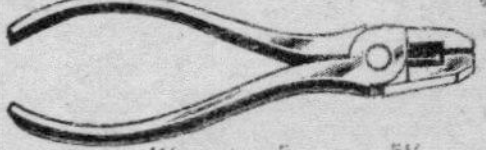

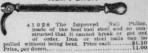

41018—Hall's Side Cutting Pliers, made from dropped forged steel.

	4½	5	5½	6 inch
Price	32c	35c	38c	40c each

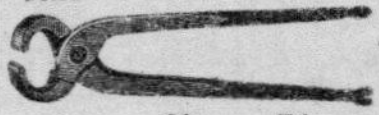

41020 Carpenters' Pincers, with claw.

	6 in.	8 in.	10 in.	12 in.
Each........	$0.15	$0.20	$0.28	$0.35
Per doz.....	1.65	2.25	3.13	3.50

Tack Claw.

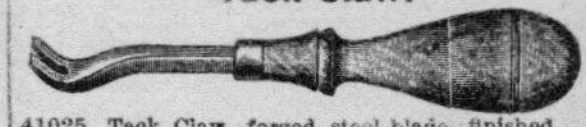

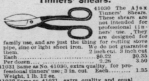

41025 Tack Claw, forged steel blade, finished handle. Each.... $0.06 Per dozen $0.65

Nail Puller.

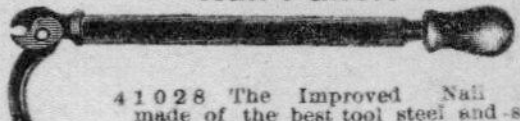

41028 The Improved Nail Puller, made of the best tool steel and so constructed that it cannot break or get out of order. Iron or steel nails can be pulled without being bent. Price each $1.10
Price, per dozen........ 11.00

Tinners' Shears.

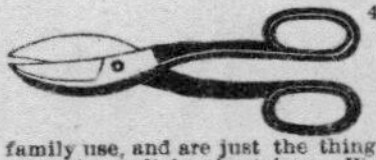

41030 The Ajax Tinners' Shears. These shears are not intended for professional tinners' use. They are designed for family use, and are just the thing for cutting stove pipe, zinc or light sheet iron. We do not guarantee them.

	2 inch cut.	3 inch cut
Each	$0.22	$0.35
Per dozen	2.28	3.50

41031 Same as No. 41030, extra quality, for professional tinners' use; 3 in. cut. Each 1.35
Weight, 1 lb. 12 oz.
41032 Same as 41031, extra quality and equal to the best in the market; 3-in. cut. Per pair... 1.00

RIM DEAD LOCKS.

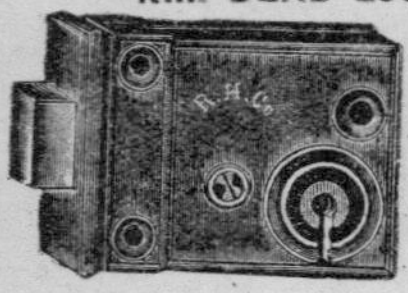

41450 Horizontal rim dead locks; size 2x-2¾, for closets or cupboard, iron bolt, 1 iron key.
Notice.— This lock cannot be used with knobs. Complete with screws and japanned escutcheons. Each........ $0.10
Per doz........ 1.00
41453 Rimmed Dead Lock (cannot be used with knobs), like cut No. 41450. Size, 2¼x3⅛ in.; with iron bolts, coppered iron key, 1 tumbler, complete with screws and escutcheons.
Price, each........$0.10. Per dozen........ 1.07
41454 Rim Dead Lock (cannot be used with with knobs), like cut No. 41450. Size, 2½x3½ in; with iron bolts, tinned malleable iron key, 1 tumbler, 12 changes, complete, with screws and escutcheons. Price, each........ .12
Per dozen........ 1.25
41455 Rim Dead Lock (cannot be used with knobs), like cut No. 41450. Size, 2¾x4; with tinned malleable keys, 1 tumbler, 12 changes complete, with screws and escutcheons. Each.. .15
Per dozen........ 1.56

"Jackson" Patent Rim Night Latch Lock.

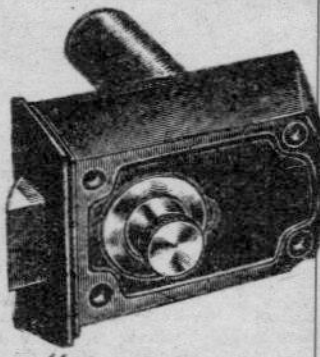

"Unpickable."

With key same as No. 41008. Adjustable to right or left hand doors; the knob rotates to fasten the bolt in or out; has japanned iron case, iron bolts, bronze escutcheon, with three keys.
41456 For doors 1 to 1⅜ in. thick, each........$0.80
41457 For doors 1⅜ to 1⅞ in. thick, each........ .90

Yale Pattern Night Lock.

Warranted to be Perfect and Equal to Any in the Market

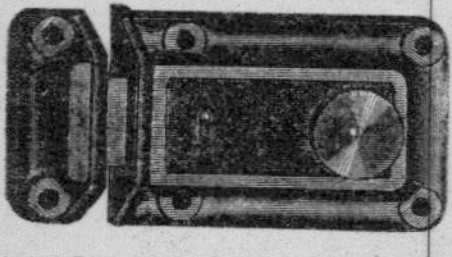

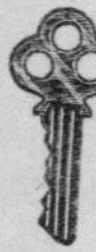

41458 Rim Night Latch, plain brass knob and escutcheon, japanned iron case; size, 3⅝x2⅜ inches; 3 steel keys. This latch is operated from the outside by the key only and on the inside by the knob, and the bolt may be fastened back at will by the spring catch on the inside of case; suitable for doors from ⅞ to 2⅜ inches thick.
Complete........$1.25

Rim Night Latches.

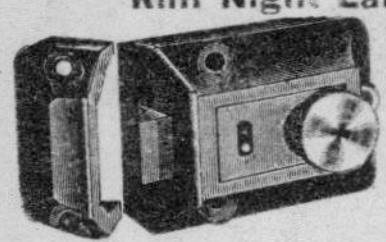

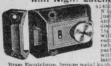

41459 Brooklyn Night Latch, adjustable to right and left hand doors, from ⅞ to 1½ inches thick, with adjustable escutcheon sleeve, two flat steel keys; packed, complete, with screws; size of latch, 2¾x3.
Brass Escutcheon, bronze metal knob, iron bolts. Price, each........$0.45
We can furnish Reverse Bevels for No. 41459 and Night Latches at same price as regular goods.

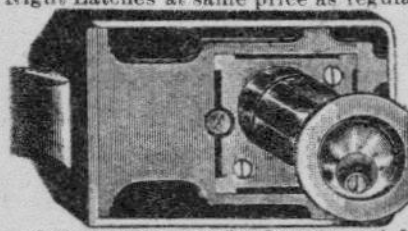

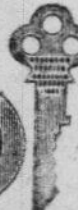

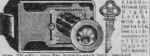

41460—Brooklyn Night Latch, with adjustable escutcheonsleeve either right or left hand; size, 3⅝x3½; two flat keys to each lock; packed, complete, with screws.
Bronze Escutcheons, bronze metal knob, bronze bolt. Price, each........$0.70

Door Latches—Continued.

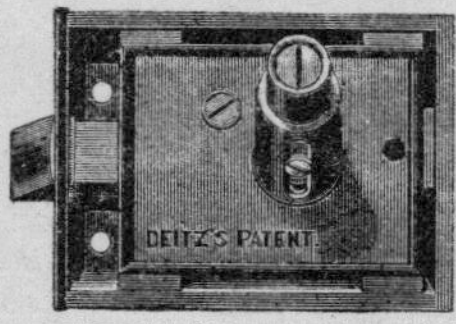

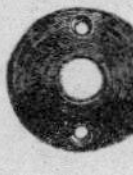

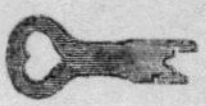

41461 Rim Night Latch, for right or left hand doors; heavy iron case, brass side and stop knob, two steel double notched tumblers for 1¼, 1½, 1¾ or 2 inch doors; state for what thickness door lock is wanted when ordering.
Weight, 1 lb. 3 oz.
Each........$0.50

Store Door Lock.

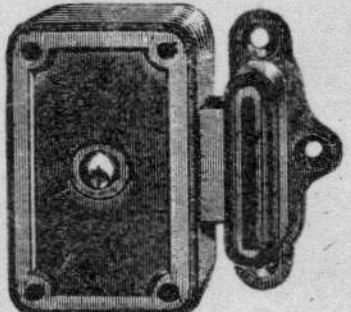

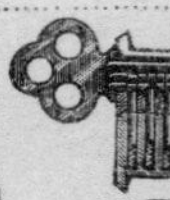

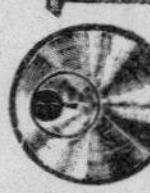

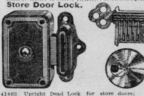

41462 Upright Dead Lock for store doors; size, 5x3, or doors 1⅛ to 4 inches thick, operated by key from both sides of door; has heavy japanned iron case, with bronze bolt 2⅛x⅛ inch, plain brass escutcheons, 3 corrugated steel keys with each lock; no two sets of keys made alike; complete; weight, 3 lbs. 5 ounces........$2.75

"Jackson" Patent Store Door Dead Lock.

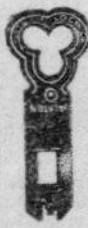

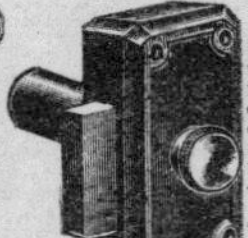

Operated by knob from inside and the key from the outside; has japan iron case, iron bolt, plated knob, bronze escutcheon, three keys. Will fit doors from 1¾ to 2½ inches thick.
41463 For doors 1¾ to 2¼ in. thick, each.$1.00
41464 For doors 2¼ to 2½ in. thick, each.$1.00

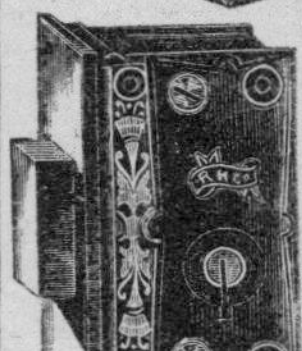

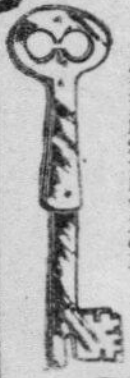

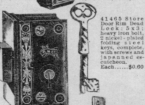

41465 Store Door Rim Dead Lock; 5x3; heavy iron bolt, 2 nickel-plated folding steel keys, complete, with screws and japanned escutcheon.
Each......$0.60

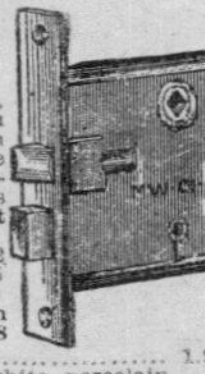

41466 Reversible Mortise Lock, like cut, lacquered iron front, iron bolt, wrought iron striking plate, tinned malleable iron key; size 3½x3½, with japanned escutcheons. Price is without screws or knobs. Weight about 1 lb
Each........ $0.12
Per dozen........ 1.25
41467 Same lock, with No. 41480 brown mineral knobs, Japan mountings. Each........$0.18
Per doz........ 1.90
41468 Same as above, with white porcelain knobs knobs, japanned mountings. Each........ .20
Per doz........ 2.16
41469 Reversible Mortise Lock, similar to cut of 41466, brass front, brass bolts, nickel plated steel keys; size, 3½x3⅜; weight, 1 lb. 3 oz. Each........ .20
Per doz........ 2.20
41470 Same lock, with No. 41480 japanned mineral knobs, japanned mountings. Each.... .26
Per doz........ 2.87
41471 Same as above, with white porcelain knobs, japanned mountings. Each........ .28
Per doz........ 2.99

Mortise Knob Locks.

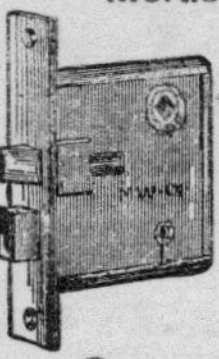

41472 Size, 3½x3½ inch, with iron front, bolts and strike plate, with steel key; 12 changes. The price of the lock is without the knob; for price of knobs, see No. 41480 to 41490.
Each........$0.20
Per doz........ 1.60

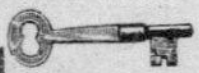

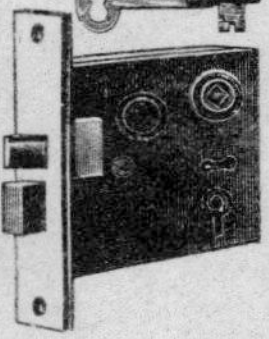

41473 Mortise Knob Lock; size, 3½x3½ inch, with plain bronze metal front and bronze bolt, brass strike plate, nickel plated steel key, with 1 tumbler, 12 changes. The thickness of case is ⅝ inch, width of face, 15-16 inch. The distance from front of lock to center of hub and keyhole, 2⅜ inches. The price of this lock is without knobs; for price of spindles, see No. 41480 to 41490.
Price, each........$0.30
Per doz........ 3.12

Door Knobs.

Weight, 1 lb.

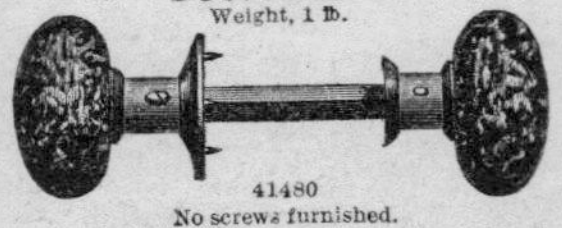

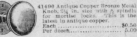

41480

No screws furnished.

See Index for screws.	Each	Per doz.
41480 Brown Mineral Door Knobs, with 5-16 inch spindles, japanned mountings, for rim locks; no screws furnished......	$0.06	$0.65
41481 Brown Mineral Door Knobs, with 5-16 inch spindles, japanned mountings for mortise lock; no screws furnished....	.06	.65
41482 White Porcelain Door Knobs, with 5-16 inch spindles, japanned mountings for rim locks........	.08	.87
41483 White Porcelain Door Knobs, 5-16 inch spindles, japanned mountings, for mortise locks; no screws furnished......	.08	.87
41484 Ebony Door Knobs, 5-16 inch spindles, japanned mountings, for rim locks.	.08	.87
41485 Ebony Door Knobs, with 5-16 inch spindles, japanned mountings, for mortise locks; no screws furnished........	.08	.87

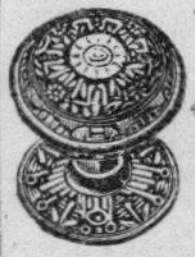

41486 Geneva Bronzed Iron Knob 5-16 inch spindles, Geneva bronzed mountings for mortise locks.
Each........$0.25
Per dozen........ 2.70
41487 Ebony Door Knobs, with 5-16 inch spindle, ornamental gold bronze mounting, for mortise locks, packed with screws to match mountings. Each..... .30
Per dozen........ 3.00
This cut shows only one-half of the knob.

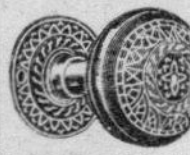

41489 Bronze Metal Door Knob, 2¼ in. size with ⅜ in. spindle for mortise locks; this knob is made of bronze metal has polished surfaces, with black background; a new and very handsome design.
Each........$0.40
Per dozen........ 4.10
This cut only shows one-half of the knob. The price includes two knobs and spindle, like cut 41480.

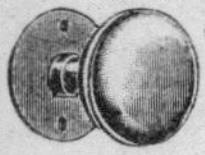

41490 Antique Copper Bronze Metal Knob, 2¼ in. size with ⅜ spindle for mortise locks. This is the latest in antique copper.
Each........ $0.50
Per dozen........ 5.00

This cut shows only one-half of the knob. The price includes two knobs and one spindle, like cut 41480.

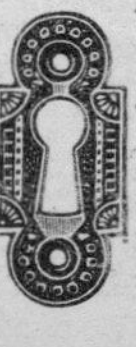

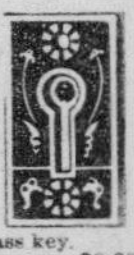

41496 Keyhole Plate or Escutcheon, japanned iron, for iron key.
Each........ $0.02
Per dozen........ .20
41497 Keyhole Escutcheon, ornamental bronze metal; with screws for steel key.
Each........ $0.03
Per dozen........ .33
41498 Keyhole Escutcheon, ornamental bronze metal; with screws for iron or brass key.
Each........$0.05
Per dozen........ .54

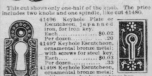

Escutcheons—Continued.   Locks—Continued.   Front Door Sets—Continued.

41499 Keyhole Escutcheon, with drop; ornamental bronze metal, packed, with screws for steel key.
Each $0.08
Per dozen............... .87
Escutcheons weigh from 8 to 15 oz. to the dozen.

Locks, Etc. Geneva Bronzed, Royal Bronze and Old Copper Finish.

Geneva bronzed goods are iron made in imitation of royal bronze. The background is finished in black, the raised surfaces (the white lines seen in cuts) are finely polished and then electroplated with bronze metal. They are handsome goods, and such a good imitation of the genuine bronze that an expert can hardly tell them apart, and being much lower in price must naturally become very popular.

Front Door Locks.
We will always send you the latest and most popular designs in Geneva bronze goods.

Front Door Lock Mortise Knob, with patent anti-friction latch ornamental bronze front (see cut of front); 2 bolts, bronze thumb-piece and rose, 1 nickel plated steel bolt key, 2 nickel plated steel night keys, ornamental solid bronze knobs, an escutcheon for outside (see cut), 1 escutcheon for inside; size of lock, 5¼x3½ inches. This lock is finely made and will last for years. When ordering, state whether right or left hand is wanted.

41508 This set comprises 1 lock 4¾x3¼, the same as shown in cut 41507. Circular fluted pattern, wrought bronze knob and escutcheon, as shown in cut.
Price per set..............$1.78
Price per dozen set..........18.75

Front Door Mortise Lock Set.

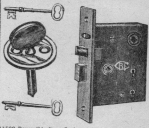

The door butts are solid bronze metal, handsomely finished, steel bushed, with steel pin; 4x4 butts weigh 1 lb. 15 oz., the 5x5 butts, weigh 3 lbs. 3 oz. We furnish the above with 4x4 or 5x5 butts.
41502 Set complete, with 4x4 butts............$4.06
41503 Set complete, with 5x5 butts............ 4.55

41504 Set of furnishings for single door, consisting of one reversible mortise lock, 3½x3¼, with bronze plated front and striking plate, brass bolts, ebony knob, bronze plated mountings and two 6-inch bronze plated steel key and a handsome pair of 4x4 bronze-plated cast butts; all packed in paper box, complete with screws. The lock alone is worth the price we ask for the set.
Weight, 4½ pounds.
Price, per set, complete...$1.10
Per dozen sets............11.00

41509 Reversible Easy Springs, with Turn Knob; size of lock 4½x3½, plain front, in old copper finish, an entirely new and very elegant design, weight per set, 3¼ lbs. Price per set, complete...$1.75
Price per dozen set, complete..............20.00

41500 Front Door Mortise Lock, royal bronze front and strike knobs and escutcheon; has bronze bolts, royal bronze turn knobs, plated steel lock key, 2 plated steel night keys. Size of lock, 4¾x3½; size of knobs, 2¼. Packed one set in a box complete, with screws, per set...... $1.25
41501 Front Door Mortise Lock same description as No. 41500; plain bronze, old copper finish; an entirely new, elegant and very popular finish. Complete, packed with knobs, escutcheon and screws, per set................... 1.55

Bronze Metal Front Door Lock.

The preceding cuts, showing lock, front door knob, escutcheon and pair of butts, represent the handsomest patterns of real bronze goods made. The finish is extremely handsome; the raised surfaces are a light polished bronze; the background a dark color, making a durable and elegant finish.

41502-3

Trimmings for Front Doors.
Front Door Sets.

41507 Eulalla Design, bronze metal, antique copper finish, size of lock 4¾ x 3¼, thickness of case ⅝ inch, width of front 1⅜ inch distance; from front of lock to center of hub and key holes, 2⅜ inch; it has 2 plated steel night keys and 1 lock key; lock has 1 tumbler on each bolt.
Price per set, as shown in cut................$1.75
Price per dozen set................18.72

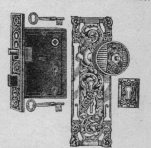

41510 Mortise Front Door Lock, bronze metal antique finish. Brass and wrought iron inside work, with night works. Size of lock, 5¼x3½. Knob and escutcheon of bronze metal, antique finish; a new and handsome design; has plated steel key with one tumbler on each bolt.
Price, per set complete, as shown in cut........$3.25

24—6th

Door Locks—Continued.

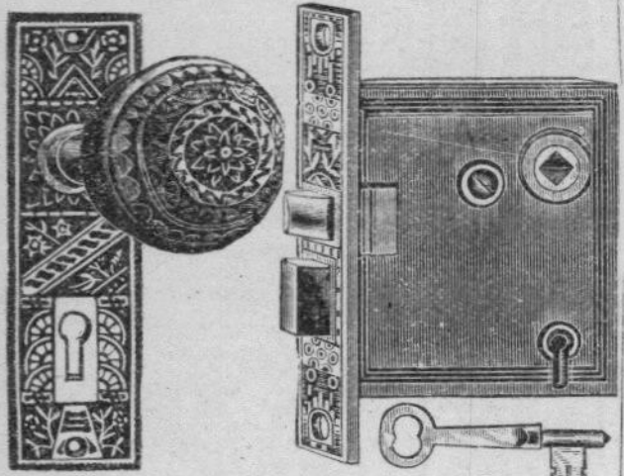

41515 Royal Bronze Mortise Knob Lock (reverse by taking off cap); size of lock, 3½x3¼; size of knobs, 2¼ inches. Has plated steel key, complete with screws $0.82

41516 Plain Bronze Mortise Knob Lock, old copper finish, an entirely new, elegant and popular finish. Knobs and inside escutcheons same as No. 41515. Packed, complete, with knobs, escutcheons and screws; per set complete...... 1.00

MORTISE KNOB LOCKS AND KNOBS.

For inside doors.

Consists of 1 mortise lock, 1 pair knobs, and two escutcheons

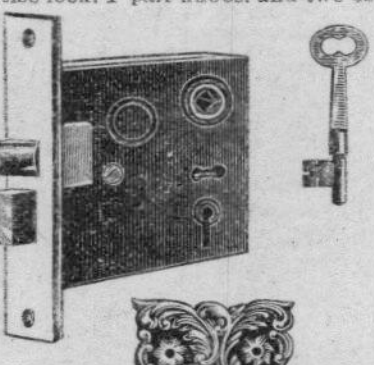

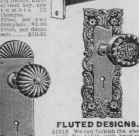

41518 A new and very elegant inside Door Set of Eulalia design. It has bronze metal front, antique copper finish with bronze metal antique copper finish knob and escutcheons. Size of lock 3¼x3¼ inches, nickel steel key, one tumble 12 changes.
Price, per set complete...$1.00
Price, per dozen sets.......$10.31

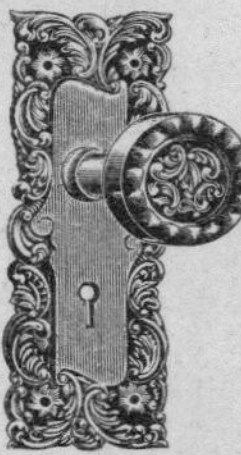

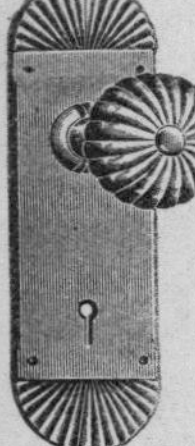

FLUTED DESIGNS.

41519 We can furnish the above lock, No. 41518, with knob and escutcheons of fluted design like cut.
Price, per set complete....$1.00
Per doz sets complete.......10.30

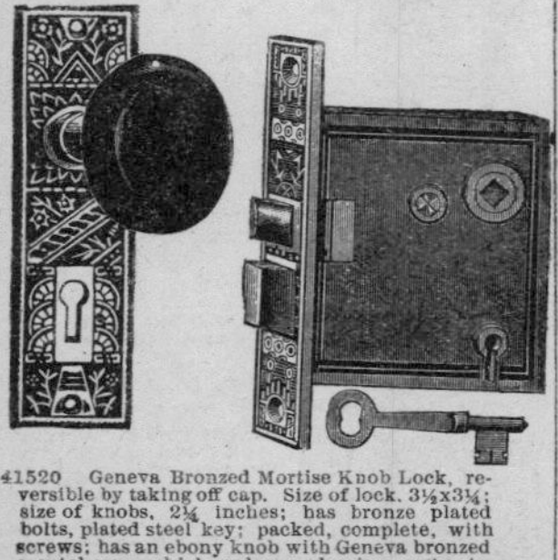

41520 Geneva Bronzed Mortise Knob Lock, reversible by taking off cap. Size of lock, 3½x3¼; size of knobs, 2¼ inches; has bronze plated bolts, plated steel key; packed, complete, with screws; has an ebony knob with Geneva bronzed escutcheons, which makes a pleasing contrast. Price, per set, complete.... $0.40 Per dozen....$4.50

Door Locks—Continued.

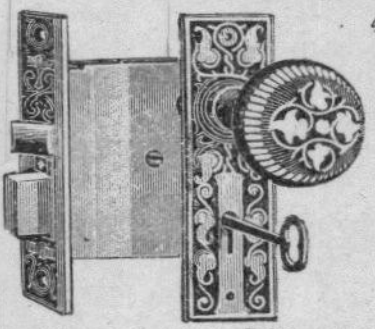

41525 Wrought Steel Mortised Lock. 3½ inch, with ornamented real bronze front, knob and escutcheons and nickel plated steel key. This is an entirely new pattern and is extremely handsome. The surfaces are polished bronze, the background a dark finish, making a very effective and attractive appearance. Price, per set, packed, complete, with screws.......... $0.88

41526 Wrought Steel Mortise Lock, 3½ inch, bronze plated knob and escutcheon, same pattern as No. 41525, but is bronze plated on iron, in place of being solid bronze metal. A very good lock for inside doors. Price, per set, with knob and escutcheon.......... .75

Inside Lock Sets.

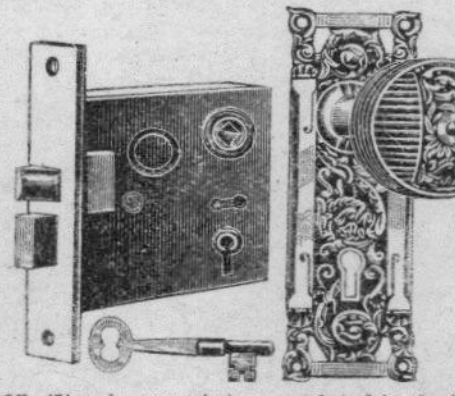

41527 The above set is bronze plated in the best possible manner and finished in antique copper, closely resembling genuine bronze in appearance. They are made from entirely new patterns and are offered with the full assurance that they are superior to any goods of this kind on the market. The size of the lock is 3¼x3¼ inch, has nickel steel key, one tumbler, 12 changes.
Price per set (consisting of one mortise lock, 2 escutcheons and 1 pair of knobs, as shown in cut).......... $1.00
Price per dozen sets.......... 10.30

Store Door Handles and Locks.

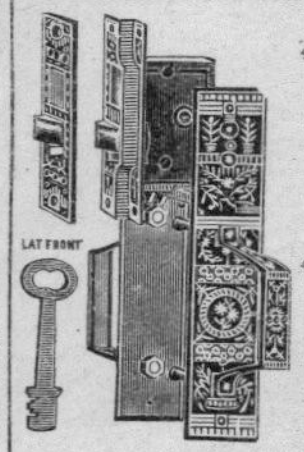

41533 **Geneva Bronzed Extra Heavy, Oblique Double Handle,** 3-tumbler, mortise lock, 4¼x3 inches; bronze metal bolts; patent anti-friction latch; 2 nickel-plated flat steel keys; flat front reversible latch.
Price per set, as shown in cut, with flat front lock.... $1.90

41534 Same as above, with full rabbet front lock, ½-inch Rabbet. In ordering parties must state if RIGHT or LEFT hand is wanted, as this latch is not reversible. Price per set, as shown in cut, with rabbet front Lock.......... $2.10

Store Door Handle.

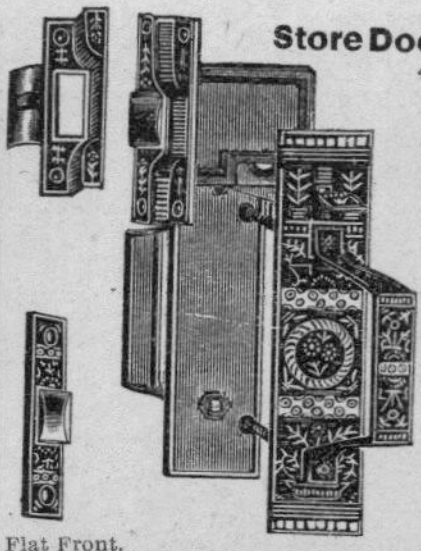

41535 Store Door Handle with Latch, rabbet front, ½ inch rabbet, like cut, oblique double handle, Geneva bronze finish. Size of latch 2¾x3¼; bronze metal bolt with anti-friction roller strike. In ordering state whether right or left-hand is wanted. Complete with screws. Per set..$1.00

Flat Front.

41536 Store Door Handle with mortise latch, same as above reversible flat front, either right or left hand, complete with screws, per set..... .85

Oblique Store Door Handles.

41538 Store Door Handle, a new pattern, Geneva bronzed, with oblique handle, either for right or left hand, complete with screws.
When ordering above store door handle, be sure to state whether for right or left hand, or we shall be obliged to omit it. Price, per set.......$0.30

Sliding Door Latch.

GENEVA BRONZED.

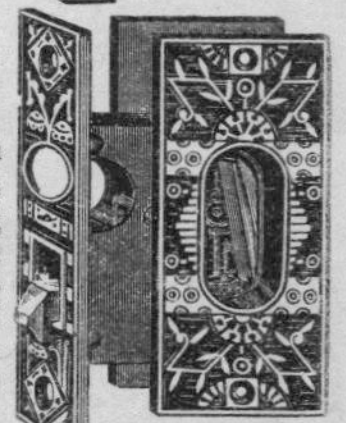

41540 Geneva Bronzed Sliding Door Latch, flat fronts; for double doors; size, 3¼x3¼ inches. Geneva bronze front and strike, bronze bolt, complete with 4 elongated flush Geneva bronzed escutcheons, one set in a box; weight, 4½ pounds.
Per set.......... $0.80

Sliding Door Locks.

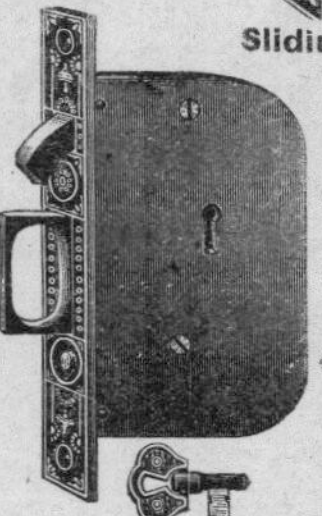

41542 Sliding Door Lock; size, 5¼x3¼; Geneva bronzed, flat front, brass bolt and pulls, bronze metal drop key, complete with 4 elongated flush Geneva bronzed escutcheons; weight, 4¼ lbs. Per set...... $1.10

41543 Sliding Door Lock, 5½x3¾, same description as above, only astragal front; weight, 4¼ lbs. Per set $1.50

41544 Sliding Door Lock, flat front, 5½x3½, same description as No. 41543 for single door; has two elongated escutcheons. These locks cannot be used on doors thicker than 1½ in. Price, complete. $0.85

Sliding Door Locks.

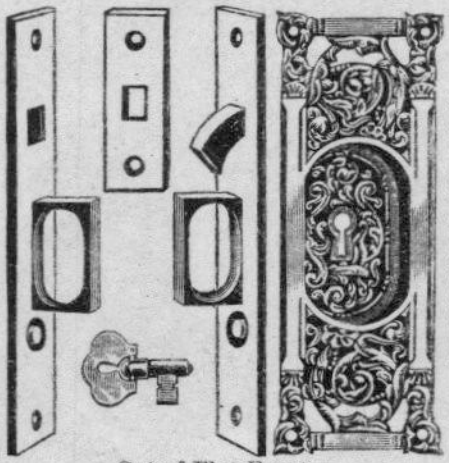

We show in the cuts only the face of the locks and one cup escutcheon. We furnish locks complete as stated below. The locks *can not* be used on doors thinner than 1⅛ inch.

Cut of Flat Front.

41545 Single Sliding Door Lock. Columbian design in iron, antique copper plated, flat front with single lock; two flush cup escutcheons. Size of lock 5¼x3½ inches. In ordering always state thickness of your door. This is very important, as keys are made for 1¼-1¾ to 2-2¼ inch doors. Price per set complete for single door.......... $1.25

41546 Sliding Door Lock for double doors, same as 41545, except that it has double locks with 4 flush cup escutcheons. Price per set complete for double doors (always state thickness of your door).......... 2.00

41546½ Same as 41546 with astragal front locks. (Always state thickness of your door.) Price per set, complete.......... 2.25

Sliding Door Lock.

EULALIA DESIGN.

Heavy Bronze metal, antique copper finish. Size of lock 5½x 3½ in. Wrought bronze flush cup escutcheons made for doors sliding in flush with the wall. These locks cannot be used on doors thinner than 1½ inch.

41547 Sliding Door Lock for single door, with flat front lock, 5½x3½ inch; two flush cup escutcheons; thickness of lock ¼ inch; width of front, 1 inch. Always state thickness of your doors. Price complete for single door....$1.25

41548 Sliding Door Locks (for double door), same as 41547, except that it has double lock with four flush cup escutcheons.
State thickness of your door.
Price per set, complete, for double doors....$2.10

41548½ Same as above, with astragal front locks.
Per set, complete....2.35

41549 Same as 41547, with fluted design cup escutcheons as shown in cut. Price per set $1.35
41550 Same as 41548, with fluted design cup escutcheons, as shown in cut. Price per set $2.35
41550½ Same as 41548½, with fluted design cup escutcheons, as shown in cut. State thickness of your door. Price per set $2.35

Chain Door Fasteners.

GENEVA BRONZED.

41551—Geneva bronzed Chain Door Fasteners, a very neat device. The door may be left slightly ajar and no one can effect an entrance from the outside. Size, 6 inches, complete with screws. Weight, 15 oz.
Each....$0.25

41552 Thumb Latches, enameled. Weight, 15 ounces. Per set, ...$0.08
Per dozen sets, ...$0.75

Door Pulls.

41553 Door Pull, Geneva Bronzed, 7 inch, oblique pattern, packed complete with screws.
Each....$0.12 Per dozen....$1.30

Door Pulls—Continued.

41554—Door Pulls, Geneva Bronzed 6 inches, straight pattern, complete with screws.
Each....$0.08 Per doz....$0.60

41556—Foot Bolt Geneva Bronzed, 6 inch extra heavy, with strike plate. Packed complete, with screws. Each....$0.25
Per doz....2.40

Chain Bolts.

41557—Chain Bolt for top of door; Geneva bronzed, 6-in., extra heavy, with strike plate.
Each....$0.25
Per doz....2.75

Door Bolts.

41558 Geneva Bronzed Door Bolt, with bronze metal knob; size of bolt, 3 inch; packed with screws. Weight, 9 oz.
Each....$0.15
Per doz....1.45

Shutter Bars.

41560 Geneva Bronzed Shutter Bars, reversible. 2¾ in.; complete with screws, weight, per doz.; 12 oz.
Each....$0.08
Per doz....90

41561 Columbian Design, antique copper plated; complete with screws. Price, each....$0.12
Per doz....1.35

Letter Box Plates.

41564 Geneva Bronzed Letter Box Plate for door, 7¾ in.; packed with screws. Weight, 12 oz.
Each....$0.20
Per doz....1.80

Door Buttons.

41566 Geneva Bronzed Door Buttons, on plate, size, 2 in.; complete with screws. Weight, per doz., 1 lb. 9 oz.
Each....$0.05
Per doz....40

Cupboard Bolts.

41568 Geneva Bronzed Flat Cupboard Bolt with bronze metal knob; complete with screws. Weight, each, 5 oz.
Each....$0.08
Per doz....87

Cupboard Turns.

41569 Columbian Design, antique, copper plated, size 2¾x2¼ inch; complete with screws. Each....$0.20
Per doz....2.75

Sash Pulleys.

41575 Geneva Bronzed Sash Pulley, 2¼ in. noiseless heavy wrought pin, turned wheel, complete with screws. Weight, 1 lb. Each....$0.12
Per doz....1.00

41576 Common Iron Sash Pulleys; 2 inches.
Per doz....$0.25

Sash Lifts.

41577 Geneva Bronzed Flush Sash Lift; size, 3 inches over all; complete with screws. Weight, 6 oz.
Each....$0.05
Per doz....45

41578 Columbian Design, antique, copper plated; has side screw holes; complete with screws. Price, each....$0.12
Per doz....1.06

41579 Eulalia Design, bronze metal, antique copper finish; has side screw holes; complete with screws. Price, each....$0.08
Per doz....75

41580 Geneva bronzed sash lift 1⅜ inches wide; complete with screws; weight, per doz., 1 lb. Each....$0.03
Per doz....25

41581 Columbian Design, antique copper plated; size, 2x1¾ inches. Complete with screws. Price, each....$0.08
Price, per dozen....75

41582 Eulalia Design, bronze metal, antique copper finish. Complete with screws. Price, each....$0.07
Price, per dozen....60

41583 Bar Handle Window or Sash Lift, Columbian design, antique copper plated. Complete with screws. Price, each....$0.17
Price, per dozen....1.70

Sash Pull Plates.

41584 Geneva Bronzed Sash Pull Plates, used in connection with pull-down hook; size, 2¼ inches; complete with screws, plates only; weight, 1 lb. 15 oz. to the dozen.
Each....$0.04
Per doz....35

Brass Butts.

41736 Wrought Brass Butts. No screws.

Sizes	¾x¾	1x⅞	1¼x⅞	1½x1
Weight, per pair	2	3	4	4 oz
Per pair	2c	3c	4c	5c
Per dozen pair	11c	13c	16c	20c
Sizes	1¾x1¼	2x1½	2½x1⅝	3x1⅝
Per pair	$0.06	.06	.07	.10
Per dozen pair	.24	.31	.50	.75

We do not furnish screws at the above prices.

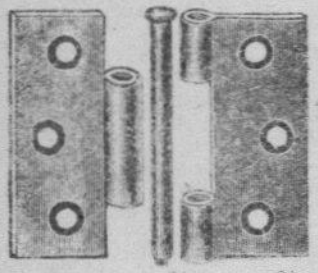

41740 Wrought steel, loose pin, light narrow butts. No screws furnished.

Size.	Size open.	Size of screw.	Per dozen.	Per pair
1½ in	1⅛	No. 5	$0.19	$0.03
1¾ in	1⅛	No. 5	.22	.03
2 in	1⅛	No. 6	.24	.04
2¼ in	1⅛	No. 6	.27	.04
2½ in	1⅛	No. 6	.30	.04
3 in	2	No. 6	.39	.05

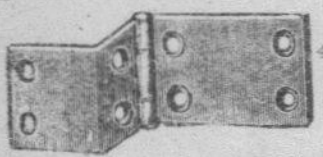

41744 Wrought Steel Chest Hinges, patent riveted. No screws furnished.

Size.	1½ inch.	2 inch.
Inside of bend to center of pin	13/16	1
Size of screw used	No. 5	
No. of screw-holes in each	8	8
Price, per pair	$0.05	$0.08
Per dozen pair	.45	.61

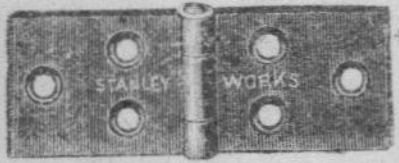

41746 Wrought Steel Back Flaps, patent riveted, 6 screw holes. No screws furnished.

Width	¾	⅞	1	1⅛	1¼	1⅜	1½	2
Length open	2¼	2⅜	2⅞	3	3¼	3¼	3½	4⅜
Size of screw used	6	6	6	6	7	7	8	8
Price, per pair	3c.	3c.	3c.	3c.	4c.	4c.	4c.	5c.
Price, pr dz. pair	16c.	18c.	20c.	22c.	24c.	27c.	30c.	35c.

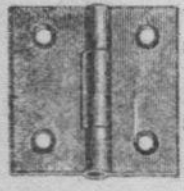

41748 Wrought Iron Butts, fast joint. (No screws furnished.)

Size	1 in.	1¼ in.	1½ in.	1¾ in.
Wgt, pr pair	2	3	4	4 oz.
Per pair	2c	2c	3c	3c
Per dozen	12c	14c	17c	20c
Size	2 in.	2¼ in.	2½ in.	3 in.
Wgt. pr pair	4	5	7	8 oz.
Per pair	4c	4c	4c	4c
Per dozen	.21c	22c	25c	32c.

41740. Wrought Steel Reversible Butts, much stronger and better than iron, with planished surface. Same as 41740, but much heavier. The price given is without screws.

Size open,	Size of screw.	Price per dozen pairs.	Per pair.
3x2½	No. 10	$0.51	$0.06
3x3	No. 10	.57	.07
3½x3½	No. 11	.81	.09
4x4	No. 11	1.00	.10
4½x4½	No. 12	1.29	.12

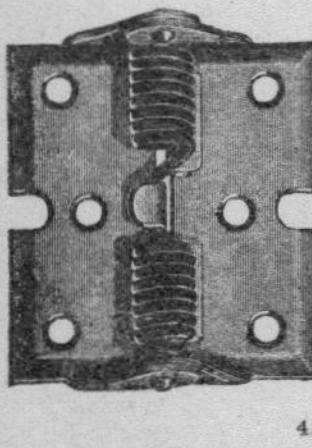

Wrought Steel Spring Hinges.

41755 Stearns' Unbreakable Steel Spring Hinge; the only wrought steel hold-back screen door hinge in the market; japanned, packed, with screws.
Price, each $0.12
Per doz 1.30

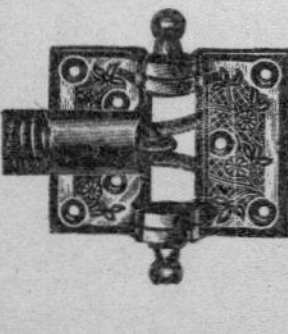

41756 Stearns' Matchless Hold-Back Spring Hinge, with covered spring, for screen doors, either right or left hand. This hinge is made extra heavy, with no light parts to break and get out of order. The spring being covered, is protected from the weather and will last longer than any other spring hinge made. It will hold the door either open or closed. Per pair, no screws furnished $0.10
Per doz. pair........ 1.00

Hinges—Continued.

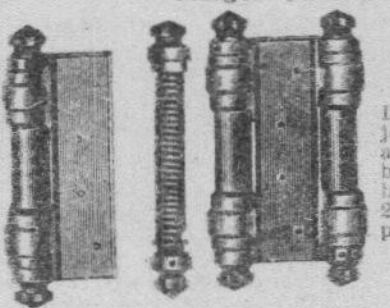

The Gem Screen Door Spring Butt, japanned, with spiral spring, reversible, for right or left hand doors; weight, 2¾ to 3¾ lbs. per pair.

SINGLE ACTION, TO SWING ONE WAY.

41757 3½-inch for doors ⅝ to 1⅛ inch, per pair..$0.50
41758 4-inch for doors 1 to 1⅜ inch, " .. .65
41759 5-inch for doors 1 to 1½ inch, " .. .80

DOUBLE ACTION, TO SWING BOTH WAYS.

41760 3½-inch for doors ¾ to 1⅛ inch, per pair..$1.10
41761 4-inch for doors 1 to 1⅜ inch, " .. 1.25
41762 5-inch for doors 1 to 1½ inch, " .. 1.60

Door Springs.

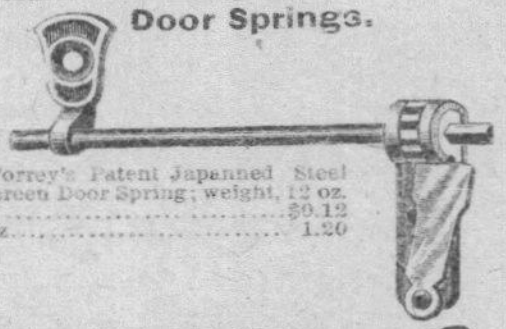

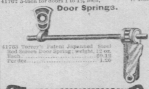

41763 Torrey's Patent Japanned Steel Rod Screen Door Spring; weight, 12 oz.
Each $0.12
Per doz 1.20

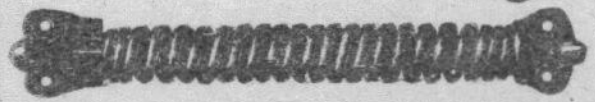

41764 Spiral Spring, made of No. 9 steel wire, japanned; weight, 11 oz. Each, 8c. Per doz...$0.87

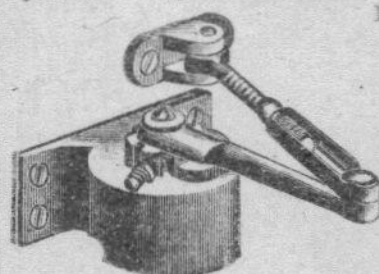

Eclipse Door Spring is suitable for either right or left hand doors. To change the doors, simply withdraw the pin at the bottom of the case and turn the spring the other side up. Directions how to apply packed with each one.

	Tuscan bronze	Nickel plated.
41765 For inside doors; weight, 3¼ lbs. Each	$0.90	$2.40
41766 For heavy outside doors; weight, 5¾ lbs. Each	1.25	2.85

Eclipse Door Check.

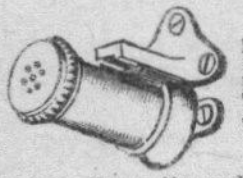

Eclipse Door Check, used to prevent doors with springs attached from slamming. Always put cylinder indoors if possible. To regulate the draft turn cap at end of cylinder.

	Tuscan bronze.	Nickel. plated.
41767 For ordinary doors; weight, 3¼ lbs., 1¾ in. cylinder. Each	$1.50	$3.00
41768 For heavy doors; weight, 4¼ lbs., 2 in. cylinder. Each	1.98	3.50

Base Knobs.

Weight, per dozen, 1¾ lbs.

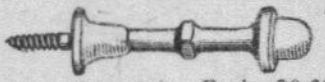

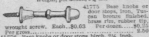

41775 Base knobs or door stops, iron, Tuscan bronze finished, brass rim, rubber tip, wrought screw. Each..$0.03 Per dozen.....$0.25
Per gross.. 2.50
41776 Base knobs or door stops, birch, 2¼ inch, with rubber tip. Each............................. .02
Per dozen.. .20
Per gross.. 1.75
41777 Same as No. 41776, walnut. Each....... .03
Per dozen........25c. Per gross................. 2.25

Padlocks.

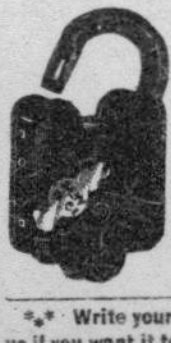

41790 Japanned iron, square, 1 wheel ward, self locking, spring shackle, brass, keyhole cover; width, 2¼ inch, a strong lock, 2 keys; weight, 7 oz,
Each $0.18
Per dozen 1.95

***** Write your name and Address on package returned to us if you want it to have attention; send letter of instructions by mail; do not put it in package.**

Padlocks—Continued.

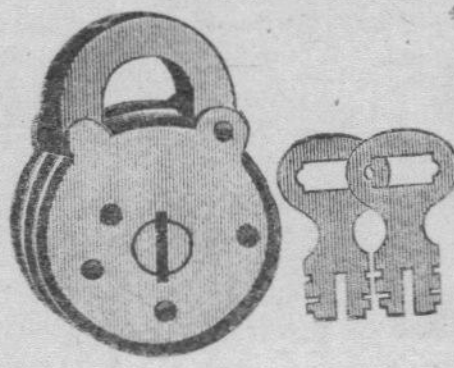

41795

41795 Eagle Padlocks, brass, plain finish, self-locking two double bitted flat steel keys with each lock, all different in a doz.
Each. $0.50
Per dozen, ... $5.40

41796 The Eagle Padlock, made of wrought iron japanned, same style as No. 41795, self-locking, two fancy double bitted keys with each, a very strong and good lock.
Each ....$0.40 Per doz. $4.40

Solid Bronze Metal.

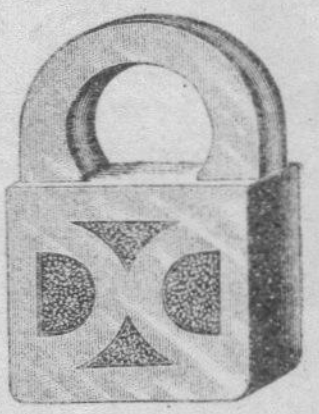

41797 Self-locking unpickable padlock, the best in the market, with two rolled steel keys, with keyhole covered by revolving brass cylinder, size, 2¼x1¾; weight 5¾ oz.
Price, each........$0.25
Price, per dozen... 2.60

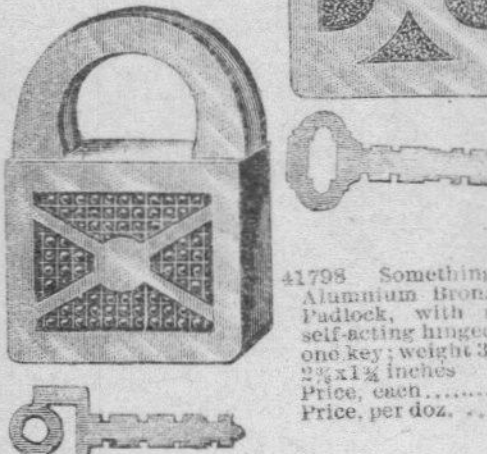

41798 Something new—Aluminum Bronze Spring Padlock, with automatic self-acting hinged shackle, one key; weight 3¼ oz., size 2⅜x1¾ inches
Price, each $0.12
Price, per doz. 1.25

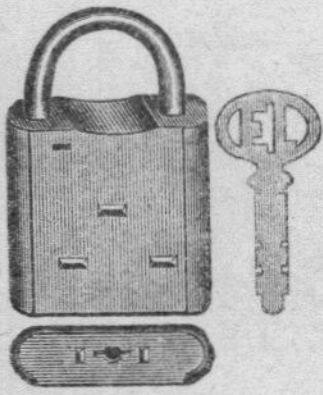

41800 The Eureka Padlock, japanned, self-locking, 1 flat steel key with each; size of lock, 1¾ inches.
Each.... ....$0.10
Per doz 1.08

The Champion 6-Lever Padlock.

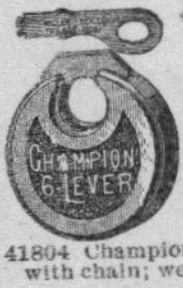

41803 6-lever Padlock made entirely of cast bronze, with interior parts of brass, warranted not to give out or rust in any climate; springs made of the celebrated phosphor bronze, keys of steel, nickel plated, no two locks take same keys, most secure and durable self-locking padlock in the market; 3¼ inches, 2 keys, hasp will pass through ⅜ inch hole. Weight, 12 ounces. Each. $0.50
41804 Champion 6-lever Padlock, same as 41803 with chain; weight, 14 ounces. Each. .60

Jackson "4-Lever Automatic" Padlock.

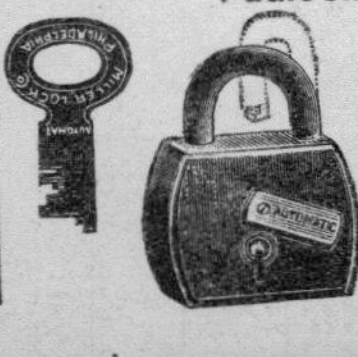

For *security*, *durability* and *convenience* these Padlocks are unequaled. Made of steel and brass.
41805 Steel dark finish. Price each $0.25
Per doz....... 2.50
41806 Brass bright finish.
Price, each $0.30
Per doz.......... 3.25

Screw Lock Padlocks.

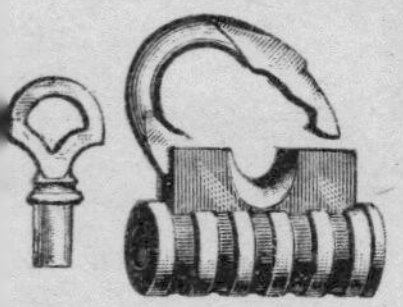

41807 Padlock, iron japanned, and self-locking, screw key; this padlock is very novel and secure; after inserting the key into the keyhole it has to be turned 3 or 4 times, or screwed into the padlock before it will unlock; two keys with each lock. Weight, 10 oz.
Price, each..........$0.25 Per dozen..........$2.70

Combination Padlocks.

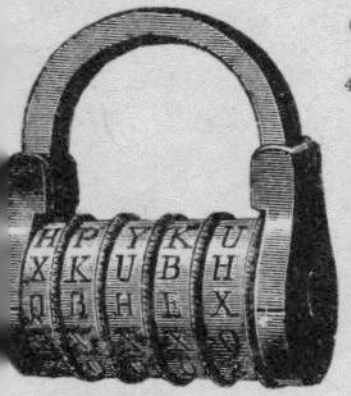

41808 Keyless Brass Padlock, without springs; 100 different changes of combination. Cut shows the full size. Weight, 3½ oz.
Price, each.....$0.65
Per dozen......7.00

Scandinavian Padlocks.

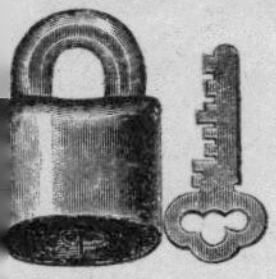

Padlock, iron case, painted red, detached shackle, two keys, good substantial lock, like cut, excepting has open keyhole and nearly square key.

1809 Size, 1⅝x2⅛.
Each..............$0.07 Per dozen..........$0.50
Extra, by mail. Each.......................07
1810 Size, 2¼x1½.
Each..............$0.08 Per dozen..........70
Extra, by mail. Each.......................11
1811 Size, 3x1¾.
Each..........$0.10 Per dozen..............80
xtra, by mail. Each........................15

Yale Padlocks.

For design, construction and finish these are undoubtedly the best line of padlocks ever made; for solidity, security, durability and convenience they are unexcelled.
1812 No. 813, Yale padlock; size, 1 inch; 2 flat keys, no chain; weight, 5 ounces.
Each...............$0.70 With chain.......$0.90

Mortise Door Bolt.

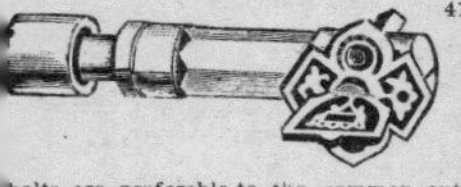

41820 Iron Mortise Front Door Bolts, ¾x3, with real bronze thumb-piece and rose. These bolts are preferable to the common outside barrel bolt, as they are not unsightly, being mortised into the door. Nothing shows but the thumb-piece, and they are the most secure fastening made.
Weight, 9 oz. Each.......$0.10 Per dozen....$0.75

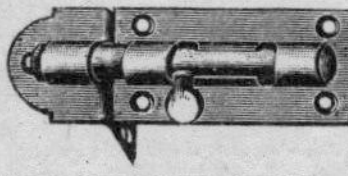

1825 Wrought Iron Barrel Door Bolts, japanned; the strongest and best bolt in the market, with best staple, which gives it greater resisting power; price is without screws.

4inch	Price each $0.07	Per dozen $0.65
5 inch	" " .08	" " .75
6 inch	" " .09	" " .85

Flush Bolts.

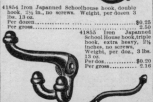

1828 Geneva Bronzed Flush Bolts, 1 inch wide; packed with screws.

	6 in.	8 in.	12 in.
Weight, each	10 oz.	11 oz.	14 oz.
Price, each	$0.12	$0.15	$0.20
Per dozen	1.25	1.40	1.75

Bolts—Continued.

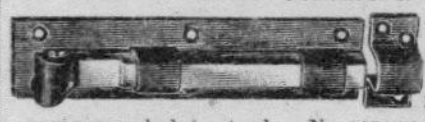

41831 Wrought Iron Square Door Bolts, with japan plates and polished bolts, steel springs and plain staple. No screws furnished at this price.

Size.	4 in.	5 in.	6 in.
Bolts,	5-16 in. sq.	⅜ in. sq.	½ in. sq.
Per doz	$0.75	$0.80	$0.85
Each	.08	.09	.10

Barn Door Bolts.

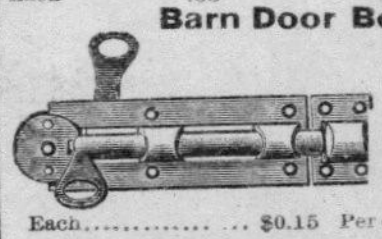

41832 Barn Door Bolts, japanned iron. This bolt is very handy; can be operated from both sides of the door; has heavy bolt 8 inch long; weighs 2 lbs.
Each..............$0.15 Per dozen..........$1.60

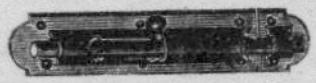

41833 Door Bolts, japanned, with brass knobs.

Sizes	4 in.	5 in.	6 in.
Weight, each	8 oz.	10 oz.	12 oz
Price, each	$0.03	$0.05	$0.06
Price, per dozen	.33	.54	.65

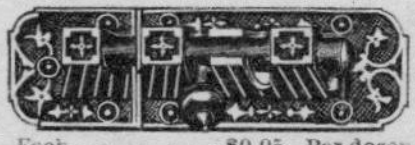

41836 Barrel Bolts, 3 inch, dark bronzed; packed with screws Weight 7 oz.
Each..............$0.05 Per dozen..........$0.50

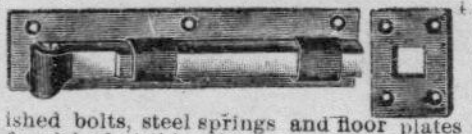

41839—Wrought Iron Bottom Bolt, with japanned plates, polished bolts, steel springs and floor plates No screws furnished at this price.

Size.	5 in.	6 in.	7 in.	8 in.
Bolts,	⅜ in. sq.	⅜ in. sq.	½ in. sq.	½ in. sq.
Per doz.	$0.79	$0.85	$1.15	$1.20
Each.	.10	.12	.15	.16

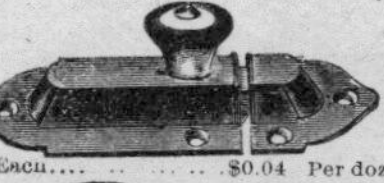

41845 Cupboard Catch, (ab), japanned iron, porcelain knob.
Weight, 4 oz.
Each..............$0.04 Per dozen..........$0.44

Door Buttons.

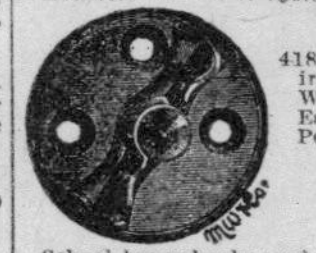

41850 Door Buttons, japanned iron, 1¾ inch.
Weight, 4 oz.
Each.....................$0.02
Per dozen.................22

Hat and Coat Hooks.

School house hooks are heavier and stronger than the ordinary hat or coat hooks and are sometimes preferred for wardrobe use for that reason.

For screws see Index.

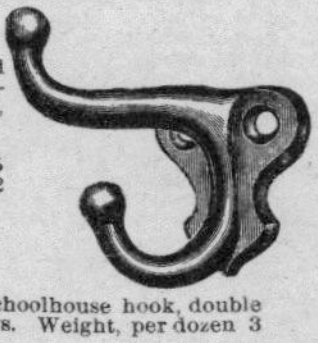

41853 Iron Japanned Schoolhouse Hook, single hook, 2½ inches, no screws.
Weight. 2¼ lbs.
Per dozen..........$0.15
Per gross..........1.62

41854 Iron Japanned Schoolhouse hook, double hook, 2½ in., no screws. Weight, per dozen 3 lbs. 13 oz.
Per dozen..................................$0.25
Per gross..................................2.50

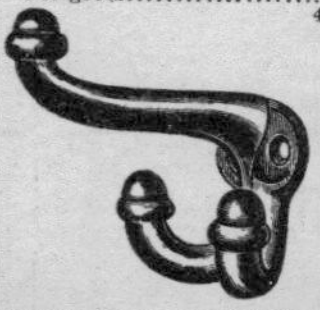

41855 Iron Japanned School House hook, triple hook, extra heavy, 2½ inches, no screws,
Weight, per doz., 3 lbs. 13 oz.
Per doz..............$0.20
Per gross............2.16

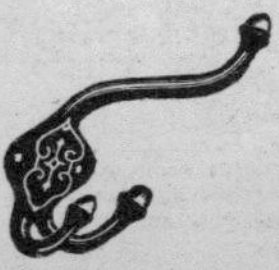

41858 Iron Japanned Hat and Coat Hook, 4 inch
Weight, per doz., 1 lb. 13 oz.
Per doz............$0.10
Per gross..........1.05

Hooks—Continued.

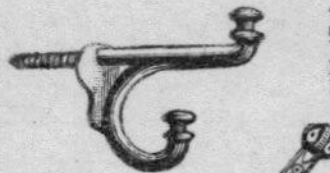

41859 Iron Japnned Hat and Coat Hook, 2½ inch.
Weight, per dozen 1¼ lbs.
Per doz...............$0.08
Per gross..............87

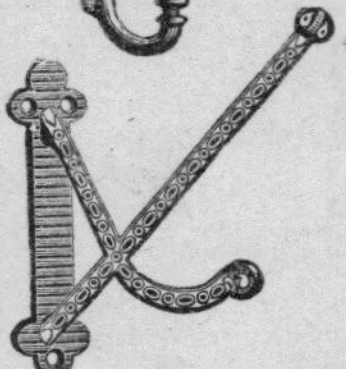

41860 Hat and Coat Hooks, bronzed iron, a very neat pattern. Weight, per dozen, 3¼ lbs.
Per doz.........$0.35
Per gross........3.88

41865 Iron Japanned Hat and Coat Hook, 3½ inch; weight, per doz., doz., 1 lb. 5 oz.
Per doz..........$0.10
Per gross..........95

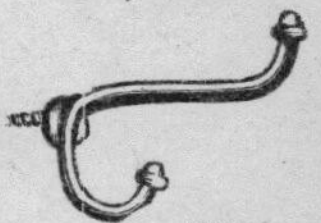

41865

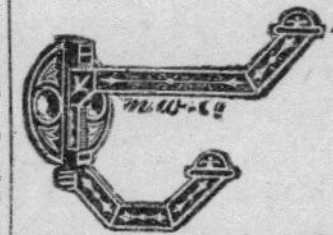

41866 Adamantine bronzed hat and coat hook, 4 inch. Weight, per doz., 2lbs. 10 oz.
Per dozen..........$0.20
Per gross..........2.16
(Screws furnished).

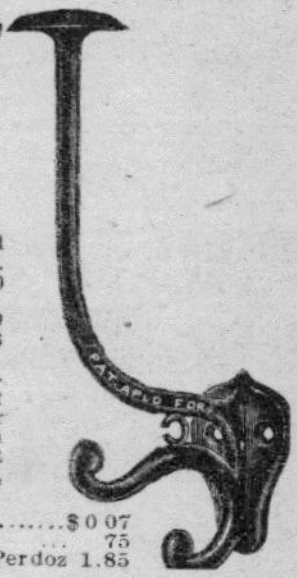

41867 Hat, coat and umbrella rack. The short hook, 4 inches long, for coat; whole length from lower hook to top of hat hook, 10 inches; weight, ½lb.
Japanned. Each...................$0 07
Per dozen.............................75
Nickel plated, each $0.17 Per doz 1.85

Geneva Bronzed.

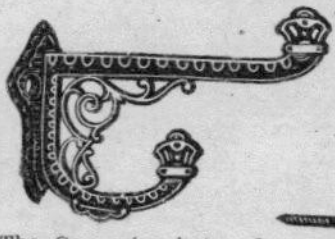

41868 Hat and coat hook, Geneva bronzed complete with screws; a very handsome pattern; size 3¼ in. weight per doz. 2 lb. 10 oz.
Per dozen......$0.45
Per gross......4.80

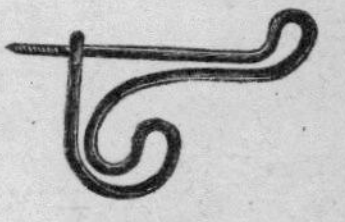

The Gem wire hat and coat hooks having gimlet screw points; they are easily put up or removed, no extra screws or tools being required.
41869-Coppered.
41870-Japanned

Size	2½	3	3½
Japanned per doz	$0.08	$0.10	$0.10
Japanned, per gross	.87	1.08	1.08
Coppered, per doz	.07	.08	.09
Coppered, per gross	.75	.87	.98

Furniture Handles.

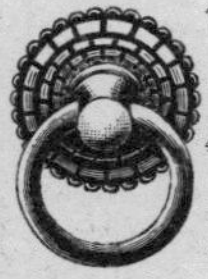

41880 Furniture Handle, ring pattern, gilt.
Weight, per doz., 1 lb. 4 oz.
Each.....$0.06
Per dozen. 67

41881 Furniture Handle, ring pattern, gilt finish: weight per dozen 15 oz.
Each.....$0.03
Per doz.. .33

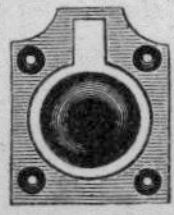

41883 Flush Brass Pulls for small drawers.

Size	1	1¼	1½	2 in.
Weight	2 oz.	2 oz.	3 oz.	3 oz.
Price each	7c.	8c.	9c.	15c.
Per doz.	$0.60	$0.80	$0.90	$1.62

Cleavers.

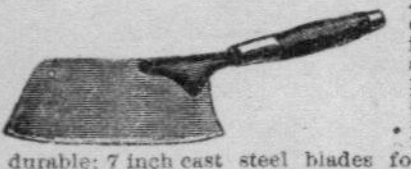

42175 Family Cleavers, with improved malleable iron shanks riveted through handles into heavy iron caps, very strong and durable; 7 inch cast steel blades forged and hardened; is a very handy household article and should be in every one's kitchen. Each........................$0.35
Per doz.. 3.78

Beatty's Butchers' Cleavers.

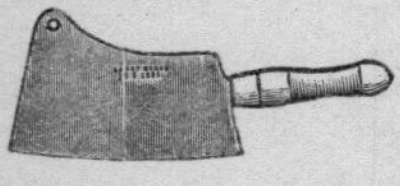

Extra Cast steel, hickory handles.

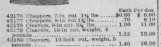

	Each	Per doz.
42176 Choppers, 7-in. cut 1½ lbs	$0.60	$ 6.90
42177 Choppers, 8-in cut 1¾ lbs	.70	8.10
42178 Cleavers, 9-in cut 3¼ lbs	1.00	11.00
42179 Cleavers, 10-in cut, weight, 4 pounds	1.12	12.00
42180 Cleavers, 12-inch cut, weight, 5 pounds	1.40	16.20

Skewers.

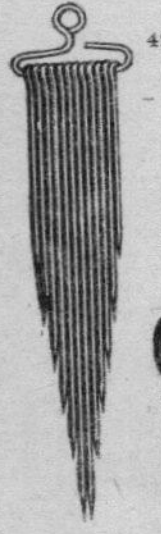

42185 Tinned Iron Skewers for kitchen use. These are superior to wooden skewers for putting up roast meat, etc., as they can be easily withdrawn and used over again. Come in sets of 12, on wire hook with eye for hanging on nail.
Per set $0.15
Per dozen set.................................. 1.50
Weight, 9 oz.

Block Scrapers.

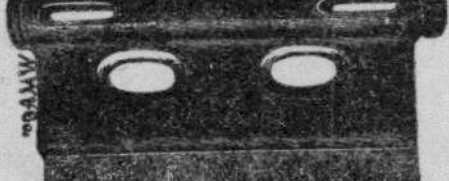

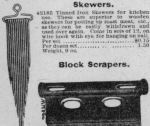

42188 Butchers' block scrapers, cast steel blades, oil tempered; weight, 1 lb., 7 oz. Each.........$0.38
Per doz.................................. 4.90

Hog Scrapers.

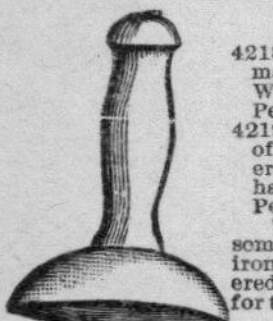

42189 Hog Scrapers, cast steel, made of No. 18 sheet steel. Weight, 12 oz. Each......$0.21
Per doz.......................... 2.25
42190 Hog Scrapers, iron, made of No. 20 sheet iron, for farmers' use, with bolt through the handle. Each..................$0.10
Per doz.......................... 1.08
These hog scrapers are shaped something like the bottom of an iron candlestick, and are considered the best instruments in use for the purpose.

Meat Cutters.

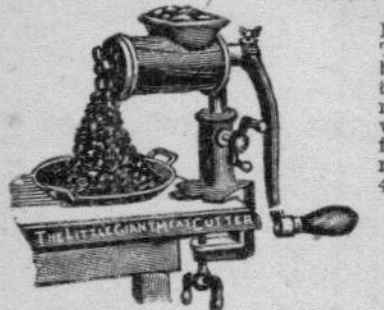

The Little Giant Meat Cutters. They combine the best qualities of all the latest improved machines, and are without doubt the fastest cutters ever made.
42196 The No. 205 size, like cut, for family use, with clamp for fastening to kitchen table; weighs 5¼ lbs., cuts 1½ lbs. per minute. Each.......................$1.50
Per doz....................................16.20
42197 Little Giant Meat Cutter, No. 210, for family or hotel use, with clamp for fastening to table, weighs 8¾ lbs., cuts 3 lbs. per minute. Each...................................... 2.00
42198 Little Giant Meat Cutter, No. 220, for hotel or butchers' use, with clamps for fastening to table; weighs 12½ lbs. cuts 4 lbs. per minute Each.............................. 2.88
Per doz..31.00
42199 Extra plates for 42196.................. .25
" knives " 42196.................. .25
" plates " 42197.................. .28
" knives " 42197.................. .28
" plates " 42198.................. .40
" knives " 42198.................. .40

Special Catalogue O.—Blacksmiths' and Wagonmakers' material. Very complete and prices low. Sent free upon request.

Sausage Stuffer, Fruit and Lard Press Combined.

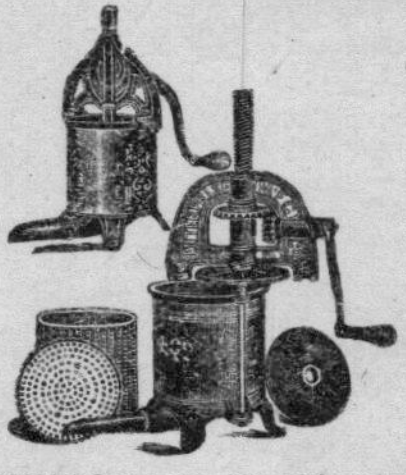

The Enterprise Combined Sausage Stuffer, Fruit and Lard Press; unexcelled for butchers' and farmers' use for stuffing sausages, and will be found useful for many purposes in every family. Directions will be found in catalogue that comes with each press.

Each.
42204 2-Quart size japanned, rack movement. Weight, 21 lbs.....................................$2.40
42205 4-Quart size, japanned, screw movement. Weight, 30 lbs.................................. 4.10
42206 8-Quart size, japanned, screw movement. Weight, 44 lbs.................................. 4.95

Sausage Filler.

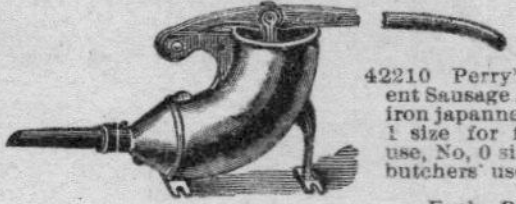

42210 Perry's Patent Sausage Filler, iron japanned, No. 1 size for family use, No. 0 size for butchers' use.

	Each.	Per doz
No. 1	$0.70	$8.10
No. 0	.92	9.94

Meat Choppers.

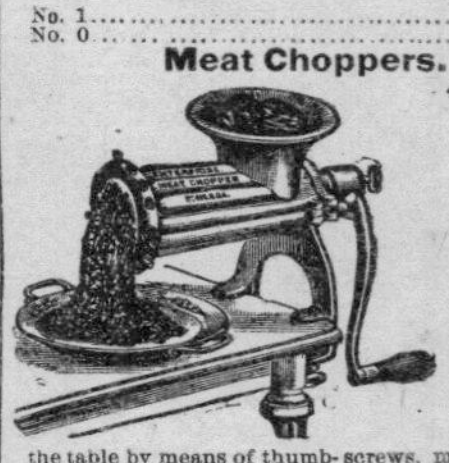

42212 Enterprise Meat Chopper will not tear the meat, but chops it precisely like the snipping process of a pair of shears. It is particularly adapted for family use being so constructed that it can be clamped to the table by means of thumb-screws, making it very convenient.

By means of an attachment Meat Choppers No's 10, 12 and 22 may be converted into excellent sausage stuffers. When in use the plate and knife are taken out and attachment secured by screwing the ring over it.

Enterprise Meat Chopper, family size No. 10, chops one pound per minute. Price each...............$2.50
42214 Price of attachment for No. 10, each...... .30
42215 Extra knives for 42212. Each.............. .25
42216 Enterprise Meat Chopper, No. 12. This chopper is exactly like 42212, only has legs instead of clamps, and is required to be screwed to the table. It is of the same capacity as 42212, and is precisely like it in all other respects. Each.. 2.00
42219 Price of attachment for No. 12, each...... .30
42220 Extra knives for 42216. Each.............. .25
42222 Enterprise Meat Chopper, No. 22. This size is especially suited to butcher, market men, farmers, hotels and restaurants. It does not fasten to table with clamps like 42212, but has legs, and screws down tight. Weight, 12 lbs; chops 2 lbs. per minute. Each.................. 3.10
42223 Price of attachment for No. 22. Each.. .45
42224 Extra knives for 42222. Each............ .45

Meat Choppers—Continued.

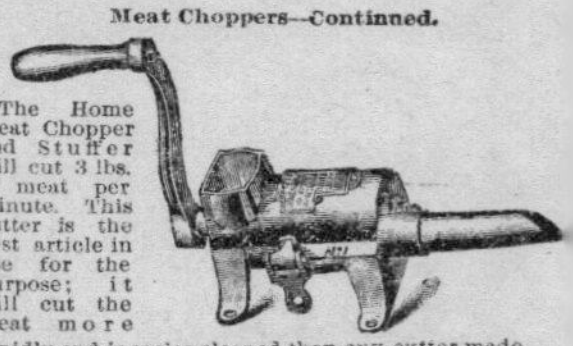

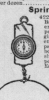

The Home Meat Chopper and Stuffer will cut 3 lbs. of meat per minute. This cutter is the best article in use for the purpose; it will cut the meat more rapidly and is easier cleaned than any cutter made.
42229 No. 1 japanned, 6 inch cylinder. Each..$0.85
42230 No. 21, galvanized, 6 inch cylinder Each.1.25
Per doz...$14.00

Wrought Iron Hooks.

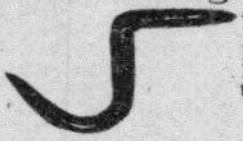

42236

42236—Wrought Iron Tinned Meat Hooks, to drive.

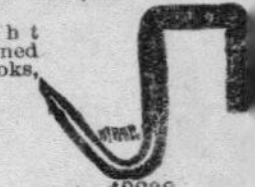

42238

Nos	1	2	3	4	5	6
Size of iron	¼	¼	5/16	⅜	⅜	⅜
Per dozen	8c	9c	10c	14c	19c	25c

42237 Wrought Iron Tinned Meat Hooks, to screw in.

Nos	1	2	3	4	5	6
Size of iron	¼	¼	5/16	⅜	⅜	⅜
Per dozen	10c	12c	16c	21c	30c	35c

42238 Wrought Iron Tinned Mutton Hooks, for 2 inch bar, made of 5/16 square iron. Per dozen.$0.45
Per gross.. 5.15
42239 Wrought Iron Tinned Beam Hooks, same shape as mutton hook, very heavy, for 2 inch bar, made of 7-16 square iron; weight, per doz., 3 lbs. 15 ounces. Per dozen $0.70
Per gross.. 7.56
42240 Wrought Iron Tinned Beam Hooks, with large round bend; very heavy, for 2 inch bar, made of ½ inch iron; weight, per doz., 9¾ lbs.
Per dozen............$0.80. Per gross $8 64

Spring Balances.

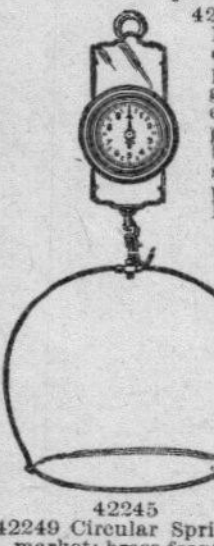

42245

42245 Circular Spring Balance, for butcher's use, weighs 30 pounds by 1 oz., has glass sash and white enameled front, tin pan, tinned iron bows and swivel: shipping weight, 5 pounds 14 oz.
Each..........$3.35

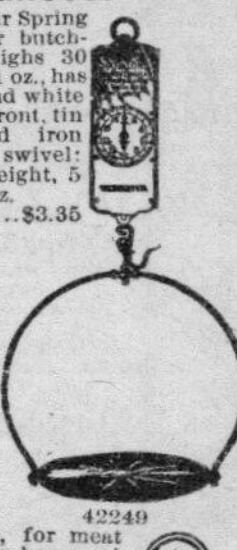

42249

42249 Circular Spring Balance, for meat market; brass front, tinned iron bows and swivel, tin pan, to weigh 30 lbs.; shipping weight, 5 lbs. Each..................$3.00

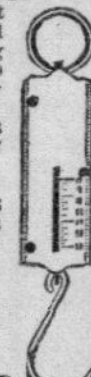

42250 Spring Balances, to weigh 24 lbs. by ¼ lb.; shipping weight 9 oz.
Each......................................$0.08
Per dozen.................................. .87
42251 Spring Balances, to weigh 50 lbs.; shipping weight, 13 oz.
Each......................................$0.16
Per dozen.................................. 1.73

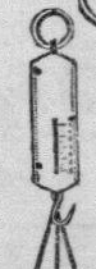

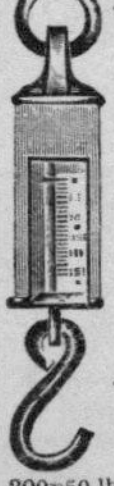

42254 Spring Balances with round tin dish very convenient for family use, for weighing butter, etc.; weighs 24 lbs. by ½ lb.; shipping weight, 2 lbs.
Each..............$0.20
Per doz............ 2.25
42257 Same as above, to weigh 50 lbs. by lbs; shipping weight, 1¾ lbs.
Each.... ....$0.35
Per dozen.......... 3.88

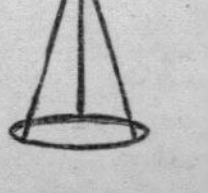

42260 Ice Balances The most durable in the market. Weight, 4¾ lbs.
To weigh:

	200x50 lbs.	300x5 lbs.	400x5 lbs.
Each	$2.35	$2.85	$3.32

Spring Balance Brackets.

42262 Iron Brackets for hanging spring balances Weight, 2 lbs. 9 oz. Each........$0.45
Per doz........4.85

Butchers' Scales.

42263 Market Scales with Marble Slab. To weigh 32 lbs. by ounces. Each.... $9.50 To weigh 64 lbs. by 2 ounces. Each........$10.50
Weight, boxed for shipment, 40 lbs.

Steelyards.

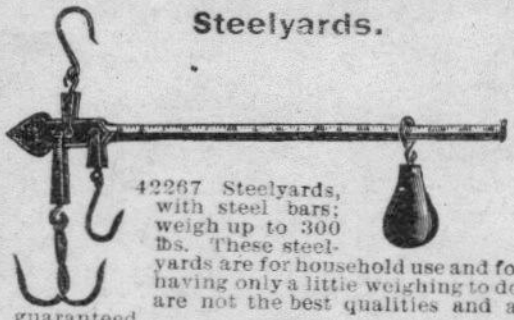

42267 Steelyards, with steel bars; weigh up to 300 lbs. These steelyards are for household use and for those having only a little weighing to do. They are not the best qualities and are not guaranteed.
The 100 to 200 lbs. Steelyards will not weigh a quantity less than 6 pounds, the 250 and 300 lbs. will not weigh a less quantity than 10 lbs.

Capacity	50	100	150	200	250	300 lbs
Price, each	27c.	37c.	47c.	53c.	60c.	65c.

42268 Steelyard with steel bars. These steelyards are guaranteed to weigh absolutely correct. They weigh up to the 50 lbs. size by ¼lbs.; above this size by ½ lbs. The 100 and 150 lbs. Steelyards do not start at zero and are not intended to weigh any quantity weighing less than 10 lbs. If you wish to weigh a smaller quantity than 10 lbs. use a 50 lb. Steelyard, as all others start at the 8 lb. point, and are accurate in weighing above 10 lbs.

Capacity	50	100	150	200	250	300 lbs.
Each....	45c.	50c.	58c.	72c.	86c.	$1.00

42269 Scale Beams with Poises. These beams are made heavy and capable of weighing to their full capacity without injury; they weigh by 1 lbs. only.

To weigh	250	400	600	1,000	1,200 lbs.
Price, each	$1.10	$1.50	$2.00	$3.50	$4.00

We furnish Poises for Scales Beams as follows:
The 250 lbs. Beam have each a 2 lb. and 8 lb. Poise.
The 400 lbs. Beam have each a 3 lb. and 12 lb. Poise.
The 600 lbs. Beam have each an 8 lb. and 16 lb. Poise.
The 1,000 lbs. Beam have each an 8 lb. and 32 lb. Poise.
The 1,200 lbs. Beam have each a 16 lb. and 32 lb. Poise.

The Standard Family Scales.

These scales are warranted correct. Are very convenient, and the best scales for family use made. There are no weights to get lost, are light and easy to handle, and do not take up much room; are japanned and beautifully ornamented in assorted colors.

42273 The family Standard Scale, to weigh 48 pounds by 2 ounces, with platform; no scoop. Weight, boxed for shipment, 9 lbs. Each..$2.56
42274 The Standard Family Scale, to weigh 12 pounds by ounces, with tin scoop. Each...... 2.25
42275 The Standard Family Scale, to weigh 48 pounds by 2 ounces, with tin scoop Each..... 2.75

42280

42278 The Novelty Family Scale, no weights needed. Weighs 12 lbs. by 2 ozs, With platform; no scoop. Each..$1.30
42279 42278-79 With platform and tin scoop........$1.40
42280 Candy Scale; weighs up to 2 pounds by ¼ oz. Hammered brass scoop. A very neat and convenient article $1.35

Scales—Continued.

42286—Platform Scale better than 42287; weight 240 lbs., by ounces all steel bearings, scales and wgts, officially sealed and each and every scale warranted. Weight, boxed for shipment, 35 lbs........$4.00

M. W. & Co.'s Scales.

42287 The Montgomery Ward Co. Platform Counter Scales, steel bearings, tin scoop, brass beam; weighing ½ oz. to 240 lbs. Warranted reliable. (See cut). Weight, boxed for shipment, 39 lbs. Price, each........$2.43

Weighs ½oz. to 25 lbs.
42288—The Housekeeper's Friend, price with platform, no scoop; shipping weight 15 lbs.; each........$1.68
42289 With tin scoop........2.00
Our scales are all packed ready for shipment.
We have some of these scales, which have been in constant use for several years, and they answer our purpose as well as those sold for $14.

Garden Trowels.

42292 Garden trowels; extra quality, cast steel; made in four sizes.

Length, inches	5	6	7	8
Price, each	$0.04	$0.05	$0.06	$0.07
Price per doz	.44	.54	.65	.75

Weeding Hooks.

42294 Weeding Hook wood handle, entire length, including handle, 10 in. This pattern is the most popular style of hand weeder; each........$0.07
Per dozen........ .75

Strawberry Forks.

42296 Strawberry Forks. Japanned iron fork, wood handle, length, including handle, 11 in. Made in two patterns, light and heavy.
Light pattern, each.... $0.08 Per doz........$0.87
Heavy pattern, each.... .12 Per doz........ 1.30

Garden Line Reel.

42299 Garden Line Reel. Malleable iron, japanned; no line furnished with reel. Each........$0.37
Per dozen........4.00

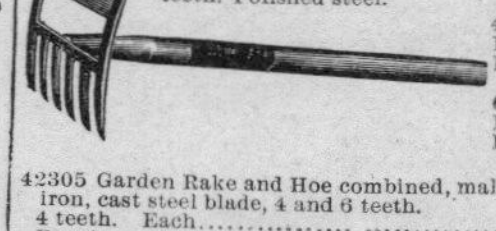

42304 Garden Rake and Hoe combined, very nice for weeding purposes 4 and 6 teeth. Polished steel.
4 teeth. Each, $0.25 Per doz. $2.70
6 teeth. Each, $0.35 Per doz. $3.85

42305 Garden Rake and Hoe combined, malleable iron, cast steel blade, 4 and 6 teeth.
4 teeth. Each........ .18
Per dozen........1.95
6 teeth. Each........ .20
Per dozen........2.16

Scuffle Hoe.

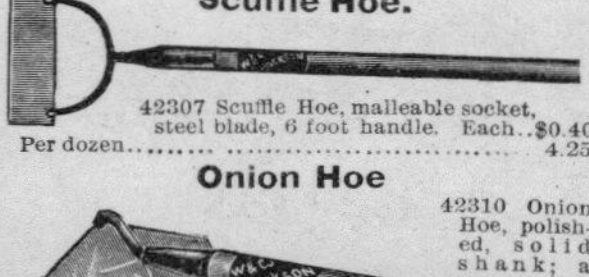

42307 Scuffle Hoe, malleable socket, steel blade, 6 foot handle. Each..$0.40
Per dozen........4.25

Onion Hoe

42310 Onion Hoe, polished, solid shank; a very convenient shape. Each. $0.25 Per doz. 2.70

All lines of merchandise very generally reduced in price.

Hoes.

42313 Garden Socket Hoes, blued.
Each........$0.30
Per dozen........3.40
42314 Garden Shank Hoes, blued. Each........ .25
Per dozen........2.75

42315 Warren Garden Hoes, extra cast steel, polished. Garden size. Each........ .40
Per dozen........4.55
Field sizes. Each........ .50
Per dozen........5.40

Garden Rakes.

42320 Garden Rake, malleable iron, polished, 12 teeth. Each........$0.20
Per dozen........2.15
42321 Garden Rake, cast steel polished, 12 teeth. Each........ .35
Per dozen........3.55
42322 14 teeth Garden Rake, cast steel. Each.... .40
Per dozen........3.90

42323 The Gibbs Lawn Rake. Improved for 1891. The teeth are made of No. 9 coppered steel spring wire, and so formed as to comb the lawn, taking up the loose grass or leaves without tearing the sod; 24 inches wide, 30 teeth. Each........$0.50
Per dozen........5.40

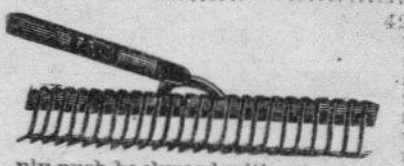

42324 The favorite Lawn Rake, strong and durable steel. Head 24 inch with 24 tinned No. 9 steel wire teeth. To unload rake simply push backward without raising it. Each.... $0.38
Per dozen........4.10
42324½ Hay Rakes, wood, made of ash; mortised head. Each........$0.15 Per dozen........1.62

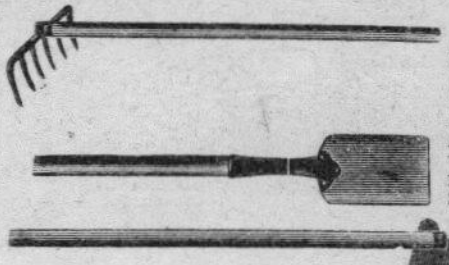

42325—Garden Tool Set, consisting of hoe rake and spade. The hoe is 3½ in. wide, rake 3 inches, spade 3x4½. Rake and hoe have 30 in. handle, spade 21 inch. Just the thing for ladies in making garden, and will furnish good healthy amusement for the children.
Per set, complete. $0.20 Per dozen sets......$2.16
42326 Garden Tool Set, same number, kind and size tools as are in number 42325 set, but are a little better finished, and made of a little better material. Per set..$0.27 Per dozen sets...... 2.92

42327 Garden Tool Set, consisting of hoe, rake and spade. Spade measures 5¾x4. Rake is 6 in. wide with 7 teeth, hoe is 3½ in. wide. Rake and hose handles are 30 in. long, spade handles are 19 in. in length with T-head. Per set..$0.40 Dozen sets $4.32

Garden Tools.

42328 Floral Set. Ladies' Favorite, for cultivating flowers, consisting of four pieces, a small rake with 7 teeth, hoe, fork used for weeding, and garden trowel, all with wood handles; entire length of rake and hoe, 13 inch, fork and trowel, 10½ inches. These floral sets are indispensable to the perfect cultivation of flowers and shrubs, and no lady who has a flower garden should be without one.
Per set complete........$0.22 Per doz. sets.....$2.38
42329 Floral Set, Ladies' Favorive, same number kind and size of tools as in No. 42328 set, but are made of a little better material and are packed in a pasteboard box. Per set complete of four tools........$0.33. Per dozen sets.... 3.57

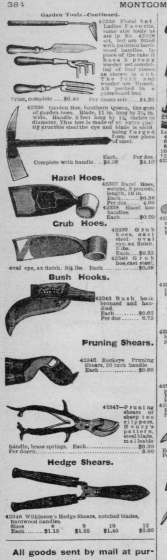

Garden Tools—Continued.

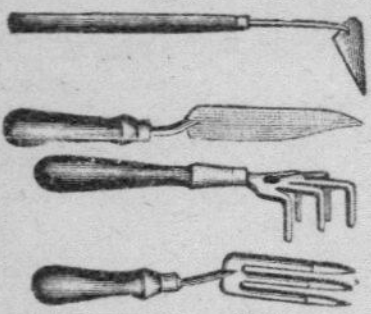

42330 Floral Set. Ladies' Favorite, same size tools as are in No. 42328 set, but are fitted with polished hardwood handles. In place of the rake it has a 5 prong weeder set consisting of four pieces as shown in cut. The fork and weeder are tinned. All packed in a pasteboard box.
Price, complete.....$0.40 Per dozen sets.....$4.32

42336 Garden Hoe, Southern Queen, the gem of garden hoes. Blade, 11 in. long by 3½ in. wide. Handle, 5 feet long by 1¼ inches in diameter. This hoe is made of an extra quality crucible steel the eye and blade is solid, being forged from one piece of steel.

	Each.	Per doz.
Complete with handle	$0.38	$4.10

Hazel Hoes.

42337 Hazel Hoes, weight, 3 pounds, length, 10 in.
Each........$0.38
Per doz...... 4.00
42338 Hazel hoe handles.
Each........$0.20

Grub Hoes.

42339 Grub hoes, cast steel oval eye, ax finish, 3 lbs.
Each....$0.35
42340 Grub hoe, cast steel, oval eye, ax finish, 3½ lbs. Each........$0.38

Bush Hooks.

42343 Bush hook bronzed and handled.
Each.........$0.62
Per doz....... 6.75

Pruning Shears.

42346 Buckeye Pruning Shears, 26 inch handle.
Each...............$0.60

42347—Pruning shears or sheep toe clippers, Henry's pattern, steel blade, malleable handle, brass springs. Each..................$0.30
Per dozen.............. 3.00

Hedge Shears.

42348 Wilkinson's Hedge Shears, notched blades, hardwood handles.

Sizes	8	9	10	12
Each	$1.15	$1.25	$1.40	$2.00

All goods sent by mail at purchaser's risk. We can assume no responsibility after goods are deposited in postoffice. We advise insuring everything of value.

Tree Pruner.

42349 Waters' Improved Tree Pruner is the best yet offered for sale. The blade being thin offers slight resistance to the wood in cutting, and does not injure the bark. It is supported on both sides by the hook which guides it and prevents its turning from a straight line; for this reason it will cut the smallest twig. With it pruning can be done standing on the ground, without climbing or using a ladder.

Length.	Weight.	Each.
4 ft	2¼ lbs	$0.45
6 ft	3 lbs	.50
8 ft	3½ lbs	.55
10 ft	4 lbs	.58
12 ft	4½ lbs	.65

42349¼ Extra knives for above pruners, each.. 20

Pruning Hooks and Saws.

42350 Diston's Pruning Hook and Saw; can be used with or without pole; the saw can be detached when the hook alone is to be used.
Each, without pole.....................$1.37

Scythes.

42356 Scythe. If you want the best, we have it; polished solid steel scythes. Each.............$0.57
Per doz.................. 6.16

42357 Scythe, extra polished web, bronzed, polished back, ground sharp. Each $0.50
per doz.................. 5.40

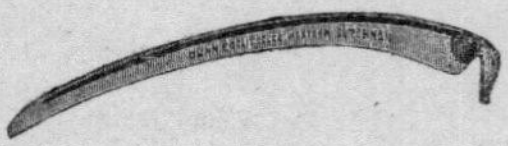

42358 Scythe, the Western Dutchman, bronzed; polished back, ground sharp.
Each.................$0.45
Per doz.................. 4.85
42359 Scythe, the Western Dutchman, solid steel,
Each.................. .50
Per dozen.................. 5.40

42360 Scythe, railroad or weed scythe, extra cast steel green ribbed.
Each.................$0.45
Per doz.................. 4.85

42363 Scythe, cast steel bush scythe.
Each.....$0.50
Per doz.. 5.46

Grass Hook or Sickle.

42366 Grass Hook or sickle.
Small size.....$0.25

Scythe Snaths.

		Each.
42369	Scythe Snath, patent loop	$0.50
42370	Scythe Snath, for bush scythe	.52

Scythe Stones.

42375 Scythe Stones, "Nova Scotia." Each.... $0.05
Per doz.................. .54
42376 Scythe Stones, "Ragg." Each.......... .08
Per doz.................. .87
42377 Scythe Stones, "Indian Pond." Each.... .06
Per doz.................. .65
42378 Scythe Stones, "Vienna." Each.......... .10
Per dozen.................. 1.08

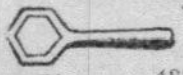

42379 Wrench for Patent Loop Snath. Each.................. .04
Per dozen.................. .44

42380 Loop for Patent Loop Snath.
Each.................. .07
Per dozen.................. .75

Hay Knives.

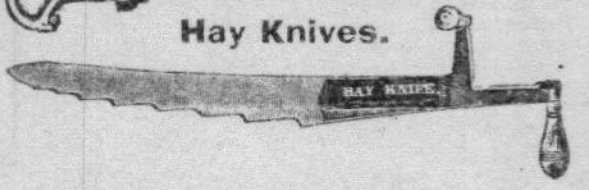

42385 Lighting Hay Knife. Best quality. Weight, 4¼ pounds.................$0.62
42386 Spear Point Hay Knife; weight, 4½ pounds .70

Corn Knives.

42387 Corn Knives, New Pattern. Excelsior Pattern, cast steel blade, length of blade 18 inches.
Price each..........$0.35 Per dozen 3.78

42388 Corn Knife, Excelsior pattern, cast steel blade, Length of blade, 15 inches; width of blade, 2½ in.
42388
Price each.............$0.25 Per dozen 2.70

Hay Forks.

Our hay forks, rakes, hoes, etc., are the very best quality; we guarantee them.

		Each.	Per doz.
42392	Hay fork, 3 tine, oval, cast steel, plain ferrule, straight handles, 4½ feet in length. Weight 3 pounds	$0.30	$3.32
42393	Same as above, only strapped ferrule. Weight 3 pounds	.35	3.75
42394	Hay Fork, 3 tine, oval, cast steel, bent handle, plain ferrule. Weight 2 pounds 9 ounces	.30	3.40
42395	Same as above only strapped ferrule, handle, 4½ to 5½ feet. Weight 3 pounds.	.35	3.90

42398 Manure Fork, 4 tine, oval cast steel, long handles, 4 to 5½ feet, plain ferrule (see cut). Weight 3 pounds 9 ounces.
Each......... .40c. Per dozen..............$4.45
42399 Same as above, only strapped ferrule. Weight 3 pounds 9 ounces. Each. .45
Per dozen.................. 5.00

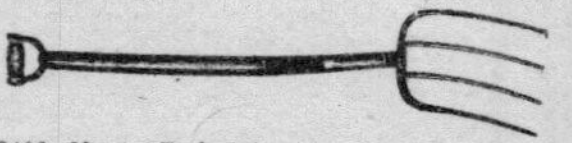

42400 Manure Forks D handle, solid steel shanks.

	Price each.	Per doz.
4 tine, Common Ferrule	$0.45	$4.80
4 tine, Strapped Ferrule	.48	5.10
5 tine, Common Ferrule	.60	6.75
5 tine, Strapped Ferrule	.65	7.42
6 tine, Common Ferrule	.75	8.38
6 tine, Strapped Ferrule	.78	8.90

Manure Hooks.

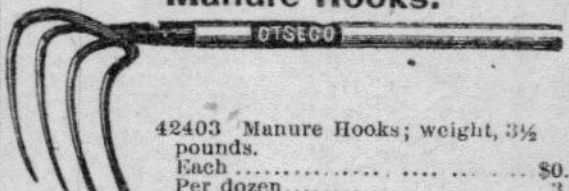

42403 Manure Hooks; weight, 3½ pounds.
Each..................$0.35
Per dozen.................. 3.90

Spading Forks.

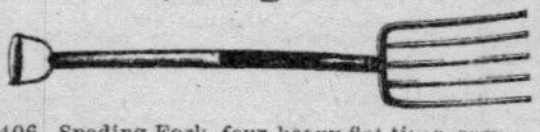

42406 Spading Fork, four heavy flat tines, common ferrule, D handle. Each..........$0.50
42407 Spading Fork, four heavy flat tines, strapped ferrule, D handle. Each.......... .55

42410 Potato Hooks, four flat tines
Each.......$0.30
Per doz....... 3.20

Heads for Fork and Shovel Handles.

42414 Malleable D heads for fork or shovel handles.
Each $0.08
Per doz .... .85

Fork Handles.

42415 Hay Fork Handles, XX, second growth ash, straight, 5 feet.
Each $0.08
Per doz .... .87
5¼ feet, each .... .09
Per dozen .... .98
6 feet, each .... .12
Per dozen 1.20

	Each.	Per doz.
42418 Hay Fork Handles, XX, second growth, bent; 4½ feet	$0.09	$0.98
5 feet	.12	1.30
5½ feet	.13	1.41
42420 Manure Fork Handles, XX, second growth, bent; 4 feet	.11	1.19
4½ feet	.12	1.20

Grass Carrier.

42422 Grass Carrier for Lawn Mower. This is a great convenience, as you do not have to use a rake. Raking a lawn is more than double the work of cutting, and this carrier catching all the grass as it is cut saves this extra work and leaves the lawn smooth and clean. It is adjustable to any size or make of lawn mower; has a strong iron frame covered with strong sail duck and enameled drill.
Price, each $1.85

Grass Catcher.

Improved.

42423 This Catcher is now made with sheet steel bottom, heavy cotton duck body, and has new device for attaching to mower. Will catch all the grass and fit any make of lawn mower.
No. 1 fits 10, 12 and 14 inch mowers.
No. 2 fits 16, 18 and 20 inch mowers.
Price, each $0.67

Lawn Mowers.

The "New York."

This Mower is made to meet the demand for a good, substantial lawn Mower at a medium low price. It has several of our latest improvements in *ratchet, back roller hanger, handle, adjustment, etc.*, and has ready sale to the large class of trade who wish to buy a first-class mower at lower price than heretofore. It has steel shafts ⅝ inch in diameter, double rachet. The knife is adjusted by one screw at each end of the knife bar, which is more simple and durable than the old plan. Its noiseless and light draft are very pleasant features with this mower, and there is more in it for the dollar than any other mower on the market. It is made in medium sizes only.
42424 12 inch, price, each $3.60
42425 14 inch, price, each 3.85
42426 16 inch, price each 4.00

Amateur Photography has come to stay. We sell all photographic instruments and supplies at less than list prices. Orders filled promptly. Every article guaranteed perfect.

25—6th

Imperial Lawn Mower.

This is our "Best Goods," and is not surpassed by any lawn mower in the market. The principal feature of this machine is that the bottom knife-bar is bolted to the sides, thus making the frame perfectly rigid, while by a new patent hanger the revolving cutter is adjusted to the bottom knife. This is the reverse of the adjustment in all other mowers. When the knives are properly adjusted a lock screw secures them in position.

The *Positive Triple Ratchet* is the simplest and most durable made. The *Gears* will wear much longer than those in other mowers, as they do not move when the machine is reversed. Our patented *Terrace Mowing Attachment* has proved a valuable addition, being very simple and effective. It is the only mower made with an arrangement for cutting terraces. This mower has been built with special reference to its durability, and we can safely say that we believe it will outwear any mower made. We make this mower with high and low wheel.

Imperial High Wheel Mower.

42427 14 Inch Cut .... Price each, $7.20
42428 16 " " .... " 7.92
42429 18 " " .... " 8.64
42430 20 " " .... " 9.36

Price of Horse Lawn Mowers furnished on application. Send for special circular.

Imperial Low Wheel Mower.

42431 12 Inch Cut .... Price each, $5.40
42432 14 " " .... " 6.15
42433 16 " " .... " 6.85
42434 18 " " .... " 7.56
42435 20 " " .... " 8.28

Shovels and Spades.

All Shovels branded "Montgomery Ward & Co." are guaranteed to be as fine as any made at any price. Shovels weigh from 4½ to 8 lbs.

42436—Shovels, D handle, back straps, square points, black iron. Each ....$0.32 Per dozen $3.38

	Each.	dozen.
42437 Shovels, D handles, back straps, square points, polished iron	$0.35	$3.62
42438 Shovels, D handle, plain back, solid steel, square points, polished	50	4.69
42439 Montgomery Ward & Co's Shovels, *warranted*, D handle, plain back, square points, patent polished, solid steel	65	7.50
42440 Shovels, Ames' D handle, plain back, square points, best quality, patent solid black steel	1.00	11.85
42441 Shovels, Ames' D handle, plain back, square points, best quality, patent solid polished steel	1.10	12.54

42442 Shovels, D handle, half polished, square point, back strap. Makes an excellent grain shovel.

	No. 1. 14x12x13	No. 2. 14x13¾x14½	No. 3. 15x13½x14½
Each	50c	55c	60c
Per dozen	$5.40	$5.83	$6.48

42443 Montgomery Ward & Co.'s Scoop Shovels, *warranted*, patent hammered solid cast steel; taper socket strap, polished. These shovels are made especially for us, and have our name stamped on the strap, and we guarantee them to be first-class in every particular.

Width of blade	12½ in.	13½ in.	14½ in.	15½ in.
Price each	$0.69	$0.72	$0.75	$0.80
Price Per dozen	7.56	7.65	8.25	9.00

42444 Scoop Shovels, Ames' extra cast steel, polished.

Width of blade	11½ in.	12 in.	12 in.	12½ in
Length of blade	15½ in.	16 in.	16½ in.	16¾ in
Price, each	$1.10	$1.20	$1.25	$1.30
Price, per dozen	11.88	12.31	12 53	12.96

By anticipating your wants and sending an order large enough to go by freight (100 lbs.) you will save money. The larger the order the more you will save.

***** MRS. HANNAH COBB'S celebrated "Home made Soap," 30 bars in a box (family or trial size). Every bar warranted. We have sold thousands of boxes and all have given entire satisfaction. Try a box and you will see why we praise it. See Grocery List for prices.**

Spades.

	Each.	Per doz.
42446 Spades, D handle, black iron, back strap	$0.32	$3.20
42447 Spades, D handle, polished iron, back strap	.35	3.50
42448 Spades, D handle, plain back, square points, solid steel, polished	.45	4.50
42449 Montgomery Ward & Co.'s Spades, warranted, D handle, patent hammered, solid cast steel, taper socket strap, polished plain back. This spade is manufactured especially for us, and has our name stamped on the strap, and we guarantee them to be first-class in every particular	.65	7.50
42450 Spade, Ames' D handle, black steel edge, plain back, fine quality	1.10	12.20

42452 Montgomery Ward & Co.'s Drain Spade, warranted, patent hammered solid cast steel, taper socket strap, D handle, plain back. These spades taper from 5¼ inches at the top to 4⅜ inches at the point.
Each.
18 inches long $0.78
20 inches long .... .85
22 inches long .... .90

Coke Forks.

42454 Coke or Coal Forks, 8 diamond tines, D handle, strapped ferrule. Each $1.50

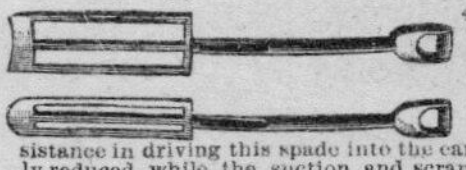

42455 The Boss Tiling spade, made of first quality cast steel. Resistance in driving this spade into the earth is greatly reduced, while the suction and scraping of ordinary spades is entirely avoided. Trenching and ditching can be done with greater ease than with any other spade. Made in 4 sizes.

Sizes, inches	4½x18	4½x20	6¼x18	6¼x20
Price, each	$1.70	$1.70	$1.85	$1.85

Drain Cleaner.

42457 Champion Adjustable Drain Cleaner, made to push or pull; can be adjusted to any angle. The most convenient and substantial tool on the market for making the oval groove in the bottom of the ditch. It is the only perfect drain cleaner made. The blade is made of solid cast steel, polished.
Size of blade, 4x15, concave. Price, each $1.25
" " 5x15, " " 1.35
" " 6x15, " 1.40

42459 Montgomery Ward & Co.'s Post Hole Spade, warranted; patent hammered solid cast steel, taper socket strap, D handle, plain back and polished. This spade is also used for drainage purposes; 5¼ inches at the step and 6 inches at the point.
18 inches long $0.75
20 inches long .... .80

Mining Shovels.

42460 Long Handled Round Point Mining Shovels, stiff polished.

	Each.	Per doz.
Price	$0.76	$8.00
42461 Long Handled Round Point Mining Shovels, half spring, polished	.75	8.00
42462 Long Handled Round Point Mining Shovels, full spring, polished	.74	8.00
42463 Long Handled Square Point Grading Shovels	.80	8.64

Our facilities for filling orders for mining supplies are unlimited. We guarantee to furnish the best of goods at the lowest possible price and will supply anything wanted not found in our catalogue if obtainable in Chicago.

Wire Clothes Lines.

Twisted Galvanized Wire Clothes Lines.

	Each.	Per doz.
42468 100 feet, No. 20 wire	$0.20	$2.25
42469 100 feet, No. 18 wire	.30	3.25

For manilla, jute or cotton lines, see Grocery List.

42470 Solid Annealed Galvanized Wire Clothes Line, preferred by a great many because they are smooth. Made of No. 9 Wire, and in coils of 100 feet. We do not sell less. Per coil....$0.50
Per dozen coils.......... 5.40

Mining Tools.

For Miners' Shovels, etc., see Index.

Railroad Picks.

42479 Picks, cast steel, ax finish; weight, 5½ to 6½ lbs. Each.......... $0.40
Per dozen.......... 4.35
42480 Pick Handles, hickory, 36 inches. Each.......... .12
Per dozen.......... 1.03

Drifting Picks.

42481 Drifting Picks, adz eye; natural finish.

No.	1	2	3	4
Weight	3 lbs.	4 lbs.	4½ lbs.	5 lbs.
Each	$0.42	$0.47	$0.52	$0.54
Per dozen	4.54	5.08	5.62	6.41

42482 Drifting Pick Handles, second growth; length, 35 inches; size of eye, 3x1. XXX quality. Each.... $0.25 Per dozen.... $2.70

Pole Picks.

42483 Pole Picks, adz eye. Nos.	1	2	3
Weight	3½ lbs.	4 lbs.	4½ lbs.
Each	$0.47	$0.50	$0.52
Per dozen	6.16	6.70	7.00

42484 Pole Pick Handles, second growth; length, 34 inches; eye, 3x1, XXX quality. Each.......$0.20
Per dozen.......... 2.16

Mattocks.

42485 Mattocks, cast steel, adz eye, ax finish, long cutter.
Weight, 6 pounds. Each.......... $0.55
42486 Mattocks, cast steel, adz eye, ax finish, short cutter: weight, 5½ pounds. Each.......... .50

Post Hole Diggers.

42489 Eureka Post Hole Digger, steel blades, 9 in.; weight, 1¾ pounds. Each........$1.00

42490 The National Post Hole Digger, the best and cheapest tool of its kind in the market. Blades and shanks are dropped out of single pieces of steel. Every digger fully warranted.
Price, each..... ....$1.00

Post Hole Augers.

42491 Vaughan's Post Hole Augers, with steel blades. The manufacturers claim that it is the most popular of any post hole auger ever invented. The blades are riveted to the bottom and can be replaced if one becomes broken. It is made in the following sizes: 6 inch, 7 inch, 8 inch and 9 inch. We send any size desired at the same price.
Each.......... $0.60
Per dozen.......... 6.90

Post Mauls.

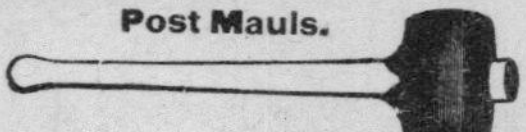

42493 Iron Post Mauls. Have heavy hickory handles, shaped like railroad pick handle, which prevents maul from coming off.

10 pounds. Each	$0.37	18 pounds. Each	$0.55
13 pounds	.44	20 pounds	.60
16 pounds	.50		

42494 Maul Handles. Price, each.......... .12

Sheep Shears.

42495 Sheep Shears, common German, bent handles; known as grass shears. Each.......... $0.25
Per dozen.......... 2.50

Wilkinson & Son's Sheep Shears.

42499 Wilkinson & Son's Sheep Shears, polished blades, swaged, single spring.	Each.	Per doz
5-inch	$0.70	$8.10
5½-inch	.70	8.10
6-inch	.75	8.70
42500 Wilkinson's Sheep Shears, full polished and etched, swaged, single spring, 5-inch	.90	10.26
5½-inch	.90	10.26
6-inch	1.00	11.34

The Hero Sheep Protector.

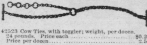

Before Taking.

42505 Is made of steel galvanized wire formed into links. Each link has two sharp projections. Each collar consists of thirteen links, which will reach around the ordinary sheep's neck. Links can be removed or more added in a moment's time; by this means you adjust the collars to the sheep's neck. These protectors are made of galvanized wire to prevent them from rusting. They will last for ten years or more. This collar adheres close to the sheep's neck and is not noticeable only for a short time after shearing. What the manufacturers claim and will guarantee: First, that sheep can not hurt themselves on these protectors. Second, that by the use of this protector 95 per cent. of the sheep killed by dogs, wolves, etc., would be saved. You say that a dog does not always catch a sheep by the neck. We say, right you are; but when they catch them elsewhere it is done to check the sheep so that they can get to its neck, and in some instances they do not lacerate the neck to speak of, but the object in catching the sheep is to cut the throat and drink the blood. In many instances one dog has killed 30 sheep in one night. In their wrestle with the sheep they are sure to come in contact with this protector. This closes the chase; they will not give blood for blood. If you will put the Hero Protector on your sheep, you can pasture them in your remotest field, and you need not lay awake at nights for fear of them being molested.

After Taking.

Price, per dozen collars.......... $1.00
" " gross " 9.00
" " 1000 " 54.60

The Nebraska Calf Weaner.

FULLERS.

42508 For calves four to eight months old.
Each.......... $0.25
Per doz.......... 2.70
42509 For calves eight months to two years old.
Each.......... $0.28
Per doz.......... 3.05
42510 For cows (without wire bits).
Each.......... $0.35
Per dozen.......... 3.78
Calf weaners, extra by mail, 25 to 40c.

Calf Weaners—Continued.

Hoosier Calf Weaners, so made that when the animal's head is lowered in the act of feeding the barbed muzzle is raised by a weight under the jaw. When the hea. is raised in position to suck, the weight forces the muzzle over the mouth. The most effectual and humane weaner in the market.

42513 No. 1, for calves, each.......... $0.40
Per doz.......... 4.55
42514 No. 2, Range Weaner, for large calves and colts. Each.......... .68
Per doz.......... 7.35
42515 No. 3, for cows.......... 1.17
Per doz.......... 12.64

Bull Rings.

42518 Bull Rings 2½ inch steel polished. Each.......... $0.10
Per doz.......... 1.08
42519 Bull Ring, 3 inch steel polished. Each.......... $0.12
Per dozen.......... 1.30
42520 Bull Rings, 2½ inch polished copper, with screw driver. Each.......... $0.12
42521 Bull Rings, 3 inch polished copper, with screw driver.. $0.15

Bull Snaps.

42522 Patent Bull Snap, tinned with 3 feet of chain and ring on end and three screw eyes; is used in connection with bull ring in leading vicious cattle; there is no handle comes with it, but a rake or hoe handle can be used. Each.......... $0.25

Cow Ties.

42523 Cow Ties, with toggler; weight, per dozen, 24 pounds. Price each.......... $0.25
Price per dozen.......... 2.50

42525 Cow Ties, closed ring, with toggle; weight, per doz, 18¾ lbs. Each.......... $0.25
Per doz.......... 2.56

Cattle Leaders.

42527 Cattle Leaders, malleable iron, brass wire spring.
Each.......... $0.05
Per doz.......... .54

Ox Balls.

Ox Balls are put on the tips of horns of vicious cattle.
42529 Ox Balls, octagon hollow.
Per dozen.......... $0.32
42530 Ox Balls, octagon, solid.
Per dozen.......... .35

Cattle Tie Irons.

42534 Cattle Tie Irons, japanned, for ½ in. rope, with patent covered snap, very convenient, as ordinary rope can be used and renewed at small expense when worn out; weight, each, 7 ounces. Each.......... $0.05
Per dozen.......... .55

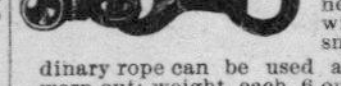

42535 Cattle Tie Irons, tinned, ½ in. rope, or smaller; with patent covered spring snap; very convenient, as ordinary rope can be used and renewed when worn out; weight, each, 6 ounces. Each.......... $0.07
Per dozen.......... .75

Picket Pins.

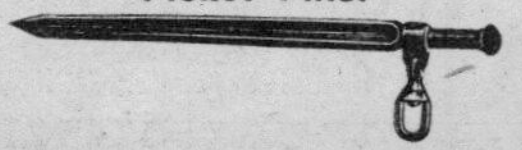

42536 Picket Pins, fluted malleable iron, 12 in long, weight, 1½ lbs. Each.......... $0.08
Per dozen.......... .87

Picket Pins—Continued.

42537—Picket Pins, spiral, ½ in., wrought iron 14½ in. long, weight 1 lb. 6 oz. Each, $0.13 Per dozen..... $1.40

Lariat Swivels.

42538 Lariat Swivels malleable iron, ⅝ and ⅝ eye, 4½ in. long.
Each.... ......$0.03
Per dozen..... .33

42539 The American Wrought Steel Lariat Swivel, the strongest and easiest working swivel in the market.
Each.............$0.04 Per dozen.............$0.44

Chains.

42540 Cable Log Chains, made of self-colored coiled chain, with large hook, grab hook and swivel, 12 and 14 feet long. The sizes given below do not indicate the size of the chain across the link, but the size of the iron the link is made of. Prices are for either 12 or 14 feet.

Size	¼	5-16	⅜	½
Price each	$1.25	$1.50	$1.75	$2.50

Coil Chains.

42542 Straight Link, hand made.

	3-16 in.	¼ in.	5-16 in.	⅜ in.	7-16 in.	½in
Weight Per foot.	8 oz.	1 lb.	1 lb. 4 oz.	1 lb. 8 oz.	2lb.	2lb. 8oz
Price per pound ..	10c.	7c.	6¼c.	5c.	4¾c.	4½c.

American Halter Chains.

American Halter-Chains are made wholly of steel and are the strongest made, as there are no welds to give way.

42543 American Halter-Chains 4½ feet long, links 1¼ in. long, ⅜ in. wide. Each............$0.10
Per dozen............ 1.00

42544 American Halter-Chain, 6 ft long, links 1⅝ in. long, 7-16 in. wide. Each .... .15
Per dozen 1.60

42545 American Halter-Chain, 6 ft. long, links 1⅞ in. long, ½ in wide. Each............ .25
Per dozen.................. 2.45

Jack Chains.

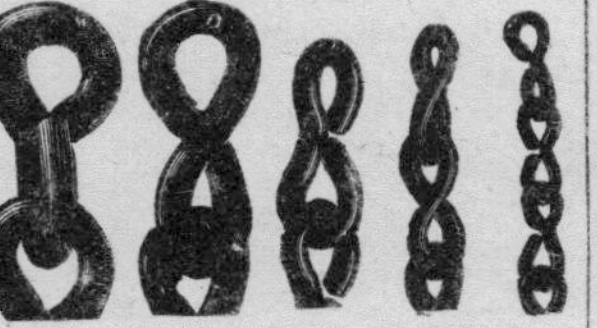

No. 8 No. 10 No. 12 No. 14 No. 16

42549 Iron Jack Chain. Cuts are exact size of chains.

Nos...........	8	10	12	14	16
Per yard..........	$0.08	$0.07	$0.05	$0.04	$0.03
Per dozen yards..	.40	.36	.20	.18	.15

42550 Brass Jack Chains. Cuts are exact size.

Nos...........	8	10	12	14	16
Per yard.......	$0.20	$0.15	$0.10	$0.08	$0.06
Per doz. yds...	2.10	1.40	.90	.60	.50

Glaziers' Points.

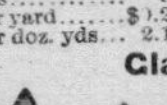

42555 Glazier's points in ¼ lb papers. Postage, 5c. per paper.
Per paper.........................$0.08
Per dozen papers .... .85

Hog Ringers and Rings.

42557 Perfection Hog Ringers, malleable iron; the most perfect and low priced ringer in the market. Weight, 13 oz.
Each......................$0.15
Per dozen.................. 1.60

42558 Perfection Hog Ring. Closes on the outside of the nose, the point passing through the loop; 100 in a box.
Per box......................$0.16
Per dozen rings.................. .03

Special Catalogue O.—Blacksmiths' and Wagonmakers' material. Very complete and prices low. Sent free upon request.

Hill's Pattern Hog Rings and Ringers.

42559 Hog Rings Per box.....$0.07
42560 Hog Ringers, each.....$0.10
Per doz.. .... 1.10

Cattle Dehorners.

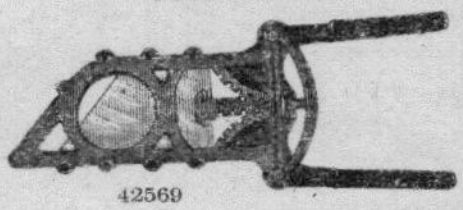

42569

Big Thing for Cattle Raisers. Newton's lately improved dehorning knife, revolving and sliding shear, each one making a draw cut. Cuts perfectly smooth, does not fracture the head or the horns; causes to heal quick.

42567 No. 1, *Intended for Calves* only, weighs 4½ lbs, and has a 2 inch opening. Price each......$3.50

42568

42568 No. ½, intended for young or medium aged cattle, with revolving cut knife. Price each...$4.50

42569 No. 3, Intended for young or old cattle, has a 4¼ inch opening, weighs 17 lbs.
Price each..................................$7.50

Hog Tamer.

42570 Hurd's American Hog Tamer, to keep hogs from rooting; made from malleable iron; three tempered steel knives, assorted sizes, furnished with tamer.
Each........$0.55
Per doz........ 5.95

BELLS IN GREAT VARIETY.

Open Polished Bells.

42575 Open Polished Bells may be used for a variety of purposes; make good sheep bells, a harness bell for milk wagons, drays, etc.

Numbers..........	1	2	3	4	5	6
Diameter of mouth in inch...........	2¼	2½	2¾	3	3¼	3½
Each...............	7c	9c	11c	13c	15c	18c
Per doz. ...	76c	98c	$1.10	$1.41	$1.62	$1.95

Hand Bells.

42576—

No.	Weight.	Diameter.	Each.
1........	5 oz..	2	$0.07
3........	10 oz........	2 13/16	.13
5........	15 oz	3 11/16	.22
7........	18 oz........	4⅛........	.35
9........	1 lb. 9 oz........	5.	.60
13........	3 lb. 15 oz	6⅞........	1.05
14........	5 lb........	7¼........	1.20

Farm Bells.

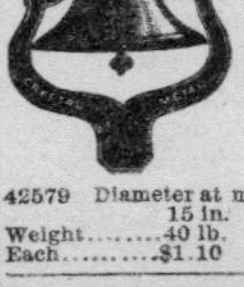

Bronzed, with iron frame.

42579 Diameter at mouth.

	15 in.	17 in.	19 in.	21 in.
Weight........	40 lb.	50 lb.	75 lb.	100 lb.
Each..........	$1.10	$1.40	$2.00	$3.00

***** It will be a favor to us (and perhaps to your friends) if you will place, where they will do the most good, any duplicate Catalogues or advertising matter which you may receive from us.**

Steel Alloy Bells

42580 Steel Alloy Church Bells, made of an alloy of cast steel and crystal metal and are of superior tone, finished and warranted against breaking with ordinary use *for two years*. For complete description send for our Special Bell Catalogue. Mailed free.

School House or Factory Bells.

BELLS ARE NUMBERED BY THE DIAMETER IN INCHES.

Number.	Bell only.	Complete.	Price.
20	105 lbs.	150 lbs.	$10.00
22	125 "	175 "	12.00
24	155 "	225 "	15.00
26	220 "	325 "	25.00
28	255 "	425 "	30.00

42581 **Church Bells.**

BELLS ARE NUMBERED BY THE DIAMETER IN INCHES.

Number.	Bell only.	Complete.	Price.
30	335 "	550 "	39.00
32	380 "	600 "	45.00
34	465 "	725 "	54.00
36	570 "	850 "	65.00
40	780 "	1200 "	90.00
44	1100 "	1600 "	120.00
54	2100 "	3000 "	225.00

The weights and prices above named are for complete bells, and include wood sills, iron wheel, and for Nos. 30, 32, 34, 36, 40, 44 and 54, tolling hammer, without extra charge.

Tolling hammers for Nos. 24, 26 and 28, when so ordered, $5.00 each extra.

These bells are cast from an alloy of cast steel and crystal metal, and can be relied on under all circumstances and in all seasons. Nos. 20 to 28 are school or factory bells, and are not suitable for churches. Nos. 30 to 54 inclusive are recommended for churches.

Send for our Special Bell Catalogue, gives full information and numerous testimonials.

Trip Gong Bells.

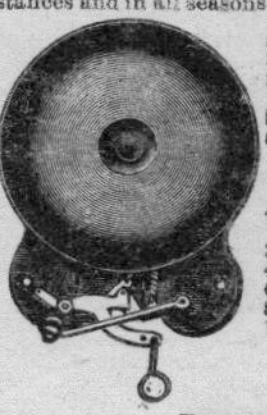

42582 Trip Gong Bells. Genuine bell metal.
3-in....wgt., 1 lb. 5 oz..$0.66
4-in....wgt., 1¾ lb .... .70
6-in....wgt., 2 lb. 13 oz 1.35
8-in....wgt., 6 lb. 2.65
10-in...wgt., 9¾ 4.00

Door Gongs.

Knocker.

Bell.

42584 Geneva Bronzed Door Bell. (Weight 2 lb. 2 oz. size 4 in.) Each.$0.42
Crank door gongs are no longer made.

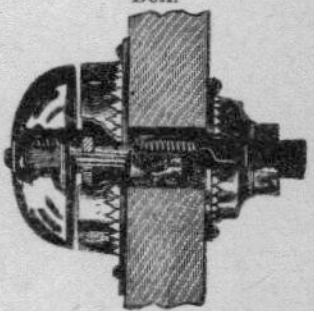

The Electric Action Door Bell; a very novel invention, durable and cheap. Easily applied.
42586 3½ inch plain gong, polished nickel plated, with genuine bronze rosette. Weight, 1 lb. 2 oz. Each...$1.00

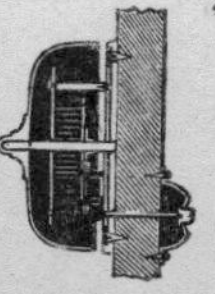

42590 The New Departure Electric Action Door Bell; winds up like a clock by turning the gong; when wound simply pushing the button will cause it to ring; will give from 400 to 500 calls at one winding, is strongly made and cannot get out of order; the most perfect and novel electric action door bell yet invented. Directions how to apply it come with each bell. Weight, 5 lbs.
4 inch, with plain bronze rosette $1.75
5 inch, with plain bronze rosette.................... 2.35

Cow Bells.

42594 The shape of these is designed to produce the loudest sound possible.

No.	0	2	3	5	7
Size of mouth...	6x4½	5½x3½	4½x3	3¼x2⅝	2⅝x1¾ in.
Height	6½	5	4¾	3⅛	2⅜ in.
Price Each	$0.40	$0.25	$0.20	$0.15	$0.10
Per dozen	4.00	2.65	2.00	1.50	1.00

42595 Cow Bell Straps, made of leather.

Width	1½ in.	1¾ in.
Per dozen	$2.50	$2.75
Each	.25	.28

Sheep Bells.

Sheep Bells, complete with straps. These bells are made of extra quality of metal and emit a sharp, tinkling sound that can be heard a greater distance than the small sized cow bell that is sometimes used.

42599 Length, 1½ inches; size across mouth of bell, 1⅛x1¼, with straps complete. Each......$0.15
Per dozen......1.60

42600 Length, 2 inches; size across mouth of bell, 1½x1¾, with straps complete. Each......$0.20 Per dozen......2.00

Sleigh Bells on Straps.
Body Straps.

42606 **24 Common Tinned Polar Bells** No. 2, (1⅛), riveted on russet or black leather strap. Price, per strap, $0.80

42608 **30 Common Tinned Polar Bells,** No. 2 (1⅛) riveted on russet or black leather strap. Price, per strap......$1.20

42610 **30 Extra White Metal Rim Bells.** No. 2 ((1⅛) riveted on russet or harness leather strap. Price per strap......1.65

42612 **36 Nickel Plated Bells.** No. 2 (1⅛) riveted on russet or harness leather strap. Price, per strap......2.25

Sleigh Bells.

Assorted Sizes on One Strap.

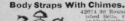

42614 19 Round Polished Bells on leather strap, wire fastened. Assorted sizes from No. 2 to No. 8 bells.

Price, per strap......$1.25

42616 23 Round Polished Bells on leather strap, wire fastened; assorted sizes from No. 1 to No. 8. Price, per strap......1.40

42618 23 Round Polished Bells on leather strap, wire fastened; assorted sizes from No. 5 to No. 13. Price, per strap......2.50

Neck Straps.

42620 9 Round Polished Bells on leather strap; assorted sizes from No. 1 to No. 5. Per strap......$0.50

42622 15 Round Polished Bells on leather strap, wire fastened; assorted sizes from No. 2 to No. 9. Per strap......95

Body Straps With Chimes.

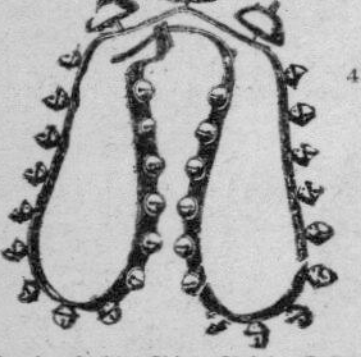

42624 30 Round Polished Bells, riveted on black leather strap with chime tinned. Per strap......$2.25

42626 Same as above, nickel plated. Per strap......$2.50

Russian Saddle Chime Sleighs Bells for single teams; see cut.
42628 Nickel plated. Each......$0.75

Chimes—Continued.

42630 Russian Saddle Chimes for single teams (see cut), nickel plated. Each......$1.25

42632 **Russian Saddle Chimes** for single or double teams; see cut; nickel plated.$2.60

42634 Same as No. 42632 only. Gold plated......$2.75

42638 **Open Shaft Bells** White Metal on shaft straps. 3 No. 1 bells on each strap.

Price per set of 2 straps......$0.31

42640 Same as 42638 with 4 No. 1 bells on each strap. Price per set of two straps......$0.40

42642 **Nickeled Gong Chime Sleigh Bells.** Extra finish, 3 bells on a strap, 6 bells to a set. Price, per set......$0.35

42644 **Nickel Plated Swiss Shaft Chimes.** 3 bells on japanned iron straps 6 bells to a set. Price per set......$0.65

42646 **Harmonized Swiss Shaft Chimes.** Nickel Plated Bells on japanned iron strap, 4 bells on a strap; 8 bells to set. Price per set......$1.00

42648 **Swiss Shaft Chimes.** Tuned. Intervals 1, 3, 5, 8; nickel plated bells, on japanned iron strap, 8 bells to set. Price per set......$1.65

42650 Common Loose Sleigh Bells for the convenience of those who wish to make their own straps of bells.

Nos......	1	2	3	4	5	6
Diameter	1⅛	1¼	1⅜	1 7/16	1⅝	1¾
Per doz..	23c	31c	41c	49c	58c	66c

Nos......	7	8	9	10	11
Diameter.	1⅞	2	2 3/16	2¼	2⅜
Per doz...	.81c	94c	$1.14	$1.35	$1.50

Ice Skates.

For 1894 we are selling the same general line of men's and women's skates as we have used so successfully for the past seasons.

In addition we would call attention to our new lines of racing and extension skates.

All of our skates are carefully mated, inspected and packed. The material which we use is of the highest grade which can be obtained, and we devote the best of oversight to our work. Our aim is to retain the reputation of selling superior skates.

When ordering skates the best and surest way to obtain the right size skate is to always send us the *length of boot or shoe in inches*. Below we give the size of skates compared with sizes of shoes by numbers.

Skates, inches..	7	7½	8	8½	9	9½	10	10½	11	11½
Number of shoe	9½	11	12½	1	2½	4	5½	7½	9	10½

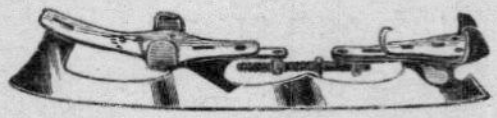

42655 This Skate is of high grade of runner, finely polished toe and heel; plates are the best quality of hot rolled Swedish steel, while the toe and heel clamps are of the best quality homogeneous steel: is easy working and sure grip; lock lever; will fit large or small boot heel; sizes, 8 to 12. Always be sure and give size in inches when ordering. Per pair......$0.35

42657 This Skate, same description as the No. 42655 skate, but nickel plated instead of plain finish. Per pair, nickel plated,......57

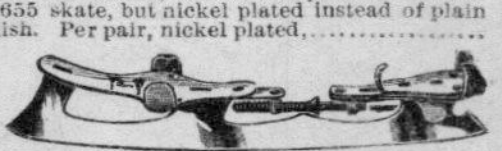

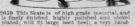

42659 This Skate is of high grade material, and is finely finished, highly polished and nickel plated; will fit large boot heel; a very handsome skate; sizes, from 8 to 12. Always be sure and give size in inches when ordering. Per pair......$1.00

42660 This Skate, same pattern as No. 42659 skate, but has hardened and welded steel runner and is nickel plated and handsomely polished on all surfaces; nothing handsomer than this skate is possible; sizes 8 to 12. Per pair......$1.75

42661 The runners of this skate are of welded iron and steel, hardened and beautifully nickel plated with bevel edges; the heel and toe plates have chamfered edges; all parts are highly polished, nickel plated and buffed; sizes 8 to 12. Per pair......$2.25

The Donoghue Racing Skate.

This skate is made under the personal supervision of Mr. Joseph F. Donoghue, World's Champion, and is made of the highest grade of material, and by first-class workmen mechanics. Mahogany tops, hardened steel runners, nickel plated, russet harness leather straps, nickel tongue buckles. This skate was designed by Mr. Donoghue, and has been used for the past five years in winning all his great races and making his wonderful records, and his success is as much due to the perfection of these skates as to his own skill.

Made in three lengths, 14, 16, 18 inches.
42665 Price, per pair......$3.25

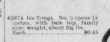

42667 The Number 28 Ladies' Wood Top Skates have finely polished beechwood top, converted steel frame runners, highly polished with finely ground cutting edge; are trimmed with the best quality oak tanned russet grained leather, nickel plated heel bands and patent buckles; is a handsome, serviceable skate; we can also furnish this skate with steel tops and russet leather toe straps at the same price. Always state which is wanted. Sizes from 7 to 10 inches. Always be sure and give size in inches when ordering. Per pair......$0.55

42669 The Number 56 Ladies' Skate. The runner is made of the best quality crucible steel, is highly polished with a fine cutting edge; best oak-tanned russet leather heel strap; patent buckles and nickel plated heel bands. Has sure grip lock lever, a very fine skate; sizes, 8 to 10. Per pair, ...$0.85

42670—The No. 59 Ladies' Lock Lever Skate, the same as No. 42669 skate, but has a welded steel runner, perfectly tempered and highly polished. The tops are all nickel plated and the heel straps have nickel plated patent buckle. Nothing handsomer in a ladies' skate made. Sizes, from 8 to 10½ inch. Per pair......$1.75

Ice Tongs.

42673 Ice Tongs. No. 1 opens 16 inches, steel point, family size. Each......$0.42
No. 2 opens 18 inches, steel, point. Each......$0.55
No. 3 opens 24 inches, steel pointed, wagon size. Each......$0.73
Weight, about 4 lbs.

42674 Ice Tongs. No. 6 opens 14 inches, with bale top, family size; weight, about 2¾ lbs. Each......$0.45

Harness Hooks.

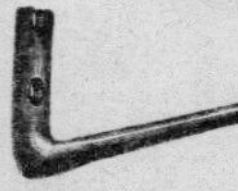

42675 Harness Hooks, japanned iron, 6 inches in length. Weight per dozen, 6 lbs. Each......$0.04
Per dozen......45

42676 Harness Hooks, japanned iron, 8 inches long; weight per dozen, 10½ lbs. Each......07
Per dozen......75

Collar Hooks.

42680 Collar Hooks, japanned iron, to hang from the ceiling. Weight, per dozen, 12 lbs. Each......$0.15

Hay Rack.

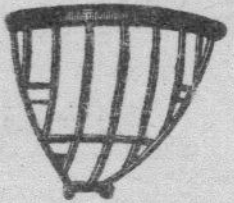

42683 Cast Iron Hay Rack, for horse stall. Weight, 29 lbs., neat and convenient; can be put up in 5 minutes. Each.......... ....$1.10

42685 Steel Hay Racks, same style as No. 42683 but made of bent steel rods. ½ inch steel, each........ ....$2.00

Feed Box.

42687 Castiron Feed Box, for horse stall; is 17 inches on each side, 10 inches deep and weighs 28 lbs.; is easily put up; fastened with screws. Each, no screws.... .....$1.00

Hitching Rings.

42689 Hitching Rings, wrought ring and swivel, no screws.

	Each.	Per doz
Japanned	$0.05	$0.54
Galvanized	.08	.87

42690 Post Caps, for fastening over top of posts to hitch horses to. Very neat and convenient; made of iron, japanned, no screws.

Size	4¾ inches.	5¼ inches.
Each	$0.20	$0.28
Per doz	2.16	3.00

Oat Sieves.

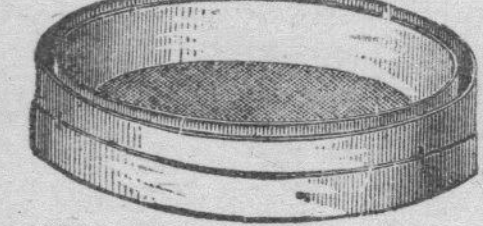

Oat Sieves made with extra heavy blued steel wire cloth. No. 12 mesh; hoops are oak; used for sifting dirt and dust out of oats and grain.

42693 14 inch, weight, 1¼ lbs., each...........$0.27
42694 16 inch weight, 1½ lbs., each.............. .32
42695 18 inch, weight, 2 lbs. each.............. .35

Boot Jacks.

Weight, 1¼ pounds.

42698 Iron Boot Jack. Each.................$0.08

42700 The American Bull Dog Boot Jack, the latest and best selling novelty out. Lacquered, each..$0.15 Per dozen.......... 1.50

Steel Safes.

42705 Steel Fire Proof Safes. These safes are made in the best material, have combination locks, are handsomely decorated and are fire proof. Satisfaction, ease of mind, a feeling of security, etc., is attained by possessing one of our safes. In all cases they will be shipped direct from the factory. Name will be put on above the door, shaded in bronze, free of charge, when specified. Allowance for slight delay in shipping must be made when this is done. Write name wanted on safe plainly, so that no mistake will be made.

	Outside Measure.			Inside Measure.			Appx Wt.	Price.
	High	Wide	Deep	High.	Wide	Deep		
3	28 in	18½	19	15	10	12	500	$20.00
4	31 in	21½	21¼	17	13¾	13¼	650	26.00
5	34½in	22¾	23¼	19¾	14¼	14½	900	34.00
6	38½in	26	26	22	16	15½	1350	50.00
7	42½in	29	29	23½	17½	18	1800	55.00
9	46½in	32	29½	27¾	21	18	2100	90.00

No 9 is a Double Door Safe.

Stencils.

Improved interchangeable Lock Stencils, made of spring brass. They will not curl up. The letters and characters are perfect in design and finish, cut in spring brass on separate plates, having a lock formed on the sides by which they can be joined one to the other. They are put up in alphabets, sets of figures and fonts. The fonts are correctly assorted as to vowels, consonants, periods, etc., by printers' rules for printing names and general use. Are especially useful to farmers for marking crates and boxes, etc.

42708 Font No. 1, 55 pieces only.

Size.........Inch	¼	⅜	1	1½
Per font	$0.55	.57	.65	.83

42709 Font No. 2, 70 pieces, letters and figures.

Size.........Inch	½	¾	1	1½
Per font	$0.70	.75	.80	$1.05

No ink or brush furnished with font No. 1 and 2.

42710 Ink for interchangeable stencils. Large cans, price each.......................$0.30
42711 Small cans, price, each.......................$0.12
42712 Stencil brushes, large. Each.......................$0.12
42713 Stencil brushes, large Each.......................$0.10
42714 House Numbers, made of brass and nicely nickel plated, each, per doz. per 100, 3 inches.

	Each	Per doz.	Per 100
Oval	$0.10	$0.80	$8.40
3 inches. 42715 Flat	.08	.60	6.25

42714

Alarm Till.

42721 Tucker Patent Alarm, Till Lock and Drawer. Hardwood, strongly dove-tailed, combination quickly changed. No keys required. Price, each..$1.45

Tap Borers.

42723 Tap Borer, weight, 1¼ lbs. Each.................................$0.55 Per dozen.................................. 5.95

Molasses Gates.

42725 Molasses Gates, Stebbins' Patent.

No.	1	2	3	4	5
Bores, inches	1	1⅛	1¼	1⅜	1½
Each	.12	.15	.16	.18	.20

Fruit, Wine and Jelly Press Combined.

42730 Combination Fruit Wine and Jelly Press; can be used for many purposes, such as making wines, jellies and fruit butter from fruits, the entire substance being extracted in one operation. Weight, 12½ lbs., Price, each.......$2.35

Twine Box.

42736 Improved Hanging Twine Box; bronzed iron; weight 15 ounces. Each.......................................$0.12 Per dozen.................................. 1.30

Fish Scaler.

42737 Fish Scaler iron, japanned, 9 inches in length, removes the scales from fish in much shorter time than it can be done in any other way. Weight, 9 ounces. Each...$0.05 Per dozen.. .54

There never was a better year to buy.

Steak Pounder and Ice Pick.

42738 The Diamond beef steak pounder and ice pick combined; made of gray iron, cast in one solid piece, nicely japanned. The best kitchen tool in the market; weight, 1 pound. Price each......$0.06. Per dozen......$0.55

Easy Can Opener.

42739 Easy Can Opener. The best cheap can opener made; cuts the entire top off the can and leaves a smooth edge. Try one. Each......$0.08 Per dozen... .87

The Improved White Mountain Ice Cream Freezer for 1895.

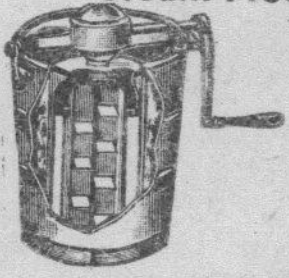

42740 As features of especial merit, we claim: A strong waterproof tub, bound with heavy, galvanized iron hoops; the gearing completely covered, so that nothing can get between the cogs; cans full size and made of the very best quality of tin-plate; beaters of malleable iron and tinned; all castings attached to the tub nicely galvanized to prevent rusting. It is the only freezer in the market having the **celebrated duplex dasher, with double self-adjusting wood scraping bar,** by the use of which cream can be frozen in one-half the time, yet finer and smoother than can possibly be produced in any other freezer now in use. Positively the best freezer in the world, and guaranteed if properly used to make ice cream in 3 MINUTES.

Size	2-qt.	3-qt.	4-qt.	6-qt.	8-qt.
Each	$1.50	$1.85	$2.20	$2.80	$3.75
Size	10-qt.	12-qt.	15-qt.	20-qt.	25-qt.
Each	$5.00	$5.80	$6.80	$9.20	$11.20

42741 Extra Fly Wheel for 25 quart Freezers. Each...$3.50

Extra Cans for White Mountain Freezers.

42743—

Quarts	6	8	10	12	15	20	25
Each	$0.90	$1.10	$1.50	$1.75	$2.00	$2.85	$4.00

Apple Parers.

42745 The '78 Parer with improved curved knife still maintains its reputation as the best in the world. All parings fall clear from the machine, and do not become mixed up in the gears. The Automatic "Push off" never fails to "push off" the apple every time after it is pared. Price each..............$0.75 Price per dozen......... 8.00

42746 Apple Parer, Corer and Slicer, "Little Star." For paring, coring and slicing; the Little Star is the simplest and best machine in use. The knife arm works on a swivel, and always faces the apple when in use; weight, 2¼ lbs. Price, each$0.45 Per doz....................................... 4.86

Wringers.

We use the Genuine Patent Rolls. Vulcanized to the shaft; the very best rolls known to the wringer business, except the old-fashioned elastic roll wringer which we quote under No. 42771. All material used in our wringers are of the best quality, and the workmanship and finish are not surpassed by any similar goods in the market. We aim to have the best goods.

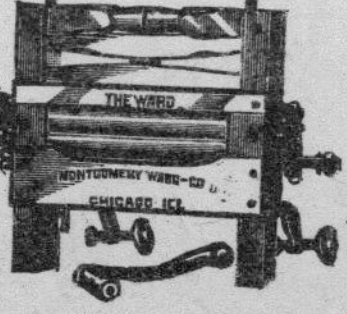

42763 Improved Montgomery Ward & Co. Wood Frame Wringer. No. 2½ like cut. Length of rolls 10 inches, diameter 1⅝ in. Price, each....$2.00 Per dozen....21.00

42764 With rolls, 11 inch long, 1¾ in. diameter, large size. Price, each....$2.50 Per dozen.... 26.50

Ore or Sand Barrows.

43448 Bolted ore barrow for ore, coal, and or dirt. The best general purpose barrow made, the side and end and piece of tray being dovetailed together and firmly strapped and nailed. Cannot come apart. Edges of tray iron strapped. Handles 5 feet long. Size of tray, 8 inches deep at the handles, 11½ inches at wheel bottom, 16½x9 inches top, 27 inches wide by 29 inches long: wheel 17 inches in diameter, tire 1⅛x3/16, spokes ⅞x1, axle bolt ½ inch. Weight, 53 lbs. Price, each........ $2.00
Per dozen........ 23.00

Stone Barrow.

43449 Bent Handle stone barrow thoroughly bolted, well ironed. Handles 6 feet long, cross pieces on legs 2x3 inches, bottom 26 inches wide by 27 inches long, 1¼ inches thick, dash 11 inches high, weight 72 lbs.
Price, each........ $ 2.50
Per dozen........ 28.00

43450 Columbus tubular steel mining and general purpose barrows. No. 6 size, tray made of No. 14 steel: capacity 3 cubic feet of earth. Weight of barrow, 80 lbs.
Price each........ $ 5.82
Per dozen........ 63.00

Sand Screens for Mason's Use.

Made of heavy parallel wires, looped to pass through the slots punched uniformly in narrow strips of sheet steel. The supporting rods are passed through the loops at the back of the sheet steel and firmly hold the wires in place. At the top and bottom wide steel plates are connected in the same manner. Weight, large size, about 42 lbs.; small size, about 35 lbs. Made in three sizes of mesh.
No. 2, about ⅜ inch between wires.
No 3, about ¼ inch between wires.
No. 4, about 3.16 inch between wires.

In ordering always state size of mesh wanted.
43451 Small size, 60 inches long, by 22 inches wide. Each........ $3.75
43452 Large size, 66 inches long, by 26 inches wide. Each........ 4.69

Quick Edge Grindstone.

43453 For the use of the farmer, butcher, carpenter, cabinet maker and pattern maker. The diameter of the stone is 17 inches, width 2¼ inches, and weighs from 45 to 50 pounds; the shipping weight it 70 lbs. It is packed for shipment, but it is a very small matter to set up the grinder for use. Each stone is plugged and center-bored true, and faced to fit the mandrel plate. Hard wood is used in its construction, and while the structure is light and convenient it is of wonderful strength and firm in operative position.
Price, each, complete, as shown in cut........ $3.50

⁂ It will be a favor to us (and perhaps to your friends) if you will place, where they will do the most good, any duplicate Catalogues or advertising matter which you may receive from us.

Ohio Mounted Grindstones.

OAK FRAME FOOT POWER.

Comes knocked down ready for shipping, can be put together in a few minutes. This is a very practical, honest machine, and for general use about a farm or shop cannot be excelled.

	43454	43455	43456
Weight of stone,	100 to 110 lb.	60 to 70 lb.	40 to 50 lb.
Each........	$2.00	$1.75	$1.60

Grindstones.

43457 Family Grindstones, with frames complete as per cut, 8-inch stone. Each........ $0.70
These are very convenient for sharpening knives and small tools, and take up little room.

Grindstone Fixtures.

43458 Grindstone Fixture similar to cut, except top bolts down instead of hinged.

15 in.	17 in.	19 in.	21 in.
For 40-lb.	60-lb.	80-lb.	100-lb. stones.
Each 25c.	28c.	30c.	35c.

Sure-Grip Steel Tackle Block.

43460 Will hold load at any point without fastening the rope; the brake is absolutely automatic; the heavier the load the better the grip. At the same time the brake is susceptible of being disengaged by very slight pressure. The body of block is made of steel plates. The pins are cold rolled steel. The essential castings are malleable iron, making the strongest and safest possible combination of materials, thus affording immunity from accidents in the highest degree. The brake is a fluted wedge dropping between two ropes in such a manner that the load is brought on all the strands of the rope at same time. The brake does not flatten the rope, consequently the wear upon it is reduced to a minimum. This machine will be found particularly valuable by boat and ship builders, contractors, dealers in hardware and machinery, grocers, truckmen, butchers, machine shops, founders and roofers in stringing heavy electric wires, handling barrels, baled hay, safes, in fact any place where hoisting blocks are used it will be found SAFE, SURE AND ECONOMICAL.
No. 5. To be used with ⅜ rope; one man can lift 400 lbs; capacity, 1,800 lbs. Price, per set.. $5.25
No. 6. To be used with ¾ rope; one man can lift 450 lbs; capacity, 2,500 lbs. Price, per set.. 6.38
No. 4½. To be used with ½ rope; one man can lift 600 lbs.; capacity, 3,000 lbs. Price, per set. 7.50
No. 5½. To be used with ⅝ rope; one man can lift 700 lbs; capacity, 3,500 lbs. Price, per set, 9.00
The price as given above does not include rope or the weight as shown in cut, but it does include one upper and one lower block.

Tackle Blocks.

43462 Improved Steel Snatch Block, edges of plates rounded to protect the rope with Ford's Patent Self Lubricating Shears, needs no oil, cost but a trifle more than iron bushed, and will do nearly double the service.

For Dia. rope	Size of shell	Price Each.
¾ in.	6 in.	$2.25
⅞ "	7 "	2.37
1 "	8 "	2.87
1⅛ "	9 "	3.38
1¼ "	10 "	4.05
1½ "	12 "	4.95
1¾ "	14 "	6.30
2 "	16 "	8.55

Iron Strapped

Single. Double. Triple.

43467 Iron Strapped Tackle Blocks, Steel Pins, Iron Sheaves. The shells have nicely rounded edges and are finished in a superior manner. When ordering always give size and state whether single, double or triple pulley is wanted. Also be very particular to state if you wish them with or without becket.

For Rope.	Size of shell.	Single pulley each.	Double pulley each.	Triple pulley each.
5/16 in......	3	$0.28	$0.50	$0.70
⅜ in......	3½	.30	.60	.80
½ in......	4	.35	.65	.85
⅝ in......	5	.38	.70	.90
¾ in......	6	.45	.80	1.20
⅞ in......	7	.55	.95	1.40
1 in......	8	.70	1.15	1.80
1⅛ in......	10	1.25	1.90	2.50
1¼ in......	12	2.00	3.00	4.25

Single pulleys weigh from ¾ to 18 pounds. Double pulleys, from 1¼ to 32 pounds. Triple pulleys from 2 to 64 pounds.

Tackle Blocks.

Rope Strapped.

Single. Double. Triple.

43468 Rope Strapped Tackle Blocks, steel pins, iron sheaves. The shells have nicely rounded edges and are finished in a superior manner. When ordering always give size and state whether single, double or triple pulley is wanted.

For rope.	Size of shell.	Single pulley Each.	Double pulley Each.	Triple pulley Each.
⅜ inch....	3	$0.30	$0.50	$0.72
⅜ inch....	3½	.32	.55	.80
½ inch....	4	.38	.65	.95
⅝ inch....	5	.40	.72	.98
¾ inch....	6	.45	.80	1.20
⅞ inch....	8	.70	1.30	1.75
1 inch....	9	.85	1.50	2.10
1⅛ inch....	10	1.10	2.00	2.65
1¼ inch	12	1.90	3.10	4.25

Single pulleys weigh from ½ lb. to 2 lbs. Double pulleys from 2 to 30 lbs. Triple pulleys from 1½ to 40 lbs.

Steel Tackle Blocks.

43470 Steel Tackle Block with loose hooks and rounded edge to protect the rope.

For Rope.	Size or shell.	Single pulley	Double pulley.	Triple pulley.
½ inch....	4 inch	$0.40	$0.80	$1.20
⅝ inch....	5 inch	.45	.86	1.32
¾ inch....	6 inch	.56	1.05	1.56
⅞ inch....	7 inch	.68	1.25	2.00
1 inch....	8 inch	.83	1.45	2.28
1⅛ inch....	9 inch	1.08	1.80	2.64
1¼ inch....	10 inch	1.40	2.30	3.25
1½ inch....	12 inch	2.30	3.75	5.88

Awning Pulleys.

43473 Awning Pulleys, galvanized iron; will not take rope larger than 5-16 inch. Single pulleys weigh 3 5 and 8 ounces, double pulleys weigh 6 8 and 12 ounces.

Size wheel.	Single pulley Each.	Single pulley Dozen.	Size of wheel.	Double pulley Each.	Double pulley Dozen.
¾ in.	$0.03	$0.30	¾ in.	$0.05	$0.50
1 in.	.04	.40	1 in.	.06	.60
1¼ in.	.08	.80	1½ in.	.11	1.15

Hot House Pulleys.

Hot House Pulleys, japanned iron, takes small rope, 5-16 or ⅜ each. Single pulleys, 13 ounces; double pulleys, 1 pound 2 ounces.

43475 Single Pulley.

Size of wheel.	Each.	Doz.
2 inch.	$0.08	$0.65

43476 Double Pulley.

	Each.	Doz.
Size of wheel, 2 in.	$0.12	$1 06

Side Pulleys.

43478 Japanned Iron Side Pulleys; will not take larger than 5-16 inch rope.

Size of wheel.	Weight.	Each.	Per doz.
1½ inches.	5 oz.	$0.04	$0.30
1¾ inches.	7 oz.	.05	.40
2 inches.	10 oz.	.06	.48
2½ inches.	14 oz.	.07	.70
3 inches.	18 oz.	.10	1.00

Screw Pulleys.

43480 Screw Pulley, japanned iron will not take rope larger than 5-16 inch

Size of wheel.	Weight.	Each.	Per doz.
1½ inch.	4 oz.	$0.03	$0.20
1¾ inch.	5 oz.	.03	.28
2 inch.	6 oz.	.04	.35
2¼ inch.	7 oz.	.05	.45
2½ inch.	8 oz.	.06	.48
3 inch.	9 oz.	.07	.65

Imitation Newhouse Traps.

43484 — Rat Traps, 3½ inch jaw with chain; weight 14 oz. No. 0. Each $0.11 Per doz. $1.25

43485 Rat Traps, 4-inch jaw, with chains; weight 14 oz. No. 1. Each .... .14
Per dozen 1.45

26—6th

Newhouse Traps.

WITH CHAINS.

The Newhouse Traps are the best in the world. They have held first place in the estimation of trappers for the last fifty years, are reliable and are sure to hold the game every time.

43490 No. 0 size. This trap is used mostly for catching the gopher (a little animal which is very troublesome to western farmers) and also rats and other vermin. It has a sharp grip, and will hold larger game, but should not be overtaxed. Spread of jaws, 3½ inches; weight 13 oz. Each $0.20 Per dozen $2.16

43491 No. 1 size. This trap is used for catching muskrats and other small animals, and is sold in greater numbers than any other size. We recommend it to the farmer, as the most serviceable size for catching skunks, weasels, rats and such other animals as may visit his poultry houses and barns. Spread of jaws, 4 inches; weight, 17 ounces. Each $0.25 Per dozen..... 2.50

43492 No. 1½ Trap. This size is called the Mink Trap. It is however suitable for catching the woodchuck, skunk, etc. Professional trappers often use it for catching foxes. It is very convenient in form and is strong and reliable. Spread of jaws 4⅞ inches; weight 1 lb., 6 oz. Each $0.35 Per dozen.......... 3.75

43493 No. 2 size. The No. 2 trap is called the Fox Trap. Its spread of jaws is the same as the No. 1½, but having two springs is, of course much stronger; weight, 1 lb. 10 oz. Each...... .48
Per dozen.......................... 5.25

43495 No. 3 size. Otter Trap, very powerful, will hold almost any game smaller than a bear. Spread of jaws 5½ inches. Double spring; weight 2 lbs. 8 oz. Each $0.65 Per dozen...... 7.00

43497 No. 4 size. This is the regular form of beaver trap It is longer than the No. 3 trap and has one inch greater spread of jaws. It is a favorite with those who hunt and trap for a living in the far West and Canada. Spread of jaws 6½ inches; weight 3 lbs., 2 oz. Each.......... .75
Per dozen.......................... 8.25

Wolf Traps.

43498 No. 4½ size, especially adapted to catching wolves. This trap has 8 inch spread of jaws, with the other parts in proportion, and is provided with a pronged "drag," a heavy snap and an extra heavy steel swivel and chain, 5 feet long, warranted to hold two thousand pounds. The trap, complete with chain and "drag," will weigh about 9 lbs.
Price, each $1.75
Per dozen 20.00

43499 No. 5 size with offset jaws. This trap weighs 17 lbs. and has a spread of jaws of 11½ inches. It is used for taking the common black bear, and is furnished with a chain and swivel sufficiently strong. Double spring. Each...... 6.25

43502 No. 6 Trap for grizzly bear. This is the strongest trap made. It will hold lion, cougar, tiger or moose, as well as the great grizzly bear. Spread of jaws 16 inches; weight, 42 lbs. Each. 11.20

Setting Clamps.

43506 For setting game traps.	Each.	Per doz.
No. 4 for setting No. 4 trap..........	$0.15	$1.25
No. 5 for setting No. 5 traps..........	.30	3.15
No. 6 for setting No. 6 Trap..........	.50	5.25

43510 The Dean Mole Trap. This is an entirely new pattern and is a decided improvement on all other makes; is more simple and less liable to get out of order. The frame is strong and terminates in two long ribbed points which anchor it firmly in the ground, (all other makes have only one point). The principal feature about it is its automatic setting device: Simply pulling up on the handle sets it. Being much more simple as to construction it can be sold at a much lower price than any other make.

DIRECTIONS FOR SETTING TRAP.

Press the dirt down across the trail; push the trap down before setting till the pan rests on the dirt; put foot on cross piece, and pull up on handle a few times to loosen dirt about the fork tines, then set it.
Price, each.......................... $1.20

Malleable Fittings for Wrought Iron Pipe.

We can furnish almost anything made in pipe fittings. Write us for prices on goods you do not find quoted. The sizes of pipe fittings are determined by the size of pipe over which they fit; thus, ¼ inch tee or elbow, etc., fits over ¼ inch pipe.

Lock Nuts.

43580—

For Pipe, in.	¼	⅜	½	¾	1	1¼	1½	2
Each........	2c	2c	3c	3c	4c	5c	6c	8c

Pipe Caps.

43581— For Pipe, in.	¼	⅜	½	¾	1	1¼	1½	2
Black, each...	2c	3c	3c	4c	5c	7c	10c	12c
43581½— Galv'd, each..	3c	3c	4c	5c	7c	10c	14c	18c

Nipples.

43582 Size, inches.	¼	⅜	½	¾	1	1¼	1½	2
Black, short, price ea.	2c	3c	3c	4c	4c	5c	6c	8c
43582½— Galv'd, short, price ea.	3c	4c	4c	4c	5c	6c	7c	10c
43583— Black, long, price ea..	3c	4c	4c	4c	5c	6c	8c	10c
43583½— Galv'd, long, price ea.	4c	5c	5c	6c	6c	7c	9c	12c

Malleable Return Bends, Open Pattern.

43585 For pipe, in.	¾	1	1¼	1½	2
Black, each,......	9c	12c	15c	23c	38c

MALLEABLE UNIONS.

43586 For Pipe, in.	¼	⅜	½	¾	1	1¼	1½	2
Black, each.......	7c	8c	10c	11c	14c	17c	23c	29c
43586½— Galvanized, each.	9c	10c	11c	15c	19c	25c	32c	40c

MALLEABLE REDUCERS.

43587 For Pipe, in.	¼	⅜	½	¾	1	1¼	1½	2
Black each......	3c	3c	3c	5c	6c	9c	12c	17c
43587½— Galvanized, each.	4c	4c	5c	6c	10c	13c	17c	26c

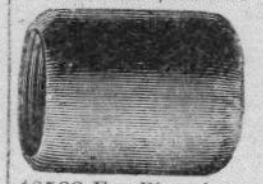

WROUGHT IRON COUPLINGS.

43588 For Pipe, in.	¼	⅜	½	¾	1	1¼	1½	2
Black, each......	3c	4c	4c	5c	7c	8c	9c	12c
43588½— Galvanized, each,	4c	5c	5c	7c	8c	10c	13c	16c

MALLEABLE ELBOWS.

43589 For Pipe, in.	¼	⅜	½	¾	1	1¼	1½	2
Black, each......	3c	4c	5c	6c	8c	9c	15c	18c
43589½— Galvanized, each.	4c	5c	6c	9c	12c	15c	22c	30c

MALLEABLE TEES

43590 For Pipe, in.	¼	⅜	½	¾	1	1¼	1½	2
Black, each......	4c	5c	6c	7c	10c	12c	17c	23c
43590½— Galvanized, each.	5c	5c	7c	10c	15c	18c	25c	35c

MALLEABLE CROSSES.

43591 For Pipe, in.	¼	⅜	½	¾	1	1¼	1½	2
Black, each......	5c	5c	6c	9c	12c	15c	23c	35c
43591½— Galvanized, each.	6c	7c	8c	10c	17c	23c	32c	50c

Plugs.

CAST IRON PLUGS.

43592 For Pipe in.	¼	⅜	½	¾	1
Black, each......	2c	2c	3c	3c	4c

For Pipe in.......	1¼	1½	2
Black, each.......	4c	5c	6c

43592½ Galvanized, each—
.3c 3c 4c 4c 5c 6c 7c 10c

Bushing.

43593 For pipe in.	⅜	½	¾	1
Black, each	3c	3c	4c	4c

For Pipe in......	1¼	1½	2
Black, each.....	5c	6c	8c

43593½ Galvanized, each—
3c 4c 5c 5c 6c 9c 12c

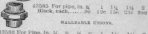

Butterfly Valves.

43608 Iron Body Brass Trimming screwed.
Size— 1½ 2 2½
Price, each $1.65 $2.15 $2.80
Size 3 3½ 4
Price,each. $4.10 $5.15 $6.65

Globe Valves.

BRASS.

43609 For pipe—
in. ¼ ⅜ ½ ¾
Price, each $0.20 $0.25 $0.32 $0.40
For pipe in 1 1¼
Price, each $0.52 $0.75
For pipe in 1½ 2 2½ 3
Price, each $1.15 $1.50 $2.90 $4.00

Brass Angle Valves.

Order No. 43610.

43610 For pipe—
in. ¼ ⅜ ½
Price, each $0.20 $0.26 $0.35
For pipe in. ¾ 1 1¼
Price, each $0.42 $0.55 $0.80
For pipe in. 1½ 2 2½ 3
Price, each $1 25 $1.65 $3.10 $4.30

Brass Cross Valves.

43612—
For pipe in. ¼ ⅜ ½ ¾
Price each $0.25 .32 .48 .60
Pipe in. 1 1¼ 1½
Price, each $0.75 1.00 1.55
Size 2 2½ 3
Price, each $2.50 4.80 7.10

Brass Steam Cocks.

Flat heads.

43614—
For pipe in. ¼ ⅜ ½
Price each $0.25 .26 .45
Pipe in. ¾ 1 1¼ 1½
Price each $0.55 .80 1.45 1.85
Size 2 2½ 3
Price each $2.68 4.95 6.90

43614

Horizontal Check Valves.

43616 For pipe—
in. ¼ ⅜ ½ ¾ 1 1¼
Price, each $0.18 .22 .28 .35 .48 .65
For pipe in. 1½ 2 2½ 3
Price, each $0.85 $1.40 $2.80 $3.90

Brass Three-Way Cocks.

43618 For pipe—
in ½ ¾ 1 1¼
Price, each $0.65 .85 $1.30 $2.10
For pipe in. 1½ 2 2½ 3
Price, each $2.70 $3.65 $6.50 $8.95

Brass Air Cocks.

Finished.

43620 Size... ⅛ ¼ ⅜ ½
Price, each. 15c 17c 20c 24c

Brass Oil Cups.

Finished

43622 All brass with screw top
Diameter of body ⅝ ¾ 1 1¼ 1½ 2
Pipe size of shank ⅛ ⅛ ¼ ¼ ⅜ ⅜
Price, each....... 10c 13c 16c 25c 32c 65c

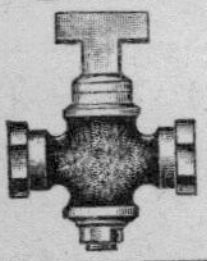

Pipe Stops.

43625 Brass rough stop, T handles round way nut and washer, screwed for iron pipe.
Size, inches..... ½ ¾ 1
Price, plain..... $0.40 $0.63 $0.93

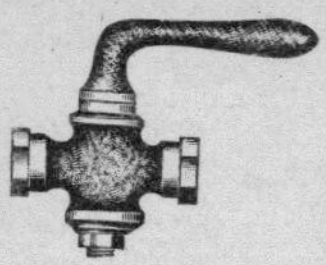

Water Pipe Stops.

43626 Brass rough stop lever handle, screwed for iron pipe.
Size, inches.......... ½ ¾ 1
Price, plain, each $0.41 $0.65 $0.95

Hydrant Cocks.

43627 Brass Hydrant Cock with T handle for iron pipe.
Size, ¾ in. 1in. 1¼ in.
Price, each, 62c. 85c. $1.30

Hydrant Clamps.

43628 Hydrant Clamps, malleable iron, with square hole. When ordering you must always give us the size of hydrant cock.
Price, each.......... $0.15

Basin Cocks.

43630 Fuller pattern, nickel plated. Price, each $1 20

Bath Cocks.

43631 Combination Fuller pattern, complete with sprinkler, nickel plated. Price, each...$3.40

Bath Cock.

43636 Compression Valve, double nickel plated. Price, each $2.20

Brass Bibs or Faucets.

43638 Hose Bibs for iron pipe. Lever handle. Size, inches, finished.
½ ⅝ ¾ 1
Price, each, $0.48 .62 .80 1.30

43640 Compression Hose Bibs, screwed for iron pipe with shoulder, finished
Size, inches—
⅜ ½ ⅝ ¾ 1
Price each—
$0.37 .40 .45 .68 1.25

43642 Compression Plain Bibbs, screwed for iron pipe, with shoulder, finished.
Size, inches—
⅜ ½ ⅝ ¾ 1
Price each—
$0.35 .40 .45 .62 1.15

Faucets—Continued.

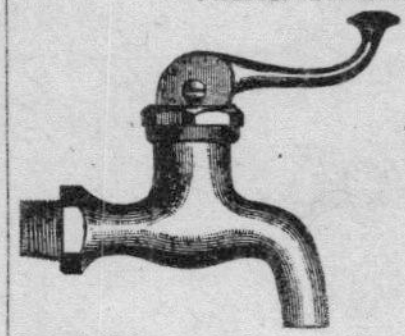

43644 Telegraph Plain Bibs for iron pipe.

Size, inches.......... ⅜ ½ ⅝ ¾
Price each, brass.......... $0 70 $0.80 $0.90 $1.25
Nickel plated.......... .80 .90 1.05 1.35

Urinals.

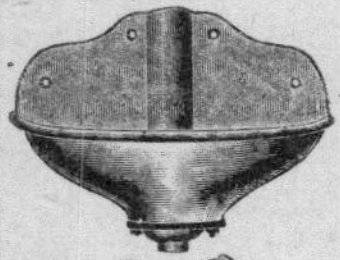

43650 Iron Corner Urinal, enameled; size, 9 inches; fitted for lead pipe.
Price, each...... $1.70

43652 Iron Half Circle Urinal, enameled; size, 12 in.; fitted for lead pipe.
Price, each.......... $1.90

43655 Ball Cocks for Iron Pipe.
Size...... ½ ⅝ in.
Each..... $0.43 $0.53
Size..... ¾ 1 1¼ in
Each..... $0.70 $1.05 $1.75

43656 Copper Ball Floats for Ball Cocks.
Size, inches....5 6 7 8 10 12in.
Price each...$0 42 $0.50 $0.73 $1.70 $3.50 $5.00

Wash Basins.

43657

43657 White Earthen Patent Overflow Wash Basin, for rubber plug for stationary wash stand, complete with chain and plug. Diameter outside.
Inches 12 13 14
Each $0.90 $1.05 $1.10
Inches..... 15 16
Each........ $1.40 $2.00

43658 Stopper with chain, for 43657 basin.
Each $0.25
Per doz 2.70
Prices in marble slabs for washstands on application.

43659

43659 Iron Wash Basins, enameled; common overflow; diameter, 14 in., complete with stopper.
Price, each.......... $2.10

43660

43660 Iron Wash Basins, enameled, patent overflow; diameter, 14 inches, complete with stopper; fitted for either iron or lead pipe.
Price, each.......... $2.67

Bibs.

43665 Fuller Pattern, Plain Bib, for iron pipe finished brass.
Sizes... ½ ⅝ ¾ 1 inch
Price ea. $0.55 $0.62 $0.82 $1.05

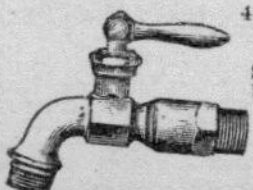

43666 Fuller Pattern Hose Bib for iron pipe finished Brass.
Sizes ½ ⅝ ¾ 1 inch
Price, ea. $0.62 .70 .85 1.20

Oil Faucet.

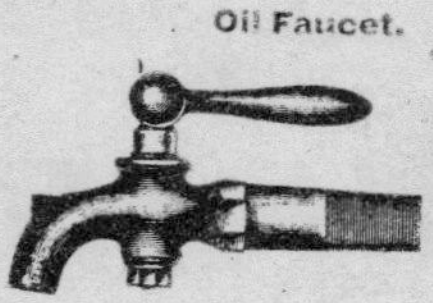

43667 The original and only genuine Frary's Patent Oil Faucet, made of iron japanned key, bushed, with brass lever handle screw shank; for oil barrel.

½ in.	$0.30
⅝ in.	.32
¾ in.	.40
1 in.	.50

Oil Faucet.

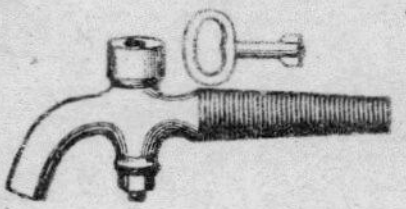

43668 Loose Key Faucets to screw, brass. These faucets are very convenient. The key may be withdrawn and the contents of the barrel cannot be drawn easily without the aid of the key to open the faucet. It is a guard against accident, as the faucet cannot accidentally be opened, as is often the case with the ordinary kind. One size, ½ inch. Each........$0.54

Sinks.

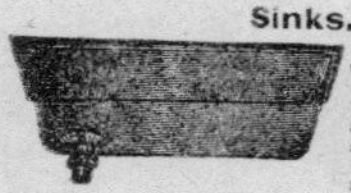

Wrought Steel Kitchen Sinks. These sinks are made from one plate of steel and are superior to cast iron sinks in every particular, being lighter, stronger and more durable, are fitted for 1¼ in. lead or 1½ inch iron pipe, and some painted or galvanized in the following sizes:

Order No. 43669 PAINTED.

Size.	Weight.	Each.	Size.	Weight.	Each.
16x24x6	8½ lbs.	$1.25	20x30x6	13½ lbs.	$2.30
18x30x6	11 lbs.	1.87	20x36x6	17 lbs.	2.77
18x36x6	16 lbs.	2.25	20x40x6	18½ lbs.	3.00

Order No. 43670 GALVANIZED.

Size.	Weight.	Each.	Size.	Weight.	Each.
16x24x6	9 lbs.	$2.00	20x30x6	17½ lbs.	$3.12
18x30x6	13 lbs.	2.55	20x36x6	18½ lbs	3.75
18x36x6	16 lbs.	3.25	20x40x6	20 lbs.	4.25

Bath Tubs.

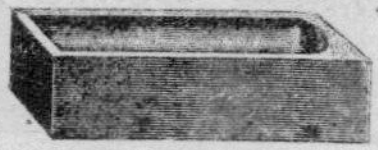

43675 Stationary Copper Bath Tub, 5, 5½ or 6 feet long, made of 12 oz. copper. Outside width at head and foot, 24 in.; outside depth, 19 inches. Prices subject to fluctuation of copper market. Price, each, for 5, 5½ or 6 feet.......$ 9.45

Stationary Zinc Bath Tubs.

43676 Same as above but lined with zinc instead of copper. Made in three sizes, 5 ft., 5½ ft. and 6 ft.
Price, each..$5.95

Iron Bath Tubs.

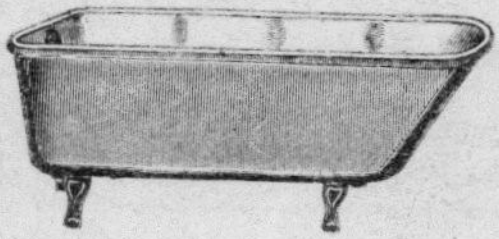

FRENCH PATTERN.

43677 The most durable and most satisfactory bath tubs made. They are easily kept clean, neat and handsome in appearance and can never rust or leak. Price, each, porcelain lined, 4½ feet, $24.45; 5 feet, $27.10; 5½ feet, $29.40; 6 feet, $32.20.
43678 Price, each, grey enameled inside, 4½ feet, $19.20; 5 feet, $23.80; 5½ feet, $26.20; 6 ft., $28.60.
43679 Price, each, painted inside, 4½ feet, $14.80; 5 feet, $16.20; 5½ feet, $17.50; 6 feet, $18.75.
For hard wood rim around top add $3.60 each.

Sink or Bath Plugs.

43680

43680 Sink or Bath Plugs.

Size	1¼	1½
Price, each	$0.10	$0.15

Our claim that this Catalogue opens the large markets to you is no idle boast. Where else can you find so much? As a genuine guide to prices it has no equal.

The Mosely Self-Heating Folding Bath Tub and Water Heater.

FOR GAS OR GASOLINE.

Is a handsome piece of furniture, of modern style, complete in all mechanical appointments, and is perfect in operation as a folding bed, giving the full equivalent of a modern bath room, as far as the bath is concerned, with the advantage of quick and independent heating, and comprises a full-sized 9-oz zinc, or 14-oz. copper-lined bath tub, water tank, heater, and waste water outlet. The cases are of modern designs, excellent quality of cabinet work and thoroughly seasoned hard lumber. The style and finish corresponds with the latest and most popular in furniture. The material used in the finish is impervious to moisture, hot or cold water, insuring a durable and permanent lustre. All burners gas or gasoline, are made expressly for the requirements of these tubs, and are unequaled. Each tub is fitted with a flexible outlet with brass couplings, one of which fastens permanently to the tub, the other may be connected to ordinary gas or lead pipe; or tubing, leading to any waste water outlet in the building, or to make an independent exit, or the contents of the tub may be emptied by means of the connecting tube into any convenient recepticle in the apartment. Having a fixed journal bearing, this tub has a positive action in raising or lowering, thus avoiding all use of casters and slides. The adjustable back supporting the water tank forms a counterbalance to the tub, rendering its manipulation sufficiently easy for a child to operate. This tub is made in two lengths, and measures 2 feet wide, 18 inches deep, and 5 feet and 5 feet 6 inches long, respectively, and occupies a floor space when closed about 26x28 inches. Weight crated for shipment about 250 pounds. This tub does not require fastening to the wall. It is an independent article of furniture, complete in itself. No cutting of carpets necessary.

GASOLINE BURNER WITH HEATER WILL BE SHIPPED UNLESS OTHERWISE ORDERED.

Tubs are lined with best quality No. 9 zinc or 14 oz. copper.

EXTREME OUTSIDE MEASUREMENTS.

5-foot tub, height when closed, 5 feet 8 inches. Length over all when open for use, 5 feet 9 inches.
5-foot 6-inch Tub, height when closed, 6 feet 4 inches. Length over all when open for use, 6 feet 5 inches.

No. 10½. Panel front oval top, antique finish. L ength 5 fet 6 in.

43685 A, Zinc-lined Tub with enameled iron heater, like cut, each....................................$27.60
B, Enamel Tub with enameled iron heater, like cut, each....................................31.59
C, Copper-lined Tub with enameled iron heater, like cut, each....................................34.50
43686 A, Zinc Tub without heater.............15.62
B, Enamel " " " 19.79
C, Copper " " " 21.68

No. 12½ Panel Front, natural, antique, or XVI Century. Polished finish, length, either 5 feet or 5 feet 6 inches. Folding legs supplied for $2.00 extra.

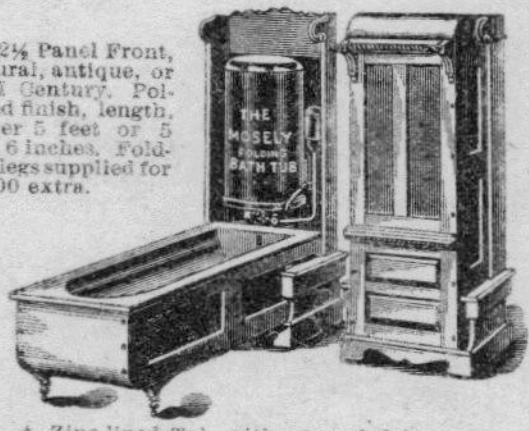

43687 A, Zinc-lined Tub, with enameled iron heater, like cut. Each..........................$33.60
B, Enameled-lined Tub, with enameled iron heater, like cut. Each..........................37.59
C, Copper-lined, with enameled iron heater, like cut. Each..........................40.40
43688 Zinc-lined Tub, without heater.........20.83
B, Enameled Tub, without heater.........25.00
C, Copper Lined Tub, without heater.........27.91

***** Freight Rates from Chicago to nearly any railroad point in America will be quoted upon application. If you have any particular class of goods in view mention same when writing. We want you to know what your goods will cost you delivered at your station, as near as possible.**

Bath Tubs—Continued.

No. 15 Beveled French Plate Mirror, 34x16, imitation drawers, natural, antique or XVI Century, Polished finish, zinc lined. Length, 5 feet 6 in. With folding legs.

43689 A, Zinc-lined Tub, with enameled iron heater, like cut. Each..........................$40.80
B, Enameled Tub, with enameled iron heater, like cut Each..........................44.80
C, Copper-lined Tub, with enameled iron heater, like cut. Each..........................47.60
43690 A, Zinc-lined Tub, without heater.........27.20
B, Enameled Tub, without heater.........31.20
C, Copper Lined, without heater.........34.00

No. 23. Full Beveled French Plate Mirror, 54 x16, Fine Raised Carvings, natural, antique or XVICentury, polished finish, zinc lined. Length 5 feet 6 inches.

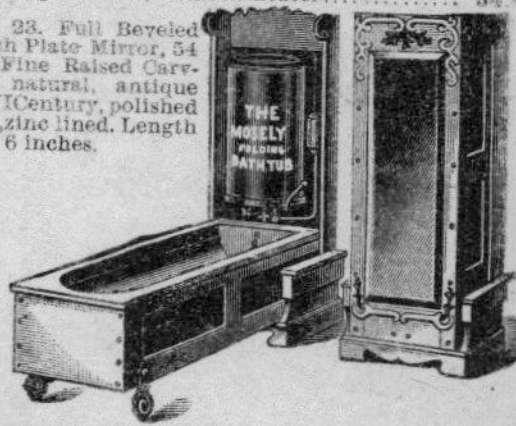

43691 A, Zinc-lined Tub, with enameled iron heater like cut. Each..........................$52.19
B, Enameled Tub with enameled iron heater, like cut. Each..........................57.20
C, Copper-lined Tub with enameled iron heater, like cut. Each..........................60.00
43692 A, Zinc-lined Tub without heater.........39.60
B, Enameled Tub without heater.........43.50
C, Copper-lined Tub without heater.........46.40

The Mosley Improved Water Heater No. 3.

WITH GAS OR GASOLINE BURNER.

Gasoline Burner.

Especially adapted for use with stationary baths, giving the advantage of QUICK AND INDEPENDENT HEATING, also for KITCHENS, LAUNDRYS, BARBER SHOPS, etc., with minimum fuel cost. PERFECT COMBUSTION. NO SMOKE. All parts clean at all times; may be used in connection with water service or otherwise. No ventilating flue required. Water tank is constructed with lid, so as to fill with bucket. Also has opening for supply pipe connecting with cut-of valve. NOT USED UNDER WATER OR STEAM PRESSURE.

43695 A, Enameled galvanized iron heaters, with bracket..........................$15.00
B, Copper heaters, with bracket..........................18.60
C, Nickel plated copper heaters..........................22.40

Brown's Adjustable Pipe Tongs.

Order No. 43696

Number	1	1½	2	3	4
Takes pipe from	½to¾	⅜to1	½to1¼	1to 2	1¼to3
Price, each......	$0.42	$0.48	$0.60	$0.90	$1.87

43697 Common Pipe Tongs. The size indicates the size of pipe they are for. Weight, from 1½ to 4 lbs.

Size..............	⅛	¼	⅜	½	¾	1
Each..............	$0.25	$0.29	$0.30	$0.35	$0.45	$0.50
Size..............	1¼	1½	2	2½	3	
Each..............	$0.60	$0.70	$0.75	$1.15	$1.57	

Seamless Brass Well Cylinder.

43968 Made with seamless brass body, iron caps and plunger. The 10-inch Cylinders has 6-inch stroke; the 12 and 14 inch cylinders have 8-inch stroke.

Diameter.	10 in. long. Each.	12 in. long. Each.	14 in. long. Each.
2¼ inch......	$2.20	$2.50	$2.70
2½ inch......	2.40	2.60	2.85
2¾ inch......	2.60	2.70	2.90
3 inch......	2.70	2.85	3.00
3¼ inch......	2.90	3.00	3.15
3½ inch......	3.10	3.20	3.35
4 inch......	3.85	4.10	4.20

43970 Foot valve and strainer, for 1¼ inch pipe. Weight, 2 pounds 15 ounces. Each..............$0.45

43971 Foot valve for 1½ inch pipe; weight, 4½ lbs. Each..............$0.55

Drive Well Points.

43972 Made of wrought iron pipe, perforated and galvanized; covered with a brass jacket of No. 36 GAUZE. This is the point in common use; we can furnish points with finer GAUZE for quicksand, etc. Prices on same will be furnished on application.

Diameter.	Length.	Each.
1¼ in.	24 in.	$0.95
1¼ in.	30 in.	1.10
1¼ in.	36 in.	1.30
1¼ in.	42 in.	1.50
1½ in.	30 in.	1.35
1½ in.	36 in.	1.70
2 in.	36 in.	2.30
2 in.	48 in.	3.30

43974 Lead Pipe. Price per pound..$0.06½

We can furnish lead pipe any size at the above price. In ordering always give the diameter and length wanted, not the weight.

Average weight per foot 1 inch 2 lbs. 8 oz.
Average weight per foot 1¼ inch 3 lbs.
Average weight per foot 1½ inch 4 lbs.

43975 Sheet Lead. Price per pound..........$0.06½

Rubber Bucket Chain Pumps.

43981 Rubber Bucket Chain Pump, complete for well 10 feet deep..............$3,50

43982 Rubber Bucket Chain Pump, complete for well 12 feet deep..............$3.60

43983 Rubber Bucket Chain Pump, complete for well 15 feet deep..............$4.00

43984 Rubber Bucket Chain Pump, complete for well 18 feet deep..............$4.35

43985 Rubber Bucket Chain Pump, complete for well 20 feet deep..............$5.50

We would not advise the use of chain pumps for deeper wells than 20 feet.

43986 Rubber Buckets for chain pumps.
Each..............$0.08
Per dozen.............. .69

Wood Pumps.

Made of good selected stock, neatly painted and decorated. Outside measurement of pumps is 6x6 inches with 3½-in bore.

43987--

Length.	Price with Plain Cylinder.	Price with Porcelain Lined Cylinder.
5 feet....	$1.65	$3.25
6 "	2.80	3.40
7 "	3.00	3.75
8 "	3.20	3.85
10 "		4.25

43988 Wood Suction Pipe. Steam tested—to fit above pumps: 4x4-in. pipe, 1⅜-in. bore 3½ tenons @ 8c. per ft.
Price is for wood pipe in 12 ft. lengths and under.

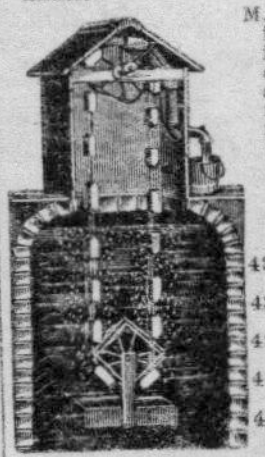

M.W.& Co's Improved water Purifying Pumps the buckets passing down into the water full of air acreates and purifies it. It always furnishes the water from the bottom of the well, as no water enters the cups until they begin to rise at the bottom. No suckers or valves or wooden tubing to rot or get rusty: buckets are made of galvanized iron; only good for dug wells.

43993 Complete for 10 foot well..............$6.00

43994 Complete for 15 foot well.............. 7.00

43995 Complete for 20 foot well.............. 8.20

43996 Complete for 25 foot well.............. 9.30

43997 Complete for 30 foot well..............10.53

Myers' Brass Spray Pump.

WITH 8 GALLON TANK.

43998 The tank is made of galvanized iron and is equipped with one of Myers' powerful brass spray pumps, as shown in cut 44000. Price, complete with 8 gallon tank, each..............$5.25

Special Catalogue "O."—Blacksmiths' and Wagonmakers' Material. Very complete and prices low. Sent free upon request.

The "Model" Hand and Garden Pump or Fire Extinguisher.

43999 For pumping from pail or tub for spraying fruit trees and bushes sprinkling lawns and flowers, washing windows and carriages; will force a ¼-inch stream from 40 to 60 feet; is furnished with a spraying attachment in the shape of a flat piece of brass; when attached to nozzle may be twisted so as to spray or to convert the stream into small drops. It is not intended for heavy work, such as extinguishing large fires, etc., but may often prove useful in putting out small blazes, thereby preventing large fires. The piece of hose which comes with pump is 28 inches long and ½ inch in diameter; cannot attach any more than this; is plenty long enough to do the work mentioned; weight, 5 pounds.
Price, each..............$2.00

The Meyers' Bucket Brass Spray Pumps.

AND FIRE EXTINGUISHER, WITH AGITATOR.

Farmers' and fruit growers' friend. Is constructed of material that is not affected by the poisonous arsenites used in the different formulas for spraying fruit trees, vines and shrubbery. The cylinder and all the working parts are brass; has rubber ball valves and is equipped with our Combination Spray Nozzle, and will throw a spray as fine as mist. The pump differs in construction from the old-line pumps of this class and is arranged so that the heavy work is done on the down stroke of the plunger and nothing on the up.

The operator is enabled to keep a constant pressure on the nozzle of from 50 to 100 lbs. with very ordinary exertion. It will throw a solid stream 50 feet, and is of unusual value for washing windows, etc. For spraying it is arranged so it discharges a fine jet in bottom of bucket to keep the solution thoroughly mixed and agitated, a feature peculiar to this pump. Will throw a solid stream 50 feet.

44000 Price of Brass Spray Pump, with agitator, complete with hose, combination, fire and coarse spray and solid stream nozzles, each..............$3.00

Our Gun Repairing Department

Is one of the largest in the country. We have as good a stocker and as good a barrel borer as there is in the country, and feel confident that we can do your repairing promptly and give good satisfaction. All work guaranteed.

Tariff Uncertainties

Caused in many cases a great reduction in price on home manufactured and imported goods. We have been able to buy with the aid of READY CASH many lines of goods direct from manufacturers at unheard of low prices, which, heretofore, we were unable to get. Upon examining quotations in this book you will find many things cheaper than ever before.

STOVE DEPARTMENT.

The Windsor Stoves and Ranges.

Montgomery Ward & Co., Manufacturers.

We manufacture all of our Windsor stoves from the very best brands of iron, and with sufficient flue capacity for soft coal, and with fire boxes, flue plates and damper arrangements of sufficient strength to be durable. We claim them to be the very best in the market, and, having confidence in our claim, we fully guarantee every Windsor Stove. Our Reservoirs as constructed are *right*, for we secure an abundance of heat under and around the tanks. All of our ranges are also arranged for *water fronts*. We use the best of iron with polished edges, nickel and tile trimmings, towel rods, pedal attachments, outside nickel oven shelf, deep ash pan, etc. Our cheap stoves are made of the same material as our higher priced stoves, and we fully guarantee each and every one.

All ranges are fitted with revolving oven bottoms. The illustrations show only complete ranges, but prices are arranged for any desired combination of low closets, reservoir, or pipe shelf with the body of the range.

Let us give you a few suggestions for operating a stove. Remember, a stove possesses no power in itself to force smoke up a chimney, that the pipe and chimney give the draft, and if these are defective, no matter how good the stove may be, it will not work satisfactorily. If the stove smokes or the soot adheres to the covers and sides of the flues, then something is wrong with the pipe or chimney, which prevents the smoke from taking its natural course up and out through the chimney. When this occurs your stove will not bake. Your fire will not burn or the reservoir will not heat, and you can be sure that the whole trouble lays in the obstruction to the draft. Therefore, to secure proper and satisfactory results with our stoves, first be sure and secure proper draft and then see that the products of combustion are not cooled off by the admission of cool air over the fire or into the flues; see that the pipe fits closely on the stove and in the chimney, and is well jointed. See that no accident has befallen the stove in transit, that every part is in its proper place; see that you understand the dampers so that you can throw the heat under the reservoir or under the oven at pleasure; see that the front grate and linings are in place. If you will follow these simple directions you will have no trouble in securing satisfactory operations in our stoves and ranges.

Our facilities for prompt shipment are now perfect, and we can also furnish without delay repairs for any of our stoves. *In ordering repairs*, state plainly what you want, giving the full name of the stove, the number and the date, and in ordering a part for the right or left side of the stove always stand in front of the fire-box and consider all parts on your right hand as the right side, and all parts on your left hand as the left side. If the part wanted is in connection with the back of the stove, specify if it is for a square or one with a reservoir.

We give you the measurements of the oven near to the floor of the oven; if we measured as other manufacturers, at the greatest swell of the oven doors, we could increase the size of our ovens from three to five inches. We measure our fire-boxes, first giving the length at the top; second, width at top; third, width at bottom; fourth, depth.

Remember, we guarantee every Windsor stove to give perfect satisfaction if the chimney is clear and has a good draft. Try one and be convinced that you save money by buying direct from the manufacturers. Cuts show but few of the forms of our ranges, but the lists indicate other forms. The closets, the reservoir and pipe shelf can be arranged in any desired form with the body of the range. Our stoves are not blacked but are as they leave the foundry. Send for our special Stove Catalogue, which is now ready. We make this Range with sufficient flue capacity for soft coal, and with properly constructed fire boxes, flue plates and damper arrangements to be durable.

We can furnish wood fixtures for the Grand Windsor Range, which includes front and bottom grates, at an extra charge of $1.00.

The Grand Windsor Range.

We make this Range with sufficient flue capacity for soft coal, and with properly constructed fire boxes, flue plates and damper arrangements to be durable.

We can furnish wood fixtures for the Grand Windsor Range (any size), which includes front and bottom grates, at an extra charge of $1.00. We do not furnish any cooking utensils, stove boards, or the first joint of pipe, with any of our ranges, at prices quoted.

44050

44050 Grand Windsor Range, 6 hole, like cut. Square Plain for Hard or Soft Coal, Coke or Wood.

Size.	Covers.	Fire box.	Shipping weight.	Size of oven.	Price.
		16x10			
8-19	8 inch.	7x6½	360 lbs.	19x18x11	$20.50
		17½x10			
8-21	8 inch.	7x6½	405 lbs.	21x20x12	23.76
		17½x10			
9-21	9 inch.	7x6½	405 lbs.	21x20x12	24.30

We can furnish wood fixtures for the above range at an extra charge of $1.00.

Water fronts, brass couplings, ground joints, all sizes; weight, 20 lbs. Price each, $4.00 extra.

44051 Grand Windsor Range, 6 Hole, with Reservoir.

Size.	Covers.	Fire box.	Shipping weight.	Size of oven.	Price.
		16x10			
8-19	8 inch.	7x6½	420 lbs.	19x18x11	$26.46
		17½x10			
8-21	8 inch.	7x6½	475 lbs.	21x20x12	29.77
		17½x10			
9-21	9 inch.	7x6½	475 lbs.	21x20x12	31.65

Water fronts; weight, 20 lbs. Price each, extra. 4.00

We can furnish wood fixtures for the above range at an extra charge of $1.00.

44052 Grand Windsor Range, 6 Hole, without Reservoir, but with low closet.

Size.	Covers.	Fire box.	Shipping weight.	Size of oven.	Price.
		16x10			
8-19	8 inch.	7x6½	410 lbs.	19x18x11	$24.62
		17½x10			
8-21	8 inch.	7x6½	465 lbs.	21x20x12	28.10
		17½x10			
9-21	9 inch.	7x6½	465 lbs.	21x20x12	28.62

Water fronts; weight, 20 lbs. Price each, extra. 4.00

We can furnish wood fixtures for the above range (any size), which include front and bottom grates, at an extra charge of $1.00.

***** Our next Catalogue will be sent only to those who send us 15 cents for postage.**

44053

44053 Grand Windsor Range, 6 Hole, with low closet and reservoir.

Size.	Covers.	Fire box.	Shipping weight.	Size of oven.	Price.
		16x10			
8-19	8 inch.	7x6½	470 lbs.	19x18x11	$30.67
		17½x10			
8-21	8 inch.	7x6½	535 lbs.	21x20x12	34.15
		17½x10			
9-21	9 inch.	7x6½	535 lbs.	21x20x12	36.00

Water fronts; weight, 20 lbs. Price each, extra. 4.00

We can furnish fixtures for burning wood in the above range, at an extra charge of $1.00.

44054 Grand Windsor Range, 6 Hole, with high shelf and reservoir.

Size.	Covers.	Fire box.	Shipping weight.	Size of oven.	Price.
		16x10			
8-19	8 inch.	7x6½	470 lbs.	19x18x11	$29.87
		17½x10			
8-21	8 inch.	7x6½	525 lbs.	21x20x12	33.27
		17½x10			
9-21	9 inch.	7x6½	525 lbs.	21x20x12	33.80

Water fronts; weight 20 lbs. Price each, extra. 4.00

We can furnish wood fixtures for the above range (any size), at an extra charge of $1.00

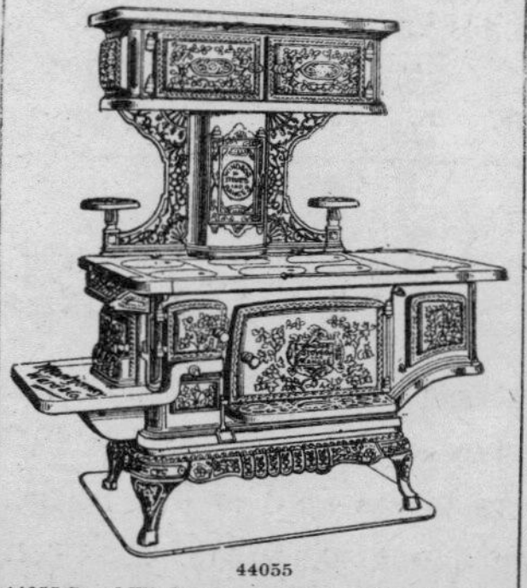

44055

44055 Grand Windsor Range, 6 Hole, with high closet and reservoir.

Size.	Covers.	Fire box	Shipping weight.	Size of oven.	Price.
		16x10			
8-19	8 inch.	7x6½	520 lbs.	19x18x11	$35.11
		17½x10			
8-21	8 inch.	7x6½	575 lbs.	21x20x12	33.73
		17½x10			
9-21	9 inch.	7x6½	575 lbs.	21x20x12	39.19

Water fronts; weight 20 lbs. Price each, extra. 4.00

We can furnish wood fixtures for the above range, which include front and bottom grates, at an extra charge of 1.00

44056 Grand Windsor Range, 6 Hole, with high and low closets and reservoir.

Size.	Covers.	Fire Box.	Shipping weight.	Size of oven.	Prices
		16x10			
8-19	8 inch.	7x6½	575 lbs.	19x18x11	$39.50
		17½x10			
8-21	8 inch.	7x6½	635 lbs.	21x20x12	43.20
		17½x10			
9-21	9 inch.	7x6½	635 lbs.	21x20x12	43.77

Water fronts; weight 20 lbs. Price each, extra. 4.00

We can furnish fixtures for burning wood in the above range (any size), at an extra charge of... 1.00

Separate Parts for making any combination desired in the Grand Windsor Range.

44057 Price of high closet only........ 8.00

44058 Price of high shelf only........ 3.95

44059 Price of low closet only.. $4.25

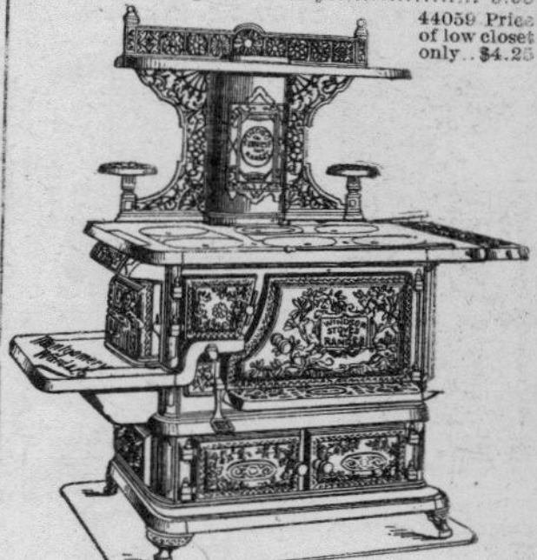

The Perfect Windsor Range is especially adapted to soft coal. The flues are very large, and the firebox is one of the best constructed. The linings are protected by air currents. The oven is thoroughly ventilated by hot air currents. Has outside nickel shelf, nickel ornaments, towel rod, ground edges, and made of the best of iron. We guarantee quick baking and quick heating of the reservoir; in fact, perfect operation with perfect draft. We furnish water fronts for all Perfect Windsor Ranges at $4.00 each extra. We can furnish wood fixtures for the Perfect Windsor Ranges, which includes front and bottom grates, at an extra charge of $1.00. We do not furnish any cooking utensils, stove boards or the first joint of pipe with any of our ranges at prices quoted.

44060 The Perfect Windsor Range, 6 hole, plain, for hard or soft coal, coke or wood. Stove *without high shelf and low closet as shown in cut.* In finish it is the same as our Grand Windsor.

Size.	Covers.	Fire box.	Shipping weight.	Size of oven.	Price.
		16x10			
8-19	8 in.	6¼x7	360 lbs.	19x19x11	$18.73
		17½x10			
8-21	8 in.	6¼x7	385 lbs.	21x21x12	22.14
		17½x10			
9-21	9 in.	6¼x7	385 lbs.	21x21x12	22.68

We can furnish wood fixtures for the above range, which include front and bottom grates, at an extra charge of $1.00. Water front, extra, $4.00.

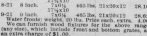

Summer Queen Oil Stoves.

44185 Summer Queen Oil Stove, one burner with 2-inch wick. Weight 2½ lbs. Price, each..$1.00

44186 Oil Stove like cut; has two burners with two 4-inch wicks. Weight 6 lbs. Price, each..$1.35

44187 Oil stove, two burners, with 4-inch wicks. Weight, 7½ lbs. Price, each..$1.85

44187½ Summer Queen Oil Stove, with three burners, each 4 inches wide. Price each..$2.40

44188 Russia Iron Oven, double lined, to fit 44186 stove. Size, 11x12x10 inches. Price, each..$1.78

44190 Russia Iron Oven, to fit above stove 44187½; doubled lined. Size, 14½x17½x 13½ in. Each..$2.95

44191 Russia Iron Oven, to fit 44187 stove. Size, 13x14x12. Price, each......$2.40

44192 Extension Top, like cut, to fit 44187 stove, with three cooking holes. Price, each.........$1.25

44193 Extension Top, to fit 44187½ stove, with three cooking holes. Price, each.........$1.30

44192

44195 Summer Queen Oil Stove, double, like cut; with four burners with four 3-inch wicks. Price, each.........................$2.80

44197 Summer Queen Oil Stove, double with four burners each; 4 inches wide. Price, each. 3.86 For Russia iron oven to fit above see No. 44192.

44199 Summer Queen Oil Stove, double; has 6 brass burners with all 4-inch wicks. Price, ea.. 4.90 For extension top to fit above see No. 44193. For Russia iron oven so fit 44199 stove see No. 44196.

Oil Stove Wicks.

44200 Cotton Oil Stove Wicks.
Width, inches........ 3   3¼   4   4¼   5
Price, each........ 2c   2c   2c   3c   4c
Per doz........ 20c   22c   25c   28c   30c

44201 Felt Oil Stove Wicks.
4 inch. Price, each....4c. Price, per dozen.....40c.
5 inch. Price, each....5c. Price, per dozen.....45c

Queen Oil Stove Iron Heaters.

Will hold Mrs. Potts' Irons.

44205 Iron Heaters like cut will fit No. 44187 and No. 44197 stoves. Price, each.....................$0.60

44206 Iron Heaters, same as cut, but will hold three irons and fits No. 44187½ and 44199 stoves. Price, each.........................$0.90

Sad Iron Heaters for Gasoline or Gas Stoves.

44208 Sad Iron Heaters, made of cast iron, will hold four irons; measures at bottom 3¼ inches. Price, each...$1.00

Broilers for Gasoline or Gas Stoves.

RELIABLE VENTILATED BROILER

44209 Broilers, made of cast iron, with tin cover. Price, each.........................$1.00

Divided Sauce Pans.

44210 Divided Sauce Pans, made of tin. Two pans, price each..$0.90 Three pans (like cut), price each............$1.00

Climax Stove.

44220 The Best Folding Pocket Alcohol Cook Stoves ever invented for the price, with boiler, cover and gridiron, complete, Each..$0.25

Pocket Stoves.

Burns Alcohol.

44221 The preceding cut shows the "Multum in Parvo Stove," with boiler. Water can be boiled in 5 minutes to make tea, coffee or other hot drinks, boil eggs, make oyster stews, etc. Packed in a box 1½ inches high and 4 inches square.

The "Multum in Parvo." Each......................$0.50 Per dozen........................ 5.25

The Excursionist's Stove.

44222 A new style stove and stand; boiler holds 3 pints, has a lip strainer, folding handle and cover. The stove will hold sufficient alcohol to burn one hour full flame or two hours small flame; will boil 3 pints of water in 15 minutes. The stand and stove fit inside the boiler, packed in a box 5 inches square, 6 inches high. There is room enough left to hold a gridiron, cups, spoons, knives and forks, and canteen to hold a pint of alcohol; weight, 1¾ pounds.
Price of Excursionist with gridiron.
Each..................................$0.85
Per dozen..............................9.50

Canteens.

44223 Canteens; nickel plated canteens for pocket cook stove; holds ½ pint of alcohol.
Each..................................$0.15

Lamp Chimney Stoves.

44225 Lamp Chimney Stove, very convenient for warming food, boiling water, etc. It is a cast iron device that can be attached to the top of any size chimney (as shown in the cut). No one should be without one of these handy little articles.
Price, each....$0.05
Per dozen.... .54

Gasoline Torches.

44250 Gasoline Torches; full one hundred thousand in use; can be used in a high wind without going out. Just the thing for campers, shows, fishing, etc.; is used extensively for fishing in boat at night; burns gasoline. ...$1.50

Out-Door Torch.

44251 For Foundries, Machine Shops, Street Salesmen, Mills; in fact for any out door use. Requires no protection, and will burn in any kind of weather. Reservoir will hold one gallon and will burn six hours; burns gasoline. Price, each.................$1.30

Gasoline Blow Pipe.

44255 The best pipe for lighting street lamps, softening paint on cars, coaches, carriages, houses, signs, furniture, etc., also for tempering drills, light brazing, thawing out frozen water pipes and for every purpose where a hot, smokeless flame is required. Made entirely of brass and warranted. Price, each.........$3.75

The "Sun" Convertible Furnace.

44256 The "Sun" Convertible Furnace is the best on the market. It will heat soldering coppers, and melt lead or solder quicker than any other furnace. It can be used as successfully on roofs as in-doors, and will positively not blow out. The burner is made with large passages, is powerful and will not clog up. Has heavy ing grilled cap; will not warp or burn out like a sawed cap. Casing is made of Russian sheet iron and malleable iron fittings. Reservoir has tinned malleable iron bottom and top, while the body is made of heavy sheet steel. The top casing being detachable, it is a great convenience for unsoldering pipes, brazing, etc. It is converted from a Tinner's to a Plumber's Furnace in a moment. Cannot be filled while burning and cannot explode. It is the strongest and most durable furnace on the market. Every furnace thoroughly tested before shipping. Height, 15 inches; with top casing off, 10½ inches. Weight, 30 lbs. boxed.
Price, each.........................$5.40

Tinners' Stoves.

44258 Tinner's Stove or Fire Pot with shaking grate, side oven hinged hearth door. The only double damper, base burning, reversible flue, tinner's stove made. To start the fire open front damper; after the fire is well started, the front damper is closed and the back damper is opened, this causes a downward draft directly on the soldering coppers, creating the densest heat where it is most required. Each pot nicely japanned. Price, each.

Tinners' Fire Pot.

44259 This Fire Pot is a universal favorite with tinners. It is lined with fire brick and made in the most substantial manner. The draft door is in two sections, which economizes fuel. Price, each,$3.00

Acme Stove Pipe.

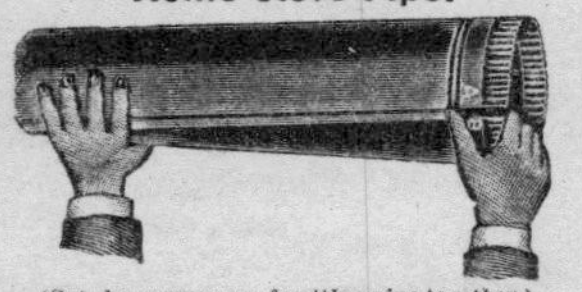

(Cut shows manner of putting pipe together.)

The only practical loose pipe made. No rivets, no malleting of seams necessary. The pipe is made from No. 26 smooth iron, and covered with a coating to prevent rust. It is a better quality of iron than has ever been used in ordinary pipe. A length of pipe properly put together cannot possibly collapse. Length of joint 24 inches.

44260 Diameter	5-inch.	6-inch.
Price per length	$0.10	$0.12
Price per crate of 25 lengths	2.25	2.35
Price per crate of 50 lengths	4.50	4.70

Universal Stove Pipe.

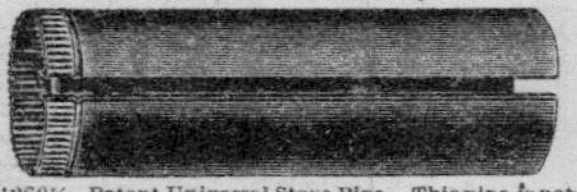

44260½ Patent Universal Stove Pipe. This pipe is not complete, but the seam is made and edges turned over, and one with a mallet or hammer can put together in a few minutes' time. It is left this way to facilitate shipping, as a dozen joints do not occupy any more space than one joint put together; it is packed in crates of fifty joints, but we will sell any quantity ordered. It is made from Planished or American Russia Iron. Length of joint, 30 inches.

Diameter	5-inch.	6-inch.
Price, per length	$0.30	$0.32

Ready Made Stove Pipe.

44265 Stove Pipe made up complete, ready to adjust to stove. Pipe shipped this way takes up considerable room, and we would advise the purchase of the patent pipe when convenient, as it can be put together very quickly; can furnish in No. 27 iron only. Length, 24 inches.

Diameter	5 in.	6 in.	7 in.
Price. per length	$0.11	.13	.20

44266 Planished or American Russia Iron Stove Pipe, same style as 44265; length, 30 inches.

Diameter	5 in.	6 in.	7 in.
Price per length	30c.	32c.	45c.

44266½ Planished Iron Elbows, corrugated, made from one piece of iron.

Diameter	5 in.	6 in.
Price each	25c	30c

44267 Planished Iron Elbows, common.

Diameter	5 in.	6 in.	7 in.
Price each	20c	25c	35c

Common Iron Elbows.

44269 Common Iron Elbows, four pieces, same style as 44267.

Diameter	5 in.	6 in.	7 in.
Price each	$0.07	$0.08	$0.15
Price per dozen	.75	.87	1.80

Stove Boards.

44275 Crystalized Stove boards, wood lined. square. The above cut does not represent the exact pattern or finish, but only the general character.

Size inches	Per dozen	Each	Size inches	Per dozen	Each
26x26	$12.25	$1.10	30x30	$15.12	$1.35
26x32	13.68	1.25	33x33	16.56	1.50
28x28	13.68	1.25	30x38	16.56	1.50
28x34	15.12	1.35	36x36	18.00	1.75

Stove Pipe Shelf.

44300 Cast Iron japanned; is 18 inches square; made for 6 inch pipe. This shelf is very complete in itself and is easily applied or raised and lowered. A heavy weight upon it strengthens its grip and assists in holding it in place, forcing the shelf farther over the wedge-shaped tin and making the grip on the pipe tighter.

Price, each ....$0.50 Per dozen.........$5.40

Chimney Thimbles.

	Diam.	Length.	Each.	Per doz.
44305—	6 x	4	$0.05	$0.50
	7 x	4	.07	.70

Stove Pipe Dampers.

44306 The Excelsior Stove Pipe Damper, 6 inch, cool, ventilated handle, easily put in. Each......$0.10
Per dozen..... 1.08
Weight, 12 oz.

Flue Stopper.

44310 The Crown Flue Stopper, brass finished, with decorated center; very handsome. Diameter, 8⅛ inches. Fits all size flues.
Each..........................$0.08
Per dozen.......... ..... .75

Flue Stoppers—Common.

	Size.	Each.	Per doz.
44311	6 inch	$0.05	$0.54

Ventilators.

	Diam.	Length.	Wt.	Each.
44315	6x4	2 lbs.	10 oz.	$0.25
	6x6	2 lbs.	10 oz.	.30
	6x10	3 lbs.	4 oz.	.38

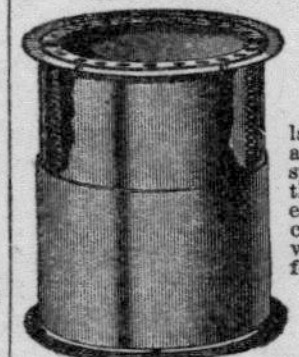

The Star Adjustable Ventilator or Register. The heads are connected by spiral steel springs, whose tension adjusts them to any thickness required; with register plate they can be used in connection with our double heating stoves for conducting heat over head

No.	Size.	Extends from	Weight.	Each.
44316	5 inch...	4 to 8 inches.	2¼ lbs.	$0.36
44317	5 inch...	6 to 12 inches.	2¾ lbs.	.40
44318	6 inch...	4 to 8 inches.	2¾ lbs.	.41
44319	6 inch...	6 to 12 inches.	3¼ lbs.	.45
44320	7 inch...	4 to 8 inches.	2 lbs., 15 oz..	.47
44321	7 inch...	6 to 12 inches.	3¼ lbs.	.55

44322 Register plates for above ventilator or register, that can be opened and closed. Price, per set, 6 in., 27c; 7 in., 35c.

Stove Shovels.

The IXL Steel Stove Shovels, made extra strong, unlike the cheap article ordinarily sold; the handle cannot be broken; it is hollow and of an oval shape and fits the hand nicely; it will outwear any other shovel.

44330 The IXL Steel Shovel No. 0. Size of scoop 5x7½; full length, 16 inches.
Each..............$0.12 Per dozen $1.30

44331—The IXL Steel Shovel No. 1. Size of scoop 5x8¼; full length, 22 inches.
Each ....$0.13 Per dozen $1.40

44332—The IXL Steel Stove Shovel No. 2. Size of scoop, 5½x9, full length, 25 inches.
Each............$0.16 Per dozen $1.75

Stove Lid Lifters.

44350 The Zero Lid Lifter, always cool, coppered iron.
Each.... .....$0.05
Per dozen.... .54

Alaska Stove Trimmings, Shovel, Poker and Tongs.

These are very elegant goods. The handles consist of spirally coiled wire which admits of a circulation of air through them, keeping them always cool. All of the implements *are handsomely nickel plated.*

44351 Alaska Fire Shovels, cool handles, nickel plated and handsomely finished: length, 17 inches. Price........ ....$0.20
Per dozen.. 2.10

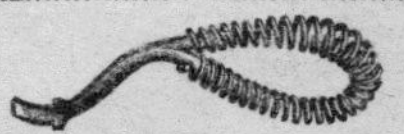

44352 Alaska Stove Lid Lifters, always cool handles, handsomely nickel plated. Price each.....$0.10
Per dozen... 1.00

44353 Alaska Stove Lid Lifters, always cool handle; a unique and very popular pattern, nickel plated. Each..................................$0.10
Per dozen.. 1.00

44355 Alaska Stove Poker, always cool handles, straight pattern, nickel plated, length 20 inches. Price, each.......................$0.10
Per dozen....................................... 1.08

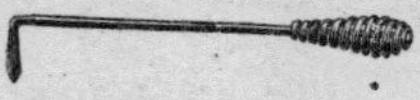

44356 Alaska Stove Poker, always cool handles, bent pattern, 22 inches in length, nickel plated. Price, each....$0.10
Per dozen.. 1.08

Adjustable Firebacks.

Readily adjusted to fit all sizes of cook stoves; made in two sizes. Send depth of fire back and fuel used. The only fireback that will adjust itself in both length and width. This fireback is so constructed that when contracted it will fit the smallest size cook stove, and when extended it will fit the largest size stove.

44366 Length, 14½ to 21 in.; width 5 to 6 in.; weight, 10 lbs. Each...................................$0.50
Per dozen.. 5.62
44367 Length, 17½ to 24 in.; width, 6½ to 7½ in.; weight, 15 lbs.
Each ....$0.85 Per dozen............ 9.10

Amateur Photography has come to stay. We sell all photographic instruments and supplies at less than list prices. Orders filled promptly. Every article guaranteed perfect.

Unique Nutmeg Grater.

45058 Unique Nutmeg Grater, the only grater that reduces the nutmeg to a fine powder, with no small pieces wasted; has an automatic cleaner which prevents clogging. No waste, no clogging, no scratched fingers, no grating finger nails in your pies or pudding; will save its price in a short time. Weight, 5 ounces. Each.......... $0.05
Per dozen........ .50

Revolving Slicer.

45060 Revolving Slicer for slicing apples, Saratoga potatoes, pumpkins, cucumbers and other vegetables; weighs 1 lb. 13 oz. Each, ... $0.25

HOUCHIN'S PAT.

Chopping Knives.

45069

45068 Chopping Knives, braced shank, wood handle, cast steel blade; weight 8 oz. Each.......... $0.03
45069 Chopping Knives (as per cut), iron handle and frame, extra cast steel blade. Weight, 12 ounces. Each.......... $0.10
Per dozen....... 1.08

45070

45070 Chopping Knives, extra cast steel double blades; tinned with malleable iron frame, wood handle. Weight, 8 ounces. Each.......... $0.06

Metallic Sieves.

Tinned Rims.

ANNEALED WIRE BOTTOM.

45075 Size of mesh, 16 to the inch.
Each.......... $0.15
Per dozen..... 1.62
45076 Size of mesh, 18 to the inch.
Each.......... $0.18
Per dozen..... 1.95

Flour Sifters.

45080 The Improved Rotary Flour and Meal Sifter, scoop, measure, weigher, mixer, rice washer, tomato, pumpkin, starch strainer, wine and fruit or jelly press combined. This is the most convenient kitchen utensil ever sold, combining, as it does, ten necessary articles for the culinary department. For mixing baking powder, etc., though flour it is almost indispensable.
Each.......... $0.10
Per dozen.......... 1.00

45081 Similar to No. 45080 but larger and with a round handle. Size, diameter 4½ inch. Height at front, 6½ inch. Height at back, 5¼ inch.
Price, each.......... $0.12
Per dozen.......... 1.35

Flour Sifters—Continued.

45082 This sifter is constructed with a bottom which can be closed when not in use, thus preventing the flour from sifting out when placed upon the table or carried about the kitchen; a decided improvement over the old style.
Price, each........... $0.18
Per dozen........ 1.75

Ice Shave.

45085 Something new, the Gem Ice Shave, constructed like an ordinary plane, having in front of the knife a receptacle closed by a lid in which the ice shaved off collects as the tool is shoved forward over a block of ice. Shaved ice can be used for making water ices or for cooling liquors, and is also very valuable as a cooling medium in the sick room. The shave is made of galvanized iron. Price, each.......... $0.40
Per dozen........ 4.32

"Magic" Milk Shake Machine.

45086 "Magic" Milk Shake Machine is a counter machine, made to do the work as effectively and satisfactorily as the famous A. & W. floor machines. It has a direct up and down movement, thoroughly by the contents of the tumblers, and there is no swinging motion which leaves the ingredient unmixed. Diameter of fly wheel, 11½ in. Machine, with four tumblers and four glass tops, price, $6.00

Egg Beaters.

45087 Easy Egg Beater. It consists of a spirally coiled wire, which in use opens and closes with exceeding rapidity, and instead of cutting the egg, as most beaters do, thoroughly aerates it, which is acknowledged by all experienced cooks to be the only correct way of beating an egg. For whipping cream it is just the thing. This egg beater is having the largest sale of any yet made; try it and you will like it.
Each.......... $0.08
Per doz......... .87

45088 Dover Egg Beaters. Each............ $0.10
Per doz.......... 1.08
45089 Surprise Egg Beater, retinned.
Each.......... $0.05
Per dozen........ .35
45090 Spoon Egg Whip, with wood handle, ½s.30 inch.
Each.......... $0.06
Per doz......... .60

Ice Chippers.

45100 The Star Ice Chipper, iron handle. By the use of this chipper ice can be chipped into small and nearly uniform pieces, the guard projecting beyond the knife making it impossible to cut off thicker pieces than the space between. Only a minute's time is required to reduce a 15 or 20 pound block of ice; cuts small pieces.

Weight 1¼ pounds. Each.......... $0.15
Per dozen........ 1.62
45101 Ice-Chisel, 3 prongs, solid steel blade. The very best ice cutter that we know of. Will cut a much larger block than any would suppose; weight 9 oz.
Each.......... $0.10
Per dozen........ 1.09

Boss Lemon Squeezer.

45105 Made of fine malleable iron, heavily tinned.
Each.......... $0.15
Per dozen..... 1.62

45108 The "King" Lemon Squeezer. This is the latest modern invention, easy to handle, will not corrode, saves all the juice, good in desirable in every particular. The receiver for the juice is of glass too thick to break, and is removable for cleaning.
Weight, 2 lbs., 7 oz. Each.......... $0.25
Per dozen........ 2.70

Measures.

45110 The Raymond funnel measures, made of steel japanned; a boon to farmers and storekeepers and any one having use for a measure. The peculiar scoop shape facilitates pouring into paper bag or basket; made in five sizes, 1qt., 2qt., 4qt., 8 qt., ½ bushel. Price per nest of five measures, $1.45

45111 Patent Iron Measures, japanned.

Size	Weight	Each
½ bushel	3 lbs., 15 oz.	$0.33
Pecks	2 lbs., 11 oz.	.25

Pantry Cabinet.

The Raymond Pantry Cabinet; a place for everything and everything in its place. Bread, crackers, dried fruit, rice, etc. Made of tin japanned, antique oak frame. Pull down the glass front of the case, take out what you want and it closes itself; contents kept free from dust, damp air, etc.

45112 No. 2, 7 cans, size of cabinet, 48 inches high, 22 inches wide; 11 inches deep.......... $6.50
45113 No. 3, 9 cans; size of cabinet, 58 inches high, 22 inches wide, 11 inches deep.......... 8.00

Flour Bin and Sieve.

The flour saved pays the cost. Keep your flour in the Columbia Flour Bin, secure from moisture, dust, dirt and vermin. This flour bin and sieve must not be confounded with others upon the market. It is unlike any other—an improvement over all. It is made of the best material, handsomely finished. It has a patent slide sieve which will do its work faster and better than any other in the market. All good cooks know the value of clean, dry sifted flour.
How to Use: Put the flour in at the top—pull the rod and the flour will be found in the drawer underneath.
45114 50 lbs. capacity.
Each.......... $1.40

Flour Bins—Continued.

45115 The Perfection Combination Flour Bin and Sieve, a very convenient household article, made of tin, japanned. It will keep flour or meal dry and free from dust, mice, rats and cockroaches, as it contains a sieve, which, by turning a crank, sifts the flour into the moveable pan at the bottom; it avoids the necessity of reaching into barrels or sacks.

100 lb. size weighs 25 lbs. Each............$2.10
50 lb. size weighs 16½ lbs. Each............1.70
25 lb. size weighs 13¼ lbs. Each............1.30

Dust Pans.

45122

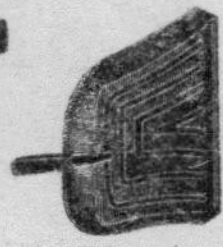

45120

45120 Dust Pan Corrugated, not covered. Each............$0.08
Per dozen............ .90
45121 Dust Pan Plain Brown, covered. Each. .12
Per dozen............1.38
45122 Dust Pan, Fancy assorted colors, with brush. Each............ .52
Per dozen............5.60

45123 The Downing Dust Pan It rests firmly on the floor and is perfectly smooth on the bottom. It has a receiving box at the back into which the dust is swept, and can be moved from one place to another with the foot without danger of spilling the contents, which is a great improvement on the ordinary kind. Price, each............$0.15
Per dozen............$1.65 - Per gross............17.40

Crumb Pans and Brush.

45125-26

45127-28

45125 Crumb Pan, with brush, plain japanned...$0.20
45126 Fancy Japanned Pan, with brush, finished nicer than 45125 Each............ .40
45127 Brass Crumb Tray and brush. Each...... .69
45128 Polished Brass, nickel plated. Each...... .80

Candle Sticks.

45135 Candlesticks, japanned.

	Each.	Per doz.
Size, 5 in............	$0.03	$0.33

Tea Tray.

45136 Tea Trays, oval japanned.

Inches.......	12	14	16	18	20
Each.......	$0.12	$0.15	$0.18	$0.23	$0.25
Per doz.	1.25	1.60	1.90	2.25	2.50
Inches.......	22	24	26	28	
Each	.30	.37	.47	.57	
Per doz.......	3.25	3.75	4.75	5.75	

CHILD'S TRAYS.

45137 The rown Child's Tray, silver finish, the best and cheapest child's tray made; complete with springs. Ready to adjust to table or high chair. Price, each ...$0.18

Knife and Fork Boxes.

45140 Knife and Fork Boxes, open top, size, 12x8............$0.35

Canisters.

45145-46

Japanned Tea or Coffee Canister.
45145 Tea Canister.
45146 Coffee Canister.

	Each.	Per doz.
1 pound.........	$0.07	$0.76
2 pound.........	.09	1.05

45148-49

Tea and Coffee Canisters, japanned tin, with hinged covers. These canisters are preferable to the ordinary kind, as the covers cannot get lost.
45148 Tea Canisters.
45149 Coffee Canisters.

To hold—	Each.	Per doz.
2 pounds............	$0.10	$1.08
4 pounds............	.15	1.50

Dredge Boxes.

45156 Japanned, large size 2½x3¼. Each............$0.04
Per dozen............ .44

45158 Clothes Sprinkler, with screw cover and handle. This is a new and very convenient article, used for sprinkling clothes before ironing. Each............$0.12
Per dozen........ 1.30

Round Spice Boxes.

Japanned, containing six small boxes and grater.
Price, per set.
45160 Size, 6¼x3½ in.......$0.35

Bread Boxes.

JAPANNED.

45165 Medium; size, 15x11½ x10¼; weight, 4¼ lbs. Each............$0.65
45166 Large; size, 19x13¾x x14½; weight, 4¾ pounds. Each $0.82

Cash Boxes with Lock and Key.

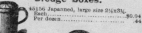

Weighs 1¼ pounds, 1½ pounds, 2 pounds; japanned.

		Each.
45168	Size, 8x5½x4	$0.55
45169	Size, 10x7x4½	.70
45170	Size, 11x8x5½	.75

Folding Cash Boxes.

Open, 9¼x8¼x2¾ inches; closed, 9¼x4½x4⅝ inches.

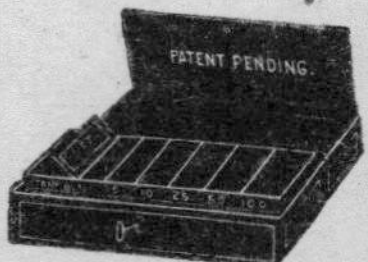

45175 The Folding Cash Box. It is made of heavy tin, well enameled, good lock. It saves time in making change and in verifying the cash. It may be used on a table or in a drawer; locked, put in a safe or vault and be ready for use the next day. It has a compartment in top part for currency, and a place under the tray for checks, drafts, money orders, postal notes, etc. It also has a tray with compartments for 31 silver dollars, 50 halves, 64 quarters, 85 dimes, 51 nickels, and 65 cents, and a box for postage stamps. The stamp box is often used for gold coin. Note our reduced price. Weight, 2¼ pounds. Each.....$1.40
Per dozen............15.96

Deed Boxes.

Weight, 1¼ to 2 pounds.

Japanned.		Each.
45176	Size, 8½...	$0.35
45177	Size, 10....	.45
45178	Size, 11....	.50

Chamber Pails.

Will hold 12 quarts each.
45185 Painted assorted colors. Each............$0.30
45186 Galvanized iron chamber pail, made of heavy iron. 12 quarts. Each............ .40

45186

45190 Agate iron ware soap dish 6½x4x1½ - Price each $0.22

Chambers.

45191 Chambers, Agate Iron Ware.

Size	7x4⅛	8½x4⅜	9¾x5¼
Each	53c.	68c.	85c.

Wash Bowls and Pitchers.

45192 Fancy japanned wash bowl and pitcher; weight, 2½ lbs. Bowl 11¼x3¾, pitcher 6¾ x10¾. Per set............$0.62

45195 Toilet stands, japanned. 30½ inches high, with japanned tin wash bowl and pitcher and soap cup, assorted colors; weight 2¾ lbs. Each, complete............$1.50
45196 Japanese Toilet Stand, with basin, slop jar, water carrier and reservoir; reservoir holds about 2 gallons; all nicely japanned and ornamented; weight, 18 lbs. Price, complete $5.95

Coffee Urn.

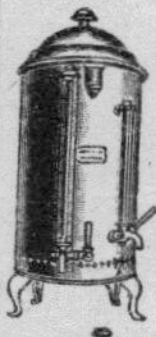

45199 Made of Copper and Nickel plated with water gauge, and so constructed that they can be easily taken apart for cleaning and repairing. The faucets and inside couplings screw together. The inside jars are enameled.

	Price, each.
Capacity, 10 gallons............	$33.75
Capacity, 8 gallons............	28.80
Capacity, 6 gallons............	27.00
Capacity, 4 gallons............	25.20
Capacity, 3 gallons............	21.60

Water Coolers.

45200

45200 Japanned Water Coolers, wrought iron body and base, stamped tin breast, stamped tin plate cover, corrugated galvanized iron reservoir, plated self-closing faucet, charcoal filled, assorted colors; artistic decoration.

Sizes, gals......	2	3	4	6	8
Price, each..	$1.28	$1.39	$1.72	$2.05	$2.73

Sheet Metals.

SHEET ZINC.

45340 This is the ordinary stock Zinc, about 26 gauge, 36 inches wide, 7 feet in length, weighs 14 lbs. Per sheet $4.15
Per one-half sheet .... .65

SHEET IRON.

45341 Common Black Sheet Iron, such as stove pipe is made of, etc. size of sheet 24x104 inches.

No.	Wt. per sheet.	Whole sheet.
24	17 lbs.	$0.76
26	14 lbs.	.66
27	13 lbs.	.60

GALVANIZED SHEET IRON.

45342 Size of sheet 30x96 inches.

No.	Wt. per sheet.	Whole sheet
24	24 lbs.	$1.30
26	18 lbs.	1.25
27	19¾ lbs.	1.20

BRIGHT TIN.

45343 IC Bright Charcoal.

Inches	14x20	20x28
No. sheets in box.	112	112
Weight, lbs.	120	240
Per sheet	$8.60	$15.67
Per sheet	.07	.15

IC ROOFING TIN.

45344 IC Charcoal.
We carry two grades of roofing tin.

Inches	14x20	20x28
No. of sheets in box	112	112
Weight of box	120 lbs.	240 lbs.
Per box	$8.60	$12.65
Per sheet	.07	.12

IX ROOFING TIN.

45345 IX Charcoal.
The IX quality is heavier than the IC.

Inches	14x20	20x28
No. sheets in a box.	112	112
Weight per box.	150 lbs.	30 lbs.
Per box	$8.25	$13.90
Per sheet	.08	.15

IC COKE TIN.

Used for making Gutters, etc.
45346 Size of sheets, 10x20. No. sheets in box 225. Weight per box, 110 lbs.
Per box $10.72
Per sheet .... .09
Owing to the constant fluctuation of the price of tin the box price is subject to change of market.

SHEET COPPER.

45347 Soft Sheet Copper, soft rolled, not polished. For sheets tinned on one side add 3 cents per sheet.

Size of sheet.	Weight of sheet	Per sheet.
14 oz.	1x18 ins.	$ 5-18 lbs. |.22½
16 oz.	14x18 ins.	4½ lbs.	1.30

The above prices of above metals subject to market changes, but will always bill them at the lowest price ruling. We do not sell less than one sheet of copper.

Post's Eureka Sap Spouts.

Over 14,000,000 Sold.

45360 Sugar makers acknowledge a very large increase in the flow of sap by the use of the Self-Sealing Air Tap in the Eureka Sap Spouts. Weight, about 70 lbs. to the 1,000; made of smooth galvanized iron 3¾ inch long.

Cut of Spout No. 1.

Spout No. 2.

No.	Price per 1000	Price per 100
1	$20.00	$2.50
2	18.50	2.35
	Per 1000	Per 100
45361 Extra Hooks for No 1 Spouts per 100....		.50
45362 Ears for Tubs No 1 Spouts....	$3.85	$0.45
		.50

Improved Farmers' Boilers.

For Wood or Coal.

For cooking feed for stock, heating water, making soap and sugar, rendering lard, washing clothes, as well as all other kinds of boiling. Give our boilers a trial and you will never buy any other.

45365 Price with cover and feet as shown in cut.

Gallons	Weight with cover and feet	With Wood Fixtures.	With Coal Fixtures.
15	200 lbs	$12.25	$15.00
20	235 "	14.00	17.28
30	305 "	17.54	20.22
45	395 "	22.58	25.66
60	434 "	29.52	31.80

We can furnish wheels in place of feet at an extra cost of $2.70 per set of 4 wheels.

Boilers—Continued.

45366 Sugar or Wash Kettles, with kettle spider and painted. No. 7, 30 gal. kettle is the largest and best kettle to's self made. Average weights of kettles are given below.

Actual Measure.	Test gal. Each.	Actual Measure.	Weight, Each.
No. 1, 5 gal	55 lbs	$1.90	No. 5, 21¼ gal.	52.26
No. 2, 10 gal.	910 in.	1.55	No. 6, 25 gal.	63 lb	2.70
No. 3, 15 gal.	42 lb.	1.28	No. 7, 30 gal.	85 lb.	3.15
No. 4, 18 gal.	28 lb.	2.07			

Dry Cold Air Refrigerators.

Our sales of refrigerators last season were way beyond our expectation, and we were compelled to disappoint some of our customers. This year we are prepared for a still larger increase in the trade and, consequently, we run at all times and a second shipments, so we live ample stock of dry hard wood lumber, with the latest improved machinery; the best of dry kilns, and the most skilled workmen. We Guarantee our refrigerators to give Perfect Satisfaction. The capacity of the factory is over two hundred complete refrigerators per day.

Points of Superiority-Scientific Insulation.

The walls of the refrigerators are constructed as follows. First, the outside case; second a layer of wood felt; third, a dead-air space; fourth, a charcoal sheathing; fifth, inside case; sixth, a charcoal sheathing which is non-odorous, waterproof and a first class insulator; seventh, a zinc lining, making complete seven walls to preserve the ice. The result is a great saving of ice and lower temperature than can be obtained in other refrigerators.

Ice being placed on the false bottom in the upper compartment, the air under the false bottom becomes very cold and heavy, and falls through the opening into the provision chamber below, forcing the warm air up through the flue, where it strikes the ice, is condensed and cooled. These crackers will keep crackers and ginger snaps crisp and dry. No refrigerator is as large a refrigerator as possible, to get the benefit of cold storage. Each size has a special design of great beauty.

The Metallic Ice Rack.

Is a very important feature of our goods, as the under side sets as a moisture condenser, while the arched center prevents the moisture from dropping through the opening into the provision chamber below. The cheeks are made of heavy galvanized iron with wide slats and rolled edges, making them very strong.

This cut shows style of our single door refrigerator.

45402 Hardwood, Antique finish, empire style. Richly carved panels and ornaments; single door. Holds 35 lbs. ice.; Length, 26½ in.; Depth, 18 in.; Height, 40 in. Price, each $7.84

45403 Same as No. 45402, except that it holds 30 lbs. of ice. Has porcelain lined water cooler. The faucet is nickel plated and the tumbler holder bronzed. We do not advise the use of melted ice for drinking water, as it is frequently impure and always has condensed on its surface the smells from the food below, so we get rid of it as soon as possible and provide a separate place for drinking water. Price each $10.09

45404 Hardwood Antique finish, richly carved panels and ornaments. Flap in front lifts up for water pan, single door. Size of opening of provision chamber 17½ in. high, 16½ in. wide, 11½ in. deep.

	Holds lbs. ice.	Length.	Depth.	Height.	Price, each.
40	28 in.	20 in.	44 in.	$9.10	

45406 Same as No. 45404, except that it holds 35 lbs. of ice. Has porcelain lined water cooler. The faucet is nickel plated and the tumbler holder bronze. Price, each $11.35

45407 Solid Ash, Antique finish, elegant hand carved ornamentation; single door. Size of opening of provision chamber 18 in. high, 20½ in. wide, 13½ in. deep; single door.

	Holds lbs. ice.	Length.	Depth.	Height.	Price.
45	32	21½	46½	10.55	

Refrigerators—Continued.

45468 Same as No. 45467 except that it holds 40 pounds of ice, has porcelain lined water cooler with nickel plated faucet and bronze tumbler holder. Price each $13.10

45409 Solid Ash, Antique Finish, hand carved ornaments. This refrigerator is deep enough to hold two rows of dishes, one behind the other, single door. Size of opening of provision chamber 29 in. high, 21½ in. wide, 17½ in. deep.

	Holds ice.	Length.	Depth.	Height.	Price.
40 lbs.	33 in.	24½ in.	49 in.	$16.30	

45410 Same as No 45404, except that it holds 35 pounds of ice, has porcelain lined water cooler. Flap in front, lifts up for water pan.

| | Price, each 15.50 |
| This cut shows style of our double door refrigerators. |

45411 Solid Ash, Antique Finish. Richly hand carved, rich hand carved double doors, removable zinc trays. Size of opening of provision chamber 18½ in. high, 22½ in. wide, 13½ in. deep. Holds 40 lbs. of ice. Length, 33 in. Depth, 24½ in. Height, 49 in. Price, each $17.85

40 pounds of ice, has porcelain lined water cooler. All goods are warranted to give perfect satisfaction. Price, each $16.61

45413 Solid Ash, Antique Finish, elegant hand carving, double door, stands with center, false bottom, and interior circulation of pure, dry, cold air. Size of opening of provision chamber 20 in. high, 23 in. wide, 14½ in. deep. See BABY FAMILY SIZE.

	Holds ice.	Length.	Depth.	Height.	Price, each.
50 lbs.	36½ in.	23 in.	50 in.	$16.69	

45414 Same as No. 45413, except that it holds 60 lbs. of ice. Has porcelain lined water cooler. Price, each 17.85

45415 Solid Ash, Antique Finish, double doors. This style has a partition through the doors, making two separate provision chambers, a most excellent family size. Size of opening of each provision chamber 20¾ in. high, 13½ in. wide, 17¼ in. deep.

	Holds ice.	Length.	Depth.	Height.	Price.
125 lbs.	41½ in.	25¼ in.	52 in.	18.10	

45416 Same as No. 45415, except that it holds 115 lbs. ice. Has porcelain lined water cooler. The large ice chamber affords room for bottles, pitchers, etc. 26.36

45417 Solid Ash. Four Doors, Antique Finish, rich hand carvings. Ice doors open in front; size of opening, 14x20 inches. Two provision chambers below. Size of each provision chamber, 22¼ in. high 13 in. wide, 19 in. deep.

	Holds ice.	Length.	Depth.	Height.	Price.
150 lbs.	41½ in.	26 in.	60 in.	$26.42	

45418 Same as No. 45417, except, that it holds 140 pounds ice, has porcelain lined water cooler. Price, each 23.90

Sideboard Style Refrigerators.

As we furnish refrigerator sideboards on orders it requires from 7 to 10 days before we can ship.

45419 Same as No. 45402, with the addition of a sideboard top. It has beveled plate glass mirror, 12x18, and convenient shelf on which things can be placed when the case is raised; 7½ inches high. Price, each $11.63

45420 Same as No. 45404, with the addition of a sideboard top, beveled plate glass mirror 12x18 inches. Height, 76 inches. Price, each 13.50

45421 Same as No. 45411 with the addition of a sideboard top. The glass is bevel plate, 12x20 inches. Price, each 19.00

Hardwood Ice Chests, antique ash finish. Made double with inside bores with lining between. This makes them triple walled and the best ice boxes in the market. They are lined throughout with zinc and furnished with metal shelves. We have an opening in the back for ventilation. We cannot guarantee them not to sweat, as we do our Dry Air Refrigerators.

	Length.	Depth.	Height.	
45422	30 in.	18 in.	27 in.	$4.50
45423	33 in.	20 in.	27 in.	5.50
45424	36 in.	22 in.	31 in.	6.75
45425	40 in.	24½ in.	33 in.	8.25
45426	44 in.	29 in.	36 in.	10.50

Table of shipping weights for the Dry Cold Air Refrigerators and Ice Chest:

Catalogue No.	Weight.	Catalogue No.	Weight.
45402	100 lbs	45415	265 lbs.
45403	105 "	45416	275 "
45404	145 "	45417	300 "
45406	150 "	45418	310 "
45407	170 "	45419	145 "
45408	175 "	45420	170 "
45409	170 "	45421	210 "
45410	175 "	45422	100 "
45411	180 "	45423	130 "
45412	185 "	45424	150 "
45413	200 "	45425	165 "
45414	210 "	45426	190 "

CUTLERY DEPARTMENT.

Our knives are selected from the most reliable manufactories, and are warranted as represented. The blades of our knives are ground as thin as a good cutting blade should be ground. If the edge gets dull sharpen by holding on the "stone" at an angle of about 40 degrees.

Ladies Knives.

Extra by mail for Ladies' Knives, 3 cents.

46000 One Blade, white handle, good steel blades. Each ... $0.10 Per dozen ... 1.13

46002 Ladies' Pearl Handle Knife, one blade and glove buttoner; best quality, finely finished, 2½ in. long. Each ... $0.34 Per dozen ... 3.60

46003 Ladies' Knife, inlaid shell handle, two blade, 2⅜ in., well finished and a good article. Each ... $0.12 Per dozen ... 1.30

46004 Two Blades, with white handle. Each ... $0.14 Per dozen ... 1.40

46005 Pearl handle. Each ... $0.20 Per dozen ... 2.16

46006 Two Blades, pearl handle. Each ... $0.22 Per dozen ... 2.35

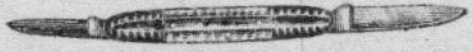

46007 Two blade Ladies' fancy pearl handle. Each ... $0.20 Per dozen ... 2.16

46008 Two blades, finest pearl handles and best finish, highest grade steel blades; an elegant article.
2½ in. handle. Each ... $0.70 Per doz ... $7.56
2¾ in. handle. Each ... .75 Per doz ... 8.10

46009 Two-blade Ladies' fancy pearl handle; a fine knife. Each ... $0.29 Per dozen ... 3.15

46010 Four blades, 2½ in., pearl handle, German silver bolster, finest finish, best of steel blades, warranted. Each ... $0.60 Per dozen ... 6.90

46011 Two blades, scored pearl handle. Each. $0.25 Per dozen ... 2.75

46012 Three blades, pearl handle; a fine knife. Each ... $0.68 Per dozen ... 7.20

46013 Three blade, 2⅜ in., pearl handle, finest finish, best quality, warranted. Each ... $0.77 Per dozen ... 8.40

46014 Four blades, shell handle. Each ... $0.45 Per dozen ... 4.27

46015 Two blade, 2½ in., pearl handle, fine finish, warranted. Each ... $0.45 Per dozen ... 4.80

46016 Two blade, 2⅜ in., pearl handle, brass lined, milled edges; a neat article. Each ... $0.39 Per dozen ... 3.50

46018 Two blade, 2⅜-inches, fine pearl handle, finely finished, and warranted finest steel blades Each ... $0.57 Per dozen ... $6.00

Men's Knives.

All of our knives are warranted. If not found as represented can be returned at our expense. Knives by mail, 3 to 5 cents extra.

46019—Four blades, stag handle, brass lined. Each ... $0.30 Per dozen ... $3.00

46021 4 blades, white handle, brass lined, a good seller. Each ... $0.30 Per dozen ... $3.00

46022 2 blades, fine ivory handle, 3¼ inch long, handsome in design and finish, the very best quality steel blades; retail price $1.00. See our price; warranted. Each $0.59 Per doz. $6.00

46023 Two blades, finest pearl handle, 3 in. long manicure file blade on back, very best quality and finish; a beauty; retail price $2.00. See our price, warranted. Each $1.12 Per doz. $12.00

46027 Three blades, cocoa handles, brass lined, warranted ... $0.30 Per dozen ... $3.25

46028 Two blades, 3 in., fine pearl handle, finely finished, warranted best quality steel blades; a very desirable article; our big seller. Each ... $0.69 Per doz ... $7.00

46029 Three blades, 3 in., finest pearl handle, German silver bolsters, finely finished; every one warranted best steel blades. Each ... $0.72 Per doz ... 8.20

46030 Three blades, 2⅝ in., pearl handles, German silver bolsters, 1 file blade; well made and durable; every one waranted best steel blades. Each ... $0.37 Per doz ... 3.90

46031 Three blades, 3¼ in., fine pearl handles, German silver bolsters, well finished. A good, strong durable article. Each ... $0.56 Per doz ... 5.75

46035 Three blades, fine buck horn handle, brass lined. German silver bolster, best quality blades, warranted, 3¼ in. handle. Retail price, $1.50. Our price, each ... $0.90 Per dozen ... $10.00

46038 Three blades, pearl handle, brass lined, German silver bolster, warranted. Each ... $0.50 Per dozen ... 5.40

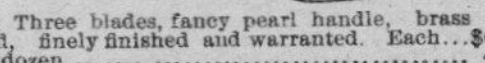

46044 Three blades, fancy pearl handle, brass lined, finely finished and warranted. Each ... $0.43 Per dozen ... 4.75

46045 Two blades, 3¼ in., dark horn handle, brass lined milled edges, crocus polished; a good office or vest pocket knife. Each ... $0.35 Per doz ... $3.60

46047 Six blades, pearl handle. Each ... $0.45 Per dozen ... 4.80

46050 Three blades 3½ in., fine pearl handle; German silver lined, German silver bolsters; abeauty; warranted. Retail price, $1.75. (See our price until sold.) Each $0.89 Per dozen ... $9.90

46053 Three blades, finest quality of steel, brass lined, 3½ in. pearl handle, German silver bolsters, nail blade, good, strong, large blade; no better knife made for durability and cutting quality. Every one warranted. Retail price, $2.00. Our price, each ... $1.50 Per dozen ... $16.43

46054 Three blades, stag horn handle, otherwise same as No. 46053. Every one warranted. Each ... $1.00 Per dozen ... $11.06

46055 Three blades, 3½ in. ivory handle, otherwise same as 46053. Every one warranted. Each ... $1.10 Per dozen ... $12.00

46056 Three blades, 3½ in. ebony handle, otherwise same as 46053, every one warranted; just the right size for a pocket knife for general use. Each ... $0.79 Per dozen ... $8.40

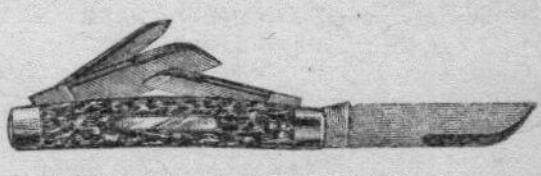

46058 Four blades, "Congress" style, 3¾-inch stag horn handle, German silver bolsters, brass lined, best steel blades; a good strong article; warranted. Each ... $0.87 Per dozen ... $9.60

46059 Three blades, fine 3¼ inch buck horn handle brass lined, German silver bolsters, brass lined; warranted. Each ... $0.63 Per dozen ... 6.62

46060 Four-Blade Congress, buck hornhandle best steel; warranted Each ... $0.63 Per dozen ... 6.62

46061 Four blades Congress, 3½ inch buck horn handle, genuine IXL Wostenholm make. Each. $1.35 Per dozen ... 14.70

46062 Three blades, fine pearl handle, German silver bolsters, warranted, a fine knife. Each ... $0.55 Per dozen ... 6.00

46063 Genuine IXL George Wostenholm, four blades, 3-inch pearl handle. It is a large size ladies' knife or a medium size for gentlemen, and a fine knife for any one. Retail price, $2.25 See our price. Each ... $1.60 Per dozen ... 17.28

Cutlery—Continued.

46064 Genuine IXL George Wostenholm, 3⅜ in., pearl handle, four blades. Is just right size for gentlemen's use. No better knife made at any price. Each.... $1.75
Per doz.... 19.00

46065 Champagne Knife, German silver lined and bolsters, best 3¾ in. shell handle. A beauty; warranted. Each.... $1.50
Per doz.... 17.00

46066 Two blades, German silver bolsters, 2¾ inches, finest pearl handles, best warranted steel; a fine little article. Each.... $0.56
Per dozen.... 6.00

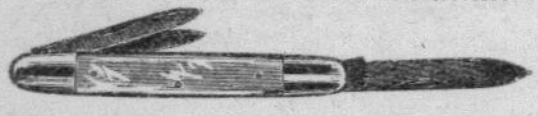

46067 Three blades, German silver bolsters, 2¾ inches, finest Pearl handle, fine finish, highest quality steel blades; warranted. Each.... $0.80
Per dozen.... 8.64

46068 Four blades, German silver bolsters, 2¾ inches, finest pearl handle, finest finish, highest quality steel blades; vest pocket size; warranted. Each.... $1.00
Per dozen.... 10.95

46069 Three blades, German silver bolsters, 2⅞ inches, finest quality pearl handles, best steel blades, best finish; handsome and desirable; warranted. Each.... $0.80
Per dozen.... 8.64

46070 Three blades, German silver bolsters, 3⅜ inches, fine pearl handles, finest finish, best steel blades, good and strong; warranted. Each.. $0.98
Per dozen.... 10.80

46071 Three blades, German silver bolsters, 2⅞ inches, finest pearl handles, finest finish, good, strong and durable; warranted. Each.... $1.15
Per dozen.... 12.50

46072 Three blades, brass lined, German silver bolsters, 3⅜ in. pearl handle, finest steel blades, finely finished, a good strong knife; warranted. Retail price, $2.50. See our price. Each.... $1.20
Per doz.... 13.00

46073 Three blades, 3⅜ in. fine pearl handle, German silver bolsters, warranted best of steel. A beauty. Each.... $1.00
Per doz.... 11.00

46074 Three blades, pearl handles, brass lined, German silver bolsters, a good strong knife, finely finished and warranted; best of steel blades. Retail price, $2.50. See our price. Each.... $1.40
Per doz.... 14.50

46075 Two blades, 3 in. pearl handle, brass lined, German silver bolsters, fine finish, best of steel blades; warranted. Each.... $0.80
Per doz.... 9.00

Cutlery—Continued.

46076 Two blade pruner and budding knife, stag horn handle, 4 in. long, finely finished and very best quality of steel blades; no better knife made; every one warranted.
Retail price $1.25. Our price, each.... $0.85
Per doz.... 9.00

46076½ Champagne knife, German silver handles, 3¼ inch long, cork screw and cigar cutter, well finished and a good strong, durable article; warranted. Retail price $1.00.
Our price, each.... $0.67
Per doz.... 7.28

46077 Champagne knife, stag horn handle, 2⅞ inches long, manicure blade and corkscrew; a general utility knife, finely finished, good and strong; warranted. Each.... $0.90
Per doz.... 9.90

Boys' Knives.

Postage, extra, 3 to 5 cents.

46078 One blade boys' knife, clip blade, 3⅜ in. cocoa handle. Each.... $0.15
Per doz.... 1.65

46079 One blade boys' knife, 3⅜ inch, cocoa handle. Each.... $0.14
Per doz.... 1.63

46080 Boys' two-blades, knife, fancy dark horn handle, brass lined, fancy bolsters, a very fine article. Each.... $0.20
Per doz.... 2.20

46081 Two blades, boys' knife, clip blade, 3¼ in., cocoa handle. Each.... $0.24
Per doz.... 2.40

46082 Two blades, boys' knife, fancy metal handle. Each.... $0.07
Per doz.... .75

46084 One blade, boy's barlow. Each.... $0.08
Per doz.... .86

46085 Two blades, boy's barlow, horn handle.
Each.... $0.12 Per doz.... $1.30

46086 Two blades, dark handle. Each.... $0.12
Per dozen.... 1.30

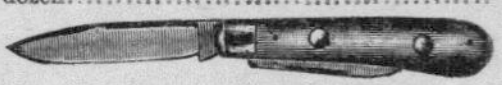

46087 Two blades, white handle.
Each.... $0.12 Per doz.... $1.35

46088 Two blades scored wood handle.
Each.... $0.12 Per doz.... 1.30

46090 Two blades, stag horn handle.
Each.... $0.20 Per doz.... 2.20

46092 Two blades, ebony handle brass lined, German silver bolsters; warranted finest quality blades,
Each.... $0.39 Per doz.... 3.95

Cutlery—Continued.

46093 Two blades, 3¼ inch, imitation stag horn handle, brass lined. Each.... $0.15
Per doz.... 1.40

46094 Two blade Barlow, 3¼ inch stag horn clip handle, point blade, English make; warranted. Each.... $0.29
Per doz.... 3.20

46095 Two blades, barlow, 3⅛ inch, stag horn handle, spear point blade, English make, warranted. Each.... $0.25
Per doz.... 2.50

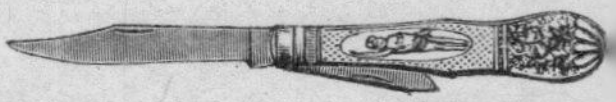

46096 Two blades, boys' hunting style knife, clip point blade, fancy nickel plated handle. Each. $0.15
Per doz.... 1.46

46097 Boys' iron handle, in imitation of buck horn, good steel blades. A strong knife; warranted. Each.... $0.09 Per dozen.... $0.96

46099 Two blades, ebony handle, better quality; warranted. Each.... $0.28 Per doz.... $3.00
46099½ Two blade, dark handle, a good strong knife. Each.... .25
Per dozen.... 2.20

46100 Two blades, white bone handle, better quality; a good knife.
Each.... $0.40 Per doz.... $4.60

Men's Heavy Pocket and Hunting Knives.

All our knives are warranted. Our prices are about one half the regular retail price. Extra by mail, 5c each.

46105 Two blades, brass lined, double bolstered, fine cocoa handle; warranted.
Each.... $0.45 Per doz.... $4.80

46106 Two blades, brass lined double bolstered, fine stag horn handle, warranted.
Each.... $0.45 Per doz.... $4.90
46107 Two blade finest quality, brass lined German silver bolsters, 3½ in. stag horn handle; a good strong article; warranted.
Each.... $0.63 Per doz.... $7.00

46108 Two blades, 3½ inch ebony handle; brass lined, fancy Germain silver bolsters, clip blade.
Each.... $0.55 Per dozen.... $6.00

46109 Two blade, fancy clip barlow, heavy capped end, 4in. handle; a good article.
Each.... $0.48 Per doz.... $4.80

46110 Two blades, 3⅞ inch, ebony handle; clip blado, brass lined, German silver bolster. Warranted. Each.... $0.55. Per dozen.... $6.00

46112 Two blades, 3¾ in ebony handle Swedish shape blade; well made and durable. Every one warranted. Each.... $0.50
Per dozen.... 5.30

46116 Two blades, 4½ in, fine ebony handles, best quality steel blades, brass lined, German silver bolsters. A large, strong and durable article. Retail price, $1.25....
See our price. Warranted. Each.... $0.79
Per dozen.... 8.82

Cutlery—Continued.

46118 One blade clip hunting style, best quality steel, 5 inch ebony handle; warranted.
Retail price, $1.00.
Our price. Each.................$0.69
Per dozen.........................7.20

46119 One blade, clip hunting style, 5¼ inch cocoa handle, spring back, brass lined, heavy and strong, best steel and warranted. Each..$1.00
Per dozen.........................11.00

46122 Two blade, 3⅜ in. ebony handle, brass lined, German silver bolsters, narrow large blade, best steel and warranted. Each........$0.50
Per dozen.........................5.40

46123 Two blades, brass lined, fine buckhorn handle, German silver lined, 3⅜ inch handle; very best quality and finest finished blades, warranted. Retail price, $1.25.
Our price. Each....$0.70 Per dozen $7.80

46127 Two blades best steel, ebony handle, brass lined, German silver bolsters, finest quality and finish, 3¼ inch handle; warranted. Retail price, $1.00.
Our price. Each....$0.49 Per dozen $5.00

46128 Two large blades, best steel, brass-lined German silver bolsters, best quality and finish, 3⅜ inch stag horn handle; warranted. Retail price, $1.25.
Our price. Each........................$0.80
....8.50

46131 Two blades, brass lined, cocoa handle; warranted. Each...$0.44 Per dozen........$4.40
46132 Two blades, 3⅜ in. ebony handle, good, strong, heavy blade. Every one warranted. The "Farmers' Favorite" and one of our best sellers.
Each.................$0.48 Per doz........$5.00

46140 Two blades, white bone handle, good and strong; warranted. Each......................$0.49
Per dozen.........................5.52

46141 Two blades, dark handle, extra heavy; warranted. Each......................$0.49
....5.52

46142 Two blades, 4 in. white bone handle, extra heavy, fine finish, brass lined, German silver bolsters; every one warranted. Each $0.60
Per dozen.........................6.00
46142½ Two blades, same as 46142, with ebony handles; a fine large knife; every one warranted.
Each.................................$0.60
Per dozen.........................6.00

46143 Two blades, 3¾ inch stag horn handle, brass lined, German silver bolsters, long, narrow large blade, best quality; warranted. A big bargain. Each......$0.42 Per dozen.......$4.80

46146 Two blades and corkscrew, white bone handle, brass lined. A handy knife to have in your pocket. Each....$0.49 Per dozen......$5.52

46147 Two blades, 3¼ in ebony handle, German silver bolsters, best steel blades; warranted. Each.................................$0.65
Per dozen.........................7.00

46149 Farmers' Knife, genuine IXL Wostenholm, two blades, black horn handle, heavy and strong; every knife warranted; 4-in. handle, the best grade manufactured. Each....$0.90
Per dozen.........................9.75
3¼ inch handle, each....$0.70. Per dozen......8.00

46150 Two blades white bone handle; warranted.
Each.................$0.49 Per dozen........$5.44

46151 Two blades, 3⅜ in. ebony handle, well made and durable. Every knife warranted. Each $0.45
Per doz.............................4.80

46154 Two blades, finest quality steel, brass lined, German silver bolsters, 3⅜ in. ebony handle; warranted. Each....$0.60 Per dozen....$6.74

46155 Two blades, finest quality steel, brass lined, German silver bolsters, 3⅜ in. stag horn handle; warranted. Retail price, $1.00.
Our price, each....$0.60 Per dozen.......$6.30

46158 Two blades; very finest quality steel, brass lined, German silver bolsters, 3⅜ in. stag horn handles; warranted. Each $0.70 per doz.$7.00

46160 Two blades 3¼-inch ebony handle, brass lined German silver bolsters. "Our big seller."
Warranted finest quality steel blades.
See our price, each....$0.65 Per dozen....$6.95

46161 Two blades, spring-back pocket hunting knife; large blade can be closed by pressing on small blade; black horn 4-inch handle, brass lined; large blade 3 inches long, best quality steel. Each.......$0.79 Per doz $9.19

46162 Two blades, carpenter's knife 3¼ in. ebony handle, both blades are large; one of the most useful knives around the shop or mill. Best quality steel blades and warranted. Each....$0.55
Per dozen.........................5.87

CATTLE KNIFE

46168 Three blades, buckhorn handle cattle knife, 3⅜ inch handle; brass lined, German silver bolsters. Each.......$0.84 Per dozen......$9.45

46169 Three blades, "Cattle Knife," finest quality steel, brass lined, German silver bolsters, 4¼ in. stag horn handle; warranted. Each $1.49
Per dozen.........................15.75

46171 Three blades, "Cattle Knife," finest quality steel, extra fine finish, brass lined, German silver bolsters, 3⅜ in. pearl handle, best quality; warranted. Retail price, $2.50.
Our price, each....$1.60 Per doz.......18.00

CATTLE KNIFE

46173 Three blades genuine IXL George Wostenholm cattle knife, heavy and strong, 3⅜ in. pearl handle, the best knife of this kind in the market. Each...........................$2.50

46174 Three blades and corkscrew, spring back, large blade closed by pressing on small blade; 4½ inch stag horn handle. Each.........$1.30
...................................14.00

46176 "The Texas Tooth Pick," 4½ inch ebony handle, 1 large clip point blade, 1 large spear point blade; a handy hunting knife; warranted; steel blades. Each....$0.70 Per dozen......$7.50

46177 Three blades frontier Hunting Knife; spring back on large blade to prevent closing while in use, 4¼ inch stag horn handle, German silver bolster; brass lined, crocus polished, heavy, strong and durable; warranted. Each...$1.25
Per dozen......................12.50

46180 Three blades, German silver bolsters, brass lined, 4½ inch stag horn handle; a fine knife.
Each.................$1.50 Per doz.....$16.00

46186 Two blades, stag horn handle, 3½ inches; physician's knife. Each....$0.49 Per dozen....$5.40
46188 Same as above, with pearl handle, finest quality and finish; warranted. Each...........86
Per dozen.........................8.37

46190 One blade, spring back, stag horn handle, 4-inch blade. Each....$0.48 Per doz.......$4.80
46191 One blade, spring back, stag handle, 4-inch blade. Same as 46190, except has "clip point" similar to 46192. Each...........$0.50
Per dozen.........................5.00

46192 Cow Boy's Pride, brass lined, stag horn handle; a fine article, spring back. Each....$1.00
Per dozen.........................11.00

46193 Three blades, 4-inch ebony handle, heavy and strong, 1 large short wide blade, 2 small blades. Very best steel in blades; every one warranted; brass lined. Each........$1.00
Each....$0.90 Per dozen.......$10.00
46194 Three blades, same style as 46193, but smaller, 3½-inch ebony handle. strong and durable, finest steel blades; warranted. Each.......$0.75
Per dozen.........................8.30

46195 One blade and corkscrew, hunting style, deer-foot handle. Each....$1.75 Per dozen....$18.00
46196 Three blades, 3⅜ inch, stag horn handle; spear marker and spay blades.
Each.................................$0.60
Per doz............................6.00

46197 Three blades, 4-inch stag horn handle, brass lined German silver bolstered, best steel. spear, marker and spay blades; warranted. Each $0.90
..................................9.29

46198 Spay, fleam and spear blades, 3⅜ inch ebony handle; warranted best of steel. Each....$0.75
Per doz...........................

Drinking Cups—Continued.

46436 Collapsing Drinking Cups, heavy white metal, nickel plated, finest finish, in neat leather cases; can be carried in vest pocket. Size, 2 5/8 x 2 1/4 inches when open. Weight, 4 oz. Each..$0.70

46437 Collasping Drinking Cup, in neat leather case, strong and durable; can be carried in vest pocket. Size, 2 5/8 x 2 3/4 in. when open. Weight, 4 oz. Each..............$0.35

Shears and Scissors.

Weights vary from 3 to 20 ounces each.

Our Shears and Scissors are the best in the market and are celebrated for THEIR GOOD CUTTING QUALITIES AND DURABILITY.

Lengths mentioned are the full dimensions from end to end.

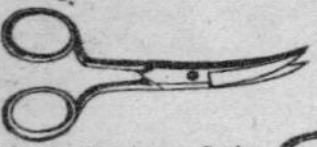

46439 Nail Scissors, used in manicuring the nails on hands or feet, 4 inch best steel, fine finish. Each $0.42

46440 Manicure Scissors, for trimming around the finger nails. Best steel, finely finished, best quality. Length.....3 1/2 in 4 in. Each.........45c. 55c.

46441 Button Hole Scissors, with inside set screw, to adjust the blades for different size button holes, 4 1/2 inch, best steel, fine finish. Each...........$0.50

46442 Buttonhole scissors, polished steel blade, adjusted by thumb screw to cut any size buttonhole, Price, pair.$0.39 Per doz...... 4.25 Postage extra.... .04

46443 Pocket Scissors, good quality, 4 in. Each.$0.20

46444 Better quality. Rogers' pattern warranted; heavy and strong. 4 in.. Each..$0.35

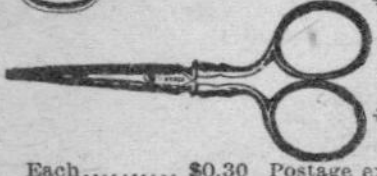

46445 Best quality, finest finished Rogers' pattern; warranted heavy; and strong. 5 in. Each.........$0.60

46446 Embroidery Scissors, good quality steel. Each......... $0.30 Postage extra............$0.04

Shears and Scissors—Continued.

46447 Fancy Embroidery Scissors, finest steel. Each $0.40

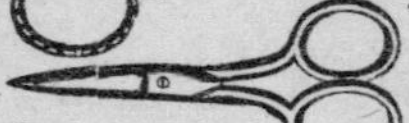

46448 Embroidery Scissors, polished laid steel and good cutters; warranted. Each. ..$0.25 Postage ext.4c

46449 Fancy Embroidery Scissors, gilt and nickel finish, best quality of steel blades; every pair warranted; 3 1/2 inch. Each...............$0.40

46450 Scissors, the best laid steel, nickel plated, best quality and finest finish.

Inches..	4 1/2	5	6	6 1/2	7
Each	$0.35	$0.40	$0.45	$0.50	$0.55

46450-51

46451 Scissors, good polished laid steel blades, round bows; every pair warranted

Length	5 in.	5 1/2 in.	6 in.	6 1/2 in.	7 in.
Each	$0.20	$0.25	$0.27	$0.30	$0.35

Postage extra, 5 to 10 cents.

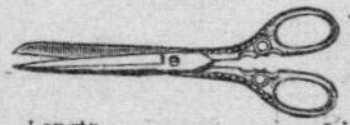

46453 Scissors, fancy gilt and nickel finished, best quality of steel blades, finely finished throughout. Every pair warranted.

Length	5 in.	6 in.	7 in.
Each	36c.	40c.	50c.

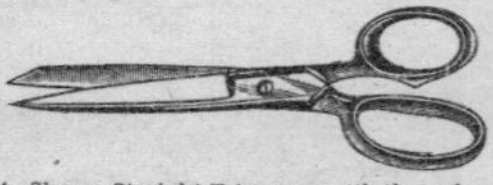

46454 Shears, Straight Trimmers, with the celebrated "brass bolt and nut" for taking up wear; full nickel plated, best steel. Every pair warranted.

Length...	8 in.	9 in.	10 in.
Each.....	50c.	56c.	68c.

46455 Shears, straight trimmers, fine laid steel blades, full nickel plated blades and handles, a good article, warranted.

Length	6in.	7in.	7 1/2 in.	8 in.	9 in.	10 in.
Each	$0.29	$0.33	$0.39	$0.44	$0.50	$0.60

Postage extra.

46456 Shears, Straight Trimmers, Japanned handles, maroon color, polished laid steel blades. Every pair warranted good cutters and good wearing qualities. The best low-priced shear on the market.

Length	6 in.	7 in.	8 in.	9 in.
Each	21c.	23c.	26c.	33c.

Shears and Scissors—Continued.

46460 Heinisch's Shears, best straight trimmers, finest laid steel, nickel plated. No better made.

Inches	6	7	7 1/2	8	8 1/2	9
Each	50c	57c	67c	74c	75c	80c

46461 Heinisch's Shears, left hand only, nickel plated, finest laid steel, 8 1/2 inch. Each $1.00

Postage, extra, 5 to 10 cents.

46462 Shears, bent trimmers, R. Heinischs Sons, nickel plated, best made; warranted.

Weight....	1/2 lb.	3/4 lb.		3/4 lb.		1 lb.
Inches......	8	8 1/2	9	10	12	13
Each	70c	75c	85c	$1.15	$1.25	$1.70

46463 Shears, Bent Trimmers, R. Heinisch's Sons best make, black Japanned handles. Every pair warranted.

Length......	8 in.	9 in.	10 in.	12 in.	13 in.
Each	56c.	74c.	90c.	$1.10	$1.20

Bent trimmers are large and strong, and made for heavy work.

46464 Paper Hangers' or Bankers' best steel; no better made.
Each, 12-inch..........$0.95 Each, 14-inch....$1.20
Postage extra.. .05

46465 Barbers' Shears, Heinisch's best japanned handles laid steel; warranted. Each, 8 1/2 inch...............$0.50 Each, 9 inch...........$0.60

46466 Left Hand Barbers' Shears, Heinisch's best, Japanned handles. 9 inch only. Each.... .80

46468 Barbers' Shears, R. Heintsch's best nickeled handles, laid steel; warranted. No better goods made.

Length	7 1/2 in.	8 in.	8 1/2 in.	9 in.
Each	70c.	75c.	78c.	85c.

R. Heinisch & Sons' shears have a world wide reputation and are acknowledged to be the best goods manufactured. No factory in the world can make better shears.

Length of shears and scissiors are for the entire length over all, from point to end of bow.

46467 The Novelty Shear and Scissor Sharpener. Any one can sharpen the dullest shear or scissors in a few seconds. Each.............. .....$0.10 Sent postpaid for 25 cents.

GUN DEPARTMENT.

All guns are guaranteed as represented, and if not found so they can be returned at our expense if FULL AMOUNT OF MONEY is sent with order, and if returned within three days from time taken from express office, properly cleaned and packed as received and in as good order as when received. If gun is as represented by us, return charges and all expenses must be paid by purchaser. Guns and rifles can be sent C. O. D. subject to examination ONLY when $5.00 is sent with ORDER anywhere this side of the Missouri River. Beyond this point full money, or $15.00, must accompany order. Send CASH with order and you run no risk and save money if you want a gun, as you then have three days for trial and examination, and also save your cash discounts and return charges on C. O. D. envelope.

Guns subject to same discount as other goods. See pages 1 and 2 for discounts.

Do not return us DIRTY and RUSTY guns and expect us to take them back, or guns that have been used until the finish has been worn off, for we cannot do so. Prices quoted on any make of gun in the market. Send full description of gun wanted, and if possible to obtain we can furnish it.

The Celebrated Chas. Daly Hammerless Guns.

46470-71
DALY EJECTOR.
Improved 1894 Model.
All bored for Nitro or Black Powders.

With all latest improvements. Improved quality. Reduced prices. Quality the best.

46470 No. 250. Diamond Quality Automatic Ejector, highest grade Damascus barrels, automatic lock, trigger safety, pistol grip, beautifully engraved Turkish walnut stock. There is no gun in the world superior to it. Will bear comparison with the finest Purdy—the highest-priced gun made; 12 and 16 gauge. Each,$222.00

46471 No. 150. Damascus Barrels, Automatic Ejector, fine plain engraving, selected stocks, matted rib. 12 and 16 gauge. A perfect ejector. Each..........$145.50
Weight, 12 gauge, 28 and 30 in., 7 1/4 to 7 3/4 lbs.

The Daly Ejectors are the handsomest, strongest and most perfect Ejectors made at any price. They are perfect in every respect. No gun in the world surpasses them in shooting or wearing qualities. Can be returned if not as represented.

Daly Hammerless.

46473
DALY HAMMERLESS.

46473 No. 120, Hammerless (not automatic ejecting), high grade Damascus barrels, beautifully finished, neatly engraved, all the latest improvements; greatly improved for this year. Shooting qualities guaranteed, best of material, finest workmanship. The best gun for the money on the market. All choke bored. Good for nitro or black powders. 12 or 16 gauge. Each.......................$110.00
Weight, 12 gauge, 7 1/4 to 7 3/4 lbs., Length of barrels, 28 and 30 inches.

46474 No. 120, 12 gauge, Feather Weights, 26 in., 5 3/4 lbs.................. 115.00

Special Bargains, $65.00.—Every one Perfect.

46475 Daly Hammerless Gun, same as No. 120, except not so finely engraved. Subject to previous sale. Built for service, and are long range, close, hard shooters, 10 gauge, 30 in., 9 1/4 to 10 lbs. Ea., $65.00; 10 gauge, 32 in., 9 to 10 1/4 lbs. Ea., $70.00
All new and in perfect order. Warranted good shooters.

THE WORLD RENOWNED W. W. GREENER EJECTOR GUNS.

WORKS, BIRMINGHAM, ENGLAND.

The Greener Gun is made as a fine gun; in fact, is the highest development of the sporting gun in every particular. Workmanship and material the very best. The ejector gun only throws out the case that is fired or both shells when both are fired. Breech action; is self fastening; the lock is self-cocking and the extractor is self-ejecting. Beautiful in design and finish. The Greener is so well known that it is not necessary to mention all of its superior qualities.

46478 No. 3 Quality Greener Ejector, hammerless, finely engraved, fine Damascus barrels, treble wedge, fastening self-acting ejector. Has all the improvements of the higher cost guns, but more plainly finished, still a very high grade gun; 12 gauge: $250.00 list. 10 gauge, $260.00 list: 12 gauge, 30 inch, 7¼ to 8 lbs. Our price.......... 210.50
10 gauge, 30 and 32 in., 8¼ to 9 lbs. Our price.......... 215.50

The "Facile Princeps" grade is the most popular gun of the Greener's. More of them are in use by noted trap shooters and sportsmen, than of any other high grade gun in the world. They are made for downright hard service, and are long range, close shooters.

Facile Princeps Greener.

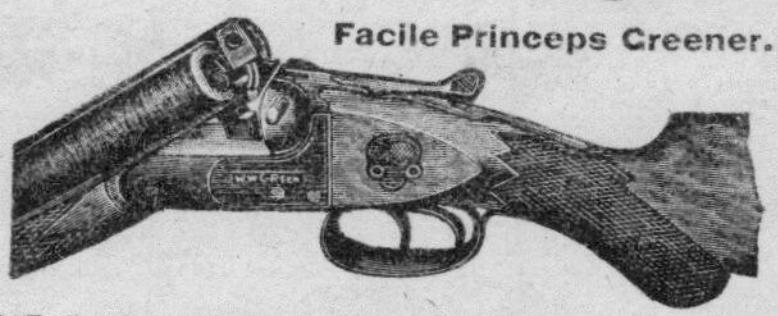

46479 "Facile Princeps" Quality, Greener cross bolt, treble wedge-fast, hammerless gun, made of best material, neatly finished, well balanced, light and strong, fine Damascus barrels, matted ribs and a good one. Made especially to our order for trap shooting. No better shooting gun at any price.
12 gauge, 30 in. barrels, 7¼ to 8¾ lbs., $125.00 list. Our price..........$105.00
10 gauge, 30 and 32 in., 8½ to 9½ lbs., $130.00 list. Our price.......... 115.00

THE IMPROVED LEFEVER HAMMERLESS AND EJECTOR GUNS.

Model 1893.

46483 Ideal.

The Lefever is a well balanced, symmetrical and well made gun, and has an unexcelled record for pattern and penetration. Compensated action to take up wear at all points. Trigger pull regulated by a screw without removing locks. Engine turned rib, all guns bored on the taper system. All warranted good shooters and latest models. All have Damascus barrels and matted ribs; 12-gauge, 30 and 32 inch, 10-gauge, 30 and 32 inch.

46483 Ideal or G Grade Damascus. English walnut stocks, full pistol grip, rubber butt, 10 or 12 gauge. Weight, 7¾ to 9 lbs..........$40.80

46484 F Grade Damascus, pistol grip, horn or steel butt plate, engraved; 12-gauge, 7¼ to 9 lbs.; 10-gauge, 9 to 10 lbs..........$57.50

46485 **Lefever Automatic Ejector**, Damascus barrels, pistol grip, beautifully checkered and engraved. Weight, 7¼ to 8¼ lbs; 30 or 32-inch barrels; 12-gauge only..........$115.00

Higher priced guns to order on short notice. The Lefever is a high grade gun, and warranted good shooter with either nitro or black powders.

COLT'S NEW HAMMERLESS BREECH LOADING GUN.

MADE BY THE COLT'S PATENT FIRE ARMS CO., HARTFORD, CONN.

Improved Model.

46494 Colt.

The 10-bore is the long range Duck Gun. $60.00 "The best gun in the world for the money;" best material, best workmanship, beautifully finished. No better shooting gun AT ANY PRICE.

Safer than a hammer gun. Simple and few parts. No better gun made for durability and shooting qualities. All have pistol grip. All are choke bored. All have extension rib. All are warranted as represented, or can be returned at our expense and money refunded. Long range, hard shooters. All warranted highest quality to the grade.

46494 Fine Damascus steel barrels, neatly engraved, fancy imported walnut stock, pistol grip, fancy rubber butt, checkered grip and fore-end, case-hardened lock plates and actions, and finely finished; 12-gauge, 30 and 32-inch barrels; 7¼ to 9 lbs. $80.00 grade. Our price.......... $58.00
10 gauge, 30 and 32-inch barrels, 8¼ to 10 lbs. Our price.......... 58.00

46495 $125.00 Grade Finest Damascus, beautifully finished and engraved, 12 or 10 gauge. Our price.......... 95.00

Higher priced guns made to order. All have the automatic safety, and every one a beauty at the trap or in the field.

Our hand-loaded shells are "hand-loaded" by men who are experts and not by boys or on "hand machines." Every motion in loading is made by hand except the crimping of the shell, which is done by electricity.

THE FAMOUS L. C. SMITH HAMMERLESS GUN.

46496
Improved for 1894.
Now made by The Hunter Arms Co., Fulton, N. Y.

All have top lever, all are choke bored, all have pistol grip, all are warranted.

46496 No. 1 quality, fine, laminated steel barrels, imported walnut stock, pistol grip, checkered grip and fore-end, rubber butt, case hardened lock plates and actions; no fancy engraving, but well made and desirable, and just as good a shooter as a higher price gun; 10, 16, or 12 gauge, 28, 30 and 32 inch barrel, 7¼ to 8¾ lbs. $40.80

46497 No. 2 quality, good Damascus steel barrels, imported walnut stock, pistol grip, checkered and finely engraved, finely finished, $80.00 grade; 10, 12 or 16 gauge, 28, 30 and 32 inch barrels. Our price.......... $57.50

46498 No. 3 quality, $100.00 grade. Our price.......... 70.00

Weights, 12 gauge, 7¼ to 9 lbs; 10 gauge, 8½ to 10¾ lbs. Higher grade guns to order. The Smith Hammerless has won more prizes than any other gun on the market. Circulars showing working parts of any hammerless gun sent on application. Boxing guns for shipment, 15 cents extra.

L. C. Smith Pigeon Gun.

46498½ The L. C. Smith Pigeon Gun. Finest "Crown steel" barrels, blued finish. Straight grip; highly finished and engraved; bored for nitro powders and made especially for trap shooting; beautifully balanced and made in the highest style of the art of "gun making" in every particular. 12 gauge, 30-in., 7¼ to 8 lbs. Each..........$100.00
Can be furnished with PISTOL GRIP stock at same price.

ALL SMITH GUNS ARE WARRANTED TO SHOOT ANY NITRO POWDER MADE; THEY NEVER CAN BE SHOT LOOSE.

Baker Hammerless Gun With Positive Automatic Block to Firing Pin. Cross Bolted.

No better shooting gun at any price;

EVERY GUN WARRANTED.
Bored for Nitros or Black Powder.

No. 46500
GREATLY IMPROVED FOR 1894.

All accidental discharge of either barrel or *simultaneous* firing of both barrels is rendered impossible. There is no condition, position or situation that this gun can be discharged other than by a pull of the triggers. The gun is locked by solidly cross-bolting the extension rib. There are no retracting bolts, in consequence of which the frame is not cut away, but is left intact, solid and strong. Beautiful in design and finish, wide breech; made for down-right hard service; not liable to get out of order; one of the best American guns on the market, and stands the "RACKET" OF ALL NITRO *Powders* EVERY TIME; 10 gauge, same price as 12 gauge.

46499 Fine Damascus Barrels, beautifully engraved; finely finished; equal to many $150.00 grade guns; 12 gauge, 28, 30 or 32 in. barrels; 7¼ to 9½ lbs. $60.00
10 guage, 30 and 32 in. barrel, 7¾ to 10¼ lbs. 60.00

46500 Fine Four-Blade Damascus Barrels, beautifully engraved, choke bored for best possible shooting. Every gun warranted. Handsome, well made and durable. 12 gauge, 28, 30 or 32 in. barrels, 7¼ to 9 lbs.; 10 gauge, 8 to 10 lbs...$37.95

46501 Finest Twist Barrels, neatly engraved, choke bored for best possible shooting. Every gun warranted, perfect and a good shooter. 12 gauge, 30 or 32 in. barrels, 7½ to 8¼ lbs., or 10 gauge, 30 and 32 in. barrel, 8 to 10 lbs. Each.......$33.00

Forester Grade Greener.

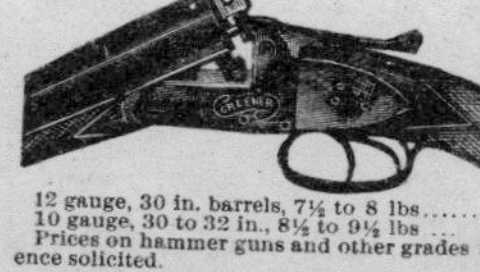

46502 No. 6 Greener "Forester's" Hammerless Gun, Anson & Deeley action, treble wedge-fast, cross-bolted, matted ribs, laminated barrels, finely finished, well balanced, choke bored, made for service, and a good shooter. The value of these guns is in the barrels and lock work, and are made especially for us. They shoot just as well as the higher costing guns, and wear just as long.

12 gauge, 30 in. barrels, 7¼ to 8 lbs..........$80.00
10 gauge, 30 to 32 in., 8¼ to 9¼ lbs.......... 84.00

Prices on hammer guns and other grades furnished on application. Correspondence solicited.

New Hammerless Double Gun.

Manufactured by Forehand Arms Company Worcester, Mass. $33.00

CROSS BOLTED.

This Gun has rebounding locks, and the *barrels can be taken off and put on again without cocking the gun*, and when cocked the hammers may be let down gradually and without the full force of the blow. It is simple in construction, having very many less pieces than any other hammerless gun. No better shooting guns at any price.

Easily Tipped and Cocked. Bored for best possible shooting. *Send for descriptive catalogue.* Small bore for nitro or black powder.

46503 Finest Twist barrels, no engraving, but finely finished 12 ga. 30 or 32 inch barrels 7½ to 8¼ lbs. Each........$33.00

46504 Fine Damascus Barrels (dark-finish), Italian walnut stock, full pistol grip, checkered grip and fore-end engraved, action and mounting handsome; well made and durable. Every gun warranted a good shooter. 12 gauge, 30 inch barrels 7½ to 8¼ lbs. Each........$37.50

The F. & W. gun is made for down, right hard service, and is a first-class gun, in every particular.

Torkelson Hammerless Gun. Manufactured at Worcester, Mass.

46506 The Torkelson Hammerless Double Barrel Shot Gun. Also sold under the brand of "Spencer Arms Co." English walnut stock-pistol grip, matted rib, beautifully case hardened frame, fine twist barrels, choke-bored; made of good material, well balanced and warranted good shooters. 12 gauge, 30 inch, 7¼ to 7⅜lbs. List price, $40.00. OUR PRICE........$23.95

This gun has been put on the market to meet the demands for a good hammerless gun without "fancy finish," that "would shoot and wear well" and "not cost too much."

THE L. C. SMITH AUTOMATIC EJECTOR, Hammerless.

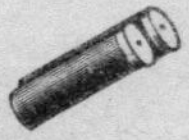

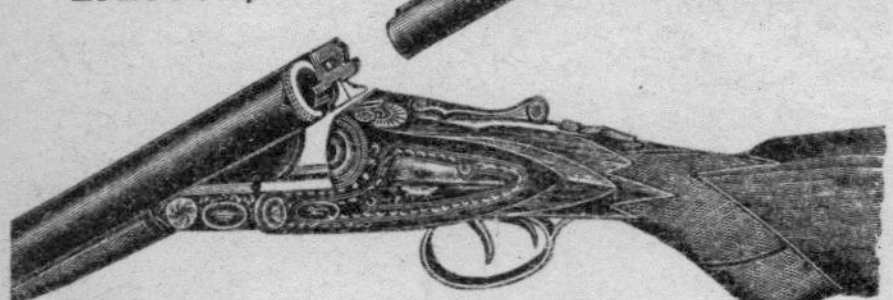

SMITH EJECTOR. Model 1894.

46514 Quality A 1. Very Fine Damascus Steel Barrels, very fine imported English walnut stocks, fine checkering and engraving. Choke bored on the multiplied system, and all warranted close hard shooters. 12 gauge, 28, 30 and 32 in. barrels, 7¼ to 8½ lbs. $117.00

Catalogue or circulars showing working parts sent on application.

THE PARKER HAMMERLESS GUN. "The Long Range Hard Shooters."

Cut shows style of engraving on $150 grade, $120 Net cash.

AMERICA'S BEST-KNOWN GUN—ALL TOP LEVER—ALL CHOKE BORED—MADE BY PARKER BROS., MERIDEN, CONN.

Fine Damascus Steel Barrels, fine figured American or imported walnut stock pistol grip; checkered, handsomely engraved, hard rubber butt plates, beautifully finished throughout. Every gun warranted; highest quality to the grade. Matted ribs. Our price.

46515 "E. H." Grade, 10 gauge, $85.00 List $62.75
46516 "G. H." Grade, 12 gauge, 16 gauge, 28, 30 and 32 inch, $80.00 List 57.50
46516¼ "D. H." 10, 12, 16 gauge, $100.00 List........ 72.00
46517 Fine Twist Barrels, 12 and 16 gauge, $65.00 List........ 44.95

Weight, 12 bore, 7½ to 9 pounds; weight, 10 bore, 8¼ to 10 pounds; length of barrel, 28 to 32 inches, "drop" of stock 2¼ to 3¼ inches. "Stocks" (measured from center of first trigger to center of butt plate) 14 to 14¼ inches. We can make shorter or longer barrels and different stocks to special orders and prices according to extra amount of labor. Circulars with illustrations of working parts sent on application. Higher priced guns made to order. Send for prices.

MODEL 1894. THE IMPROVED ITHACA HAMMERLESS.

46518

Bored for nitro and black powders

Barrels can be put on and taken off same as a hammer gun, whether gun is cocked or not. Locks are rebounding, automatic safety, can be changed to independent by the touch of the thumb for rapid firing. All HAVE PISTOL GRIP, all HAVE EXTENSION RIB, ALL CHOKE BORED, all finely finished and greatly improved for this year. All have matted ribs. "The Stub Twist" barrels used on these guns are better than laminated or cheap Damascus barrels. 30 inch barrels, 12 gauge, 7¼ to 8½; 32 inch 7¾ to 9¼. 30 inch barrels 10 gauge, 8½ to 9½; 32 inch 8¾ to 11 lbs.

12 gauge, 7¼ to 9¼ lbs.; 10 gauge, 8½ to 11 lbs.; 16 gauge, 6½ to 7½ lbs.

46518 Fine English stub twist barrels, American walnut stock pistol grip, checkered line engraving, No. 10, 12 or 16 gauge........$33.75

46519 Fine Damascus Steel Barrels, English walnut stock, pistol grip, checkered, neatly engraved, No. 10, 12 or 16 gauge........$40.00

ITHACA HAMMERLESS.

46521 ITHACA.

HANDSOME, WELL MADE AND DURABLE.

Bored for nitro and black powders.

46521 Fine Damascus steel barrels, selected English walnut stock, pistol grip, checkered, fancy finished breech action, neatly engraved A handsome finely finished gun. All warranted for shooting qualities and wear. 10 and 12 gauge, 28, 30 and 32 inch barrels........$54.00

Higher priced guns to order, $65.00, $75.00, $115.00 to $150.00, on short notice.

THE WELL-KNOWN PARKER GUN. Latest Improved.

See that your Parker guns are stamped Parker Bros.—All others are only IMITATIONS, and cheap grade of common guns.

Cut shows "D" grade.

Breech loading, double gun, top lever, made by Parker Bros., Meriden, Conn. All grades of this gun, as quoted below, are breech loading. All have the top lever action, double bolt and improved check-hook and pin, fore-end lock, solid head plunger, extension rib, rebounding locks and low hammers. In ordering guns, give first and second choice on weights and dimensions. We shall always do our best to give the "first choice," and generally will be able to do so. All Parker guns are choke bored for close shooting, and are accompanied by target made at factory. 12 gauge, 7¼ to 9¼ pounds; 10 gauge, 9¼ to 10¼ pounds. Length of barrel, 30 to 32 inches.

Our guns are the very best made in these grades. Every gun warranted. All bored for long range, and the cheapest will shoot as well as the most expensive.

	12 gauge.	10 gauge.
46522 Parker, twist barrels, American stock, engraved and checkered pistol grip	$40.00	$44.00
46523 Parker, fine Damascus steel barrels, fine figured American or imported stock, engraved rubber butt plate, checkered pistol grip	57.50	62.75

REMINGTON NEW BREECH LOADING DOUBLE BARREL SHOT GUNS.

Look out for the old-models. The new ones all have matted ribs.

Manufactured by the Remington Arms Co., Ilion, N. Y. The latest improved model Top lever, extension rib, rebounding bar locks, large head strikers, patent fore-end. All have pistol grip and all are choke bored. Every gun is carefully and rigidly tested before leaving the factory, and satisfaction is guaranted. Lengths, 12 gauge, 30 and 32 inches. Weights, 10 gauge, 8¾ to 9¾ lbs. Lengths, 10 gauge, 30 inches. Weights, 12 gauge, 7¼ to 8¾ lbs.

The barrels of Remington guns are choke bored on the best principle, and the parts are interchangeable. Only the best material and workmanship are used in the construction of these guns.

All have matted ribs and circular hammers.

46525 Grade (2). Twist barrels, selected walnut stocks, 10 or 12 gauge, pistol grip, $45.00 List. Our price........$22.95

46526 Grade (3). Damascus steel barrels, selected walnut stocks, pistol grip, 10 and 12 gauge, $50.00 List. Our price........ 24.50

Higher priced guns made to order.

Regular length stock, 14 inches; drop, 2⅞ to 3½ inches. Any deviation will cost extra

REMINGTON AUXILIARY RIFLE BARRELS.

46526½ These barrels extend the entire length of the breech-loading shot gun barrels, and are held firmly in place by a thumb nut at muzzle. They shoot accurately. Can be inserted in any shot gun. Each barrel has an extractor. For 30 and 32 in. barrels, 10 or 12 gauge, calibre 32, W. C. F., 32-40, 38-55, 45-70. Price........$8.00

THE IMPROVED NEW BAKER GUN—Breech Loader. $19.90.

Manufactured by The Baker Forging and Gun Co., Batavia, N. Y. Just the gun you have been asking us for—plain, but a good one.

THE BEST GUN FOR THE MONEY EVER PUT ON THE MARKET. MONEY WILL NOT BUY A BETTER SHOOTING GUN.

CROSS BOLTED.

The makers claim for this gun "even pattern, powerful shooter, and challenge any gun in the market to equal it for durability and simplicity." Best English steel twist barrels, extension ribs, checkered pistol grip, English walnut stocks, rubber butt plate, low circular hammer, solid strikers, rebounding locks, top snap action, interchangeable parts, choke bored, unless otherwise ordered. No better shooting guns at any price. A plain, well balanced, neatly finished gun, made of best material, compensating fore-end, cannot get loose and shaky in hinge joint. In fact just the gun for business at a moderate price. Every gun warranted. All have matted ribs.

46527 $30 grade, 12-gauge, 30 and 32-in. barrels, 7¼ to 10½ lbs....... $19.90
46528 10-gauge, 30 and 32 in.-barrels, 8½ to 11 lbs....... 19.90
Every gun warranted.

46529 Fine Damascus Barrels, finely finished, engraved, fine case-hardened lock plate and action, choke bored for nitro or black powder. 12-gauge, 30 and 32-inch barrels, 7½ to 9 pounds....... $24.50
10-gauge, 32 inch-barrels, 9 to 10½ pounds....... 24.60

N. B. The "Baker" is well-known as the "long range Duck Gun"

THE NEW ITHACA GUN. Improved Model.

(Manufactured by the ITHACA GUN COMPANY, Ithaca, N. Y.)

$23.65.

Made of best materials. Simplest and best locks. Low hammers, Top lever swinging over them when cocked. Self compensating, taking up wear at every point. Never get loose and shaky. Matted rib, and all have walnut pistol grip, stock checkered, case hardened lock plates and blued mountings.

All guns are choke bored to shoot the closest pattern. No extra charge for a No. 10-gauge over a No. 12-gauge, or a heavy weight over a light gun. Only the best English twist and Damascus steel barrels are used.

All have Rubber Butt. All have Top Lever. All have Extension Rib. All are Choke Bored. Every gun warranted. All have Matted Rib.

46531 Fine English Stub Twist Barrels; American walnut stock, pistol grip, checkered, No. 10, 12 or 16-gauge, neatly engraved....... $23.65
46532 Fine Damascus Steel Barrels, selected American walnut stock, pistol grip, checkered, No. 10; 12 or 16-gauge, engraved....... $35.90

10-gauge, length of barrel, 30 and 32 inches; 12-gauge, 30 and 32-inch barrel; 12-bore, weight 7¾ to 10½ lbs.; 10-bore, weight, 8½ to 11 lbs.; 16-gauge, 28, 30 and 32-inch barrels, 6¾ for 28 inch up to 8 lbs. for 32 inch.

N. B.—No better shooting gun at any price. The "Boss" Duck Gun.

New Model Machine Made Breech Loaders. (Made by H. Pieper.)

HERE YOU HAVE IT. A GOOD GUN FOR A LITTLE MONEY.

Handsome, well made, finely balanced, good shooting, machine made gun, at popular prices by a well-known maker. The machine-made gun has come to stay, and is vastly superior in every way to the old-style hand made article.

Modified Diana Pattern Machine-Made Breech Loading Shot Guns.

The barrels are screwed in the breech; they remain perfectly round and straight and are not pinched together as is the case in the old way of manufacture. The lumps and the steel breech are one solid piece, thus avoiding lumps becoming loose. The barrels being independent of each other, the expansion is even, and the penetration and shooting qualities in general are thereby increased. The steel breech is level with the barrels; in this it differs from the Diana Gun, where the breech projects, and the new system is therefore called the "Modified Diana"

Top Lever — Back Action.

Barrels are choked after the most approved system.

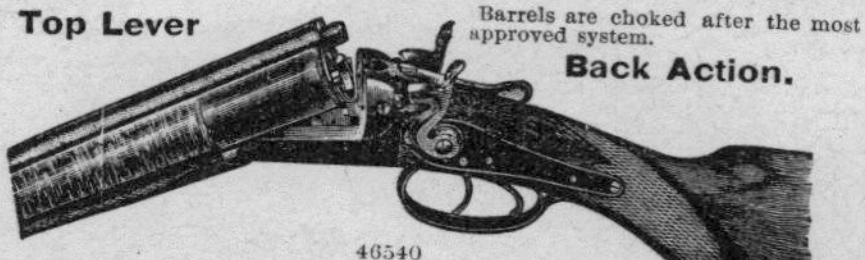

46540

46540 Top Snap, Modified Diana Pattern, back action, two spring rebounding locks, pistol grip, matted rib, rubber butt, extension rib, left barrel choke bored, genuine twist barrels. Warranted. Locks are polished inside, and are as good and will wear as long as the bar locks. Low circular hammers.
12-Gauge, 30 or 32 in., 7¾ to 8¾ lbs....... $16.00
10-Gauge, 30 or 32 in., 8¾ to 9¾ lbs....... 16.50

Top Lever — Bar Locks.

46541

46541 Top Snap, Modified Diana Pattern, genuine laminated twist barrels, bar rebounding locks, extension rib, low circular hammers, pistol grip, rubber butt, matted rib, left barrel choke bored. A good one. Warranted.
12 Gauge, 30 or 32 in. barrels, 7½ to 8¾ lbs. each....... $19.50
10 Gauge, 30 or 32 in. barrels, 8½ to 9¾ lbs. each....... 19.90
16 Gauge, 28 or 30 in., 6½ to 6¾ lbs....... 20.75

46542 Top Snap, genuine laminated twist steel barrels, double bolt, bar rebounding locks, extension rib, matted rib, low circular hammers, pistol grip, rubber butt, Deely & Edges' fore-end, fine engraving on barrels, best finish, rubber cap on pistol grip, both barrels full choke bored. A fine gun.
12 Gauge, 30 and 32 in. barrels, 7¼ to 8¼ lbs., each....... $23.00
10 Gauge, 30 and 32 in. barrels, 8¾ to 9½ lbs., each....... 23.00
16 Gauge, 28 and 30 in. barrels, 6½ to 7 lbs., each....... 23.75
20 Gauge, 28 inch barrels, 6½ to 6¾ lbs. each....... 23.70

MODIFIED DIANA PATTERN.

Cross Bolted.

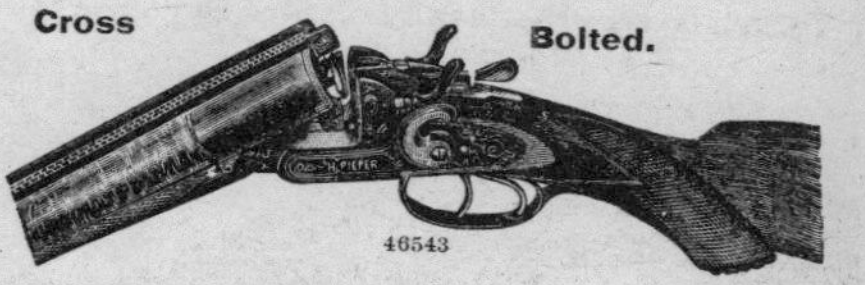

46543

46543 Modified Diana Pattern, Greener cross bolt, top snap. Damascus barrels, bar rebounding locks, extension rib, matted rib, double bolt, Deely & Edges fore-end, new style low circular hammers, nicely engraved, pistol grip with rubber cap, rubber butt, full choked both barrels, fine finish. Built for service and a fine gun in every particular.
12 Gauge, 30 and 32 in., 7¼ to 8¾ lbs., each....... $27.50
10 Gauge, 30 and 32 in., 8¾ to 9¾ lbs., each....... 27.90
16 Gauge, 30 inches, 6½ lbs....... 28.00
20 Gauge, 28 inches 6¼ to 6¾ lbs....... 28.60

L. C. SMITH HAMMER GUN.

Cross Bolt. Choke Bored.

Factory Price, $55.00.

The New L. C. Smith Hammer Gun, Cross Bolted, Pistol Grip, circular hammer, matted extension rib, choke bored, good for nitro or black powder. A long range, hard shooting gun, not liable to get "loose or shaky" in the joints. Finest stub twist barrel.
46544 12 gauge, 30 or 32 inch barrels, 7¾ to 8¾ lbs. Each....... $23.75
46544½ 10 gauge, 30 or 32 inch barrels, 8¾ to 9¾ lbs. Each....... 23.90

Belgian Double Barrel Breech Loader.

46547 Belgian Double Barrel Breech Loader, top lever bar action locks, rebounding hammers, extension rib, pistol grip, patent fore-end, matted rib, circular hammers, engraved lock plate and action, steel barrels, finished in imitation of Damascus; can hardly be told from genuine Damascus. A showy gun for the money.
12 gauge, 30 or 32 inch barrels, 7¾ to 8½ lbs Each....... $13.65
10-gauge, 30 and 32 inch, 8¾ to 9¾ lbs. Each....... 13.90

Our hand-loaded shells are "hand loaded" by men who are experts and not by boys or on "hand machines." Every motion in loading is made by hand except the crimping of the shell, which is done by electricity.

THE RICHARDS.—Double Barrel Gun.

Extension Rib.

46550

46550 Richards' Breech Loaders, double barrel, back action locks, top lever, low hammers, pistol grip, checkered grip and fore-end, and brass studded on grip and fore-end, both lumps through frame nickel-plated locks, *extension rib*, guard and butt plate; neatly engraved, a showy gun and a good one. Blued steel barrels, left barrel choke-bored for close shooting. 10-gauge, 30 or 32 inch, 8¼ to 9 pounds........................$10.94
12 gauge, 30 or 32 inch, 7¼ to 8 pounds........................ 10.50

THE CELEBRATED PRIZE MACHINE GUNS.

Cross Bolted.

46556.
THE PRIZE MACHINE.

46556 The Prize Machine Double Barreled Breech Loader, Greener treble wedge fast cross bolt top lever, bar rebounding locks, pistol grip, solid strikers, double bolt, extension matted rib, rubber butt, circular hammers, D. & E. patent fore-end, nicely engraved, left barrel best taper choked, well made, well balanced, and a handsome gun, laminated steel barrels. All good shooters, and made for service in the field or at the trap. (List price $35 00.) Our price.
12 gauge, 30 and 32 inch, 7¾ to 8½ lbs. $21.50
10 gauge, 30 and 32 inch, 8¾ to 9¾ lbs. 21.50

Elegant guns for the money.

Each gun tagged with record of shooting.

46557
The best material and finish.

46557 The Prize Machine Breech Loading Double Barreled Shot Gun, top lever, bar rebounding locks, patent fore-end, solid large head strikers, double bolt, extension matted rib, pistol grip, rubber butt, new style circular hammers, laminated steel barrels, made of best material, well finished, well balanced, choke bored, and a good gun at a moderate price. All good shooters. (List price $30.00) Our price.
12-gauge, 30 and 32 inch, 7¾ to 8¼ lbs. $18.95
10-gauge, 30 and 32 inch, 8¾ to 9¾ lbs........................ 19.45

COMPLETE BAR LOCK.—Double Guns.

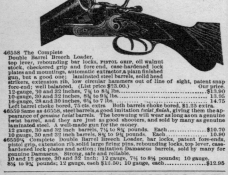

46558 The Complete Double Barrel Breech Loader, top lever, rebounding bar locks, PISTOL GRIP, oil walnut stock, checkered grip and fore end, case-hardened lock plates and mountings, automatic extractor, a plain finished gun, but a good one; laminated steel barrels, solid head strikers, extension rib, low circular hammers out of line of sight, patent snap fore-end; well balanced. (List price $23.00.) Our price.
12-gauge, 30 and 32 inches, 7¾ to 8¾ lbs........................$13.90
10-gauge, 30 and 32 inches, 8¾ to 9¾ lbs........................ 13.95
16-gauge, 28 and 30 inches, 6¼ to 7 lbs........................ 14.75
Left barrel choke bored, 75 cts. extra. Both barrels choke bored, $1.25 extra.

46559 Same as 46558, steel barrels, a good imitation *twist finish*, giving them the appearance of *genuine twist* barrels. The browning will wear as long as on a genuine twist barrel, and they are just as good shooters, and sold by many as genuine laminated steel. A well-made gun for the money.
12 gauge, 30 and 32 inch barrels, 7½ to 8¾ pounds. Each................$10.70
10 gauge, 30 and 32 inch barrels, 8¾ to 9¾ pounds. Each................ 10.90

46559½ Complete Double Barrel Breech Loader, bar locks, patent fore-ends, pistol grip, extension rib, solid large firing pins, rebounding locks, top lever, case-hardened lock plates and action; imitation Damascus barrels, sold by many for genuine Damascus. Strong, safe and reliable.
10 and 12 gauge, 30 and 32 inch; 12 gauge, 7¼ to 8¼ pounds; 10 gauge, 8¼ to 9¾ pounds; 12 gauge, each $12.50; 10 gauge, each................$12.95

OUR GUN REPAIRING DEPARTMENT IS ONE OF THE LARGEST IN THE COUNTRY.

Special Complete. Bar Lock Guns.

46560
46560 Special Machine Finished Complete Double Barrel Breech

Loader, Top Lever, Bar Rebounding Lock, locks polished inside, pistol grip, oiled walnut stock, checkered grip and fore-end, case-hardened lock, plates and mountings, laminated steel barrels, large head firing pins, extension rib, low circular hammers out of line of sight, patent snap fore-end, well balanced, well made, finely finished locks and action. The best gun for the money ever put on the market. Good shooters. 12-gauge 30 and 32 inches, 7¼ to 8¾ lbs.$17.00
10-gauge 30 and 32 inches, 8¼ to 9¾ lbs., choke bored........................ 17.50

46560¼ Special Complete Double Barrel Breech Loader. Bar rebounding locks, pistol grip, solid head firing pins, patent fore-end, extension rib, case-hardened lock plates and action, top lever. Well made and a good gun; left barrel full choke-bored, laminated steel barrels.
12-gauge, 30 and 32 inch, 7¼ to 8¼ lbs. Each........................$15.00
10-gauge, 30 and 32 inch, 8¼ to 9¾ lbs. Each........................ 15.50

TOP LEVER, BACK ACTION.

46561 Special Complete Double Barrel Breech Loader, top lever, snap action, fine rebounding back action locks, walnut stock, checkered grip and fore-end, fine case-hardened lock plates and mountings, automatic shell extractor. A good, honest well made gun, and a good shooter, well balanced. Fine laminated steel barrels, extension rib, patent fore-end. (List price, $18.00) Our price.
12 gauge, 30 and 32 inch barrel, 7½ to 8¾ lbs........................$10 90
10 gauge, 32 inch barrel, 9 to 9¾ lbs. 11.00
16 gauge, 28 and 30 inch barrel, 6¼ to 7¼ lbs. 11.50
With one barrel full choked, 75 cents extra. With both barrels full choked, 1.25 extra, and shooting qualities guaranteed.

46561½ Same style as 46561, Imitation twist barrels, not as finely finished as the genuine twist, cannot be told from genuine and the browning will wear just as long. A good gun for the money.
12 gauge, 30 and 32 inch, 7¾ to 8¼ lbs. Each $9.75

Top Lever, Back Action, High Grade.

46562 Machine Finished, Complete Double Barrel Breech Loader, fine polished rebounding back action locks, top lever, extension rib, pistol grip, patent fore-end, case hardened lock plates and action, low circular hammers, well balanced, finely finished for the grade, strong, well made and durable, safe and reliable. A good all-around gun. (List price, $20.00.) Our price.
12 gauge, 30 and 32 in., 7½ to 8½ lbs........................$13.00
10 gauge, 30 and 32 in., 8½ to 9½ lbs........................$13.40

BLUED SIDE LEVER. Double Barrel.

$8.50 $8.90

46563 Double Barrel Breech Loader, side lever, snap action, automatic shell ejector, walnut stock, checkered grip, patent fore-end, case-hardened mountings, BLUED BARRELS, low hammers out of line of sight, well balanced. A good, safe gun. 12 gauge, 30 inch barrels, 7½ to 8½ lbs. Each........................$8.50
10 gauge, 30 and 32 inch barrels, 8¼ to 9¼ lbs. Each........................ 8.90
One barrel full choked, 75 cents extra; both barrels, $1.25 extra.

OUR SPECIAL SIDE LEVER. Double Barrel.

$9.25 $9.50

46564

46564 Double Barrel Breech Loader, side lever, snap action, automatic shell extractor, case-hardened mountings, PISTOL GRIP, patent fore-end, walnut stock, checkered grip, GENUINE TWIST BARRELS, safe and reliable and a good gun for the money. Low circular hammers out of line of sight, well balanced.
(List price $18.00.) Our price.
12 gauge, 30 inch, 7¼ to 8¼ lbs. Each........................$ 9.25
10 gauge, 30 and 32 inch, 8½ to 9¾ lbs........................ 9.50
16 gauge, 28 and 30 inch, 6 to 6¾ lbs 10.50
With one barrel full choked 75 cents extra. With both barrels full choked $1.25 extra.

THE CELEBRATED LEFAUCHEAUX ACTION GUNS.

CENTER FIRE BRASS OR PAPER SHELLS ARE USED IN ALL OF OUR LEFAUCHEAUX GUNS.

$6.80 **$6.57**

Celebrated Lefaucheaux Action. **BREECH LOADERS.**
N. B.—Observe Price.

46565 The Celebrated Lefaucheaux Action, double barrel, breech loading shot gun, blued decarbonized steel barrel, back action lock, checkered grip, bottom lever, (not pistol grip), 12 gauge automatic shell ejector, 30 and 32-inch barrel, weight 7¼ to 8¾ lbs. List price, $12.00. Our price........$6.57
10 gauge, 8½ to 9½ lbs........ 6.80
16-gauge, 30 and 32-inch........ 7.50

$8.75 **$9.00**

46566

46566 Lefaucheaux Action, double barrel, rubber butt, pistol grip, laminated steel barrels, rebounding locks, double key, 12 gauge, 30 and 32 inches, 7¼ to 8½ lbs........$8.75
10 gauge, 30 and 32 inches, 8¾ to 9½ lbs........ 9.00
16 gauge, 30 and 32 inches, 6½ to 7 lbs........ 9.90
N. B.—Any gun purchased of us not described as choke bored, we will full-choke bore one barrel for 75 cents, or both barrels for $1.25; and warrant them to be close shooters. All Breech Loaders use brass, or paper shells, center fire

A NEW SHOT GUN.—WINCHESTER, MODEL 1893. $16.88

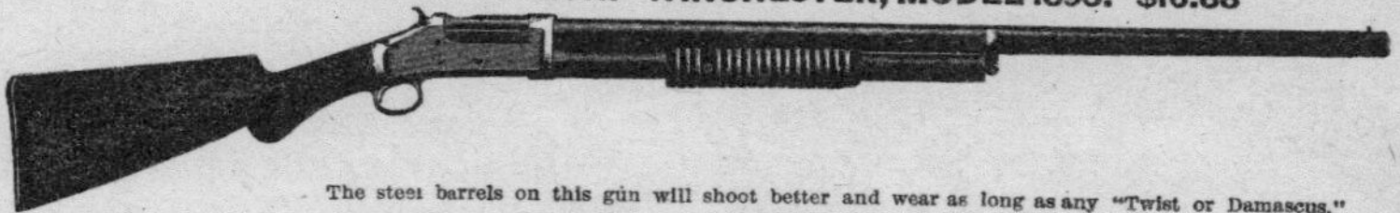

The steel barrels on this gun will shoot better and wear as long as any "Twist or Damascus."

Winchester Repeating Shot Gun, Model 1893.

The arm is operated by a sliding fore-arm below the barrel. When the hammer is down, the backward and forward motion of this slide unlocks and opens the breech-lock, ejects the cartridge or fired shell and replaces it with a fresh cartridge. The construction of the arm is such that the hammer cannot fall, or the firing-pin strike the cartridge until the breech-lock is in place and locked fast. While the hammer stands at the full cock notch, the gun is locked against opening. In this position the firing-pin must be pushed forward to open the gun. When the hammer stands at half-cock, the gun is locked both against opening and pulling the trigger.

To Load the Magazine.—Turn the gun with the guard upward. Lay the cartridge on the underside of the carrier and push it into the magazine.

12 Gauge only; no other gauge made.

46568 Rolled Steel Barrels, plain walnut pistol grip stock. Length of stock, 13 inches; drop of stock 2¾ inches, 7¾ lb. weight; 6 shot. 12 gauge only; 30 or 32 inch barrels........$16.88
All guns choke-bored for best possible shooting unless otherwise ordered. This new gun has few parts and not liable to get out of order.

The Burgess Repeating Shot Gun. $30.00

46569 The Burgess Single Barrel Repeating Shot Gun, walnut stock, Damascus barrels, bored for long range close shooting. This gun has the sliding pistol grip movement for loading and ejecting shell. Made of best material, has few parts and not liable to get out of order. Barrel can be separated from stock in an instant. 12 gauge, 30 or 32 inch, about 7½ pounds weight; 6 shot........$28.00
Circulars giving full description of Burgess Gun sent free on application.

THE DALY THREE-BARREL BREECH LOADER.

46570 Damascus barrels, selected English walnut stock, extension rib, open sights, and fine folding rear sight. (The plunger for rifle barrel is set by pushing the lever slightly to the left, and is fired by the right hand hammer.) The rib is matted, and locks and body neatly engraved.
12 bore, 30 inch, 8 to 9 lbs., 38-55 and 32-40 caliber rifle........$75.00
10 gauge 45-70 caliber, 30 inch barrels, 9½ lbs........ 80.00
This is the most attractive three-barrel breech-loader yet produced.
It is a marvel of beauty; the rifle barrel is made of such a quality of steel that the addition to the weight is not noticed at all. The putting together of the three barrels is perfect, so that the utmost accuracy with shot and bullet is guaranteed. The sight on the tang can be used the same as the Lyman sight. The demand has surpassed our expectations. We have never bought anything which achieved such marked success in so short a time.

PIEPER'S COMBINED SHOT GUN AND RIFLE BREECH LOADER.

46571-5

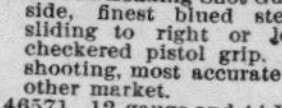

The rifling is the best and accuracy and range as good as the best rifle in the market. The Boss Gun to have around the farm. Pieper's Patent "Reinforce" Breech Loading Shot Gun and Rifle Combined, barrels side by side, finest blued steel barrels and steel butt plate, sporting rear sight, sliding to right or left, white metal front knife sight, shot gun stock, checkered pistol grip. This is without doubt the handsomest and strongest shooting, most accurate and combined arm ever offered for sale in this or any other market.

46571 12 gauge and 44 W. C. F caliber, 30 in. barrels, weight about 8½ lbs. $23.45
46573 Pieper's Patent Combined Shot Gun and Rifle, 12 gauge and 38 caliber; 55 grains powder, 255 grains lead; barrel, 30 inches; 8½ lbs., using cartridge 47222........$23.45
46574 Pieper's Patent Combined Shot Gun and Rifle, side snap lever, blued barrel, good on game up to 300 yards; accurate and reliable. 12 gauge and 32 W. C. F. caliber, using cartridge 47193; 30 inch; 9¼ lbs........$23.45
46575 Pieper's Combined Shot Gun and Rifle, side lever, blued barrels, 12 gauge and 40-60 caliber (using No. 47232 cartridge) 30-inch 8¾ to 9¼ lbs. Each, $23.45

BEST RIFLING. **MERWIN, HULBERT & CO.'S COMBINED SHOT GUN AND RIFLE.** **A GOOD GUN.**

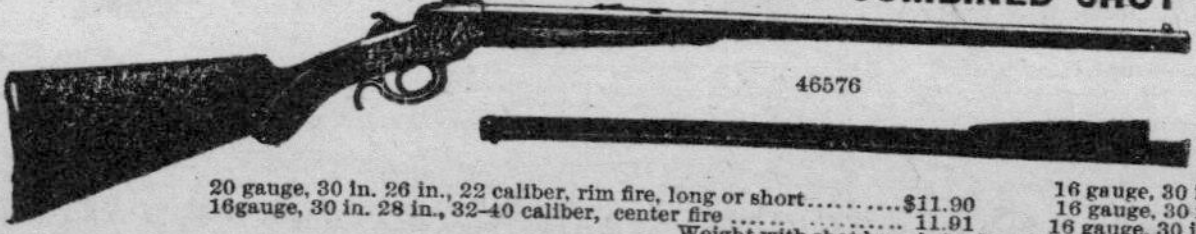

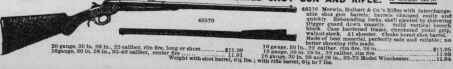

46576

46576 Merwin, Hulbert & Co.'s Rifles with interchangeable shot gun barrels; barrels changed easily and quickly. Rebounding locks, shell ejected by throwing trigger guard down smartly. Solid vertical breech block. Case hardened frame, checkered pistol grip, walnut stock. A1 shooter. Choke bored shot barrel. Made of best material, perfectly safe and reliable; no better shooting rifle made.

20 gauge, 30 in. 26 in., 22 caliber, rim fire, long or short........$11.90
16gauge, 30 in. 28 in., 32-40 caliber, center fire........ 11.91
16 gauge, 30 in., 22 caliber, rim fire, 26 in........$11.95
16 gauge, 30 in. 28 in., 32 caliber, rim fire........ 11.93
16 gauge, 30 in. 26 and 28 in., 32-73 Model Winchester........ 11.94
Weight with shot barrel, 6½ lbs.; with rifle barrel, 6½ to 7 lbs.

THE NEW MODEL SPENCER REPEATING SHOT GUN. $28.00.

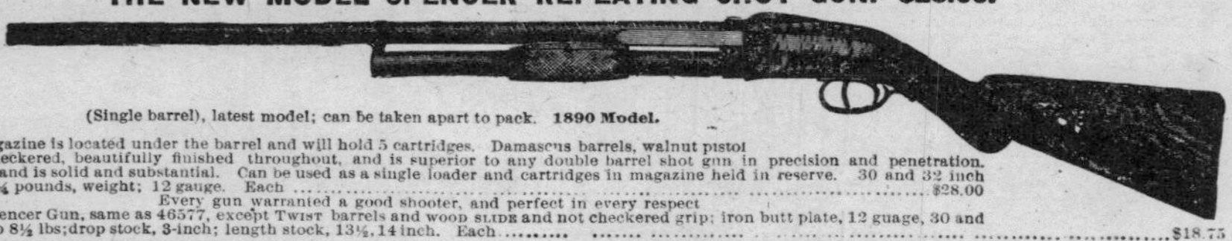

(Single barrel), latest model; can be taken apart to pack. **1890 Model.**

46577 The magazine is located under the barrel and will hold 5 cartridges. Damascus barrels, walnut pistol grip stock, checkered, beautifully finished throughout, and is superior to any double barrel shot gun in precision and penetration. Has few parts and is solid and substantial. Can be used as a single loader and cartridges in magazine held in reserve. 30 and 32 inch barrels, 7¾, 8¼ pounds, weight; 12 gauge. Each $28.00

Every gun warranted a good shooter, and perfect in every respect

46577½ The Spencer Gun, same as 46577, except TWIST barrels and WOOD SLIDE and not checkered grip; iron butt plate, 12 guage, 30 and 32-inch, 7½ to 8½ lbs; drop stock, 3-inch; length stock, 13½, 14 inch. Each $18.75

THE WINCHESTER REPEATING SHOT GUN.

Price, $16.88.

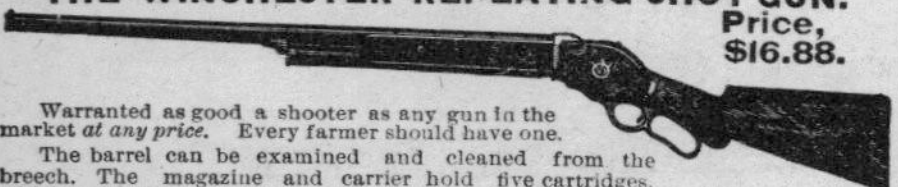

Warranted as good a shooter as any gun in the market *at any price*. Every farmer should have one.

The barrel can be examined and cleaned from the breech. The magazine and carrier hold five cartridges, which, with the one in the chamber, makes six at the command of the shooter. The forward and backward motion of finger lever, which can be executed while gun is at shoulder, throws out empty shell, raises a new cartridge from magazine and puts it into the barrel. The gun is then ready to be fired. Rolled steel barrel, case-hardened frame and pistol grip, stock of plain walnut, not checked. All guns are full choked, and no gun will be sent out that will not make a good target. The standard gun will have a stock 12¾ inches in length and 2⅝ inches drop, and any variation from standard length or drop will be charged for extra.

46578 Winchester Repeating Shot Gun, rolled steel barrel, with plain pistol grip stock, 30 and 32 inch barrel, 12 gauge; weight 7¾ lbs. Factory *net cash* price, $25.00; Our price .... Net cash $16.88

For 10 gauge, 30 and 32 inch, 9 lbs. weight .... Net cash 16.88

For 10 gauge, 2⅞ inch paper shells. 12 gauge, 2⅝ inch paper shells.

This gun has the largest sale of any gun on the market. Buy one; you will like it. Everybody does who tries one. N. B. The blued steel barrels used on this gun are made by the Winchester Arms Company, and will wear as long and shoot as well as any Damascus or twist barrel.

BREECH LOADERS—Single Barrel.
FOREHAND AND WADSWORTH GUNS.

Manufactured at Worcester, Mass.

$6.50

46579 The F. & W. Top Snap Single Barrel Breech Loading Gun, rebounding locks, pistol grips, snap fore-end, solid block strikers, choke bored. Finest blued steel barrels, just as durable as twist steel barrels, just as strong and just as good shooters, using paper or brass center fire shells.

12 guage, 30 and 32 inch barrels, 7 lbs. weight. Each $6.50

BREECH-LOADERS.
The Great Long-Range Duck and Goose Gun.

Single Barrel.

American Trigger Action.

46580 American Trigger Action, Single Barrel Breech-Loader, pistol grip, fine twist barrel, rebounding lock, case hardened mounting, *choke bored*, oiled walnut stock; front trigger throws the barrel open, self-acting shell ejector, strong, simple and durable action; 8 gauge, 36 inch barrel, weight about 12 to 13 lbs. The 8 gauge is the long-range goose gun. The 10 and 12 gauge are made in the same style as the 8 gauge, but of course will not shoot as far. Price $24.25

46581 10 gauge, pistol grip, 32 to 34 inch barrel, 8 to 9½ pounds 14.00

46582 12 gauge, pistol grip, 32 inch, 7 to 7¼ pounds 10.90

This gun (46580, 8 gauge) is without doubt the "best and most substantial long-range single breech-loader ever built." It is made with a special view to hard service, with heavy charges of ammunition and long range shooting. No. 3 or larger shot should be used, for an 8 gauge is not good with smaller shot using paper or brass shells, center fire. See "Remarks" about ammunition, and how to load.

The Remington Semi-Hammerless. Single Barrel. Handsome and Well Made. $6.90.

46583 Remington Semi-Hammerless Single Gun. Top lever, blue steel barrels, choke bored, side cocking lever, case-hardened frame and butt plate, pistol grip stock, rebounding lock. The material, finish and shooting qualities are the same high standard as the double guns. Every gun warranted perfect and a good shooter. 12 gauge; 30, 32 and 34 inch barrel; 6 to 6½ pounds weight. Each $6.90

16 gauge, 30 inch, 6 to 6½ lbs 6.85

20 gauge, 30 inch, 6 to 6½ lbs 6.80

THE FOREHAND HAMMERLESS. $12.50.

Finely Finished. Good Shooter.

The Hammerless Gun is the coming gun, and is safer and more durable than the *hammer gun*.

46584 The F. & W. Hammerless Single Barrel Breech Loading Shot Gun, top snap, pistol grip, snap fore-end. Automatic action, with an absolute safety catch to lock the trigger to prevent accidental discharge, simple in construction, perfectly safe, and made of best material. Choke bored, twist steel barrels, using brass or paper shells, center fire, 12 gauge, 30 inch barrel, 7 lbs. weight. Each $12.50

THE PERFECTION BREECH-LOADER.

Single Barrel. Price $7.90

46585 The Improved Perfection Single Barrel Breech-Loading Shot Gun, walnut stock, pistol grip, improved fore-end, rebounding lock, plated frame, twisted steel barrel, medium *choke bored*, shell extractor, center fire, top lever; as good a shooter as any double barrel gun of the same caliber. This gun is all that its name ("Perfection") implies, and in its manufacture the best ideas of years of experience have been embraced, and *it is* the most perfect single barrel breech-loader *ever produced*. Its *simplicity* and *perfection* of action render it almost equal to a *double* breech-loader. For strength, beauty, penetration, and *general* shooting qualities it is without a rival. Using paper or brass shells, center fire; 30 and 32 inch barrels, 6½ to 7 lbs., 12 gauge. Each $7.90

16 gauge. Each 7.85

46586 The Victor Single Barrel Breech Loader, same as 46585, with fine decarbonized steel barrels; 12 gauge, 30 and 32 inch barrels, 6½ lbs. weight. A fine gun and a good shooter Each $6.35

Top-Snap Champion Single Breech-Loading Shot Gun.

MANUFACTURED BY JOHN P. LOVELL'S SONS.

Champion, 46587

46587 Champion Single Breech-Loader, top lever (that can be operated either to right or left), choke bore, rebounding lock, patent fore-end fastening, pistol grip, oiled walnut stock, nickel-plated frames, a fine shooter and a well-made and durable gun. Fine twist barrel, 12 gauge, 32 inch, 6¼ pounds; 30 in. 6lbs.... $8.40.

Every gun warranted a good and reliable shooter. Just as long range as the double guns.

The Boys' American Side Snap. $5.85. The Boss Single Gun. Big Bargains.

46588 The New American Side Snap. Pistol grip, fine quality, plain blued barrels, nickel plated mountings, rubber butt plate, choke bored, 12 gauge only, 30 inch barrel, weight, 6½ pounds, using paper or brass shells, center fire Each...$5.85

This is not a *toy gun*, but a handsome, well-made, safe, reliable, accurate shooting gun, and made of the best material. Every gun warranted. Order one, and if not found as represented can be returned at our expense both ways and money will be refunded.

THE NEW HOPKINS & ALLEN SHOT GUN. $6.50.

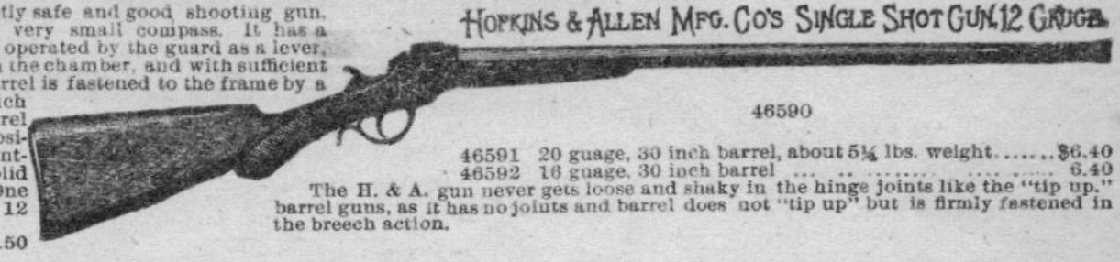

46590

46590 The New Hopkins and Allen Shot Gun, a perfectly safe and good shooting gun, that can be taken apart without tool and put into very small compass. It has a rebounding lock and a vertical sliding breech block operated by the guard as a lever, which when thrown down ejects the empty shell from the chamber, and with sufficient force to carry it 6 to 8 feet from the shooter. The barrel is fastened to the frame by a tapering screw key, easily removed by the hand, which passes through the frame and section of the barrel laterally, keeping the barrel always in its proper position. Finest blued steel barrel, case-hardened mountings, choke bored. The barrels are bored out of solid metal; oiled walnut pistol grip stock, double bolt. One of the strongest and best made guns in the market. 12 guage only, 30 inch barrels, 6½ to 7 pounds. Each $6.50

46591 20 guage, 30 inch barrel, about 5¼ lbs. weight $6.40
46592 16 guage, 30 inch barrel 6.40

The H. & A. gun never gets loose and shaky in the hinge joints like the "tip up." barrel guns, as it has no joints and barrel does not "tip up" but is firmly fastened in the breech action.

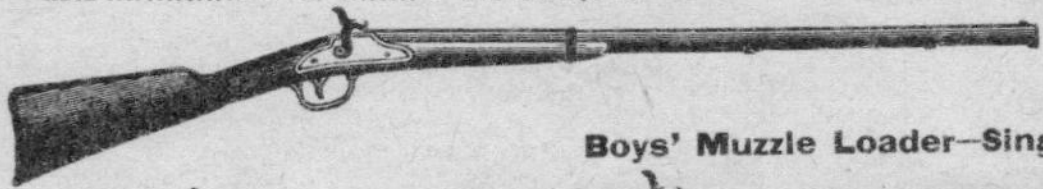

46595 Cut Down Muskets 32 in. barrels, 16 gauge, walnut stocks, blued finish, muzzle-loading single barrel, weight about 6¼ lbs. Each $2.90

Boys' Muzzle Loader—Single Barrel.

46596 The Boys' Muzzle Loader, single barrel, wood ramrod, pistol grip, blued barrels, a good safe gun, small nipple for G. D. or E. B. caps, 31 inch barrels, 4½ lbs. weight, 16 gauge. Each $3.50

MUZZLE LOADERS—Double Barrel.

This cut represents as near as possible a Double Barrel Muzzle Loader, with back action locks.

46597 Imitation Twist Barrels, back action lock, plain breech, guage 11, 12, 13 and 14, Belgian manufacture. Price $5.40

46598 Double Barrel Muzzle Loader, Belgian manufacture, genuine twist steel barrels, oiled walnut stock, patent breech and break off back action locks, checkered grip, 12 to 14 bore; weight 7 to 8½ pounds; length 30 to 34 inches. A good, safe and reliable gun.. $8.00

DOUBLE BARREL MUZZLE LOADERS.

With bar lock. All have patent breech and break off.

46600-3.

Cut showing Bar Locks, Pistol Grip.

46600 Double Barrel Muzzle Loader, laminated steel barrel, bar locks, oiled walnut stock patent breech and break off, checkered pistol grip, German manufacture, 12 to 14 gauge, 7 to 8½ pounds, 30 to 34 inch barrels. Price $9.00

46603 Genuine Twist barrels, bar locks, walnut stock, checkered grip, gauge 11 and 12, English manufacture. Length of barrel 30 to 34 inches, weighs 7½ to 8½ lbs. Pistol grip $9.75

COLT'S NEW LIGHTNING MAGAZINE RIFLES.

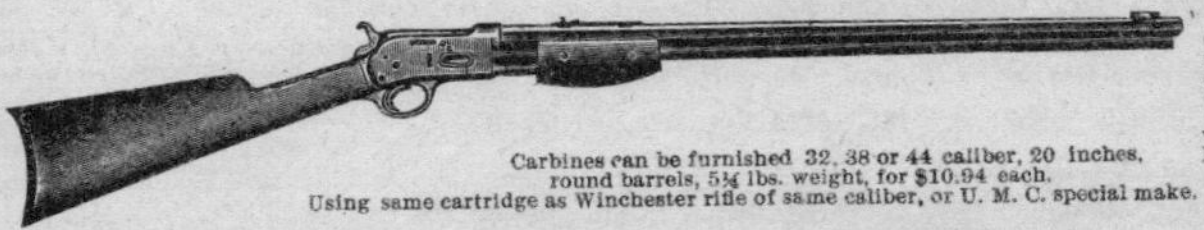

Manufactured by Colt's Patent Fire Arms Manufaturing Co., Hartford, Conn. Constructed upon entirely new principles. The workmanship is of the same high standard as that of the other arms manufactured by this company. Old shell ejected and new cartridge inserted by sliding motion of the forearm, and as it can be done with the left hand it is at once convenient and rapid. Every rifle warranted. ALL CENTER FIRE.

Carbines can be furnished 32, 38 or 44 caliber, 20 inches, round barrels, 5¾ lbs. weight, for $10.94 each.

Using same cartridge as Winchester rifle of same caliber, or U. M. C. special make.

	Reduced Prices.	Factory Price.	Our Price
46616	32 caliber, 15 shot, weight 6¾ lbs., 26 inch round barrel, using 47192 cartridge	$16.50	$10.94
46617	32 caliber, 15 shot, weight 7¼ lbs., 26 inch octagon barrel, using 47192 cartridge	18.00	11.86
46618	38 caliber, 15 shot, weight 6¾ lbs., 26 inch round barrel, using 47201 cartridge	16.50	10.94
46619	38 caliber, 15 shot, weight 7¼ lbs. 26 inch octagon barrel, using 47201 cartridge	18.00	11.86
46620	44 caliber, 15 shot, weight 6¾ lbs., 26 inch round barrel, using 47214 cartridge	16.50	10.94
46621	44 caliber, 15 shot, weight 7¼ lbs., 26 inch octagon barrel, using 47214 cartridge	18.00	11.86
46624	38-56 caliber, 28 inch octagon barrel, using 47225 cartridge, 10 shot	20.50	14.20
46625	45-85 caliber, 28 inch octagon barrel, weight 10 lbs., using 47246 cartridge, 10 shot	20.50	14.20
46626	40-60 caliber, 28 inch octagon, 10 lbs., using 47227 cartridge 10 shot		14.20
46627	40-60 caliber, 28 inch round barrel, 9½ lbs., using No. 47227 cartridge 10 shot		13.20

COLT'S LIGHTNING RIFLE—22 Caliber. $9.72.

46629 22 caliber, 15 shot, rim fire, long or short, weight 5¾ lbs. 24 in. octagon barrel. Each $9.72
Using 47155 to 59 cartridge.

Colt's 22 Caliber Magazine Rifle. The BEST in the market. Extra for Colt Rifles. Fancy pistol grip stock, checkered grip and fore-end, $12.00 extra. Extra length barrels, $1.00 per inch.

WINCHESTER RIFLES. All Warranted. Highest Grade Made.

These Rifles are all perfectly new and direct from the factory, and are fully warranted by the Winchester Company and by us. They are among the very best sporting and target rifles manufactured in the world. There are no poor ones. Every one is perfect. The extremely low prices at which we are now offering them place them within the reach of every man and boy in the land. There are no later models in any grade than those we have listed. The 1873 and 1876 models are exactly the same in design; the only difference is caliber, length and weight.

For additional length of barrel and magazine add to price $0.75 per inch. For set triggers on models 1873, $2.00.

Extra for set trigger case hardened mountings and lock plates and extra finished plain stocks, $3.75.

Extra for plain walnut, pistol grip, stocks not checkered, $4.75. Extra for fancy walnut pistol grip, stocks checkered, $11.00.

All have oiled walnut stocks. Sling strap and swivels, $1.50 per set.

Prices on extra parts and fancy styles and cuts of same furnished on application.

For Cartridges see Index. For Reloading Tools and Sights see Index.

46736 Winchester Carbine, 32 caliber, center fire (model 1873), 20-inch round barrel; 12 shot; using No. 47193 cartridge. Each $10.94
46737 Winchester Carbine, 38 caliber, center fire (model 1873), 20-inch round barrel; 11 shot; using No. 47200 cartridge. Each 10.95

Carbine 1873 Model.

46738 Winchester Carbine, 44 caliber (model 1873.) center fire, 20-inch round barrel, 12 shot, weight 7¼ lbs., using No. 47208 cartridge. Price $10.94

46739 Winchester Carbine (model 1876), 22-inch round barrel, stock full length of magazine, number of shots 9, weight 8¾ lbs., 45-60 caliber, using No. 47240 cartridge. Price $13.00

46740 40-60 caliber, using No. 47230 cartridge. Price 13.00

WINCHESTER RIFLES—MODEL 1873.

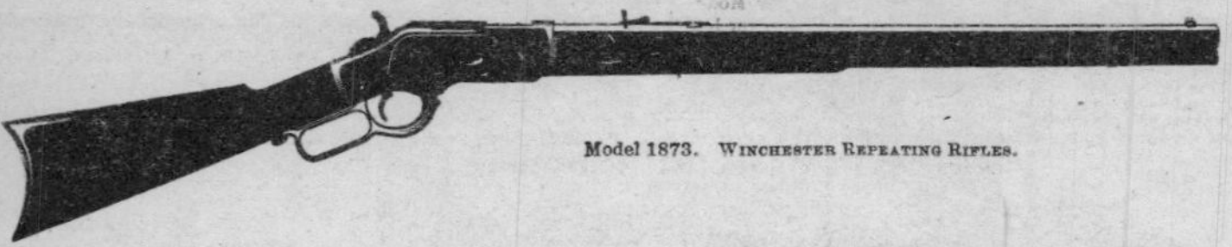

Model 1873. WINCHESTER REPEATING RIFLES.

46744 Winchester Sporting Rifle (model 1873), repeating, round barrels; length of barrel, 24 inches; center fire; caliber, 44; number of shots, 15; weight, 8¾ lbs.; using 47208 cartridge. Price $10.94

46745 Octagon Barrel; length of barrel, 24 inches; center fire; caliber, 44; number of shots, 15; weight 9 lbs.; using No. 47208 cartridge. Each $11.86

46746 Octagon Barrel, 24 inches, 15 shot; weight, 9 lbs.; 38 caliber; using No. 47200 cartridge only (model 1873). Each. $11.86

46747 Round Barrels, 24 inches, 15 shot; weight, 8¾ lbs.; 38 caliber, using No. 47200 cartridge only (Model 1873)). Each........ 10.94
46748 Octagon Barrels, 24 inch, 15 shot; weight, 9 lbs.; 32 caliber, using No. 47193 cartridge *only* (Model 1873). Each........ 11.86
46749 Round Barrels, 24 inch. 15 shot; weight, 8¾ lbs.; 32 caliber, using No. 47193 cartridge *only* (Model 1873). Each........ 10.94
46750 Octagon Barrels, 24 inch, 25 shot; weight, 9 lbs.; 22 caliber, *rim fire short only*, using No. 47156 cartridge *only* (Model 1873). Each........ 11.86

THERE IS ONLY ONE QUALITY OF MATERIAL USED IN WINCHESTER RIFLES, AND THAT IS THE BEST. YOU GET THE SAME WHATEVER PRICE YOU MAY PAY.

WINCHESTER CENTENNIAL SPORTING (MODEL 1876) REPEATING RIFLE.

Winchester Rifles are the best in the World for the Money.

Net Price.

46756 Octagon Barrel, 28 inch, 12 shot; weight, 10 lbs.; 40-60 caliber (Model 1876), using No. 47230 *cartridge only*. Each........ $14.90

YOU CANNOT BUY ANY BETTER QUALITY of Winchester Rifles, for they are not made. Only one kind of material is used in Winchester Rifles, and that is the best. Boxed for shipment, rifles weigh 20 to 25 pounds each.

WINCHESTER 22-CALIBER REPEATING RIFLE—Model '90. "Take Down."

Winchester Model 1890 Repeating Rifle. Loads and ejects the shell by the sliding motion of the forearm. All 24-inch octagon barrels, all 5¾ pounds weight.

46757 For 22 Caliber Rim Fire Short, only 15 shot, using No. 47156 Cartridges. $9.72

46758 For 22 Caliber Rim Fire Long, 12 shot, using No. 47159 Cartridges. $9.72

46759 For 22 Caliber Rim Fire Special Winchester Lubricated Bullet Cartridge, using No. 47165 Cartridges .... $9.72 The same rifle will only load the one length of shell.

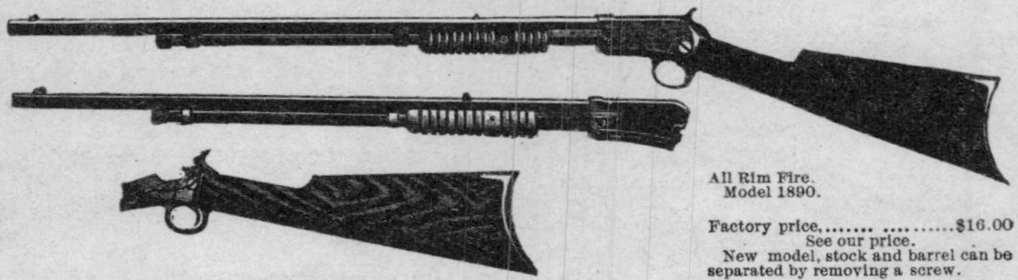

46757-9 Taken apart.

All Rim Fire.
Model 1890.

Factory price........ .... $16.00
See our price.
New model, stock and barrel can be separated by removing a screw.

TESTING GUNS FOR ACCURACY.

In testing guns for accuracy, sit down when firing, resting the muzzle on some solid object, and if possible securing a solid rest for the arms and body. In this way extreme accuracy can be obtained—sufficient for the testing of the gun. Do not in any case attempt to get accuracy by screwing the gun in a vise. No reliable result can be had in this way.

WINCHESTER REPEATING RIFLES—Model 1886.

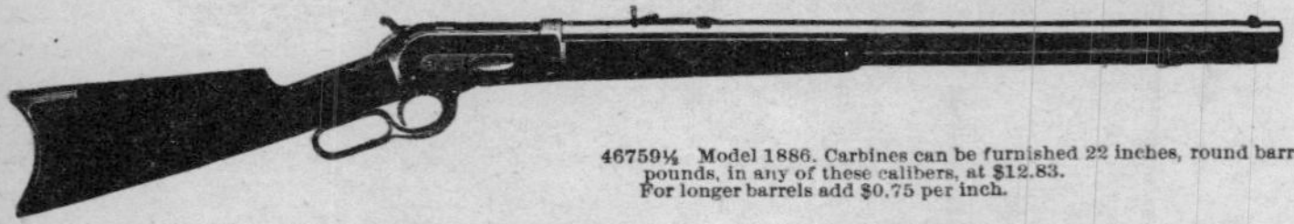

All have case-hardened lock plates and mountings.
Prices on longer or shorter barrels on application.

46759¼ Model 1886. Carbines can be furnished 22 inches, round barrels, 8 pounds, in any of these calibers, at $12.83.
For longer barrels add $0.75 per inch.

		Factory prices.	Our prices.
46760	Octagon Barrel, 26 inches or under, 9¼ lbs., 40-82 caliber, 260 grain bullet, 8 shot, using No. 47234 cartridge	$21.00	$14.18
46761	Round Barrel, 40-82 caliber	19.50	13.16
46762	Octagon Barrel, 26 inches or under, 9¼ lbs., 45-70 caliber, 405 grain bullet (using a regular Government cartridge), 9 shot	21.00	14.18
46763	Round Barrel, 26 inches or under, 9 lbs., 45-70 caliber	19.50	13.16
46764	Octagon Barrel, 26 inches or under, 9¼ lbs., 45-90 caliber, 300 grain bullet, 8 shot, using No. 47249 cartridge	21.00	14.18
46765	Round Barrel, 26 inches or under, 9 lbs., 45-90 caliber, using No. 47249 cartridge	19.50	13.16
46766	Octagon Barrel, 26 inches, 9¼ lbs., 38-56 caliber, 8 shot, using No. 47225 cartridge	21.00	14.18
46767	Round Barrel, 26 inches, 9¼ lbs., 38-56 caliber	19.50	13.16
46768	Octagon Barrel, 26 inches, 9¼ lbs., 40-65 caliber, using No. 47231 cartridge	21.00	14.18
46769	Round Barrel, 26 inches, 40-65 caliber	19.50	13.16
46770	Octagon Barrel, 26 inches, 50-110 Express, using No. 47262 cartridge	21.00	14.18
46771	Octagon Barrels, 26 inches, 9¼ lbs., 38-70-255 caliber, using No. 47226 cartridge	21.00	14.18
46772	Octagon Barrels, 26 inches, 9¼ lbs., 40-70-330 caliber, using No. 47228 cartridge	21.00	14.18

The standard length of barrel will be 26 inches. Guns taking the 45-70 cartridge will have the Sporting Leaf Sight, and all others the Sporting Rear Sight.
Plain walnut pistol grip stocks not checkered, $4.75; extra barrels can be made any length from 20 to 36 inch; add $1.00 per inch for barrels over 26 inch.
Cleaning Rods will not be put in butt stocks, but each gun will be accompanied by a slotted hickory rod without charge.
All extras same as other Winchester Repeating Rifles.
Set Triggers, $2.25 extra.

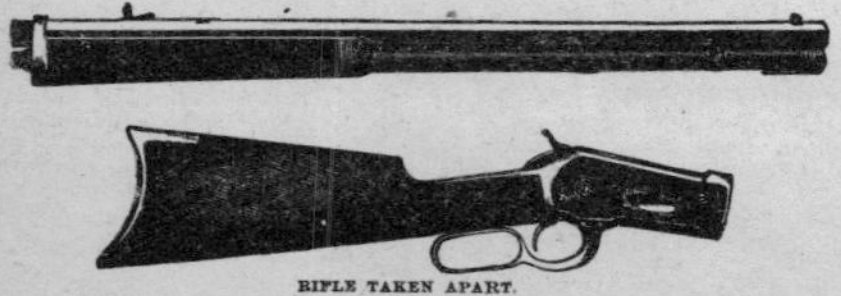

RIFLE TAKEN APART.

WINCHESTER REPEATING RIFLES, "TAKE DOWN"—Model 1886.

46771½ Winchester Repeating Rifles, model 1886 "Take Down," 26 inches, octagon barrels, any caliber from No. 46760 to 46772........ $17.60
No other lengths made in the "Take-Down" style.

A NEW REPEATING RIFLE.

The Winchester Model 1892.

The system is the same as the model of 1886. Loaded and discharged by a finger lever. The firing pin is first withdrawn, the gun unlocked and opened, the shell ejected, and a new cartridge presented and forced into the chamber of the barrel. The locking bolts are always in sight, and when the gun is closed support the breech bolt against the force of the explosion. The rifle is light, strong, handsome and simple in construction. Cleaning rods *will not* be put in butt stocks, but each rifle will be accompanied with a slotted hickory cleaning rod.

They will only be made with 24 inch barrel. (Factory price on Octagon barrel) $19.50
They will only be made with plain triggers. (" " " Round ") 18.00
They will only be made with straight grip stocks.
They are only made as quoted below, using the same tools and cartridge as the model 1873. See Index for quotations on Tools and Cartridges.

Winchester Model '92 Repeater.

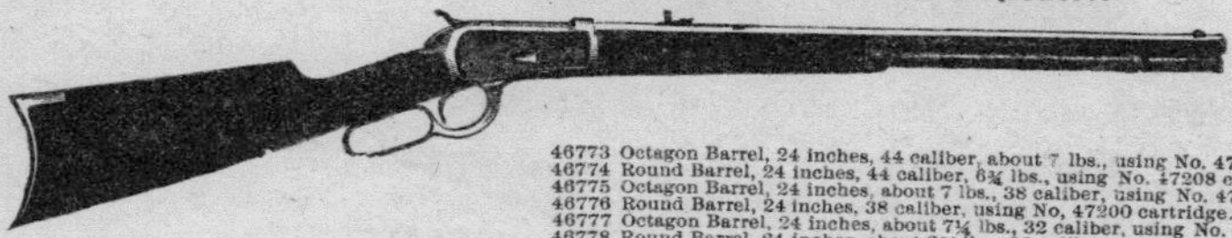

	Our Price Each.
46773 Octagon Barrel, 24 inches, 44 caliber, about 7 lbs., using No. 47208 cartridge	$11.86
46774 Round Barrel, 24 inches, 44 caliber, 6¾ lbs., using No. 47208 cartridge	10.94
46775 Octagon Barrel, 24 inches, about 7 lbs., 38 caliber, using No. 47200 cartridge	11.86
46776 Round Barrel, 24 inches, 38 caliber, using No, 47200 cartridge	10.94
46777 Octagon Barrel, 24 inches, about 7¼ lbs., 32 caliber, using No. 47193 cartridge	11.86
46778 Round Barrel, 24 inches, about 6¾ lbs., 32 caliber, using No 47193 cartridge	10.94

Winchester Model '92 Carbine.

46778½ Carbines with 20 inch round barrels, full magazine, in 32, 38 or 44 caliber, 6¼ lbs. weight, Each $10 90

THE WINCHESTER REPEATING RIFLE. Model 1892. "Take Down."

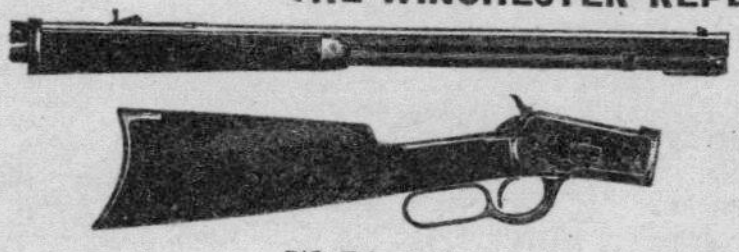

Rifle Taken Apart.

46779 Winchester Model '92—Take Down Repeating Rifle.
24-inch Octagon Barrels, made in 32 W. C. F. Caliber, 38 W. C. F. Caliber, and 44 W. C. F. Caliber. Each $15.20
Operates same as No. 46773-75-77, and takes same cartridges. No other length of barrels or style of rifle made in this Model "Take Down."

Marlin Safety Rifle. Model 1893. Side Ejector.

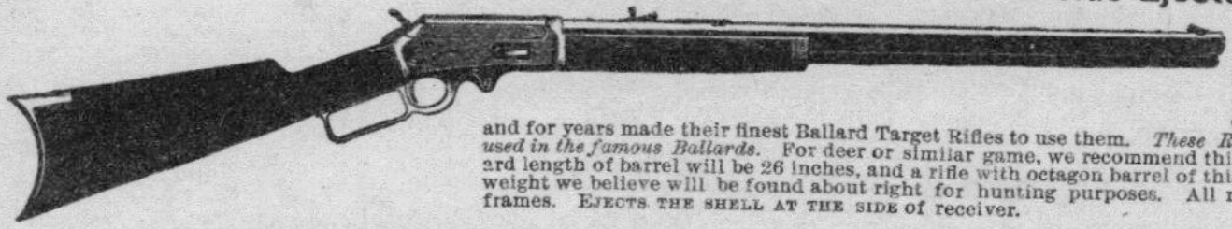

This model is similar in principle to the 1889 Model, and is made in response to the many demands for a rifle in 32-40 and 38-55 calibers. It is the only repeater on the market using these cartridges. The Marlin Fire Arm Co. were the originators of these cartridges, and for years made their finest Ballard Target Rifles to use them. *These Rifles are to have exactly the same barrels as were used in the famous Ballards.* For deer or similar game, we recommend this model above any in the market. The standard length of barrel will be 26 inches, and a rifle with octagon barrel of this length will weigh about 7¾ pounds. This weight we believe will be found about right for hunting purposes. All rifles of this model will have case hardened frames. EJECTS THE SHELL AT THE SIDE of receiver.

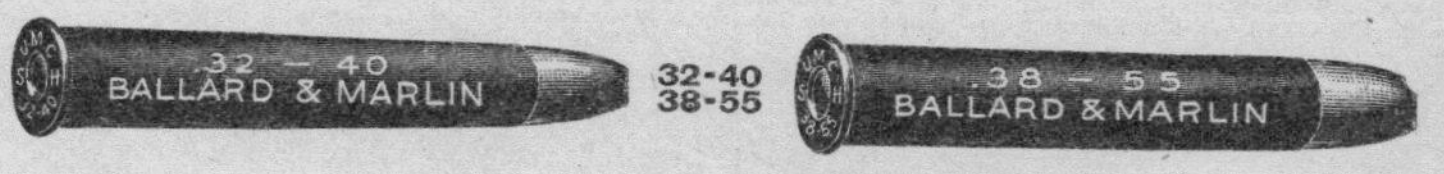

46780 Marlin Rifle, 26 inch octagon barrel, 10 shot, 32-40 caliber (using No. 47220 cartridge), 7¾ lbs. weight	$14.18
46781 Marlin Rifle, 26 inch round barrel, 10 shot, 32-40 caliber (using No. 47220 cartridge), 7½ lbs. weight	13.16
46782 Marlin Rifle, 26 inch octagon barrel, 38-55 caliber (using No. 47222 cartridge), 10 shot, about 7¾ lbs. weight	14.18
46783 Marlin Rifle, 26 inch round barrel, 38-55 caliber (using No. 47222 cartridge), 10 shot, about 7½ lbs. weight	13.16

We can furnish either the 32-40 calibre or 38-55 caliber with 28 inch octagon barrels, at $15.66 each; with 30 inch octagon barrels, $17.25. If not on hand, would take a few days to have them made.

Marlin Rifle. Model 1893. "Take Down."

46783½ Marlin Rifle, Model 1893, made to separate barrel from stock easily, 26-inch octagon, 32-40 and 38-55 calibers. Each $17.65

Marlin Rifles. Model 1889-1894. Side Ejector.

Can furnish Carbines 32, 38, or 44 caliber, 15 or 20 in. round barrels, 6 lbs.... $10.94

NEW MARLIN RIFLE.

An entirely new model. Every rifle warranted. Model 1889 and '94. The easiest working and handiest rifle in the market. Ejects the empty shell at the side instead of at the top. The newest feature in Repeaters. Simple in construction, and accurate shooters. Not liable to get out of repair. The system of rifling is the same as in the world-renowned Ballard rifles.

46784 Marlin Repeating Rifle, 15 shot, 32 WCF caliber, 24-inch octagon barrel, 6¼ lbs., using No. 47193 cartridge	$11.86
46785 Marlin Repeating Rifle, 15 shot, 38 WCF caliber, 24-inch octagon barrel, using No. 47200 cartridge, weight 6½ lbs	11.86
46786 Marlin Repeating Rifle, 15 shot, 44 WCF caliber, 24-inch octagon barrel, using No. 47208 cartridge, weight 6¼ lbs.	11.86
26-inch barrel, octagon, either caliber .... $13.50 | 28-inch barrel, octagon, either caliber	14.50

Model 1889 Rifle not made with set trigger. Extra for plain walnut, pistol grip stocks, checkered grip and fore-end $4.00 on Marlin 1889 or 1894 model.
Extra for selected walnut stock, checkered grip and fore-end, $12.00.

46787 24 in. round barrel .... $10.95 26 in. round barrels. Each 12.96

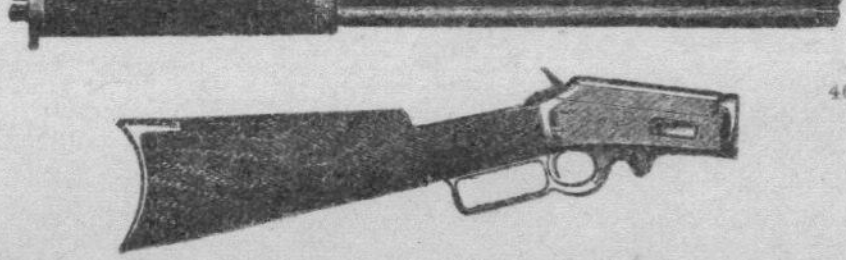

Marlin Rifles. Model 1894. "Take Down."

46787½ Marlin Rifles, Model 1894, made so that barrels can easily be separated from stock, 32, 38 and 44 calibres; oththerwise same as Nos. 46784 to 46786, with 24-inch octagon barrels. Each $15.20

MODEL OF 1891.--Marlin Repeater. Side Ejector. $11.86

Rim fire. Center fire.

The styles of cartridges for No. 46788.

Rim fire. Center fire.

46788 Marlin Repeating Rifle, Model 1891, 32 caliber, rim or center fire, 24 inch octagon barrel, weight 6½ lbs, interchanging firing pins. 24 in. $11.86; 26 in. $13.80; 28 in. $14.80.

No of shots: short cartridge 18, long 15. Using Nos. 47170, 47171, 47189 and 47190 cartridges

Rifle will be shipped with rim fire, firing pin in rifle. An extra firing pin for center fire will be sent with each gun. Rifle is loaded same as the 22 caliber, by drawing out magazine.

MARLIN MODEL 1891. 22 Caliber Repeater. $11.86.

Full length Magazine.

DISMOUNTED TO CLEAN.

SIDE EJECTOR.

46789 Marlin Repeating Rifle, model 1891, 20 to 25 shot, 22 caliber, rim fire, 24 inch octagon barrel, side ejector, magazine full length of barrel, using Nos. 47155, to 47160 cartridges; weight 6 lbs........................$11.86

Same rifle, model 1891, will use both short and long rim fire, 22 caliber cartridges without any changes. 20 long or 25 short cartridges can be put in magazine Accurate and reliable.

THE FAMOUS WINCHESTER SINGLE SHOT RIFLE. $10.13.

Illustrations of the Plain, Straight Grip Rifles, as quoted below.

The Winchester Single Shot Rifle, Breech Loaders.

Showing lever thrown down to receive cartridge.

Manufactured by the WINCHESTER REPEATING ARMS CO., New Haven, Conn.

Although this rifle is a recent production it has become almost as famous as the "Winchester Repeater," and stands in the "front rank" with the very best target rifles of this and other countries.

This gun has the old Sharp's breech block and lever, and is as safe and solid as that arm. The firing pin is automatically withdrawn at the first opening movement of the gun and held back until the gun is closed. The hammer is centrally hung, but drops down with the breech block when the gun is opened, and is cocked by the closing movement. It can also be cocked by hand. This arrangement allows the barrel to be wiped and examined from the breech. In outline everything has been done to make the gun pleasing to the eye. All of these rifles have case-hardened lock plates and dark walnut stocks. Other styles and calibers made to order.

Every rifle warranted perfect and accurate. These rifles are not made with *double trigger*. The set locks are adjusted by a little screw in rear of trigger, and can be set to pull as desired or not used at all. Pushing the trigger *forward* places it in the "hair pull" notch, same as working a double trigger. All rifles have sporting rear sights. CAN BE RETURNED AT OUR EXPENSE if not found as represented.

WINCHESTER SINGLE SHOT RIFLES.

		Each
46790	22 caliber, *rim fire*, BB caps, short or long cartridge, 24-inch octagon barrel; weight 7 lbs., plain trigger	$10.13
46791	22 caliber, *rim fire*, BB caps, short or long cartridge, 26-inch octagon barrel; 7 lbs. weight, plain trigger	11.00
46794	32 caliber, *rim fire*, extra short, short or long cartridges, 26-inch octagon barrel; 7 lbs. weight, *plain trigger*	10.13
46796	22 caliber, *center fire*, using No. 47186 cartridge, 26-inch octagon barrel; 7 lbs. weight, *plain trigger*	10.75
46797	25 caliber, *center fire*, using No. 47187 cartridge, 28-inch octagon barrel; 7 lbs. weight, *plain trigger*	10.13
46798	32 caliber, *center fire*, using No. 47193 cartridge, 28-inch octagon barrel; 8½ lbs. weight, *plain trigger*	10.40
46799	32-40 caliber, *center fire*, using No. 47220 cartridge, 30-inch octagon barrel, 9 lbs. weight, *plain trigger*	10.13
46800	32-40 caliber, *center fire*, using No. 47220 cartridge, 30-inch octagon barrel; 9 to 9½ lbs. weight, *set trigger*	12.13
46801	38 caliber, *center fire*, using No. 47200 cartridge, 28-inch octagon barrel; 8½ lbs. weight, *plain trigger*	11.00
46802	38-55 caliber, *center fire*, using No. 47222 cartridge, 30-inch octagon barrel; 9 lbs. weight, *plain trigger*	10.13
46803	38-55 caliber, *center fire*, using No. 47222 cartridge, 30-inch octagon barrel; 9½ lbs. weight, *set trigger*	12.75
46804	40-60 caliber, *center fire*, using No. 47230 cartridge, 30-inch octagon barrel; 9½ lbs. weight,	10.13
46805	40-82 caliber, *center fire*, using No. 47234 cartridge, 30-inch octagon barrel; 9½ lbs. weight, *plain trigger*, long range	10.13
46806	40-90 caliber, *center fire*, using No. 47237 cartridge, 32-inch octagon barrel; 9¼ to 11 lbs., *set trigger*	14.75
46808	45-70 caliber, *center fire*, using No. 47243 cartridge, 30-inch octagon barrel, 9½ lbs. weight, *plain trigger*, long range	11.00
46810	40-65 caliber, *center fire*, using No. 47231 cartridge, 30-inch octagon barrel, 9½ lbs., a good target rifle. Each.	11.00
46812	45-90 caliber, *center fire*, using No. 47249 cartridge, 30-inch octagon barrel; 9½ lb., long range. The "Boss" *Bear and Deer Rifle*	11.00
46813	40-70 caliber, using No. 47233 cartridge, 30-inch octagon barrel; 9½ lbs., *plain trigger*	10.13
46813¼	30, U. S. caliber, using No. 47219 cartridge, 30-inch special round barrel; 9¼ lbs., *plain trigger*	23.00

Extras on Winchester single shot rifles. Barrels can be furnished up to 36 in. Extra for longer barrels than quoted, $1.00 for every two inches. Barrels making gun weigh 1 to 1½ lbs. more, $2.00 extra. Barrels making gun weigh about 12 lbs., $8.00 extra. Set trigger, $2.00 extra.

It may take 10 to 20 days to have guns made extra lengths or otherwise different from our regular quotations. Fancy walnut pistol grip stock, checkered, extra $11.00; plain pistol grip stocks, $4.75 extra; 22 and 25 caliber not made over 28 inches.

Keep Your Rifles Bright and Clean Inside or They Will Not Shoot Well.

NEW MODEL STEVENS' RIFLE.—"Sure Shot."

46814 The "Sure Shot" is an entirely new model. The barrel swings to extract the shell instead of "tipping up" as in the old models. Barrels are rifled same as in the higher grades, and is a wonderful shooter. Frame nickel plated, walnut stock, re bounding lock, German silver front sight, finely finished throughout. Stock and barrel easily separated to clean or pack. Barrel 20 inches. entire length 34 inches, weight 3½ lbs., 22 caliber, rim fire short, long, or long rifle cartridge. Every rifle warranted as long range and as accurate as any 22 caliber rifle in the market. Each..................$6.49

J. Stevens & Co.'s Single Breech Loading Rifles.

Manufactured at Chicopee Falls, Mass. In all styles the barrel "tips up" at the breech the same as a breech loading shotgun. Stock and barrel can be easily separated and packed in a trunk or case. All have nickel-plated frame and mountings, oiled walnut stock, blue barrels and are finely finished throughout. Every rifle is rigidly tested at the factory and warranted perfectly accurate and reliable. There are no better shooting rifles in the market. There are more of these rifles in the shooting galleries than of any other make. There are no better ones.

Stevens' "Expert" Rifles No. 5, Vernier and Open Back Sight and Beach Front Sight.

Weight of Rifles boxed for shipment 15 to 25 pounds, each; 25 caliber rim or center fire same prices as the 22 calibers.

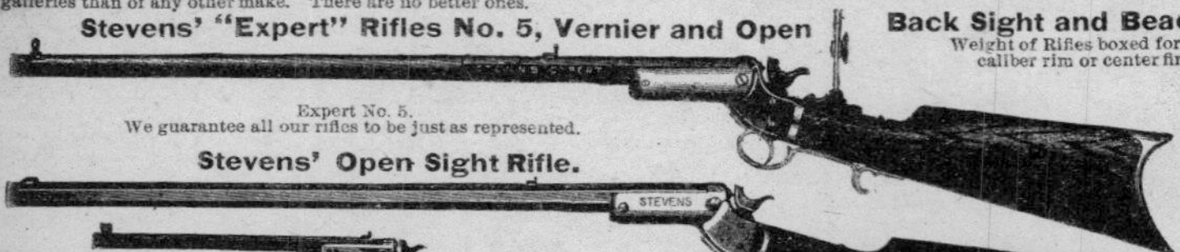

Expert No. 5.

We guarantee all our rifles to be just as represented.

46815 Stevens' Rifle No. 5, 22 caliber, rim fire, weight, 6¼ to 7¼ for 24 in.; 7 to 7¾ lbs. 28 in.

	Each.
24 in. barrel	$15.00
28 in. barrel	17.49

Stevens' Open Sight Rifle.

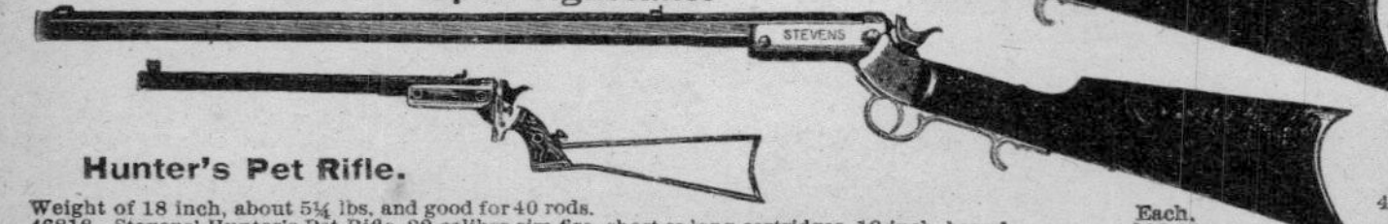

46816 Stevens' Open Sight Rifle, 22 caliber, rim fire, short or long cartridges. Weight, 6½ to 7½, 24 in. 7½ to 8 lbs. 28 in.

24 in. barrel	$12.00
28 in. barrel	14.40

46817 Stevens' Open Sight Rifle, 32 caliber, rim fire, short or long cartridges and 25-20 caliber center fire.

24 in. barrel	$12.00
28 in. barrel	13.20

Hunter's Pet Rifle.

Weight of 18 inch, about 5¼ lbs. and good for 40 rods.

		Each.
46818	Stevens' Hunter's Pet Rifle, 22 caliber rim fire, short or long cartridges, 18 inch barrel	$12.15
46819	Stevens' Hunter's Pet Rifle, 32 caliber, rim fire, 18 in. barrel	12.15
	20-inch barrel..............(22 and 32 caliber, same price)	13.00

The Stevens' New Model Pocket Rifles.

A fine target or squirrel rifle; good for 100 yards.
46820 Stevens' New Model Pocket Rifle, 22 caliber, rim fire, short or long cartridge, and BB cap cartridges, 22 caliber.

	Each.
12 inch barrel, 2¼ lb. weight	$8.95
15 inch barrel, 2½ lb. weight	10.13

Cut of sights, plain open, such as will be sent on rifle.

46821 Stevens' Diamond Model Pistol, single shot, tip-up, blued barrels, long plain grip stock, plated frame, chambered for 22 rim fire short or long rifle cartridges, plain open sights.
Weight, 10 oz. 6 inch barrel, good for 50 yards, each.........$4.75
Weight, 12 oz. 10 inch barrel, good for 20 to 100 yards...$6.75
The Stevens' pistols are all made of the very best material, and are all warranted accurate shooters.

Stevens

46822 Stevens' Single Shot Pistol, tip-up barrel, plated finish, 3½ inch barrel, 22 caliber, rim fire, a fine target pistol..........$2.15
30 caliber, rim fire, short.......... 2.10
No better material put in rifles; weight, 8 oz.
Stevens' 25 Caliber Rifles, rim or center fire, can be furnished at same prices as the 22 caliber styles. See "Cartridges" for prices on ammunition. Can furnish any style to order.

Stevens' New Model Favorite Rifle.

As well rifled as the higher cost rifle.

46823 The Favorite is an entirely new model Stevens' rifle. The barrel is held to stock by a set screw, and easily separated or put together. Rifling and quality of barrel same as the higher cost rifle, case-hardened frame, walnut stock, finely finished, warranted accurate, rim fire, 22 caliber; using long or short cartridges. Each
22 in. barrel, about 4½ lbs. weight..........$6.95
46823½ Steven's Favorite Rifle, 25 calibre, rim fire, 22 inch barrel. Weight 4½ lbs. Each..........$6.95

REMINGTON No. 3 RIFLES. The Boss Long Range Rifle.

Made by Remington Arms Company, Ilion, N. Y.
Over a Million Sold, Pretty Good Recommendation. Latest Model, and Every One Perfect and New.
No better target rifle in the market. We have full octagon only in stock. All Warranted.

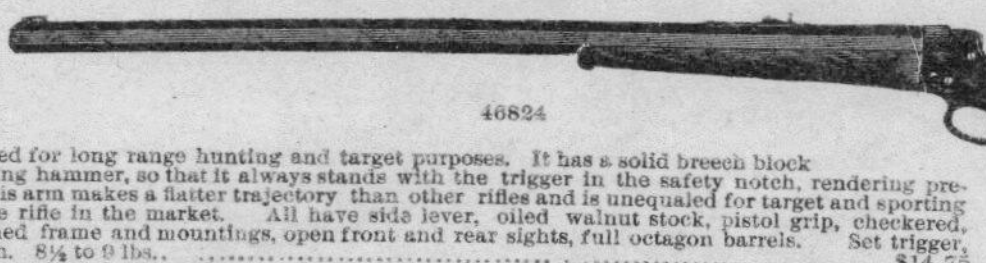

46824

This rifle is especially designed for long range hunting and target purposes. It has a solid breech block with direct rear support, rebounding hammer, so that it always stands with the trigger in the safety notch, rendering premature discharge impossible. This arm makes a flatter trajectory than other rifles and is unequaled for target and sporting use. No better or more accurate rifle in the market. All have side lever, oiled walnut stock, pistol grip, checkered, rebounding hammer, case-hardened frame and mountings, open front and rear sights, full octagon barrels. Set trigger, $2.75 (extra). 32-30 Caliber 30 in. 8¾ to 9 lbs..........$14.75

46824 32-40 caliber, 30-inch octagon barrel, 8½ to 9 lbs. weight, using No. 47220 cartridge *only*. The Boss 200 yd. off hand..........$14.75
46825 38-55 caliber, 30-inch octagon barrel, 8¾ to 9¼ lbs. weight, using No. 47222 cartridge *only*. Good for 100 to 500 yards..........14.75
46826 40-65 caliber, 30-inch octagon barrel, 8¾ to 10 lbs. weight, using No. 47268 cartridge *only*. Good for 150 to 600 yards..........14.75
46827 40-90 caliber, 32-inch octagon barrel, 10 to 11 lbs. weight, using No. 47237 cartridge. Long range..........16.75
46828 45-70 caliber, 30-inch octagon barrel, 10 lbs., using No. 47244 cartridge. Good for 200 to 1,000 yards..........14.75

Our Remington rifles are the best, and every one warranted. Can be returned at our expense if not found as represented.
Remington Match and Fancy Target Rifles made to order. The Remington Rifle is used by many of the best shots in the world. The system of rifling is the best and material finest.

REMINGTON SINGLE SHOT RIFLES.—Elegant Shooters.

Fine Target Rifles.

46828¼ Rim Fire, 22 caliber, using BB cap, or 22 long or short cartridges.
24-inch octagon barrel, 5¼ 6 lbs.......... $8.72
46829 Rim fire, 32 caliber, using long or short rim fire cartridges.
28-inch octagon barrel, 5¾ to 6 lbs.......... 8.75

Remington Rifles No. 4, oiled walnut stocks, case-hardened frames and mountings, open front and rear sights. As finely rifled as any rifle in the market, and made of the very best rifle material, perfectly accurate, and every one warranted. No better or longer range rifles made of these calibers. Warranted as represented.

46830 Remington No. 4 Rifle, 22 caliber, rim fire, 22¼-inch octagon barrel, 4½ lbs. weight, rifle butt, a fine little rifle and an accurate shooter, each..........$5.00
46830½ Remington No. 4, 32 caliber, rim fire, 24-inch barrel.......... 5.00

MERWIN HULBERT & CO.'S RIFLE.

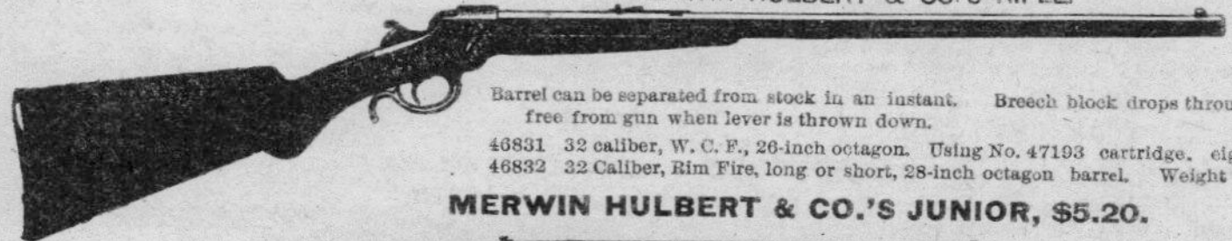

FINE TARGET RIFLES.

Barrel can be separated from stock in an instant. Breech block drops through frame to load, and ejects the shell free from gun when lever is thrown down.

46831 32 caliber, W. C. F., 26-inch octagon. Using No. 47193 cartridge. eight, about 7 lbs..........$8.75
46832 32 Caliber, Rim Fire, long or short, 28-inch octagon barrel. Weight 7 lbs.......... 8.90

MERWIN HULBERT & CO.'S JUNIOR, $5.20.

The 22 calibers are good for 100 yards on rabbits, squirrels and small game. Elegant shooters.

Showing operation of lever.

46833 M. H. & Co.'s Junior Target Rifle, single shot, barrel easily removed from stock for packing or cleaning, blued barrels; case-hardened lock plates, 22-inch ROUND BARRELS, about 4¼ pounds' weight, perfectly reliable and accurate, barrel as well rifled as the best rifles; 22 caliber, RIM FIRE, using BB caps and 22 long and short cartridges. Ejects the empty shell free from gun, when lever is *thrown down*. Each..........$5.20

46833½ 32 caliber, 26-inch round barrel, Rim fire, long and short cartridge, Ivory bead and Sporting rear sights.......... $6.75

NO. 3 REMINGTON MATCH RIFLE.

THE LONG RANGE TARGET RIFLE.

46833¾ A quality ½ octagon barrel, rebounding hammer, oiled walnut stock, pistol grip, checkered, nickel plated Swiss butt plate, case-hardened frame, Beach combination front and tang graduated rear sights, 32-40 caliber, using No. 47220 cartridge, 28-inch barrel; weight 8½ to 9 lbs..........$18.75
38-55 caliber, using No. 47222 cartridge, 30-inch barrel, weight 9 to 10 lbs..........$19.50

There are no better Target Rifles.

FLOBERT—Remington Action. $2.35.

A cleaning rod is sent with each rifle quoted in this catalogue.
Short cartridges are better than long for any 22 caliber rifle, and Flobert's are not made for 22 long cartridges.

Don't expect a Stevens or Winchester in a Flobert rifle.

46835 Flobert Gallery Rifle, Remington action, 22 caliber, BB caps, round and conical, and 22 short *rim fire cartridge*, 24 inch octagon barrel; weight, 6 to 6¼ lbs.; is a good short range target or squirrel rifle, oiled walnut stock, shell extractor, rifled barrels, PISTOL GRIP $2.90

We do not guarantee any Flobert rifle in the market with a long cartridge. They shoot the short cartridge the best.

46834 Flobert Gallery Rifle, Remington action; shoots 22 caliber cap cartridge or 22 short *rim fire cartridge*; oiled walnut stock, pistol grip, octagon barrel, well rifled and a good shooter. Shell extractor. Weight, 4½ lbs.; length of barrel, about 22 inches. Price $2.35

RIFLES, $3.25.

New Model Solid Breech.
The Best Model.
46836-38

46838 Flobert Rifle, new model; Warrant action, oiled walnut stock, checkered pistol grip, 24-inch octagon barrel, 6 lbs. weight, shell extractor, 22 caliber, RIM FIRE, short or long cartridge, rifled barrels........................$3.40
N. B.—In ordering any 22 caliber rifle we advise only using the short cartridge for accurate work.

46836 Flobert Rifle. Warrant action, new model, oiled walnut stock, checkered pistol grip, 24 inch barrel, 22 caliber, SHORT rim fire, shell extractor. A good, strong shooting rifle, heavy octagon barrel, 6½ lbs., rifled barrel $3.25
Prices subject to market changes on Flobert Rifles.

STEVENS' NEW IDEAL RIFLE—1894 Model.

46838½ Ideal Rifle, No. 109 Half octagon barrel, wind gauge front and mid-range Vernier back sight, no rear barrel sight, fore-end and stock varnished. Frame case hardened and Swiss butt plate, nickel plated. Stock easily separated from barrel when desired.
28-inch, 7 lbs., 25-20 caliber, using No. 47187 cartridge.........................$21.90
30-inch, 8¼ lbs., 32-40 caliber, using No. 47220 cartridge....................$22.60
Other lengths and weights can be furnished if desired. Prices quoted on application.

FLOBERT RIFLES. $2.55.

46839 Warnant Action Flobert Rifle, oiled walnut pistol grip stock, checkered, octagon barrels, blued finish and rifled, safe and reliable, good shooter, 22 caliber, rim fire, shoots BB caps, or 22 short or long cartridges, 22 inch barrels, 4 to 4½ lbs., weight. Each $2.55

H. M. Quackenbush's Safety Cartridge Rifle—A Fine Target Gun, $4.75.

Something entirely new. The best accurate rifle yet offered for the money.
Globe and peep sights, per set $1.50

46840 It has a rifle steel barrel, automatic cartridge extractor, and adjustable rear sight; stock is of black walnut handsomely finished, and so fastened to the barrel that the two may be easily and quickly separated, making the arm handy to carry in a trunk, valise or package. The barrel and parts are well and durably nickeled, except the breech block, which is case hardened in colors. Whole length, 33 inches; 18 inch barrel; weight, about 4½ pounds; 22 caliber for regular *rim fire* "BB" or long and short cartridges. Plain open sights, as shown in cut. Price, 18-inch barrel.....................$4.75
22-inch barrel 5.00

THE CHICAGO AIR RIFLE. "OLD RELIABLE." $0.89.

It is not a Spring Gun. The ball is thrown by compressed air.

46841 The Chicago Air Rifle shoots common BB shot and darts; will kill small game at 50 feet, with the BBs, costs 1 cent to shoot 100 times; the stock and frame are maple, nicely varnished and stained, representing rosewood. The air chamber and inserted barrel are made of drawn brass, accurately bored and polished. The ball is held tight in place in barrel. Plunger and piston made of best steel. Made to stand hard usage. Not liable to get out of order. No smoke, no noise, no caps, death to sparrows and rats, etc. Entire length, 33 inches. Each.....................$0.89
Postage, extra, 25c. BB Shot, 5 pounds for 40c. Darts, per dozen, 35c. Mainsprings, each, 10c.

SOMETHING NEW, BOYS.

A Repeating Air Rifle That Shoots 65 Times Without Reloading. $1.75.

46842 Hart's Repeating Air Rifle. Don't expect these guns to shoot like a first-class rifle. Blue finish metal barrel, black walnut stock, adjustable sights. Just the thing for old or young for amusement and practice. No smoke, no noise, no smell; easy to handle, effective at short range on sparrows, rats and other small game. Shoots "BB" shot, and 65 shot can be placed in the magazine at one time. Only one shot can be discharged at one time. Entire length, 35½ inches, weight, 2¼ pounds. Price, $1.75.
Full directions for loading and handling, with 65 shot and 10 paper targets, accompanies rifle.
BB shot per bag of 5 pounds, 40 cents. Mainsprings, 25 cents. Do not snap these guns unless you have shot in the barrel.

THE DAISY AIR RIFLE, IMPROVED. $1.00.

46845 The Daisy Air Rifle has been improved in many parts and is now one of the best of all metal air rifles in the market. It shoots BB shot, one at a time. All of the parts are made of good strong metal and are not liable to get out of order.
Each $1.00
BB Shot per sack of 5 lbs., 40 cents.

THE KING AIR RIFLE, $0.90 EACH.

46846 The King Air Rifle. The barrel is made of one continuous piece of Brass, with no soldered joints or levers to break. Neatly nickel plated. Working parts can easily be removed when desired to clean or repair. The latest thing in air guns. Shoots BB shot. One of the strongest and most durable on the market.
Each $0.90
BB shot per sack of 5 lbs. ....

THE QUACKENBUSH JUNIOR SAFETY RIFLE—Finely Rifled—$4.00.

A perfect shooting, all steel Rifle for little money.

46849 The Quackenbush Junior Rifle, steel nickel plated skeleton stock which can easily be detached for carrying in small space. Nickel plated barrels. Whole length 33 inches. Weight about 4 lbs. 22 caliber rim fire only. Using No. 17163 to 17169 cartridges. Safe, accurate and reliable.
Each $4.00

Junior Quackenbush.
Stock can be separated from barrel to pack in trunk or valise. A handy little rifle.

M. H. & CO.'s FANCY JUNIOR RIFLE—Highest Grade Rifling. Accurate.

46851 Marwin, Hubbert & Co., Octagon Barrel, Fancy Junior Rifle, rebounding locks, case hardened frame, solid breech-block, polished and checkered walnut stock and fore-end, sporting rear sight. Lyman ivory

bead front sight, nickel plated butt plate, 22 caliber, rim fire, short or long cartridge. 22 inch octagon barrel. 4½ lbs. weight. Safe, accurate and reliable. Barrels easily separated from stock in a moment. Each $6.60

THE NEW YORK CLUB RIFLE.

46853 The New York Club Rifle. Automatic extractor, case hardened frame, walnut stock, barrel separates from stock by a set screw on the side of frame, finely finished, accurate and strong; 24 inch, Octagon barrels, about 4½ lbs. A big seller, and a good one. 22 caliber, rim fire. Long or short cartridge $5.00

46854 New York Club Rifle. Same as No. 46853. 32 caliber short or long rim fire, 24 inch Octagon barrels. A fine shooter, accurate and reliable. Each $5.00

The Boys' Delight Snip Snap.

46855 The most accurate and durable Snip Snap ever manufactured.
Each complete, 5 in. handle $0.09
Per dozen, complete 98
46856 Extra Rubbers, each, 6c; per doz. 65
Postage on Snip Snap 5 cents each.
46857 Snip Snap, 2½-inch iron handle and rubber. Each $0.05
Per dozen 40
Extra rubber, each 04
Per dozen 36

Rifle Sights.

When ordering sights for Winchester or other Rifles, mention caliber and model, as the same sights will not fit all calibers. Sights by mail 1 to 4 cents extra.

Lyman's Patent Rifle Sights.

The optical principle involved in these sights is entirely new in its application. When aiming, this sight has the appearance of a ring or hoop, which shows the front sight and the object aimed at, without intersecting any part of the view.

The cut gives an approximate idea of how the sight appears when aiming it will be noticed that the top of rifle barrel and front sights are seen as distinctly as if no rear sight was used.

46857½ Lyman's New Front Target Sight, with globe or aperture combination. See No. 46866 for "globe" illustration. Each $1.15

It Would be Poor Policy

To misrepresent our goods knowingly, therefore do not hesitate to place confidence in our Buyers' Guide. If goods are not as represented we will cheerfully refund purchase price and pay all transportation charges.

29—6th

Lyman's Patent Combination Rear Sight on Rifle.

46858

Anyone can attach these sights to a rifle in a few minutes. Lyman sights of all kinds can be furnished for almost every kind of rifle on the market.

Lyman's Patent Combination Sight.

46858 Showing "point blank" stop pin in the right stem. Price of this sight $2.45
These sights more than double the value of a rifle, either for hunting or target shooting, for instantaneous aim can be taken with great accuracy. The sights are made in all sizes. When ordering, give the make and gauge of rifle.

46858

Lyman's Patent Wind Gauge Sight

46859 Used without the large disk, the principle of this sight is the same as the Combination Sight. For target shooting it is unequaled, and it is an improvement on the Combination Sight for hunting. Price $4.00

Lyman's Patent Ivory Bead Front Sight.

46861 This Sight gives the sportsman a clear, white bead, which can be seen distinctly against any object in the woods, or in bright sunlight.
Price $0.80

Lyman's Patent Improved Ivory Front Sight.

46862 This Sight is better than the Bead Sight for a hunting rifle. The ivory is so well protected by the surrounding metal that there is no danger of its being injured. Price $0.42

46863 Blank Piece to replace the rear Crotch Sight, which is usually on the barrel when the rifle is purchased. This Sight should always be removed when Peep Sights are used.
Price $0.25

46864 An excellent Spirit Level, which can be used in place of blank piece. Price $0.85

. Freight Rates from Chicago to nearly any railroad point in America will be quoted upon application. If you have any particular class of goods in view mention same when writing. We want you to know what your goods will cost you delivered at your station, as near as possible.

Lyman's Leaf Sight (Rear).

Both leaves folded down.   Using the - straight bar.   Using the crotch.

46853   Each $0.75

One leaf is a bar with a triangular ivory center, the other is a wide open V crotch.

Many sportsmen who use the Lyman rear sights do so with the ordinary crotch sight on the barrel. This is much in the way and the shooting is done at a great disadvantage. Lyman's leaf sight can be put in place of it. It folds down close to the barrel, allowing the shooter to use the combination sight in an unobstructed manner, and the result is that the shooting is twice as good as when the ordinary crotch sight is on the barrel. Although the shooter should in any case use the Lyman tang sights for nearly all shooting, he has the satisfaction of knowing that if he wishes to use this leaf sight that it is the best form of crotch and bar sight in use. The bar leaf is excellent as a twilight sight or when used at night with a back.

The right-hand screw, as indicated by arrow, adjusts the leaves to fold as tightly as desired.

(Front) Wind-Gauge Target Sight.

Showing Aperture.   Showing Globe.

46866   Each $2.40

This is the best wind-gauge ever made for a match rifle. It has a reversible globe and aperture which can be changed quickly. It is compact in form, being close to the barrel. When set for a given point of wind it is locked by a spring clamp firmly in position.

Notice.

The front sight, blank, spirit level and leaf sight should be driven into the barrel slot from the right-hand side.

Combination Rear Tang Sight, With Cup Disk.

46867 ....$2.65

This sight has a large detachable disk and is intended for match rifles and gallery rifles. It is not as good for "all round" shooting as the 46858 combination sight. Many target shooters like it, as it is much better than the Vernier peep sight.

The disk is easily removed, and for most work is not needed.

For gallery practice the aperture in the disk can be enlarged to advantage.

When ordering give the make and size of rifle.

Sporting Wind-Gauge Sight.

46868 ....$2.27

A good sight for general shooting. It is the combination front sight on the wind-gauge base. Price..................................$2.27

Lyman's Patent Combination Ivory Front Sight.

46870   One cut shows the Sight with the ivory open part in use, and the other with the globe turned up Each $0.80

46877   Knife Blade Front Sight, German Silver, Price..................................$0.48

46877   46879
46878   Knife Blade, Front Sight, Ivory. Price...$0.45
46879   Sporting Front Sight. Price.............. .30

Sights—Continued.

46880   Sporting Leaf Rear Sight. Price..................................$1.30

46885   Sporting Rear Sight Price..................................$0.78

46886   Wind Gauge Sight, with spirit level and 3 discs.

46887   Without spirit level. $2.95

ALWAYS MENTION NAME AND CALIBER OF RIFLE WHEN ORDERING SIGHT.

46890   Beach Combination sight. Price..................................$0.75

As Open.   As Globe.
46890   46890

46891
46891   Globe Sight with interchangeable disk. Price..............$1.20
46892   Graduated Peep Sight, complete, with screws to fasten to stock of rifle. Each.........$2.25
46893   Mid Range Vernier Peep Sight, complete with screws to fasten to stock of rifle.
Each..................................$3.90

The Lyman, Vernier and Graduated Peep Sights can be put on rifle in five minutes by any person with screw driver.

In ordering sights state caliber and maker's name of rifle, as the sights are made to fit only one special rifle and the same base will not fit all rifles.

46896   Winchester express front sight. Each..................................$0.45

46897   Winchester Express Rear Sight. Each..................................$1.48

Ballard and Marlin Sights.

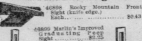

46898   Rocky Mountain Front Sight (knife edge). Each..................................$0.43

46899   Marlin's Improved Graduating Peep Sight $2.25
46900   Rocky Mountain Rear Sight, similar to No. 46898 ....$0.75
46901   Gallery Peep Sight $2.00
46902   Globe Front Sight similar to 46891. No extra disks. Each..................................$0.95

Always give name and caliber of rifle when ordering parts.

46901   46899

Lyman's Patent Ivory Shot Gun Sights.

A New System of Sighting Shot-Guns.

Postage extra 11 cent.

46904   The left hand cut shows the large muzzle or front sight. The right hand cut, the small rear sight. This sight is placed 18 inches from the muzzle sight.

The first engraving gives the appearance of the sights when aiming at a straight-a-way bird. The elevation of the gun is right, but the rear sight shows that the gun is out of line, which would not be discovered if these sights were not used. This system is a great help both in the field and at the trap. Price, per set $0.85

Gun Repairing Department.

We have the largest jobbing gun repair shop in the country. None but experienced workmen employed, and each one an expert in his line. We have one of the best stockers and one of the best barrel borers in the world, and can guarantee the highest grade work in every particular on the finest guns. Give us a trial. We guarantee satisfaction. All kinds of repairing done; fine work a specialty. Price as low as first-class work can be done.

We do not change muzzle loaders to breech loaders, for it costs more to do it than you would have to pay for a first-class breech loader ready-made.

Stocks bent, stocks straightened; new stock made same drop as old one, or changed any way you may desire.

When you send us a gun, rifle or parts, send us a letter at the same time, giving full description of the article, name of the gun, style, etc., and also state plainly what you want done.

Gun Material and Gun Repairing.

N. B.—These parts are not fitted or case hardened and are for band-made guns only and require fitting. We cannot fit them unless we have the gun here, and then we would have to make an extra charge for the labor. Always send the old part you wish duplicate for, if possible, as no two guns have parts just alike, and a part that would fit one gun would not fit another of the same make and cost. Hammers, etc., for American machine made guns cost much more than those quoted here. Parts for all American made shot guns and rifles, in stock, are furnished on short notice.

Flobert Rifle Parts.

By mail, 2 to 4 cents extra.

These parts are soft iron in the rough, and not fitted, but plain as shown in cuts. They are blocked out large, and require a great deal of filing to fit them to the rifle. We cannot fit them unless we have the rifle here, and then we would have to make an extra charge for the labor.

No two rifles are just alike, and all Flobert rifles are hand made, and all are imported from Europe.

46905   Flobert Hammers, Remington action, cut nose, not fitted. Each $0.50

46905½
46905½   Flobert Breech Block for new model Warrant rifles, filed, just blocked out. Each $0.80
46905¾   Flobert Hammer for new model Warrant, not fitted. Each $0.50

46906½
We can often repair hammers where the nose or top breaks off, and make stronger than new for 75 cents

46907   Flobert Breech Block for Remington Action, not fitted. Each $0.40
46908   Flobert Breech Block for old model Warrant action, not fitted. Each $0.60
46908   46907
46908¾   Hammers for Warrant Action Rifles, not fitted. Each $0.45
46909   Hammers for Warrant 6 lb. Rifles. $0.70

46908½   46909½
46909½   Flobert Trigger, not fitted. Each $0.15
46910   Flobert Extractor for Remington Action, not fitted. Each $0.20
46911   Flobert Thumb Extractor, not fitted. Each $0.26

46912—Flobert Mainspring, not fitted. Each ..$0.25

46912   46911

Rifle Parts—Continued.

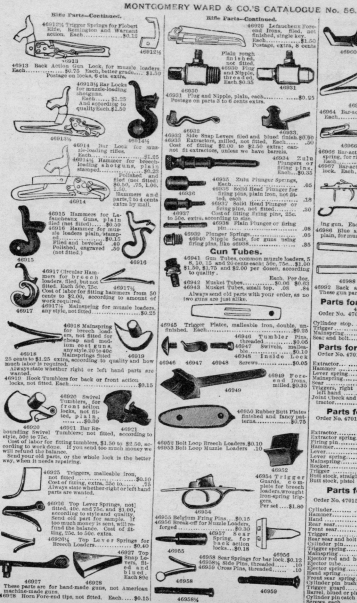

46912½ Trigger Springs for Flobert Rifle, Remington and Warnant Rifles. Each..........$0.12

46913 Back Action Gun Lock, for muzzle loaders. Each..........$0.75, better grade.. $1.50
Postage on locks, 6 cts. extra.

46913½ Bar Locks for muzzle-loading shotguns. Each..........$1.25 And according to quality Each.$1.50

46914 Bar Lock for muzzle-loading rifles. Each..........$1.25
46914½ Hammer for breech-loading shotguns, plain stamped..........$0.23
Polished and filed (not fitted) $0.50, .75, 1.00, 1.50.
Hammers and parts, 2 to 4 cents extra by mail.

46915 Hammers for Lefaucheux Guns, plain filed (not fitted)..........$0.50
46916 Hammer for muzzle loaders plain, stamped..........$0.15
Filed and beveled.. .40
Polished, engraved.. .50
(not fitted.)

46917 Circular Hammers for breech loaders, filed, but not fitted. Each 50c, 75c.
Cost of labor for fitting hammers from 50 cents to $2.00, according to amount of work required.
46917½ Mainspring for muzzle loaders, any style, not fitted..........$0.25

46918 Mainspring for breech loaders, not fitted for cheap and medium cost guns, any style, 20 to 40c
Mainsprings fitted 25 cents to $1.25 extra, according to quality and how much labor is required. Always state whether right or left hand parts are wanted.
46919 Hook Tumblers for back or front action locks, not fitted. Each..........$0.15

46920 Swivel Tumblers, for front action locks, not fitted, any style. Each..........$0.15
46921 Bar Rebounding Swivel Tumblers; not fitted, according to style, 50c to 75c.
Cost of labor for fitting tumblers, $1.50 to $2.50, according to work done. If you send too much money we will refund the balance.
Send your old parts, or the whole lock is the better way, when it needs repairing.

46925 Triggers, malleable iron, not fitted..........$0.10
Cost of fitting, extra, 35c to.....75
Always state whether right or left hand parts are wanted.

46926 Top Lever Springs, not fitted, 40c. and 75c. and $1.00, according to style and quality. Send old part for sample. If too much money is sent, will refund the balance. Cost of fitting, 50c to 50c. extra.
46926½ Top Lever Springs for Breech Loaders..........$0.40

46927 Top Snap Levers, filed and blued. Each 89c
46928 Horn Fore-end tips, not fitted. Each..........$0.15
These parts are for hand-made guns, not American machine-made guns.

Rifle Parts—Continued.

46929 Lefaucheux Fore-end Irons, filed, not finished, single key. Each..........$1.50
Postage, extra, 8 cents

Plain rough finished, not fitted.
46930 Plug and Nipple, threaded. Each..........$0.35

46931 Plug and Nipple, each..........$0.25
Postage on parts 3 to 6 cents extra.

46932 Side Snap Levers filed and blued. Each..........$0.90
46933 Extractors, milled, not fitted. Each......50
Cost of fitting $2.00 to $2.50 extra; cannot fit extractors, unless we have barrels.

46934 Zulu Plungers or firing pins. Each..........$0.35
46935 Zulu Plunger for firing pins, each..........05
46936 Solid Head Plunger for firing pins, not fitted, each..........18
46937 Solid Head Plunger or firing pins, not fitted, each..........30
Cost of fitting firing pins, 25c. to 50c. extra, according to size.
46938 Plain Plunger or firing pin..........08
46939 Plunger Springs..........05
46940 Nipple Seats, for guns using firing pins, like 46938..........85

Gun Tubes.

46941 Gun Tubes, common muzzle loaders, 5, 8, 10, 15 and 20 cents each; 50c, 75c...$1.00, $1.50, $1.75 and $2.00 per dozen, according to quality.

	Each. Per doz.
46942 Musket Tubes	$0.06 $0.63
46943 Musket Tubes, small top	.05 .84

Always send old parts with your order, as no two guns are just alike.

46945 Trigger Plates, malleable iron, unfinished. Each..........$0.25
46946 Tumbler Pins, threaded..........$0.05
46947 Swivels, malleable..........05
46948 Inside Lock Screws..........05
46949 Fore-end Irons, milled. $0.35

46950 Rubber Butt Plates finished and fancy patterns..........$0.75

46952 Bolt Loop Breech Loaders .$0.10
46953 Bolt Loop Muzzle Loaders .10

46954 Trigger Guards, complete for breech loaders, wrought iron-spring triggers. Per set..........$1.80

46955 Belgium Firing Pins..........$0.15
46956 Break-off for Muzzle Loaders, forged..........$0.30

46957 Sear Spring for back action locks..........$0.18

46958 Sear Springs for bar lock $0.12
46958½ Side Pins, threaded..........10
46959 Cross Pins, threaded..........10
46956 Bar lock..........

Rifle Parts—Continued.

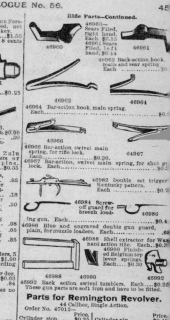

46960 Sears Filed, right hand. Each.....$0.75
46961 Sears Filed, left hand, 75c
46962 Back-action hook, main and sear spring. Each..........$0.

46964 Bar-action hook, main spring. Each..........$0.

46966 Bar-action swivel main spring, for rifle lock. Each..........$0.30
64967 Bar-action swivel main spring, for shot gun lock. Each..........$0.

46982 Double set trigger, Kentucky pattern. Each..........$0.7

46984 Screw-off guard for breech loading gun. Each..........$0.4

46986 Blue and engraved double gun guard, plain, for muzzle loaders. Each..........$0.

46988 Shell extractor for Warnant action rifle. Each..........$0.3
46990 Finish-ed Belgium top lever springs. Each..........$0.30

46992 Back action swivel tumblers. Each..........$0.25
These gun parts are soft iron and have to be fitted.

Parts for Remington Revolver.

44 Caliber, Single Action.
Order No. 47012—

	Price.		Price.
Cylinder stop	$0.35	Cylinder pin	$0.45
Trigger	.20	Hammer	1.90
Mainspring	.30	Hand and spring	.20
Sear and bolt	.20		

Parts for Remington Shot Gun.

Order No. 47013—

	Price.		Price.
Extractor	$0.85	Sear and spring	$0.30
Hammer	1.60	Solid head plungers	.20
Lever spring	.30	Tumblers	.60
Mainspring	.30	Tumbler pins	.15
Sear	.35	Tumbler stirrup	.15
Triggers, right and left hand	.25	Trigger plates	1.00
Joint Check and Extractor	.25	Guard bow	1.00

Parts for Remington Rifle.

Order No. 47014—

	Each. Nos. 1, 1½, 2 Rifles.	Each. No. 3 Rifles.
Extractor	$0.35	$0.45
Extractor spring	.25	.25
Firing pin	.25	.27
Hammer	1.15	1.20
Lever	.35	1.69
Lever spring	.20	.45
Mainspring	.45	.45
Rocker		.15
Trigger	.49	.75
Butt stock, straight grip	2.00	.50
Butt stock, pistol grip		4.00

Parts for Colt's Revolver.

Order No. 47015—

	Army double.	38 and 41 single action.	Army single.
Cylinder	$3.00	$2.25	$3.00
Hammer	1.50	1.10	.97
Hand		.25	.25
Rear sear	.60	.30	
Front sear	.30	.25	
Trigger	.55	.56	.35
Rear sear and bolt spring		.30	
Cylinder pin		.49	.49
Trigger spring	.49	.25	
Mainspring	.60	.40	.49
Ejector rod and head	.70	.50	.70
Ejector tube	1.65	1.25	1.69
Ejector spring	.15	.10	.15
Hand spring		.10	
Front sear spring		.10	
Cylinder pin bushing	.45		.45
Trigger guard	1.75	1.50	1.75
Barrel, blued or plated	3.75	3.15	3.75
Cylinder pin catch complete	.30	.25	
Screws, each	.10	.10	

Parts for Remington No. 4 Rifle.
.22 and 32 caliber.
Order No. 47016.

	Each.		Each.
Extractor	$0.50	Firing pin	$0.30
Trigger block and extractor pin	.25	Main spring	.40
		Trigger	.50
Hammer	.50	Butt stock	1.25

Parts for Smith & Wesson Revolvers.
Postage 2 to 3 cents extra.

Order No. 47017.	32 Single Action.	32 Double Action.	38 Single Action.	38 Double Action.	Hammer.	44 Single Action.	44 Double Action.	38 and 44 Target.
Barrel catch	$0 40	40	40	40	40	15	15	1.10
Cylinder stop	30	30	45	35	45	35	1.35	29
Extractor	87	85	85	85	85	1.10	1.10	1.00
Extractor spring	10	10	10	10	15	15	15	15
Front sear	...	40	...	35	45	...	45	...
Guard	...	60	60	60	55	55	55	55
Hammer	50	85	50	85	85	85	85	85
Hand	30	30	30	35	35	40	40	40
Hand spring	12	12	12	15	15	15	15	15
Main spring	30	30	30	35	35	35	35	35
Rear sear	...	40	...	...	30	...	30	...
Rear sear spring	...	45	...	25	...	25	...	...
Side plate	30	35	30	45	35	40	40	35
Triggers	30	30	30	40	30	40	30	30
Trigger spring	12	12	12	12	12	30	30	30

Parts for Ballard.
State caliber and our catalogue number on rifle when ordering parts.
Order No. 47018.

	Each.		Each.
Trigger, plain	$0.50	Front set trigger spring, No. 5 rifle	$0.25
Front set trigger, No. 5 rifle	.65	Rear set trigger spring, No. 5 rifle	.25
Rear set trigger, No. 5 rifle	.65	Mainsprings	.40
		Extractors	.40

State caliber and number of rifle in ordering parts.

Marlin Rifle Parts.
Order No. 47019. Model 1881.

No.		Price.	No.		Price.
4	Carrier block	$1.40	26	Side cover spring	$0.07
5	Carrier block spring	.05	28	Trigger spring	.05
7	Bolt	2.20	29	Trigger spring screw	
8	Firing pin	.75			.07
10	Extractor	.04	31	Mainspring	.45
11	Extractor screw	.06	33	Magazine tube stud	.10
12	Ejector	.04	34	Magazine tube stud screw	.06
15	Hammer bushing	.12	38	Magazine foil'w'r	.10
16	Hammer screw	.10	42	Tang screw	.12
18	Lever screw	.15	45	Forearm tip screw	.05
19	Lever pin screw	.06	46	Hammer fly	.22
20	Lever spring	.25	48	Mainspring screw	.05
22	Mortise cover	.40	49	Sear spring	.24
24	Side cover	.45	50	Front set trigger	.70
25	Side cover stud	.20			

Marlin Repeating Rifle, Model 1893.
Order No. 47019½.

		Price.			Price.
1	Barrel, Carbine, 20-inch	$4.15	17	Firing Pin (2 pcs)	$0.90
1	Barrel Round Rifle 24-inch	4.68	18	Firing Pin Spring	.05
			19	Firing Pin	.04
3	Barrel Octagon or ½ Oct. Rifle, 24 inch	6.00	20	Finger Lever(with ejection plunger	2.00
			26	Hammer	2.00
4	Breech Bolt	2.50	28	Locking bolt	.75
5	Bolt	1.50	37	Receiver	8.00
8	Carrier	1.90	38	Loading Spring	
11	Carrier Rocker	.35			.10
			40	Trigger	.45
11	Carrier Rocker Spring	.05	42	Trigger Spring	.15
12	Carrier Rocker Pin	.04	44	Trigger Plate	2.00

Parts for Stevens' Rifles.
32 and 22 Caliber.
Order No. 47020.

	Price.		Price.
Hammer	$0.70	Mainspring	$0.19
Trigger	.45	Sear spring	.19
Barrel catch and spring	.36	Barrel Screw	.13
Barrel Catch nut	.15	Firing Pin	.22
Extractor	.39	Firing pin screw	.38
Extractor bar	.40	Extractor spring	.39

Parts for Stevens' Tip-up Pistol.
Order No. 47021.

	Price.		Price.
Hammer	$0.39	Barrel catch nut	$0.15
Mainspring	.17	Extractor	.30
Trigger and spring	.34	Extractor spring	.30
Barrel catch and spring	.27		

Parts for Winchester Shot Gun.
Lever Action.
Order No. 47022.—Price.

	Price.		Price.
Mainspring	$0 50	Cartridge lifter	$0.25
Firing pin	.25	Mainspring screw	.05
Firing pin spring	.10	Trigger	.45
Extractor, single	.30	Carrier screws	.05
Extractor pin and spring	.15	Breech block stud	.30
Hammer	.75	Butt stock	2.50
Extractor, left hand	.30	Carrier, right	.60
Extractor, right hand	.30	Carrier, left	.60

Component Parts of the Winchester Repeating Rifle, Model 1892.
Order No. 47022⅔.

	Price.		Price.
Barrel, Round	$4.30	Firing Pin Stop Pin	$0.05
Barrel, Octagon	5.40	Fore-arm	.60
Barrel, Carbine	4.20	Fore-arm Tip Pin	.05
Breech Bolt	2.75	Fore-arm Tip Screws (2), each	.03
Butt Stock	1.45	Fore-arm Tip Tenon	.40
Butt Plate	.60	Hammer	.50
Butt Plate Screws(2), each	.05	Hammer Stirrup	.15
Carrier	.90	Hammer Stirrup Pin	.05
Carrier Stop	.10	Hammer Screw	.05
Carrier Stop Pin	.05	Locking Bolt, right hand	.60
Carrier Stop Spring	.05	Locking Bolt, left hand	.60
Carrier Screws (2), each	.05	Locking Bolt Pin	.05
Cartridge Guide, right hand	.30	Locking Bolt Screw	.05
Cartridge Guide, left hand, 32 caliber	.30	Mainspring	.20
		Mainspring Screw	.05
Cartridge Guide Screws (2), each	.05	Mainspring Strain Screw	.05
Cartridge Stop	.30	Magazine	.90
Cartridge Stop Pin	.05	Magazine Follower	.20
Cartridge Stop Spring	.15	Magazine Spring	.20
Ejector, with Collar and Spring	.45	Magazine Plug	.10
		Magazine Plug Screw	.05
Extractor	.62	Magazine Ring	.40
Finger Lever	1.40	Magazine Ring Pin	.02
Finger Lever Pin	.20	Receiver, complete with Tang	5.40
Finger Lever Pin Stop Screw	.05	Receiver Tang	1.10
Friction Stud	.15	Spring Cover	.30
Friction Stud Spring	.07	Spring Cover Screw	.04
Friction Stud Pin	.02	Trigger	.45
Firing Pin	.50	Trigger Pin	.05
		Trigger Spring	.10
		Trigger Spring Screw	.05
		Tang Screw	.10

Parts for Winchester Single Shot Rifles.
Order No. 47023.

	Price.		Price.
Mainspring	$0.40	Butt stock	$1.40
Extractor	.40	Finger lever	1.50
Sear spring	.30	Trigger	.50
Hammer, plain lock	.90	Receiver tang, separate from receiver	1.20
Firing pin	.30	Sears	.30
Ejector spring (22 cal. only)	.30	Knock-off spring for set lock	.30
Hammer set lock	1.00		

Parts for Winchester Repeating Rifle, Model '90, Take-Down.
Order No. 47023½.

	Price.		Price.
Carrier	$1.00	Extractor	$0.25
Firing pin	.50	Hammer	.50
Mainspring	.30	Firing pin stop	.05
Trigger	.45	Butt stock	1.40

In ordering Carrier state if for 22 caliber short, 22 long, or 22 W. R. F. cartridge.

Parts for Winchester, Model '86, Rifle.
Order No. 47024.

	Price.		Price.
Cartridge stop	$0.35	Ejector spring	$0.10
Cartridge guide	.30	Spring cover complete	1.15
Carrier spring	.50	Set sear	.05
Extractor	.25	Butt stock	1.40
Carrier hook	.55	Finger lever	1.50
Trigger	.45	Mainspring	.30
Trigger spring	.05	Carrier	2.00
Lower tang	2.00	Firing pin	.50
Hammer, plain lock	.50	Magazine springs	.20
Hammer, set lock	.90	Screws, each	.05
Ejector	.35		

Winchester Repeating Shot Gun Parts.
Order No. 47024¼.—Model 1893, 12 ga. only.

	Price.		Price.
Action Slide	$1.50	Magazine Band	$0.70
Action Slide Stop Pin	.05	Magazine Band Screw	.05
Action Hook	.30	Magazine Follower	.45
Action Hook Screws	.05	Magazine Plug	.50
Barrel, plain	7.50	Magazine Plug Screw	.05
Breech-block	3.00	Magazine Spring	.20
Butt Plate	.60	Mainspring	.30
Butt Plate Screws, ea.,	.05	Mainspring Strain Screw	.05
Butt Stock	2.00	Receiver, complete with Guard	7.50
Carrier	1.75	Receiver Bolt	.40
Carrier Pin	.05	Receiver Bolt Washer	.05
Cartridge Stop, right or left hand, each	.35	Receiver Shank	.45
Cartridge Stop Base	.20	Sear	.45
Cartridge Stop Screw	.05	Sear Pin	.05
Cartridge Stop Spring	.10	Sear Spring	.05
Extractor	.30	Sear Spring Screw	.15
Extractor Pin	.05	Slide Handle	.85
Extractor Spring	.05	Slide Handle Esectheous, 2, each	
Firing Pin	.30	Slide Handle Screws, 2, each	.05
Firing Pin Nut	.05	Stirrup	.05
Firing Pin Lock	.50	Trigger	.45
Front Sight	.25	Trigger Pin	.05
Guard Bow	.45		
Hammer	.60		
Hammer Pin	.05		
Magazine	.90		

Always write your name the same way.

Parts for Colt's Rifle.
Order No. 47025—

	22 Cal.	32 to 44 Cal.	38-56 to 45-85 Cal.
Magazine cartridge stop	$0.75	$0.55	$0.75
Mainspring	.50	.26	.44
Hammer	1.10	.92	.97
Firing pin	.80	.44	.55
Trigger	.45	.40	.45
Carrier levers	.75	.52	.77
Shell extractor	.30	.28	.33
Trigger spring	.20	.16	.20
Tang screws	.10	.10	.10
Butt stock	2.75	2.15	2.25
Magazine spring	.30	.35	.40

Component Parts
OF THE
MARLIN SAFETY REPEATING RIFLE.
MODEL 1891.
Order No. 47026.

Component Parts
OF THE
MARLIN SAFETY REPEATING RIFLE.
MODEL 1889.
Order No. 47027.

Winchester Rifle Parts.
Order 47028.

MORTISE COVER
Each 30c.

Model 73
$6.60.
RECEIVER

Model 76,
$7.75.

M. COVER
STOP
Each 10c.

SPRING COVER
Each 30c.

BREECH PIN BASE
Each $1.10.

EXTRACTOR
Each 25c.

LEFT HAND LINK
Each 55c.

BREECH PIN COMPLETE
Each $2.20.

RIGHT HAND LINK
Each 55c.

FIRING PIN
Each 60c.

FINGER LEVER
Each $1.00.

CARRIER BLOCK
Each $1.10.

HAMMER
Each 50c.

CARRIER LEVER
Each 35c.

FINGER LEVER SPRING
Each 20c.

MAIN SPRING
Each 30c.

CARRIER LEVER SPRING
Each 20c.

SAFETY CATCH
Each 40c.

RETRACTOR
Each 25c.

CATCH HOOK
SPRING
Each 15c.

SEAR SPRING
PLAIN
Each 5c.

SEAR SPRING SET
Each 10c.

SAFETY CATCH
SPRING
Each 10c.

KNOCK OFF
SPRING
Each 30c.

SET SEAR
Each 60

PLAIN SEAR
Each 40c.

RIGHT HAND SIDE PLATE

CATCH
HOOK

KNOCK OFF

SET TRIGGER

PLAIN TRIGGER

Model 73, 80c.   Model 76, 90c.   Each 50c.   Each 60c.   Each 60c.   Each 30c.
Hammer, Set Lock, 60c each.   Screws, each, 5c.   Magazine Springs, 20c. each.

In ordering parts state caliber of rifle and send old part for sample when possible to do so, and mention model of rifle. Parts by mail, 1c. to 5c. extra.

PARTS FOR QUACKENBUSH SAFETY RIFLE.

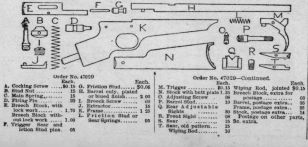

Order No. 47029.

	Each.		Each.
A. Cocking Screw	$0.15	G. Friction Stud	$0.06
B. Stud Nut	15	H. Barrel only, plated	
C. Main Spring	15	or blued finish	2.00
D. Firing Pin	20	I. Breech Screw	08
E. Breech Block, with		J. Extractor	15
lock work	1.70	K. Frame	1 25
Breech Block with-		L. Friction Stud or	
out lock work	1.00	Sear Springs	05
F. Trigger Sear and			
iction Stud pins	05		

Order No. 47029—Continued.

	Each.		Each.
M. Trigger	$0.15	Wiping Rod, jointed	$0.15
N. Stock with butt plate	1.35	Breech Block, extra for	
O. Adjusting Screw	08	postage	03
P. Barrel Stud	10	Barrel, postage extra	15
Q. Rear Adjustable		Frame, postage extra	25
Sights	30	Stock, postage extra	14
R. Front Sight	08	Postage on other parts,	
S. Sear	15	3c. extra.	
T. Sear, old pattern	15		
Wiping Rod	10		

REVOLVERS.

REVOLVERS.—The following quotations do not include cartridges.

All revolvers can be sent by mail when so ordered. Postage, 1 cent per ounce in weight.

47032

Defender, wood stock, full nickel plated, plain cylinder, 7-shot. 22 caliber, rim fire, long or short, 2¼ inch barrel; weight 7 ounces. Safe and reliable. Each.........$0.74

Postage, extra, 10 cents.

47033 Eclipse vest pocket single shot pistol, nickel plated wood stock, 3¼ inch barrel; weight 5 ounces; for BB and conical caps and 22 caliber short cartridge, safe and reliable, barrel swings to the right to load.
Each.........$0.50
By mail, extra.........05

47034 Rosewood stock, 7-shot, full nickel plate, 22 caliber long or short, rim fire; weight 7 oz., 2¼ in. barrel; entire length 5¼ in., safe and reliable.
Each.........$0.79
Using No. 47155 cartridges.

47035 Rubber Stock, 7-shot, 22 caliber, long or short. 2½ inch barrel, rim fire, entire length 5¼ inches, full nickel plated, weight 7 ounces, rifled barrels. (See cut 47034.)
Each.........90c.   Extra by mail....10c
Using No. 47155-59 cartridge.

47036 Czar, a good target pistol, rubber stock, long handle, fluted cylinder, nickel plated finish, caliber 22 long or short, rim fire, 3½ inch octagon barrel, entire length 7 inches, weight 9 oz., well rifled and a good one, 7-shot. Price.........$1.75
(Using 47155-59 cartridges.) Extra by mail....110

Revolvers—Continued.

47037 Blue Jacket, No. 1½, a fine shooter, 22 caliber, long or short cartridges, round barrel, rubber stock, full nickel plate, saw handle, length of barrel, 2½ inches; entire length, 6 inches; weight 9 oz., using No. 47155-59 cartridge, well rifled, and a good one.

Price each, 7 shot, $1.35. By mail, extra, 12c.

47039 Wood Stock, plain cylinder, 5 shot, 32 caliber, long or short, rim fire, 2½ inch barrel, weight 12 oz., full nickel plate, entire length 6½ inches. Rifled barrels. Price.... $1.00
Using No 47169-70-71 cartridge.
Extra by mail, 15c. Safe and reliable.

Rifled Barrel.

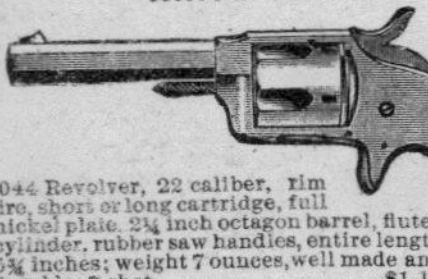

47044 Revolver, 22 caliber, rim fire, short or long cartridge, full nickel plate, 2¾ inch octagon barrel, fluted cylinder, rubber saw handles, entire length 5¾ inches; weight 7 ounces, well made and durable, 7 shot.... $1.10

Using No. 47155-59 cartridge. Extra by mail, 15 cts.

47045 Revolver, 32 caliber, rim fire, long or short cartridges, full nickel plated, 2½ inch octagon barrel, fluted cylinder, rubber saw handles; entire length, 6¾ inches; weight 10 ounces. Price, $1.25. Using 47169-70-71 cartridges. Extra by mail, 15 cents.

47046-47

47046 Forehand & Wadsworth's New Double Action Self-Cocking Revolvers, full nickel plated, rubber stocks, rifled barrels, safe, reliable and accurate. Rebounding locks and parts are interchangeable. 32 caliber, 2½ in. octagon barrel, 6 shot, 12 oz. weight, using No. 47188 cartridge.... $1.40
47047 38 caliber, 2½ in. octagon barrel, 5 shot, weight about 15 oz., using No. 47194 cartridge. 1.40
Postage, extra, 17c.

47048 Forehand & Wadsworth Safety Hammer Double Action Revolvers, full nickel plated, rubber stocks, rifled barrels, rebounding lock; safe, reliable and accurate, 32 caliber, 2½ in. octagon barrel (using No. 47188 cartridge), 6 shot, about 12 oz. weight.... $1.50
47048½ 38 caliber, 2½ in. octagon barrel, 5 shot, about 15 oz. weight, using No. 47194 cartridge.. 1.50
Postage extra, 17c.

Big Bargains.

(Retail Price, $5.00. See our price.)

Harrington & Richardson's Improved Automatic Shell Extracting Double Action Self-cocking Revolver (modeled on the Smith & Wesson pattern), beautifully nickel plated, rubber stocks, as accurate and durable as any revolver in the market, equal to a Smith & Wesson in shooting; weight, 18 to 20 ounces; 3¼ inch barrel
47049 6 shot 32 caliber, center fire, using 47188 cartridge. By mail, 21 cents extra.... $3.25
47050 5 shot 38 caliber, center fire; using 47194 cartridge. By mail, 23 cents extra.... 3.25

Revolvers—Continued.

Forehand & Wadsworth's New Hammerless Revolver. Automatic Shell Ejector double action, self-cocking, rebounding lock, absolute safety catch to lock hammer, made of best material, beautifully finished throughout; accurate and reliable, no better shooters in the market, all center fire. Length of barrel, 3¼ inches; entire length 7¾ inches Weight, 17 ounces, nickel plated, 38, 5 shot.
47051 32 S. & W., center fire.... $4.75
47052 38 S. & W., center fire. Each.... 4.75
Either caliber, 5 inch barrel.... 5.40

47053 Forehand & Wadsworth's Improved New Model Revolver. Automatic Shell Extracting, Rebounding Locks, double action, self cocking. Simple and accurate: interchangeable parts made from *Drop forgings:* the frame is cast steel; *no malleable iron about it.* Nickel plated, rubber stocks. WARRANTED. Length of barrel, 3¼ in. Weight, 17 oz.; entire length 7¾ in. This is the best selling revolver in our stock, having contracted for several thousand. 32 Caliber, S. & W., center fire cartridge. Each, 6 shot $3.35
47054 38 Caliber, S. & W. center, fire cartridge. Each, 5 shot.... 3.35
Either above calibers with 5 in. barrel. Each.. 4.50

47058 Hopkins & Allen Automatic Hammerless Double Action Revolver. High grade finish, fine adjustment. Its trigger locking device makes it one of the safest revolvers to carry in the pocket. Automatic shell ejector, rebounding lock, safety trigger, locking device, chambered cylinder, rifled barrel, nickel plated, 32 caliber, S. & W. small frame, 5 shot, weight 13 oz.; length of barrel 3 inches, using cartridge 47188. (Retail price, $7.50.) Our price.... $5.50
47059 38 caliber, S. & W. large frame, weight 18 oz., length of barrel 3¼ in. Price, $5.50. Using cartridge 47196. Either of above calibers in blued finish same price. Pearl stocks, $3.00 extra. Postage, extra, 22 cents.

47061 Frontier Bull Dog, for home protection, beautifully nickel finished, 6 shot, double action, self-cocking, rubber stock, rifled barrels, 44 Winchester center fire, cartridge No. 47208, 4¾ in. barrel; weight, 18 oz. Good, strong and durable. Each.... $3.85
Postage, extra, 23 cents.

47062-63

Hopkins and Allen Acme Hammerless Double Action Revolver. Rebounding lock, safety trigger, locking device, chambered cylinder. Safe, reliable and accurate. (Retail price, $5.00.)
47062 32-caliber, using No. 47188 cartridge, 5 shot, 11 oz., 2¾ in. octagon barrel.... $2.65
Postage, extra, 13 cents.
47063 38-caliber (using No. 47194 cartridge), 3 in. octagon barrel, 5 shot, 17 oz.... 2.65
Postage, extra, 19 cents.

Revolvers—Continued.

47073 Young America, double action, full nickel plated fluted cylinder, rubber handles, 2 in. barrel, full length, 6 in.; weight, 9¼ oz., 32 caliber, center fire, using No. 47188 cartridge, only 5 shot. Each.... $1.20
By mail, 12 cents extra.
47074 Young America, 22 caliber, rim fire; length of barrel, 2 in., entire length 6 inches. 8 oz.; using No. 47155-59 cartridge, 7 shot. Each.... $1.20
By mail, 8 cents extra.

Big Bargains. American Bull Dog Revolvers.

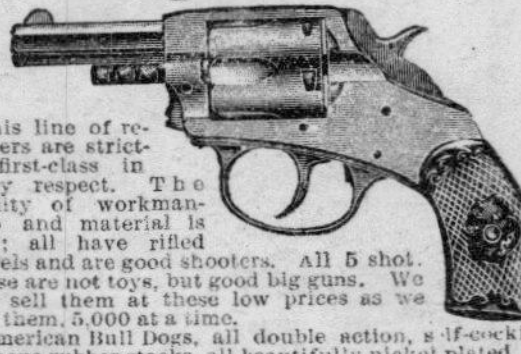

This line of revolvers are strictly first-class in every respect. The quality of workmanship and material is best; all have rifled barrels and are good shooters. All 5 shot. These are not toys, but good big guns. We can sell them at these low prices as we buy them, 5,000 at a time.

American Bull Dogs, all double action, self-cocking all have rubber stocks, all beautifully nickel plated, all have saw handles, all have fluted cylinders, all have octagon barrels, all warranted new and in perfect order.
47075 32 caliber center fire, 2½ in. barrel, 13 oz. weight.... $1.10
47078 32 caliber, center fire, 4½ in. barrel, 16 oz. weight.... 1.55
47079 32 caliber, center fire, 6 in. barrel, 17 oz. weight. All 32 caliber use No. 47188 cartridge. 1.89
47080 38 caliber, center fire, 2½ in. barrel, 16 oz. weight.... 1.10
47081 38 caliber, center fire, 4½ in. barrel, 17½ oz. weight.... 1.55
47082 38 caliber, center fire, 6 in. barrel, 18 oz. weight.... 1.89
All 38 caliber use No. 47194 cartridge
Postage, when sent by mail, 18 to 20 cents extra.
Revolvers of all kinds can be sent by mail; postage is 1 cent per ounce in weight.

X. L. Double Action.

WITH FOLDING HAMMER.

GOOD ONES.

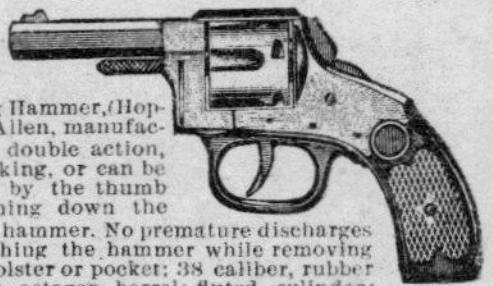

47090—X. L. Double Action. Folding Hammer, (Hopkins & Allen, manufacturers), double action, self-cocking, or can be cocked by the thumb by turning down the folding hammer. No premature discharges by catching the hammer while removing from holster or pocket; 38 caliber, rubber handles, octagon barrel; fluted cylinder; length of barrel, 3 inches; entire length, 7 inches; weight, 16 oz.; center fire, using Smith & Wesson's 38 caliber cartridge; nickel plated. Safe, accurate and reliable. Each.... $2.40
By mail, 20c extra.
47090¼ Same, 38 S. & W. caliber, blued finish.. 2.65
47091 X. L. Double action same as 47090, except 32 caliber, center fire, 3 in. barrel; entire length, 8 inches; weight, 16 oz.; using Smith & Wesson's 32 caliber cartridge, 6 shot, each.... 2.40
By mail 19c extra.
47091¼ Same, 32 S. & W. caliber, blued finish.. 2.65
47092 X. L. Double action, same as 47090, except 22 caliber, rim fire, 2¼ in. barrel; entire length, 6 inches; weight, 12 oz; the best double action 22 caliber in the market; using No. 47155-59 cartridge. By mail, 13c extra. Each, 7 shot.... 2.50
47092½ Same, 22 caliber, blued finish.... 2.65

Handsome Revolvers.

ACCURATE. RELIABLE.

47093 Hopkins & Allen Automatic Shell Ejecting Center Fire, Double Action, Self-cocking, Folding Hammer Revolvers, 38 caliber, 3¼ inch barrel, nickel plated, rubber stocks, using 47194 cartridges, finely made and accurate, rifled barrels. Each, 5 shot, 17 oz.... $4.45
47093¼ Same, 38 S. & W. caliber, blued finish.. 4.48

Revolvers—Continued.

47094 Hopkins & Allen Revolver, same as No. 47093, except 5½ inch barrel, plated rubber stock, 38 caliber, using 47194 cartridge. Weight 19 oz. By mail, 23c. extra. Each, 5 shot......$5.10
47094½. 32 caliber, 3 in. barrel, 11 oz.; using S. & W. cartridge. Each.............................. 4.65
47094¾ Same, 32 S. & W. caliber, blued finish.. 4.68

A Fine Target Pistol.

47099 X. L. Double Action Target Revolvers, regular hammer, self-cocking, full nickel-plated, rubber stock, 4½ inch octagon barrel, 7 shot weight 12 ounces, 22 caliber rim fire, using long or short cartridges, accurate and durable revolver. Each...$3.00

Colt's Revolvers.

Manufactured by the Colt's Patent Fire Arms Co., Hartford, Conn. No better revolvers manufactured in the world than the Colts. They are in use all over the globe.

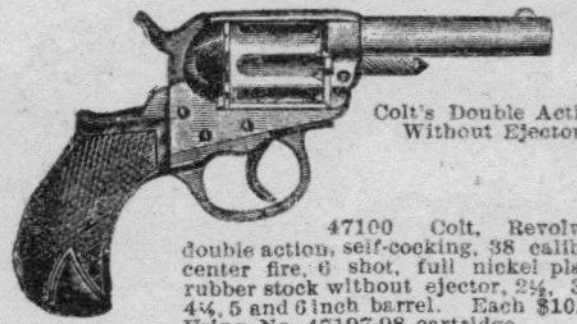

Colt's Double Action Without Ejector.

47100 Colt, Revolver, double action, self-cocking, 38 caliber, center fire, 6 shot, full nickel plate, rubber stock without ejector, 2½, 3½, 4¾, 5 and 6 inch barrel. Each $10.00 Using No. 47197-98 cartridge. By mail, 32 cents extra.
47100½ Same as 47100, except blue finish....... 10.00 (Factory price, $15.00.)

Colt's Double Action, Sliding Ejector. Every one warranted.

47101 Colt's Revolver, double action, 38 caliber, center fire, 6-shot, 4¾, 5 and 6 inch barrels, rubber stock, nickel plated, with sliding spring ejectors. Using 47197-98 cartridge. Each.................................$11.20 By mail, 32 cents extra.
47101½ Colt's Revolver, same as 47101, except blued finish. Each.......................... 11.20
47102 Colt's Revolver, double action, 41 caliber, center fire, rubber stock, nickel plated frames and barrels, 6 shot with sliding spring ejector, 4¾, 5 or 6 in. Using No. 47203 cartridges. Each.. 11.20 By mail, 32 cents extra.
Extra for pearl stock on either of above numbers. Each.................................. 4.25
47102½ Colt Revolver; same as No. 47102 *except* blued finish. Each........................... 11.20
Postage, extra, 32 cents.

New Single Action Frontier and Peacemaker. Every one warranted. (Regular price $16.00.) See our price.

47103 Colt Revolver, single action, sliding ejector, 38 caliber, using 38 caliber Winchester rifle cartridge, model '73, 4¾, 5½ and 7½ inch barrels, rubber stock, nickel plated. 6 shot. Our price.............................. $12.00
47103½ Colt Revolver, same as 47103, *except blued* finish. Our price........................ 12.00
47104 Colt Revolver, single action, sliding ejector, rubber stocks, 32 caliber, using Winchester rifle cartridge, 32 caliber, model '73, 4¾, 5½ and 7½ inch, nickel plated, using 47192-93 cartridge 12.00
47104½ Colt Revolver, same as 47104, *except blued* finish, 6 shot. Our price.................. 12.00
47105. Colt Revolver, "Frontier," 44 caliber, single action, sliding ejector, using Winchester 44 caliber, model 1873 cartridge, central fire, nickel finish, rubber stocks, 6 shot, 4¾, 5½, 7½ inch barrel. Each................... 12.00 Postage extra, 54 cents.
47105½ Colt Revolver, same as 47105, except blued finish.................................. 12.00
47106 Colt Revolver, "Peacemaker," single action, sliding ejector, rubber stocks, 45-caliber, central fire, nickel plated, 6 shot, 4¾, 5½ and 7½ in. barrel. Using No. 47216 cartridge. 12.00
47106½ Colt Revolver, same as 47106, except blued finish.................................. 12.00
47107 Colt Revolver, single action, sliding ejector, 41 caliber, center fire, 4¾, 5½, and 7½ inch, nickel plated, rubber stocks, using 47203 cartridge...$12.00 Extra for plain pearl stocks. 8.00
Extra for pearl stocks, carved ox head or eagle 13.00
47107½ Colt Revolver, same as 47107, except blued finish...........$12.00 By mail, extra... .52

Revolvers—Continued.

Colt's Double Action, 44 and 45 caliber. Every one warranted. Made by the Colt's Pat. Fire Arms Co., Hartford, Conn. (List price $20.00.)

47108 Colt Revolver, army size, double action, self-cocking, 44 caliber Winchester, center fire, case-hardened, NICKEL plated, rubber stock with sliding spring ejector, 4¾ inch, 5½ inch or 7½ inch barrel, 6 shot...$13.00
47110 Colt Revolver, 44 caliber, same description as No. 47108, except BLUED finish......... 13.00
47112 Colt Revolver, army size, double action, self-cocking, 45 caliber, center fire, case-hardened, 4¾, 5½ and 7½ inch barrel, NICKEL plated, 6 shot, rubber stock, with sliding spring ejector 13.00
47114 Colt Revolver, 45 caliber, same description as No. 47112, except BLUED finish........ 13.00
47115 Colt Revolver, double action, self-cocking, 4¾, 5½ and 7½ inch barrel, 38 caliber, using 38 Winchester rifle cartridge, model '73, NICKEL plated.. 13.00
47116 Colt's Revolver, same as No. 47115, BLUED finish....................................... 13.00
Extra for plain pearl stock on 44 or 45 caliber, double action, $4.50. By mail, 50 cents extra.

Smith and Wesson Revolvers.

Look out for imitations. There are many on the market All genuine Smith & Wesson revolvers are stamped on the barrel, "Smith & Wesson, Springfield, Mass."

Genuine Smith & Wesson Hammerless

47118 Smith & Wesson's Hammerless Revolver, automatic ejector, 32 caliber, center fire, 3½ inch barrel, nickel plated, double action, self-cocking; weight, 16 ounces, 5 shot. Each.............$11.50 By mail, extra.. .19
47119 Smith & Wesson's Hammerless Revolver, automatic ejector, double action, self-cocking, 32 caliber, center fire, using No. 47188 cartridge, blued finish, double action; weight, 16 ounces, 5 shot...............$11.65. By mail, extra....... $0.19
47120 38 caliber, 3¼ inch barrel, nickel plated, double action; weight, 20 oz., 5 shot...... 12.00 By mail, extra.. .23
47121 38 caliber, 3¼ inch barrel, blued finish, using No. 47194 cartridge; weight, 20 oz., 5 shot By mail, extra, 23c. Each....12.55

Genuine Smith & Wesson Single action 32 caliber. Manufactured at Springfield, Mass.

32 CALIBER, CENTRAL FIRE, 3½ INCH BARREL, AUTOMATIC EJECTOR, LATEST MODEL WITH HAMMER.
47125 32 caliber, 5 shot, blued, rubber stock, single action; weight, 13 oz................... $8.95 By mail, extra.. .18
47126 32 caliber, 5 shot, blued, double action, self cocking, 32 caliber; weight, 13 oz....... 10.65 By mail, extra... .18

Manufactured by Smith & Wesson, Springfield, Mass. S. & W. 32 D. A.

47127 32 caliber, 5 shot, nickel plate, rubber stock, single action; weight, 13 oz.... $9.00 By mail, 15 cents extra.
47128 32 caliber, 5 shot, plated, double action, self-cocking; weight, 13 oz......................$10.65 By mail, 18c. extra.
47129 32 caliber, 5 shot, blued or plated, 6 in. barrel, rubber stock, double action, using 47188 cartridge; weight, 15 oz......................... 12.00
Extra, for pearl stock.................................... 2.00

Cut shows 38-caliber, center fire, 3¼ in. barrel, automatic ejector, latest model, with hammer.

47135 38 caliber, 5 shot, blued, rubber stock, single action; weight, 16 oz.........$10.35 Extra by mail.................................... .23

Revolvers—Continued. Each

47136 38 caliber, 5 shot, blued, double action; weight, 18 oz..$11.40
47137 38 caliber, 5 shot, nickel plate, rubber stock, single action; weight 16 oz.................10.40
47138 38 caliber, 5 shot, plated, double action; weight 18 oz.......................................11.40
47140 38 caliber, 5 shot, blued or plated, 4 or 5 in. barrels, rubber stocks, double action; weight, 18 oz., using 47194 cartridges..........12.00
Extra for pearl stocks..................................... 3.25
Extra by mail... .23

Smith & Wesson.

47141 44 caliber, 6 shot, blued, rubber stock, single action, 6½ in. only; using 47208 cartridges; weight, 40 oz..$12.50 Extra by mail..$0.52
47142 44 caliber, 6 shot, blued finish, rubber stock, double action, 6, 5 or 4 in.; using 47208 cartridges; weight 40 oz. $14.40. Extra by mail .48
47143 44 caliber, 6 shot, nickel plate, rubber stock, single action, 6 in. only; using 47208 cartridges; weight, 44 oz..............................12.60
Extra by mail.. .52
47144 44 caliber, 6 shot, Smith & Wesson, plated, rubber stock, double action, 6, 5 or 4 in.; weight 40 oz., using 47208 cartridge...............14.75
47145 44 caliber, Russian model, double action or self cocking, blued, 4 in., 5 in., 6 in. barrel; weight about 40 oz., using No. 47204 cartridge. Each........... $14.55 Extra by mail............ .48
Extra for pearl stock.................................. 4.00

Colt's New Navy.

Made by the Colt's Pat. Fire Arms Co., New Haven, Connecticut.

This revolver has been adopted by the U. S. Navy and every one has to pass a rigid inspection.

47146 Colt's New Navy, double action, self cocking, shell-ejecting revolver, nickel plated or blued finish, rubber stock, beautifully finished, finest material; length about 12½ in., 6 shot, weight, 2 lbs.; 4½ or 6 in. barrels, 38 caliber, using No. 47198 cartridges, 6 shot. Each..........................$12.00
41 caliber, using No. 47203 cartridge, 6 shot. Each..$12.00
By mail, 35 cents extra.

Colt's Special Target Pistol.

47147 Colt's Special Target Pistol, single action, six shot, rubber stock, solid frame: the best quality and finish; warranted accurate and perfect in every detail. Nickel plated or blued finish. Barrel 7½ in., length 12½ in.; 32-44 S. & W....$16.50 Weight 2 lbs. 5 oz., 38-44 S. & W. target caliber $15.75
44 S. & W. Russian caliber............................ 15.75

COLT'S ARMY MODEL 1892. 38 & 41 CALIBRES.

Ejects the shells the same as No. 47146.
47150 Colt's New Army Revolver, Double Action, Self Cocking, Shell Ejecting, Model 1892. Adopted by the Ordnance Bureau U. S. Army. Nickel plated, rubber stocks. Every one warranted perfect. Length of barrels 3 inch, 4½ inch and 6 inch. Weight about 2 lbs. 38 Caliber, using No. 47197 or 47198 cartridges......$13.00 Postage, 35 cents extra.

Colt's New Pistol.

47151 Colt's New Pocket Revolvers, Double Action, self-cocking, - shell ejecting. Beautiful in design and finish; perfectly accurate and reliable. Full nickel plated; rubber stocks, Length of barrel, 3½ in. Weight, 20 ounces; 32 caliber, using No. 47189-90 cartridge. Blued finish same price. Each.....$10.00 Postage, extra, 25 cents.

LOADED METALLIC CARTRIDGES.

We do not send Cartridges C. O. D. Cartridges cannot go by mail. We can furnish all kinds of cartridges not in this list at lowest market price.

CARTRIDGES CAN BE SHIPPED WITH OTHER GOODS BY EXPRESS OR FREIGHT.

Prices subject to changes without notice. U. M. C., U. S., Lowell and Winchester Makes, all the same price and kept in stock.

RIM FIRE CARTRIDGES.

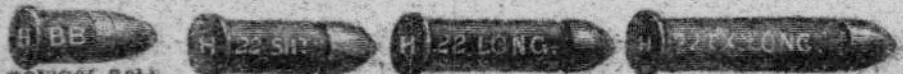

CONICAL BALL 47154 47158 47159 47161

47153 Cartridges, 22 caliber, BB cap, 100 in box. Per box........................$0.14
Per 1000 ....$1.31 Weight, ¼ lb. per box.
47154 Conical Ball Cap Cartridge, 22 Caliber, rim fire, box of 100.. .... .22
Per 1000.............................$2.00 Weight, ¼ lb. per box.
47154½ Conical Ball Cap Cartridge U. M. C. make, powder loaded. 22 caliber, per 100.......................$0.22 Per 1000. .... 2.00
47155 Cartridges, 22 caliber, short, rim fire, U. M. C. make, "U," 100 in box .24
Per 1000 .... 2.25
47156 Cartridges, 22 caliber, short, rim fire, Winchester make, "H," 100 in box .24
Per 1000... 2.25
47157 Cartridges, 22 caliber, short, rim fire, U. S. make, 100 in box. .... .24
Per 1000... 2.25
47158 Cartridges, 22 caliber, short, rim fire, 100 in box....$0.25 Per 1000... 2.25
47159 Cartridges, 22 caliber, long, rim fire, 100 in box.......................... .30
Per 1000...............................$2.85 Weight, 1¼ lbs. per box
47160 Cartridges, 22 caliber, long rifle, rim fire, 100 in box...................... .30
Per 1000... 2.85
47161 Cartridges, 22 extra long, rim fire, 100 in box............................ .47
Per 1000...............................$4.60 Weight, 1¼ lbs. per box.

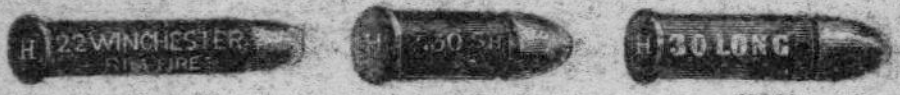

47165 47167 47168

47165 Cartridges, special 22 caliber, for Winchester model '90, repeating rifle, 7 grains powder, 45 grains lead. Per 100....$0.48 Per 1000........$4.57
47166 Cartridges, 25 caliber, for Stevens, Maynard and Winchester single shot rifles, 11 grains powder, 65 grain ball, rim fire, 50 in box.................. .40
Per 100.. .70
47167 Cartridges, 30 short, rim fire, 50 in box $0.23 Per 100 .... .44
Weight, ¼ lb. per box.
47168 Cartridges, 30, long, rim fire, 50 in box.$0.28 Per 100. .... .51
Weight, ¼ lbs.

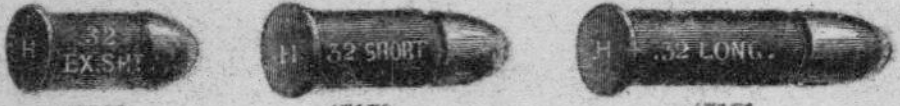

47169 47170 47171

47169 Cartridges, 32 caliber, extra short, rim fire, 50 in box..................$0.25
Per 100. ....$0.46 Weight, ½ lb. per box.
47170 Cartridges, 32 caliber, short, rim fire, 50 in box $0.26 Per 100........ .48
Weight, ¾ lb.
47171 Cartridges, 32 caliber, long, rim fire, 50 in box $0.30 Per 100......... .56
Weight, 1 lb.

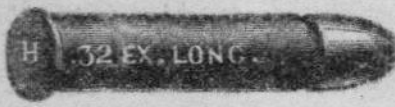

47172

47172 Cartridges, 32 caliber, extra long, rim fire, 50 in box, 48c.

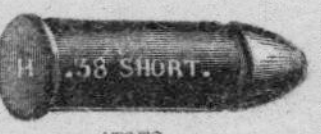

47173

Per 100..............................$0.80 Weight, 1¼ lbs. per box.
47173 Cartridges, 38 caliber. short, rim fire, 50 in box.........................$0 42
Per 100..............................$0.79 Weight, 1¼ lbs.

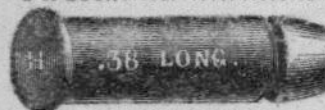

47174

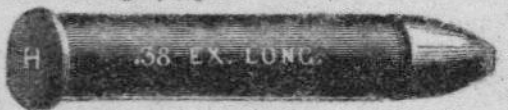

47175

47174 Cartridges, 38 caliber, long, rim fire, 50 in a box........................$0.47
Per 100 ....$0.87 Weight, 1½ lbs.
47175 Cartridges, 38 caliber, extra long, rim fire, 50 in box...................... .65
Per 100............................$1.20 Weight, 1¾ lbs.

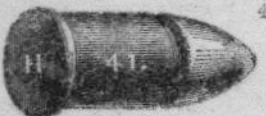

47176

47176 Cartridges, 41 caliber, rim fire, for Remington Derringer pistol.
Per box of 50......$0.40
Per 100........... .72
Weight, 1¼ lbs.

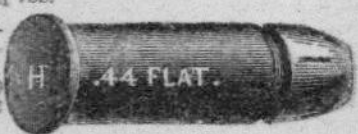

47178

47177 Cartridges, 41 caliber, long, rim fire, 50 in box. Weight, 2 lbs $0.45
Per 100.. .85
47178 Winchester, model '66, rim fire, 28 grains powder, 200 grain ball, 50 in box........................... $0.62 Per 100...... .... 1.17
Weight, 1¼ lbs. per box.

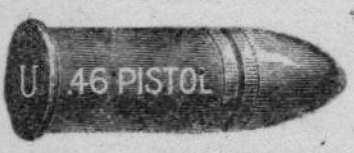

47180

47180 Cartridges, 46 caliber, rim fire, short, for Remington revolvers and Kentucky Ballard rifles,
Box $0.65
Per 100.. 1.20
Weight, 2¼ lbs.

47181 Cartridges, 46 caliber long rim fire for Remington revolvers and Kentucky Ballard rifles, 50 in box...$0.86
Per 100.............................. 1.61
Weight, 3½ lbs per box.

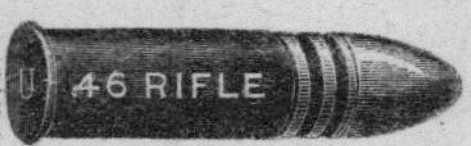

47181

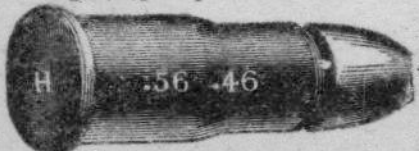

47182

47182 Cartridges, 56-46, Spencer Carbine, rim fire, 25 in box......................$0.52
Weight, 2 lbs. Per 100.................. 1.94

47183 Cartridges, 56-50 Spencer carbine, rim fire, 25 in box.......................$0.52
Weight, 2¼ lbs. per box. Per 100... 1.94

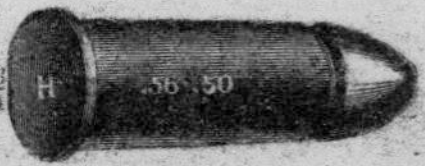

47183

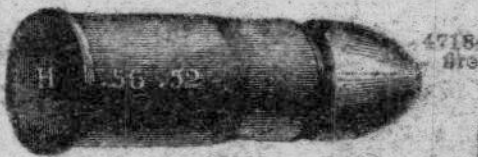

47184

47184 Cartridges, 56-52, Spencer rifle, rim fire, 25 in box. $0.52 Per 100......$1.94

47185

47185 Cartridge, 56-56, Spencer Carbine, rim fire, 25 in box. $0.52
Per 100...................................... 1.94
Weight, 2½ lbs. per box.

Center Fire Pistol and Rifle Cartridges.

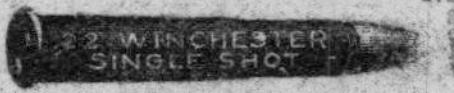

47186 Cartridges, 22 caliber, center fire, 13 grains powder, 45 grain bullet for Winchester *single shot* rifle, box of 50.. $0.53
Per 100.. 1.10
Weight, 1 lb. per box.

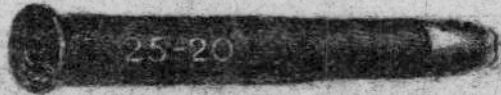

47187 Cartridges, 25-20 caliber 19 grains powder, 86 grain ball, for Stevens, Maynard and Winchester single shot rifles, box of 50...$0 75
Per 100 .... 1.35
Weight, 1½ lbs.

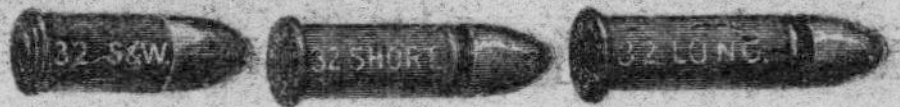

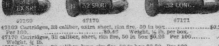

47188 47189 47190

47188 Cartridges, 32 caliber, Smith & Wesson, center fire, 50 in box...........$0.44
Weight, 1¼ lbs. Using No. 1 primers if made by W. R. A. Co Using No. 0 primer if made by U. M. C. Co. Per 100.. .80

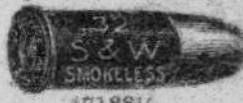

47188½

47188½ Cartridge, 32 S. & W. Smokeless Powder loaded: for Smith & Wesson revolvers of this caliber.
Per box of 50...$0.50
Per 100 .... .92
47189 Center fire, 32 caliber, short, for Colt's revolver, 50 in box............. .44
Weight, 1½ lbs. Per 100 .... .80
47190 Center fire, 32 caliber, long, Colt's or Ballard, 50 in box .... .48
Weight, 1½ lbs. per box. Per 100.................................... .88

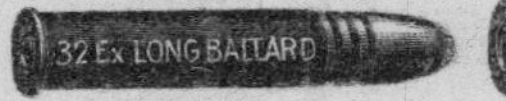

47191

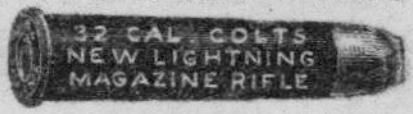

47192

47191 Cartidges, 32 caliber, extra long, center fire, 50 in box.................$0.72
Per 100..............................$1.32 Weight, 1¾ lbs.
47192 Cartridges, center fire, 32 caliber, for Colt's lightning repeating rifle. 20 grains powder, 100 grains lead, box of 50................................ .64
Per 100..............................$1.16 Weight, 1¾ lbs. per box.

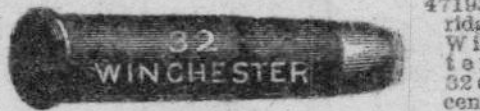

47193

47193 Cartridges for Winchester rifle, 32 caliber, center fire, 20 grains powder, 115 grains lead. Weight, 1¾ lbs. Per box of 50, using No. 1 primer......................$0.64 Per 100..............................$1.16

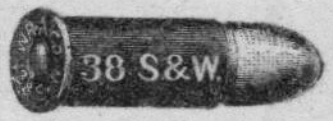

47194

47194 Cartridges, 38 caliber, center fire, Smith & Wesson, 50 in box.......... .54
Per 100..........................$0.98 Weight, 2 lbs. per box.
47195 32 Ideal Cartridge, 1¾ in. straight shell, 25 grains powder, 150 grains lead. Per box of 50, $0.75 Per 100..... ....$1.40

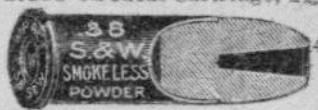

47196

47196 Smokeless Powder, 38 S. & W., 7 grain powder, 135 grains lead adapted to Smith & Wesson revolvers. Per box of 50 cartridges.................$0.58
Per 100................................... 1.05

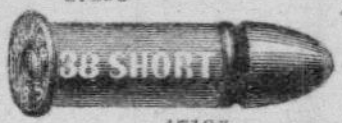

47197

47197 Center fire, 38 caliber, short, for Ballard rifles and Colt's and Remington revolvers, 50 in box.

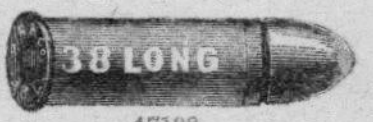

47198

Weight. 2 lbs. Per box. ....$0.54 Per 100 ....$0.98
47198 Center fire, 38 caliber, long, for Ballard rifle and Colt's revolvers, 50 in a box.................................$0.58 Per 100........................... 1.05
Weight, 2¼ lbs. per box.
47198½ Cartridges for Colt New Navy and New Army Revolvers, 38 long inside lubricant 50 in box. Per box..........$0.59. Per 100...................$1.05

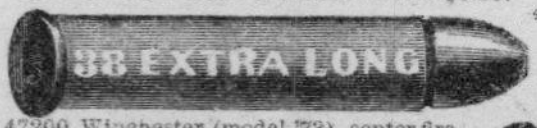

47199 Center fire, 38 caliber, extra long, 38 grains powder, 148 grains lead, for Ballard rifle No. 2, 50 in box. Per box....$0.92
Per 100.....................1.67
Weight, 2½ lbs.

47200 Winchester (model '73), center fire, 38 caliber, 40 grains powder, 180 grains lead, 50 in a box, using No. 1 primer.
Per box.............................$0.69
Per 100.............................1.38
Weight, 2¾ lbs. per box.

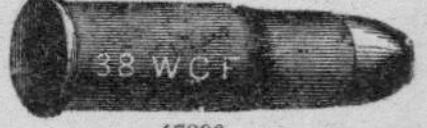

47200

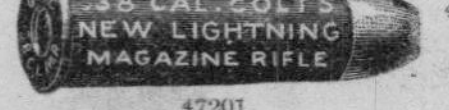

47201

47201 Cartridges, center fire, 38 caliber for Colt's Lightning Repeating Rifle, 40 grains powder, 180 grains lead, per box of 50. ....$0.70
Per 100,...................................1.87
Weight, 2¾ lbs. per box.

Cartridges—Continued.

47203 Colt's Revolver, caliber 41, center fire, (long DA), 50 in a box. Per box........$0.70
Per 100.......................................1.28
Weight, 1½ lbs.

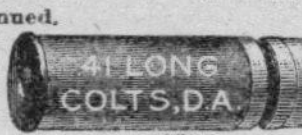

47203

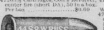

47203½ Cartridges, Colt's Revolver, 41 caliber, center fire (short DA), 50 in a box.
Per box..................$0.60 Weight 1½ lbs. per box. Per 100......$1.15

47204 Cartridges, 44 caliber, Smith & Wesson, center fire, No. 3 Russian, 50 in a box.
Per box..$0.80
Per 100..1.42
Weight, 2¼ lbs.

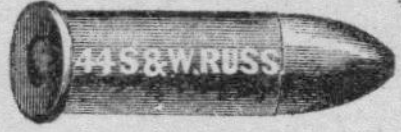

47204

47205 Smith & Wesson, American model, 44 caliber, center fire, 50 in a box.
Per box..................................$0.76
Per 100..................................1.38
Weight, 2¼ lbs.

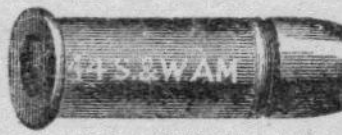

47205

47207 Cartridges for Colt's Pistol, 44 caliber, center fire, 50 in a box. Per box..............................$0.80
Per 100..................................$1.45 Weight, 2¼ lbs. per box.

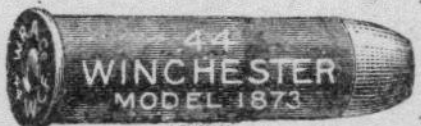

47208

47208 Cartridges for Winchester Rifle, Model 1873, 44 caliber, center fire, 40 grains powder, 200 grains lead, 50 in a box, using No. 1 primer. Per box $0.70
Per 100..1.38
Weight, 1¾ lbs.
Per box.........................$0.88

47209 Cartridges, 44 caliber, long, center fire, for old Ballard rifles, 50 in a box.
Per 100..............$1.60. Weight, 2¼ lbs.

47210 Cartridges, Evans' New Model Repeating Rifle, 44 caliber, 42 grains powder, 280 grains lead, 50 in a box. Per box $1.00
Per 100..................................1.89
Weight, 3¼ lbs. per box.

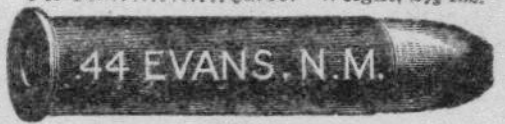

47210

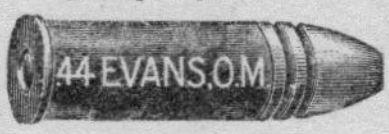

47211

47211 Cartridges, Evans' Old Model Repeating Rifle (34 shot), shell 1 inch long, 33 grains powder, 220 grain bullet, 50 in a box.
Per box..$0.88
Per 100..1.69
Weight, 2½ lbs.

47213 Cartridges, 44 caliber, Webley center fire, for bull dog revolver, 50 in a box. Per box........$0.68
Per 100..1.20
Weight, 2¼ lbs. per box.

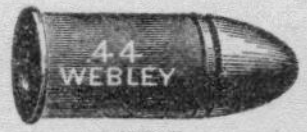

47213

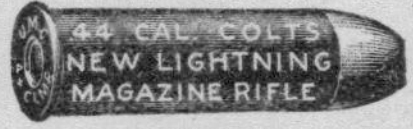

47214

47214 Cartridges, center fire, 44 caliber, for Colt's Lightning Repeating Rifle, 40 grains powder, 217 grains lead, per box of 50..........$0.70
Per 100..1.37
Weight, 2¾ lbs.

47216 Colt's Army and DA Revolvers, 45 caliber, center fire, 50 in a box.
Per box.............................$0.84
Per 100.............................1.57
Weight, 3¼ lbs. per box.

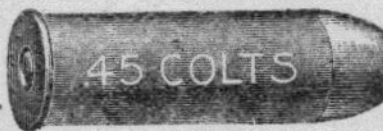

47216

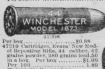

Center Fire Cartridges for Target and Sporting Rifles.

Five per cent discount for cash in case lots if 1,000 of one kind are ordered.

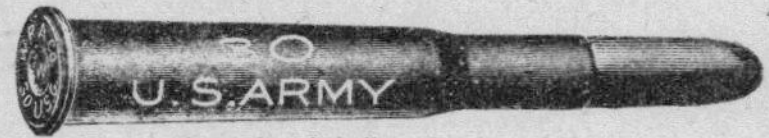

47219 U.S. Army Cartridge, smokeless powder, steel jacketed bullet, 40 grains powder, 220 grain bullet. Per box of 20..........$0.90
For Winchester single-shot rifle, per 100..........4.25

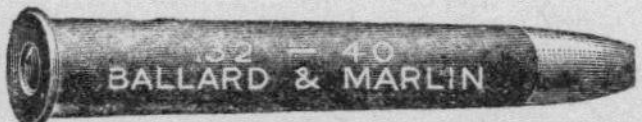

Per 100.

47220 Cartridges, for Ballard, Marlin and Winchester Single Shot Rifles, center fire, 32 caliber, 40 grains of powder, 165 grains lead. Weight, 1¼ lbs. Per box of 20 ....$0.47 $2.29
47221 Cartridges, for Ballard, Marlin and Winchester Single Shot, Short Range, 32-40 caliber, 13 grains powder, 98 grains lead. Weight, 1¼ lbs. Per box of 20..........................48 2.33

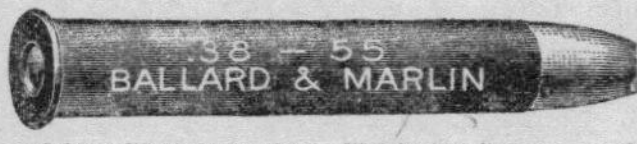

47222 Center Fire 38-55 caliber, powder 55 grains, lead 255 grains for Ballard and Marlin and Winchester Single Shot Rifles of this caliber; 20 in a box. Weight, 1½ lbs..........$0.60 Per 100...$2.72
47223 Cartridges 38-55 Express for Marlin and Winchester Rifles, 38-55 caliber. Box of 20..........$0.63. Per 100..........$2.96
47224 Cartridges, for Ballard, Marlin and Winchester Single Shot, 38-55 caliber, SHORT RANGE, 20 grains powder, 155 grains lead; same length shell as No. 47222. Per box of 20. $0.60. Per 100..........$2.72

47225 Cartridges, for Winchester Rifle, Models 1886, 38-56 caliber, 255 grains. Weight, 1⅞ lbs. Per box of 20.
Per box..........$0.60 Trade price per 100..........$2.70

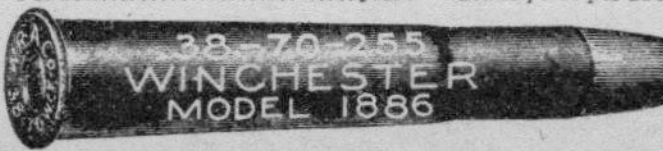

47226 Cartridge for Model, 86, Winchester Rifle, 38-70-255. 20 in a box.
Per box. Per 100
$0.60 $2.85

Cartridges—Continued.

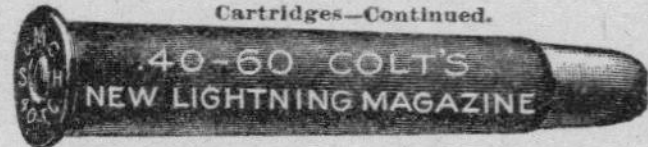

47227 Cartridges, center fire for Colt's Lightning Rifle, 40 caliber, 60 grains powder, 260 grains lead. Weight, 1¾ lbs. Box of 20.
Per box..........$0.55 Per 100..........$2.62

47228 Cartridges, for Winchester Rifle, Model '86, 40-70-330, 20 in a box.
Per box...$0.65
Per 100. 3.00

47230 Cartridges, for Winchester Rifle, 40-60 caliber, 60 grains powder, 210 grains lead. 20 in box.
Per box..............$0.54
Per 100..............2.62
Weight, 1⅛ lbs.

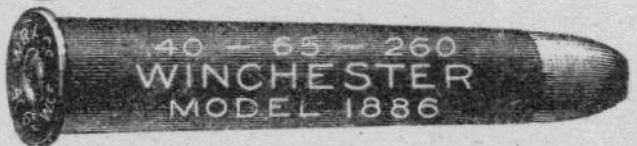

47231 Cartridges, for Winchester Repeating Rifle, Model 1886, 40-65-260 caliber, center fire. 20 in box.
Per box.........$0.59
Weight, 1½ lbs.
Per 100........2.70

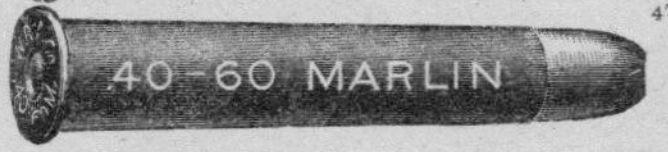

47232 Cartridges, for Marlin Rifle, 40-60 caliber, center fire, 60 grains powder, 260 grains lead, 20 in a box.
Per box.........$0.59
Weight, 1⅛ lbs.
Per 100.....2.70

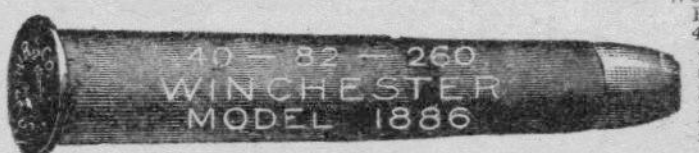

47233 Cartridges, 40-70-330 straight shell, grooved ball, 20 in box.
Per box......$0.64
Per 100........2.95
Weight, 1⅜ lbs.

Per 100.

47234 Cartridges, 40 caliber, 82 grains powder, 260 grain bullet, center fire, for Winchester Rifle, Model 1886. Per box of 20, $0.64 $2.97
47235 Cartridges, 40-75-260, hollow point express bullet, for Winchester Rifle, 40-82 caliber. Per box of 20..........$0.75 3.20

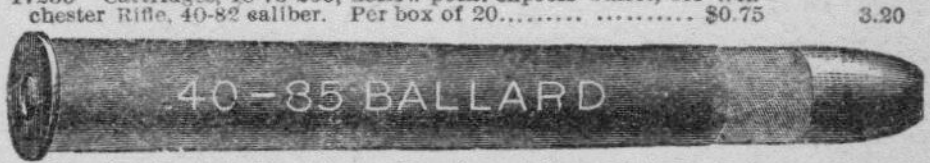

Per 100

47236 Cartridges, 40-85 caliber, center fire, straight shell, for Ballard Rifle; this caliber, 85 grains powder, 370 grains lead. Per box of 10..........$0.45 $4.12
47237 Cartridges, for Sharp's Rifle, 40-90, Sharp's, Remington and Winchester Single Shot Rifles, center fire, 3¼ inches, straight shell, 90 grains powder, 370 grains lead. For shape of shell see 40-85 Ballard. Per box of 10..........$0.45 4.12
47239 Cartridges, 40-110 Express, 3¼ inch shell, 110 grains powder, 260 grains lead. Per box of 10..........$0.72 6.80

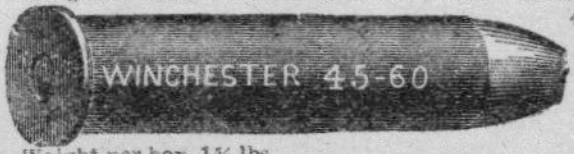

47240 Cartridges, for Winchester Rifle, Model 1876, 45 caliber, center fire, straight shell, 60 grains of powder, 300 grains of lead. 20 in box.
Per box..............$0.60
Per 100..............2.72
Weight per box, 1⅝ lbs

47242 Cartridges, for Winchester Rifle, Model '76, 45 caliber, center fire, 75 grains powder, 350 grains lead, 20 in box.
Per box............$0.63
Per 100............3.00
Weight per box, 1⅛ lbs.

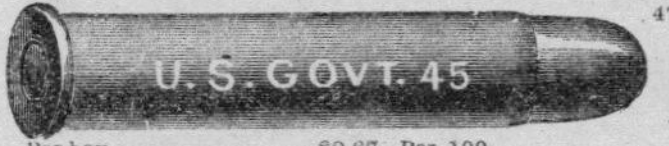

47243 Cartridges, 45 caliber, center fire, for Winchester Rifle, Model 1886, 70 grains powder, 405 grains lead, 20 in box. Weight per box, 36 oz.
Per box..............$0.67 Per 100..........$2.98
47244 Cartridges, for Marlin Rifle and Winchester Model '86 Rifle, 45 caliber, center fire, 70 grains powder, 405 grains lead, 20 in box.
Per box..........$0.67 Per 100..........$2.98. Weight per box, 36 oz.
47245 Cartridges, for single shot rifles, 45-70 caliber, for armory practice, 5 grains powder, 140 grains lead, round ball, per box of 20.
Per box..........$0.67 Per 100..........$2.98 Weight per box, 20 oz.
47246 Cartridges, for Marlin Rifle or any other 45-70 caliber rifle, 45 caliber, 85 grains powder, 285 grain bullet, per box of 20..........$0.67
Weight per box, 30 oz. Per 100..........2.98
47247 Cartridges 45-70-330, hollow bullet, for Winchester Rifles, 45-70 caliber.
Per box of 20..........$0.70 Per 100..........$2.97

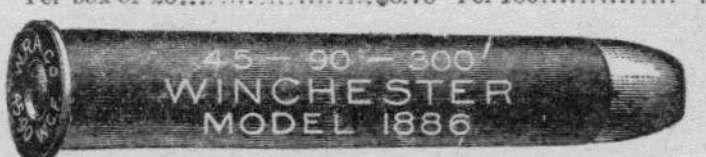

47249 Cartridges for Winchester Repeating Rifle model 1886, 45 caliber, 90 grains powder, 300 grain bullet.
Weight per box, 28 oz. Per box of 20......$0.70 Per 100..........$3.17
47250 Cartridges 45-90-300, hollow point express bullet, for Winchester Rifle, 45-90 caliber. Per box of 20..........$0.75 Per 100..........$3.25
47254 Cartridge, Sharp's only, 2¼ in. necked shell, 44-77-405. Per box of 20 .80
Per 100..........3.62
Weight, per box 30 oz.
47255 Cartridges, U. S. Government 45 caliber, 70 grains powder, 2⅛ inch shell, 500 grain ball, special long-range target, for Winchester and other 45-70 caliber rifles, 20 in box.......... .72
Weight per box, 36 oz. Per 100..........3.25

Cartridges—Continued.

	Per Box.	Weight.	Per 100.
47257 Cartridges, 50 caliber, U. S. Government center fire, 70 grains powder, 1¾ inch shell, per box of 20	$0.58	44 oz.	$2.85
47258 Cartridges, Regular and Remington, 44-77-470, necked 2¼ inch shell, per box of 20	.80	44 oz.	3.62
47259 Cartridges, Sharp's straight 2⅞ inch shell, 45-105-550, per box of 20	1.08	55 oz.	4.84

47261 Cartridges, 50-95 Winchester Express Rifle, 95 grains powder, 300 grains bullet, 20 in box.
Price per box, $0.76. Per 100, $3.35

	Per Box.	Weight.	Per 100.
47262 Cartridges. 50-110-300, Winchester Express, per box of 20	.87		3.92

Cartridges for Remington Rifle.

	Pr bx.	Wgt. pr. bx	Per 100
47264 32 caliber, center fire, 30 grains powder, 125 grains lead, per box of 50	$0.90	36 oz.	$1.70
47265 38 caliber, center fire, 1¾ inch, 40 grains powder, 245 grains lead, straight shell, per box of 20	.60		2.65
47266 38 caliber, center fire, 2¼ inch straight shell, 50 grains powder, 245 grains lead, per box of 20	.63		2.88
47267 40 caliber, center fire, 45 grains powder, 265 grains lead, 1⅞ inch straight shell, per box of 20	.62	24 oz.	2.88
47268 40 caliber, center fire, 65 grains powder, 330 grains lead, 2¾ inch straight shell, per box of 20	.71	38 oz.	3.30

Cartridges—Continued.

47271 32-44 caliber, center fire, S. & W. Target Cartridges, grooved ball, 19 grs. powder, 83 gr. ball; per box of 50..$0.71

47272 32-44 S. & W. Gallery Cartridges, center fire, round ball, 6 grains powder, 50 grain bullet, per box of 50 .... $0.68
47273 38-44 caliber, center fire, S. & W. Target Cartridges, grooved ball, 23 grains powder, 140 grain ball, per box of 50 .... .87
47274 38-44 caliber, center fire, S. & W. Gallery, round ball, 6 grains powder, 70 grain ball, per box of 50 .... .70

Patent Metal Patch Bullet Cartridges.

These Cartridges are made up with the regular shell, and vary only in charge of powder and weight and kind of bullet. The Patent Metal Patched Bullet gives increased accuracy, penetration and cleanliness. The bullet has a covering of copper.

47275 Metal Patch Cartridge, 38-56-255 for Winchester Mod. '86 rifle. Per box of 20 .... $0.65. Per 100 .... $3.00
47276 Metal Patch Cartridge, 40-65-245 for Winchester Rifle Mod. '86. Per box 20 .... $0.65. Per 100 .... $3.00
47277 Metal Patch Cartridge, 40-82-245 for Winchester Rifle Mod. '86. Per box of 20 .... $0.68. Per 100 .... $3.20
47278 Metal Patch Cartridge, 45-90-295 for Winchester Rifle. Per box of 20 .... $0.75. Per 100 .... $3.36

Blank Cartridges. Order No 47280.

Primed and regular powder charge, but without ball. Weight per box of fifty, ¾ to 1¼ lbs.

22 caliber, rim fire, per box of 100	$0.18
32 caliber, rim fire, per box of 50	.22
45-70 caliber, per box of 25	.57
50-70 caliber, per box of 25	.72

Empty Rifle and Pistol Shells. Order No. 47281.

Sold in any quantity from one shell to a thousand. All center fire. Shells can be sent by mail.

	Weight.	Per 100
22 caliber, Winchester	1 lb.	$0.77
25-20 caliber	1 lb.	1.02
32 caliber, for Smith & Wesson	1⅛ lb.	.55
32 caliber, for Winchester, 1873 model	1⅜ lb.	.75
32-44 S. & W., gallery	¾ lb.	.90
32-44 S. & W., target	¾ lb.	.91
32 caliber, for Colt's Rifle	1⅜ lb.	.78
38 caliber, for Smith & Wesson	1⅛ lb.	.64
38 caliber, for Colt's Pistol	2 lb.	.63
38 caliber, for Winchester, model '73	1¾ lb.	.85
38-44 S. & W., gallery	1⅛ lb.	1.08
38-44 S. & W., target	1⅛ lb.	1.08
41 caliber, for Colt's Long D. A. Pistol	2 lb.	.63
44 caliber, for Smith & Wesson, Russian	2 lb.	.85
44 caliber, for Winchester, model '73	1¾ lb.	.85
44 caliber, for Colt's Lightning Rifle	1¾ lb.	.86
44 caliber, for Evan's Rifle, new model	1 5/16 lb.	1.00
44 caliber, Webley	⅞ lb.	.68
45 caliber, for Colt's Revolvers	1 5/16 lb.	.90
32-40 caliber, Ballard & Marlin	2 lb.	1.30
38-55 caliber, Ballard & Marlin	2½ lb.	1.50
40-60 caliber, Winchester, model '76	2¾ lb.	1.68
40-85 caliber, Ballard	2¾ lb.	2.20
40-65 caliber, Winchester, model '86	2¾ lb.	1.55
45-60 caliber, Winchester, model '76	2½ lb.	1.68
40-82 caliber, Winchester, model '86	2¾ lb.	2.00
45-70 caliber, U. S. Government	2¾ lb.	1.90
45-75 caliber, Winchester, model '76	2¼ lb.	1.75
44-77 caliber, Sharp's only, necked	2¼ lb.	2.00
40-90 Ballard	2¾ lb.	2.20
45-90 Winchester	2⅞ lb.	2.00
50-70 Government	2¾ lb.	1.80
40-70 Remington, Straight	2½ lb.	1.85
40-90 Sharp's Straight	3¼ lb.	2.26
38-56 Winchester	2⅞ lb.	1.60
40-90 Sharp's necked	2⅝ lb.	2.20

Prices of cartridges, shot and ammunition in general are subject to market changes without notice.

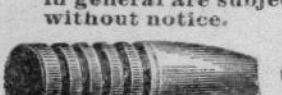

Grooved Bullets. Order No. 47285.

Weight, per 100, 1¾ lbs. to 4 lbs., according to size.

32-165

Sizes.	Description.	Weight Grains.	Price Per 100.	Weight Per 100.
22	Winchester	45	$0.21	1 lbs.
32-40	Short Range	98	.45	2 lb.
38-55	Short Range	155	.63	2¼ lbs.
25-20	Stevens'	86	.35	1¾ lbs.
32	Smith & Wesson	85	.25	1¾ lbs.
32-73	Winchester	115	.35	2 lbs.
32-40	Ballard & Marlin	165	.60	2½ lbs.
32-40	Ballard & Marlin	185	.81	4 lbs.
32-44	S. & W.	83	.47	1 lb.
32-44	S. & W., round ball	146	.36	1½ lbs.
38-44	S. & W.	140	1.08	1¼ lbs.
38-44	S. & W., round	70	.37	1 lb.
38	Smith & Wesson	145	.38	3 lbs.
38-73	Winchester	180	.42	4 lbs.
38-55	Ballard & Marlin	255	.78	4 lbs.
40-60	Winchester	210	.66	3½ lbs.
40-60	Marlin	260	.75	4½ lbs.
45		285	.95	4½ lbs.
44-73	Winchester	200	.50	3¼ lbs.
44	Smith & Wesson, Russian	256	.54	4 lbs.
45	Colt D A	260	.58	4¼ lbs.
45-60	Winchester	300	.75	4½ lbs.
45-75	Winchester	350	.79	5¼ lbs.
45-70	Government	405	1.00	6 lbs.
45-70	Government	500	1.25	7¼ lbs.
50-70	Government	450	1.35	6¾ lbs.
50-95	Hollow Ball Express	300	.90	5¼ lbs.
50-95	Solid Ball Express	312	.76	

Patched Bullets. Order No. 47286.

Size.	Description.	Weight Grains.	Weight Per 100.	Price Per 100.
32-40	Ballard	185	3¼ lbs.	$0.82
38-55	Ballard	255	4¼ lbs.	.85
40-85	Ballard	370	5¾ lbs.	1.05
40-90	Sharp & Winchester, straight	370	5¾ lbs.	1.05
44-77	Remington	470	7 lbs.	1.35
44-90	Remington	550	8 lbs.	1.40
45-70	Sharp's	420	6¼ lbs.	1.25
45-105	Sharp's	550	10¼ lbs.	1.89
45		500	7½ lbs.	1.48
40		330	5 lbs.	.96

Metal Patched Bullets.

Order No. 47287.

	Price Per 100
38-56—245 grains	$1.00
40-65—245 grains	1.00
40-82—245 grains	1.00
45-90—295 grains	1.00

The metal patched bullet is adapted to Winchester rifles of above calibers.

Everlasting Shells.

No.	Size.	Description.	Each.
47294	45-70	Ballard Everlasting Shells	$0.08
47295	45-100	Ballard Everlasting Shells	.07

By mail, 1 cent extra.

Shot Cartridges.

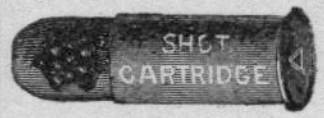

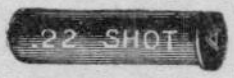

Loaded with shot instead of ball. For use in rifles and revolvers.

	Weight.	Per 100.
47300 22 caliber, rim fire, 50 in box, per 100	¾ lbs.	$0.55
47301 32 caliber, long rim fire, 25 in box, per 100	2 lbs.	1.10
47303 32 caliber, S. & W., center fire, 50 in box, per 100	2 lbs.	1.17
47304 38 caliber, S. & W., center fire, 50 in box, per 100	4 lbs.	1.30
47305 44 caliber, Winchester, model 1873, center fire, 50 in box, per 100	5 lbs.	1.64
47307 32 caliber, center fire, Winchester model 1873, 50 in box, per 100	2½ lbs.	1.36
47308 38 caliber center fire, Winchester model 1873, 50 in box, per 100	4¼ lbs.	1.65
47309 56-52 caliber, Spencer rim fire, per 100		2.50
47309½ 56-56 caliber, Spencer rim, per 100 25 in a box		2.50

Pin Fire Pistol Cartridges.

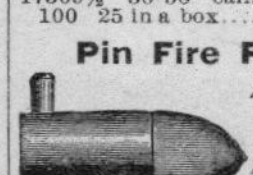

47310 7 M-M per box of 50, weight 18 oz. $0.30

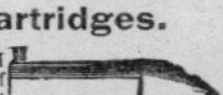

47311 9 M-M. per box of 50 weight, 24 oz. $0.45

In sizes 7 M-M is 32 caliber, 9 M-M is 38 caliber, 12 M-M is 44 caliber.

47312 12 M-M per box of 50 weight, 24 oz. $0.58

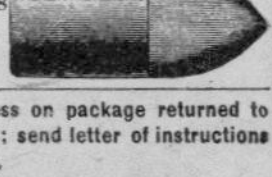

***_** Write your name and Address on package returned to us if you want it to have attention; send letter of instructions by mail; do not put it in package.**

Machine-Loaded Paper Shot Shells.

Every Shell warranted.

Loaded Shells can go by freight or express, alone or with other goods.

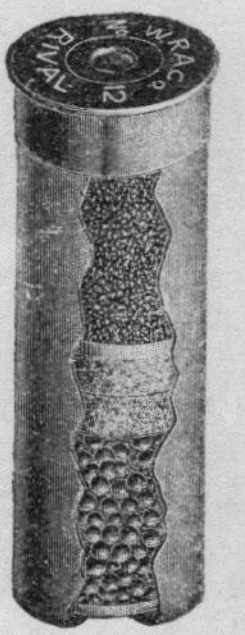

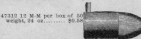

The shells used are the celebrated WATERPROOF RIVAL and Club, U. M. C. and Winchester make. (Waterproof paper shells.) Put up in boxes of 25 shells, 20 boxes or 500 shells to the case. These shells are loaded with two thick black edge wads, and one CARDBOARD wad over the powder, and one thin cardboard wad over the shot.

NO BETTER MADE.

The uniformity of the mateial used and the regularity of the machine work, insure level seating of wads and even pressure of powder, the compression being such as to secure the *highest explosive force*, thereby giving absolute perfection of loading, and becoming at once the most salable form of fixed ammunition. We can usually furnish these goods, loaded with Dupont, Laflin & Rand, or Hazzard American dead shot powder.

PRICES SUBJECT TO CHANGE WITHOUT NOTICE.

Weight, per case, 12 gauge, 65 lbs.; 10 guage, 77 lbs.; 500 shells in a case.

5 per cent. discount for cash on 1,000 lots or over.

Order No. 47315. 12 Gauge.

Black Powder.

Load No.	Am't. of powder	Am't. of shot	Size shot	Adapted to shooting.	Price per Box 25	Price per 100
701	3 dr.	1 oz.	10	Woodcock	$0.34	$1.22
703	3¼ dr.	1⅛ oz.	9	Snipe	.35	1.29
705	3¼ dr.	1 oz.	8	Quail	.34	1.24
707	3¼ dr.	1⅛ oz.	8	Quail & Prairie cks	.36	1.29
709	3½ dr	1⅛ oz.	8	Prairie chicken	.37	1.31
711	3 dr.	1¼ oz.	8	Inanimate Targets	.37	1.31
713	3¼ dr.	1¼ oz.	8	Inanimate Targets	.38	1.34
715	3½ dr	1¼ oz.	8	Live Pigeons	.38	1.34
717	3¼ dr.	1¼ oz.	7	Clay Pigeons	.38	1.34
719	3¼ dr.	1⅛ oz.	7	Ruffed Grouse	.36	1.29
721	3½ dr.	1⅛ oz.	7	Teal	.37	1.32
723	3½ dr.	1¼ oz.	7	Live Pigeons	.39	1.37
725	3¼ dr.	1⅛ oz.	6	Bluebill	.36	1.29
727	3½ dr.	1⅛ oz.	6	Pintail	.37	1.32
729	3½ dr.	1⅛ oz.	5	Mallard	.37	1.32
731	3¾ dr.	1⅛ oz.	4	Red-head	.38	1.34
733	3¾ dr.	1⅛ oz.	3	Canvas-back	.38	1.34
735	4 dr.	1⅛ oz.	2	Turkey	.38	1.37
737	4 dr.	1⅛ oz.	1	Brant	.38	1.37
739	4 dr.	1⅛ oz.	BB	Goose	.45	1.54
741	3 dr.	1 oz	9		.34	1.22
743	3 dr.	1 oz.	8		.34	1.23
745	3 dr.	1⅛ oz.	8		.36	1.27
747	3 dr.	1 oz.	7		.34	1.22
749	3 dr.	1 oz.	6		.34	1.22
751	3¼ dr.	1⅛ oz.	5		.36	1.29
752	3 dr.	1⅛ oz.	7		.35	1.27
753	3 dr.	1¼ oz.	7		.35	1.30

TOYS FOR THE CHILDREN.

Our line of toys and games consists of all the latest articles upon the market. Prices very low this season. **See pages 219 to 234.**

Order No. 47316. 10 Gauge.

Machine Loads. Black Powder.

Load No.	Am't of powder	Am't of shot.	Size shot.	Adapted to shooting.	Price per 25	Price per 100
700	4 dr.	1⅛ oz.	10	Woodcock..........	$0.40	$1.41
702	4 dr.	1⅛ oz.	9	Snipe..............	.40	1.41
704	4 dr.	1⅛ oz.	8	Quail.............[en	.38	1.42
706	4¼ dr.	1⅛ oz.	8	Quail & Prairie Chick-	.40	1.44
708	3¾ dr.	1¼ oz.	8	Inanimate Targets.	.40	1.44
710	4 dr.	1¼ oz.	8	Inanimate Targets.	.41	1 46
712	4¼ dr.	1¼ oz.	8	Inanimate Targets.	.42	1.49
714	4½ dr.	1¼ oz.	8	Live Pigeons.......	.42	1.51
716	4¼ dr	1¼ oz	7	Clay Pigeons.......	.42	1.49
718	4¼ dr.	1⅛ oz.	7	Ruffed Grouse......	.40	1.44

Order No. 47316. 10-Gauge—Continued.

Load No.	Am't of powder	Am't of shot.	Size shot.	Adapted to shooting.	Price per 25	Price per 100
720	4½ dr.	1⅛ oz.	7	Teal............ ..	$0.41	$1.46
722	4½ dr.	1¼ oz.	7	Live Pigeons.......	.42	1.51
724	4¼ dr.	1⅛ oz.	6	Bluebill	.42	1.44
726	4½ dr.	1⅛ oz.	6	Pintail..............	.41	1.46
728	4½ dr.	1⅛ oz.	5	Mallard..............	.41	1.46
730	4½ dr.	1⅛ oz.	4	Red-Head	.41	1.46
732	4¾ dr.	1⅛ oz.	3	Canvas-Back	.42	1.49
734	5 dr.	1⅛ oz.	2	Turkey..............	.42	1.51
736	5 dr.	1⅛ oz.	1	Brant...............	.42	1.51
738	5 dr.	1⅛ oz.	BB	Goose..............	.55	1.66
740	3½ dr.	1¼ oz.	8	....	,40	1.41
742	3½ dr.	1⅛ oz.	7	....	.39	1.37
744	3¾ dr.	1⅛ oz.	6	....	.39	1.39
746	4 dr.	1⅛ oz.	6	....	.40	1.41
748	4 dr.	1⅛ oz.	7	....	.40	1.41
750	4¼ dr.	1⅛ oz.	5	....	.40	1.44

Order No. 47318. 16 Gauge.

Machine Load Black Powder.

Load No.	Am't of powder	Am't of shot.	Size shot.		Price per 25	Price per 100.
800	2½ dr.	⅞ oz.	10	....	$0.33	$1.20
802	2¾ dr.	1 oz.	10	....	.37	1.27
804	2½ dr.	⅞ oz.	9	....	.35	1.20
806	2¾ dr.	1 oz.	9	....	.37	1.27
808	2¾ dr.	1 oz.	8	....	.37	1.27
810	2¾ dr.	1 oz.	7	....	.37	1.27
812	2¾ dr.	1 oz.	6	....	.37	1.27
814	3 dr.	1 oz.	6	....	.38	1.30
815	2½ dr.	1 oz.	8	....	.37	1.25
816	2½ dr.	1 oz.	7	....	.37	1.25

M. W. & Co.'s Prices for Hand-Loaded Shells.

USE OUR HAND-LOADED SHELLS AND IMPROVE YOUR SCORES 10 TO 20 PER CENT.

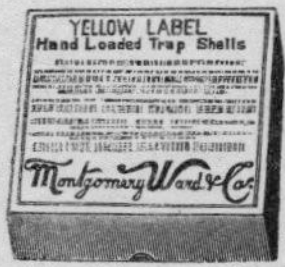

Your ammunition is only second in importance to your gun. Your gun may be of the highest grade, but with improper ammunition a cheaper gun properly loaded might prove more effective at the trap or in the field. Knowing this to be a fact we have added this new department and placed it under the supervision of a well-known trap shooter who has had long experience in loading shells for the most prominent trap shooters in the West. Shooting and testing all kinds of guns and experimenting with all kinds of powder for years, assures us that we can guarantee our hand loaded shells to be as good as it is possible to obtain anywhere in the world. A trial will convince you that our claim is good.

Our Famous $2.00 Load.

S. S.", "E. C." OR DUPONTS SMOKELESS POWDER.

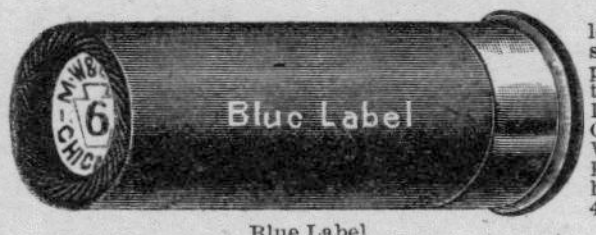

Blue Label.

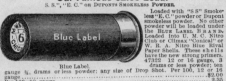

Loaded with "S S" Smokeless "E. C." powder or Dupont smokeless powder. No other powder will be loaded under the BLUE LABEL BRAND. Loaded into U. M. C. Nitro Club or Climax "Conical" or W. R. A. Nitro Blue Rival Paper Shells. These shells have the new strong primers.

47322 12 or 16 gauge, 3 drams or less powder; ten gauge ¾, drams or less powder; any size of Drop Shot. Per 100, 12 or 16 gauge..$2.00
Per 100, 10 gauge..2.35

Our World-Beater $2.40 Load.--(Yellow Label).

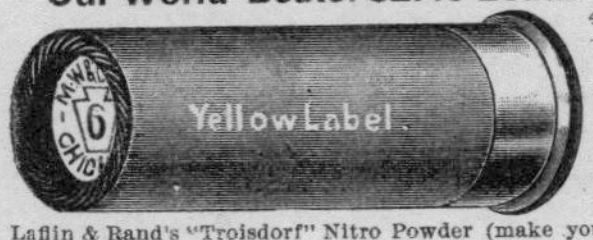

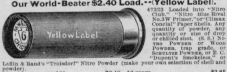

47323 Loaded into "Nitro Club," "Nitro Blue Rival No.3W Primer," or "Climax Concial" Paper Shells. Any quantity of powder, any quantity or size of drop or chilled shot. (S. S.) NITRO POWDER or WOOD POWDER, trap grade, or SCHULTZE POWDER, or E. C. "Dupont's Smokeless," or Laflin & Rand's "Troisdorf" Nitro Powder (make your own selection of shell and powder).
12 or 16 gauge, per 100................$2.40 10 gauge.........................$2.85

Our Yellow Label $2.85 Load.

47324 Loaded in the new U.M.C.Red Color "Smokeless" Grade Shells with the No. 3 long quick primer, or Winchester "Leader," or U. S. "Rapid" Nitro Shells. These shells are made especially for nitro powders. Any quantity of Wood, Schultze, E. C. (SS) Smokeless, or "Dupont's Smokeless," or Laflin & Rand's "Troisdorf" powder. Any quantity of chilled or soft shot. Wadded and loaded in the most scientific manner, by a well-known trap shooter.
12 ga. per 100......................$2.85. 10 ga...........................$3.35
No "hang fires" when you use our S. S. Loads. Every shell warranted.

Our Trap Shooters' Delight $3.40 Load—(Yellow Label).

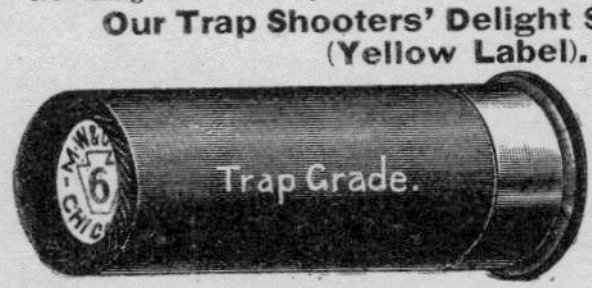

Yellow Label.

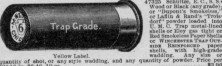

47325 Schultze, E. C., S. S., Wood or Black (any grade), or "Dupont's Smokeless," or Laflin & Rand's "Troisdorf" powder loaded into U. M. C. Trap metal-lined shells or Eley gas tight or Red Smokeless Paper Shells or WINCHESTER TRAP OUTSIDE REINFORCED paper shells, with high-grade wadding. Any size or quantity of shot, or any style wadding, and any quantity of powder. Price per 100 12 ga. $3.40. 10 ga.......................................$3 90

Every one of our hand-loaded shells are warranted the best possible to furnish. No two guns will shoot exactly alike, whether made and bored by the same man or not. This being a fact your only safe way is to test your gun with different loads until you find the load or the loads it will shoot the best.

Black Powder Hand Loaded Shells.

47326 Black Powder, Dupont, Laflin & Rand, American Dead Shot F. G., F. F. G., F. F. F. G., loaded into Club, Climax or Rival paper shells.

Drams	2½	3	3½	4	4½	5
Per 100 12 ga., 16 ga.	$1 80	1.90	2.00	2.10	2.20	2.30

10 ga. loads, 20 cents per 100 higher than 12 gauge.

If your gun don't shoot to suit you, order some of our hand-loaded shells.

Try (SS) Smokeless Powder. It's the best nitro on the market.

Our hand-loaded shells are "hand loaded" by men who are experts and not by boys or on "hand machines." Every motion in loading is made by hand except the crimping of the shell, which is done by electricity.

Price for Shells Loaded with "Walsrode" Powder and Wads Only, Without Shot.

NET PRICES; NO DISCOUNT.

47327 Climax Shells or Blue Rival, primed, 12 bore, $1.90 per 100, per M net, $16.00; Climax Shells or Blue Rival, primed, 10 bore, per 100, $2.25, per M net, $20.00; U. S. or U. M. C. No. 3 primer, "Walsrode" Shells, 12 bore, per 100, $2.50 per M net, $22.50; U. S. or U. M. C., No. 3 primer, "Walsrode" Shells, 10 bore, per 100, $2.75; per M net, $25.50.
Load—12 ga., 29 or 31 grains; 10 ga., 35 or 38 grains.
Add for shot to all above shells $0.60 per 100, $6.00 per M net.

Shot Spreaders—Patented.

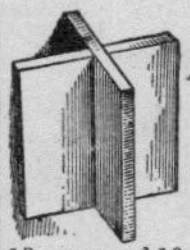

47329 Full Chokes made to spread MORE than cylinders. SHOT SPREADERS do it. A FULL CHOKE makes a circle of only 12 inches at 15 yards. Shot Spreaders make the same gun scatter from 24 to 30 inches. No use of carrying two sets of barrels on a hunting trip. They are made of pasteboard, and pass loosely through the choke. Very successful in the bushes where shooting is done at short range. Just right for quail, woodcock, partridge and rabbits. Do not mangle the game at close quarters. No trouble to load them.
12 gauge and 10 gauge. To load: in a 2⅝ inch shell use 2¾ drs. powder; 1 B, edge and 1 card wad on powder. Drop the spreader down onto the powder wads, and then pour in 1⅛ ounces shot. 1⅛ ounce fills the spreader and a little over. Lay on an ordinary card wad and turn over the shell. If your shell is more than 2⅝ inches long use any load of powder and wads you have room for.
Price per hundred...........................50c. Box of fifty...........................25c

Empty Paper Shot Gun Shells.

· Pin-Fire.

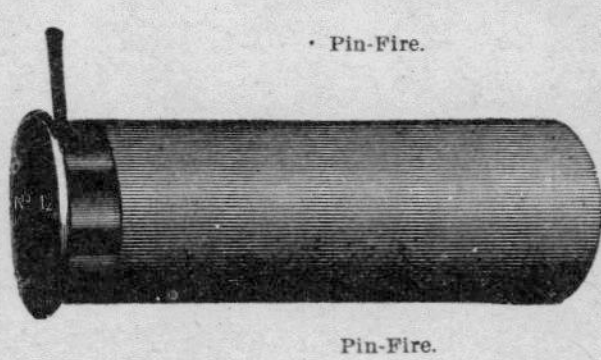

Pin-Fire.

47335 Pin-fire Paper Shells, 20 gauge; per box of 100 weight, 2 pounds, ...$0.70
47336 Pin-fire Paper Shells, 14 gauge; per box of 100, weight 2 pounds, ...$0.70
47337 Pin-fire Paper shells, 16 gauge; per box of 100, weight 2 pounds, ...$0.70
47338 12 gauge; per box of 100, pin-fire, weight 4¼ pounds.........$0.90
47339 10 gauge, pin-fire paper shells, per box of 100.................$1.45

U. M. C. "Walsrode" Paper Shell.

(Salmon.)

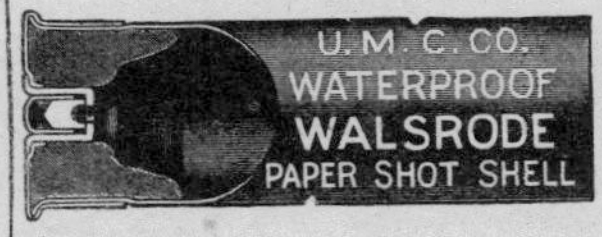

4734 3 U. M. C. Walsrode Paper Shell, Salmon Color No. 3 primer and battery cup, made especially for any proper charge of "Walsrode" powder. It is not adapted to any other powder.

—100 in a box—	Per box.	Per 1,000.
12 Guage, 2⅝ in..	$0.90	$7.98
12 Gauge, 2¾ in..	.97	9.50
10 Gauge, 2⅞ in..	.97	9.50
16 Gauge, 2 9-16 in....................................	.90	8.75

U. M. C. Smokeless Paper Shells.

(Salmon.)

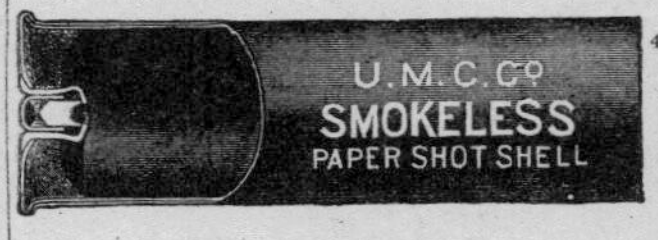

The Smokeless Shell is the Boss Paper Shell.
47601 The New U. M. C. Smokeless Red or Salmon Color Paper Shell, made expressly for (SS) smokeless powder' and the best low-priced shell for E. C. Schultze and Wood powders, using the LONG, STRONG No. 3 primer made by the U. M. C. Company. only. With "Nitro" powder of any kind this is much the *quickest* and strongest shell now upon the market for the price. See that your shells take the LONG No. 3 PRIMER, for they are *much* the *best*. (The long No. 3 primer is twice as long as other primers.)

		Per 1,000.
12 gauge, 2⅝ in., per box of 100, Weight 2¼ lbs................	$0.83	$7.80
12 " 2¾ in., " " " " 2½ "	.89	8.50
10 " 2⅞ in.. " " " " 2¾ "	.89	8.50
16 " " " " " "	.86	8.25

Dupont Smokeless Powder.

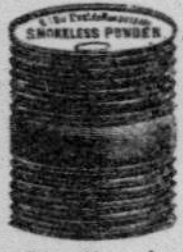
SMOKELESS POWDER

47428 Dupont Smokeless Nitro Powder is a hard, fine grain powder and is quick, clean and smokeless. It is not affected by the extremes of heat, cold or moisture. It may be loaded the same as black powder, except the quantity should be less; use paper shells only; load measured in a regular powder measure. 16 ga. 2 to 2½ drams; 12 ga. 2½ to 3 drams; 10 ga. 2¾ to 3¼ drams.
12½ lb. cans, equal in bulk to 25 lbs. black powder......$16.50
6¼ " " " 12½ lbs. " " 8.44
3½ " " " 6¼ lbs. " " 4.30
½ " " " 1 lb. " " ...... .75

Directions for loading with each can.
N. B.—All nitro or smokeless powders can be shipped by express or freight, either alone or with other goods.

THE NEW GRADE. (S. S.) Smokeless Powder.

THE BEST.

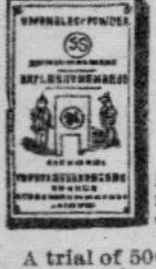
SMOKELESS POWDER
SS

47429 The New Smokeless (S. S.) Shot Gun Powder; does not weigh as much bulk for bulk as black powder.
1 pound can (bulk). Price $0.65
10 pound cans (bulk) 5.80
100 pound cans (bulk)............58.00
"S. V." Smokeless Powder for revolvers, 1-pound can......... 1.00
"S. R." Powder for rifles1 pound can............ 1.00

The superiority of the (S. S.) powder consists in its high velocity, long range, reduced recoil, reduced smoke, reduced fouling and more regular patterns. (S. S.) is the highest development in "Nitro" compounds. In consequence of the absence of "jar" and the reduced recoil it is the most agreeable of powders to shoot.

A trial of 500 of our hand loaded shells, will convince the most pronounced advocate of any other powder that the (S. S.) is all we claim for it.

(S. S.) The Best Smokeless or Nitro Powder Yet Produced.

Comparative Table of Nitro-Powders.

	Wood or Schultze.	"S. S."	"E. C."
2½ drs. (Black Powder measure) equal	35 grains.	34 grains.	36 grains.
2¾ " " " " "	38 "	36 "	40 "
3 " " " " "	42 "	38 "	44 "
3¼ " " " " "	45 "	40 "	47 "
3½ " " " " "	48 "	43 "	50 "
3¾ " " " " "	51 "	46 "	53 "

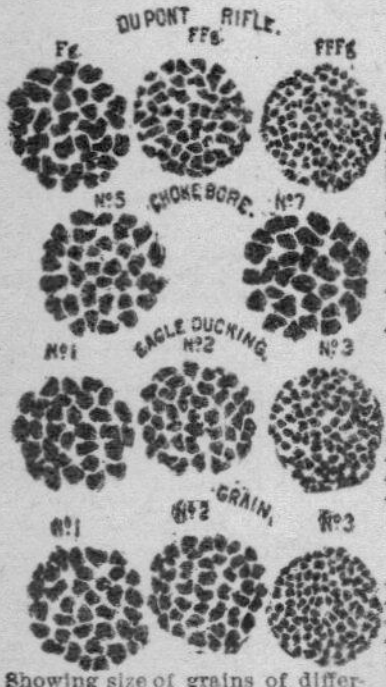
DUPONT RIFLE.
Fg
FFg
FFFg
No5
CHOKE BORE.
No7
No1
EAGLE DUCKING
No2
No3
No1
No2
GRAIN.
No3

Showing size of grains of different powders. Hazard Powder same price as Dupont.

Dupont Rifle and Shot Gun Powder (Black.)

The Messrs. Dupont & Co are the oldest powder makers and have the most extensive works in the country. We consider their powder the best. Every pound warranted *good* and clean, In air-tight metallic kegs; Fg, coarse; FFg, medium; FFFg, fine.
47430 Kegs, Fg. FFg, FFFg, 25 pounds, $3.25
47431 ½ Kegs, Fg, FFg, FFFg, 12½ pounds............ 1.90
47432 ¼ Kegs, Fg, FFg, FFFg, 6¼ pounds............ 1.15
47433 1-pound cans, Fg, FFg, FFFg, per can............ .30

Choke Bore.

47438 Kegs, Nos. 5 and 7, 25 lbs $4.86
47439 ½ kegs, Nos. 5 and 7. 12½ lbs..... 2.70
47440 Kegs, Nos. 5 and 7 6¼ lbs.. .... 1.50
47441 1 pound cans, Nos. 5 and 7 .... .40

Dupont Eagle Duck.

47444 Kegs, Nos. 1, 2, 25 pounds........$11.00
47445 ½ kegs, Nos. 1, 2, 12½ pounds.... 5.75
47446 ¼ kegs. Nos. 1, 2, 3, 6¼ pounds.. 3.00
47447 1-pound cans, Nos. 1, 2 and 3 ...... .60
Powder cannot be shipped by express, but must be sent in separate kegs or cases, and marked "gunpowder," and sent by freight Freight charges are double first-class rates on powder.

Walsrode Smokeless Shot Gun Powder, Nitro.

47450 This powder must only be used in high grade guns, and must only be loaded according to directions on each package; in no case must a larger quantity be used than the directions specify, for it is dangerous to do so.
SINGLE CANISTERS....................$0.85 DRUMS............................$8.50
A single canister will load 120 12-gauge shells; a drum will load 1200 12-gauge shells. Use "Climax" or "Blue Rival," or "Walsrode," U. M. C. paper shells. The Climax or Blue Rival should be primed with about ⅓ grain of black powder.
47451 "Walsrode" Special Powder Measures..............................$0.30
10 or 12 gauges; mention gauge wanted and grain. 29 or 31, 12-gauge; 35 or 38 grain, 10 gauge.
47454 Laflin Rand's "Troisdorf" Smokeless Shot Gun Powder, Nitro.
1 pound cans (bulk), each........$0.68 6½ pound drums (bulk), each... $3.95

"V. C. P." Dupont's "V. C. P."

47455 The new Trap Powder--black, moist, quick, clean and strong (not a nitro). 12½ pound kegs.............................. $2.00
6¼ pound kegs.............................. 1.15

Prices Quoted on Any Make of Powder in the Market.

GUN REPAIRING DEPARTMENT.

Our shop is now one of the largest in the country. We have nothing but first-class workmen, and have as good a stocker and as good a barrel borer as there is in the country. We feel confident that we can do your repairing promptly and give good satisfaction. All work guaranteed.

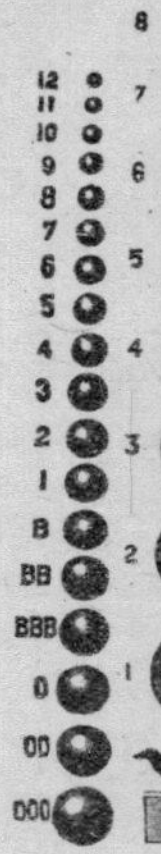
8
12
7
11
10
9
6
8
7
6
5
5
4
4
3
2
3
1
B
2
BB
BBB
1
0
00
000

Shot and Bar Lead.

Subject to market changes without notice.

Chilled and drop shot in sacks of 5 pounds and 25 pounds at lowest market rates. *We do not sell less than a sack.* The price of shot fluctuates so much that we cannot quote permanent price.
47457 Drop Shot, all sizes, 1 to 12, per 25 pound sack..$1.25
47458 Drop Shot, all sizes, 1 to 12. Per 5 lb. sack... .40
47459 Chilled Shot, all sizes, 2 to 10. Per 25 lb. sack. 1.50
47460 Chilled Shot; all sizes, 2 to 10. Per 5 lb. sack. .45
Buck Shot, B to No. 1, 25 lb. sack 1.50
Buckshot, B to No. 1, 5 lb. sack.................. .45

In case of fluctuation chilled shot is always 25 cents higher in 25 lb. sacks and 10 cents higher in 5 lb. sacks than drop shot. We will always bill shot at the lowest market rates.
47461 Bar Lead for running bullets at market price, average price about 6¼ cents per pound.

We will always bill at lowest market prices.

We guarantee lowest market price on cartridges, shells, primers, powder, shot, etc.

Prices subject to change without notice.

We cannot sell 5 lb. sacks at 25 lb. sack rates.

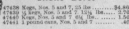

Gallery Targets.

BIRD AND STAR TARGET.

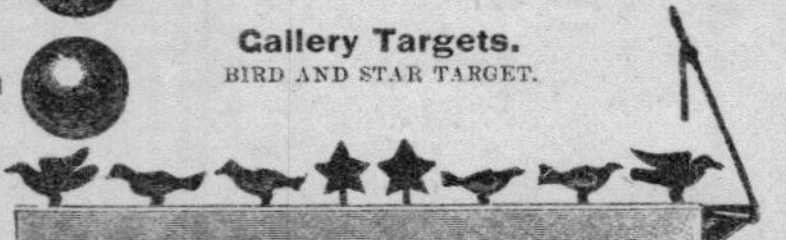

The birds and stars fall back out of sight when hit, and are reset by rope from shooting stand. It is one of the most satisfactory targets in the market, and is made to last. Heavy wrought iron face plate.
47465 Target of 6 extra heavy birds and stars; weight, 14 to 18 pounds. Each....................................... $2.30
47466 Target of 8 extra heavy birds and stars; weight 18 to 22 pounds 2.65

Round Iron Targets.

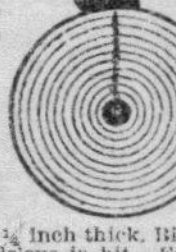

Bell rings when bullseye is hit, and self setting, round iron; no figure.
47468 12 in. diameter, for Flobert ball caps; weight, 12½ pounds..............................$0.90
47470 12 in. diameter, heavy, for 22 cartridges....... .35

Round Iron Figure Targets.

Figure springs up and rings bell when bullseye is hit; reset with rope from shooting stand.
47471 12 inch diameter, for Flobert ball caps; weight, 15 lbs.........................$1.95
47473 12 inch diameter, heavy, for 22 cartridges; weight 15 to 18 lbs.........................$2.25

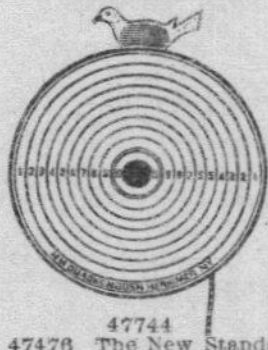

47474 12 inch diameter, steel faced, ¼ inch thick. Bird is thrown up and bell rings when bulls eye is hit For air guns or cartridges not larger than 22 long; weight, 12½ lbs. Each.............................$2.90
Paper Targets for rifle and pistol practice furnished. Write for prices.

Standard Keystone Trap and Target.

47744

47476 The New Standard Keystone Target, improved in every way; best target yet made. Can use in any trap except the Peoria Black Bird trap. Try 1,000 and you will not use any other target
Per (barrel) 500 targets.......$2.90
Per 1,000 Targets............. 5.75
Weight, 148 lbs. per barrel.
In 10,000 lots or over per M... 5.50

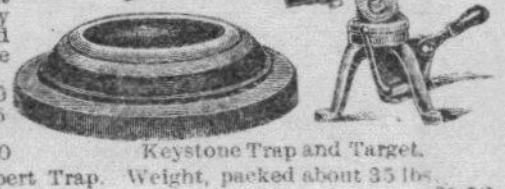

Keystone Trap and Target.

47477 The Standard Keystone Expert Trap. Weight, packed about 35 lbs. Each..$5.50

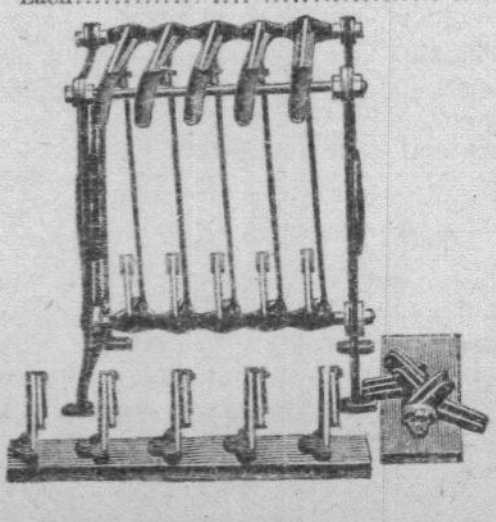

Other targets same price as Keystones.

47478 The Standard Keystone Trap Puller, made entirely of iron; ropes or wires can be used to pull the trap.
Price, 3 trap pull..............$3.75
Price, 5 trap pull.............. 6.00

We can furnish Score Cards free.

THE GUN CLUB SCORE BOOK.

COPYRIGHTED.

100 sheets ruled with 25x25 spaces; alternate sheets perforated to tear out and mail for publication or otherwise. Pocket with three sheets of carbon paper in rear. Bound in cloth with gold side stamp. Price, per copy, $0.75.

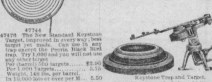

Blue Rock and Trap.

Blue Rock Extension Trap.

47481 Blue Rock Extension Traps. Each $4.50
Standard Keystone Targets work just as well in Blue Rock Traps as other targets.

Other Targets same price as Keystones.

We Furnish Score Cards Free.

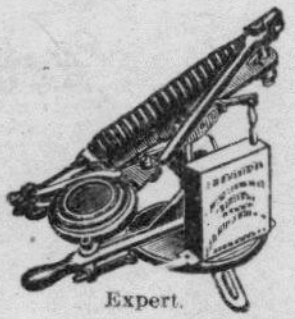

Expert.

47482 The New Blue Rock "Expert" Traps. Each $6.50
47483 Paul North's Electric Trap Pulls, complete with wire and battery. Weight, 35 lbs.

For One Trap	$10.00
For Three Traps	25.00
For Five Traps	30.00

SHOOTING CLUBS are being formed all over the country, even among the farmers. They find it pays in the increased amount of "work" the boys and "hired" men perform.

Midget Traps.

47485 U. S. Midget Traps. The smallest trap made; will throw U. S. pigeons, Blue Rocks, or Standard Keystones 40 yds. Weight, 13 lbs. Each $2.50
Prices on targets are subject to market changes.

Rudolph's Ground Pigeon Trap.

47488—closed.

47488 Rudolph's Ground Pigeon Trap, for live pigeon match shooting. The most satisfactory trap for the purpose and used by many of the State Associations for 8 years. Made of heavy galvanized sheet iron. This trap has filled a long felt want for a good trap at a reasonable price. Every club should have a set.
Each $2.60
Weight, 6¼ lbs. each.

Winchester Make Reloading Tools, Including Bullet Molds, Complete Set.

47510

A set of implements comprises the reloading tool, a bullet mold and charge cup. The reloading tool removes the exploded primer and fastens ball in the shell, at the same time swaging the entire cartridge to the exact form and with absolute safety. Wood handles on bullet molds. Blued finished and polished. Perfect in every respect.

47510 Extra by mail 42 and 45 cents.	Per set.
22 caliber, center fire, Winchester	$1.70
25-20 caliber, center fire, Winchester	1.71
32 caliber, center fire, Winchester model '73	1.76
38 caliber, center fire, Winchester model '73	1.77
44 caliber, center fire, Winchester model '73	1.78
32 caliber, center fire, S. & W	1.68
38 caliber, center fire, S. & W	1.69
38-90 Winchester Express	2.75
44 caliber, center fire, Webley cartridge	1.80
40-90 caliber, Sharps's Patched Straight	2.80
40-70 Ballard Patch Ball	2.81
40-110 caliber, Winchester Express	2.40
40-60 caliber, Winchester	2.15
44 S. & W. Russian	1.80
44 S. & W. American	1.80
45-75 caliber, Winchester	2.26
50-95 caliber, Winchester Express	2.70
50-70 caliber, U. S. Government	2.50
45-60 caliber, Winchester	2.22
50-110 Express	2.40
47511 Reloaders, only 22 to 44 caliber	1.45
Reloaders, only from 40-90 to 45-60 caliber. Each	1.85
47512 Bullet Molds, any caliber. Each	.75
47512½ Brass Charge Cups	.10

Mention caliber when ordering tools.

New Model Winchester Tool, including Bullet Mold and Complete Set. Reloads and Resizes the Shell.

Polished blued finish. Wood handles on bullet molds. Perfect in every respect.

47513 Weight 4¼ pounds.	Per set.
38-56 Winchester	$2.12
40-65 Winchester	2.13
40-82 Winchester	2.14
45-90 Winchester	2.15
45-70 Winchester	2.16
45-70 Gov't, 405	2.17
45-70 Gov't, 500	2.18
50-110 Winchester Express	2.45

N. B.—When we are out of 47513 we shall send No. 47514. No more 47513 to be made after these are gone.

**** ERRORS.—We make them; so does everyone, and we will cheerfully correct them if you will write to us. Try to write us good-naturedly, but if you cannot, then write us any way. Do not let an error pass unnoticed, or complain to your friends or neighbors about it. We want an early opportunity to make right any mistakes that may occur.**

Reloading Tools—Continued.

WINCHESTER NEW MODEL TOOL, including bullet mold with wood handles. A complete set. Reloads and resizes the sheel. Weight, 3¼. Polished blued finish. Perfect in every respect.

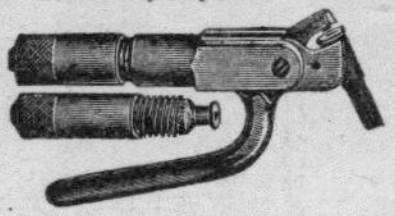

47514

47514—	
32-40 Caliber	$2.15
38-55 Caliber	2.16
38-70 Caliber	2.17
40-70 Caliber	2.17

Ideal Combined Reloading Tools.

IDEAL RELOADING TOOLS.

These tools will reload shells using patched balls, but to run smooth balls you require an extra bullet mold.

47515

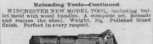

A set of reloading tools includes: Bullet Mold, Recapper, Decapper, Ball Seater, all in one tool. Powder Measure with each set.

IDEAL RELOADING TOOLS.

47515 Any caliber. State caliber wanted.

	Per set.
22 caliber, center fire U. M. C	$1.59
32 caliber, short	1.59
32 caliber, long	1.59
32 caliber, S. & W	1.59
32 caliber, extra long	1.59
38 caliber, short	1.59
38 caliber, long, outside lubricator	1.59
38 caliber, extra long	1.59
38 caliber, S. & W	1.59
41 caliber, Colt's D. A. pistol	1.59
41 caliber, long, Colt's D. A. pistol	1.59

Postage on above tools about 30c. extra

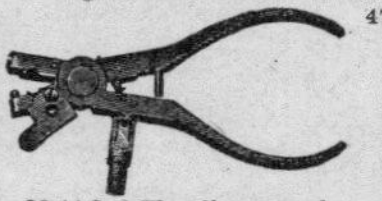

47517 Ideal Tools. State caliber when ordering.
32-44 S. & W. grooved ball. Per set $3.50
32-44 S. & W. gallery round ball.
38-44 S. & W. target grooved $3.50
38-44 S. & W. gallery round 3.50
38 Long Colt Pistol, inside lubricator, per set ... 3.00
Postage on above tools about 40c. extra.

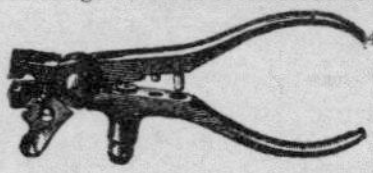

47518 Ideal Tools. 25-20 caliber, Winchester. Per set $1.70
32 caliber, Colt's Lightning Rifle. Per set $1.71

	Per set.
32 caliber, Winchester Rifle	$1.72
32-20 caliber, Marlin	1.73
32-30 caliber, Remington	1.75
38-40 caliber, Winchester Model '73	1.74
38-40 caliber, Colt's Rifle	1.75
38-40 caliber, Marlin Rifle	1.76
44-40 caliber, Colt's Rifle	1.77
44-40 caliber, Winchester Model '73	1.78
44-40 caliber, Marlin	1.79
44 caliber, S. & W. Russian Model	1.80
44 caliber, S. & W. American Model	1.80
45 caliber, Colt's Pistol	1.70

Postage on above tools about 40c. extra.

Reloading Tools—Continued.

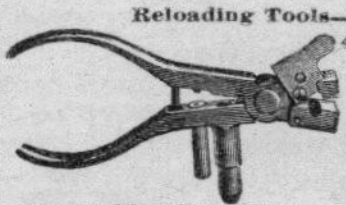

47519 Ideal Reloading Tools. State caliber wanted.
32-40 Ballard and Marlin. Per set $2.10
32-40 caliber, Remington. Per set ... $2.11

	Per set.
38-40 caliber, Remington	$2.12
38-50 caliber, Remington	2.13
38-55 Marlin	2.14
38-56 Winchester and Colt	2.15
40-60 Winchester	2.16
40-60 Colt and Marlin	2.17
40-65 Winchester	2.18
40-70 Sharp's straight grooved	2.70
40-82 Winchester	2.19
44 Evans' new model	2.30
45-60 Winchester	2.20
45-70 405 Government	2.12
45-70 500 Government	2.24
45-70 Marlin	2.14
45-85 285	2.25
45-90 Winchester	2.22
50-70 Government	2.24
40-90 Sharp's straight 3¼ in. shell	3.00

Postage on above tools about 45c. extra.
Can furnish any other caliber in the Ideal Tools that are made, including those for Winchester rifles, etc.

47534 Shell Reducer and Resizer for any size, from 32-40 and larger. Each, $1.75
Order size wanted.
Every good rifle shooter needs these tools.
Postage, extra, 15c.

47535 Ideal Bullet Sizer for making bullets to exact size, and one standard die.
Each $1.50
Extra dies .... .50
You require a die for each style of bullet. Postage, extra, 18c.

47536 Ideal Re-and-De-capper for pistol cartridges. One tool will only re-and de-cap the one size shell. Each .. $1.00
Postage, extra, 8c.

FOR NITRO & BLACK POWDER.

47538 Ideal Loading Flask. Holds ¾ of a pound of black powder; accurate and reliable for either black or nitro powder. Directions for using with each flask.
No. 1 for Rifle, 38 to 50 caliber $2.25
No. 2 for Rifles and Pistols, 38 to 22 caliber 2.20
Extra shell receiver from 22 to shot gun size .... .50
Postage, extra, 20c.

Bullet Molds Only.

Be sure and give size wanted.
For all sporting and military sizes of cartridges.
Extra by mail 16c

	Each
47540 To make Grooved Balls	$0.85
47541 To make Express Balls	1.25
47542 To make Round Balls	1.15
47543 To make Smooth Balls for Cartridges made only with patched bullet	1.00

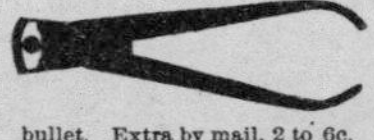

47544 Bullet Molds for making round bullets, from 16 to 120 bullets to the pound. One mold will only make one size of bullet. Extra by mail, 2 to 6c. Each $0.25
47545 Patch paper for cartridges, using patched ball. Per quire .... .70
Per sheet .... .07

Gun Cases—Continued.

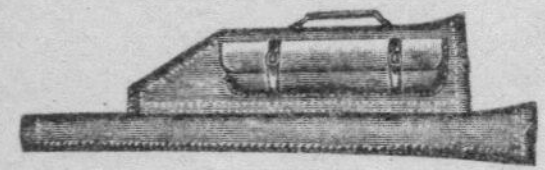

47752-3-5

47752 Victoria Gun Case, extra heavy russet leather, good, strong and durable. 30 and 32 inch barrels, with tool pocket outside......$2.40
47753 Victoria Gun Case, heavy russet sole leather, cotton flannel lined, tool pocket outside, 30 and 32 in. barrels. Weight 36 oz. Each...... 2.63

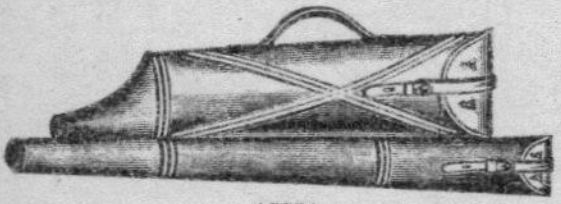

47754

47754 Victoria Gun Case, extra heavy leather, good, strong and durable, no outside pocket, 30 and 32 in. barrels. Each...... 2.00
47755 Victoria Gun Case, extra heavy russet colored sole leather, highly finished, with tool pocket, flannel lined, 30 and 32 inch barrels. Weight, 44 oz. Each...... 2.75

47755½ California style gun case. Heavy brown canvas, leather muzzle protector, tool pocket and sling strap. Well made, strong and durable. Each...$1.00
Postage, extra, 25 cents.

47756½

47756½—Victoria Gun Case, heavy waterproof canvas, reenforced on stock and barrel with pocket for cleaning rod, also shell bag to hold 50 shells. The most complete cover offered to sportsmen and trap shooters. Each......$1.27
Postage, extra, 35 cents.

Weight 40 to 60 ounces.

47757 English Victoria Gun Case, extra heavy oak tanned russet leather, embossed, nickel plated trimmings, patent fastening, staple for lock. A fine case, well made and very durable, 30 and 32 inch barrel. Each......$4 00

47758 English Victoria oak tanned russet colored leather, brass trimmings, a beauty; 28, 30 or 32 in. barrels. Flannel lined, each ...$4.75
47758½ Same as 47758 with tool pocket on outside. Each...... 5.25

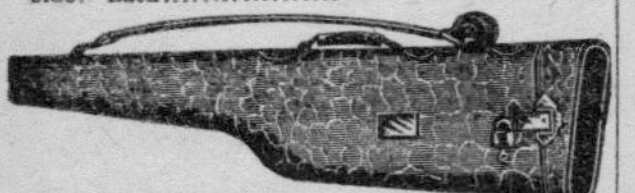

47759

47759 English Victoria, imitation alligator, chestnut colored leather, heavy and strong, a fine case. Each......$4.60
Any of above cases lined with lambskin with the wool left on for $2.00 extra, to order chamois lined $2.50 extra.
47760 English Victoria Gun Case, made of the very best orange color finish sole leather, burnished brass trimmings, made up in the very best style; no tool pocket; elegant in design and finish. Each...... 5.50
47761 Victoria Case, same as 47760, with tool pocket on the outside. Each...... 6.00
All leather Victoria cases are the best and handsomest covers for guns. The leather being thick and heavy protects the guns from being injured or getting rusty. These cases are called sole leather and are almost as heavy as sole leather. (Mention length of gun barrels.)

Hunting and Fishing Case.

47763 Adjustable Revolving Seat Hunting and Fishing Case. Made of copper or galvanized iron. Height, when closed, 9 inches; length, 12 inches; width 6 inches. It will hold 250 No. 10-gauge cartridges. The cover laps over the side when closed and fastens with a spring. The handle is of leather, large and easy on the hand, lies flush with the top when used as a seat, making a perfectly smooth surface. The cover is used as a seat and rises automatically with with a spring to any height desired. It is held firmly in position desired by a catch bolt easily operated. When the spring raises the cover above the box it will revolve. All hunters know the advantage of a revolving seat when shooting on the wing, as one can follow the game with the gun perfectly. For pass shooting it has every advantage. One can mark the game both ways without twisting or getting cramped in the neck, besides having a perfect and a sure aim to the right or left.
Galvanized iron, each......$2.50
Copper, each...... 4.25

Leather Trunk Gun Cases.

For breech loading guns with 30 to 32 in. barrels. Weight, 8 to 10 lbs.

47764 Sole leather trunk case, nickel corners-iron frame, shell top, holding 75 shells for 30 or 32 in. barrels, each......$10.00
47765 Sole Leather Trunk Case same as 47764, without metal corners or shell top, for 30 or 32 in. barrel, each...... 8.90
47766 Heavy Leather Trunk Case, same as 47764, metal corners and without shell top, 30 or 32 in. barrel, each...... 6.25
In ordering trunk cases, give length of barrel.

Shell Boxes.

Weight, 5 lbs.

47767 Sole Leather Shell Boxes, tin lined, with compartments, nickel plated trimmings. Dimensions: 12¾ in. long, 6 in. wide, 7½ in. high; holding 200 shells. Each......$2.95
47768 Sole Leather Shell Boxes, same as 47767, dimensions: 13¾ in. long 8½ in. wide, 8 in. high; holding 300 shells, each...... 3.50

47769 Metallic Shell Box; length, 11 in.; width 6½ in.; depth, 5 in.; capacity 100, No. 12. Each......$1.75
Weight, 3 lbs.
47769½ Length, 13 in.; width, 8½ in.; depth, 7½ in.; capacity, 400 No. 12. Each.$2.75
The material of this box is very heavy, so it could be used for a seat or a stool to sit upon without damage. All are nicely painted and ornamented. Weight about 4 lbs.

47770 Trap Shooter's Leather Ammunition Cases, heavy russet sole leather, tin lined, partitioned for 25 shells in each space; tray for cleaning rod and three partitions for sundries; holds 150 shells. Each......$4.96
Weight 5 lbs.

Pistol Holsters.

47771 Russet Leather Pocket Holster (as adopted by police officers), heavy russet leather, for 3½ in. barrel, 32 and 38 caliber. Made to wear in the hip pocket; sweat proof. The best pocket holster in the market, made to fit the hip pocket, and not necessary to remove it when you take out the revolver.
Each......$0.30
Per dozen...... 3.24

Army and Navy Holster. By mail 5c. extra.

47772-73

47772 Pistol Holster with loop similar to cut, heavy russet leather, 32 caliber. Each......$0.25
47773 Pistol Holster, with loop similar to cut, russet leather, 38, 44 and 45 caliber. Each.... .38

47774 Rubber Pocket Holster with steel hook.
32 caliber......$0.50
38 caliber...... .60
44 caliber...... .80
Postage, 4 cents extra.

The rubber Holster is rust proof, and being soft and pliable, it is the best and most convenient holster ever made to carry a revolver in the pocket. Will hold revolvers with 3½ in. barrel or shorter.

Pistol Holsters—Continued

47776 Pocket Pistol Holster, soft russet leather (no loop for belt) for pocket use only, 22, 32 and 38 calibers. Each.$0.15
Per dozen...... 1.65
Postage, 3 cents.

Pistol Holsters.

(By mail, 5 cents extra.)

47777 Pistol Holster with loop for belt, heavy russet leather, 22 and 32 caliber. Each......$0.26

47778 Pistol Holster, with loop for belt, best russet leather, 38 caliber...... Each $0.25
47779 Pistol Holster, with loop for belt, best russet leather, 44 caliber...... .30
47780 Pistol Holster, with loop for belt, best russet leather, 45 caliber...... .35

47782 Mexican Holster, best russet leather, heavy and durable, 32 and 38 caliber...... .40
44 caliber...... .47
45 caliber...... .50
By mail 6c. extra.

Leather Belts.

Our Leather Goods are the Best in the Market.

47783 Belts only, russet leather, without loops for cartridges. By mail, 5c. extra.
Each......$0.15

47784 Belts only, russet leather, with loops for cartridge; 32 and 38 caliber, 1½ inches. Wide plain roller buckle. By mail, 5c. extra. Each...$0.30

47785 Belts only, fine russet leather, with loops for cartridges. 32, 38, 44 and 45 caliber, 2⅛ inches wide, large nickel plated buckle.
By mail, 10c. extra. Each......$0.45

Rifle Cartridge Belts.

By mail, 5 cents extra. Be sure and mention caliber of cartridge you wish to carry.
47786 Web Rifle Belt, 32, 38, 44, 45 caliber, heavy and strong......$0.35
47787 Leather Rifle Belt, 32, 38, 44, 45 caliber, 2⅛ inches wide, best quality, heavy...... .50

Cartridge and Shot Belts.

47788 The Woven Cartridge Belt, invention of Col. Anson Mills, U. S. A. The main body of the belt, as well as the loops which hold the cartridge, is woven in one solid piece. The belt is soft and pliable, particularly adapted to rifle cartridges. In ordering be sure to give caliber and name of cartridges you wish to carry. 32 to 50 caliber. By mail, 20 cents extra. Each......$1.20

47789 The Anson Mills Woven Shot Shell Belts, 10-gauge and 12 and 16 gauge, with shoulder strap and game hooks. By mail, 22 cents extra.$1.50

Shell Belts.

47790 Anson Mills Hunters' Belt. The loops are woven, closed at the bottom, protecting the crimped end of shell, no sewing on the belt whatever: weight, 5 oz. 10 or 12 gauge. Each.. $1.20
47790½ Light Web Shell Belts, no shoulder straps or welt on bottom; weight, 4 oz...... .18

Belts—Continued.

47791 Canvas Shell Belts, 10, 12, 16 and 20 gauge, with shoulder strap; weight, 15 oz............................$0.40

47792 Russet leather Shell Belt, with shoulder strap, 10, 12, 16 and 20 gauge Each....................$0.46

47793 Russet leather Shell Belt with shoulder strap, 8 gauge only. Each........$1.00

By mail, extra............................16

47795 Mexican Combined Cartridge and Money Belt, made of the very best russet leather; belt 3 inches wide, soft and pliable and will not get hard and crack; neatly embossed, 32 and 38 caliber.......................$0.95
44 caliber..........$0.96 45 caliber.........97
By mail, 13c extra. Don't forget to state caliber wanted.

47796 "The Pop" Shoulder Holster, with breast and shoulder strap to wear under coat on left side, as shown in cut. Made of fine soft russet leather, any caliber or length of barrel. Each.........$0.63
Extra by mail, each 7c. Always forget to state caliber if you are in a hurry for your goods, and then it will be necessary to write us for size.

Money Belts.

By mail, 3 cents extra.

47797 Money belts, chamois skin, with 3 compartments, width 3 inches; to be worn around waist under clothing. Each......$0.40 Per dozen.......$5.00

47798 Money Belts, soft, pliable leather, 3 compartments, sweat proof, never get hard or stiff, the best thing in the world. Each.........................75
Per dozen..................7.70

47799 Heike's Hand Protector, for shot gun barrels, a protection from cold barrels or hot barrels, made of spring steel, leather

MEDIUM CUT.

covered. A necessity to trap shooters. Each...$0.69
By mail 3c. extra.

Recoil Pads.

By mail 5c extra.

47800 Rudolph's Popular Recoil Pad, leather, with lacing; will not become loose. Each............$0.95
Postage extra......10

47801 The Rubber Recoil pad, made entirely of rubber, well padded and will fit any gun, its elasticity keeping it in position, and preventing the shock of the recoil doing injury to the shoulder. Price, each.......$0.35 Per pair........$3.95

47801-2

47802 Pure Red Rubber Recoil Pad, the best pad in the market. Two sizes, No. 3 and 4. No. 3 smallest. Give length of heel plate on gun for which you want the pad. Each.............75
Postage extra..........................07

47803 Silver's Patent Recoil Pad and Butt Piece combined, making a hard rubber butt plate and a flexible rubber pad; for 10 or 12 gauge gun. The screws from old butt plate can be used to hold it on. Each......$3.70
By mail, 10 cents extra.

47804 The "Cow Boy" Holster, made of heavy red, oiled leather, raised embossed work; made to match in color and style our Cow Boy Saddles. The best holster on the market. 38 caliber.....................$1.40

44 caliber.....$1.50 45 caliber........1.60
Postage extra.........................11

47805 The "Cow Boy" Combined Cartridge and MoneyBelt; made of heavy red, oiled leather; strong and durable, designed to match our Cow Boy Saddles. 38, 44 and 45 caliber. Each...........$2.25
Postage extra.............................08

We supply the best standard books at regular jobbers' prices.

Hunting Knives.

All these knives are of very best quality steel.

47807 Deer Foot

47807 Hunting Knife, deer's foot handle, 7-inch clip blade, best steel leather sheaths, with loops to attach to belt, nickel bolstered (see cut).....$1.85

Spear blade / Club blade

47809 Hunting Knife, buckhorn handle, 6-inch best steel blade, leather sheath, with loop to attach to belt; entire length, 11 inches. By mail, 8c extra......................$0.90

47810 Woolenholm I X L Hunting Knives, fine staghorn handle, 6 inch. clip point blade, with leather sheath, finest quality. Each.....2.25

47811 Hunting Knife, same description as No. 47809, 6 inches, spear point. By mail, 8c extra. .95

47812 Hunting Knife, same description as No. 47809, 9 inches, spear point; weight, 13 oz 1.65

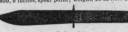

By mail, 8c extra.

47813 Hunting Knives, scored ebony handle, bolstered with guard, best steel blade, 6-inch blades. Each...............................$0.50
6½ inch blades. Each...........................60
7-inch blades. Each..............................70

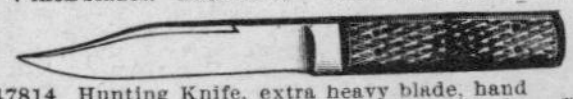

47814 Hunting Knife, extra heavy blade, hand forged, ebony handles, 6 inch clip blade. Each.......70

Sheaths and Belts.

By mail, 8c extra.

47815 Leather Knife Sheaths.
6 in. 7 in. 8 In. 9 In.
$0.10 .12 .15 .18

47816 Leather Belts for knife sheaths, 1¼ in. wide.....................................$0.15

Hunter's Ax.

Hunters' Ax and Sheath.

47818—Hunters' Ax, with handles, extra cast steel, steel poll; wt., per cut. This is a very convenient tool. It makes a light ax or a heavy hatchet. Price each......$1.40

1¼ lbs; with heaviest russet leather sheath, as per cut.

Pocket Oilers.

47819 The C. & D. Perfection Gun Oiler, the best and handiest gun and revolver oiler in the market. Each...................................$0.23

47820 The Pocket Oiler, flat, nickel plated with brass screw on top, entirely preventing the escape of oil, can be carried in the vest pocket; about the size of a watch. Each.......................$0.12
Per dozen....................................1.25
Extra, by mail, 2c

Gun Oils, Etc.

Winchester Gun Grease, put up by the Winchester Repeating Arms Company.

47820

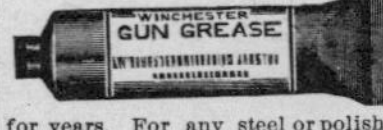

47821 The Winchester Gun Grease is the best rust preventer manufactured. It has been in use in this factory for years. For any steel or polished iron surface and for inside or outside of gun or rifle barrels it has no equal. Put up in neat metallic tubes. Per tube..$0.11
Per box of 10 tubes.............................1.15
Postage 12c. extra, per ten tubes.

47821½ Gunoleum Lubricant, for protecting and preserving all metals from rust and tarnish. Especially adapted to guns, revolvers and fine machinery. Put up in metallic tubes. Per tube..$0.12
Per dozen...1.13
One-half-pound cans, each........................45
One-pound cans, each..............................60

47822 Paraffine Gun Oil, put up exclusively for guns, gun locks, and fine machinery and furniture; removes rust and will not gum, 2 oz. bottles. Price per dozen..............................50
3 bottles for...15

Gun Oils—Continued.

47823 Montgomery Ward & Co's Popular Lubricating Oil, best oil in the market for guns, locks, sewing machines, bicycles and any small machines; will not freeze, gum, rust, or corrode or become rancid. Per bottle.......................$0.08
Per dozen...80
Unmailable.

47825 Rust Remover, coarse, for removing rust from iron, steel, brass or any metal where cutting properties are desired. Per bottle...............20
47826 Rust Remover, medium............................18
47827 Rust Remover, fine................................19
Postage, 5c. extra.

47830 Wood Polish. Nothing like it for bright, clean and lustrous polish on furniture, desks, gun stocks and all walnut, oiled or varnished furniture. Per bottle....................................20
Unmailable.

47833 Cook's Black Fly and Mosquito Paste. It is the nicest, most pleasing and effectual mosquito and fly starter in the country. A little rubbed on the face and hands will positively keep them off, as well as keep off fleas, wood ticks, forest, sand and house flies, and all similar pests. Per bottle.................$0.20
Postage, 10c. extra.

Bird Calls.

By mail, 2 to 3 cents each.

47835 Grubb's Improved Illinois River Duck Call. The most natural toned call made; easy to blow; not easy to get out of repair, having a fine tempered reed; makes it so you can call teal, woodduck and bluebill, as well as mallard. This is the only call you can do this with. Each...........................$0.60

47836 The Perfection Duck call, made of red cedar, silver mounted, with silver reed which gives it perfect tone. This is the finest duck call made, perfect, similar in style to the Grubb's call, and is warranted. Each.........$1.00

47841 Allen's improved wood Duck Caller, the most natural toned, easiest blowing. Used in the field by all the best duck shooters in America. Each..........................$0.45

47842 Duck Calls, horn, with rosewood mouth piece. Each..............$0.33

47843 Turkey Calls, horn, with rosewood mouth piece. Each...........$0.32
Extra by mail 3c.

Allen's Duck Call. Turkey Call.

47844 Snipe Calls (no cut). Each...............$0.21
Postage, 2c. extra.

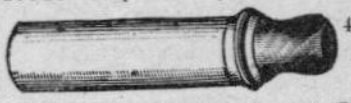

47845 Fuller's Metallic Wild Goose Caller. Each.............................80c.
Extra by mail 5c.

Barnum's Patent Game Carrier.

By mail, 3 cents each.

Barnum's.   Rudolph

47848 Worth its weight in gold; a blessing to feathered game shooters; weight, 2½ ozs., folded, 8½ inches long; ¼ inch thick; can be carried in the pencil pocket, yet holds securely 18 ducks, balanced on the shoulders, on the belt, gun barrel, or in the hand. Price, each........$0.15
Per dozen.............1.40

47849 Rudolph's Compact Game Carrier, with leather shoulder strap. Each..$0.30 Per dozen $3.00
By mail, 3c extra.

Decoys.

In making these decoys great care has been used to select only sound white cedar for their construction and to secure a perfect balance. They are light, substantially and naturally painted. Assortments; Mallard canvas back, red head, blue bill, teal, pin or sprig tails. Weight, per dozen, 35 to 40 pounds.

47850 No. 1 Best Decoy Ducks (glass eyes). Per dozen...$3.75
47851 No. 2 Good Decoy Ducks (metallic eyes) Per dozen..2.75
47852 Cords and Anchors for Decoys. Per dozen....15
We do not handle the No. 3 decoy, as they are too poorly finished.

Catchers' Masks.

Warranted the best mask made. It is made of the best material well padded, and by an ingenious arrangement of the wires an unobstructed view is obtained. It is far superior to the old style of wire mask, or the heavy, dangerous steel bar mask.

Each

48169 New neck protecting mask, best wire, best padding, soft and pliable $3.60
48170 Extra Heavy Special League Masks, the very best made, warranted 2.97
48171 Regulation League Masks, heavy wire, and warranted first-class in every respect 2.50
Extra by mail, 30c.
48172 Amateur Men's Masks. We guarantee this mask to be equally as good as many dealers sell for the best league mask 1.50
48173 Amateur Boys' Masks. This mask is the same as the men's masks, only smaller, to fit a boys' face 1.35
Extra by mail, 20c
48174 Youths' Masks, without head or chin piece. .80
48175 Boys' Masks, light wire, without head or chin piece .... .40

Base Ball Belts.

Extra by mail. 3 cents. Each. Per dz.

	Each.	Per dz.
48190 Cotton Web Belts, 2¼ in. wide, leather mounted, single strap and buckle, colors: Red, blue, white, maroon, navy blue, red, white edge, blue, white edge, red, white and blue, red and white stripe, blue and white stripe	$0.14	$1.50
48191 Cotton Web Belts, 2¼ inch double strap, nickel buckle (same colors as 48190)	.23	2.30
48192 Worsted Web Belt, 2¼ in. single leathered covered buckle, colors: Red, blue, navy brown, black, white, maroon and old gold	.32	3.40
48193 Worsted Web Belt, 2¼ in. double leathered covered buckles (same colors as 48192)	.35	3.60
48194 Special League Belt, worsted web, large nickel plated buckle (same colors as 48192)	.45	4.70

Spalding's Base Ball Goods.

Base Balls.

Extra by mail, 10c each. Net cash.
48219 Spalding's League Base Ball, per dozen. $13.90
Sold in any quantity at the above price.

Bats.

Weight, 22 to 40 ounces. Per doz.
48225 Spalding's Best Second Growth Ash Bat, wagon tongue, new rough handle $11.95
48226 Spalding's Second Growth Ash, Black Band League Bat, polished, rough handle (special weight, same price) 9.00
48231 Spalding's Trade-Marked Black Band Willow Bat 4.00
Sold in any quantity at above prices.

Catchers' Mitts.

Front

Throwing Glove.

Each.

48235 Spalding's Special League Mitt, finest quality drab buckskin, new model, laced, with patent short-fingered throwing-glove $5.90
48236 Spalding's League Mitt, hogskin, with patent throwing glove 4.25
48239 M. W. & Co.'s New League Mitt, best buckskin, fingerless throwing glove padded with extra thick felt, heavy rubber welt around front of fingers, fingers heavy leather tipped, as good as the best; once used you would have no other kind. As well padded and as good quality in every way as the best glove in the market; warranted 4.85
48240 M. W. & Co.'s Horsehide Back Locked Elastic Fastening League Mitt and Throwing Glove, same make as No. 48239. Made of good leather, soft and pliable 3.00
48241 M. W. & Co.'s Goatskin League Mitt and Throwing Glove, thick felt pad with welt around front of fingers. A good one 2.30
48242 M. W. & Co.'s Boys' League Mitt and Throwing Glove, laced fastening, heavy padded, fingers well protected, the best boys' mitt in the market 2.25
48243 Men's Goatskin Mitt and Throwing Glove, well padded 1.50
48244 Boys' Mitt and Throwing Glove, padded; good and strong .... .50

Masks.

48249 Spalding's Sun-Protecting Base Ball Mask. Each $4.25
48250 Spalding's New Patented Neck Protecting Mask 3.75
48251 Spalding's Special League Mask, used by all the leading professional catchers, extra heavy wire, well padded with goat hair, padding faced with best imported dogskin 3.45
48252 Spalding's Regulation League Mask made of heavy wire, well padded and faced with horsehide, warranted first-class in every respect. 2.95
Weight 2¾ to 3½ lbs.

Catchers' and Umpires' Breast Protectors.

Nicely made, and well padded and quilted, and are used by nearly all professional catchers and umpires.
48260 Chamois and canvas Weight, 1 lb. Each $2.90
48262 Spalding's League Body Protector, inflated $9.75
48263 Spalding's Amateur Body Protector $5.75

Indian Clubs.

Sold in pairs only, and made of the best rock maple and finely polished. Weight given is the weight on each club. If you order one pair 1 lb. clubs, you get two 1 lb. clubs, etc.

		Per pair
48270	1 lb.	$0.26
48271	1¼ lbs.	.30
48272	2 lbs.	.35
48273	3 lbs.	.50
48274	4 lbs.	.66
48275	5 lbs.	.80
48276	6 lbs.	.90

Boxing Gloves.

48281

Weight, 3 to 4 pounds, packed for shipment. Our Boxing Gloves are the latest designs and are the best gloves in the world for the money.
Average weight, men's sizes, about 7 oz. each.
48281 Boxing Gloves, the California patent, padded on end of fingers, side heel pads, dark buff color; weight, each glove, 8 oz.
Per set $6.00

48282-85

48282 Boxing Gloves, new style, ends of fingers padded inside as well as out, very best quality with kid finish $5.75
48283 Boxing Gloves, same style as 48282 except black goat finish, quality not as good, but strong and durable $3.79
48284 Boxing Gloves, same style as No. 48282, but not as good quality. Color white. Per set $1.95
48285 Boxing Gloves, same style as No. 48282, better quality, color black. Per set $2.40

48290-99

48290 Boys' sizes, well stuffed white kid, tan colored palms, good size, made of same material and just as well as the men's size.
Per set of 4 gloves $1.87
48291 Men's sizes, same as 48290. Per set of 4 gloves, well made and durable 2.25
48292 Men's sizes, well stuffed and extra tan leather, palms and wrists bound with fancy leather. Per set 2.85
48293 Men's sizes, same as No. 48292, better quality, heel padded. Per set 3.75
48295 Same as 48292, best quality, heel padded.. 4.85
48296 Kid Gloves, with best tan palms 4.95
48297 Finest Kid Gloves with ventilated palm, very best quality. Per set 5.50
48298 Same as 48297, heel padded 5.75
48299 Chandler's Professional Kid Glove, for sparring exhibitions, being small and compactly stuffed, 6, 4 or 2 oz 5.50
We cannot furnish any better gloves than what we quote above, as there are no better ones in the market at any price.

Dumb Bells.

48300 Our Iron Dumb Bells are cast from pure gray iron, and are very much stronger and more durable than those ordinarily sold, which are usually made from scrap iron, tin, etc., and are very brittle and break easily. We make them with weights as follows: 1 lb. 2, 3, 4, 5, 6, 8, 10, 12, 14, 15, 20, 25 pounds each. Sold by the pound. Price per lb., 4c; 50 lbs., 5c; 75 lbs, 6c; 100 lbs, 6c. per lb.
48301 Wood Dumb Bells, made of polished maple.

Weight	1 lb.	2 lb.	3 lb.	4 lb.
Per pair	30c	36c	55c	70c

Foot Balls.

48302 The Association "Match" Foot Ball, genuine, made of best India rubber bladder, with fine leather outside case, hand sewed, laced, round. Postage, about 20c. extra.

Each.

22-inch circumference $2.00
24-inch circumference 2.45
27-inch circumference 2.68
30-inch circumference 2.90
33-inch circumference 3.90

48303 Rugby Foot Ball, College "Match," oval shape, made of the best India rubber bladder with outside leather case, hand sewed, laced. Best quality.

Each.

22-inch circumference $2.00
24-inch circumference 2.50
27-inch circumference 2.65
30-inch circumference 2.93
33-inch circumference 3.90

Rugby Bladders.

Association Bladders.

48304 Extra Foot Ball Bladders for either Rugby or Association Foot Balls. In ordering state which kind is wanted. Each.
For 22-inch ball, weight, 8 oz $0.57
For 24-inch ball .... .69
For 27-inch ball .... .73
For 30-inch ball .... .76
For 33-inch ball .... .79

Rubber Foot Balls.

48305 American Round Rubber Foot Ball. By mail, 7 to 12c extra.
No. 1, 6 in. diameter $0.57
No. 2, 7 in. diameter .... .68
No. 3, 8 in. diameter .... .79
No. 4, 9 in. diameter .... .90
No. 5, 10 in. diameter 1.00
No. 6, 11 in. diameter 1.15
48306 Extra keys for foot ball, etc .... .10
48307 Rubber Foot Ball Inflaters, nickeled tubes for filling up bladders .... .40
48308 Rubber Foot Balls, Rugby shape, made of heavy rubber, one size only, regulation, No. 5. Each 1.90

Foot Ball Inflaters.

48309

48309 Foot Ball Inflaters, solid brass metal, new design and the best. Each $0.75
By mail, 6c. extra.

Foot Ball Suits.

Foot Ball Canvas Jackets.
48310 Best $1.35
48311 Medium .... .85
Foot Ball Canvas Pants.
48312 Best, padded 2.25
48313 Medium, padded 1.50
Moleskin Pants, padded.
48314 Best 4.50
48315 Medium 3.15
These goods are made to order. Give full measurements when ordering.

GYMNASIUM GOODS.

Improved Striking Bags.

FOR PHYSICAL CULTURE.

Refines, elevates and ennobles; adds to our courage, zeal and health and thereby to our happiness.

The bag is intended to strengthen the arms, wrists, shoulders, back, loins and particularly the muscles of the abdomen, and will teach the striker how to deal a blow. It is of inestimable value to everyone, especially to those whose business requires confinement.

48317 Canvas Striking Bags, about 14 inches long with rubber bladder inside; good and durable. Each $1.75
48318 Leather Striking Bags with rubber bladder inside; good quality. Each 2.88
48319 Rubber Bladder for striking bags. Each 1.20

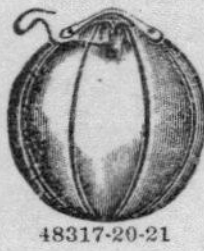
48317-20-21

48321 Best Quality Striking Bags, leather cover, with rubber bladder inside, strong, durable, lace up tops. Each..$3.95
48323 Rumsey's Patent Striking Air Bag with cords and screw eyes, complete, ready to set up; weight, 3 lbs. Each. $5.00

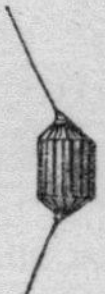

Horizontal Bars.

Weight, 4½ to 6 lbs.

Made of best quality second growth straight hickory, square ends.

		Each.
48345	4 ft. long	$0.50
	4½ ft. long	.60
	5 ft. long	.70
	5½ ft. long	.95
	6 ft. long	1.20

Trapeze Bars.

Weight, 2 to 3½ pounds.

Made of the best second growth hickory. Without ropes.

		Each.
48346	2 ft. bar, without ropes	$0.45
	2½ ft. Bar, without ropes	.48
	3 ft. Bar, without ropes	.55
	3½ ft. Bar, without ropes	.60
	4 ft. Bar, without ropes	.70

We make any length of rope to order, 8 cents per foot

Goodyear's Round Rubber Health Pull.

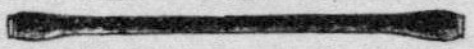

Each

48351 For ladies and children, 14 years and upward..... $1.25
48352 For men of moderate strength..... 1.45
48353 Used by ladies, children or men; is fitted with screw eye to attach to wall or floor..... 1.90
48354 For men of extra strength, made like No. 48353 ..... 2.40

Eastman's Calisthenics.

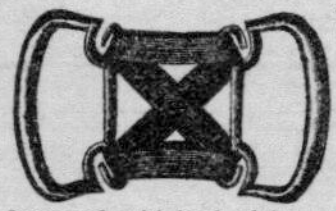

48361 A complete system of Calisthenics brought within the compass of a single instrument of not above a pound in weight. The handles are of iron and are connected with rubber bands.

Japanned, with book of instructions. Pair.......$0.47

Fencing Foils, Masks and Gloves.

All goods standard make and quality.

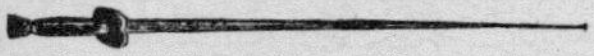

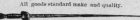

Weight, 24 to 32 ounces per pair.

48363 Fencing foils with steel blades, iron mounted handles. Per pair $1.50
48364 Fencing foils, steel Solingen blades, brass mounted, bell guard. Per pair..... 2.50
48365 Fencing foils, best steel Solingen blades, brass mounted, wound handles. Pair..... 3.75

Fencing Masks.

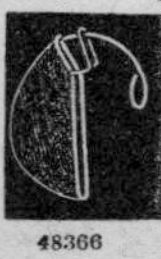
48366

Weight, 24 to 28 ounces.
48366 French pattern, standard quality. Per pair........$2.30
48367 French pattern, standard quality, with ears. Per pair........$2.75

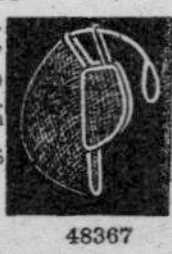
48367

Fencing Gloves, Buckskin.

Weight, 10 to 15 ounces.

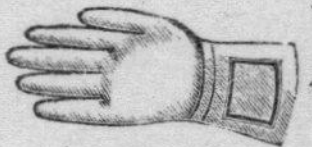
48369

48368 Fencing Gloves, without gauntlet. Per set of 2 gloves. $1.75
48369 Fencing Gloves, with gauntlet. Per set of 2 gloves. $2.70

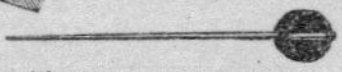

48370 Fencing Sticks, with cane, willow basket hilt. Per pair..... $0.60

Athletic Clothing.

(See Index for Bicycle Clothing.)

Give chest measure when ordering shirts; waist measure when ordering tights.

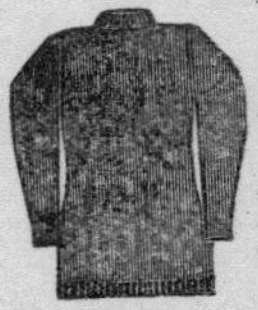

48371 Sweaters, made of lamb's wool, the best in the market, full length sleeves, heavy. Sizes, 34, 36, 38, 40, 42, 44..... $3.75
Light weight..... 2.75
48372 Worsted Full sleeve shirts, with collar, black worsted; heavy, good for trap shooters' use also..... $2.40
48373 Worsted full sleeve shirts, with collar, black or navy blue, extra heavy. $3.25
48374 Shirts, long sleeve, worsted, black or navy blue, light weight, good for trap shooters also..... $1.80

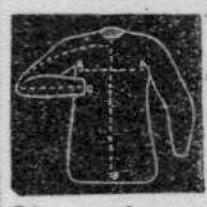

48375 Long sleeve shirt, worsted, navy blue or black, better quality $2.30
48376 Shirts, fast black, silk finish cotton, long sleeve shirts..... $1.30
48377 Shirts, fast black, silk finish cotton, long sleeve, standing collar $1.35
48378 Shirts, Black Polo cotton, long sleeve..... $1.15

Sleeveless Shirts 30, 32, 34 and 36 Chest.

48379 Worsted, any color, plain, seamless..... $3.00
48381 Cotton, white or flesh color..... .75
By mail, extra..... .10
University or Quarter Sleeve Shirt, 26, 28, 30, 32 and 36 chest measure. Each.
48382 Shirts, worsted, plain, any color, seamless. $3.10

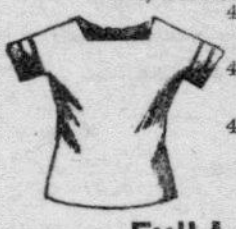

48383 Shirts, worsted, ¼ sleeve, black or navy blue, medium weight..... 1.55
48384 Shirts, cotton, ¼ sleeve, white or flesh color, good weight ..... .72
48384½ Shirts, cotton, ¼ sleeve, flesh color, white finish, fast colors, light weight, but firm and good wearing goods..... .55

Full Length Tights.

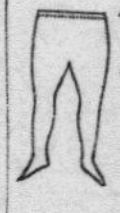

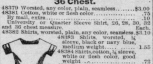

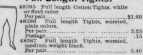

48385 Full length Cotton Tights, white or flesh color
Per pair..... $1.60
48386 Full length Tights, worsted, plain colors.
Per pair..... 3.25
Postage..... .15
48387 Full length Tights, worsted, medium weight black.
Per pair..... 2.40

Knee Tights.

48390 Knee Tights, cut Jersey goods, plain black, per pair $1.40
48391 Worsted, plain black, per pair..... 2.00
48392 Worsted, plain colors, per pair..... $2.60
48393 Cotton, white or flesh color; also make good bathing trunks, per pair..... $0.50
By mail, extra..... .10
48395 Trunks, worsted, black, navy, flesh or maroon, per pair..... $1.50
48396 Bathing trunks, fancy colored cotton in stripes, assorted sizes, ... $0.20

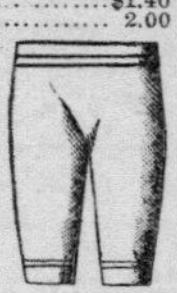

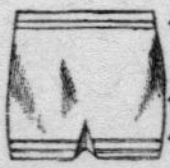

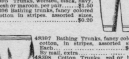

48397 Bathing Trunks, fancy colored cotton, in stripes, assorted sizes, Each..... $0.30
By mail, extra..... .05
48398 Cotton Trunks, red or blue, Trunks. Per pair..... $0.55
48399 Puffed Velvet Trunks, black, red, navy or maroon, per pair..$1.00

N.B.—Give waist measure for gymnasium goods.

INSURE YOUR PACKAGES.—Mail packages may be insured against loss by paying a fee of 5 cents for each $5.00 in value. Write "Insured Mail" on your order, enclose the money, and we will do the rest.

Bathing Trunks—Continued.

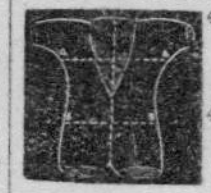
48401

48401 Full Fashioned Leotars, worsted, black or tan color.
Each..... $3.75
48402 Morton's Perfect Supporter, the best fitting, most comfortable and effective supporter yet devised. Used by ball players, athletes and the theatrical profession generally; made of best quality Canton flannel, laced front, cool and pleasant to wear.
Each..... $0.35 Per doz..... $3.30

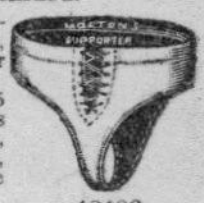

48402

Give waist and hip measure for supporters. Send us your order for anything in the athletic goods line. We will take good care of you both as regards quality and price.

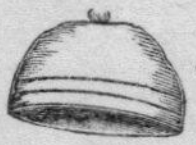

48403 Skull Caps, worsted.
Each $0.50

The Whitely Exerciser.

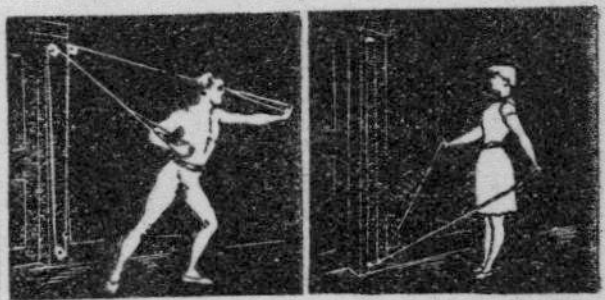

48403½ An ideal gymnasium for home or traveling use; noiseless; warranted to remain so; weighs less than two pounds; can be carried in your pocket or corner of valise and used in hotel, sleeping car or state room of steamer; a special attachment enabling travelers to suspend the Exerciser anywhere in a second; can be put up permanently in two minutes without tool of any kind; with a few extra hooks can be used in every room in the house; the hooks are of steel wire, though small, and do not injure the woodwork; no straps to buckle; no weights to change; self-adjusting resistance of two to forty pounds; no jerks, no dead weights—you'll think its alive. Exercises all the muscles, not the upper limbs only; attachment for foot movements; makes all movements that can be made on weight machines, and many others that would break any pulley weight machine all to pieces; a thing of beauty and a hustler forever; equally adapted to ladies, gentlemen or children; written endorsements from the very highest authorities; ask for pamphlet containing them; World's Columbian Exposition medal and diplomas awarded for merit and general superiority; will do the work of several cumbrous machines, aggregating a cost of fifteen to thirty dollars. Price, complete with illustrated book of instruction..... $4.00

Chest Weights.

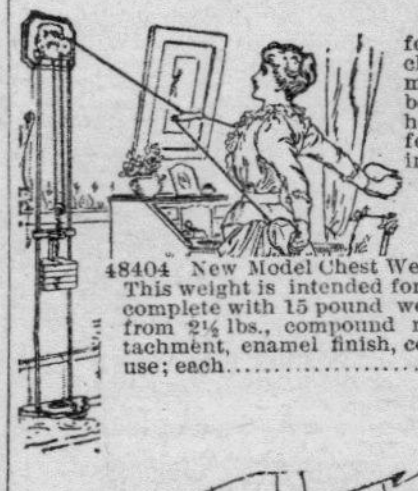

Improved Pattern for development of chest and all the muscles of the body. The most healthful exercise, for indoors, ever invented.

48404 New Model Chest Weights, single pull. This weight is intended for home use. Sent complete with 15 pound weights, adjustable from 2½ lbs., compound rope and floor attachment, enamel finish, complete ready for use; each..... $5.00

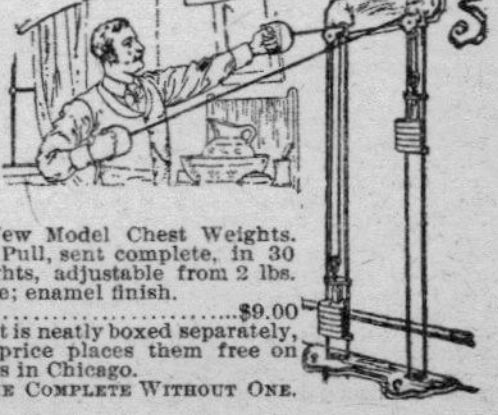

48405 New Model Chest Weights. Double Pull, sent complete, in 30 lb. weights, adjustable from 2 lbs. on a side; enamel finish.
Each..... $9.00
Each set is neatly boxed separately, and the price places them free on board cars in Chicago.

NO HOME COMPLETE WITHOUT ONE.

FISHING RODS, TACKLE, ETC.

FISHING RODS.

In selecting the goods in this department it has been done with a view to get standard and reliable goods only, and we know of no single article in the following list that is not the best obtainable of its grade. Made of the best quality woods, warranted clear timber, free from knots and flaws. Weight given is for rods alone, and does not include cases. Any rod not found as represented can be returned at our expense and money refunded if returned as soon as examined.

Wood Rods.

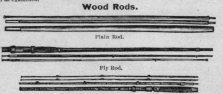

Plain Rod.

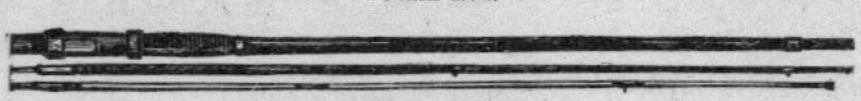

Fly Rod.

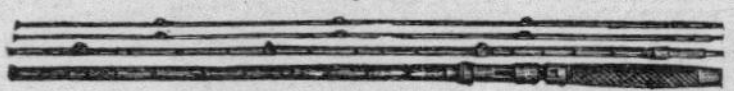

Bait Rod.

Our prices are lowest jobbing prices on fishing tackle. That is why the prices may seem low to you for GOOD goods.

	Feet.	Each.
48410 Fish Rod, 3 pieces, jointed, single brass ferrule; about	10½	$0.12
48411 3-Piece Jointed Rod, single brass ferrule, ringed for line	10½	.15
48412 4 Piece Jointed Rod, varnished, single brass ferrule, ringed for line, natural color	12	.20
48413 3-Piece Light Bass, stained, double ferrules, rings and reel bands, brass capped butt	10½	.38
48414 Fish Rod, 3 pieces, fly or light bait, stained dark, double ferrule, brass butt cap, ringed for line, brass reel bands	10	.47
48415 4-Piece Bass or Bait Rod, stained lancewood tip, guides and reel bands, brass butt cap, double brass ferrules, finely finished	12	.75
48416 3-Piece Bait Rod, stained ash and lancewood tip, *brass mounted*, guides and reel bands	9½	$0.75
48417 3-Piece Light Bass Rod, varnished ash with lancewood, tip full mounted, in *nickel*. A good rod	10	1.20
48418 3-Piece Fly Rod, ash butt and second joint, nickeled lancewood tip, full mounted, a light, fine rod, covered dowels, 8 oz	10½	1.30
48421 4-Piece Fine Stained General Rod, covered dowels, reel bands, brass mounted, hollow butt, extra lancewood tip, braided butt	.12	1.80
48422 4-Piece California General Rod, lancewood except first joint, ash butt, nickeled, full mounted, solid metal reel seat, silk wound, anti-friction tie guides and silk wound at short intervals, reel seat above hand, in cloth bag, 3 rods in one, good anywhere. One extra short tip and one extra heavy tip	.12	3.00

Steel Rods.

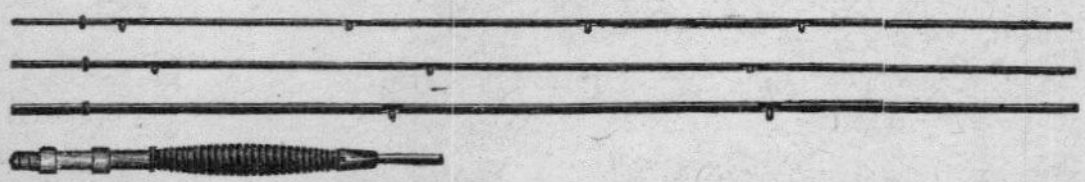

The Bristol Steel Fishing Rods. They are a marked departure from all rods of the past, and your fishing outfit is incomplete without one. Every rod guaranteed against breakage from reasonable use or from defects in manufacture.

48423 (1) Bass Rod, telescopic, 9 ft. 6 in., full nickel, mounted with solid reel seat above hand, line runs through the center of the rod; when telescoped the rod is 32 in. in length, all closed within the butt length, with celluloid wound handle. Weight, 12½ oz. Price $4.25

48423¼ (5) Fly Rod, 9 ft. 6 in., reel seat below hand, otherwise same style and description as No. 1. Weight, 11¾ oz. Price 4.20

48424 (8) Fly Rod, 10 ft., full nickel mounted, with solid reel seat below hand. This rod is jointed, has standing line guides on outside, does not telescope. Weight, 9½ oz., with celluloid wound handle. Price 5.00

48424¼ (13) The St. Lawrence Bass Rod, 7 ft. 6 in., full nickel mounted with solid reel seat above hand. This rod is jointed, has standing guides and 3 ringed tip. This is one of the best bait-casting or boat rods on the market. Weight, 9¼ oz., with celluloid wound handle. Price 5.00

Lancewood Rods.

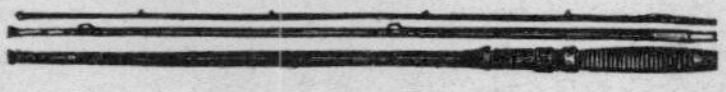

Lancewood Bait Rod.

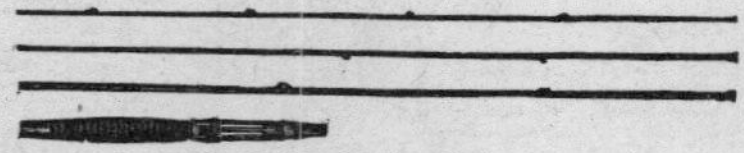

Showing Short Butt.

Weights on rods may vary 1 to 3 oz.

	Length Feet.	Each
48425 3-Piece All Genuine Imported Lancewood Fly Rod, finely nickel plated, improved shoulder ferrules, silk wound tie guides, covered dowels, solid nickel reel seat below hand, fancy or corrugated hand grasp, with one extra tip, in cloth bag, partitioned, a BARGAIN. Fly rod, heavy	10½	$1.25
Fly rod, light	10	1.35
48427 3-Piece All Genuine Imported Lancewood Fly Rod, in wood case or form, finely finished, full nickel plated shoulder ferrules, fancy silk wound tie guides, covered dowels, solid nickel reel seat below hand grasp, corrugated zylonite butt, with one extra tip. A good one	10½	1.95
48428 3-Piece All Genuine Imported Lancewood Bass Rod finely nickel plated, improved shoulder ferrules, silk wound tie guides, covered dowels, solid nickel reel seat above hand, cane wound or zylonite butt, with one extra tip, in cloth bag, partitioned; a very fine rod (a bargain)	9	$1.25
48429 3-Piece All Genuine Imported Lancewood Bass Rod, in wood form, varnished and polished, nickel plated, solid reel seat, shouldered ferrules, covered dowels, metal plugs, fancy silk wound tie guides for line, wound or fancy butt stock, one extra tip (a bargain) Bass rod	9	1.95
Bait rod	7½	2.00

48430 3-piece and extra tip, all best Jamaica lancewood carefully selected and thoroughly tested, patent hard rubber butt and extra fine finish, welt ferrules and metal plugs. Each rod in wood form, full nickel plated mountings, fancy silk winding between joints.

	Feet.	Each
Fly rod, reel seat below hand	10	$2.95
Bass rod, reel seat above hand	9	3.00
Bait rod, extra heavy	8	3.05

48430½ Trout or Black Bass Rod, best Jamaica lancewood, for bait casting, has rubber butt, full nickel plated mountings, fancy silk windings. Two piece, extra tip, in wood form, 6½ 3.00

Henshall Bass Rods.

48431 Henshall Bass Rod, all genuine Jamaica lancewood, solid rubber butt. German silver mountings, extra fancy silk windings. Each rod put up in lined wood form. The best lancewood rod in the market at any price. No better rod made. Generally retails at $8.00. 8 ft. 3 in. long. Our price 4.75

48431½ Jamaica Lancewood Short Bait Rod, genuine, 3-piece with extra tip, cork butt and aluminum reel seat, extra fancy silk windings, full German silver mountings, in lined wood form.
8 ft. bait 5.00
9¼ ft. very light fly 4.95

Combination Lancewood Rod.

48432 7-Piece Combination Lancewood Rod, corrugated black celluloid grip, shouldered and trimmed ferrules, nickel plated trimmings, silk wound tie guides, bass bait, trout bait and trout fly combination, 1 short butt, 1 long ash butt. When short butt is used will make a difference of 24 inches in length of rod, in any combination 7 to 10 feet; one of the best and handiest rods in the market. Will make 6 different rods. Each $2.75

48433 Florida Bass Rod, extra heavy, all lancewood, selected wood, rubber hand grasp, silk wound throughout, nickel plated mountings, metal plugs, 3-piece, extra tip; length, about 8½ feet. Each. $2.60

48434 Tarpon or Florida Bass Rod, combined rod, will make a 3-piece rod, 8½ ft., 18 oz., and a 2-piece rod 5¾ ft., 16 oz. Jamaica Dagame wood, double tie guides, solid nickel reel seat, nickel mounted corrugated zylonite butt. Heavy, strong and durable. The 2-piece rod is a good tarpon or gogebec trolling rod. Everything about this rod is finely finished, and the wood resembles lancewood very closely. Each... $3.95

Jointed Bamboo Fishing Rods.

The Bamboo Rods are light, handy and strong, can be used with or without reels. The best trolling rods in the market.

	Length, feet.	Each.
48435 2-Piece. Japanese bamboo, double ferrules, plain straw color	8 to 9	$0.15
48436 3-Piece, Japanese bamboo, double ferrules, plain straw color	14 to 18	.36
48437 4-Piece, Japanese bamboo, double ferrules, ringed, plain straw color	14 to 16	.44
48439 3-Piece, Calcutta bamboo, double ferrules, ringed, reel bands and capped butt	10 to 12	.55
48440 4-Piece, Calcutta Bamboo, double ferrules, ringed and capped butt	14 to 17	.65
48441 4-Piece, Calcutta bamboo, double ferrules, ringed, reel bands, capped butt	14 to 17	.80
48442 4-Piece, Calcutta bamboo, double ferrules, reel bands, capped and cane wound butt	13 to 16	1.10
48443 3-Piece, Calcutta bamboo, double ferrules, standing guides, reel bands, capped and cane wound butt, nickel mounted	10 to 12	.86

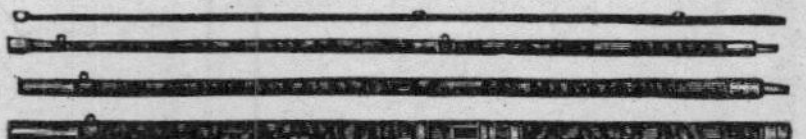

Bamboo 4-Piece Rod.	Length, feet.	Each.
48444 5-Piece Calcutta bamboo, double ferrules, standing ring guides, reel bands, and cane wound below hand, one extra tip in butt	18 to 20	$2.20
This is a great favorite with the trade where an extra long, strong rod is wanted.		
48445 3-Piece, Calcutta bamboo, improved shoulder ferrules, wound tie guides, covered dowels, solid reel seat, nickel plated trimmings, capped and zylonite or cane-wound butt, extra lancewood tip, in cloth bag	9 to 11	1.90
48446 4-Piece, Calcutta bamboo, bass rod, nickel plated, improved shoulder ferrules, full mounted extra lancewood tip, standing guides, metal reel seat, cane-wound butt	14 to 16	2.00
48447 Jap Boat Rod, 2-piece Japanese Bamboo Boat Rod, with 14 in. corrugated black zylonite butt or grip, nickel plated mountings, solid reel seat, tie guides, tube tips. Length, 6½ to 8 feet		.75
48448 Oconomowoc Bass Rod, 1 corrugated short butt, with 1-piece Japanese bamboo, 7 to 8 feet long, brass mounted, tube tips, reel seat above hand. A big seller		.65

Split Bamboo Rods.

Our Split Bamboo Rods are the best in the market at anywhere near the prices we offer them, and are warranted as represented.

ALL OUR RODS ARE GUARANTEED *just as represented.* Any not found so can be RETURNED at our expense. Our "Split Bamboo" prices are 50 to 100 per cent. lower than regular retail prices.

FLY ROD.

WOOD FORM

BAIT OR BRASS.

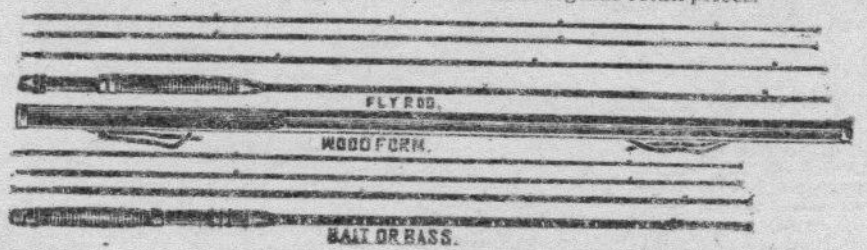

48448½ The "Baby Brook" Fly, the very best 3-piece all hand-made, six strip, split bamboo polished orange wood butt, full German silver mountings, first-class in every particular. the equal to if not better than the best rods made by anybody. Each rod, with extra tip, in flannel lined wood form, with canvas case. Weight 7¾ ounces, 7½ feet long. Price $25.00

48449 3-piece genuine six strip hexagonal split bamboo rods. Patent zylonite butts, full nickel plated mounting, well fitted ferrules, metal plugs, solid reel seat, fancy silk windings, 1 extra tip. Each rod in a wood form. Fly rod, reel below hand, 8 oz., 10¼ feet 3.50
Bait casting rod, reel above hand, 9 oz., 7½ ft .. 3.55
Long bait rod, reel seat above hand, 13 oz., 10½ feet 3.90

48450½ Three-piece hexagonal six strip Bamboo Rods, welted waterproof ferrules, metal plugs, full nickel plated, fancy silk windings, fancy celluloid wound butt, inlaid with cedar, each rod in lined wood form. These rods are beauties. Fly rod, weight about 7 oz.; length 10 feet 5 00
Bait rod, weight about 9 oz.; length, 8½ feet 5.10

48451 The very best 3-piece all hand-made six strip hexagonal split Bamboo Rods Patent hard rubber butts, full German silver mounted, waterproof welted ferrules, metal plugs, fancy silk windings, first class in every particular. Each rod in lined wood form, with canvas bag and extra tip. This is the rod that usually retails at $25.00, and is good value even at that price. It is the best rod that we can get made up. Fly rod, reel seat below hand, 7 oz., 10 feet 16.50
Bait rod, reel seat above hand, 10 oz., 8½ feet .. 16.55

48452 Three-piece split Bamboo Rods genuine six strip hexagonal patent rubber butts,full German silver mountings, solid metal reel seats, welt ferrules, metal plugs, fancy silk wound. Each rod in a lined wood form, extra tip. The best rod offered by *anybody* for *anything* like the *price* we name.
Fly rod, reel seat below hand, 8 oz., 10¼ feet.. 6.00
Bait rod, reel seat above hand, 11 oz., 8½ feet 6.00

48452½ Trout Fly Rod, 3-piece split bamboo, six strip, cork butt, aluminum reel plate, full German silver mountings, with extra tip, fancy silk windings. Each rod in a lined wood form, the best rod for the price ever offered. Very light; 5 ounces; length, 9 feet. Each 6.00

48453 Three-piece hexagonal six strip genuine Bamboo Rods. Welted waterproof ferrules, metal plugs, full German silver mounted, fancy silk windings between ferrules, inlaid cedar butt. Each rod in wood form, lined; extra tip. These rods we believe to be better than most $12.00 to $15.00 rods on the market. *They are good ones.* Fly rods, reel seat below hand, 6 oz., 9½ feet 8.90
Fly rods, reel seat below hand, 8 oz., 10½ feet.. 8.95
Henshall bass rod, 9 oz., 8 feet 3 in. long 9.00

48454 Three-piece genuine six strip hexagonal Split Bamboo Rods, full nickel plated mountings, silk wound tie guides, solid reel seats, metal plugs, corrugated zylonite butts, each rod in wood form; 1 extra tip. Fly rod, reel seat below hand, 10 feet 1.25
Bait Rod, reel seat above hand, 9½ feet 1.30
Wood case weighs 10 oz., where rod is described in wood case or form.

48455 Three-piece, six strip, hexagonal split Bamboo Rods, full nickel plated mountings, silk wound tie guards, solid reel seats, metal plugs, zylonite Patent Holder a dozen, each rod in wood form, extra tip, selected stock. Fly rod, weight about 8 oz; length, 10½ feet 1.80
Bait rod, weight about 12 oz; length, 9½ feet.... 1.85

48456 Three-piece, six strip, hexagonal split Bamboo Rods, with cork grip, nickel plated mountings, solid metal reel seats and metal plugs in wood form. An extra tip. Fly Rod, weight about 8 oz; length, 10½ feet 2.80
Bait Rod weight about 12 oz; length, 9½ feet.... 2.85

48457 Four-piece, six strip, hexagonal split bamboo rods, with zylonite strips, nickel plated mountings, solid metal reel seat and metal plugs in wood form, without extra tip. Bait rod only, weight about 13 oz; length, 10 feet 1.45

ALL OF OUR RODS ARE GUARANTEED just as represented. Any not found so can be RETURNED at our expense. Our "Split Bamboo" prices are 50 to 100 per cent lower than regular retail prices.

Trunk Rods.

48459 Five-piece Trunk Rod, varnished; Feet. long double nickel ferrules, covered dowels, nickel butt cap, one light, one heavy tip, making a good bass or bait, and also a light fly rod, ring guides, reel bands,lancewood tips, a very good, handy and cheap rod, ... 11 $1.20

48460 Five-piece Trunk Rod, natural wood finish, varnished,double brass ferrules, lancewood tip, ring guides, brass butt, cap, fine little rod .... 10 .75

48461 Five-piece Bamboo Trunk Rod,plain brass-finished mounting, ring guides, 11½ to 12. .90

48462 5-piece Bamboo Trunk Rod, improved and rimmed shoulder ferrules, covered dowels, silk-wound tie guides, metal reel seat, extra lancewood tip, a fine rod 2.60

48463 5-piece trunk rod, all genuine lancewood, butt varnished and polished, shouldered ferrules, fancy finish, nickel plated, whole rod made of lancewood, fancy silk windings and tie guides, solid metal reel seat, one extra tip; 10 to 15 oz., a good, honest rod. Fly Rod,reel below hand, about 9¼ feet 2.50
Bait Rod, reel above hand, about 8½ feet 2.55

48464 Five-piece Trunk Rod genuine hexagonal split bamboo zylonite butts,nickel plated mountings, solid metal reel seat, metal plugs, fancy silk windings and a handsome rod. Each rod in a partition cloth bag. An extra tip with each rod.
Fly rod, reel below hand, about 8 oz , 10 feet.. 3.50
Bait rod, reel above hand, about 12 oz., 9½ feet. 3.55

Rod Cases.

48465 Round Rod Case, embossed russet leather, copper riveted, nickel trimmed, capped end, fastened with strap and buckles, 40 in, 2 inch diameter. Each $2.85
50 in., 3 in. diameter. Each ....
Cheaper quality leather neatly finished, 40 to 50 in. long, 2 in. diameter. Each 1.80

48466

48466 Canvas Rod Cases,leather top and bottom,a dandy for the money. Weight, 6 to 8 ozs.—40 to 50 in. long $0.60
48466½ Canvas Rod Case, plain, heavy canvas. Each 40

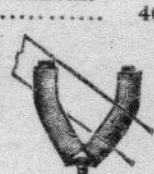

48467 The"Handy"Fish Rod Holder,can be fastened in the vest pocket; screws on gunwale of boat; is covered with rubber. Ordinary size, each....$0.15
Large size, each .... .15

48468

48468 Fish Rod Holder, a good one for the money; screws on any part of the boat; forks covered with Rubber. Each $0.35

48469 Leather Reel Cases are made of bleached oak, finest leather, felt lined,with leather covered buckles.

48469

No. 11, to hold small single action reel $0.75
No. 12, to hold large single action reel .... .88
No. 13, to hold small multiplying reel .... .88
No. 14, to hold large multiplying reel 1.00

The Universal Fish Rod Holder.

48510 For trolling and still fishing in a boat. It can be fastened either to the gunwale or seat. It enables a person, if he desires,to go fishing without a guide to row for him,or to have two or three rods in use without their being all over the bottom of the boat to be stepped on and broken. By means of a thumb-screw it can be adjusted to any angle or any direction, as it works on a ball and socket joint. It is neatly and strongly made, and forks are covered with rubber; it will take any rod from ½ to 2 in. diameter at butt. Weight, 26 oz. Each $1.10

Fishing Reels.

(Reels by mail, 10 to 15 cents extra.)

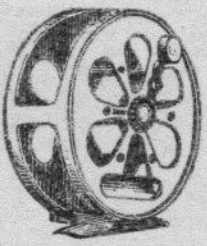

48511 The Expert Reel. This reel has an entirely new device for use in casting or "playing" a fish whereby the angler may vary the reel from a free running to a delicate drag, heavy drag, or bring it to a complete stop, simply by the pressure of the thumb upon the guard. By this device the line may be stopped instantly at any desired point when casting. This guard is made of extra hard spring metal so that no matter how often used or struck by accident it will resume its original position. These reels, having a large diameter of spool, will reel in a line faster than the best quadruple multiplying reel. All finely polished, heavy nickel plated and well made; 40 yards, 2¼ in. diameter, with click. Each $1.55
Extra by mail, 6c.
70 yards, 3 in. diameter, with click. Each 1.70
Extra by mail, 7c.

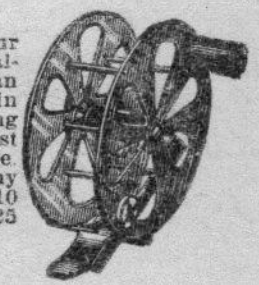

48512 The Famous Amateur Drag Reel, fine nickel plate, allowing tip to dry quickly; can be changed to a free runner in an instant by simply pressing down on spring. Beats the best multiplier in reeling in the line. Very light weight, and fits any reel band. Small $1.10
Medium 1.25
Extra by mail, 5c.

48513 The Competitive Reel, brass finish, plain, no click or drag, light and strong. Plain, free runner. Each $0.10
Extra by mail, 3c.

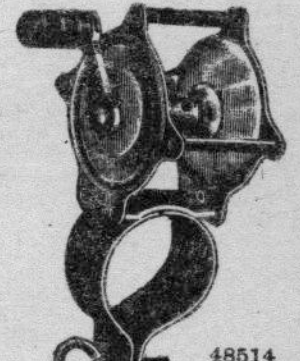

48513

48514 Brass Free Running Reel, with band to screw on rod, 25 yards. Each $0.30

48514

48516 Rubber Side Plate Reel for light trout fishing, a good and strong reel.
25 yards, each $0.45
40 yards, each .... .50
60 yards, each .... .60
Extra, by mail .... .05

48517 Polished Brass raised pillar, star pattern, with click, 25 yards, 1⅜ inches diameter of plate. Each $0.20
40 yards, 2 inches diameter of plates. Each $0.23
60 yards, 2 3-16 in., diameter of plates. Each $0.30
Extra, by mail .... .04

48518 Raised Pillar, polished brass, free running no click or drag.

48517

25 yards, each $0.20
40 yards, each .... .25
60 yards, each .... .30
Extra by mail .... .06

Fluted Spoon Bait.

48742 Fluted trolling spoon, full nickel plate, same shape spoon as Skinner's and same size hook, treble hook and fly, a first-class spoon. No. 1, smallest, 1¼ inch in spoon. Nos. 1, 2, 3, 4, 4½.
4¾. Each $0.09
Nos. 5 and 6. Each .... .10
Nos. 7 and 8. Each .... .12

Chapman's Allure Baits.

One of the finest spinners and best killing baits in the market; designed by an old fisherman. Gold color and nickel on opposite sides. A perfect bait for bass, pickerel and pike.

48743—
No. 1—0, large, 2¾ in. spoon $0.44
No. 2—6, largest, 3 in. spoon, heavy and strong. .50

Fancy American Spinner.

48746 Best Plated Spoon, one-half hammered; best material and a rapid spinner, for bass, pickerel, etc. Nos. 2, 3, 4, 5 and 6, smallest. Each ... $0.35
Per dozen 3.60

Lightning Ball Bait.
A Big Seller.

It's a good one.

48747 Best Nickel-plated Spoon, finest material throughout, and easy spinner that does not get easily tangled. This is the latest thing out in spoon baits, treble hook and fly; same size spoon and hook as Skinner baits. Smallest, Skinner No. 4.

	Each	Per doz.
Nos. 2¼, 3, 3½, Trout, small bass	$0.25	$2.55
Nos. 4, 4½, 5 Pickerel	.35	3.50
Nos. 7 and 8, muskallonge, etc	.40	4.00

Spoon Minnows.

48748 Fine Nickel-plated Spoon, rubber minnows, best material, treble hook; a good bait for large fish, Nos. 4, 5, 3½. Each $0.65
Per doz. 4.70

Hammered Spoon Baits.

In ordering state kind of fishing wanted for.

48749 Best Nickel plated Spoon, feathered treble hook. One of the most successful baits in the market. No. 7 smallest, 1 in.; No. 1 largest, 1 in. Nos. 1, 2, 3, 4, 5, 6, 7.
Each $0.10
Per doz. 1 00

48750 Ball Bait, good nickel plate spoons, feathered treble hook. No. 1, smallest, for small bass. Larger ones for pickerel, pike and muskallonge. Nos. 1, 2½, 3, 3½, 4, 5, 6 and 7. No. 7, largest about 2¼ in.
Each $0.20
Per dozen 1.95

48751 Salmon Trout Bait, plated spoon, one hook. No. 6, smallest, 2½ in. long; No. 1 largest, 4 in. long.
3¼ in. long. Each .$0.25 Per doz. $2.40

48752 Trolling Squids Diamond Block, tinned, No. 1 smallest, 3 in. long, 15c.; No. 2, 3½ in. 20c.; No. 3, 4 in. 25c.; No. 4, 4½ in. 35c.

The Muskallonge or Tarpon Baits.

The herculean strength of this bait will tell its own story to the fisherman in the pursuit of large game. For the St. Lawrence, the Western lakes and rivers and the coast of Florida they fill the bill to perfection.

48753 Fine Nickel Plated Spoon; treble hook, feathered, very best material. 2¾ inch spoon for 10 to 25 lb. fish.
Each $0.25
Per dozen 2.70
3¼ inch spoon, for 30 to 100 lb. fish.
Each .... .30
Per doz. 3.00

48753½ Muskallonge Trolling Minnow, solid rubber accurately decorated to represent the live minnow, the finest bait in the world to capture "Muskey," entire length of minnow 6½ inches.
Price, each $1.35

48754 Adirondack Spinner Spoon Fly, smallest nickel spoon, feathered hook for small trout, etc. Small, about ½ inch spoon; medium, 1 inch; large, 1¼ inch. Each $0.20
Per dozen 2.25

The Patent Luminous Fish Bait.

The most attractive lure for day fishing and the only successful bait in deep and roily water, and after dark. Every suitable size, style and pattern made for bass, pike, pickerel, muskallonge and other game fish of America. As game fish do most of their feeding by night, luminous bait is the best bait to fish with.

DIRECTIONS.—For day fishing, use same as ordinary baits. For night fishing, expose baits to light during the day.

48755 Luminous Soft Rubber Grasshopper. The most natural and most durable article on the market.
Each $0.49

48756 Luminous Soft Rubber Frogs. This bait is a lasting one, combined with luminous qualities. It is a decided improvement over live frogs.
Each $0.45

48757 Luminous Fluted Bait, with gimp leader and swivel .... Nos. 5 7 9
Each .... 35c. 36c. 45c. 48c.
Number 5 smallest, about size of Skinner's bait No. 4.

48759 Luminous Hard or Soft Rubber Minnow, indestructible. The best imitation of a minnow, finely colored. The "cut" is poor but the bait is the best in the market.
No. 7, No. 8, No. 9. Price each, all sizes, 45c.

48760 Luminous Crystal Minnow, a very attractive lure, and often successful when all others fail.
Price, each .... 35c. No. 1. 45c. No. 2.

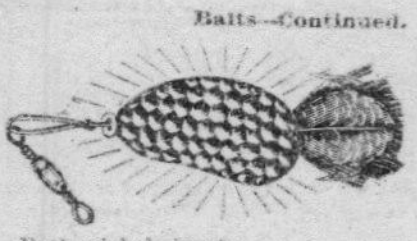

48761 Luminous Kidney baits.
No. 1 for trout ... $0.25
No. 4 medium small bass $0.28
Nos. 5 and 4, large, big bass ... $0.37
Each, nickel plated $0.3

Caledonia Minnows.

48762 No. 8, largest, 60c.; No. 7, 50c.; No. 6, 45c.; Nos. 5, 4, 3 and 2, 45c.

Protean Minnows.

48764 Flexible Rubber.
Nos. 2, 3, 4 5 6 7 8
Each 35c 48c 50c 58c 64c

Phantom Minnows.

48765 One of the most successful baits made. The body is made of silk waterproofed, nicely mounted, assorted colors and shades.
Nos. 1, 2, 3, 4, 5 6 7 8
Each 45c 49c 55c 60c

Helgamites.

48769 Helgamite or Dobson soft rubber, with swivel.
Each $0.25

48770—Large Crawfish, soft rubber.
Each $0.29

48771 Shrimps, small.
Each $0.20

48772 Shrimps, large.
Each .... .27

Artificial Baits.

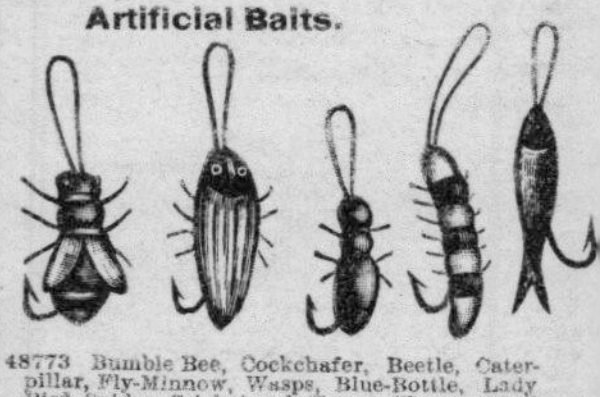

48773 Bumble Bee, Cockchafer, Beetle, Caterpillar, Fly-Minnow, Wasp, Blue-Bottle, Lady Bird, Spider, Cricket and House Fly; assorted colors. Each $0.15
Grasshopper, small. Each .... .18
Grasshopper, large. Each .... .25
48774 Frogs, small; soft rubber. Each .... .20
48775 Frogs, large; soft rubber. Each .... .25

48776 Angle Worms; a perfect imitation. Each .... .20

••* No one enjoys eating from chipped or cracked dishes. Why not get a new set? Prices low.

Fish Hooks—Continued.

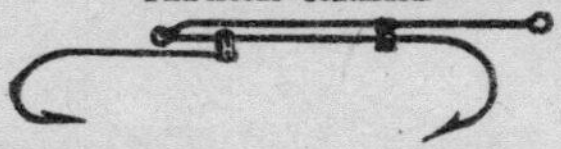

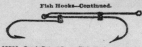

48780 Geer's Patent Lever Fish Hook; no more fish lost and baits to reset; no coming home without your largest fish; a dead sure thing on getting your fish if it bites; it is easily adjusted to all kinds of fishing, by sliding the little clamp on the rod; made on 3-0 Carlisle hooks. Each........$0.15 Per dozen..........$1.25

Spring Hooks.

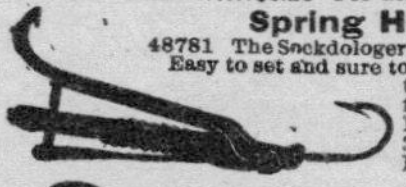

48781 The Sockdologer Spring Fish Hook. Easy to set and sure to catch any fish that takes it. For large fish. No. 1 small, No. 2 medium, No. 3 large. Each..........$0.25

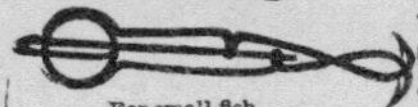

For small fish

48782 The Snap and Catch 'Em Spring Fish Hook. Easily set. Fish cannot get away once he is hooked.

No. 20 small, No. 19 medium No 18 large. Each $0.15

Fish Stringers.

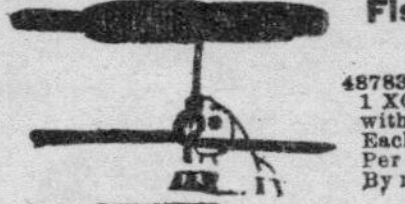

48783 Fish Stringer, No. 1 XC plate, complete with line. Each........... $0.05 Per dozen........ .45 By mail, 2c extra.

Chain Fish Stringer.

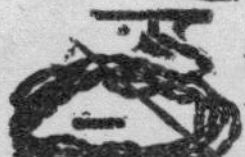

48784 Chain Fish Stringers brass links, heavily nickel plated, strong and durable, will hold 100 pounds of fish and not break. Each.........$0.35

Nickeled Steel Combined Fish Hook Extractor and Fish Stringer.

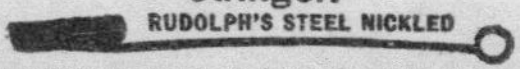

48785 Extracts the hook instantly. Saves time, line, hook and fish. Each..........$0 18
Per dozen.......... 1.55

Clearing Rings.

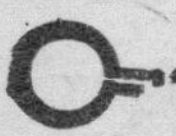

48786 Clearing Rings to free the hook when it gets caught under the water. Each..........$0.54

Frog Spear.

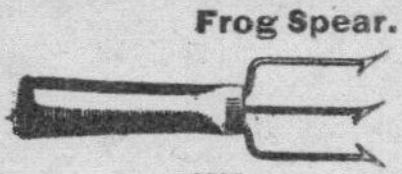

48787 Frog Spear, 3 tines, with socket to put pole in. Each $0.15

48787

Fish Spears.

Lengths given the entire length of prongs; weight, 8 to 12 ounces each.

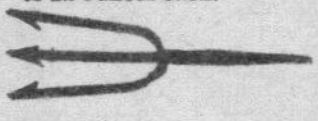

48787½ 3 Prongs, 2¼ in. long tanged. Each..........$0.25
48788 5 Prongs, 4 inches long, tanged. Each $0.30

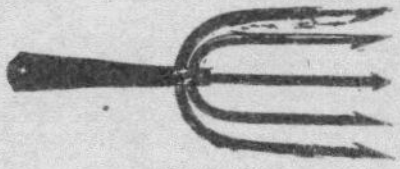

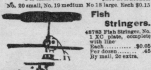

48789-90

48789 5 Prongs, 4½ inches, with sockets. Each..$0.50
48790 5 Prongs, 5 inches, with socket. Each ..... .65
Lengths given are length of prong.

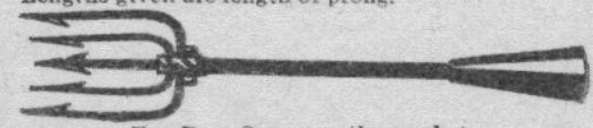

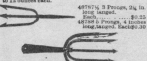

THE BEST SPEAR on the market.

48791 Hand made Fish Spear, all best steel, except socket and wedge; beards of each tine made on solid shank, screws into socket and makes its own thread in wood (of handle); the outside tines can be removed if smaller spear is wanted at any time by putting in larger wedge; width about 4½ to 4½ inches; entire length of tines, about 6½ inches; entire length, 22 inches; Weight about 1¼ lbs. Each ....$ 2.25
Per dozen 24.00

Fishing Tackle Boxes.

The very best in the market.

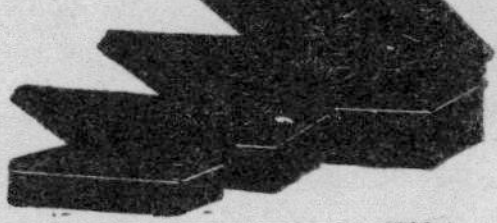

Showing comparative sizes of 48793-4.

This is a very practical and ornamental box made of heavy tin, double seamed and soldered, and will stand hard service.

48793 Single outfit tackle box, 10 spaces, 1 tray and space for small reel; length, 8¼; width, 5¼; depth, 2¼ in. Each..........$0.75
48793½ Double outfit tackle box, 10 spaces, 1 tray space for large reel; length 10¼; width, 6¼; depth, 4 inches. Each.......... 1.10
48794 Stock tackle box, 15 spaces, 2 trays, space for three reels; any amount of lines, hooks, etc. They must be seen to be appreciated. All are made black finish, gilt stripe and ornamentation. Length, 12¼; width, 8¼; depth, 6 in....1.88
48795 Pocket Tackle Box, 7x4x1½ inches. Has center leaf which projects slightly beyond the two halves of the box, so that when the box is opened this leaf is caught and raised with the half uppermost, thus retaining in their places the tackle in that half. Has corks for hooks. Space for gang hooks attached to the trolling spoons. Each.......... .84

Borcherdt's Fishing Tackle Box.

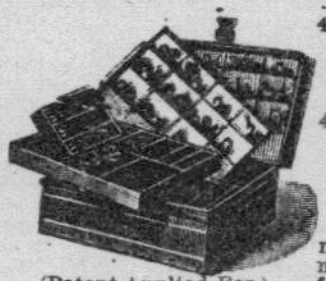

(Patent Applied For.)

48796½ Size, 8½x7x3, has three trays, space for two reels and any amount of lines, hooks, etc. Each..........$2.97
48797 12¼x8x4½. has three trays, space for 2 reels, trolling line, etc., and 24 pockets. Each..........$3.97

These boxes were planned by a practical fisherman, and have given satisfaction to all. They are all made of heavy stock, double seamed and soldered, smoothly made and elegantly painted and ornamented.

Pocket Tackle Books.

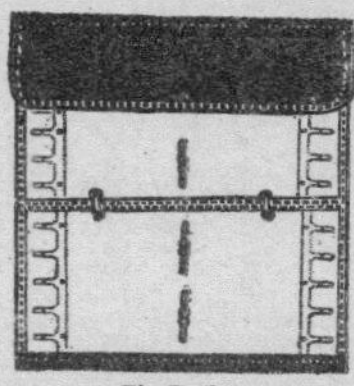

Fly Book.

48798 Solid Leather Tackle Books, bound and stitched edges, strap fastening, 6 compartments,
6 inches long..$1.65
7 inches long.. 2.13
48799 Pocket FlyBook patent celluloid leaves clip fly holders, morocco leather covered, snap fastening; a good book.
7 inches long..$1.50 Each.

48800 Pocket Fly Book, made of good strong morocco colored leather, snap fastening, made of best materials throughout, not a cheap article, but made for service, patent clips; a fine book. 8 leaves, 64 clips, 7 in., each..........$1.83
48803 Pocket Fly Book, leather covered, patent fastenings, well made, patent clips, parchment leaves, 7 inch. Each.......... 1.00
48804 Pocket Fly Book, leather covered, patent clips, snap fastening, good shape, parchment leaves, but not made of fine material, 6 in. long. .50
48805 "Best South Side" solid leather, fine quality, celluloid leaves, two compartment pockets, two leather pockets, clips to hold 5 dozen flies, felt pads for keeping flies moist; size of book 7x4. An elegant book for the money. Price.......... 3.00

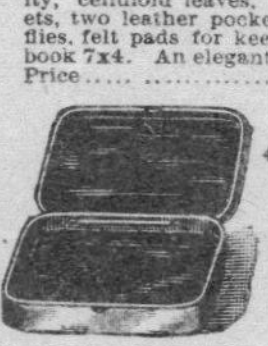

48806 Leader Boxes, heavy nickel plated leader boxes; size, 4½x3¼; has felt pad to keep leaders moist; no more whipping off of leaders or wasting of time trying to get them in shape after you are at your fishing grounds. Each..........$0.50

Amateur Photography has come to stay. We sell all photographic instruments and supplies at less than list prices. Orders filled promptly. Every article guaranteed perfect.

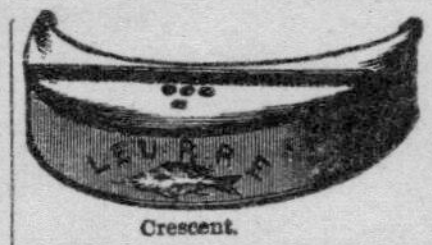

Bait Boxes.

Crescent.

		Each.
48807	Oval Pattern	$0.09
48808	Padlock Pattern	.09
48809	Ketchem Pattern	.09
48810	Crescent	.18
48811	Bait Box straps, leather, ⅜ in. wide, 36 in long	.20

The Harvard Ice Top Minnow Pail.

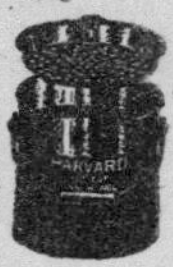

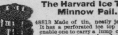

48813 Made of tin, neatly japanned. It has a perforated ice top cover to enable one to carry a lump of ice to keep the water cool and minnows fresh.

	6 qt.	8 qt.	10 qt.
Each	58c.	73c.	80c.

Rudolph's Celebrated Floating Minnow Buckets.

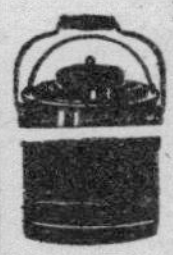

48816 Handiest, lightest, noiseless and most complete minnow bucket ever put on the market. Will not sink, free circulation of air and water, attracts the fish to it, thereby making good fishing around the bucket. No loss of bucket or bait should you drop it overboard. Ice top to carry ice, if desired, to keep the minnows fresh while in transit. When you arrive at the lake drop inside bucket into the water, where it will remain on the surface, the waterproof wire making it so open that it affords full flow of fresh water all the time, bringing to your minnows the insect food upon which they exist, as well as attracting other fish to it; weight, 3½ to 5½ pounds.

Quart	6	8	10	12
Each	$1.15	$1.35	$1.55	$1.65

Floating Minnow Pocket.

(Rudolph's Patent.)

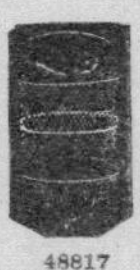

48817 When in use.

When several ladies and gentlemen go fishing together, they may provide themselves with Floating Minnow Pocket each so that when they arrive at the fishing grounds each may have their own minnows, avoiding the necessity of more than one minnow bucket in the party. When not in use are so small that they will go in an ordinary coat pocket and no thicker than your hand.
48817 Floating Minnow Pocket. Each..........$0.90

Live Nets.

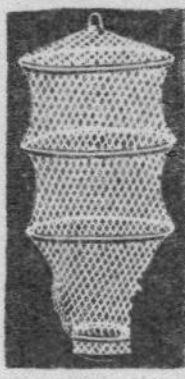

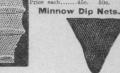

48818 These nets are to put fish in when caught, keeping them alive.

Inches	10	12	14
Price each	45c.	50c.	55c

Minnow Dip Nets.

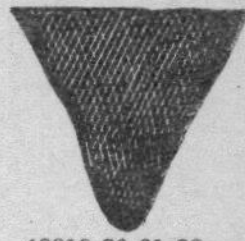

48819-20-21-22

48819 (Linen) Minnow Dip Nets.

Inches deep	16	18	20	24	30	36
Each	35c.	40c.	45c.	50c.	73c.	$1.00

Linen Landing Nets

48820 Inches	20	24	30
Each	25c.	30c.	40c.

Braided Waterproof Landing Nets.

(Cotton.)

48821 Inches deep	24 in.	30 in.
Each	60c.	78c.

48822 Crab Nets, made of 12-thread cotton seine twine, regulation meshes.

Inches deep	16 in.	20 in.	24 in.
Each	12c.	15c.	20c.

Our claim that this Catalogue opens the large markets to you is no idle boast. Where else can you find so much? As a genuine guide to prices it has no equal.

Improved Perfection Trammel Net.

It has three nets hung upon a single top and a single bottom line. Of the three nets, two have large meshes of cotton seine twine. The inside net is made of best linen gilling twine, which is hung slack, forming a bag in which fish coming from either side are caught, unable to escape. These nets are not "drag seines" but are to be "set" in the water the same as a gill net.

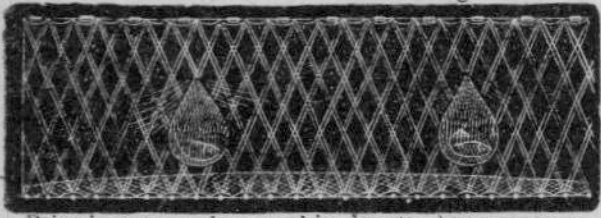

Price is per running yard in length, hung measure, the three nets combined complete with leads and floats. Square mesh. Weigh per yard about ½ lb.

No	Depth.	Outside Mesh.	Inside Mesh.	Inside Linen Twine.	Outside Cotton Twine.	Price Per Yard.
49010	3½ ft.	6 in.	¾ in.	No. 25	No.	$0.22
49011	3½ ft.	6 in.	1 in.	No. 25		.21
49012	3½ ft.	6 in.	1¼ in.	No. 25		.19
49013	4 ft.	6 in.	1 in.	No. 25		.24
49014	4 ft.	6 in.	1¼ in.	No 25		.22
49015	4½ ft.	7 in.	1¼ in.	No. 20		.24
49016	4½ ft.	7 in.	1¼ in.	No. 25		.22
49017	4½ ft.	7 in.	1½ in.	No. 18		.23
49018	4½ ft.	7 in.	1¾ in.	No. 18		.22
49019	4½ ft.	7 in.	2 in.	No. 18		.21
49020	5 ft.	8 in.	1 in.	No. 25		.28
49021	5 ft.	8 in.	1½ in.	No. 18		.24
49022	5 ft.	8 in.	2½ in.	No. 18		.20
49023	5 ft.	8 in.	3 in.	No 18		.19
49024	6 ft.	8 in.	1 in.	No. 25	All No. 16, Soft Laid.	.34
49025	6 ft.	8 in.	1½ in.	No. 18		.27
49026	6 ft.	8 in.	2 in.	No. 18		.26
49027	6 ft.	8 in.	2½ in	No. 18		.21
49028	6 ft.	8 in.	3 in.	No. 18		.20
49029	7 ft.	8 in.	1½ in.	No. 18		.35
49030	7 ft.	8 in.	2 in.	No. 18		.33
49031	7 ft	8 in.	2½ in	No 18		.24
49032	7 ft.	8 in.	3 in.	No. 18		22
49033	8 ft	8 in.	1¼ in.	No. 18		39
49034	8 ft.	8 in.	1¾ in.	No. 18		.37
49035	8 ft.	8 in.	2 in.	No. 18		.34
49036	8 ft.	8 in.	2½ in.	No. 18		.26
49037	8 ft.	8 in.	3 in.	No. 18		.24

Other styles made to order. Meshes as given above are diamond square. Hung complete for use except hauling lines. When ordering nets, give SIZE, PRICE and CATALOGUE number

Gill or Set Net.

A gill net is a single net, hung with floats and leads complete, without hauling lines. Made of best imported linen twine. These nets cannot be used for "drag" seines, the twine being too fine. They are set in the water, and allowed to remain from 5 to 24 hours. Commencing at one end "lift" gently when taking up net. The fish are caught by the gills, hence the name "gill" or "set" net.

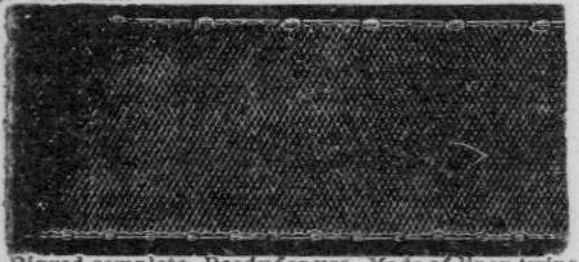

Rigged complete. Ready for use. Made of linen twine; Price is per running yard in length, hung measure. Weight, per yard, about ¼ pound.

No.	Depth	No Twine. Linen.	Size of Mesh Square.	Price per Yard.
49045	3½ feet.	40	2 inch.	$0.13
49046	4 feet.	40	1 inch.	19
49047	4 feet.	40	1¼ inch.	15
49048	4 feet.	35	1½ inch.	16
49049	4 feet.	35	1¾ inch.	14
49050	4 feet.	40	2 inch.	15
49051	5 feet.	40	1 inch	22
49052	5 feet.	40	1¼ inch.	19
49053	5 feet.	35	1½ inch.	18
49054	5 feet.	25	1¾ inch.	17
49055	5 feet.	40	2 inch.	16
49056	5 feet.	40	2¼ inch.	15
49057	5 feet.	40	2½ inch.	16
49058	6 feet.	40	1 inch.	25
49059	6 feet.	40	1¼ inch.	22
49060	6 feet.	35	1½ inch.	20
49061	6 feet	35	1¾ inch.	19
49062	6 feet.	35	2 inch.	18
49063	6 feet.	40	2¼ inch.	17
49064	6 feet.	40	2½ inch.	16
49065	7 feet	25	1½ inch.	22
49066	7 feet.	20	1¾ inch.	21
49067	7 feet.	20	2 inch.	20
49068	8 feet.	25	1½ inch.	24
49069	8 feet.	20	1¾ inch.	23
49070	8 feet.	20	2 inch.	22

Other styles made to order. Our Gill nets are made of Knox best Scotch linen twine.

Seines or nettings made to order cannot be returned.

Cotton Trot Line.

49089. Cotton trot line in 50 feet coils (6 connected), best quality, sold in any quanity at dozen rates.

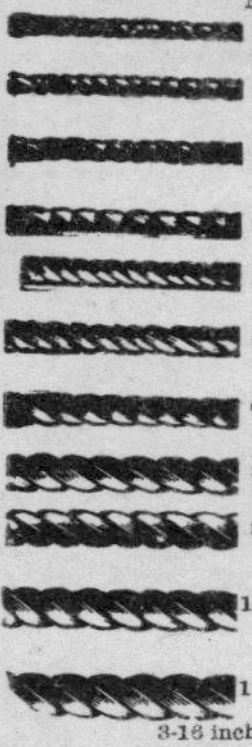

No.	Per doz. coils.	Wt. Per doz.
1	$0.38	15 oz.
2	.47	16 oz.
3	.49	19 oz.
4	.67	20 oz.
5	.76	23 oz.
6	.88	24 oz.
7	.95	32 oz.
8	1.05	36 oz.
9	1.20	44 oz.
10	1.35	52 oz.
11	1.60	56 oz.
3-16 inch diam.	2.00	96 oz.

Gilling Twine.

The best quality imported.

Gilling twine is a small all linen twine, used for gill or set nets, and cannot be used to make a drag, lake or river net.

No		Per lb.
49090	Linen gilling twine, No. 12, 3 cord.	$ 0.78
	Linen gilling twine, No. 14, 3 cord	.82
	Linen gilling twine, No. 16, 3 cord	.95
	Linen gilling twine, No. 20, 3 cord	.98
	Linen gilling twine, No. 25, 3 cord	1.10
	Linen gilling twine, No. 30, 3 cord	1.15
	Linen gilling twine, No. 35, 3 cord	1.30
	Linen gilling twine, No. 40, 3 cord	1.50
	Linen gilling twine, No. 50, 3 cord	1.85

Gilling twine comes in ¼ lb. balls.

Seine Twine.

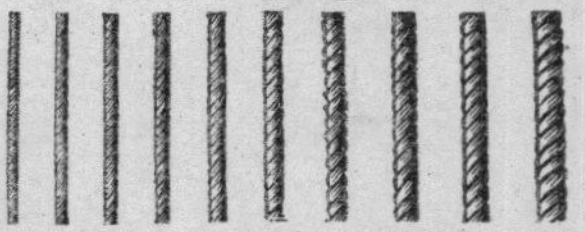

Showing sizes of seine twine as near as possible. These illustrations appear larger than the twine.

Our Seine Twine is the best in the market, laid smooth and even, and uniform in size. We do not handle the loosely laid, bunchy cheap goods.

49091 White Seine Twine soft laid, in skeins of about 1 to 1¾ lb. each. Nos. 6, 9, 12, 16, 20, 24, 28, 32, 36, 40, 44, 48, 60; No. 6, smallest, No. 60, largest; 32 to 48 is the proper size for fly nets; 16 to 24 is the hammock size.
Per lb. in less than 5 lb. lots $0.22
Per lb. in 5 lb. lots and over .... .19

49092 White Seine Twine, medium laid, for Seines and Hammocks, in skeins. Nos. 9, 12, 15, 18, 21, 24, 27, 30, 36, 39, 42, 48, 54, 60. (No. 9 smallest.)
Per lb in 5 lb. lots or over .... .21
Per lb .... .24

49093 White Seine Twine, hard laid, in skeins, Nos. 9 to 60, same size as in medium laid.
Per lb. in 5 lb. lots or over .... .23
Per lb .... .26

N. B —In the small size the hanks weigh about one lb. In the larger sizes they run about 1¼ lb. to the skein. We do not break skeins.

Colored Twine for Hammocks and Fly Nets.

49094 Colored Seine Twine, for hammocks and fly nets; colors: Blue, red, brown and orange; Nos. 24 and 32 only. (No. 24 for hammocks and No. 32 for fly nets.)
Per lb $0.30

Price on Rope and Seine Rigging quoted on application. We can furnish nearly everything in this line at low prices.

Seine Needles.

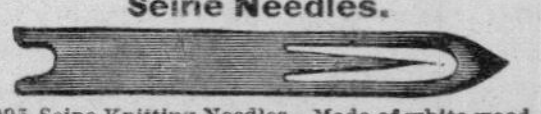

49095 Seine Knitting Needles. Made of white wood.

	½ in.	¾ in.	1 in.	1¼ in.	1½ in.
Each	10c	12c	15c	16c	17c

For quotations on Sailors' Palms, Needles and Twine, see Index.

Hammocks.

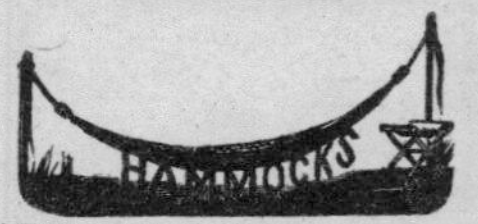

49100 Hammocks for children, open mesh, cotton cord, mixed bright colors, strong and durable, 7 ft. bed by 4 ft wide; weight, 8 oz. Each .. $0.50

49102 Hammocks, full size, made of heavy double seine twine, full width, entire length end to end 14 ft., fancy bright colors; weight, 2 lbs. Each .. 1.25

49105 Hammocks, Mexican, white, entire length 14 ft., bed 6 ft. 6 in. long; weight 3½ lbs. .... .70

49106 Hammock, Mexican, assorted colors, same size as No. 49106; weight, 3 lbs. .... .85

The Mexican Hammocks are made of a sea grass and are light and strong and among the most durable in the market.

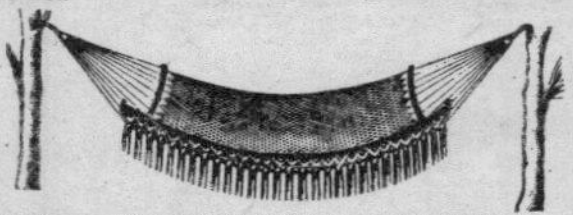

49107 Hammocks, Mexican, woven, made of sisal sea grass, yellowish white bed, fancy colored valance on each side, bright colored end strings, clinch thimble on end, entire length 14 ft., length of bed 6 ft. 6 in., full width; a showy, well made, strong and durable article; weight, 4 lbs. Each $1.59

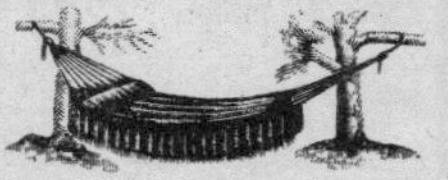

49108 Hammocks, close woven body, cotton weave, in bright fancy colors mostly red mixed with other bright colors, wide valance on each side, with pillow, 42x84 in. heavy and strong. Weight about 6 pounds. Each $4.00

49109 Hammocks, close woven body, cotton weave, in bright fancy colors mostly red mixed with other bright colors, wide valance on each side, curved spreader on each end, with pillow. One of the most comfortable and showy hammocks, well made, strong and durable, bed 42x84 in., entire length 13 ft.; weight, about 5 lbs. Each 2.95

49111 Hammock, close woven body, cotton weave, modest pale colors mixed with white, with valance pillow and curved spreaders on each end, bed 40x80 in., entire length 12½ ft., well made, strong and durable and much more comfortable than the open mesh style; weight, about 5 lbs. Each 2.65

49112 Hammocks, close woven body, cotton weave, white mixed with pale modest colors, valance on both sides, curved spreaders in each end, no pillow, bed 42x84 in., entire length 13 ft.; weight about 4½ lbs., well made and durable. Each 2.35

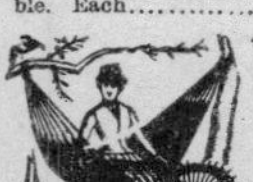

49113 Hammocks, close woven body, cotton weave, fancy mixed colors (no valance) with pillow, curved spreaders in each end, well made, strong and durable, bed 40x80 in., entire length 12½ ft.; weight about 4½ lbs, strong and durable. Each $1.85

49114 Hammocks, close woven body, cotton weave, fancy bright colors, without pillow, curved spreader in each end, bed 42x84, entire length 13 ft. well made and durable; weight, 3¾ lbs. Each 1.65

49115 Hammocks, close woven body, cotton weave, white and pale mixed colors, without pillow, curved spreaders in earch end, bed 42x84, entire length 13 ft.; weight, 3¼ lbs, well made, strong and durable. Each 1.45

49116 Child's Hammock, double cord open mesh, bright colors, curved spreaders on each end entire length from end to end 9 ft., spreaders, 2 ft. 6 in. long, strong, well made and durable; weight, 1½ lbs. Each .... .50

Peerless Hammock Spreader.

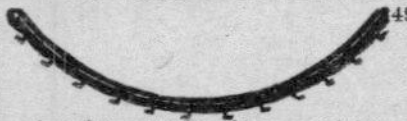

49130 Is made of a solid hard piece of hard wood, bent bow shape with hooks on its lower edge. It is designed to sustain a heavy weight, and is so simple in its construction and application that all will understand how to use it.
Each .... $0.08 Per doz $0.75
Weight 1 lb. each.

Hammock Ropes and Hooks.

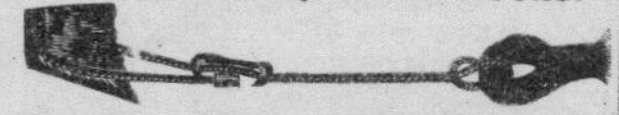

49133 Hammock Ropes, 7 feet long, with galvanized iron anchor fastening that remains where you place it; no knots to tie after attached to hammock, no slipping, while in hammock. Hammock can be raised and lowered in an instant.
Each..............$0.08 Two for..............$0.15

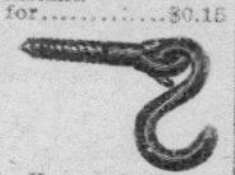

49136 Screw Hammock Hooks, tinned, 7-16 inch diameter, to screw in. Each $0.06
Per doz. .... .65

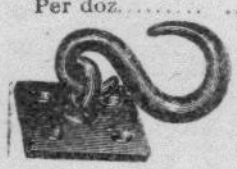

49137 Plate Hammock Hooks, tinned, 7-16 inch in diameter, to screw on. Each $0.09
Per doz 1.00

"A" or Wedge Tents.

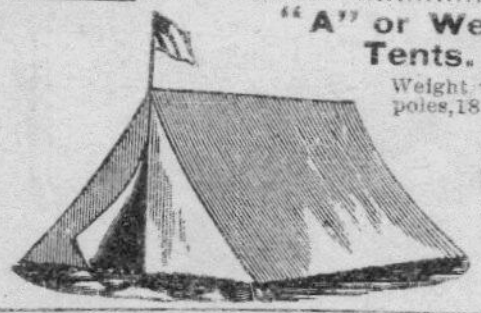

Weight without poles, 18 to 40 lbs.; weight of poles, 14 ounces to the foot in length.

Order No.	Length and Breadth. Feet.	Height Feet.	Price 8 oz. Duck.	Price 10 oz. Duck.	Price 12 oz. Duck.
49190	7x7 ft.	7 ft	$3.35	$3.90	$5.15
	7x9 ft	7 ft.	4.00	4.70	6.20
	9x9 ft.	7 ft.	4.45	5.25	6.95
	9½x12 ft.	7½ ft.	5.45	6.40	8.55
	12 x14 ft	9 ft.	7.85	9.25	12.35

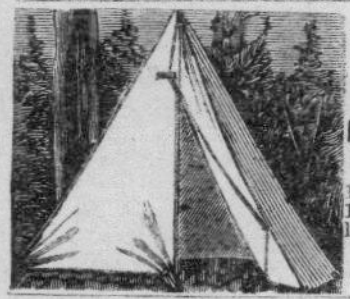

Miners' Tents.

Weights without poles 14 to 30 pounds; poles 13 ounces per foot in length.

49195	Price, Complete.			
Size of Base.	Height.	8 oz. Single Filling Duck.	10 oz. Single Filling Duck.	12 oz. Double Filling Duck.
7 ft.x7 ft.	7ft.	$2.35	$2.70	$3.75
9 ft.x9 ft.	8ft.	3.50	4.00	5.60
12 ft.x12 ft.	9ft.	5.35	6.15	8.50

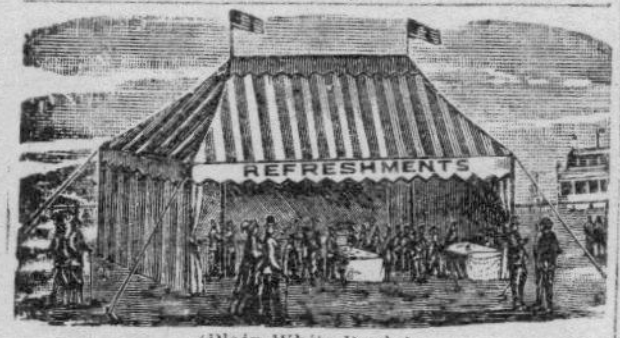

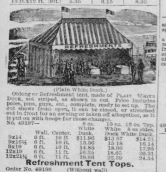

(Plain White Duck.)

Oblong or Refreshment tent, made of Plain White Duck, not striped, as shown in cut. Price includes poles, pins, guys, etc., complete, ready to set up. The cut shows front open, it can be closed, or stretched out in front for an awning or taken off altogether, as it is put on with hoops for these changes.

No. 49197—	Wall.	Center.	8 oz. White Duck.	10 oz. White Duck	12 oz. Top. 8 oz sides. White Duck.
9x14	6 ft.	10 ft	$11.96	$13 57	$14.21
9x16½	6 ft.	10 ft.	13.36	15 18	16.14
9x19	6 ft.	10 ft.	14.85	18.00	17.95
12x19	6 ft.	11 ft.	16.35	18.65	20.31
12x21½	6 ft.	11 ft.	19.66	22.39	24.54

Refreshment Tent Tops.

Order No. 49198 (Without wall)

	Center.	8 oz. White Duck.	10 oz. White Duck.	12 oz. White. Duck.
9x14	10 ft.	$6.90	$7.48	$9.19
9x16½	10 ft.	7.78	8.54	10.64
9x19	10 ft.	8.87	9.62	11.97
12x19	11 ft.	9.89	10.85	13.85
12x21½	11 ft.	12.19	13 37	17.00

Wall Tents.

We can furnish tents in large or small quantities on short notice generally. Our tents are the best quality; they are *all full size*, and all have a *good* "pitch" to roof, to turn rain, and all made in a durable and substantial manner. Prices in lots of 5 or more furnished on application. Tents will not be sent C. O. D., as they have to be made to order. We warrant them to be exactly as represented. In ordering give catalogue number, length and breadth and price.

We can make to order all kinds of tents, canopies, etc.

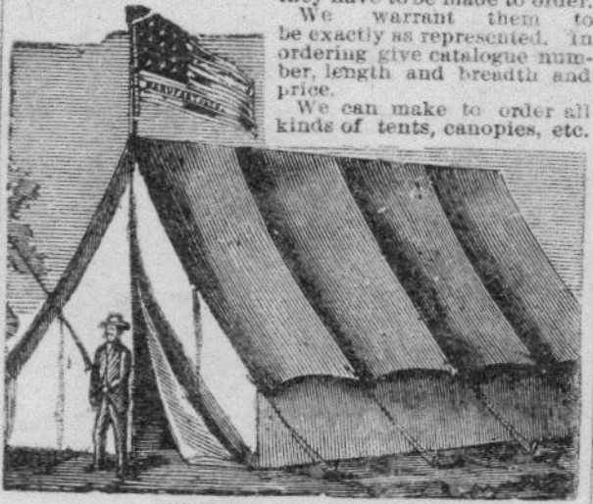

Wall Tent No. 49215

Wall Tents.

Weights without poles, 7x7, 30 lbs.; 9½x12, 40 to 50 lbs.; 14x16, 66 to 76 lbs.; 16x24, 120 to 130 lbs.; 18x32, 147 to 160 lbs. Ridge poles weigh 22 ounces to the foot. Upright poles, 14 oz. to the foot. Pins weigh ¼ to ¾ pounds each. All of our 12 ounce duck tents are double filling, best quality.

No.	Length and Breadth Feet	Height Wall Feet	Height Pole Feet	Price with Poles, Pins, Guys, etc Complete ready to set up: 8 oz. Duck.	10 oz. Duck.	12 oz. Duck.
Order 49215	7 x 7	3	7	$4.25	$4.95	$6.50
	7 x 9	3	7	5.00	5.85	7.80
	9 x 9	3	7½	5.80	6.80	9.00
	9½ x 12	3	7½	6.85	8.00	10.60
	9½ x 14	3	7½	7.80	9.10	12.00
	12 x 12	3½	8	8.10	9.50	12.60
	12 x 14	3½	8	9.20	10.70	14.20
	12 x 16	3½	8	10.20	11.90	15.50
	12 x 18	3½	8	11.35	13.22	17.40
	14 x 14	4	9	10.95	12.80	17.00
	14 x 16	4	9	12.00	14.15	18.80
	14 x 18	4	9	13.45	15.75	20.90
	14 x 20	4	9	14.95	17.35	22.80
	14 x 24	4	9	16.85	19.55	25.50
	16 x 16	5	11	14.10	16.60	22.05
	16 x 18	5	11	15.50	18.20	24.15
	16 x 20	5	11	17.05	19.80	26.10
	16 x 24	5	11	19.45	22.60	29.55
	16 x 30	5	11	23.50	27.40	35.75
	16 x 35	5	11	26.30	30.65	40.10
	18 x 18	5	11	17.70	20.80	27.60
	18 x 20	5	11	19.50	22.85	29.85
	18 x 24	5	11	21.80	25.45	33.25
	18 x 30	5	11	26.15	30.45	39.95
	18 x 35	5	11	29.10	33.90	44.55

Poles and pins included in above prices. Prices on any size of wall tent not mentioned above given on application. Can furnish any style of tent wanted.

A tent fly makes an extra movable or double roof to a tent, and affords a greater protection from sun and rain, and can be made to serve as an awning, either in front or rear of tent. They are not really necessary, and are not included in prices of tents, but we can furnish them, if ordered, at one-half the price of tents of corresponding size and quality.

Photographers' Tents.

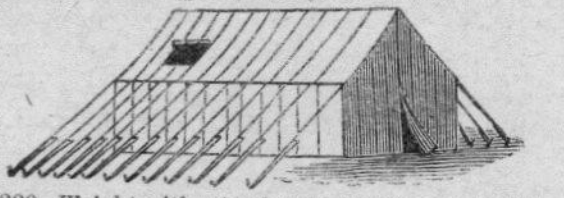

49220 Weight without poles, 66 to 176 pounds Ridge Poles, 22 to 25 oz. per foot in length.

Size.	Pole.	Wall.	Price complete without dark room: 8 oz. single fill'g duck.	10 oz. single filling duck.	10 oz double filling duck.
12x16 ft....	11 ft.	6 ft.	$15.78	$17.69	$20.11
12x21 ft....	11 ft.	6 ft.	19.24	22.19	27.56
14x16 ft....	12 ft.	6 ft.	17.64	20.84	25.11
14x21 ft....	12 ft.	6 ft.	21.38	24.59	29.67
16x18 ft....	13 ft.	6 ft.	20.84	24.33	29.14
16x24 ft....	13 ft.	6 ft.	25.65	29.93	35.54

Photographers' Tents—Continued.

Prices on tents include poles, pins, guys, etc. Tent complete ready to set up.

Dark rooms extra, 6x6 feet, $7.80; 4½x4½ feet $6.50. Our dark rooms are made of same material, same weight and color as the tent—all white. We make the room only, the artist can darken it to suit his own taste. Some use black Silesia, some yellow, etc.

The above prices include poles, pins, guys, etc., ready to set up tent. Quotation on other sizes on application and at bottom prices.

Prices on stable tents, stable, tops, Sibley tents, canopy tops without wall, photographers' tents, square hip-roof tents, or any other style, given on application and at bottom prices.

Palmetto, or Lawn Tents.

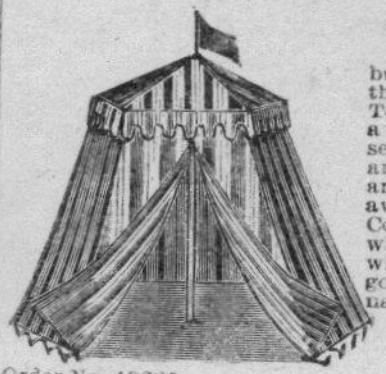

These tents have but one pole, and that is in the center. Top is supported by a light iron frame sewed into tent around eaves. They are made of 8 ounce awning material. Color, blue and white, brown and white, blue and old gold, etc., in alternate shades.

Order No. 49225— Size of Base.	Size of Eaves.	Height Center.	Price.
7x7 ft.	2 ft. 4 in.	7½ ft.	$4.95
8x8 ft.	2 ft. 4 in.	8 ft.	5.80
10x10 ft.	3 ft.	9 ft.	8.30

Black Oiled Wagon Cover.

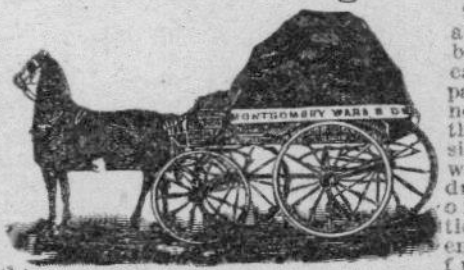

These covers although black and called tarpaulins, have no tar in their composition. Our water proof dressing is an oil preparation, and is entirely free from anything calculated to rot or burn the canvas, but adds to the durability of the cover, being impervious to water, and very soft and pliable. It will neither rot nor mildew from damp, nor break from being too hard. They are invaluable to all persons who are shipping and receiving goods which are liable to damage from wet weather. In ordering, give catalogue number, size and price.

Weight 9 to 28 pounds. 6x12, 12 lbs; 6x9, 9 lbs; 7x12, 16 lbs; 7x14, 19 lbs.

Order No.	Feet	Oz.	Each.	Feet.	Oz.	Each
49227			$	7x9	8	$3.30
	6x8	8	2.50	7x12	8	4.40
	6x9	8	2.85	7x14	8	5.10
	6x12	8	3.75	8x12	8	5.15
				8x14	8	5.85

Wagon Covers.

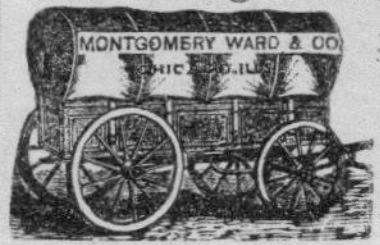

49228 Wagon Covers white duck (see cut). Always give size when ordering. Weight, 7 to 50 lbs., 10x10, 8 oz., 7 lbs., 10x13, 10oz., 16 lbs.; 12x22, 40 to 50 lbs.

Size—Feet.	8 oz. Duck.	10 oz. Duck.	12 oz. Duck.
10x10	$1.50	$1.95	$2.00
10x12	1.80	2.31	3.44
10x14	1.98	2.50	3.75
10x15	2.39	2.90	4.39
10x16	2.46	3.25	4.68
11x13	2.25	2.85	4.25
11x15	2.57	3.24	4.94
11x18	3.13	3.93	5.95
12x15	2.85	3.60	5.50
12x16	3.00	3.85	5.84
12x20	3.95	4.80	7.10

We sell more SEWING MACHINES than any other house in the world.

Why?

• • See our Prices • •

Stack, Machine and Merchandise Covers, Called Paulins.

Weight from 15 to 100 lbs.
16x14, 10 to 20 lbs; 14x20, 25 to 30 lbs.
20x20, 38 to 45 lbs.

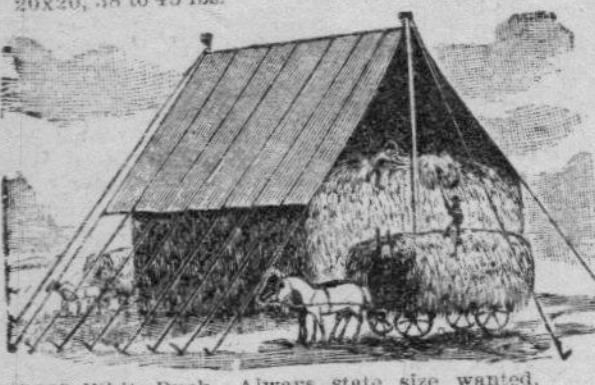

49229 White Duck. Always state size wanted, when ordering. Prices quoted on application, on sizes not mentioned here. Our 12 ounce duck is best double filling. These goods are not tents, but "stack covers" or paulins.

Size.—Feet	8 oz. Duck.	10 oz. Duck.	12 oz. Duck.
10x16	$ 2.22	$ 2.75	$ 4.25
10x18	2.50	3.07	4.80
12x14	2.42	3.00	4.60
12x16	2.85	3.42	5.30
12x18	3.15	3.81	5.89
12x20	3.50	4.27	6.65
14x16	3.70	4.53	6.30
14x18	4.16	5.11	7.20
14x20	4.65	5.70	8.00
14x24	5.55	6.81	9.60
16x16	4.25	5.20	7.30
16x18	4.75	5.84	8.20
16x20	5.30	6.50	9.15
16x24	6.35	7.80	10.95
18x20	5.95	7.30	10.25
18x24	7.15	8.75	12.30
18x28	8.35	10.20	14.35
18x30	8.95	10.95	15.35
20x24	7.95	9.71	13.68
20x36	11.90	14.60	20.50
24x30	11.95	14.65	20.55
24x36	14.30	17.50	24.65
24x40	15.87	19.45	27.35

Stack covers have short ropes, but no poles, machine and merchandise covers have eyelets around side. Any other size furnished on short notice. Prices on application.

Binder Covers.

49230 Weight, 6¼ to 7¼ lbs. Fitted to cover the binder and not the whole machine. Will fit any binder. Made of white duck.

	8 oz.	10 oz
Price, each	$1.85	$2.15

Stockmen's Bed Sheets.

Weights, 10 to 22 lbs. Fitted with snap rings or eyelets as may be ordered.
Made of very best heavy white duck.

Order No.	Feet.	13 oz.	15 oz.	18 oz.
49231	6x12	$2.54	$3.00	$3.66
	6x14	2.92	3.55	3.82
	6x15	3.15	3.81	4.09
	6x18	3.75	4.54	4.88
	7x12	2.95	3.52	3.89
	7x14	3.38	4.00	4.49
	7x15	3.51	4.38	4.85
	8x12	3.67	4.48	4.82
	8x14	4.23	5.00	5.57

Arctic Sleeping Bags.

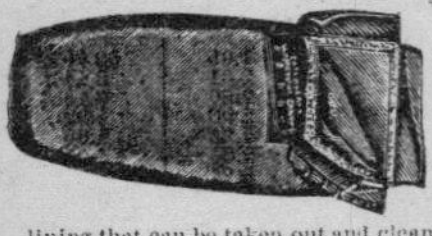

49240 The Improved. Made of heavy water-proof tan-colored duck, lined with sheepskin, with the wool left on, inside of sheepskin lining is a heavy drill lining that can be taken out and cleaned at any time; large enough to cover any man entirely, can cover up "head and ears" and still have plenty of air. Loops on sides so that it can be hung up with ropes if desired. With these bags all bed and bedding can be dispensed with; it rolls up into small package, so that it can be fastened to a saddle, or "packed on back." The best bed ever invented for outdoor sleeping or tent camping. Weight, about 20 lbs. Each........$15.50

Campers' Clothes Bag.

49241 These bags are made of heavy white duck, round bottom, drawing string top fastening, handy for extra clothing, shells, boots and other "truck." Regular sailor's bag. Don't cost much, always useful. Every family needs them.
Each $0.75

Campers' "Carry-All" Bag.

(Try one on your next outing trip.)

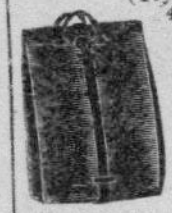

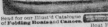

49243 This bag is made of heavy water-proof tan colored duck, with leather lap over mouth, leather lock strap fastening, mail bag style. Durable and strong, large size. The BEST and most USEFUL bag a "cow-boy," hunter or camper could suggest. No campers' outfit complete without one; about 20x30 inches.
Each $3.50

Kit Bag.

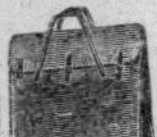

49245 Made of 10 oz. brown canvas, fastened with straps and buckles, neat, handy and durable. Length, 27 inches; width, 20 inches.
Each......................................$0.75

Folding Canvas Boats.

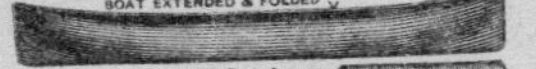

Send for our Illust'd Catalogue of Folding Boats and Canoes.

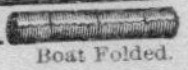

Boat Folded.

The Acme Folding Canvas Boat.

49252 (2) The Acme Folding Canvas Boat. Painted dark green. Length 12 feet, beam 45 inches, depth at stem and stern 22 inches, depth amidships 14 inches. Weight, light form, 35 pounds, weight complete 46 pounds; capacity, two and three passengers. Complete with 1 pair 6½-foot oars, pair adjustable oar locks, 2 folding seats, 1 adjustable back and shipping case. Price complete..........................$35.00

This is our most popular boat. It is a good general purpose boat. It can be made up in a light form weighing but 35 pounds by leaving out some of the parts which are necessary only when the boat is loaded to its full capacity. It can be made up into two bundles of equal size and weight. For from one to three passengers we would recommend it above any of the other sizes.

The Eureka Canvas Folding Boat.

49255 No. 1.—Length, 10 feet; beam 36 inches; depth at ends, 20 inches; depth at center, 12 inches; weight, 35 pounds; capacity, one to three passengers. Price with one pair 6-foot ash oars, malleable rowlocks and two folding seats, Grade A..........................$24.00

The No. 1 has a full model, the full beam being carried well up to the ends. It has great carrying capacity for a boat of its length and weight, and is very steady on the water. It is a boat capable of carrying safely two or three persons, yet light enough and compact enough to be easily carried long distances by hand.

The Eureka does not fold as compactly as the Acme, and of course is not as well made, but yet is strong and durable.

The Koshkonong Hunting Skiff.

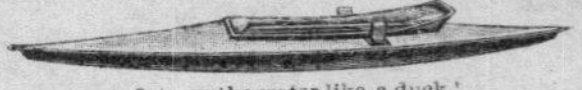

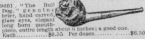

" Sets on the water like a duck."

49260 The Celebrated Koshkonong Hunting Boat is without doubt the best in the world, all things considered. Fifteen feet long, three feet beam, cockpit five feet long, two feet wide, pointed at both ends, deck boarded and canvas covered—can walk all over deck. Folding canvas wing around cockpit. Oarlocks not fitted, can put on any kind of locks desired. Water and air tight chamber in each end, good in open rough, as well as shallow water. Cannot be tipped over, easy rowing, foot rack in bottom made especially for running easily over grass and weeds, sets low on the water. Capacity 1,200 to 1,500 lbs. Just what every hunter and fisherman has been looking for; "easy as a rocking chair." Boat only $25.00
Weight, about 90 lbs.

Camping Outfits.

The best in the market.

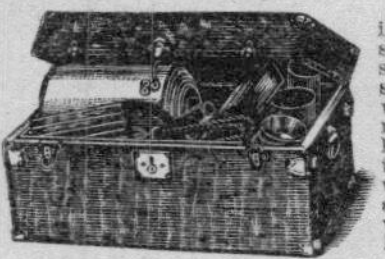

Everything packs in box, including stove. Put up in a strong, well-made, stained wooden box, with metal trimmings and durable lock. Length, 28 in.; depth, 13 in.; width, 19 in., wt. about 77 lbs. and will stand lots of hard usage.

49278 No. A. Contents. 1 stove, 4 lengths pipe, 1 elbow, 1 baking pan, 1 frying pan, 1 wash bowl, 3 camp kettles, 1 coffee pot, 6 knives and 6 forks, 1 carving knife, 1 basting spoon, 6 teaspoons, 6 enameled cups, 6 enameled plates.
Price complete...$22.50

49279 No. B Outfit, Contents same as No. A, except tin cups and plates in place of white enameled ware. Price complete......................18.00

Stove is made of heavy Russia sheet iron, has 4 lids, oven is placed on top of stove when in use. Stove does not knock down; fire is built on ground; fuel door in front. The stove just fits easily into box mentioned above, and of course is just a little smaller than dimensions of box. There are cheaper outfits on the market, but this is a first-class one in every particular.

United States Flags.

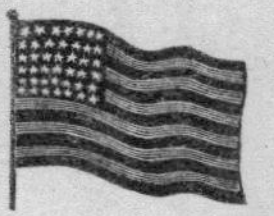

Made of Standard Bunting.

Prices are for flags only, without staff or tassels.

49280

Length	3 ft.	4 ft.	5 ft.	6 ft.	7 ft.	8 ft.	10 ft
Each	$1.50	1.60	2.30	2.70	3.50	3.70	4.90
Length	12 ft.	14 ft.	16 ft.		18 ft.	20 ft.	25 ft.
Each	$5.40	7.00	8.50		9.70	11.50	17.00
Length	28 ft.	30 ft.	32 ft.		35 ft.		
Each	$21.10	23.90	28.00		30.47		

N. B.—A 6 ft flag is the smallest that 44 stars can be put on. All flags 6 ft. and over have 44 stars.

Procession Flags.

Made of Standard Bunting.

49290 6x6½ feet, with staff, spearhead, tassel and boot; complete $9.75
49291 Flag only...................................... 4.50

U. S. Muslin Flags on Stick.

To amuse the children and for decorating purposes.

		Per doz.	Per gross.
49295	Size 2x3 inch	$0.03	$0.22
	Size 2½x4 inch	.04	.27
	Size 3½x6 inch	.05	.43
	Size 4½x7½ inch	.09	.60
	Size 6x9½ inch	.14	1.15
	Size 9x14 inch	.25	2.25
	Size 12x18 inch	.40	3.35
	Size 13x23 inch	.45	
	Size 18x27 inch	.65	
	Size 22x36 inch	1.00	

Burgees, Streamers and Campaign Flags furnished on short notice. Prices on application.

LOWER PRICES than you ever saw before on Wall Paper, Rugs, Mats, Curtains, etc. See Index for quotations.

SMOKERS' ARTICLES, PIPES, ETC.

You will find our prices on pipes from 25 to 75 per cent less than regular retail prices. Moisten your wood pipes with water before smoking to prevent burning the pipes. Postage, 3 to 5 cents extra on pipes

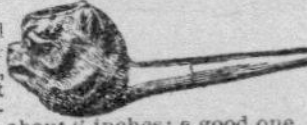

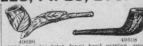

49601 "The Bull Dog," genuine brier, hand carved, glass eyes, elegant long horn mouthpiece, entire length about 6 inches; a good one.
Each..............$0.55 Per dozen..........$6.50

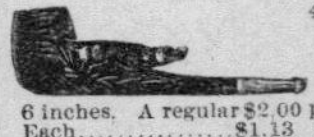

49602 Genuine brier, hand carved, assorted designs or stems, genuine amber mouthpiece; an elegant pipe. Entire length about 6 inches. A regular $2.00 pipe at retail.
Each.....................$1.13 Per dozen..........$11.00

49603 Genuine brier, assorted designs, same shape as 49602. English amber mouthpiece. A GOOD PIPE. Generally sold for highest quality for $1.00 to $1.50 each. Our price, each .75
Per dozen 8.40

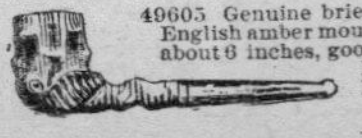

49605 Genuine brier, hand carved, long English amber mouthpiece, entire length about 6 inches, good large bowl.
Each...............$0.35
Per dozen 3.00

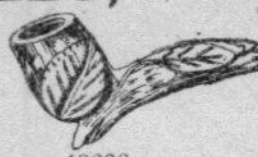

49606

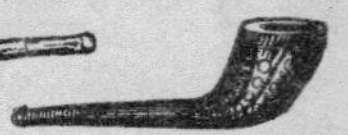

49608

49606 Genuine briar, fancy hand carving, *genuine* amber mouthpiece, large bowl; a fine pipe.
Each ....$0 75 Per dozen..............$8.00

49608 Genuine carved briar, "Woodstock shape," English amber mouthpiece, good heavy bowl, and a desirable pipe; about 5¾ inches entire length, one of *our best sellers.*
Each............$0.25
Per dozen....... 2.70

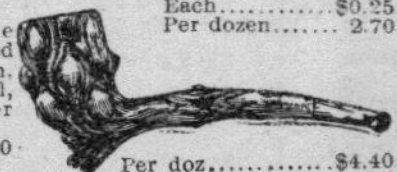

49610 Genuine brier, carved bowl and stem, good large bowl, genuine amber mouth piece.
Each........$0.40
Per doz..............$4.40

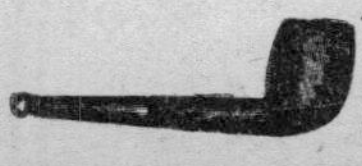

49612 Genuine brier, English amber mouthpiece, good, thick bowl, length about 6 in.
Each $0.35
Per dozen......... 3.60

Pipes—Continued.

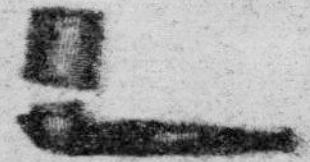

49615 Genuine brier, screw-off bowl, nicotine cup, metal screw, rubber stem.
Each..........$0.33
Per dozen..........3.50

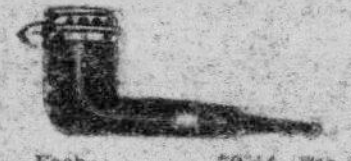

49616 Dark rosewood finish, heavy nickel cover, band on stem, good heavy horn mouthpiece, large bowl and stem, a very durable pipe, elegantly finished.
Each..........$0.44 Per dozen..........$4.73

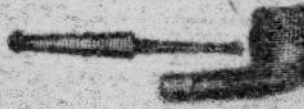

49617 Genuine brier, self-cleaner, band on stem, fine horn mouthpiece with cleaner.
Each..........$0.28
Per dozen..........3.00

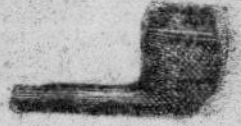

49618

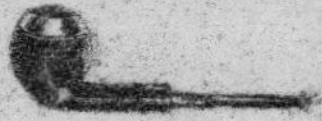

49620

49618 Self cleaner, French brier bowl, rubber stem, horn cleaner, entire length about 5½ in. assorted shaped bowls, English bull-dog and egg shape, in dark colors.
Each..........$0.32 Per dozen..........$3.00
49620 Dark rosewood finish, English shape, heavy nickel band on top of bowl and on stem. English amber mouthpiece, entire length about 5¼ inches. A very handsome pipe.
Each..........$0.25 Per dozen..........$2.75

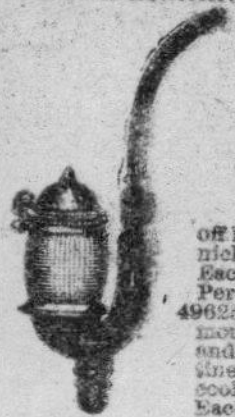

49624

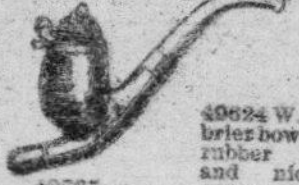

49625

49624 W.R.Co. brier bowl, long rubber stem and nicotine cup, screw-off bowl and screw-off nicotine cup, nickel and gilt cover, cool smoker.
Each..........$0.35
Per dozen..........3.38
49625 Genuine brier, fine horn mouthpiece, band on stem, nickeled and gilt cover, horn screw-off nicotine cup on end of stem. A handy, cool smoker.
Each..........$0.47
Per dozen..........4.80
49650 Pipes, polished applewood
Each..........$0.05
Per dozen..........45

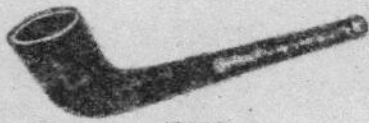

49654

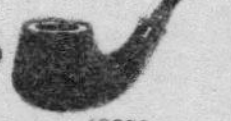

49650

49654 Brier Pipes, imported, assorted shapes, in dozens, and similar to cut, second in quality, but just as good as the best for a good smoke. Each..........$0.15 Per doz..........$1.40
49655 French Brier Pipes, round stem, amber mouthpiece, medium size, straight stem (style 49654). Each.......... .20
49658 French Brier Pipe, flat stem, amber mouthpiece, large size, straight stem. Each.......... .25

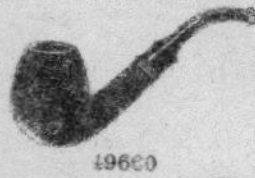

49660 Pipes, brier, polished amber mouthpiece.
Each..........$0.25
Per doz..........2.50

49660

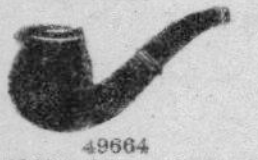

49664

49666

49664 Pipes, applewood, polished, with cover, rubber stem. Per doz.....$1.20 Each..........$0.12
49666 Pipes, applewood, with patent adjustable perforated cover, rubber mouthpiece.
Each..........$0.12 Per dozen..........1.15

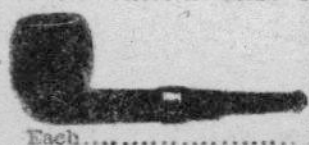

49676 English Brier Pipe, finished in dark colors, a large heavy pipe, with light colored horn mouthpiece, nickel band on stem. A very durable pipe.
Each..........$0.35
49678 French Brier Pipe, finished in natural color of wood; a large heavy pipe. Light colored horn mouthpiece; same shape as No. 49676. Each.. .25
49679 English Brier Pipe, finished in dark colors, rubber bit, nickel band on stem; a good medium size pipe, same shape as No. 49676. Each...... .30

Pipes—Continued.

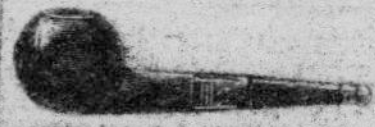

49682 Brier Pipe, Egg shape, cannot tip over when laid on table or shelf. English amber mouthpiece, entire length 5½ inches. Each..........$0.25
Per dozen..........2.75

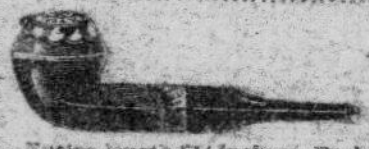

49683 Fine Brier Pipe, nickel cover, band on stem, rubber mouthpiece, "bull dog" style. Entire length 5¼ inches. Each..........$0.35
Per dozen..........3.85

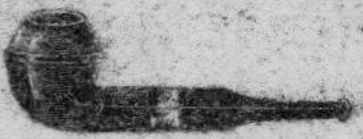

49684 Applewood Pipe, band on stem, "bull dog" style, rubber mouthpiece, strong and durable. Each..........$0.13
Per dozen..........1.40

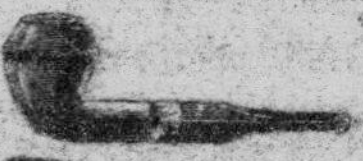

49685 Bull Dog Brier Pipe, nickel band, rubber stem, good large bowl, strong and durable. Entire length 5½ inches.
Each..........$0.18
Per dozen..........2.00

49686 Genuine Brier Pipe, horn mouthpiece, carved bowl, a very neat little pipe. Each..........$0.18
Per dozen..........1.70

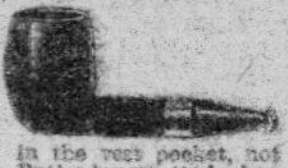

49687 Genuine Brier Pipe, "The Teamster's Favorite." Large deep bowl, short heavy stem, English amber mouthpiece, made strong and durable, can be carried in the vest pocket, not liable to get broken. Entire length 4½ inches. Each..........$0.35
Per dozen..........3.60

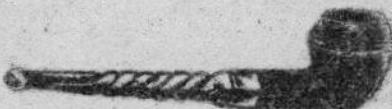

49688 Fine brier, "bull dog" shape, nickel band on stem, 3½ inch twisted English amber mouthpiece, handsome and durable—a fine smoker. Each..........$0.65
Per dozen..........7.00

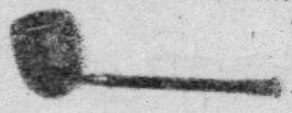

49738 Genuine Brier Bowl, 4 inch rubber stem; a neat, tidy little pipe.
Each..........$0.08

49739 Pipe, brier, rubber stem, nickel cover, a good and durable pipe.
Entire length 5⅜ in., each..........$0.25
Per dozen..........$2.70

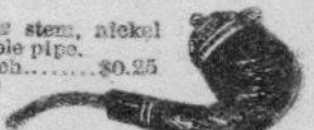

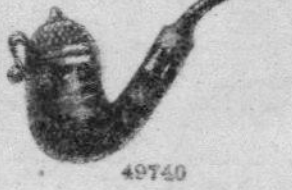

49740

49740 Brier Pipe, nickel band on stem, fancy nickel cover, bent stem, English amber mouth-piece, entire length 5¼ inches.
Each..........$0.42
Per doz..........4.60

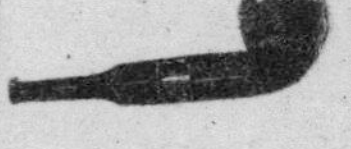

49753 Real French Brier, English bulldog shape, heavy diamond square stem, horn mouthpiece, fancy silver plated band on stem and top of bowl, entire length 5¼ inches. Each..$0.40

Bull Dog

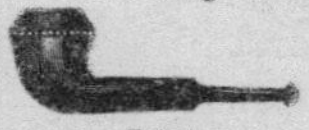

Bull Dog.

49755 Imported Brier Pipe, London shape, heavy and strong, fine horn mouthpiece.
Each..........$0.45
Per dozen..........4.80

49756 French Brier Bowl, Bull Dog shape, diamond square stem, fine amberite mouthpiece, heavy and durable, English bulldog style.
Each..........$1.00

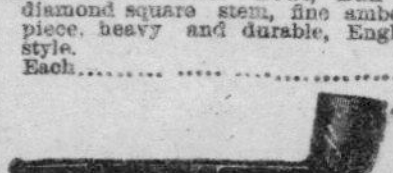

49765 Genuine Brier Pipe with genuine amber mouthpiece, finished in natural color of wood.
Each..........$0.59
Per doz..........6.00

Pipes—Continued.

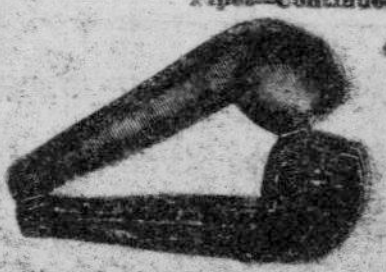

49767 Pipe, warranted finest quality French brier, English shape bowl, finest finish, diamond square stem, 2½ in., fine amber mouthpiece, silver band on stem. Entire length 5½ in., in leather covered, satin and velvet lined case, heavy and durable and a beauty. Each..........$3.00

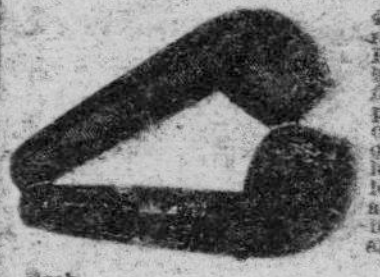

49768 Pipe, warranted fine quality French brier, English bull dog shape, 2½ in. fine amber mouthpiece, German silver cap on bowl and band on stem. Entire length, 5½ in.; in fine leather covered, satin and velvet lined case, beautifully finished and an elegant article.
Each..........$2.40

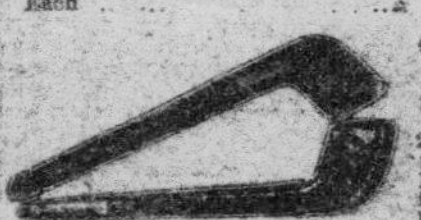

49773 Pipe, warranted French brier, finely finished, assorted shapes, 2 in. oval amber mouthpiece. Entire length, 5 in. medium sized bowl, a cool, nice smoker, in leather covered, satin and velvet lined case. Each..........$2.00

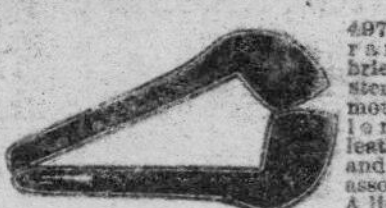

49774 Pipe, warranted French brier, fine finish, round stem, 2 in. amberite mouthpiece. Entire length, 5 in. In leather covered, velvet and satin lined case, assorted.
A little dandy smoker.
Each..........$1.00

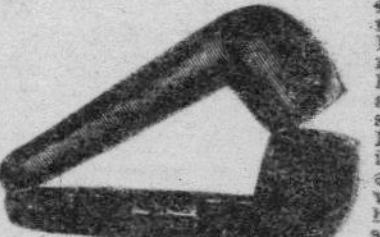

49775 Pipe, warranted finest French brier, diamond square stem, heavy 2½ inch fine amber mouthpiece, silver band on stem. Entire length, 6 in. In leather covered, satin and velvet lined case. A handsome and durable article.
Each..........$2.98

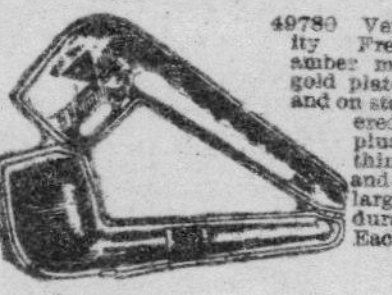

49780 Very finest quality French brier, fine amber mouthpiece, heavy gold plated band on bowl and on stem, in leather covered case, fine silk plush lined, just the thing for Christmas and birthday presents; large, handsome and durable.
Each..........$4.75

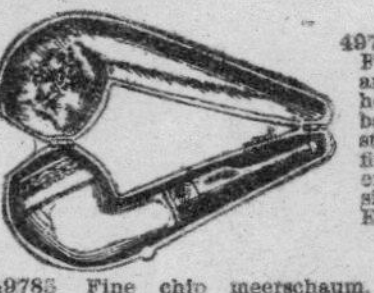

49784 Very finest French brier, fine amber mouthpiece, heavy gold plated band on bowl and stem, highest quality finish, in leather covered case lined with silk plush, a beauty.
Each..........$4.50

49785 Fine chip meerschaum, same style as 49784, fine amberite mouthpiece, silver plated band on bowl and stem, in leather covered case, silk and plush lined, a good pipe and a handsome one. Each..........$1.75
Per doz..........18.00

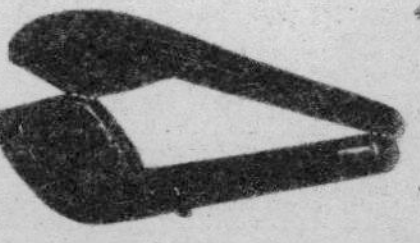

49790 Genuine brier pipe, genuine amber mouthpiece, finished in natural color of wood, in leather case silk and velvet lined, assorted.
Each....$0.98

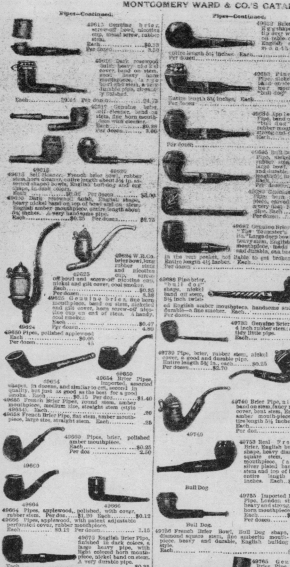

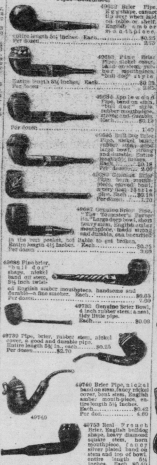

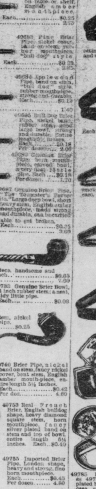

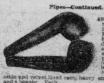

Cigar Cases—Continued.

49935 Cigar Case, finest fancy finished leather, handsome figured bronze and gilt bronze frame, leather and satin lined, elegant floral designs in silk and gilt inside, full sizes, made in best manner; a gem.
Each.......... $3.00

49936 Cigar Case, alligator leather, satin and leather lined, nickel frame, well made and durable.
Each $1.15

49937 Cigar Case, genuine lizzard leather, gray and buff color, leather lined, nickel frame; a very desirable article.
Each.......... $1.30

	Each.	Per doz.
49940 Cigar Case, Turkish leather, telescope style (see cut)........	$0.30	$3.00

49941 Cigar Case, telescopic style, heavy embossed leather.
Each.......... $0.35
Per dozen.......... 3.40

Cigar Cases—Continued.

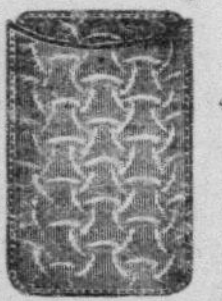

49942 Cigar Case, telescope style, soft leather, embossed finish.
Each.......... $0.23
Per dozen.......... 2.30

49945 Cigarette Case, telescopic style, all leather, vest pocket size, good and durable.
Each.......... $0.18
Per dozen.......... 1.60

Snuff and Tobacco Boxes.

49971 49973

49971 German rustic design wood covered with birchbark buckskin string lift
Each.......... $0.06

49973 Snuff or Tobacco Box, fine black colored composition, strong and durable; 3¼x2 inches
Each.......... .17

49974 49975

49974 Snuff or Tobacco Box; ebony composition inlaid pearl on cover. 3x1½ in. Each.......... $0.25

49975 Snuff or Tobacco Box, composition imitation ebony and tortoise shell, 3¼x1⅞, strong and durable. Each.......... .29

Tobacco Boxes—Continued.

49977 Tobacco Box, finest nickel plated metal, spring cover, good and strong, keeps tobacco clean and fresh.
Each.......... $0.20
Per dozen.......... 2.25

49978 Cigarette Case, fine nickel plated metal, embossed raised figures around sides, metal spring holder; inside, spring cover; keeps the cigarettes fresh and in perfect order. Neat and desirable.
Each.......... $0.25
Per dozen.......... 2.40

Cigarette Machine.

49990 The Champion Cigarette Maker. The frame consists of a single piece, nickel plated and polished. There are two rollers, one moves back and forth in a slot and around these is a piece of flexible rubber cloth. It is handsomely made, strong, simple and durable; can be carried in the vest pocket, being but 3 in. long, 1½ in. wide by ¾ in. thick. Each.......... $0.25

SMOKING TOBACCOS.

We carry a fine line. See our Monthly Grocery List, columns 59 and 60, for prices.

BOOT AND SHOE DEPARTMENT.

150,000 pairs sold in 1893.

Our yearly output of boots and shoes is now on a scale of such magnitude that we can still further reduce our well-known moderate percentage of profit without affecting our gross earnings, as the prices below will indicate.

In all cases send the size you want when you know it; otherwise send us the length and shape of the foot, drawn with a pencil while standing on a piece of clean white paper; instep, ball and other measurements not necessary. From length and shape of this outline we can determine, from our knowledge of measurement, what size and width will fit your foot the best.

We would call special attention to goods in this department marked "warranted." We mean by "WARRANTED" just this: If at any time a pair of WARRANTED boots or shoes give out without just cause, report the fact to us and we will pay for repairing them, replace them with others or refund the money paid for them, according to the circumstances of the case. We do not warrant boots and shoes against fire. We will not allow for damages incurred by wetting and then burning shoes.

We will not warrant "Calf or Light Kip-Boots" to endure usage that only a "Stoga Boot" was designed for.

The meaning of the different letters representing the widths on the inside of ladies' shoes are as follows: (A) extra narrow; (B) very narrow; (C) narrow; (D) medium; (E) wide; (EE) very wide. The same applies to men's shoes. Pegged and nailed boots and shoes not made in half sizes

Ladies' Hand Turn Shoes.

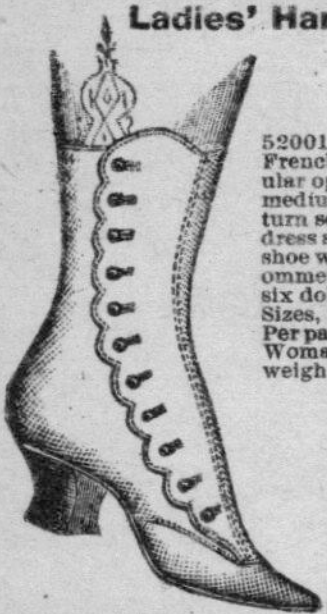

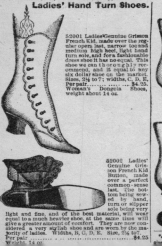

52001 Ladies' Genuine Grisson French Kid, made over the regular opera last, narrow toe and medium high heel, light hand turn sole, and for a fashionable dress shoe it has no equal. This shoe we can thoroughly recommend, and is equal to any six dollar shoe on the market. Sizes, 2½ to 7; widths, C, D, E. Per pair.......... $4.25. Woman's Dongola Shoes, weight about 14 oz.

52002 Ladies' Genuine Grisson French Kid Button, made over a perfect common-sense last. The bottom being sewed by hand, turn or slipper sole being very light and fine, and of the best material, will wear equal to a much heavier shoe, at the same time will give a greater amount of comfort. They are now considered a very stylish shoe and are worn by the majority of ladies. Widths, B, C, D, E. Size, 2½ to 7.
Per pair.......... $4.25
Weight, 14 oz.

52003 Ladies' Satin Kid, light weight bottom, opera last, narrow toe, and medium high heel, turn sole with thin bevel edge, giving the shoe a light, dressy appearance. This shoe is designed specially for fine dress wear. Sizes, 2½ to 7; width, B, C, D, E. Per pair $3.00

Weight, 14 oz.

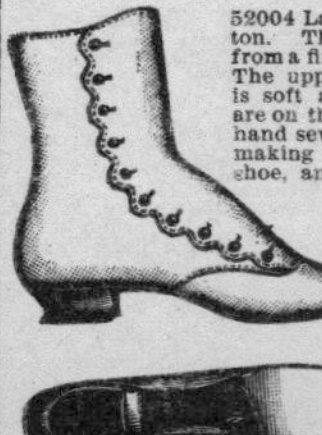

52004 Ladies' Common-Sense Button. The stock in this shoe is cut from a fine selection of Paris Kid. The upper has a rich luster and is soft and glove like. The soles are on the slipper or turn order, hand sewed, with thin bevel edge, making a very light and dressy shoe, and will wear equal to a much heavier shoe. Sizes, 2½ to 7. Widths, B, C, D, E.
Per pair... $3.00
Weight, 15 oz.

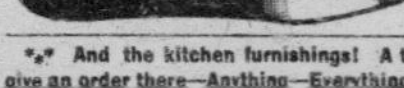

₊ And the kitchen furnishings! A treat for a woman to give an order there—Anything—Everything.

The Feather Weight.

52005

52005 Ladies' Hand Turn Shoe. This shoe is made over the opera last with long patent leather tip and the stock is cut from a good quality of bright Dongola, and we claim it to be as good as any $4.00 shoe on the market; will give the wearer the same amount of comfort as a high price shoe and will wear equally as well; sizes, 2½ to 7; widths, C, D, E.; per pair.......... $2.75
Weight, 15 oz.

52006 This Common-Sense Shoe is made from the same stock as 52005, the only difference being the style of last, which calls for a low heel and wide toe. This being a very popular style, we claim for it to be equal to any $4.00 turn shoe on the market. Sizes, 2½ to 7; widths, B, C, D, E. Per pair.......... $2.75
Weight, 15 oz.

Extra High Cut Shoe.

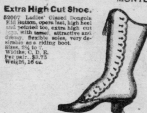

52007 Ladies' Glazed Dongola Kid Button, opera last, high heel and pointed toe, extra high cut legs, with tassel, attractive and dressy, flexible soles, very desirable as a riding boot. Sizes, 2½ to 7; widths, C, D, E. Per pair..........$3.75
Weight, 16 oz.

Goodyear Welt Shoes.

52608 This shoe is made from a very fine selection of Vici Kid of high grade finish, much more so than the ordinary Dongola stock. The style is the very latest narrow square toe, with long patent leather tip, and medium heel with half stitch around outside of sole. This shoe is adapted to all kinds of wear, has a very graceful appearance when on the foot. Do not pass this shoe when selecting, for they will give excellent wear. Sizes, 2½ to 7; widths, B, C, D, E. Per pair..........$3.15

52609 Ladies' Genuine Vici Kid Button, Philadelphia square toe last, with patent leather tip and medium Goodyear welt soles, slightly extended, with half stitch around outside. This style takes the place of a full common sense last, which is not so wide and clumsy looking, and at the same time gives the required width across ball of foot. One of the prevailing styles at present, fits neat and looks well, and will give excellent service for a fall and winter shoe, has no equal. Sizes, 2½ to 8; widths, A, B, C, D, E, and EE. Per pair..........$3.10

Ladies' Walkenfast.

52611 This shoe is made from a very fine grade of satin finish Dongola. The tops are also a Dongola, but a dull finish. The bottoms are a Goodyear welt, making a perfectly smooth inner sole and free from all imperfections. The toe is a medium width with a long perforated patent leather tip and extension sole; medium weight, becoming very flexible after wearing a few times. This shoe is a perfect beauty, a good fitter and a good wearer, and for ease and comfort in walking it has no equal. Sizes, 2½ to 7; widths, C, D, E, and EE. Per pair..........$3.30
Weight, 17 oz.

The Zephyr.

52012 Ladies' American French Kid Button, medium square toe, with long patent leather tip, the heel of a medium height, making a very attractive and dressy shoe. The stock used in the manufacture of this brand has the appearance of a French kid, being soft and glove like, enabling it to readily adjust to the foot, insuring a perfect fit. We think it superior to French Kid, being less liable to chip or crack and much more durable. Sizes, 2½ to 7; widths, B, C, D, E, and EE. Per pair..........$3.00
Weight, 16 oz.

52013 Ladies' American French Kid, Button, same as 52012, only made on Common Sense last. Low heel and broad toe, giving ample room across the ball of foot, making a comfortable shoe for tender feet, and will not create corns or bunions; sole light and flexible. Sizes, 2½ to 7. Widths, A, B, C, D, E. Price..........$3.00
Weight, 16 oz.

Our Wonder.

52014 This shoe is made from a very choice selection of Dongola Kid, with patent leather tip, open toe and medium heel. This shoe we may well call a wonder, for it contains all of the good qualities of the higher grade shoes both as to style, fit and finish. We have this shoe made special for our own trade, and we claim for it to be the best shoe in the country for the money; do not be afraid to order; they will wear you well. Sizes, 2½ to 7, C, D, E, EE. Per pair..........$2.00
Weight, 16 oz.

Ladies' Dongola Blucher.

52015 You will notice the novel and very peculiar way in which this shoe is constructed; unlike any other shoe in the book, making one of the newest patterns in Ladies' Shoes. The uppers are made from fine satin finish Dongola Kid, handsomely trimmed with patent leather; medium weight soles, making a very neat and stylish dress boot; narrow square toe with long patent leather tip. Sizes, 2½ to 7, B, C, D, E. Per pair..........$3.00
Weight, 15 oz.

Ladies' Tan or Russet Shoes.

Weight, 17 oz.

52016 This shoe is made from a very fine quality of russet or tan colored Dongola, front lace with light flexible soles. Picadilly toe with long perforated tip. This shoe requires no blacking or dressing and will be all the rage for the coming season. We have taken special pains to secure a shoe that will give good, honest service, and for style and finish will have no equal. Do not fail to order if you want a slightly and stylish shoe at a price that cannot be beaten. Sizes 2½ to 6; widths, C, D, and E. Per pair..........$2.75

M. W. & Co.'s Wear Resisters.

Weight, 16 oz.

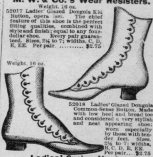

52017 Ladies' Glazed Dongola Kid Button, opera last. The chief feature of this shoe is the perfect fitting qualities, combined with style and finish; equal to any four-dollar shoe. Every pair guaranteed. Sizes, 2½ to 7; widths, C, D, E, EE. Per pair..........$2.75

52018 Ladies' Glazed Dongola Common-Sense Button. Made with low heel and broad toe and considered a very stylish and neat appearing shoe; worn especially by those with tender feet. Sizes, 2½ to 7; widths, B, C, D, E, EE. Per pair..........$2.75

Ladies' Spring Heel.

Weight, 17 ounces.

52019 This shoe is made from fine Glazed Dongola Kid and a shoe that will meet the desired wants of a great many. In the past the largest size attainable in this style was No. 2. In the last year we have had hundreds of orders, which we are unable to fill. Now we can offer you a shoe we can recommend, and we trust will be appreciated by those of our customers that could not obtain them heretofore. Sizes, 2½ to 6. Widths, C, D, E and EE. Per pair..........$2.50.

The Princess.

52020 Ladies' Glazed Dongola Button, opera last, medium high heel, pointed toe, with fancy patent leather tips, giving an attractive and dressy appearance; beveled edge, single soles, suitable for general wear. Sizes, 2½ to 7. Widths, C, D, E and EE. Weight, 16 oz. Per pair..........$2.55

The Sunbeam.

52021 Ladies' Glove Top Button, opera last, popular style heel and toe; flexible, single soles. The vamps or front are of soft, pliable Dongola Kid, with dull glove kid tops. A well made and thoroughly reliable shoe of standard value. Sizes, 2½ to 7. Widths, D, E, E and EE, only. Weight, 15 oz. Per pair..........$2.56

Our Solid Comfort Line.

Weight, 17 oz.

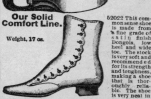

52022 This common sense shoe is made from a fine grade of satin finish Dongola, low heel and wide toe. The stock is very soft and recommended for its strength and toughness, making a shoe that is thoroughly reliable. The shoe is very neat in appearance and a perfect fitter. We can recommend it as being first-class. Sizes, 2½ to 6, C, D, E and EE. Per pair..........$2.50

Shoes—Continued.

52411 Men's Oil grain Plow Shoes, high cut; extra quality; all solid, good value; sizes, 3 to 11.
Per pair................$1.35
Weight, 40 oz.

52415 Men's Whole Stock Kip Brogans, lace, half double soles, pegged, all solid; sizes, 6 to 11.
Per pair..........................$1 15
Weight, 41 oz.
52416 Men's Whole Stock Kip Brogans, lace, all solid; good value; sizes, 6 to 11. Per pair....... 1.00
Weight, 41 oz.

M. W. & Co.'s Cotton King.

52420 This shoe is made from Milwaukee oil grain leather, solid counters and insoles with bellows tongue, or dirt excluder. This shoe we claim to be the best on earth for the money. Sizes, 6 to 12. Per pair....$1.15
Weight, 36 oz.

Men's Grain Creedmoors.

52425 Men's English Grain "Creedmoor" hook lace, extra high cut, bellows tongue, calf lined, very desirable for hunting or wet weather wear; double soled and tap nailed and as near waterproof as leather can make it; sizes, 6 to 11; full width. Per pair.....$3.50
Weight, 57 oz.

Base Ball Shoes.

Weight, 22 oz.
52430 Men's Heavy Canvas Base Ball Shoes, calf trimmed solid leather soles and counters, extra quality; sizes 6 to 11.
Per pair............................$1.10
52431 Boys' Heavy Canvas Base ball Shoes, calf trimmed, all solid, best grades; sizes 1 to 5.
Per pair...........................$1.00
Weight, 20 oz.

Black Tennis Bals.

(Weight, 20 oz.)

52440 Men's Black Canvas Tennis Bals, corrugated rubber soles, with leather insoles.
Size, 6 to 10.
Per pair, $1.00

52441 Boys' Black Tennis Bals, corrugated rubber soles, with leather insoles. Sizes, 1 to 5.
Per pair...........................$0.95
Weight, 17 oz.
52442 Ladies' Black Tennis Bals, corrugated rubber soles, with leather insoles. Size, 2½ to.7.
Per pair..........................$0.90
Weight, 17 oz.

Black Tennis Oxfords.

52445 Men's Black Tennis Oxford, corrugated rubber soles, with leather insoles. Sizes, 6 to 11.
Per pair, $0.85

52446 Boys' Black Tennis Oxford, corrugated rubber soles, with leather insoles. Sizes, 1 to 5.
Per pair............................. .75
Weight, 15 oz.
52447 Ladies' Black Tennis Oxfords, corrugated rubber soles, with leather insoles. Sizes, 2½ to 6.
Per pair............................. .75
Weight, 15 oz.

Check Tennis Bals.
Weight, 20 oz.

52450 Men's Check Tennis Bals, corrugated rubber soles with leather insoles.
Size, 6 to 11.
Per pair, $1.00

52451 Boys' Check Tennis Bals, corrugated rubber soles, with leather insoles. Sizes, 1 to 5½.
Per pair............................$0.95
Weight, 17 oz.
52452 Ladies' Check Tennis Bals, corrugated rubber soles, with leather insoles. Sizes, 2½ to 6.
Per pair............................$0.90
Weight, 15 oz.

Check Tennis Oxfords.

Weight, 17 oz.
52460 Men's Check Canvas Tennis Shoes, with corrugated rubber soles, best quality; sizes 6 to 11. Per pair..................$0.85
52461 Boys' Check Canvas Tennis Shoes, with corrugated rubber soles, best quality; sizes, 1 to 5½. Per pair..................... .75
52462 Ladies' Check Canvas Tennis Shoes, with corrugated rubber soles; best quality; sizes 2½ to 6. Per pair.................. .75
Weight, 15 oz.

Running Shoes.
Weight, 11 oz.

52470 Men's English running Shoes, made of fine cordovan leather, with English steel spikes inserted between the soles; hand sewed, sizes 6 to 10. Per pair...........................$3.50
Weight, 13 oz.

52471—Men's American Running Shoes, made after the style of the English shoe, cordovan leather, steel spikes, machines sewed; a desirable shoe for amateurs; sizes, 6 to 10. Per pair..........................2.40

Canadian Snow Shoes.

52474 The appending cut illustrates the manner in which they are used. We are prepared to furnish snow shoes, which, for lightness and elegance of workmanship, cannot be equaled by other manufacturers; made from the choicest material, and will give excellent good service.
Width. Length.
Size...16x44....Per pair. $6.50
Size....16x42....Per pair. 4.50

Dancing Shoes.
Weight, 25 oz.

52475 Men's Song and Dance Shoes, made of calfskin, with extra heavy soles, machine sewed; sizes, 14 to 16 inches long. Per pair............$4.50

Weight, 21 oz.
52476 Men's Dancing Clogs, made of red, blue or black morocco leather, wood soles, all one piece; sizes, 6 to 10, full width. Per pair.........$2.50
52477 Brass Jingles for above, per set............ 25

52478 Wooden Shoes for clog dancers and comedians, also extensively used in dyeing establishments, laundries, cellars, dairy farms, etc.

Weight, 33 oz.
Men's sizes, 6 to 11. Per pair............$0.50
Boys' sizes, 1 to 5. Per pair............. .50
Women's sizes, 2 to 7. Per pair......... .50

Shoe Pacs.
Weight, 29 oz.
52479 This Pac is made with an oil grain top, and oil tanned Pac leather uppers and soles with low flat heels, making a very light and serviceable shoe for all kinds of wear. Sizes, 6 to 12.
Per pair................$1.75

Lumbermen's Pacs.
Weight, 41 oz.
52480 The accompanying cut represents our best hand sewed Pac with the inch leg of oil grain leather and oil tan Pac leather uppers; the soles are doubled, sewed and inserted with round coneheaded Hungarian nails, which adds to the wearing qualities. The sole is light and flexible, and very easy to walk in, and does not slip. Sizes 6 to 12. Per pair $2.35

Wood Shoes with Leather Uppers.

Weight, 21 oz.
52481 This shoe is made with wooden bottoms and leather uppers. They are used in laundries, dairies, and are also very useful on the farm; are very light and durable. Sizes, 5 to 12. Full width. Per pair.......................$0.80

Wood Sole Clip-Clap Slippers.

Weight, 20 oz.
52482 The Old Style Clip-Clap Slipper, wood sole and leather, vamp light and durable, and very useful on the farm, for out door choring; sizes, 4 to 12. Per pair.......................$0.50

Men's Slippers.

52485 Men's Silk Plush Chenille Embroidered Slippers, fancy shades, opera cut, extra fine quality and finish, hand sewed, turn soles. These are decided novelties in slipper line and cannot fail to please; sizes, 6 to 11. Weight, 13 oz.
Per pair..................................$1.65
52487 Men's Everett Cut Slipper, velvet embroidered, is very serviceable and stylish. Sizes, 6 to 11.
Per pair..................................$0.75

52488 Men's Velvet Embroidered Slippers, good style and quality, sewed; sizes, 5 to 11.
Weight, 15 oz. Per pair..........$1.00

52489 Men's Genuine Alligator Slippers, opera cut; hand sewed sole and edge slipped; sizes 6 to 11. Per pair..... $2.16
Weight, 13 oz.

Slippers—Continued.

52490 Mens' Tan Color Slippers, made opera cut, very soft and fine; lined, hand sewed, turned sole, flexible; very popular for fine wear; sizes, 6 to 11.
Per pair...................$1.50

The Romeo (Nullifiers.)

52491 This is the most popular and sensible slipper ever put before the public. Any man who has ever worn a pair will never wear any other kind. Its great and principal advantage is in the fact that the ankle and instep being covered protects the health by preventing colds which arise from drafts that are constantly passing over floors; can be worn as a light summer street shoe. There is no slipper or shoe made which gives so much comfort to the feet; color, black. Sizes, 5 to 11; width, C, D, E and EE. Per pair.....................$1.65

52492 This shoe is made exactly as the above, only the stock is of a tan color, morocco calf and a much finer quality, being a turn sole, light and serviceable and of a very stylish last; in fact the very latest in gentleman's slippers. If you want something fine and for solid comfort they have no equal. Sizes, 5 to 10; widths, B, C, D. Per pair........................$2.50

52495 Men's Goat Slippers, dark maroon, patent leather trimmed, turn soles, hand sewed, opera cut; sizes, 6 to 11.
Per pair.......................$1.40

52496 Men's Goat Slippers, black; Everett cut, turn soles, sewed, solid comfort; sizes, 6 to 11.. 1.25

52497 Men's German Cloth Embroidered Slippers, all solid, broad and roomy, nothing better for style; sizes, 6 to 11................1.00

52498 Men's Oil Grain Slippers, machine sewed, damp proof, strong and serviceable, for house or outdoor wear, all solid; sizes, 6 to 11.. .85

Men's Carpet Slippers.

52499 Men's Brussels Carpet Slippers, best quality; bound and stayed, leather soles and heels, sewed; sizes, 8 to 11...................$0.42
We think we sell first-class goods. Let us know if your shoes don't wear well and give us an opportunity to make them satisfactory.

Cowboys' or Ranchmen's Boots.
Weight, 53 ounces.

The "Opera."

52500 Men's Calf "Opera Cowboy" Boots, sewed, extra long goat leg, fancy stitched front and back (see cut), 2-inch heel, 18 inch leg; sizes, 6 to 10.
Per pair...................$5.00

The "Montana."

52501 This boot is made from the very best tannery calf skin, all solid, and after the style of the regular cowboy boot; extra high heel and medium toe; very serviceable, and a boot that is adapted to all kinds of wear. Sizes, 5 to 10.
Per pair.............$3.25
Weight, 56 oz.

The Soudan.

Weight, 46 oz.
52502 Men's Soudan Calf "Cowboy" Boots, sewed, 19-inch leg, stitched and ribbed, 2-inch heels; very dressy, fine quality and finish; sizes, 5 to 10.
Per pair...............$4.75

Cowboys' Pride.

Weight, 56 oz.

52505 This boot is made from the finest of tannery calf skin and over the regulation cowboy last, high heel, short shank and medium toe. The heel on this boot is set under well and made from solid leather, also a solid counter and an extra steel shank, making a boot that will stand a hard strain before giving way; it also has a fancy nailed bottom. The boot is very slightly and one we can recommend. Sizes, 5 to 10. Per pair $4.75

"The Cattle Trail" Boot.
Weight, 56 oz.

52504 Men's All Calf "Cowboy" Boots, fancy scolloped top, half double soles, hand pegged, solid and serviceable, 15 in. leg, 2 in. heels; sizes, 4 to 11.
Per pair..........$4.00

Men's Calf Opera Boots.
Weight, 41 oz.

52510 Men's Calf Opera Boots, goat leg, single sole, hand welt, low, broad heels, for fine wear; quality guaranteed; sizes, 6 to 11.
Per pair................$4.75
52511 Men's Calf Opera Boots, goat leg, machine sewed, half double soles, low heels, solid and well made; sizes, 6 to 11.
Per pair.................$4.00
Weight, 57 oz.

Mens' Calf Boots, Pegged.

52515 Men's Genuine French Calf Boots, half double soles, medium low heels, custom-made throughout, hand pegged and hand sided. This boot we claim to be genuine French calf and no imitation, and our experience for the last 18 years in handling this work is sufficient evidence to convince most any one that the boot must be just what we represent it to be. Every pair warranted for fair and reasonable amount of service. Sizes, 5 to 11. Per pair...$4.10

52523

Tap Sole Calf Boot.

Weight, 5* oz.

52517 This is a genuine custom-made calf boot, backs and fronts of the best of calf skin, half double sole, with an extra tap, making one of the best wearing boots on the market; made over a neat last, with medium heel and toe. Warranted for reasonable service. Sizes, 5 to 12.
Per pair....................$3.85

The Farmers' Pride.
Tested for twenty years."

52519 This boot we have constantly sold for the last eighteen years, and has stood the test so well and has given such good satisfaction that we cannot say too much in its praise. This is what it is made up of: The calf skin is the first selection, the bottom from first quality sole leather and over the regulation cowboy last; and from the quality of stock that we use and the workmanship, we cannot hesitate to warrant this boot to give entire satisfaction, not to be used as you would use a common man's store boot. Sizes, 5 to 11; no half sizes.
Per pair....................$3.75
Weight, 53 ounces.

52520 This boot contains the very choicest of stock, carefully selected and carefully put together by experienced boot makers. We can cheerfully recommend this boot to our customers to give good service; calf backs and fronts and strictly solid. No shoddy used in any of our foot wear. Sizes, 6 to 12. No half sizes. Per pair....................$3.00
Weight, 60 ounces.

The Tornado.
Weight, 55 ounces.

52521 This boot we claim to be the best boot ever offered by any house in this country for the price. Genuine calf skin, calf backs and fronts, solid counters and inner soles and a regular custom appearance. This boot we have made especial for our own trade and can thoroughly recommend them to those wanting a first-class calf boot for a little money. Sizes, 6 to 12.
Per pair............$2.50

Men's Light Kip boot.
Weight, 70 ounces.

52525 Men's Genuine French Kip Boots, half double sole pegged, 16-inch leg, all hand made, warranted; sizes, 6 to 11.
Per pair.............$4.50
Weight, 76 oz.

52526 Men's Light Veal Kip Boots, half double sole, hand pegged, whole stock and solid throughout, warranted; sizes, 5 to 12. Per pair.......$3.56
Weight, 60 ounces.

52527 Men's Fine Kip Boots, half double sole, whole stock, well made and durable; sizes, 6 to 11.
Per pair.............$2.85
Weight, 64 ounces.

CROCKERY DEPARTMENT.

We invite a careful inspection of our Crockery Department, in which will be found an attractive line of decorative dinner, tea and chamber sets, all v desirable ware of the best English, French and American manufacturers' make. The following advantages to be derived from buying these goods from us worthy of your consideration. First, you do not have to take the large, expensive, and sometimes superfluous dishes that come in regular made dinner sets, as all our dinner ware is open stock, and you can buy as many or as few dishes as you like. Second, we can supply the missing pieces of sets that are broken within one year from date of purchase. The prices are lower than can be obtained elsewhere.

SPECIAL NOTICE.

We have taken considerable pains in selecting our made-up Dinner and Tea Sets, and cannot change the combination by adding or deducting any piece We use every precaution when packing crockery or glassware, "employing none but experienced men for that purpose," and cannot allow claims for breakage. Wh goods of this character are returned package must contain full amount of straw, otherwise they will be receipted for as "damaged" and allowance made only such pieces as are taken from package in good condition.

Myrtle Pattern.
Manufactured by Burgess & Leigh, Burslem, England.

Genuine English semi-Porcelain, body decorated with a neat border design of small flowers and leaves in a light brown or choc'late color, warranted not to crack or wear off; scalloped edge plates. This pattern is of exceptionally good value, being of the best English make, and priced nearly as cheap as plain white ware of a like quality.

Order No. 54001.

	Per doz.		Per doz.		Each.
1 Tea Cups and Saucers with handles	$1.45	11 Bone Dishes	$1.28	22 Covered Butter Dishes	$0.60
2 Coffee Cups and Saucers with handles	1.75	11½ 3-inch 'Bakers' (used as side dishes)	1.28	23 Sauce Boat	.37
				24 Pickle Dish	.20
			Each.	27 Teapot	.50
4 Plates, scalloped edge, 5 inch	.85	12 Platter, 8 inch	$0.16	28 Sugar Bowl	.42
5 Plates, scalloped edge, 6 inch	1.05	13 Platters, 10 inch	.28	29 Cream Pitcher	.20
6 Plates, scalloped edge, 7 inch	1.20	14 Platters, 12 inch	.47	30 Bowl, 5 inch	.15
		15 Platters, 14 inch	.64	31 Cake Plate	.27
7 Plates, scalloped edge, 8 inch	1.40	16 Platters, 16 inch	1.02	32 Pitcher, ¼ pint	.18
8 Plates, scalloped edge, 7 in. Soup	1.20	18 Soup Tureen and ladle	2.75	33 Pitcher, 1 pint	.20
				34 Pitcher, 1 quart	.25
9 Sauce Plates, 4-inch	.55	19 Sauce Tureen Stand, cover and ladle	.95	35 Pitcher, 2 quart	.40
				36 Pitcher, 3 quart	.60
10 Individual Butters	.38	20 Covered Dishes, 9 inch	.75	37 Bowls, ½ pint	.20
		21 Casserole Square Covered Dish	.89	38 Bowls, 3 inch	.33
				39 Bowls, 1 pint	.14
				40 Pitcher, Bowls, 1 pint	.14

41 Baker, 7 inch	$0.19	42 Baker, 8 inch	$0.28

Utopian Pattern.
Manufactured by Henry Allcock & Co., Hanley, England.

Superior grade of English Royal semi-porcelain, decoration of small forget-me-not flowers, handsomely put on under the glaze; all the pieces are shapley and he richly gold trimmed edges and handles; plates are scalloped on the edge. This very handsome table set and can be furnished in two colors, fawn and green, is equally attractive. When ordering be sure to state which color you prefer.

Order No. 54005.

	Per doz.		Per doz.		Each
1 Tea Cups and Saucers, handled	$2.15	13 Bowls 1 pint	$2.14	31 Pitchers, 2 quart	$0.
2 Coffee Cups and saucers, handled	2.48	14 Oyster bowls 1 pint	2.14	32 Pitchers, 3 quart	
		15 Oatmeal bowls 1 pint	2.10	33 Covered Dishes, 9 inch	
3 After Dinner Coffee Cups and Saucers, handled	1.80		Each.	34 Casserole (square covered dish) 9 inch	
4 Plates, 5 inches	1.29	16 Platters, 8 inch	$0.25	35 Soup Tureen and ladle (no stand)	4
		17 Platters, 10 inch	.40		
5 Plates, 6 inches	1.47	18 Platters, 12 inch	.67	36 Sauce Tureen with ladle and stand	1
6 Plates, 7 inches	1.75	19 Platters, 14 in	.94		
7 Plates, 8 inches	2.00	20 Platters, 16 in	1.47	38 Sauce Boat	
8 Soup plates, 7 inches	1.75	21 Bakers, 7 inch	.27	39 Covered Dish	
9 Sauce plates	.80	22 Bakers, 8 inch	.40	40 Pickle Dish	
10 Individual butters	.54	24 Scalloped Nappies 7 inch	.27	41 Cake Plate	
		25 Scollloped Nappies		42 Covered Butter Dish	
11 Bakers 3 inch (used as side dishes)	1.87	28 Pitchers, ½ pint	.40	43 Teapots	
		29 Pitchers, 1 pint	.27	44 Sugar Bowls	
12 Bone dishes	1.87	30 Pitchers, 1 quart	.32	45 Cream Pitchers	

Evangeline Pattern.
Manufactured by Johnson Bros., Hanley, England.

English semi-porcelain ware; thin and pure white. The glaze is burnt on and will not crack or chip with ordinary use. The shape is of the very latest design and the raised scroll work is handsomely ornamented with neat gold decorations. Pure white dinner ware of this quality with gold decoration is unusually attractive and sure to please. We shall be pleased to furnish any quantity you may desire.

Order No. 54004.

	Per doz.		Each.
1 Tea Cups and Saucers, 12 cups and 12 saucers	$2.00	10 Bone Dishes	$1.75
		11 Bowls, 1½ pt	2.00
2 Coffee Cups and Saucers, 12 cups and 12 saucers	2.35	12 Oyster Bowls, 1½ pints	2.00
		13 Oatmeal Bowls, 1 pint	2.00
3 Plates scalloped edge, 5 inches	1.12		Each.
4 Plates, scalloped edge, 6 inches	1.37	14 Bakers, 8 in	.37
		15 Bakers, 8 in	.37
5 Plates, scalloped edge, 7 inches	1.63	16 Platters, 8 inch	.22
		17 Platters, 10-inch	.37
6 Plates, scalloped edge, 8 inches	1.88	18 Platters, 12-inch	.63
		19 Platters, 14 inch	.88
7 Soup Plates, 7 inches	1.63	20 Platters, 16 inch	1.37
		21 Covered Dish, 8 inch	1.00
8 Sauce Dishes, 4 in	.51	
9 Individual Butter Plates	.51	

22 Casserole, Square Covered Dish, 8-in	$1.13
23 Soup Tureen, Cover and Ladle (no stand)	3.65
24 Sauce Tureen, complete with cover, ladle and stand	1.25
25 Sauce Boat	.34
26 Pickle Dish	.25
27 Covered Butter Dish, with drainer	.75
28 Pitcher, ¼ pint	.25
29 Pitcher, 1 qt	.39
30 Pitcher 3 qt	.75
31 Tea Pot and Cover	.67
32 Sugar Bowl and Cover	.56
33 Cream Pitcher	.25
34 Cake Plate	.34

Columbia Pattern.
Manufactured by Johnson Bros., England.

Semi-porcelain ware, thin and very shapely; decoration consists of flowe leaves and the spray in neutral brown color, warranted not to wash or wear o scalloped edge plates. This is a very desirable pattern and cannot fail to plea We will sell you as few or many pieces as you wish.

Order No. 54007.

	Per doz.		Per doz.		Each.
1 Tea Cups and Saucers with handles	$1.50	13 Oyster Bowls, 1 pint	$1.67	27 Sauce Tureen, with ladle and stand	$1.
2 Coffee Cups and saucers with handles	1.90		Each.	28 Sauce Boat	
3 Plates, scalloped edge, 5 inches	.94	14 Bakers, 7 inches	.32	29 Covered Butter Dish	
		15 Bakers, 8 inches	.43	
4 Plates, scalloped edge, 6 inches	1.10	16 Platters, 8 inches	.17	31 Covered Vegetable Dish	
		17 Platters, 10 inches	.28	
5 Plates, scalloped edge, 7 inches	1.36	18 Platters, 12 inches	.51	32 Casserole (square covered dish)	
		19 Platters, 14 inches	.94	
6 Plates, scalloped edge, 8 inches	1.56	20 Platters, 16 inches	1.05	33 Tea Pot	
		21 Scalloped Nappies, 7 inches	.22	34 Sugar Bowl	
7 Plates, scalloped edge, 7 in., Soup	1.36			35 Cream Pitcher	
		24 Scalloped Nappies, 9 inches	.42	36 Cake Plate	
8 Fruit Saucers, 5 in.	.94			37 Pitcher, 2 quarts.	
9 Individual Butters	.42	26 Soup Tureen, with ladle and stand	3.95	38 Pitcher, 3 quarts.	
10 Bone Dishes	1.47			39 Pitcher, 1 quart.	
11 Bakers (used for side dishes), 3 in.	1.87			40 Pitcher, 1 pint.	
12 Bowls, 1 pint	1.87			41 Pitcher, ½ pint.	

Dove Premier Pattern.

Manufactured by John Maddock & Sons, Burslem, England.

A superior grade of English semi-porcelain, thoroughly vitrified and thin, unexcelled in finish and durability. The decoration is a reproduction of a Royal Worcester design in a soft dove color, underglazed and relieved with neat gold trimmings. We shall be pleased to furnish any quantity.

Order No. 54009.

Per doz.		Each
1 Tea Cups and Saucers, with handles	$2.00	13 Footed Oyster Bowls, 1 pint $2.00	30 Pitchers, 1 pt.... $0.26
2 Coffee cups and saucers, with handles....	2.35	14 Bakers, used for side dishes, 3-inch 1.75	31 Pitchers, ½ pt.... .22
3 After Dinner Coffee Cups and Saucers.......	1.67	15 Bakers, 7-inch $0.26	32 Soup Tureen, and Ladle 3.75
4 Plates, 5 inch....	1.12	16 Bakers, 8-inch .38	33 Sauce Tureen, complete 2.00
5 Plates, 6 inch....	1.28	17 Bakers, 8-inch .25	34 Covered Dish 9 in. 1.00
6 Plates, 7 inch....	1.62	18 Platters, 8-inch .26	35 Casserole, Square Dish 1.15
7 Plates, 8 inch....	1.88	19 Platters, 12-inch .55	37 Pickle Dish .... .26
8 Soup Plates, 7-in.	1.62	20 Platters, 12-inch .53	38 Sauce Boat ..... .34
9 Fruit saucers, square	.65	21 Platters, 14-inch .88	39 Cake Plate ..... .34
10 Individual Butters	.50	22 Platters, 16-inch 1.88	40 Tea Pot..... .88
11 Bone Dishes	1.75	23 Scalloped Nappies, 7-inch...... .26	41 Sugar Bowl ..... .56
12 Bowls, 1 pint	2.00	24 Scalloped Nappies, 8-inch .38	42 Cream Pitcher .... .30
		25 Pitchers, 3 qt.... .75	43 Covered Butter.... .75
		26 Pitchers, 2 qt.... .50	44 Celery Tray ..... .50
		29 Pitchers, 1 qt.... .30	45 Double Egg Cups 1.75

Lexington Pattern.

Manufactured by Johnson Brothers, Hanley, England.

English semi-porcelain, a very pretty shape, decorated with a light brown Begonia leaf, enameled with blue forget-me-nots and warranted not to wash or wear off; scalloped edge plates, gold traced handles. We shall be pleased to have your order for any quantity, no matter how small.

Order No. 54011.

Per doz.		Per doz.
1 Tea Cups and Saucers, with handles...	$2.00	12 Bakers (used for side dishes) 3 in. $1.75	24 Pickle Dish..... $0.26
2 Coffee Cups and Saucers, with handles ...	2.35	13 Oyster Bowls, 1 pint 2.00	25 Covered Butter Dish ...... .75
3 Plates, scalloped edge, 5 inches ..	1.12	14 Bakers, 7 inch .$0 27	26 Covered Vegetable Dish, 9 inch.. 1.00
4 Plates, scalloped edge, 6 inches ..	1.38	15 Bakers, 8 in..... .38	27 Casserole (square covered dish).. 1.15
5 Plates, scalloped edge, 7 inches ..	1.63	16 Platters, 8 in.... .22	28 Tea pot ..... .68
6 Plates, scalloped edge, 8 inches ..	1.88	17 Platters, 10 in.... .28	29 Sugar Bowl ..... .56
7 Soup Plates, scalloped edge, 7 in. Soup.	1.63	18 Platters, 12 in.... .63	30 Cream Pitcher ... .26
9 Fruit saucers, 4 in.	.75	19 Platters, 14 in.... .88	31 Cake Plate ..... .34
10 Individual Butters	.50	20 Platters, 16 in.... 1.88	32 Pitcher, ½ pt..... .26
11 Bone Dishes	1.75	21 Soup Tureen with ladle 3.75	33 Pitcher, 1 qt..... .30
		22 Sauce Tureen with ladle and stand 1.25	34 Pitcher, 2 qt..... .50
		23 Sauce Boat ..... .34	35 Pitcher, 3 qts.... .75

Pearl Flora Pattern.

Manufactured by W. H. Grindley & Son, Tunstall, England.

Order No. 54013.

Per doz.		Per doz.
1 Tea Cups and Saucers, handled....	$1.47	14 Oyster bowls, 1 pint $1.47	32 Pitchers 3 quart $0.63
2 Coffee Cups and saucers, handled...	1.72		33 Covered Dishes, 9 inch ..... .95
		16 Platters, 8 inch... $0.18	
4 Plates, 5 inches.	1.02	17 Platters, 10 inch... .35	34 Casserole (square covered dish) 9 inch ..... .95
5 Plates, 6 inches...	1.20	18 Platters, 12 inch... .51	
6 Plates, 7 inches...	1.38	19 Platters, 14 inch... .93	35 Soup Tureen and ladle (no stand) 2.36
7 Plates, 8 inches...	1.57	20 Platters, 16 inch... .91	
8 Soup plates, 7 inch	1.38	21 Bakers, 7 inch..... .21	36 Sauce Tureen with ladle and stand.. 1.00
9 Soup plates	.73	22 Bakers, 8 inch..... .42	39 Sauce Boat ..... .28
10 Individual butters		24 Scalloped Nappies 8 inch ..... .21	40 Pickle Dish ..... .21
11 Bakers 3 inch (used as side dishes)	1.28	25 Scalloped Nappies 8 inch ..... .28	41 Cake Plate ..... .28
12 Bone dishes	1.20	29 Pitchers 1 pint ... .21	42 Teapots ..... .56
13 Bowls 1 pint	1.47	30 Pitchers 1 quart.. .28	43 Sugar Bowls..... .42
		31 Pitchers 2 quart.. .42	45 Cream Pitcher ... .28

English semi-porcelain ware, thin and light, decorated in print with border pattern and blackberry blossom, and sprays in bluish-gray colors; all the pieces are of latest shape, and will be sure to please. See order No. 54014, next column.

Yale Pattern.

Manufactured by Doulton & Co., Burslem, England.

English decorated semi-porcelain, manufactured by Doulton & Co., Burslem England, who are world renowned as makers of the most reliable goods. The decoration is a handsome design of blackberry blossoms and vines in a neutral of slate blue color, put on under the glaze; new graceful shapes, neat gold trimmings, scalloped edge plates. We shall be pleased to be favored with an order for any quantity, no matter how small.

Order No. 54014.

Per doz.		Each		Each
1 Tea cups and saucers, handled.... $2.35	24 Platters, 10 inch.. $0.51	31 Sauce tureen (with ladle and stand) $1.00
2 Coffee cups and saucers, handled.... 1.65	25 Platters, 12 inch.. .51	32 Sauce boat.... .28
3 Pie plates, 5 inch.. .89	26 Platters, 14 inch.. .71	33 Pickle Dish .... .23
4 Plates, 6 inch.... 1.15	27 Platters, 16 inch.. 1.12	34 Covered butter dish. .62
5 Plates, 7 inch.... 1.30	18 Bakers, 7 inch.... .21	
6 Plates 8 inch..... 1.50	19 Bakers, 8 inch.... .23	35 Covered vegetable dish. .88
7 Soup plates, 7 inch 1.30	21 Scalloped Nappies, 7 inch.... .20	36 Casserole (square covered dish).. .84
8 Fruit saucers .... .65	22 Scalloped Nappies, ½ pt.... .19	37 Teapot ..... .54
9 Individual butters .44	26 Pitchers, 1 pt..... .20	38 Sugar bowl .... .46
10 Bakers, 3 inch (for side dishes).... 1.45	27 Pitchers, 1 qt..... .28	39 Cream pitcher ... .20
11 1 pt. bowls 1.50	28 Pitchers, 2 qt..... .42	40 Cake plate .... .28
12 1 qt. oyster bowls 1.60	29 Pitchers, 3 qt..... .62	
13 Platters, 8 in.... .30	30 Soup tureen (with ladle and stand) 3.75	

Dove Spray Pattern.

Manufactured by Alfred Meakin, Tunstall, England.

Genuine semi-porcelain, made by Alfred Meakin, Tunstall, England. The decoration is a delicate spray in dove color, put on under the glaze and guaranteed not to wash or wear off.

Order No. 54015.

Per doz.		Per doz.		Each
1 Tea Cups and Saucers, with handles $1.85	10 Bone Dishes $1.87	22 Covered Butter Dishes $0.50
2 Coffee Cups and Saucers, with handles.. 2.48	11 3-inch Bakers (used as side dishes).... 1.87	23 Sauce Boat ..... .36
		24 Pickle Dish ..... .27
3 Plates, scalloped edge, 5 inch... 1.26	Each.	25 Teapot .... .71
	12 Platters 8 inch..$0.25	26 Sugar Bowl ..... .60
4 Plates, scalloped edge, 6 inch... 1.47	13 Platters, 10 inch .40	27 Cream Pitcher .... .27
	14 Platters, 12 inch .67	28 Cake Plate ..... .36
5 Plates, scalloped edge, 7 inch... 1.75	15 Platters 14 inch.. .93	30 Pitcher, ½ pint.... .23
	16 Platters, 16 inch 1 47	31 Pitcher, 1 quart... .32
7 Plates, scalloped edge, 8 inch... 1.88	18 Sauce Tureen (cover, ladle and stand 5.25	32 Pitcher, 2 quart... .58
7 Plates, scalloped edge, 7 in. Soup. 1.75	19 Sauce Tureen Stand, cover and ladle..... 1.35	36 Pitcher, 3 quart... .80
8 Sauce Plates, 4 inch .... .80	20 Covered Dishes 9 inch 1.20	37 Nappies, 7 inch.... .28
9 Individual Butters .... .55	21 Casserole Square Covered Dish.. 1.20	38 Nappies, 8 inch.... .40
		40 Bowls, 1 pint..... .19
		40 Oyster Bowls, 1 pint .19
		41 Baker, 7 inch..... .27
		42 Baker, 8 inch..... .40

Order No. 54016.

Per doz.		Per doz.		Each.
1 Tea Cups and Saucers, handled.... $1.47	14 Oyster bowls 1 pint $1.47	32 Pitchers 3 quart $0.63
2 Coffee Cups and saucers, handled.. 1.72		33 Covered Dishes, 9 inch ..... .95
	16 Platters, 8 inch... $0.18	Each.
4 Plates, 5 inches. 1.02	17 Platters, 10 inch... .35	34 Casserole (square covered dish) 9 inch ..... .95
5 Plates, 6 inches... 1.20	18 Platters, 12 inch... .51	
6 Plates, 7 inches... 1.38	19 Platters, 14 inch... .93	35 Soup Tureen and ladle (no stand) 2.36
7 Plates, 8 inches... 1.57	20 Platters, 16 inch... .91	
8 Soup plates, 7 inch 1.38	21 Bakers, 7 inch..... .21	36 Sauce Tureen with ladle and stand.. 1.00
9 Soup plates ..... .73	22 Bakers, 8 inch..... .42	39 Sauce Boat ..... .28
10 Individual butters	24 Scalloped Nappies 8 inch ..... .21	40 Pickle Dish ..... .21
11 Bakers 3 inch (used as side dishes) 1.28	25 Scalloped Nappies 8 inch ..... .28	41 Cake Plate ..... .28
12 Bone dishes 1.20	29 Pitchers 1 pint ... .21	42 Teapots ..... .56
13 Bowls 1 pint 1.47	30 Pitchers 1 quart.. .28	43 Sugar Bowls..... .42
	31 Pitchers 2 quart.. .42	45 Cream Pitcher ... .28

Glassware—Continued.

The Vigilant Class Assortment.

Plain and engraved. Cuts show it engraved.

Hero Ruby and Engraved Assortment.

55004 The Ray Table Set; exceedingly neat and attractive, very smooth and every piece perfect.
Per set $0.50

55006 The Sylvan Glass Table Set is made of an extra quality of fine glass, and finished to perfection. We heartily recommend this set to any one wishing an attractive medium priced set. Per set $0.55

Parian Glassware "Ruby."

55011 Hero Ruby Engraved Combination Glass assortment; the smooth part of this pattern is of a rich ruby color, engraved in a pretty design, as shown by cuts. Engraving on ruby is very effective, as the part engraved is clear crystal, and the combination of crystal and ruby is very striking. Another thing that makes this pattern extra desirable is on account of the figured part being clear crystal, well finished glass; in fact, it must be seen to be appreciated. It is composed of the following pieces: one butter dish, one sugar bowl, one cream pitcher, one spoon holder, one large sauce or berry dish, six large sauce or berry dishes, one half gallon pitcher, six tumblers, one bon bon or candy dish, one vinegar or oil bottle, and three each salt and pepper shakers. We pack securely in a strong box, and it weighs ready for shipment about 35 pounds. Price........... $6.0

Water Sets.

55007 The Parian Glass Assortment contains nothing but useful pieces of glassware, such as come constantly into use, as will be seen by the following articles they are all hand-made, of the very best quality lead-blown glass, and warranted perfect: Table set, consisting of butter dish, sugar bowl, spoon holder and cream pitcher; one large berry dish, six small sauce dishes, one half-gallon pitcher, six tumblers, one oil bottle, one syrup can, one small night lamp, three salt bottles, three pepper bottles and one toothpick holder. They are packed securely in a strong wooden box and weigh about 40 lbs.
Per set.............................. $5.40

55008 This line of glassware is pronounced by experts to greatly excel all efforts in the past in the way of plain patterns, and is the acme of perfection. It is extra heavy, substantial and undoubtedly pretty; every piece is oil finished and perfect in shape. We pack them in assortments containing the following pieces: 1 butter dish, 1 sugar bowl, 1 spoon holder, 1 cream pitcher, 6 table tumblers, ½ gallon tankard, 1 8-inch berry dish, 6 small sauce dishes, 1 7-inch footed bowl, 1 pickle dish, 1 celery holder, 1 molasses or syrup pitcher, 1 oil or vinegar bottle and 3 each salt and pepper shakers.
Price, plain................................ $3.25
Price, engraved.......................... 4.50

55013 Glass Water set, a new and a very fancy pattern; fancy stripes as shown in cut can be had in either blue, opal or crystal opal; set consists of ½ gallon pitcher, two tumblers and slop bowl and 13-inch embossed tin tray.
Per set complete $0.5

55016 Same as No. 55013, but has six tumblers.
Per set, complete 1.0

Florence Assortment.

55020 Our Florence assortment is composed of pieces of glassware most commonly used on the table; the pattern is pretty and substantial; all the pieces are finished perfectly smooth. The following is a complete list of the articles it contains: One butter dish, one sugar bowl, one cream pitcher, one spoon holder, one 9-inch berry dish, 12 small sauce dishes, one tall fruit bowl, one cake salver, six salt and six pepper bottles, one celery holder, 6 goblets, 1 half gallon pitcher and 6 table tumblers. It is packed by experienced packers in a good strong box, so that there is very little danger of breakage. Weight. 50 lbs. Price..............$3.60

ARE YOU A SHREWD BUYER?

If you are, you can find in this catalogue just what you are looking for and that is nothing more than low prices and the best quality of goods for the money. Remember that we buy direct from the manufacturers and therefore can offer our goods at very reasonable prices. We are *Importers, Manufacturers* and *Jobbers*, and can supply you with anything from a needle to a steam engine. Try us and you will be convinced that we give good values for the money.

Water Sets.

55025 Frosted Glass Water Set, a new design; consists of two tumblers, 1 slop bowl, 1 half gal. jug and 10 inch glass tray; this is the best and cheapest set we have ever been able to offer.
Per set,..............$0.55
Per doz. sets,..........$5.94

55029 Engraved Water or Lemonade Set; consists of ½ gallon tankard shape jug, 6 engraved tumblers, and 13 inch hammered brass tray....$1.95

55033 These handsome sets are made of the best quality lead glass and are decorated by hand with a beautiful flower and spray, and warranted not to wash off. They are equal in quality and appearance to the finest imported ware that sells at three times the price we ask for these; set consists of half gallon pitcher, six tumblers and fine embossed white metal tray.
Ruby, per set, $2.50. Green, $2.35. Crystal...$1.90

55037 Water or Lemonade Set. Fancy globe shape pitcher with tumblers to match, made of thin blown colored glass, set consists of ½ gallon pitcher, 6 tumblers and hammered brass tray. Price, Ruby opalescent...
..............$2.10 Price
Blue...$1.55
Crystal. 1.55

55041 Tankard shape Lemonade Set, very best quality lead glass, hand decorated with flowers and sprays in colors; will not wash off; set consists of one half gallon, tankard pitcher, six tumblers and embossed white metal tray.
Crystal, per set..............$2.40
Ruby, per set.............. 2.75

Exposition Ruby Water Set.

55044 The Exposition Set is an exceedingly handsome pattern in crystal and dark ruby colors. The dark pieces in cut indicate the rut...; very latest shaped pitcher, holding half gallon, six tumblers and hammered brass tray. Price..............$2.50

55045 Water Set, light blown colored glass, big spot pattern, handsome shapes; pitcher holds half gallon. Six tumblers and hammered brass tray complete.
Price, ruby opalescent..............$1.90
Blue opalescent.............. 1.55
Crystal opalescent.............. 1.55

55047 Glass Pitcher, finely engraved, very delicate and handsome pattern. The glass is of a very fine quality and heavy. Price..............$0.65
55049 Fine crystal glass, half gallon water pitcher, rich and sparkling. Price.............. .45

55051 Hob-nail, half gallon Pitcher, very strong, made of good, clear glass. Price..............$0.23
55053 Tankard shape, half gallon Water Pitcher, extra well finished and very nobby in shape, nothing better in plain glass manufactured. Price.............. .85

55055 Imitation cut glass, half gallon Water Pitcher, rich and sparkling well finished and heavy. Price..............$0.39

Rose Bowls—Continued.

55485 Imitation Cut Glass Rose Bowl, 6½x7 inches, best and closest imitation of cut glass yet brought out. Makes a very pretty ornament. Each $0.25

Bouquet Holders.

55487 Glass Bouquet Holder, made of fine glass; is a very handsome pattern; stands 7 inches high. Each..................$0.15
Per dozen..................1.62
55489 Same as above; 6 inches high.
Each..................10
Per dozen..................1.02

Genuine Imported Bisque Figures.

55490 Imported Bisque Figure, stands 7¾ inches high; subjects are children in various costumes. These are not toys, but real works of art, and at the price we ask for them are remarkably cheap. Price..................$0.25
Per dozen..................2.70

Are you an Artist? We can supply your paint box with the best that artists require.

Bisque Figures—Continued.

55493 Swing Bisque Figure, 3 inches high, beautifully tinted and decorated. Each..................$0.30
Per doz..................3.24
55496 Bisque Figure, representing a boy carrying a small sail boat; these make pretty mantel ornaments; they stand 7 inches high and are handsomely colored.
Each..................$0.20
Per pair..................38
55498 Bisque toothpick holders, this is a very neat article and represents a child with a willow basket strapped on her back, nicely colored and stands five inches high.$0.10

Art Majolica Ware.

55500 English Majolica Vase, gold trimmed and ornamented with raised work, flowers and leaves. This makes a ver. handsome ornament, as it is quite large, standing 14 inches high.
Price..................$ 1.50
Per dozen..................16.20

Majolica Ware—Continued.

55501 English Majolica double handled vase, raised ornamentation of flowers and leaves. This is a very handsome piece of ware and will be sure to be appreciated wherever seen. It stands 10½ inches high.
Price..................$1.25
Per dozen..................13.50

55502 English Majolica handled vase, stands 8 inches high, it is ornamented with raised flowers and leaves in very pleasing colors, this makes a very handsome mantel ornament.
Price..................$0.65
Per dozen..................7.05

55503 English Majolica flower vase; it is ornamented in the same manner as the larger ones; it stands 5½ inches high and is used largely for cut flowers dried grass, etc. Price..................$0.25
Per dozen..................2.70

55504 English Majolica flower vase or bouquet holder, ornamented with raised work flowers and leaves, tinted in natural colors; it stands 4½ inches high and makes a very desirable, low priced article.
Price..................$0.20
Per dozen..................2.16

LAMP DEPARTMENT.

We respectfully call our customers' attention to the handsome line of hanging, table, piano and banquet lamps we are offering this season. We think they are finer than any we have yet shown. They are entirely new designs, and from the low prices we are enabled to offer them at, we predict a large sale. They are packed by experienced and careful men and the chance of breakage is very slight.

55510 Polished bronze metal, ball weight hanging lamp; length closed, 44 inches; extended 59 inches; complete with 14 inch opal cone shade, one No. 2 sun burner, taking one inch wick and ordinary No. 2 chimney.
Price..................$1.75

55512 Polished bronze metal hanging lamp, improved spring extension; length closed, 32 inches; extended, 80 inches, complete with 14 inch plain white dome shade, No. 2 chimney and burner.
Price..................$2.15

55514 Polished bronze metal. patent improved extension; length, closed, 35 inches, extended 81 inches; fancy hand decorated and tinted 14 inch dome shade and fount to match, with climax burner, chimney and 1¼ inch wick, giving a large and steady light.
Price..................$2.75

55518 Polished Bronze Metal Hanging Lamp, with pull-down ornament, plated bright silver, patent improved spring extension; length, closed, 37 inches, extended; 83 inches, fancy tinted and decorated 14 inch dome shade and fount to match, fitted with large burner taking 1¼ inch wick and chimney; a good light giver and sure to please..................$3.00

55520 Polished Bronze Metal Hanging Lamp, patent spring extension; length, closed, 35 in.; extended, 81 in.; fancy hand decorated and tinted 14-inch dome shade and fount to match; cut glass crystal prisms, climax burner chimney and 1¾ inch wick, gives a brilliant light.
Price..................$3.65

55524 Polished Bronze Metal Hanging Lamp, patent improved spring extension; length, closed, 34 inches; extended, 80 inches, hand decorated satin finish 14-inch dome shade and fount to match; fitted with climax burner and chimney, giving large light; cut glass crystal prisms around edge of shade.
Price..................$3.90

55528 Polished Bronze Metal Hanging Lamp, patent improved spring extension; length closed 38 inches; extended 84 inches, tinted decorated satin finish 14-inch dome shade and fount to match, cut glass crystal prisms, climax burner and chimney.
Price..................$4.15

55530 Polished Bronze Metal Hanging Lamp, with cast brass silver plated ornaments, patent spring extension, length closed 37 inches; extended, 83 inches; crystal cut glass crystal prisms, fancy decorated 14-inch dome shade and fount to match, trimmed with climax burner and chimney.....$4.25

55531 Polished Bronze Metal Hanging Lamp, with pull-down ornaments plated bright silver, patent improved spring extension; length, closed 39 inches; extended 85 inches; handsome satin finished hand-decorated 14-inch dome shade and vase to match; removable oil fount fitted with 80 candle power central draft burner giving an extra large light; takes number 2 Rochester chimney and wick; crystal glass cut prisms.
Price..................$6.15

Lamps—Continued.

55534 Polished Bronze Metal Hanging Lamp, with strap work on harp and pull-down, ornaments plated bright silver, improved spring extension; length, closed, 39 inches; extended, 85 inches, satin finish fancy hand decorated 14-inch dome shade and vase to match, removable oil founts (easy to clean and fill), central draft burner giving 80 candle power light; cut glass crystal prisms.
Price..............$5.45

55536 Polished Bronze Metal Hanging Lamp, improved spring extension; length, closed, 39 inches; extended, 85 inches; adapted for either high or low ceilings, satin finished decorated 14 inch dome shade and vase to match, large central draft burner giving 80 candle power light; ornamented with cut glass crystal prisms.
Price..........$4.95

55538 Polished Bronze Metal Hanging Lamp, improved spring extension; length, closed, 38 inches; extended, 84 inches; adapted for either high or low ceilings; handsome hand decorated and tinted; 14-inch dome shade and vase to match, on satin finish body; has removable oil fount (easy to fill or trim); fitted with central draft, 80 candle power burner, which throws a powerful light; ornamented around shade with cut glass crystal prisms.
Price..............$4.60

55541 Polished Bronze Metal Hanging Lamp; improved spring extension; adapted to low or high ceilings; length, closed, 38 inches; extended, 84 inches; satin finish; hand decorated; 14-inch dome shade and vase to match; removable oil fount (easy to fill and clean); fitted with central draft, 80 candle power burner; ornamented with cut glass crystal prisms.
Price..............$4.75

34—6th

Lamps—Continued.

55545 Polished Bronze Metal,; length closed, 26 inches; length, extended, 47 inches. Has sun burner with pearl top lead glass chimney. Choice of etched crystal globe, ruby globe, or blue, pink, rose or crystal opalescent globe, all at same price. This is the cheapest and best article we have ever been able to offer in the line of a moderate size ball lamp, and is the latest production.
Price...........$1.80

55546 Hall Lamp made of polished bronze metal and trimmed with pink rose globe and No. 2 unique burner, which can be lighted without removing chimney. Length, closed, 30 inches; extended, 48 inches.
Price..............$2.50

55545 Zenith

55546

55548 Hall Lamp, polished bronze, fitted complete with crystal etched globe and No. 1 sun burner and chimney; length, closed, 30 inches; extended, 48 inches.
Price..............$2.45

55549. Polished Bronze Metal Hall Lamp; length, closed, 29 inches; extended, 47 inches; square shape, with crystal etched glass; size of glass 6x8 inches; trimmed with No. 1 sun burner and chimney.
Price..............$2.65

55548   55549

Lamp and Chandelier Hooks.

GENEVA BRONZED.
55550 Lamp or Chandelier Hook, with plate, and 4 in. screw. Each...........$0.10
Per dozen..........1.05

Ceiling Hooks.
55552 We recommend the use of our rich gilt ceiling hook, as it compels the chandelier or lamp to remain exactly where placed on hook.
Each.................$0.22
Per dozen..........2.50

Chandeliers.

55553 Polished bronze extension chandelier, complete with crystal etched pan globes and embossed metal central draft burner, which gives four times the light of an ordinary burner. This is an ornamental fixture for the parlor and is used extensively in churches, halls, etc. Always gives good satisfaction.
3-light trimmed, complete $16.50
4-light trimmed, complete...................20.00

Chandeliers—Continued.

55554 Chandeliers, antique brass, with patent spring extension; length, closed, 37 in. extended, 55 inches; spreads 30 inches; is fitted with unique burners which enable you to light it without removing chimney or globe.

We can furnish this chandelier with either etched or colored globes as desired.
Price, three-light complete.....................$11.25
Price, four-light complete...................... 13.25

55556 Polished Bronze Metal Chandelier, improved spring extension, adapted to either high or low ceilings; length, closed, 40 inches; extended, 58 inches; spread of arms, 30 inches; fitted with 4-inch wave top-etched globes and No. 2 Unique burners, which can be lighted without removing chimney or globe.
2-light, trimmed complete......................$7.95
3-light, trimmed complete 10.00
4-light, trimmed complete 12.00
55558 Same Chandelier as No. 55556, but fitted with metal oil founts, having 50-candle power burner, which gives an extra brilliant light. This fixture meets all requirements and si suitable for dwellings, churches and halls.
2-light, trimmed complete..................... 9.25
3-light, trimmed complete...................12.00
4-light, trimmed complete...................15.00

Piano Lamps.

55562 Gold finish metal Piano Lamp; has extension rod which runs through center of table, and prevents it from being easily tipped over. Genuine Mexican onyx top 8x8 inches, fitted with removable oil fount, and large central draft burner and handsome 20-inch silk shade, with 8 inch lace border. Height to top of chimney, 50 inches; extended, 75 inches.
Price.......... $12.85

Lamps—Continued.

55614   **55617**

55614 Decorated Stand Lamp, metal foot, Japan finish, colored center and crystal glass fount, complete, with No. 2 Sun burner, chimney and fancy Japanese paper dome shade; height to top of chimney, 21 inches. Price...... .....$0.85
55617 Crystal Glass Stand Lamp; neat, plain pattern. We keep three sizes.
19 inches high to top of chimney, and trimmed with No. 2 burner, chimney and wick, complete. Price..... .35
18 inches high to top of chimney, and trimmed with No. 2 burner, chimney and wick, complete. Price..... .30
16 inches high to top of chimney and trimmed with No. 1 burner, chimney and wick, complete. Price.... .25

55619 Crystal Glass Stand Lamp; has clinch collar put on under several hundred pounds pressure; no cement or plaster clinched on collars, never come off, and the process of putting them on breaks all the imperfect lamps, consequently a clinch collar lamp is superior and safer than those having collars put on with plaster paris.
19 inches high to top of chimney and trimmed with number 2 burner; chimney and wick complete. Price...... .$0.45
18 inches high to top of chimney and trimmed with number 2 burner; chimney and wick complete. Price........ .$0.37
16 inches high to top of chimney and trimmed with number 1 burner; chimney and wick complete. Price........$0.30

55624   **55623**

55623 Crystal Glass Night Lamp; will hold enough oil to burn all night and is fitted with a burner, wick and chimney, complete. Price............$0.16
55624 Footed crystal Glass Hand-Lamp, heavy foot, not easily upset, complete with No. 1 Sun burner, chimney and wick. Price .... .20

55626 Footed Crystal Glass Hand-lamp, with patent clinch collar, put on under several hundred pounds pressure; no cement or plaster; can never come off; extra heavy foot; complete with No. 1 Sun burner, chimney and wick. Price....$0.25

Use Corticelli Sewing and Embroidery Silks.

Fancy Metal Table Lamps.

55631 Metal Parlor Table Lamp; bright silver finish; a very handsome and substantial lamp; made of heavy cast metal, open work design; has removable oil fount fitted with 80 candle power, center draft burner, 10 inch; handsome, tinted and decorated satin finished dome shade; height to top of chimney, 20¼ in. Price......$6.00

55632 Metal Parlor Table Lamp, rich gold finish, extra heavy metal cast open work design, removable oil fount, fitted with 80 candle power, center draft burner, giving a large and brilliant light, 10-inch dome shade, handsomely tinted and decorated; height to top of chimney, 19 inches. Price...........$4.50

55632

55633 Metal Parlor Table Lamp, silver finish, trimmed with 10-inch tinied and decorated dome shade; has 80 candle power, center draft burner; height to top of chimney, 18 in. Price............$3.50

55633

Montgomery Ward & Co.'s Central Draft Metal Table and Hand Lamps.

We have selected this burner (after a careful comparison with all others) as being the very best; it will give more light according to the amount of oil consumed than any other lamp made. Try one and you will be more than pleased.

55634 Our World Beater Central Draft Table Lamp made of polished and embossed brass, good size; will hold more than enough oil for a long evening; trimmed complete with tripod, chimney, wick and 10-inch plain dome shade. Price........$1.75
55636 Same as 55634, Nickel plated. Price......2.00

55638 The Rochester Junior is designed for a night or bedroom lamp. It stands about 9¼ inches to top of burner and is fitted with 6-inch plain dome shade. It will not smoke or smell if turned low and will hold sufficient oil to burn all night. Price....$0.90
55641 Plain White Dome Shades, to fit 55638 lamp.
Each............................$0.20
55642 Chimneys to fit 55638 lamp. Each............$0.05
Per doz....... .... .55

Student Lamps.

55643 This is the best Student or Library Lamp we know of. Gives a perfect and uniform light, is cool, absolutely safe, is adjustable in height and is in every way a perfect lamp. Price, complete, packed for shipping. Each $3.50. Extra chimneys for students' lamp.
Per bundle of 6.....$0.20

55644 Rochester Study Lamp, detachable fount with wick, chimney and 10-inch plain dome shade as shown in cut. Add 40 cents to prices below if wanted with decorated dome shade.
Brass $3.75
Nickel plated..... 6.00
Weight, 25 lbs, packed.
55646 Central Draft Bracket Lamp, made entirely of polished brass, furnished with chimney and wick (no shade). Price.......................$1.90

55647 Brass Swing- **55646** ing Bracket Lamp, square arm, with 12 in. spread, trimmed with No. 2 unique burner and 5 in. etched globe; can be lighted without removing chimney or globe.
Price........$2.15

55648 Two Joint Brass Swinging Bracket Lamp, closed 12 in., extended 20, trimmed complete with fancy colored dew drop globe in blue or light ruby; has No. 2 unique burner and chimney, and can be lighted without removing either Price........$2.75

55649 Non-explosive Hand Lamp, bronze finish. This lamp is absolutely non-explosive; can be carried around without the slightest danger it gives an excellent light; furnished complete with wick and chimney as shown in cut. Price......$0.85

Genuine Rochester Bracket and Harp Lamp.

55651 Rochester Bracket or side lamp, metal fount, 9 inches high, holds 2 qts. of oil; gives immense light for factories, mills, engine rooms, etc. Complete bracket, reflector, 8 in. metal fount, wick and chimney. Each $2.00
55653 Rochester Lamp, complete with tin shade, and wire harp, 30 inches in length, to hang from ceiling; for shops, factories, stores etc.; fount trimmed with wick and chimney complete. Each.... $2.25
Per dozen.................... 24.50
55654 Rochester Lamp, same as No. 55651, in wire harp, 30 in. in length and in tin shade, to hang from ceiling, for shops, factories, stores, etc. Fount complete, with wick and chimney. Each $2.10
Per dozen................$22.75

Lamps—Continued.

55656 The Rochester Combination Oil Stove and Lamp. The oil fount holds 2½ quarts and will burn twenty hours. When used as a stove it will boil water in a few minutes. The chimney is of Russia iron, having nice window and malleable iron base. The whole top easily lifts off and a glass chimney can be put on, thus changing it into a real Rochester lamp. There is real merit in this article, as it combines two of the most useful and necessary household utensils.
Price..............................$2.50

The Banner Mammoth Lamp.

400 Candle Power Light.

55658 The mammoth lamp gives a strong and brilliant light, and has a fount holding one gallon of oil; it is the only mammoth lamp with extra wick feeder to supply oil to the burning wick; suitable for all places where a large and steady light is required; 20 inch embossed tin shade harp, smoke bell and chimney; ready for use.
Price......$3.25

55661 The mammoth lamp, with spring extension and 14 inch white porcelain shade; this makes a very neat appearing lamp and is especially adapted for use in churches, school houses, halls, etc.
Price..............................$4.75

Extra Chimneys to fit mammoth lamp. Each.....$0.25

All Steel Kitchen and Night Lamps.

55663 Reflector lamp made of steel, riveted together; will last a life time; the polished tin reflector is removable, and if at any time it is not required can be taken off; it is fitted as shown in cut, complete with number 2 burner, wick and chimney. Price..............$0.46
Per dozen 5.52

55663
55664 All steel side lamp with polished tin reflector; it is fitted with bandied fount which can be taken from frame when required; this will be found to be a very convenient lamp; it is fitted with number 2 burner chimney and wick complete.
Price..............................$0.40
Per dozen 4.35

55666 All steel side or reflector lamp, very useful, as it may be hung up or placed on shelf; the frame is so constructed; that it can be carried in the hand without the least danger of upsetting; trimmed complete with No. 2 burner, chimney and wick. Price........$0.35
Per dozen 3.80

Lamps—Continued.

55668 Swing bracket lamp, made of steel and riveted together, finished in black enamel and bronze stripes; fitted with No. 2 burner, 8 inch reflector and chimney complete.
Each $0.65
Per dozen 7.00
Same as No. 55668, but without reflector. Each....$0.49
Per dozen 5.40

55669 Swing bracket lamp, all steel and riveted together; finished in black enamel and bronze stripes; fitted with No. 2 burner, illuminator and shade as shown in cut; does not require any chimney.
Price............................$0.84
Per doz 8.60

Lamp Shades.

55678   **55680**
55678 Porcelain Lamp Shade, plain white, 7 in., for standing lamps. This pattern is intended to be used on illuminator. Each, plain $0.25
Same as above, decorated 40
55680 Porcelain Lamp Shades, cone shapes, 10 and 14 inch decorated, assorted decorations, not alike in cut; 10 inch for parlor stand lamp; 14 inch for hanging or library lamps.

Size	10 in.	14 in.
Plain, each	60c.	73c.
Decorated	80c.	90c.

55682 Porcelain Lamp Shades, dome shape, 10 and 14 inch. Plain and decorated, assorted decoration; 10 inch for parlor stand lamps; 14 inch for library lamps.

Size	10 in.	14 in.
Plain	50c	75c.
Decorated	75c.	$1.00

Paper Shades.

55684 The Queen Folding Paper Shade, to cover the ordinary plain cone shade table lamp a nd give it the appearance of a nice shade lamp. There are innumerable uses to which the Queen may be put, such as covering up unused stove pipe holes, decorating the walls, covering flower pots, etc. Can be had in red, blue or green.
Each, $0.15 Per doz...........$1.62
55687 Holders for Queen Folding Shade; will fit any chimney. Each, $0.10 Per doz....1.08

Linen and Silk Piano and Banquet Lamp Shades.

55688 Fancy silk shades for banquet and piano lamps, latest styles and artificially made; best China silk used; ton cannot be ruffled or damaged by heat, as it is protected by a metal band. The frame on which they are made fits any four inch holder. Choice of the following colors: Red, lemon, orange, pink, nile green, and old gold.
15 inch with 6-inch lace border. Price.......$1.85
15 inch with 6-inch embroidered chiffon border. Price 2.10
18 in. with 8 in. lace border. Price..............2.75
18 in. with 8 in. embroidered chiffon border. Price..3.15
18 in. with 8 in. embroidered chiffon in colors. Price..3.40
Note.—15-inch shades are used on banquet lamps; 18 on piano lamps.

Shades—Continued.

55689 The same material is used in the construction of this shade as 55688, the difference being in shape only.
15 inch, with 6 inch lace border. Price......$1.85
15 inch, with 6 inch chiffon border. Price......2.10
15 inch, with 6 inch chiffon border embroidered in colors. Price..............................2.25
18 inch, with 8 inch lace border. Price......2.75
18 inch, with 8 inch embroidered chiffon border. Price..............................3.15
18 inch, with 8 inch embroidered chiffon borders in colors. Price..................3.40
20 inch with 8 inch lace border. Price......3.50
20 inch, with 8 inch embroidered chiffon border. Price..............................3.90
20 inch, with 8 inch embroidered chiffon border in colors. Price..............................4.25

55691 Isabella Linen Shades and Holder for banquet lamps; entirely new shape, made of best quality linen with 3 inch silk fringe; it comes only in one size, 16 inches in diameter, and can be had in any of the following colors: Red, lemon, orange, pink and nile green.
Price, with holder, complete.................$0.65

55740 Linen shades, 7-inch with 2-inch silk fringe and holder complete.
Each.....$0.25
Per doz 2.70
55742 Linen shade 9 in., with 3-inch silk fringe and holder complete. Each......$0.40
Per doz 4.32
55743 Linen Shade 12-inch, with 3-inch silk fringe. Each..............................50
Per doz 5.40
55744 Linen Shade, 14-inch with 3-inch silk fringe. Each........................67
Per doz 7.42
55745 Brass Shade Holders, suitable for 10, 12, or 14 inch shades, and will fit any chimney. Each...35

Firemen's Lanterns.

55748 This lantern is made of solid brass of extra heavy quality, and intended for firemen's use; the shield on top of globe is for the purpose of keeping water and steam from entering the globe when in burning buildings; it is fitted with number one burner, taking ⅝ inch wick, and uses the ordinary lantern globe.
Solid brass, each....................$1.65
Solid brass nickel plated, each . 2.10

Stockmen's and Shippers' Lanterns.

55749 This lantern is made especially for rough use, being used very extensively on railroads by car inspectors, as they need a very strong light; it is made of the very best quality block tin, nicely japaned; it has a four-inch silver plated reflector and five inch beveled edge, front glass; the oil pot is large, holding sufficient oil to burn all night; we recommend it wherever a strong and powerful light-giving lantern is desired.
Price..............................$1.85

The Modern Progress Burner.

This burner takes a special chimney and cannot be used with any other.

55925 The New "Modern Progress" Burner emits a very large, beautiful white flame, fits all ordinary large stand lamps. It burns a moderate amount of oil, breaks few chimneys, does not smoke or get very hot, never gets out of order, it is safe and reliable, takes ordinary plain top chimney. Order one, and if not found as represented, send it back at our expense. Each with chimney and two extra wicks.
Price.......................$0.68
Weight, complete, 16 oz.

***** Our next Catalogue will be sent only to those who send us 15 cents for postage.**

The P. & A. Duplex Burner.

This burner takes a special chimney and cannot be used with any other.

55930 This is, without doubt, the most complete, strongest and best constructed burner now in use. It takes two wicks, has a patent extinguisher to put out the light, emits a large brilliant and steady light and is suitable for fine parlor, vase or library lamps.
Price, with extinguisher, reducing collar and ring for globe..........$0.80
Per dozen.......................8.64

Return at our expense if not satisfactory.

55932 Extra chimneys for P. & A. Duplex Burner. Each $0.08 Per dozen.................. .87
Weight, 12 ounces.

Prisms.

55934 Crystal Glass Prisms, for ornamenting hanging lamps. We do not have them in any other color. Each.......................$0.03
Per dozen....................... .35

Lamp Wicks and Candle Wicking.

55940	Candle wicking, per pound..............	$0.22
55941	Lamp wicks' No. 0, ⅝ inch, per doz.......	.03
55946	Lamp wicks, No. 1, ⅞ inch, per doz.......	.04
55949	Lamp wicks, No. 2, 1 inch, per doz.......	.05
55950	Lamp wicks, No. 3, 1½ inch, per doz.....	.08
55952	Lamp wicks to fit No. 55925 burner, per doz..............	.36
55953	Lamp wicks to fit No. 55650 lamp, per doz..............	.75
55954	Lamp wicking No. 0, ⅝ inch, roll 32 yds..	.27
55955	Lamp wicking No. 1, ⅞ inch, roll 32 yds..	.35
55956	Lamp wicking No. 2, 1 inch, roll 32 yds..	.60
55957	Lamp wicking No. 3, 1½ inch, roll 32 yds..	.80

BICYCLES AND BICYCLE SUNDRIES.

In selecting our line of Bicycles for this season we have had in mind the unusual depression in all kinds of industries, and aimed to procure a stock of good, substantial and reliable machines at prices to conform with the times. In this respect we think we have been eminently successful. Our selection embraces machines for the use of adults of both sexes and boys and girls of all ages. If, in our descriptions of the various styles, we have not been sufficiently explicit we shall at all times be pleased to answer any and all inquiries regarding same. Our Special Bicycle Catalogue will be ready April 1st. Free upon request.

56000—The Bicycle shown in above illustration is made of the best weldless steel tubing and steel drop forgings. It has a perfect diamond frame, and is in every respect a high-grade and serviceable machine. The wheels are 28 inches in diameter and are fitted with 1⅜-inch pneumatic tires, ball bearing to all parts, including head and pedals. The finish is high-grade jet black enamel, with the usual parts nickel-plated. Gear, 59 inches; weight, crated for shipment, about 90 lbs.
Price.......................$49.50

56004 — The above machine is intended for youths having a leg measurement from 26 to 32 inches; it is made of the best weldless steel tubing and steel drop forgings; the wheels are 26 inches in diameter and fitted with 1¼ inch pneumatic tires; ball bearings to all parts, including head and pedals; it is finished in high grade jet black enamel with usual parts finely nickel plated. Gear, 52 inches. Weight, crated for shipment, about 80 lbs. Price....... $40.00

56005 The above is a handsome and well proportioned Bicycle capable of being ridden by a lady of any weight; it is made of the best weldless steel tubing and steel drop forgings; the wheels are 28 inches in diameter and fitted with 1⅜ inch pneumatic tires; ball bearings to all parts, including head and pedals; the finish is high grade jet black enamel with the usual parts nickel plated. Gear, 54 inches. Weight, crated for shipment, about 90 lbs.
Price.......................$49.50

56007 The above machine is of the combination style, capable of being used by either boys or girls, from the ages of 10 to 18 years; in fact is strong enough to carry a person of almost any weight. It is made of the best weldless steel tubing and steel drop forgings. The wheels are 26 inches in diameter and fitted with 1¼ inch pneumatic tires; ball bearing to all parts except head. The finish is high grade jet black enamel, with the usual parts nickel plated. Weight, crated for shipment, about 75 pounds. Gear, 49 inches. Price.......................$39.75

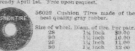

56009—The above machine is intended for boys having a leg measurement from 22 to 28 inches. The frame is of the double diamond pattern, made entirely from steel tubing and steel forgings. It is full ball bearing with the exception of the head. The wheel are 24 inches in diameter, fitted with 1⅛ inch pneumatic tires. The finish is high grade jet black enamel, with the usual parts nickel plated. Gear. 48 inches. Weight, crated for shipment, about 65 pounds. Price $34.50

24 Inch Wheels, 1 Inch Elastic Cushion Tires.

56014 The above machine is intended for boys having a leg measurement from 20 to 26 inches. It is a strictly juvenile wheel, and should not be ridden by full-grown people. The main reach and cross bar are tubular, with semi-hollow front and rear forks; adjustable steel cone bearing to head and all wearing parts. The finish is high grade jet black enamel, with the usual parts nickel plated. Gear, 43 inches. Weight, crated for shipment, about 64 pounds.
Price.......................$18.00

Morgan & Wright Pneumatic Tire.

In producing the Morgan & Wright Pneumatic Tire the aim of the manufacturer has been to make it as thin and resilient as possible, and at the same time of sufficient strength to endure service. The outer cover is of a fine fabric of special quality and weave, resilient and hard to puncture. The inner tube is flat, with closed ends; this makes the tube draw easily through the tire. These tubes are three-ply and are without any seam or joint, and the ends are closed by vulcanizing. The valve is self-contained and replacable; it is light, small and practical.

	Inside diam. tire.	Diameter rim
26 inch	22¼ inches	22½
28 inch	24¼ inches	24½
30 inch	26¼ inches	26½

56017 Price per pair, complete with pump, any of above sizes.......................$10.00

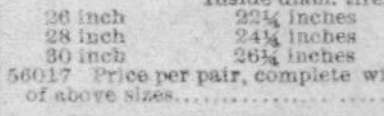

56019 Pumps to fit Morgan & Wright pneumatic tire.......... .50

56020 Bicycle Tires made of best quality solid rubber. We can furnish them in any of the following sizes.

Size of wheel.	Diam. of tire.	Per pair.
24	¾ inch	$2.60
26	¾ inch	2.90
28	¾ inch	3.10
30	¾ inch	3.40

Size of wheel.	Diameter of tire.	Per pair.
24	⅞ inch	$3.30
26	⅞ inch	3.70
28	⅞ inch	4.00
30	⅞ inch	4.40

56022 Cushion Tires made of the best quality gray rubber.

Size of wheel.	Diam. of tire.	Per pair.
28	1⅜ inch	$9.00
30	1⅜ inch	10.00
28	1½ inch	11.00
30	1½ inch	12.00

56024 Molded Pedal Rubbers, best quality, 4x1⅛, 3x1¼, 3¾x1⅛. When ordering be sure to say which size is wanted and whether round or square hole in center. Per set of four..........$1.25

Bicycle Sundries.

56026 The Hart Saddle. State if ladies' or gentlemen's is desired; not fitted with tool bag. This is a beautiful saddle and as comfortable as a rocking chair.
Price $4.00

Belts.

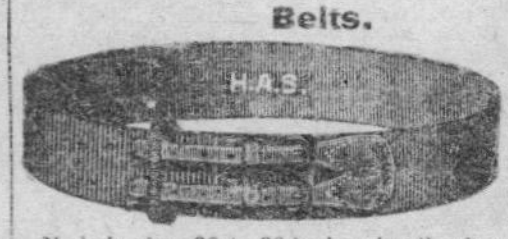

56029—Our Belts are made especially for cyclists, of fine worsted, or cotton webbing.

Made in sizes 32 to 38 inches, in all colors.
Worsted belts, each.......................$0.35
Per dozen....................... 3.75
Cotton belts....................... .25
Per dozen....................... 2.70

Bells.

56032 The Favorite, 2¼ inches in diameter, and has full nickeled gong and fastenings; gives a sharp clear note; this is as good as bells sold by retail dealers at 50c.
Our price.......................$0.35
Per dozen....................... 3.78

56034 Same as 56032, 3 inches in diameter. This is a favorite bell; you will have to pay a retail dealer $1.00 for one like it. Our price......... .60
Per dozen....................... 6.48

56035 The London Chime, 3 inches in diameter, sounds two distinct musical notes, the handsomest and cheapest bell on the market.
Price.......................$0.95
Per dozen.......................10.00

56037 The New Electric Stroke Bell. As a test this bell was attached to machinery and rung continuously for two hours, striking over one hundred and ninety-one thousand distinct blows without in the least destroying the effectiveness of its ring, and showing only slight wear of the parts. We consider this a thorough test of its durability.
Nickel-plated. Price.......................$1.25

56039 The New Departure Bell, a double electric alarm for each pressure on lever. This was last season the most popular bell on the market, and with the new and unique lock and key fastening is destined to enjoy an increased popularity.
Large size.......$1.65
Small size....... 1.40

Bicycle Lamps.

Our lamps all have finely polished front and heavy ruby side lights, detachable reflectors and noiseless spring backs, and all are formed with locked and folded seams and joints, no solder being used except in the oil reservoir, so that they cannot be melted apart.

The Rambler Lamp.

56041 This is one of the best lamps; is fitted with a new style fastening which will fit any style bracket. Price, large size, ja-panned..................$1.95
Price, large size, nickeled.. 2.35
Price, medium sized, ja-panned....................1.50
Price, medium size, nickeled 1.95

The Perfection Lamp, No. 5.

56044 The per-fection is a small sized lamp, but will give good serv-ice; throws a strong light, does not rattle, and will not jar out. Price, ja-panned..$0.75

56044   56045.
56045 Chicago Headlight, No. 3, japanned finish.
Price..................$0.90

The Luster Lamp.

56047 The Luster is one of the neatest and most expensive lamps made, is furnished with a bullseye lense 3¼ inches in diameter, and an adjustable socket fastening; will fit any style of lamp bracket. This is absolutely the highest grade lamp manufactured.
Price, japanned..................$2.75
Price, nickeled.....................3.25

56049 The Cyclone Bicycle Lamp, one of the neatest and most expen-sive on the market; the lens, which is imported and the very best money can buy, costs more than a great many lamps to produce; it is very light, weighing about 11 ounces, has a ¾-inch wick, but will throw more light than the majority of lamps with 1-inch wick; the fount slides and is locked in place by the sliding side light. To those in search of a supe-rior lantern, one that will be sure to give satisfaction, we strongly recommend the Cyclone; it comes nicely japanned with nickel trimmings. Price..........$3.00

Tool Bag.

56052 This Tool Bag is the best adapted for wheelman's use of any yet made. It is made of the best leather throughout.
Price..................$0.60
Price, better quality.................$0.75

56059 A specially de-signed bag of latest ap-proved shape, for use on machines of the dia-mond frame pattern, hand made of best se-lected russet leather; has a side opening, afford-ing easy access to tools. It is large size and will hold wrench, oiler,
pump and repair outfit. Price..................$1.15

56063 Square Telescope Tool Bag, made of the best leather, light rus-set, with extra smooth finish, will carry a pneumatic pump wrench and oil can. Price $0.75

56064 Cyclists' Belt Pouch, a convenient means of carrying watch, wrench or money with-out fear of their being lost or damaged, made of first qual-ity leather.
Price..................$0.75

Wrenches.

56065 Tower & Lan Pocket Wrench, drop forged from bar steel and case hardened. These wrenches are unequaled in material, strength and ef-ficiency and are warranted in all respects a first-class article. Nickeled, each............$0.50
Per dozen....................5.40

56069 The Acme Bicycle Wrench; for strength, durability, and easy action, this wrench is un-surpassed; being made entirely of iron, it will stand more hard usage than any monkey wrench made; with wood cushioned handle, 5 in. long.
Price..................30

Bicycle Locks.

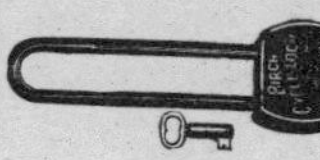

56070 The Birch all steel Automatic Bicycle Lock is without doubt the most secure and hand-somest in the market; it will lock a bicycle by either drop-ping through the links of the driving chain or fitting over the rear fork and through the wheel; it weighs but a trifle and read-ily fits the vest pocket or tool bag. Price..................$0.50
Per dozen....................5.40

56072 Pure Aluminum Bicycle Lock; all are finished with raised parts highly polished and de-pressed parts luster polished. They are spring, self-locking with spring shackles and fitted with 16-inch strong and shapely chain.
Each..................$0.35
Per dozen....................3.80

56074 Gun Metal Bicycle Lock, made on same principle as rail-road switch lock, all parts very stout and strong and nickel plated, the chain is 16 inches long, made of stout hard cut steel, spring self-locking, spring hinged shackles.
Each..................$0.45
Per dozen....................4.86

56075 Bicycle Lock, made of bronze metal, highly polished and nickel plated, spring self-locking, with automatically opening pivoted shackles, fitted with 17-inch steel chain.
Each..................$0.25
Per dozen....................2.75

The Bridgeport Cyclometer.

56078 The Bridgeport Cy-clometer registers accurately up to 1,000 miles and re-peats, or can be set back at will, adjustable to any bicy-cle and can be read from the saddle. We guarantee it to be absolutely reliable and equal in quality and durability to any. It weighs only 6⅜ ounces and is made to fit 28 or 30 inch wheels. Be sure to say what size it is wanted for when ordering. Price..................$3.50

Bicycle-Tire Cements—Enamel, Oil, Graphite, Etc.

56080 Best imported Tire Cement. Price per pound..................$0.65
56082 2 oz. cake..................10
56085 Bicycle Enamel, quick drying; will not crack or peel off; ½ pint can with brush. Price..................30
56090 Electric Cycle Oil, in 4 oz. screw top cans. Each..................12
56091 Same as above, 8 oz. cans, with oiler spout. Each..................20
56092 Illuminating Oil, made specially for bicycle lamps, and put in ½ pint cans. Each..................30
56093 Standard Rubber Cement, for cementing cuts in, or splicing rubber tires; 2 oz. bottles with directions how to use. Price..................18
56094 Cycle Chain Graphite or Plumbago is a fine dry powder, and the only satisfactory lubri-cant for cycle chains. Put up in bottle, enough to last one year. Price..................15

56097 Steel Balls, perfectly true and case hard-ened, for bicycle bearings.
Size	A	B	C
Each	$0.04	$0.05	$0.06
Per dozen	.44	.54	.65

56099 Tire Tape, thin as paper, strong as leather; is used to fasten a loosened tire quickly, and without heat. It is one of the essential ac-cessories, and should be found in every cyclist's tool bag. Per package..................12
Per dozen packages..................1.20

56100 Star Enamel, easily applied with a flat brush, produces a brilliant and lasting surface like ivory, and is as washable as porcelain. One bottle is sufficient to enamel a bicycle; it comes in the following colors: Pure white, ivory white, blue, pink, green, yellow, red and black. Per bottle..................$0.18   Per dozen bottles.... 1.95

There never was a better year to buy.

Pedals.

56103 High grade ball bearing roadster, rat trap Pedals, ta-pered covered center, hardened cups, cones perfectly true, dust proof caps, coppered and nick-el plated, weight per pair 13 ounces.
Per pair..................$5.00

56104 High grade ball bearing racing rat trap Pedals, tapered ends, with properly hardened cups and perfectly true cones, coppered and nickel plated, weight per pair 11 ounces. Pair.. 6.00

56105 High grade rubber ball bearing pedals, tapered covered centers, hardened cups and cones, ground perfectly true, dust proof cap, coppered and nickel plated, weight per pair 14 ounces.
Per pair..................$5.00

Hose Supporters.

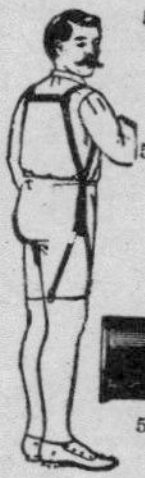

56110 Hose Supporter; consists of a belt to go around the waist with elastic straps, with patent fastenings to attach to the hose to hold them smoothly in their place. They are adjustable to waist and length of limb. State size of waist when ordering. Per pair...$0.35

56114 Shoulder Stocking Supporter; an article that meets the popular demand of wheelmen. These supporters do away with elastic bands which bind upon the limbs, causing numbness or swollen veins. Adjustable for any size person. Price per pair..................$0.45

Oilers.

PERFECT POCKET OILER

56116 Perfect Pocket Oiler. The clean-est and handsomest pocket oiler in the world. Price..................$0.25
56120 Bicycle Oiler, can be carried in pocket. Price, each, tinned..................$0.08
Each, nickeled..................12

56122 The Little Beauty Oiler; made like cut, emits only a small quantity at each pressure. The nee-dle which screws into spout keeps it always free and clear from dirt and grit.

56120
Each..................$0.15
Per dozen..................1.32

Tire Heater.

56124 Perfection Tire Heater, a practical article for cementing rubber tires. Price..................$0.60

Spoke Grip.

56126 The Chicago Spoke Grip. Best on earth. Price..................$0.50

56128 The Staythere Nipple Grip for tightening the nip-ples on tangent spoke wheels. This is a standard article of necessity, a great labor saver and useful tool. Price..$0.25

Bicycle Whistles.

56130 The Duplex Whistle; gives two clear and distinct notes; made of brass, heavily nickel plated, com-plete with chain and hook.
Price..................$0.25

56132 The Gem Whistle gives a soft, loud alarm; a favorite whis-tle. Price, with chain..$0.20

Carriages—Continued.   **Carriages—Continued.**   **Carriages—Continued.**

56356   Baby Carriage, reed body, shellaced, upholstered in silk plush, brussels carpet, silk satin, unlined parasol, with lace edge; springs and 20x22 inch steel wheels, brightly plated. Price...$9.95
56358   Same in every respect as 56356, but is upholstered in American damask, with silk plush roll. Price..................................... 9.10

56367   Baby Carriage, reed body, shellaced, upholstered in silk plush, brussels carpet, silk satin, unlined parasol, with lace edge, springs and 20x22 inch steel wheels, brightly plated. Price........$10.50
56369   Same, in every respect, as 56367, but is upholstered in American damask, with silk plush roll. Price...................................$9.65

56375   Baby Carriage, reed body, shellaced, upholstered in silk plush, brussels carpet, silk satin parasol, with lace edge, and lined with silesia, springs and 20x22 inch steel wheels brightly plated. Price..................................$11.95

56360   Baby Carriage, reed body, shellaced, upholstered in silk plush, brussels carpet, silk satin, unlined parasol, with lace edge; springs and 20x22 inch steel wheels, brightly plated. Price..................................$10.15
56362   Same in every respect as 56360, but is upholstered in American damask, with silk plush roll. Price...................................... 9.20

56370   Baby Carriage, reed body, shellaced, upholstered in silk plush, brussels carpet, silk satin parasol, lined with silesia, and lace edge, springs and 20x22 inch steel wheels, brightly plated. Price..................................$11.50

56377   Baby Carriage, reed body, shellaced, upholstered in silk plush, brussels carpet; fine silk satin parasol, with silk lace edge, and lined with seteen; springs and 20x22 inch steel wheels, brightly plated. Price..................................$13.35
56380   Same, in every respect, as 56377, but is upholstered in silk brocatelle. Price..............$13.35

56364   Baby Carriage, reed body, shellaced, upholstered in silk plush, brussels carpet, silk satin, unlined parasol, with lace edge, springs and 20x22 in. steel wheels, brightly plated. Price..............$10.50
56365   Same in every respect as 56364, but is upholstered in American damask, with silk plush roll. Price..................................$9.65

56372   Baby Carriage, reed body, shellaced, upholstered in silk plush, brussels carpet, silk satin parasol, with lace edge, and lined with silesia; springs and 20x22 inch steel wheels, brightly plated. Price..................................$11.75

56382   Baby Carriage, reed body, shellaced, upholstered in silk plush, brussels carpet; fine silk satin parasol, with silk lace edge, and lined with sateen; springs and 20x22 inch steel wheels brightly plated. Price..................................$14.50
56385   Same, in every respect, as 56382, but is upholstered in silk brocatelle. Price...............$14.50

Baby Carriage Parasols, Rods, Wheels Etc.

Prices quoted below are for parasols only. No rod. Parasols will fit only rods same as those used on our carriages.

All satin parasols can be furnished to match upholstering in the following colors: Cardinal, bronze, gold, olive, peacock blue, pomegranate, light tan, wine gobelin blue, golden brown and light coral.

The silesia and satin parasols can be furnished in all colors but goblin blue, light coral and light tan.

56420 Silesia Parasol	$0.36
56425 Sateen Parasol	.45
56429 Sateen Parasol, with lace edge	.70
56430 Silk Satin Parasol, unlined, with lace edge	1.15
56432 Silk Satin Parasol, lined with silesia with lace edge	1.60
56435 Silk Satin Parasol, fine quality, lined with sateen, with silk lace edge	2.00
56437 Fine Silk Satin Parasol, lined with silk satin, with silk lace edge	2.55
56438 Finest Silk Satin Parasol, lined with satin, with point d' Ireland lace edge	3.75
56442 Pongee Silk, cord color only, lined with silesia	1.60
56445 Pongee Silk, corn color only, lined with silesia, with silk lace edge	1.80
56450 Front-Carriage tinned, each	.18
56451 Back springs, tinned, each	.15
56452 Back springs, tinned, each	.21
56454 Parasol rods with fixtures, tinned	.45
56455 Parasol rods with fixtures, nickeled	.60
56457 Steel wheels, tinned, 19x20, per set of four	1.44
56459 Steel wheels, tinned, 20x22, per set of four	1.44

Lace Covers.

56460 No. 1 Nottingham	$0.25
56462 No. 2 Nottingham	.40
56465 No. 3 Nottingham	.60
56467 No. 4 Nottingham	.80
56468 No. 5 Swiss point	.95
56470 No. 6 Swiss point	1.35
56472 No. 7 Irish point, Escurial	2.20
56474 No. 8 Oriental	2.75
56475 No. 9 Dotted Swiss with pleated flounces	2.00
56479 No. 10 Dotted Swiss with Oriental lace flounces	2.90
56482 No. 11 Oriental lace with five flounces	4.00
56485 No. 12 Oriental lace with six flounces	4.55

Children's Carriage and Parasol Protector.

56486 The Protector is made of the best waterproof material and will protect both mother and baby if caught out in the rain; when not in use it may be folded and carried under the seat. Price $1.00

Tothill's Spring Chair.
For Children and Infants.

This chair is by far the most simple, practical and durable of anything of the kind yet offered to the public. It can be readily adjusted to any position desired, and combines both chair and crib, in which the youngest infant can be placed with no possibility of falling or getting out. As can be seen at a glance, it is simple and practical; it is provided with a foot rest, which, by a slight adjustment, either increases the width of the seat or acts as a footboard to the crib. Should the child fall asleep while occupying the chair, it will not be annoyed or disturbed by adjusting the chair to a bed, as it can be readily be changed from an upright to a reclining position.

56487 Price, with veneer seat and back	$1.50
56489 Price, with cretonne upholstered seat and back	2.00

Baby Swings or Jumpers.

Baby Swing, made of wood, smoothly finished, seat upholstered in cretonne; can be hung up anywhere, in a doorway or from a bracket or support of any kind. The swing is so arranged that it is impossible for the child to fall out; folds into a very small space and weighs about 4 pounds complete with hooks and cotton rope.

56494 Price, each	$0.40
Per dozen	4.35
56498 Baby Swing Springs, coil steel springs; diameter, 1¼ in., length 15 inches. Each	.40

*** All orders are filled from the latest Catalogue. We always, whenever possible, on orders from old Catalogues, give the nearest we have, and wish to explain that we change our quotations so as to be able to give the latest styles and better values.

Boys' Velocipedes.
WROUGHT IRON FRAME.

The frame is made of wrought iron with malleable iron head and neck, cow horn handle bars; suspension saddle, with coil springs, metal pedals and detachable pedal pins.

We have selected this velocipede as being the best of the many now on the market. Weight, from 12 to 25 pounds.

PATENT STEEL WIRE WHEELS.

56500 16 inch drive wheel	Price	$1.55
20 inch drive wheel	Price	1.75
24 inch drive wheel	Price	2.25
26 inch drive wheel	Price	2.75
28 inch drive wheel	Price	3.00

Rubber Tire Velocipedes with Patent Steel Wheels. Note reduced prices.

56505 18 inch drive wheel	Price	$3.00
20 inch drive wheel	Price	3.75
24 inch drive wheel	Price	4.15
26 inch drive wheel	Price	4.50
28 inch drive wheel	Price	5.00

Little Beauty Tricycle.

The cut fully illustrates the Little Beauty Tricycle for crib. The frame is made of tubing, very strong and light. The propelling is by means of levers pivoted to the center frame, and connected to the double crank shaft, which is made of steel. The seat can be adjusted in height without the use of a wrench, a handle being attached to the set screws for that purpose. Has a very elastic spring. The tricycle is highly finished; the frame is black, neatly striped; wheels, handles, levers and springs are brightly tinned. Weight, from 30 to 45 pounds.

56507	Steel Wheel Tricycle.			56508	Rubber Tire Steel Wheel Tricycle.	
Front wheel.	Rear wheel.	Price.		Front wheel.	Rear wheel.	Price.
12 in.	20 in.	$3.95		12 in.	20 in.	$6.70
12 in.	24 in.	5.40		12 in.	24 in.	8.25
14 in.	28 in.	6.50		12 in.	28 in.	8.25
14 in.	32 in.	7.50		14 in.	28 in.	10.00
				14 in.	32 in.	11.75

No charge made for crating.

BOYS' WAGONS, WHEELBARROWS, CARTS, ETC.
NEW PATENT IRON FRAME.

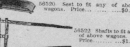

The handsomest and best boys' wagon made. All iron.

56509 Body 11x12 in, wheels 8x11	Price	$1.40
	Weight, 15 to 25 lbs	
56510 Body 12x24 inches, wheels 9x12 inches. Price		$1.57
56512 Body 13x26 in.; wheels 10x14	Price	1.75
56515 Body 14x28 in.; wheels 12x16	Price	2.00
56519 Body 15x30 in.; wheels 14x18	Price	2.25

56520 Seat to fit any of above wagons. Price $0.45

56522 Shafts to fit any of above wagons. Price $1.15

Police Patrol Wagon.

56523 An exact imitation of the patrol wagon used by the police department of all large cities, strong and well made; body 21x38 inches, with front seat, also two seats running lengthways of wagon, brass rails along side, seats are upholstered, has a brass gong and whip socket in front, a step on the rear and one in the front, are strongly braced with iron, wheels are extra heavy, 15 inches in front and 23 in rear, welded tires, staggered spokes and hub caps, all parts are nicely painted; the body in blue and running gear in red. Price $7.50

Boys' Farm Wagon.

56524 An exact imitation of a regular farm wagon, body 18x36 inches, with hardwood frame, the sides and ends can be taken off, leaving bed with stakes. The gearing is made like a farm wagon, having bent hounds and adjustable reach; all parts are strongly ironed and braced; wheels are 14 and 20 inches, heavy welded tires, hub boxes and hub caps, has seat, handle and a pair of hardwood shafts for dog or goat. It is handsomely ornamented with landscapes and scroll work, and is without doubt the handsomest, strongest and best made boys, wagon in the market. Price $6.75

56525 Wood Axle Wagon, body 12x25 inches; front wheels turn under body; varnished and stenciled, with rim and base painted red, wheels 10 and 14 inches. Weight, 12 lbs. $0.75

56527 Same as 56525 but has iron axle in place of wood. Weight, 12 lbs. Price .... .85

56530 Steel Wheel Express Wagon, on wooden body, 12x25 inches; wheels 10x14 inches, body nicely striped and red. Has malleable iron handle connection and fifth wheel, making a very neat durable wagon. Weight, 15 pounds. Price $1.70

56532 Body 14x28 inches, otherwise same as 56530. Weight, 15 pounds. Price 2.00

56534 Wagon with dashboard and seat, body 15x30 inches, handsomely painted and scrolled, wheels 12x18, iron braces in hub, heavy iron axles; bolsters are well braced with heavy iron; tin malleable iron draw and circle plate; a very fine and substantial wagon. Weight, 24 pounds. Price $2.25

Same as 56534 with seat boxes 2.95

56535 Rack Dray, made of hardwood, capable of sustaining a heavy load; it slopes toward the center, and will carry boxes or baskets without being tied on; body measures 18x36 inches; has iron axles and 11x12 inch strong wood spoke wheels, has malleable iron tongue fastening and fifth wheel, iron braces and bent handle, nicely striped and varnished. Weight, 16 lbs. Price $1.65

56537 Toy Cart, body 6¼x11 in., 6 in. wheels; painted and striped in assorted colors. Each $0.14
Per dozen 1.50

Hook and Ladder Truck.

56539 Hook and Ladder Truck. 5 feet long, wheels 10 and 12 inches, sweet sounding bell on steel spring, side ladders, 4 feet; middle ladder 5 feet, side ladder coupled together 7¼ feet, heavy iron axles and braces. Hardwood throughout, strongly constructed and firmly bolted together. The running gear is bright red, the ladders navy blue. The splendid contrast of colors, with the artistic striping and varnishing, makes it a handsome and very fascinating toy. Weight 35 lbs. Price..................$2.25

Doll Carriages.

56540 Doll Carriage. willow body; 18 in. long, made of selected white willow; wheels, 6 inches; No parasol or rod.
Each..........$0.45
Per dozen.... 4.86

56545 Same as above, with parasol and rod
Each..........$0.65
Per dozen.... 7.02

56547 Doll Carriage, body 21 inches, wheels 8 inches and spring bars.
Each..........$0.70
Per doz... 7.50

56548 Same as 56547 Doll Carriage, but fitted with parasol and rod.
Each..........$0.90
Per dozen.... 9.00

56550 Same as above but has folding parasol, with plated rod; lined half way around and trimmed with lace upholstered seat. Each.$1.00
Per dozen.... 10.70

56551 White Enamelled Doll Cab body 21 inches long carpet mat, lined body and upholstered seat, steel springs, axles and wheels, front 10 and rear 12 inches in diameter, folding parasol.
Each..........$1.50
Per dozen.. 16.80

56552 Fancy Doll Cab, body 23 inches long, enamelled and trimmed with gilt knobs, seat upholstered and back lined with cretonne; it has steel springs, axles and wheels, front 10 and rear 12 inches in diameter. Folding parasol.
Each.....$ 2.25
Per dozen.. 24.30

56552

Doll Carriages—Continued.

56553 Fancy Doll Cab, body 27 inches long, upholstered in fancy colored cretonne with folding parasol to match. Steel springs axles and wheels, front 12 and rear 14 inches in diameter. This is a very taking design and modeled after the regular style baby carriage.
Each..................$ 3.50
Per dozen..................37.80

Improved Garden Wheelbarrow.

The body is made of sheet steel with edges wired with suitable wire. The frame is made of well seasoned material; no amount of knocking around can hurt it. Nicely painted and ornamented.
    Each.

56554 Body 9x12 by 5 inches high, wheel 8 inches......................$0.75
56556 Body 11x14 by 5½ inches high; wheel 10 inches.......................85
56558 Body 13x16 by 6 inches high; wheel 13 inches....................... 1.00

Improved Dump Wheelbarrow.

Solid steel body, strong hardwood shafts well bolted painted and ornamented very tastily. A good and serviceable article.
    Each

56560 Body 12x13, wheel 8 inches................$0.75
56562 Body 13x16, wheel 10 inches................90
56564 Body 16x18, wheel 12 inches............... 1.00

Improved truck, made very substantial and is without doubt the strongest truck made, nicely painted and ornamented; guaranteed to carry 400 pounds; the sideboards, stakes and standard can be removed; gear and wheels painted black.

56566 Platform 13x28, wheels 8 and 10 inches....$3.00
56568 Platform 14x31, wheels 8 and 10 inches... 3.50
56570 Platform 15x33, wheels 10 and 12 inches.. 3.75

Goat Sulky.

Goat or Dog Sulky, is made entirely of hardwood and painted vermilion, has patent steel wheels and springs; will carry safely 125 pounds; this is without doubt the finest article on the market, and is suitable for children from 3 to 15 years old. Weight, crated, 25 lbs.
56572 22 inch steel wheels.
Each..................$ 3.50
56574 28-inch steel wheels.
Each.................. 5 00

Goat or Dog Harness.

56575 Fine set of goat or dog harness, lines and bridle, made of good strong harness leather, are adjustable to fit any size dog or goat.
Price..................$1.98

Patent Swing Horses.

56580 Swing Horse, 18 in. high from floor to saddle. This horse requires very little strength to operate and for that reason is a decided improvement over the old style rocking horse.
Each..........$1.95

56582 Swing Horse 21 inches high from floor to saddle, otherwise same as No. 56580.
Each..........$2.45

56584 Swing Horse, 22 inches high from floor to saddle, and trimmed in a superior manner.... 3.00

Patent Swinging Shoo-Fly Rockers.

56585 Swinging Shoo-fly, easy to operate, no danger of child falling out, nicely upholstered in cretonne and painted dapple gray.
Each..........$1.80
56586 Same as above, but extra large.
Each..........$2.25

Shoo-Fly Rockers.

56587 Shoo-fly 12x40 inches; painted and dappled, has painted hardwood seat, bent rocker and hair tail.
Price..........$0.75
56588 Shoo-fly, same as 56587, but is upholstered in cretonne.
Price..........$0.90

56589 Shoo-fly 12x44 inches, neatly painted and dappled, has box in front, to hold a child's toys, and is upholstered in cretonne; hair tail, bent rocker. Price..........$1.10
56590 Shoo-fly, same as 56589, except that it is upholstered in satin finished damask, and is extra trimmed. Price.................. 1.35

Childs' Cutters.

56592 Swell Body Childs' Cutter, made of hardwood in a very substantial manner, nicely painted and decorated, has a large, deep body and seat, push handle, round side fenders, brightly plated braces, half round shoes; not upholstered. Price..................$3.00
56593 Same as 56592, but is upholstered in plush. Price.................. 5.00

Bent Knee Sleds.

56594 Dragon Head Sleigh, as shown in cut; size 15x36 inches, finished on the wood with fancy painted top, round side fenders, three knees with iron braces, flat shoes. Price..................$0.75
Per dozen.................. 8.10

56595 Same as No. 56594, except it has half-round shoes. Price.................. $1.00
Per dozen.................. 10.80

56596 Boys' Knee Sleds, finished in natural color of wood, with top board neatly scrolled; has two bent knees, square tenon round, flat shoes; size 12x33 inches. Each..........$0.35
Per dozen.................. 4.22

Clipper Sleds

56397 Clipper Bob Sleds, 11x36, varnished, with the top board neatly ornamented; flat shoes. Each $0.39
Per dozen........4.22

Clipper Sleds—Continued.

56398 Clipper Bob Sleds, 11x36; painted and varnished, and neatly ornamented side handles, oval shoes. Each..........$0.49
Per dozen..........5.30

All lines of merchandise very generally reduced in prices.

Clipper Sleds—Continued.

56399 Clipper BobSled, 12 x36 inches long; made of hardwood, nicely ornamented and varnished; has full round shoes, hand holes on the side.
Each..........$0.76
Per dozen..........8.18

There never was a better year to buy.

TRUNKS.

We will cheerfully answer letters of inquiry concerning any other style trunk or traveling bag than those illustrated by us. Large trunks weigh from 30 to 70 lbs.

Patent Square.

Imitation leather.
56600 Round top, iron bound, spring lock.

Inches.	Wgt.	Price.	Inches.	Wgt.	Price.
24	13 lbs.	$0.50	30	18 lbs.	$1.00
26	15 lbs.	.70	32	20 lbs.	1.10
28	17 lbs.	.90	34	22 lbs.	1.20

Patent Crown Prince.

Imitation leather—men's trunk.

56602 Barrel Stave Top iron bound, long, hardwood slats, bumpers, hasp lock with patent bolt lock on each side, stitched leather handles with cap, rollers. Iron hinges, high set up tray, covered and nicely trimmed.

28 inch..$1.60 30 inch..$1.85 32 inch..$2.05

Crystal Globe.

56604 Barrel Stave Top Trunk; corner doubled iron bound, reverse strips on top, hasp lock, bolt locks on each side; tray with covered bonnet or hat box; a good, substantial trunk for the money.

	Each.		Each
26 inches	$1.65	32 inches	$2.40
28 inches	1.95	34 inches	2.65
30 inches	2.10		

Crystal Superior.

IRON BOTTOM.

56607 Extra High and Wide Trunk; iron bottom cross bar, slats on top and on front. Flat steel key lock, buckle bolts, set-up tray with covered bonnet box.

	Each.		Each.
28 inches	$2.25	34 inches	$2.95
30 inches	2.50	36 inches	3.20
32 inches	2.70		

Crystal Don.

56608 Extra high and wide trunk, wide iron bound, five cross bar slats on top, body and end slats, malleable iron corner shoes, bumpers, cross strip clamps, skeleton bands, rollers, large double hasp spring lock, patent bolts, stitched leather handles; covered tray with bonnet or hat box, parasol case and side compartment, fall in top, glove box; all linen faced.

	Each.		Each.
28 inches	$4.85	34 inches	$5.50
30 inches	5.15	36 inches	6.40
32 inches	5.30	38 inches	7.25

Crystal Maine.

56609 Barrel stave top, double iron bound corners, four reversed hardwood strips on top and front, valanced all around, stitched leather handles, hasp lock, bolt locks on each side, iron bottom; deep tray, with covered hat box, hardwood bottom cleats.

	Each.		Each.
26 inches	$2.15	32 inches	$2.95
28 inches	2.40	34 inches	3.15
30 inches	2.65		

56615 Fancy metal covered flat top with front and back rounded, hardwood reverse bent slats over entire top, body and end seats, malleable corner bumpers, clamps, bottom rollers, good strong lock and patent bar bolts, heavy strap hinges, tray with bonnet box all in top and side compartment, all separately covered.

	Each.		Each.
28 inches	$3.00	34 inches	$3.75
30 inches	3.25	36 inches	4.00
32 inches	3.50		

56617 Barrel Stave top Trunk side iron bound, five cross bar slats on top, and upright on front, and slats malleable iron corners and shoes, stitched leather handles, Excelsior lock, patent bolts; covered tray with bonnet box, parasol case and side compartment, fall in top.

	Each.		Each.
28 inches	$3.40	34 inches	$4.15
30 inches	3.65	36 inches	4.40
32 inches	3.90		

Crystal Gibson.

56620 Barrel Stave, top, fancy size covered, double iron bound, iron bottom, five cross stripe on top, two on front, also on end, good spring lock, covered body tray with covered hat box, fall in top, extra large and well made, iron bottom.

	Each.		Each.
30 inches	$3.45	34 inches	$4.00
32 inches	3.70	36 inches	4.35

We want you to know that we are Manufacturers of Ready-Made Wrappers.

Crystal Magic.

56625 Large barrel stave top, corners double wide iron bound, five heavy hardwood strips reversed on top and front, and two on ends, all tipped with malleable iron and braced with a new style of malleable iron corners and scroll binding, stitched slides leather handles, iron bottom, three hardwood bottom cleats, heavy malleable iron corner rollers, valance all around, heavy strap hinges. Monitor lock, heavy patent bolt lock on each side, malleable iron corner clamps on valance; hinged body tray, with separate parasol case, packing partition and bonnet box all covered, large glove box and fall in top faced with linen.

	Each.		Each.
30 in	$6.25	32 in	$6.75
36 in	7.75	38 in	8.50

56627 Large barrel stave top, double iron bound corners, five wide hard wood strips reversed on top and front, all tipped with heavy iron, all corners and strips protected with new style malleable iron corners and clamps, extra heavy malleable iron corners on valance, brass Excelsior lock, heavy side bolts, stitched leather sliding handles, japanned iron, with three hardwood bottom cleats, heavy malleable iron corner rollers; deep hinged body tray with hat box, packing partition and separate parasol case, all covered, large glove box and fall in top, faced with linen, extra dress tray. Sizes 30 32 34 36 38
Prices......$7.75 $8.25 $8.75 $9.25 $10.00

56630 High Barrel Stave Top Trunk, corners double iron bound, heavy hardwood strips reversed on top, front and ends, fancy scroll binding, heavy malleable iron corners, Excelsior lock, iron bottom and hardwood bottom cleats, hinged body tray with hat box, covered, packing partition and parasol case, fall in top.

28 in	$4.00	30 in	$4.25
34 in	4.75	36 in	5.00
		32 in	$4.50
		38 in	5.50

56635 New style trunk, flat top with round corners, double iron bound, reverse stripe on front, ends and top, the latter bent to extend over round corners, from front to back and valance, strap hinges, half Excelsior lock, with flat steel key, iron bottom, hardwood bottom cleats, stitched leather handle rollers, hinged body tray, with covered hat box, packing partition, fall in top, neatly faced and trimmed.

	Each.		Each.
30 inches	$6.00	34 inches	$4.00
32 inches	4.20	36 inches	4.35

We also make Dresses in most fashionable styles. Our Dressmakers are experts in their line which insures superior style and finish for all of our garments.

Free—Write for Dressmaking Catalogue No. 2.—Free.

* Read pages 1 and 2 before ordering goods. You obtain a discount by sending money with order. Send money by Express, Draft on Chicago or New York, Post Office Money Order, or Registered Mail.

TEA GOWNS AND DRESSES.

Lamb's Adjustable Animal Power For Churns, Etc.

56830 This power is built to be operated by two dogs, sheep or goats, and will furnish sufficient power to run a "Safety" separator, corn sheller, fan mill, sawing machine, churn, pump, washing machine, etc. Balance wheel is banded for 2½ and 3 inch belt; weight crated, 180 pounds. Price........................$30.00

First Prize Dog Power.

56831 This power can be operated by a dog, goat or sheep; yields 25 per cent. more power from a given weight of animal than any other, and with adjustable bridge to regulate the required power and motion, a 30 pound animal will do the churning; if you keep a dog make him "work his passage." The power can be connected to any churn sold by us. Price........................$16.25

The Star Barrel Churn.

This style of churn is old, tried and reliable, easy to operate and keep clean; it is absolutely impossible for this churn to leak as the wear can be taken up as simply as any one can turn a thumb nut. The fastenings are attached to the outside of the churn, and it will be seen from the cut that the bails and cover fastening is a compound leverage which increases the pressure ten times more than any other make of churn.

56850 Five Gallon Barrel Churn, for one or two gallons of cream.
Each........................$3.00
56852 Nine Gallon Barrel Churn for 1 to 4 gallons of cream.
Each........................$3.25
56854 Fifteen Gallon Barrel Churn, for 2 to 7 gallons of cream.
Each........................$3.50
56856 Twenty Gallon Barrel Churn, for 3 to 9 gallons of cream.
Each........................$4.00
56859 Twenty-five Gallon Barrel Churn, for 4 to 12 gallons of cream.
Each........................$4.95
56860 Thirty-five gallon Barrel Churn for 5 to 16 gallons of cream. Each........................6.00

Rectangular Churns.

56861 The Rectangular Churn works the easiest and quickest of any churn on the market. At the Dairy Fair, held in Chicago, December 1878, it received the highest award, a cash premium and diploma in competition with the world, Wisconsin butter won five medals at the Centennial Exhibition, at Philadelphia, and four of these were awarded to butter made in the Rectangular Churn.

No.	holding	Price
No. 0	7 gallons	$3.50
No. 1	10 "	4.00
No. 2	15 "	4.35
No. 3	20 "	4.80
No. 3½	26 "	6.00
No. 4	40 "	7.65
No. 5	60 "	11.00

The Nos. 4 and 5 are adapted for use in small creameries and large dairies, and fitted with cranks at both ends, and so arranged that a pulley can be attached for connecting with power. Full capacity of churns are given; when in use they should be only half full.

FOR THE LADIES.

Our new Dressmaking Department will be glad to send you a Catalogue showing styles and prices of dresses made to measure. Order Catalogue E. Mailed free.

Curtis' Improved Square Box Churn.

56862 Its compactness, durability and efficiency make it very desirable for a dairy of one cow or fifty. It is a great favorite and has been improved in many respects, until it is believed to be absolutely the most perfect box churn to be found anywhere. The cover is of heavy tin and securely fastened. The corners are protected with iron caps and are so constructed that when the buttermilk is drawn out and cleaned it will drain perfectly dry.

Holding 7 gal. churns from 1 to 3 gal.	Price	$3.50
" 10 "	2 to 4 "	4.05
" 12 "	2 to 6 "	4.35
" 20 "	3 to 9 "	4.80
" 26 "	4 to 12 "	6.00

Union Churn.

The Union Churn. You can make, gather, work and salt your butter without removing from the Union Churn, or without touching the butter with your hands. It churns with ease by the extra power and motion gained by gear wheels.
56863 Union Churn, holding 5 gallons.
Each........................$4.00
56864 Union Churn, holding 7 gallons.
Each........................$4.25
56866 Union Churn, holding 10 gallons.
Each........................$4.75

Improved Cedar Cylinder Churn.

56869 This we consider by far the best small cheap churn on the market. It is made from the best Virginia cedar; it has a double dasher, and the crank is locked to the churn with a clamp and thumbscrew, which prevents leakage. Lock cannot break. The top is large and dasher easily removed galvanized iron and will not rust. The hoops are of

No.	1	2	3	4	
Will hold....				7	10 gallons.
Will churn..	3	3	3	4	5 gallons.
Price....	$1.50	$1.90	$2.25	$2.50	

Dash Churns.

Common Dash Churns. A long handle goes through the cover at the top, with a dasher at the bottom, which is worked up and down inside the churn.

	Each	Per doz.
56870 3-gallon dash churn........	$0.56	$6.00
56872 4-gallon dash churn........	.70	7.56
56874 5-gallon dash churn........	.85	9.18
56875 6-gallon dash churn........	.96	10.37

Dash Churns, Striped Cedar, with Brass Hoops.

	Each	Per doz.
56878 3-gallon...	$0.95	$10.26
56880 4-gallon...	1.00	10.80
56882 5-gallon...	1.10	11.88
56885 6-gallon...	1.20	12.26

See Index for Stoneware Dash Churns.

Reid Butter Workers.

56887 Size 14 x28 inches, to work 8 lbs. of butter. Each, $3.60
56888 Size 17 x27 inches, to work 18 lbs. Each, $4.25
56889 Size, 20x36 inches, to work 25 lbs. of butter. Each........................4.80
56890 Size, 23x36 inches, to work 50 lbs. of butter. Each........................5.75

Lever Butter Workers.

56891 The Lever Butter Worker; its simplicity, saving of time, ease of operation and very low price, commend it as an indispensable adjunct to every dairy.
No. 0 size, 20 inches wide, works 15 lbs. Each........................$3.50
No. 1 size, 30 inches wide, works 25 lbs. Each........................$4.95
56892 No. 2 size, 40 inches wide, works 35 lbs. Each........................5.00

Cottage Butter Workers.

56893 A convenient low-priced worker that is placed upon a table when in use. The end is placed over the side of the table and the drip falls into a vessel upon the floor.

For 1 or 2 cows.	$2.50
For 2 or 3 cows.	3.00
For 4 or 5 cows.	3.50

Cheese Factory Milk Cans.

GENUINE STEEL.

56895

Holds	Gallons	Price
15	"	$3.90
20	"	4.32
30	"	4.92
40	"	5.76

Weighing Cans.

56898 Made of heavy tin with 3 inch perfection gate and sloping bottom.

Holds	Gallons	Price
40	"	$6.00
60	"	7.20
80	"	8.40

Milk Cans.

The illustration below shows the improved breast used on all our milk cans; the most important feature is to make a breast that is proof against being "jammed in." Our heavy half oval hoop accomplishes this; the hoop is forced onto the breast in the block, securely fastened and afterward ralined, which makes it absolutely safe against being knocked off.

THE IMPROVED BREAST

56901 Sturges' or Teet's Pattern Railroad Milk Can.

	Wgt.	Each	Per doz.
8 gallons, 15 lbs.		$1.98	$22.58
10 gallons, 17½ lbs.		2.10	23.95

56903 Elgin Pattern. All Steel Railroad Milk Can with improved breast.

	Wgt.	Each	Per doz.
8 gallons 18 lbs.		$2.25	$25.65
10 gallons 22 lbs.		2.45	27.93

Milk Cans—Continued.

56905 Iowa or Dubuque Pattern Railroad Milk Can, with improved breast.

	Weight	Each.	Per doz.
8 gallons,	18 lbs.	$1.98	$22.75
10 gallons,	21 lbs.	2.10	23.95

56907 Chicago Pattern. All Steel Railroad Milk Can, with improved breast.

	Weight	Each.	Per doz.
5 gallons,	14 lbs.	$2.25	$25.35
8 gallons,	18 lbs.	2.45	27.95
10 gallons,	22 lbs.	2.80	31.95

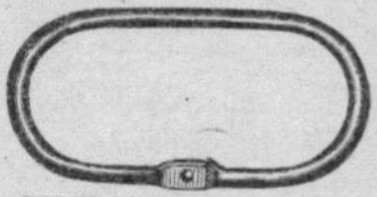

Milk Can Links and Washers. We always use this washer to strengthen can and prevent its wearing. We can fit any of our milk cans with link and washer at an additional charge of 5 cents per can.

Brass or Steel Milk Can Letters; size, 1¾ inches, soldered onto can at 1½ cents per letter; when ordering state which is desired, otherwise copper letters will be used.

The above illustration shows ⅜ inch brass faucet fitted to milk can or bucket for delivery purposes. When desired it can be put on any of our cans at an additional cost, including price of faucet and labor.......$1.50

56909 Milk or Cream Pails, tin, with bails.

	Each.	Per doz.
1 quart	$0.12	$1.30
2 quarts	.15	1.62
3 quarts	.20	2.16
4 quarts	.25	2.80

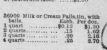

56911 Milk peddling cans. They are made of 4X tin with heavy brass hoop on top and bottom, spout tipped with brass, a very strong and serviceable article. Capacity two gallons.
Each........................$1.50

56913 Milk measure graduated, made of good quality tin and holds 1 quart.
Each........$0.08
Per dozen.........$0.87

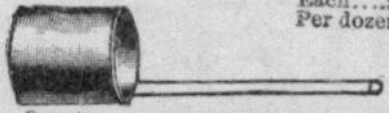

56915 Milk dippers, made of tin, with long handle.

Quarts	½	1	2
Price, each	10c	15c	20c	25c

56917 Conical Milk Skimmer, well made of good stock.
Each..........$0.08
Per dozen.....90

56919 Extra Heavy 4X Tin Milk Dippers capacity, 1 gallon. Each................$0.45

56921 Milk Can Strainers. These are made of heavy tin and have a 4-inch brass wire strainer; it will fit a milk can, cooley or our regular cream setters.
Each...........$0.80

Howard Patent Milk Cooler.

56923 This valuable implement is made to fit any can. As the milk is poured into one side it is strained, and runs in very fine streams into the can below. It cools the milk in the operation, and takes from it the animal odor.
Each...................$2.40

Curtis Babcock Farm Tester.

56925 Every dairyman or farmer who keeps a half dozen cows ought to provide himself with one of these milk testers, if he cares the snap of his finger to know whether he has a cow in the herd that is worth keeping. (More than one cow "eats her head off" every year she is kept.) This tester is designed especially for farm use, and so low a price put on it that every man who owns two cows can have a four-bottle machine.

4 Bottle tester, complete	Price	$5.00
6 " "	"	6.00
8 " "	"	7.00

With each machine there is a pipette acid measure, a bottle of acid and directions for operating.

Babcock Milk Test.

With Roe's improved swinging heads.

56927 4-bottle tester complete. Price..............$8.00
6-bottle tester complete. Price...........10.00
12-bottle tester complete. Price...........14.00
24-bottle tester complete. Price...........21.00

With each machine is included testing bottles, pipette acid measure and acid for 50 to 200 tests, according to size, and full directions for operating

Strainer Pails, Tin.

| 56931 | 56929 |

They will not hold as much as represented.

56929 10 quarts.....$0.25 14 quarts.........$0.30
56931 Milk Pail, with strainer, extra heavy tin, stamped seamless, holds 12 quarts.
Each............$0.90 Per dozen...........9.72

The Dairyman's Favorite.

56933 The accompanying cut represents an article having all the essential points of a perfect Strainer Pail. Among its points of excellence we mention the breast and front half of the pail being formed to fit nicely into place, making but two up and down seams in the body. It will be noticed that the breasts funnel-shaped, and will not slop over in pouring. Besides the wire gauze strainer there is a brass spring clamping around the mouth to hold a cloth, thus making a double strainer without extra labor or loss of time. Another important feature is—there is no part but what can be thoroughly washed, no rough and unsoldered seams in which dirt can accumulate and sour.

12 quarts, per doz.	$5.40	Each	$0.50
14 quarts, per doz.	6.05	Each	.56

Cream Setter.

56935 This Cream Setter has tinned iron bottom, glass panel in graduate case. The glass panel in can is graduated so that if parties are buying cream two degrees will make one pound of butter. Thousands of them are in successful and satisfactory operation. They are easily cleaned and raise as much cream and as quickly as any other cream setting can in the market. The can has a bail on it so that a man can carry two of them at a time. Size, 8¼x20 inches. Weight 4¼ lbs.
Each.........$0.60 Per dozen.........$6.48
56937 Cream Setters, same as above, without gauze. Each $0.55 Per doz. $5.95
For dairy thermometers see Index.

Plain Cooley Can.

56938 The submerged system of setting milk for gathered cream is recognized everywhere as a superior way of raising cream. The milk is away from the flies and dust, and any foul odors that may be floating in the air from the barnyard or pig sty. The milk is set in cold water immediately after milking. The cream is all thrown up in twelve hours The can holds 18 quarts. Each.. $1.25

Cooley Can With Bottom Faucet.

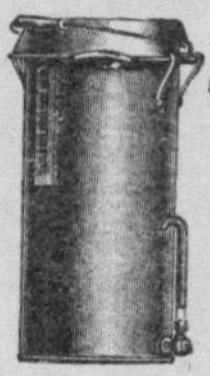

56939 For private dairies this can has no equal. The milk is drawn off through the bottom faucet, leaving the cream in the can to be poured into the cream pail. The value of sweet skim milk over sour milk for feeding purposes will more than pay for the cans every three months. All of the Cooley cans are made from the best in obtainable. They hold 18 quarts. Each............$1.75

Family Cheesemaking Apparatus.

ARMSTRONG'S FAMILY CHEESE MAKING APPARATUS

56941 This is a very simple apparatus, adapted to the wants of all farmers or dairymen who keep from two to ten cows or more. It will make from two to ten pounds of cheese each operation, according to the quantity of milk; so simple that any boy or girl of average intelligence can learn the process in a very few operations. It makes a perfect cheese each time, whether two pounds or ten pounds.

You will admit that two cows give at least six quarts at a milking, making six gallons a day. A gallon of milk will make a pound of cheese. Six gallons make six pounds—for 30 days is 180 pounds of cheese, which at 10c per pound is $18 for one month. This is a low wholesale price. The milk is heated by a coal oil lamp, which is easily kept under control. The heating vat is so constructed that the lamp gives all the heat that is necessary. The management of the heat is the secret of success in making good cheese. The entire apparatus is so light in weight that a lady can move it from one place to another with ease. It does not take up quite as much room as an ordinary kitchen table. A lady can make cheese in the kitchen or pantry and carry on her household work at the same time. With each machine we send simple and full instructions how to make cheese successfully. Each apparatus is complete with heating vat, press, curd knives, lamp and thermometer; made of good material, strong and well finished. The apparatus is guaranteed to do the work exactly as represented. Price...........$12.00

Flat Side Curd Pail.

56943 This is a strongly built pail from the best 4X tin, used for lifting the curd from the vat.
Price................$0.95

Curd Scoop.

56945 These scoops are made of heavy tin and all seams are wire carefully soldered. Price.......$0.50

Extension Ladders.

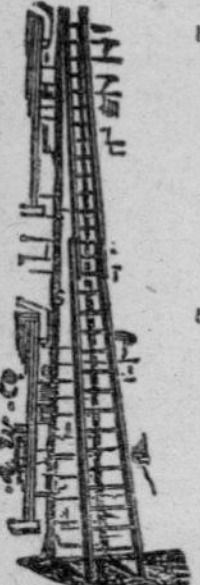

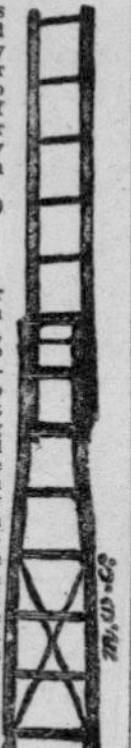

57153 Extension Ladders are made from selected Norway pine and hickory rungs. Put together with screws; gotten up in a tasty manner, of sufficient strength for safety, and not too heavy to carry. Extension ladders all lengths.
Per foot............$0.20

Extension Step Ladder.

57155 Cut shows ladder extended; upper part can be instantly lowered, making an ordinary step ladder. When in position as a step ladder, two persons can work on it at the same time, being very strong and well braced; does not require strings to keep it from spreading. It is easily adjusted to the position as a long ladder, and often of great convenience in reaching high ceilings or skylights. Can also be used as a trestle, and in the several positions can readily be appreciated by the carpenter, painter and fruit grower. It recommends itself to everyone who has use for a ladder.

Length.	Weight.	Each.
6 ft. step, extended, 11 ft	20 lbs	$1.75
7 ft. step, extended, 12 ft	23 lbs	2.00
8 ft. step, extended, 15 ft	26 lbs	2.25
9 ft. step, extended, 17 ft	30 lbs	2.50
10 ft. step, extended, 19 ft	35 lbs	2.75
11 ft. step, extended, 21 ft	40 lbs	3.00
12 ft. step, extended, 23 ft	46 lbs	3.25

The "Gardner" Clothes Bar.

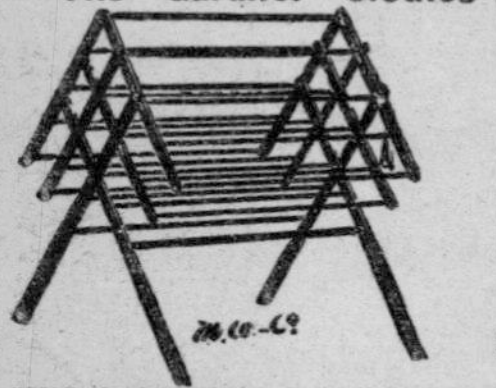

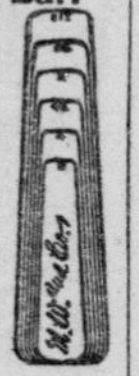

57157 Gardner Clothes Bar, all hardwood, has 60 lineal feet drying surface; something new; weight, 17 lbs. Each..$0.70 Per dozen.........$7.56

57163 Ironing Boards, made of poplar wood:

	Weight.	Each.	Per doz.
3 feet	3 lbs.	$0.25	$2.70
4 feet	6 lbs.	.33	3.57
4½ feet	7 lbs.	.37	4.00
5 feet	7½ lbs.	.42	4.54
5½ feet	9 lbs.	.46	4.97
6 feet	11 lbs.	.50	5.40

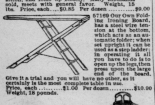

Cut shows board closed (opens to table height.

57164 The Excelsior Folding Skirt Board, all hardwood, adjustable to standing or sitting position, and folds up closely. Many thousands sold, meets with general favor. Weight, 15 lbs. Price, each....$0.85 Per dozen $9.00

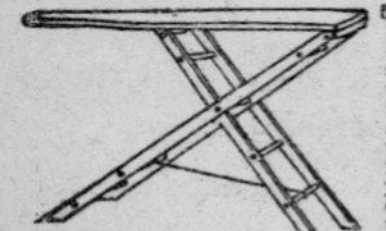

57169 Our Own Folding Ironing Board, has a steel wire tension at the bottom, which acts as an automatic folder; when set upright it can be used as a step ladder; in operating it all you have to do is to open up the legs, then press upon the large end of the board. Give it a trial and you will have no other, as it certainly is the most complete table in use.
Price, each ....$1.00 Per dozen..........$10.90
Weight, 18 pounds.

57170 The Champion Bosom Board and Stretcher; the most complete in the market. After you have once used this board you will never be without one.
Price........................$0.40

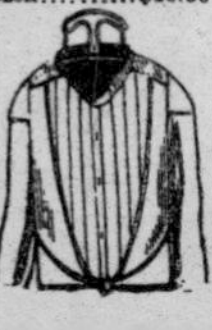

Eureka Adjustable Clothes Bar.

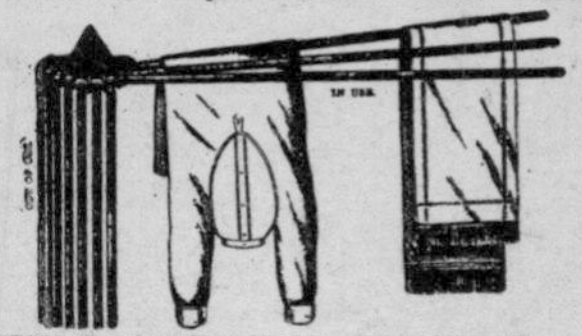

57171 Eureka Adjustable Clothes Bars, intended to fasten to the wall. When not in use takes the space of an ordinary broom. The bars are three feet in length, with gilt tips; a very convenient household article. Weight, 4 lbs.
Each................$0.39 Per dozen..............$4.22

57173 Same as 57171 with 6 bars 2 feet long.
Each................$0.25 Per dozen............$2.70

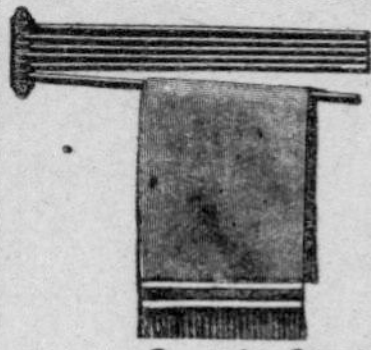

57175 The Excelsior Clothes Dryer; is made of picked ash bars 11-16 of an inch thick, folds up snug against the wall when not in use, takes up less space and has more capacity than any other bar made.
10 bars, 36 inches long.
Each.........$0.30
Per dozen..... 3.24
6 bars, 24 inches.
Each..........$0.27
Per dozen.... 2.92

Curtain Stretcher.

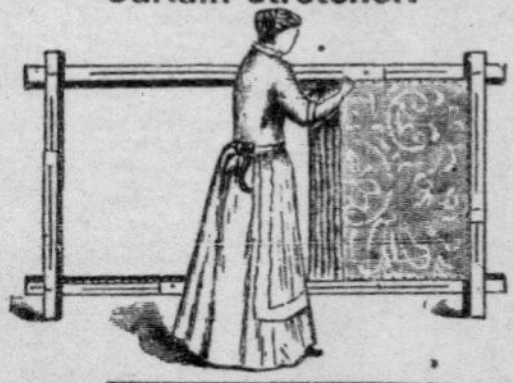

57177 Folding Curtain Stretcher, made of poplar, for stretching lace curtains, shawls, blankets, etc. Adjustable to any size. As will be observed, the frame is secured at the corners with adjustable screw clamps, and the bars are provided with plate hooks 1½ inches apart, set in coped recess below the surface, so that the bars pass each other, allowing a free extension and contraction. Each..............$1.75

Schmuck's Mop Wringer.

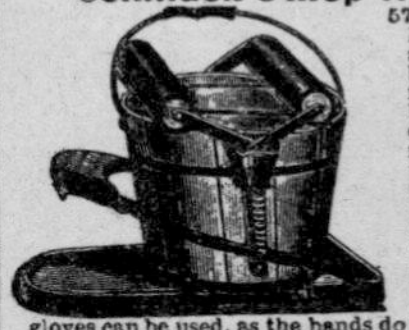

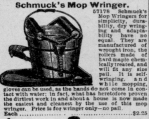

57178 Schmuck's Mop Wringers for simplicity, durability, dry wringing and adaptability have no equal. They are manufactured of wrought iron, the rollers made of hard maple chemically treated, and will fit any size pail. It is self-wringing, and while mopping, gloves can be used, as the hands do not come in contact with water; in fact, what has heretofore proven the dirtiest work in and about a house is now made the easiest and cleanest by the use of this mop wringer. Price is for wringer only—no pail.
Each $2.25

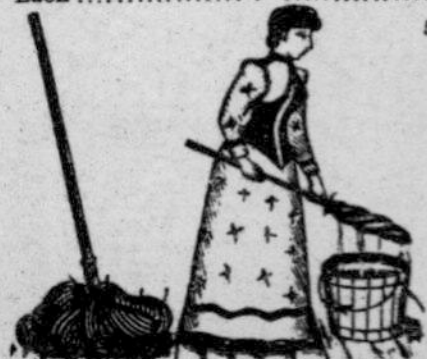

57181 The Globe Perfect Self-Wringing Mop. The mop is made of cotton coils, large and full size. We believe this to be the most acceptable and best wearing wringing mop ever offered for sale.
Each....$0.25
Dozen.. 2.80

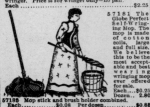

57188 Mop stick and brush holder combined.
Each..............$0.08 Per dozen...............$0.85

Hand Laundry Steam Generators.

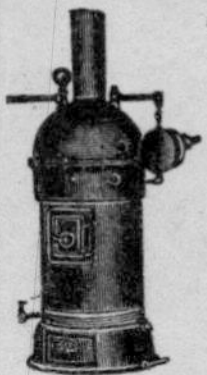

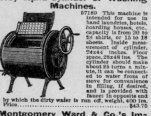

57183 These steam generators are intended for heating water, boiling clothes, making starch, etc., in hand laundries. They are tested at about forty pounds pressure. The water supply to the boiler is automatically regulated by a brass float and valve which shuts off the water when it reaches the right height and allows more to enter as needed. The float and valve are placed in an iron float-box (Z) outside of the dome, but attached to the latter by pipes, (2,4). Where the generators are to be used in cities or towns having waterworks the water supply pipe (B) is attached directly to a hydrant. Where there is no hydrant pressure a strong, tight barrel or tank is placed on a support opposite the top of the generator, and filled with water from a hole in the head, which is then plugged up. A small pipe from the dome carries steam to the top of the barrel to force the water into the generator through a pipe from the bottom of the barrel. A pipe (E) carries steam to where it is needed for use; more pipes can be used if desired. The safety valve (N) is combined with a vacum valve to prevent matter being sucked up into the boiler through the steam pipe when there is no steam up. Full instructions for setting up and using are sent with every generator. Please state in ordering whether the water connection will be made with a hydrant or supply barrel. The fixtures include an ash box, grate, shaker, combined safety and vacum valve, gauge cocks, blow-off valve, and 3¼ feet of ¾ inch, steam hose with 2½ feet of iron pipe to convey steam for heating. We also furnish ¾ inch angle valve and nipple to connect with a water supply pipe for a hydrant, or, 5½ feet of ½-in. rubber hose and 4¾-inch iron nipples to make the two connections with a water supply barrel. Two horse power, diameter 22 inches, height 56 inches, size of fire box, 16x26 inches. Weight, 900 pounds.
Price...$70.00

Troy Hand Cylinder or Washing Machines.

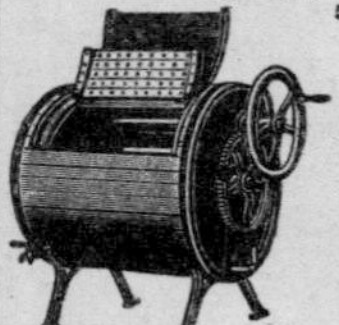

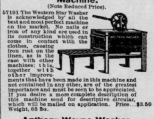

57189 This machine is intended for use in hand laundries, hotels, boarding houses, etc., capacity is from 20 to 24 shirts, or 15 to 18 sheets. Inside measurement of cylinder, 24x44 inches. Floor space, 28x48 ins. The cylinder should make about 25 turns a minute, it can be connected to water front of stove for convenience in filling, if desired, and is provided with faucet in opposite end by which the dirty water is run off, weight, 400 lbs.
Price...$43.75

Montgomery Ward & Co.'s Improved Western Star Washing Machine.

(Note Reduced Price).

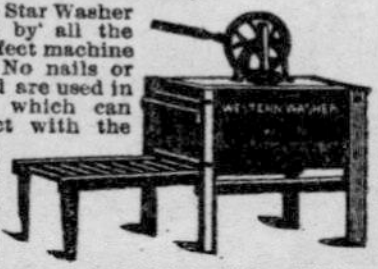

57191 The Western Star Washer is acknowledged by all the best and most perfect machine on the market. No nails or iron of any kind are used in its construction which can come in contact with the clothes, causing iron rust on the linen, as is the case with other machines; this, together with other improvements that have been made in this machine and not contained in any other, are of the greatest importance and must be seen to be appreciated. If you desire a more complete description of this machine send for descriptive circular, which will be mailed on application. Price...$3.50
Weight, 65 lbs.

Anthony Wayne Washer.

Note reduced price.

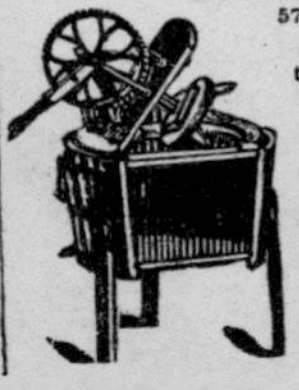

57193 The Anthony Wayne Washer, with corrugated stave and bottom. This is the best round washer made. Some prefer the round washer to the square; we have selected the Anthony Wayne as being the best on the market, and we offer it at a price which places it within reach of all.
Price...... ....$3.50
Weight, 50 lbs.

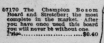

New Combination Washer.

57194 Were's shirt ... boiler ... the Waste ... New Washer ... be used is a ... Dr. Wove ... are ... we ... found that the late ... of family ... washing is ... washer ... visible movement ... of the water ... shallow. The ... great that no family ... is machine is that a ... work fully one-third easier ... than any other machine that ... use ... with a gun-wheel ... it takes less ... all the parts, and that ... it is a simple in construction ... machine, when used in locks too ... without a wringer can ... be attached on the wringer-board without lifting it, a ... small key inserted in the ... prevent it from tilt-ing when full to prevent accidents of any kind. The ... ... well made out of the best of yellow poplar. ... large, ... size and a ... of style, and we can recommend ... as ... the same as the best ... family washing ... Weight, 66 lbs. $4.25

Cline's Improved Steam Washer.

57195 Cline's Improved Steam Washer has several new features that the Windsor does not have. Has a corrugated cylinder; sliding cover and a faucet attached to the boiler for removing the water without lifting the boiler from the stove, which is a decided advantage. Weight, 32 lbs. Price, each $6.00

American Household.

Mangle and Wringer.

57198 In the saving of labor and the perfection of work, these machines hold the same relative position in the laundry that the sewing machine does in its place in the household economy. They are specially adapted for ironing table linens, bedding, underclothes and all plain ironing, and save a wonderful amount of labor. The driving gear is far superior to that of any other mangle ever offered, and the power required to operate it is about half that necessary to work any other. Every family should possess one of these machines, and our price is such as to place them within the reach of all. Directions for use furnished with every machine. Description: Hard wood rolls 24 inches long 5 inches in diameter; the machine stands 4 feet high and weighs 125 pounds. Price......................$19.00

Troy Polishing Machine.

Weight, 120 lbs; floor space, 30x30 inches.

57202 The shirts must first be prepared by dampening skirts and wringing them as dry as possible by hand, then fold the skirts over the bosom with the wristbands inside, and roll them up tightly. After remaining this way for about an hour and a half they are ready to be ironed. Set the machine level and adjust the springs by means of the set screw on the swinging arm, so as to give about 40 pounds, or the desired pressure, on the polishing iron. Set the table straight at right angles with the machine, and secure it in this position by the set screw underneath; stretch the shirt over the table and commence to iron by setting up the neck band first; then do the wrist bands and then the bosom, always iron straight with the linen up to, but not on, the neck band. This is the original hand-ironing machine, and if instructions are followed an ironer can do twice as much with this machine as by hand alone. It will polish a shirt bosom perfectly, giving it a very high finish. Collars and cuffs are done on it equally as well as shirts. The double-jointed arm allows the iron to be moved in any direction while the pressure is obtained by the powerful spring. Three polishing irons are included with each machine. Price $24.00

Troy Hand-Power Collar and Cuff Ironer.

57204 ... machine is ... for laundries ... iron ... of large ... each ... iron ... will give ... iron from tilt-ing ... be moved in ... the eye ... spindle or ... to produce ... reach of any ... with either gas ... a floor space of ... this ... all directions ... a ... No. Utica, $75.00

or gasoline burner ... which is desired which ... will be sent. The ... $62.50 inches an ... for operating are sent with each machine.

Troy Combined Collar, Cuff and Shirt Ironer.

57205 This will be found to be the best and most convenient hand collar, cuff and shirt, ironer on the market. It will give a gloss finish and can be used with either gas or gasoline burner. These are always included with machine, but at time of ordering, do not neglect to say which is desired. It takes a floor space, 36x40 inches and weighs 650 pounds. Full directions for operating are sent with each machine. Price, $150.00

Wash Boards.

	Doz.	Each
57207 The Northern Queen, single face, perforated zinc, a very excellent and fast selling board......	$2.50	$0.24
57209 The Globe Washboard, double faced. This is considered the very best washboard now in use................	2.70	.25
57211 Favorite Wassboard............	1.85	.17

Folding Wash Benches.

57213 Folding Double Wash Bench, made of hard wood and nicely finished. The upright piece is constructed so that any kind of a wringer can be fastened to it, and room enough each side of it for tubs. When not in use it may be folded up so it will occupy much less space than an ordinary wash bench. Weight, 25 lbs. Price.............$1.54

57215 Tripod Wash Bench made of hard wood; very strong and durable, taking up less room than any other. Price.........$0.95

Hat and Coat Racks.

57217 The Perfection Iron Hook Hat Rack, with wood frame, to hang on the wall; the long or extension hooks can be used for hats, the shorter ones for clothing.

	Each	Per doz.	Weight
Five hooks	$0.18	$1.95	22 oz.
Seven hooks	.23	2.16	29 oz.

Hat and Coat Racks—Continued.

57219 The Improved Hat Rack will hold any kind of a hat. The iron hooks are japanned or lacquered, and the wood frame nicely finished, very handsomely.

	Each.	Per doz.	Weight
Six hooks	$0.20	$2.16	34 oz.
Seven hooks	.30	3.24	48 oz.

57221 Hat and Coat Racks, iron hooks, wood frame, to hang on the wall, 4 and 6 hooks.

	Each.	Per doz.	Weight.
Four hooks	$0.07	$0.76	13 oz.
Six hooks	.08	.87	18 oz.

Lap Cutting Boards.

57223 Lap Cutting Board, striped, oil finished and polished, with yard measure stamped on it; size 20x36.
Each $0.65
Per doz 7.03
Weight, 4½ lbs.

57225 Lap Cutting Board, same shape as 57123, made of white wood, plain, 20x36.
Each.............. $0.52 Per dozen.......$5.94

57227 Folding Striped Lap Board, hand oil finish, can be rolled up and put into small space, and be put out of the way; it measures 20x36 inches, and has a yard measure printed on the edge.
Price, each...........$0.85
Per dozen........... 9.20

Bread or Pastry Boards.

57229 Bread or Pastry Boards, made of poplar wood.

Size	Weight	Each	Per doz.
18x22	4½ lbs.	$0.28	$3.15
18x24	5½ lbs.	.33	3.60
20x27	5½ lbs.	.42	4.50
20x30	6½ lbs.	.46	4.95

57231 Fancy hardwood and hand carved Bread Plate. Everybody needs one of these for slicing bread.
Each..............$0.18
Per dozen........ 1.93

Slaw Cutters.

57233 Slaw Cutters, one knife.
Each.............. $0.22
Per doz....... 2.56

Adjustable Knife Kraut Cutters.

57235 Kraut Cutters, 8x26inches, 3 cast steel knives with slide box.
Each .... $1.00   Per dozen.....$10.95
57237 Kraut Cutters 30x9 inches; 3 cast steel knives, with slide box.
Each........... $1.75   Per dozen.....$19.00

LADIES' FINE SHOES.

LARGE VARIETY. NEW STYLES.

Bread or Butter Bowls.

	Crates contain	Price Per doz.	Price Each
57450 15 inch	1 doz.	$3.60	$0.35
57451 17 inch	1 doz.	4.50	.45
57452 19 inch	½ doz.	5.40	.52

Spittoons.

57453 16 in	½ doz.	$7.50	$0.68
57455 13 in	½ doz.	4.95	.46
57457 12 in	½ doz.	4.50	.43
57459 9½ in	½ doz.	4.05	.38

Handy Dishes.

57460 8 qt.	1 doz.	$2.95	$0.28
57462 6 qt.	1 doz.	2.65	.27
57464 4 qt.	1 doz.	2.50	.26

Milk Pans.

57466 Standard size, 3 dozen in crate.
Per doz $2.25
Each .... .22

Wash Basins.

57467 12½ inch (one size only), 2 doz. in crate. Each $0.20
Per doz 2.15

Slop Jars.

57469 12 quart (one size only), ½ dozen in crate.
Each $0.67
Per doz 7.65

Slop Jar Mats.

57470 17 inch; crate contains 1 doz. Each $0.33
Per doz 3.60
57471 21 inch; crate contains 1 doz. Each .... .45
Per dozen 4.95

Chamber Pails.

57475 12 quart, concave tops; crate contains ½ dozen.
Each $0.67
Per doz 7.65

BUGGY AND WAGON DEPARTMENT.

We handle a greater variety and wider range of vehicles than any other house.

We have every quality from the common to the most expensive. We class our grades as common, medium, standard, standard extra and special, the last named ranking with the very finest work sold, though our prices are much lower than dealers obtain for this high grade of work.

For full description of our different vehicles see our special catalogue, C, which we mail upon receipt of 3 cents to pay postage.

WIDTH OF TRACK.

There are two standard tracks in use, measured from center to center of tire on the ground, one narrow track, 4 ft. 8 in., and one wide, 5 ft. 2 inches. These two tracks are in use often in the same section, and its frequently impossible to decide which is wanted, unless stated in the order. If purchasers fail to state which track is wanted, we cannot be responsible for the selection made, or for delays incident in writing for width of track, where we are in doubt as to which is required.

IN ORDERING ALWAYS GIVE WIDTH OF TRACK.

Buggies and spring wagons crated are usually shipped at *once and one-half first-class rate, actual weight*. Purchasers must pay their own freight. We mail freight rates, which will show cost of delivery. Nothing is gained by prepaying freight. We make no charge for crating or cartage.

Top Buggy Elliptic Springs.

ELLIPTIC SPRINGS PIANO BODY.

70002 Price, F.O.B cars, crated, medium grade, $47.60 Standard grade ..... $54.40 Standard Extra Grade ...... $58.90 Special grade $69.50 Without top (open buggy) Standard grade
Weight, crated, 425 pounds. Price $44.50

Surprise Piano Box, End Spring. Surprise Piano Box, Brewster Spring.

70004 The Surprise Piano Box, end springs.
70005 The Surprise Piano Box, Brewster springs. Price of either of these buggies, $45.75 Silver hub bands and silver dash rail $2.00 extra. Weight 425 lbs. Best leather quarter top, heavy English cloth trimming.

We propose to take the lead in offering the largest and best variety of buggies ever catalogued, and at prices from which any of our customers can make a satisfactory selection. These two Indiana buggies are a new addition to our list. Vehicles both alike, except style of springs; weight and price the same.

Back of body covered with a good rubber boot.

Furnished only according to these specifications. No changes made.

AXLES—Double collar, swedged, made of steel, 15/16 inch, ⅞ inch boxing.

BODY—25x50 inches; made from the best of materials and superior workmanship.

DASH—No. 1 Patent Leather.

FORGINGS, CLIPS AND BOLTS are all of Norway iron.

GEAR—Made from best second growth hickory, ironed with Norway iron; double reach.

Bodies black; gear dark green.

TOP—Best leather quarter, lined with broadcloth. Always shipped with 3 or 4 bowed top, as ordered.

TRACK—4 ft. 8 in., or 5 ft. 2 in., whichever is ordered.

TRIMMING—Cushions and back, English body cloth; upholstered with hair; Brussels carpet; boot and storm apron.

WHEELS—Sarven or Shell Band, bolted between each spoke; 3 ft. 4 in. in front, 3 ft. 8 in. in rear, ⅞ in. tread.

Brewster Springs, Corning Buggy.

70006 Brewster Springs Corning Body, like cut.
70007 Brewster Spring Piano Box at same price, if preferred. Unless otherwise specified will send piano box. Standard Grade .. $54.40 Standard Extra Grade 58.90 Special Grade, $69.50 Without Top (open buggy) Standard Grade $44.50
Weight, crated, 435 lbs. Weight, crated, open, 400 lbs.

Top Buggy, Cross or Timken Spring.

70009 Corning or Piano Body, Medium Grade $49.50 Standard Grade, $56.50, Standard Extra Grade, $61.87 Special Grade, $70.00 Weight, crated, 440 lbs. Price without top (open buggy), Standard Grade, $45.50 Weight, crated, 410 lbs.

Montgomery Ward & Co.'s "Silver Star."

70010 "Silver Star," End Spring, Piano Box or Corning Body. "Silver Star," Brewster Spring Piano Box or Corning body. Standard ...... $53.25 Weight, Crated 440 lbs. Standard Extra, $60. Special $74.00. Weight, crated open, 410 lbs; Standard, no top, $48.00. Elegantly striped and highly ornamented; has silver hub bands, silver axle nuts, silver dash rail, silver handles on seat, silver whip socket, silver trimmed boot on back, silver joints on brace irons to top, silver top nuts, silver fastenings to back curtains. Ornamental silver star and monogram showing initials of purchaser on both sides of body. Be sure to give initials wanted, and make them plain

Top Buggy, Maud S Springs.

MAUD S. PIANO BOX.

70014 The great length of the springs makes them ride with great ease and evenness of motion. Size of Body 25x50, larger cannot be used on this gear. Piano Box or Corning body. Price, F. O. B cars, crated.
Medium Grade $58.00
Standard Grade, $62.00 Standard Extra Grade, 66.50
Special Grade 75.00
Weight, 415 lbs. Crated 445 lbs.
Without top (open buggy) Standard Grade 51.00

Texas Ranger.

70015 Corning or Piano Box Body; extra long body and reach, hung on long Concord Springs, 1⅛ axles, 1-inch tire; made heavy and strong to withstand hard usage. Weight, crated, 520 lbs.
Standard Grade, $64.00. Standard Extra Grade. $68.50
Special Grade 83.00

Heavy Concord, Piano Box.

70016 Heavy Concord. Price, Standard, $65.25 Standard Extra, $69.75 Special. $84.50 Standard, Without top. $54.24
Brake, extra, $5.00

Hung on heavy Concord spring made especially for drummers' and livery use. Springs 1¼ inches, 5 plate, with equalizers, body of extra width and length and extra roomy seat. Height above ground, 34 inches; will carry 600 pounds. Body length, 54 ins; breadth, 28 ins.; depth, 8½ ins.; width of seat inside at bottom, 29 ins.; between axles. 56 in.; wheels, front, 42 ins.; rear, 46 ins.; 1 inch tire; axles, 1¼ ins., with 1¼ spindle; hub, 7x3 in.; actual weight, 425 lbs.; shipping weight, crated, 500 pounds.

Economy Business Wagons.

70017 Roomy spindle body on end springs. Sarven patent wheels. Medium Grade, Price, $32.50. Standard Grade, $37.50. f.o.b. Chicago. For description of grade see Vehicle Catalogue C. State whether narrow track, 4 feet 8, or wide, 5 feet 2, is wanted. Price is with shafts. Pole, whiffletrees and yoke adds $3.00 to price. Weight crated, 350 lbs.

Road Wagons.

70018 Spindle Body Road Wagon, trimmed in corduroy or imitation leather. Long side springs, end springs, or Brewster springs, as preferred; 1 in. axle, 1⅛ inch spoke, felloe ⅞ inch wide; full width of tire 1 inch, weight with shafts 300 pounds. Price, medium grade $31.00
Common grade 28.00
With rubber top, add to price 8.50
With lined leather quarter top, add to price 13.50
Pole in place of shafts adds $3 to price.

Jump Seat Buggy.

Weight, boxed for shipment 500 lbs. (Cut shows vehicle with two seats.)

Jump Seat, Three Springs

The back seat swings on wrought prop iron and does not mar the body like those moved on slides. 1⅛ axle and shafts are furnished with this buggy at following price:

	Medium.	Standard.	Standard Extra.	Special
70019 Jump Seat, three springs, Corning body.	$70.25	$76.00	$80.50	$91.50
70020 Jump Seat, side bar	70.25	76.00	80.50	91.50
Pole in place of shafts....				4.00

Elliptic Spring Road Wagon with Top.

70021 Medium grade imitation leather or corduroy trimming, low hung, steel axles with wood beds, shafts; weight, 400 lbs. Price with rubber top, Medium Grade $40.00
Common Grade 36.00
Price with leather quarter top 45.00

Our prices on cutlery are 25 to 50 per cent. below regular retail prices.

Phaetons.

Three-Spring Phaeton.

Brewster Phaeton, superior in style of body and strength of gear to any in the market. Body is hung low, making it very easy of access. Very popular with ladies elderly persons and physicians. High, full back and very roomy

	Standard.	Standard Extra.	Special.
70022 Two-Spring Phaeton..	$70.00	$75.00	$87.00
70023 Three-Spring Phaeton.	75.00	80.00	92.00

Weight, crated, 525 pounds.
Fine wing dash and silver rail, extra.......... 4.00

Three-Spring Phaetons.

70025 Three-Spring Phaeton, with wing dash and lamp-holes and lamps.
70026—Two-Spring Phaeton, with wing dash lamp holes and lamps.

70025 Standard, 3 springs $82.50
70025 Standard Extra 87.50
70025 Special 100.00
70026 Standard, 2 springs 77.50
70026 Standard Extra " " 82.50
70026 Special " " 95.00
Weight, crated, 537 pounds.
Above prices are with shafts; pole, extra, in place of shafts 4.00
State whether narrow track, 4 ft. 8; or wide, 5 ft. 2, is wanted. Delivered free on board, Chicago.

Canopy Top Surrey.

70027—Canopy Top Surrey, straight sills on end springs.
70028—Canopy Top Surrey, straight sills on Brewster springs.

Price same for either style.
Medium grade, with pole $78.75
Standard grade, with pole 99.00
Special grade, with pole 112.00
Weight, crated, 775 pounds.
A very nice carriage. State whether wide or narrow track is wanted. 1¼ in. axle in place of 1⅛ in., adds $3.00. 1¼ in. wheels instead of 1 in., adds $1.50.

Family Carriages.

70029 Four-passenger extension top carriage, substantial, light and durable. The body hangs low and is easy of access. Very roomy; light enough for one horse, furnished with lamps, leather fenders and pole, three spring gear, best construction. Full back on front seat if preferred. Standard grade $140.00
Special grade 155.00
Shipping weight, 650 lbs.

Write out what you want, enclose the money, tell where to send and we do the rest. Easiest thing in the World.

Spring Wagons.

70033 Two-seated platform, half-spring wagon, pole, whiffletree and yoke, two full backs, leather trimming throughout. Price,.......... $49

The very best wagon for the money ever offered, d end gate, round-cornered body; 1⅜ springs, 1¼ t This is a special vehicle, built in standard grade or The best wagon of this pattern made. Best Sar patent wheels. Weight, crated, 625 lbs., intended carry 1,000 lbs.; body 88 inches long, 33 wide; b from ground, 32 inches.

Two-Seat Business Wagons.

70034 Price, with shafts, $32.00 Pole, whiffletrees and yoke in place of shafts, adds to price, $3. Weight, 500 pounds, crated.
Made in the common grade only.
Drop axles and single half-end springs. Sarven pa ent wheels. For full description, see our Special Bug Catalogue.

Light Delivery Wagons.

70035 Price, with shafts, $32.00. Pole, whiffletrees and yoke in place of shafts, adds to price $3.0 Weight, 500 lbs., crated.
Drop axles and half-end springs. Sarven paten wheels.
Has side boards or wings on body; very handy fo light or medium delivery up to 600 lbs. Made only i the common grade.

Studebaker Spindle Body "Clipper."

70044 Length of body, 5 feet 3 inches; width, 2 feet 4 inches; depth of box, 4½ inches. The axles are 1 inch double collar steel; wheels, Sarven patent, with steel tires; Studebaker's veneer seat, nicely trimmed. Wine, carmine or green, gearing, natural wood finish body and seat. For cut see our Buggy Catalogue. This is a standard grade job, finely finished, and should have a large sale, as price is low considering quality. Price, with shafts.......... $32.00
Weight, crated, 300 lbs.

Road Carts.

Road carts are usually shipped crated at one and one-half first-class freight. Wrapped, not crated, double first-class. Light carts can often be wrapped and shipped cheaper than if crated.

General Purpose Cart.

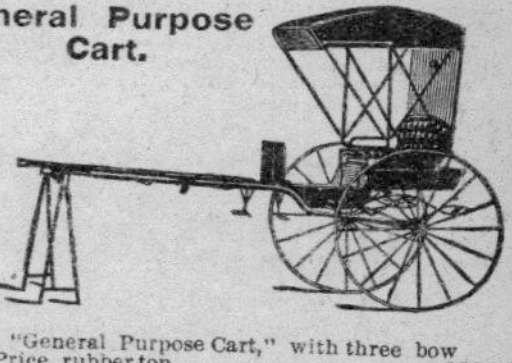

70045 "General Purpose Cart," with three bow top. Price, rubber top $39.50
Leather quarter top 40.50
Full leather top 45.00
Weight, crated, 319 lbs.
Spring heavy, to carry top. One of the most popular top carts made.

The Eureka Two Wheeler.

70048 Absolutely without horse motion.

Easier to ride in than a buggy. A more useful cart would be hard to find. It has the utility of a road cart, and is as roomy as a buggy. Made and finished in best buggy style. Weight, 250 pounds; with top, 300 pounds. Price, open...$30.00
Price, with rubber top............................ 40.00
Weight, crated, 305 pounds.

The Favorite No. 3 Cart.

70050 Our Improved Favorite Road Cart. This is one of the most popular low-priced carts made; built light and neat; Sarven patent wheels, double collar steel axle braced throughout. Long oil tempered spring hung over the axle. Finish natural wood only. Weight, wrapped for shipment, 120 pounds; width of seat, from rail to rail, 30 inches.
Price...$9.00

The Studebaker Road Cart.

70052 The Studebaker Coil Spring Road Cart. The construction of the cart is of the well-known Studebaker style. Substantial and well made. The frame and seat rests are of angular steel and supported at four points by elastic springs, ⅞ inch axle, painted in wine or finished in natural wood, striped and well varnished; weight, about 125 pounds; crated, 150 pounds. Price, crated, on board car...$17.00

The "Dream."

70055 Double bent shafts, body mounted on axle only. Width of seat, rail to rail, 32 inches. Easy riding. Weight, 280 lbs.
Price...$29.00
70056 Miniature Dream, for pony..........$29.00

70060 Our Improved No. 4½ Phaeton Cart
Price..............$14.50
Shipping weight, 150 lbs

This is one of the most saleable carts we handle, long spring hung on loops under shafts, good wheels and axles, dash board, cushion and lazy back. Upholstered in imitation leather, box under seat for halter, etc. Seat, 30 inches wide. A good reliable cart.
No such cart sold anywhere at less than 30 to 40 per cent. advance on our price.

Universal Tire Setter.

70061—This implement will set a tire on any buggy or wagon with a tire up to 4 in. wide. It is made of the best steel and galvanized iron and neatly finished. No injury whatever need be done in tightening tires by this tire setter to the finest painted wheels. Weight, 10 lbs.
Price for tire up to 3¼ in. wide.................$1.75
70061¼ For tire over 3¼ in. wide.................. 2.00
Felloes are immersed in boiling linseed oil; kerosene is burned under tank. Oil cannot catch a fire.

Our Celebrated Racine Farm Wagon.

Shipped at first-class freight, actual weight.
70062 Is made on our special order by one of the largest and best known builders in the country, and whose name alone is a guarantee of perfection in material and excellence in construction. For prices see next column.

This self-oiling patent Thimble Skein, used only on this wagon, renders it unnecessary to remove the wheel while oiling. Has perfect fitting sand bands, which exclude the sand and retain the oil. The following prices are for the very best farm wagons made and by the most celebrated manufacturers. Common work sold everywhere could be furnished at a much less price.

Racine Farm Wagons—Continued.

We will quote freight rates to any part of the United States.

No. 1.	No. 3.	No. 5.	No. 7.	No. 9
2¼x8	2⅝x8¼	3x9	3⅛x10	3⅝x11

Capacity:

No. 1	No. 3.	No. 5.	No. 7.	No. 9.
1,500	2,000	2,500	3,800	4,500

Price, gears, pole and whiffletrees, and weight:

No. 1.	No. 3	No. 5.	No. 7.	No. 9.
$28.90	$30.90	$33.25	$34.78	$37.00
575 lb.	625 lb.	700 lb.	725 lb.	750 lb.

Price of wagon, top box and seat. If brake is on gear it adds to price, $5.00; on box, $2.50.

No. 1.	No. 3.	No. 5.	No. 7	No. 9.
$32.95	$42.88	$45.59	$47.47	$49.70
790 lb.	840 lb.	915 lb.	1025 lb.	1085 lb.

WE EMPLOY NO AGENTS.—Beware of anyone soliciting orders for us.

70063 **Our Reliable Clinton Farm Wagon**; following prices are without brake. Brake on box extra, $2.50; on gears, $5.00. The Clinton wagon has skeins of regular construction, not self-oiling.

Order No. 70063.

PRICES AND DESCRIPTION.	No. 1	No. 3.	No. 5.	No. 7.	No. 9.
Size of skein	2¼x8	2⅝x8¼	3x9	3⅛x10	3⅝x11
Size of tire	1½x⅜	1⅝x7-16	1½x½	1¾x9-16	1⅝x9-16
Capacity, pounds	1,500	2,000	2,500	3,800	4,500
Height of lower bed in inches	11	12	13	14	14
Height of top box in inches	6	8	8	9	9
Gears with whiffletree, neckyoke and staychains	$24.00	$26.50	$28.00	$30.50	$32.50
Low bed	6.25	6.25	6.25	6.25	6.25
Top box	2.00	2.00	2.00	2.25	2.25
Spring seat, with two-leaf springs	2.50	2.50	2.50	2.50	2.50
Wagon with above parts	35.00	37.50	39.00	41.50	43.50
Weight of gears, pole and yoke	575	625	700	725	750
Weight of box and brake	215	215	215	300	335
Weight of complete wagon and brake	790	840	915	1,025	1,085
Feed box, extra	$1.00	$1.00	$1.00	$1.00	$1.00
Bows and staples, per set, extra	1.50	1.50	1.50	1.50	1.50
With steel skeins, extra	4.00	4.50	5.00	6.00	6.00
Tubular axles, extra	2.56	3.50	4.35	7.00	7.00

70064 One-horse Farm Wagon, with shafts, top box dash and one spring seat.

Size of skeins	2¼x7	2½x8	2⅝x8¼
Size of tire	1¼x⅜	1¼x⅜	1⅜x7/16
Weight, pounds	700	735	800
Capacity, pounds	1,000	1,300	1,600
Price, complete	$35.72	$37.13	$39.48
Gears only	25.50	26.50	28.75

Pole and yoke in place of shafts..........$2.00 extra.
Pole with shafts.............................. 5.00 extra.
Two spring seats instead of one............ 2.50 extra.
Brake on gears................................. 5.00 extra.
Brake on box.................................... 2.50 extra.

Dump Cart.

Shipped 1st class.

Order No. 70065.

WITH WOOD AXLE

Number	74.	76.	78.
Size of Skeins	2⅝x8¼	3x9	3¼x10
Size of Tire	1½x⅜	1¾x9-16	1⅝x9-16
Capacity, pounds	1000	1300	1600
Weight, pounds	445	495	565
Price	$32.50	$35.00	$37.50

Iron axle adds to price $2.50.

M. W. & Co.'s Farm Truck.

70066 Wheels, 24 inches in diameter; 5 inch tire; hub, 7½ inches long; axles, 2 inch solid iron; bolsters, 2¾ thick, faced with iron; removable stakes, 2¾ round; reach 2x4¾ wide. This is a special manufacture, made to meet a most urgent demand. Weight, about 1,000 pounds.
Price, without whiffletree and yoke...............$32.50
Whiffletrees and yoke, extra........................ 3.00

Watch and Jewelry Repair Department.

We have the best of workmen in this department, and are prepared to do all kinds of repairing and altering at reasonable prices. We guarantee all work.

Our Scoop Board.

70079 The simplest, best, cheapest and strongest board made; used for corn, potatoes, turnips, cobs, etc.; wood bottom, steel sides, iron braces and supports. Weight, 45 lbs.
Price...$2.00

Tornado Tank Pump.

For Steam Thresher Use.

70085 This is the only tank pump in the market that has a tight discharge from the cylinder to the tank, and with a shut-off valve in this discharge to close when using the pump to wash out or fill the boiler with or transferring water from one tank to another. Also has a clevis for the 2-inch suction hose. It can also be taken entirely apart, even to the bucket in the cylinder and shut off valve and repacked with one common wrench. It is a strong, simply constructed and easy working pump for raising and forcing large quantities of water quickly. It has important advantages. Tank pump only, as shown in cut, $9.90. 2-inch suction hose in 15, 20 and 25 foot length, per foot, 45c.; 1-inch discharge hose, per foot, 12c. Brass couplings and nozzle to screw on, for discharge hose, 50c. Strainer for 2-inch suction, hose, 65c. 1-inch discharge hose is used in case of fire.

Cutters and Sleighs.

SHIPPED AT DOUBLE FIRST-CLASS FREIGHT.

The following cutters have back, dash and sides made from lumber sawed in a circle around the log in the same direction as the bark is peeled off. This gives material entirely free from knots or checks and of any desired width. There are no joints in any of the lumber used except bottom boards. Every part is cut out of one solid piece. All of our cutters and sleighs have clipped knees—that is, braces are not riveted, but bolted on with clips or strap bolts and furnished with the best steel shoes.

Order sleighs early. We will not guarantee to carry an unlimited supply of cutters to be called for, only in case there is plenty of sleighing the coming winter.

Prices on all single seated sleighs include shaft.

Poles in place of shafts with any single seated sleigh, extra (neck yoke included)..............................$3.00
Poles alone...... 6.00

Swell Body Cutter.

SWELL BODY CUTTER.
70200 This is our Standard Grade Cutter, well braced and finished. State trimming wanted. No charge for crating or cartage. Shafts furnished.
Trimmed in velour or raw silk..... $16.00
Trimmed in red worsted plush.19.00
Trimmed in red plain mohair........................ 20.00
Trimmed in red crushed mohair..................... 22.00
Weight, 165 pounds.

Cutters—Continued.

REAL COMFORT SWELL BODY CUTTER.

70202 This is the roomiest and widest swell side cutter made. Extra finished and trimmed. Shafts furnished; knees clipped.

Solid Comfort Swell Body Cutter.

Trimmed in moquette....................$23.00
Trimmed in red wool plush.................25.00
Trimmed in red mohair plush...............27.00
Trimmed in red car plush..................30.00
Weight, 175 pounds

70204 Extra Portland Cutter. Extra fine throughout.
Trimmed in velour, ...$19.00
Trimmed in broadcloth $20.50
Weight, 150 pounds.

Extra Portland.

70205 Medium Grade Portland, trimmed in moquette..........$22.00

Cutters—Continued.

RUNABOUT CUTTER.

70206 Runabout Cutter (called also square box or piano box). Plain and substantial; construction as fine as possible. Trimmed in velour or corduroy.
Weight, 140 lbs.
Price..............$14.00 Lazy-back, extra....$1.00

70208 Two-seated sleigh; has no equal for all-around country use. Trimmed in velour or corduroy.

Two-seat Square Box.

Price with shafts, no pole..................$22.00
With pole and yoke, no shafts...............25.00
Pole, extra, without neck yoke..............5.50
Pole, extra, with neck yoke.................6.00
Lazy-backs, extra, each.....................1.00
Weight, 200 pounds.

Orders for the following sleighs must be placed with us before December 1st, as they will have to be built to order. We do not carry them in stock.

For Guns and Sporting Goods, we are headquarters. Remember this.

Shifting or Jump-seat Cutter

70209 This, for a l ness, pleasure family sleigh c bined, is the best cheapest in the r ket. Adjusted so either two or persons can ride c fortably. Front folds down dire under the move back seat, leaving the space in rear for packages, etc.
Price, moquette plush, with shafts..............$33
Price, fine mohair plush, with shafts.............36

Standard Mortise Knee Bob Sled

FOR FARM AND ROAD USE.

70212 Price, No. 7—4-knee, 2 front and 2 rear..$13
Price, No. 10—5-knee, 3 front and 2 rear.......15
Price, No. 12—6-knee, 3 front and 3 rear.......16

Oviatt Carriage Runner.

70214 Possessi more points of periority tha any other runn in the marke Price per set:
No. 1, and linc capaci 1000 lbs. $ 8.
No. 2, 1⅛ and 1¼ inch; capacity, 2000 lbs .... 10.
No. 3, 1⅜ and 1½ inch; capacity, 3000 lbs.... 12.

AGRICULTURAL IMPLEMENT DEPARTMENT.

Montgomery Ward & Co.'s Duplex Mill, with Stand.

Send for our new special Agricultural Catalogue, containing 225 pages of the most desirable farm implements and machinery. One of the most complete catalogues of its kind. Postage, 4 cents.

70302 Weight, 50 lbs. Price, without stand $5.60

70303 Same as above on stand, wt. 105 lbs. $7.90

Shells corn and grinds all kinds of grain.

Where a corn sheller and a family grist mill are both required it is much better to have them combined in one machine. The corn sheller is better because the shelled corn can not scatter and the balance wheel makes it more efficient. If mounted on bench or table, make opening at least 3 inches long or cobs will not discharge. We recommend our customers to buy these mills mounted on stand.

All grinding and bone mills are shipped second-class freight.

Montgomery Ward & Co.'s Triple Bone Mill, Grain Mill and Corn Sheller Combined

Triplex Mill.

70304 Shells corn, grinds all kinds of grain, and grinds dry bones and oyster shells for chickens. Mounted on stand same as 70303, wt. 112 lbs $11.00
70305 Same mill without stand, wt. 65 lbs......... 8.50

This mill has three hoppers; one B to shell corn; one A for shelled corn or any other kind of grain, and one C for dry bones or oyster shells. A family grist mill and bone grinder on legs; a corn sheller separate would cost $13.30. We here have them all in one machine on stand for $11.00, or for $7.90 without the bone grinder attachment.

Wilson's $5 Hand Bone Mill No. 1.

70308 We have sold thousands of these mills and our customers speak only their praise.

The teeth of a bone mill are strong and coarse and will not grind grain for family use.

Allow fresh bones to dry before grinding. Will not grind green bones. Weight, 35 lbs. Our Price, each...$4.00

I X L Bone Mill.

70310 Wilson's Patent Bone Mill. No. 1, same as 70308, but with iron legs; weight, 65 lbs. Price, each..........$5.85

70311 No. IXL. Bone Mill, weight 30 lbs. A little lighter and easier to handle than No. 1. Grinds Dry Oyster shells and dry bones perfectly. Price..............$3.60

Mann's Bone Cutter.

These mills are bone planers or cutters. Will cut perfectly green bones as they come from the butcher; prepares butchers' refuse perfectly as food for poultry.

70313 Mann's No. 2 mill, weight, 140 pounds $18.40

70315 Mann's No. 6 mill, weight, 100 pounds. $16.00

No. 2 Stand. 6 Post.

Our Family Grist Mill.

70316 If you own one of these mills you can have at all times fresh graham flour, fresh corn meal, fresh hominy, split peas, cracked wheat, fine table or butter salt. In fact, everything that is ground at a custom mill except fine bolted family flour.

The grinding surfaces are of a very hard material, especially made for this purpose, and are ground off perfectly true on emery wheels and will last for years. Burrs, 4½ in. diameter.

This is the same mill as is combined with our grinder and sheller No. 70302-5.

Every one guaranteed to work as represented.

Will not grind bones.

Price, each................................$4.10
Weight, 35 lbs.

Wilson's No. 1 Mill and No. 1 Green Bone Mill, Combined.

70318 Two mills mounted on one strong stand. Weight, 175 lbs. For grinding dry bones, shells and all kinds of grain, green and greasy bones and offal from the table. Anything at all that is to be ground can be done with either one or the other of these mills. The No. 1 has a sieve and each mill has a pan.

Price, complete..............................$21.00

***** Read pages 1 and 2 before ordering goods. You obtain a discount by sending money with order. Send money by Express, Draft on Chicago or New York, Post Office Money Order, or Registered Mail.**

Oriole Farm Grist Mill No. 2½.

Shipped second-class freight.

70320 Weight 150 lbs. Can be ru with one or two horse power. For grin ing corn, fine corn meal an graham flour for table use. It is mad in the most durable way possible, run easy and has an automatic feed.

This mill will grind from 5 to bushels per hour. One set of burrs wi grind 2,000 bushels of grain befo they are worn out. They can be r placed for $1.25. Speed of this mill about 800 revolutions per minut Size of pulley, 8 in.; diameter of burr 7 in. An extra set of burrs furnishe with each mill free of charge. Doe not grind bones. Price.......................$20.0
Burrs, per set.................................1.2

70322 No. 3 Farm and Bone Mill combined. Similar in appearance to No. 2½ above. See large cut in Agricultural Implement Catalogue. Will grind green bones direct from butcher, dry bones, greasy bones, corn and cob and grain. Capacity on bones from 500 to 1000 lbs. per day. Capacity on grain from 5 to 12 bushels per hour. Weight, 300 lbs Price.....................................$ 45.0
Burrs, per set...................................2.0

Daisy Bone Cutter.

70324 Knives operate like a common wood hand-plane; except that they are notched and cut bone into small pieces. The knives can be taken out when dull, sharpened and replaced in a few minutes. *A large or small bone* can be cut up at once. Very little pressure on the lever is required. The cutter is always ready for work. Turns easy, cuts fine and fast. *Is simple in construction;* nothing to get out of order. Can be turned by hand or power, by running a belt on hand wheel. Capacity by hand, ½ lb. per minute; by power, about 60 lbs. per hour.

Weight, 140 lbs. Price.........................$16.00

BIG GIANT.
Improved Grinding Mills.

All mills shipped second-class freight.

A mill with the greatest capacity and most even grinding of all kinds of grain ever offered to the farmer. Automatic in feeding, simple in construction, scientific in principle, looked upon by feeders as the gem of all grinders; requires from 2 to 10 horse power, according to size and speed.

70344 The No. 1 size Belt Mill, 5⅜ in. burrs; capacity, 10 to 20 bushels per hour; weight, 175 pounds. Price, burrs, $1.00 per set. Mill......$20.75

70346 The No. 2 size, 5¾ inch burrs, geared for attachment to tumble rod; capacity 10 to 20 bushels per hour; weight, 225 pounds. Price, burrs, $1.00 per set. Price of Mill...... $23.75

Drag Saw Machines.

Shipped Second-class.

Our Drag Sawing Machine can be attached to any kind of power or motion, tumbling rod or belt. The self-feed moves carriage with logs any desired distance for sawing stave lengths, cord wood, stave bolts, heading, etc. Can be used with two or four horse power. Capacity of self-feeding machine, 30 to 40 cords of wood per day; one saw sent with each machine. Price to attach to tumbling rod or belt.

70417 Hand feed, weight 1050 lbs. Price........$45.00
70418 Self-feed, weight 1100 lbs. Price........ 52.50
70419 Extra saw for Drag Saw Machine........ 5.25

See description and illustrations of our Drag Saws in Agricultural Implement Catalogue.

Improved Cider Mill.

Shipped Second-Class.

70420 These mills have hard wood frames strongly bolted together. The beams are heavy cast iron; the screws are wrought iron, capable of standing the most severe pressure applied by the lever; have long crushing roller and large crates. Made in three sizes.

Price of Senior, weight 410 lbs $20.50
Price of Medium, weight 230 lbs.................. 17.50
Price of Junior, weight, 165 lbs.................. 13.75

Lard and Wine Presses.

70421 The inside crate is 12¼ inches in diameter, and 10 inches deep. The screw is 1¼ inches in diameter, and 18 inches long. Price..............................$7.90

70422 Cider and Cheese Press Screws Cast iron whole length; 4 foot screw, 3¾ diameter. Weight, about 50 lbs. Price, each..................$14.00

Fanning Mills.

Shipped K. D., First-class.

"Minnesota Chief" Fanning Mill, shipped knocked down so as to secure a lower rate of freight; just as good a mill as there is made. Made by a well-known manufacturer: 1 wire wheat hurdle (3 sieves), wheat screen, wheat grader, corn and oat sieve and barley sieve.

Identically the same mill, No. 1 is sold by agricultural dealers for $20 00 to $25.00, which we sell for $11.90.

70424 No. 1 Farm Mill, 120 lbs., sieves 24 in. wide, 60 to 90 bushels per hour..............$11.90
70426 No. 2 Farm Mill, 125 lbs., sieves 30 in. wide, 100 to 125 bushels per hour.............. 15.85
70428 No. 2 Warehouse Mill, 175 lbs., sieves 40 in. wide, 200 to 300 bushels per hour.......... 34.00
70430 No. 3 Warehouse Mill, 200 lbs., sieves 48 in. wide, 300 to 400 bushels per hour.......... 43.50

For price of grass seed attachments, see our Agricultural Catalogue.

Paint Mills.

Shipped Second-class.

70432 Paint Mills for grinding colors in oil.
No. 1 Large power mill with clutch..................$36.00
No. 3 Small power mill.................. 11.25
No. 4 Medium hand mill.................. 9.00
No. 5 Small hand mill... 7.50

Corn Shellers.

Shipped First-class.

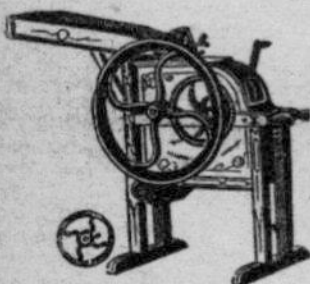

70434 The "Sheller" Valley is the best one-hole corn sheller in the market. Has the largest balance wheel put upon any sheller, being 27 inches in diameter and weighing 35 lbs.; is a right hand sheller with end delivery. One-Hole Sheller, with fan and feed table. Weight, 150 lbs. Price..............$5.40

Pulley, extra, 50c.

70436 Hocking Valley Two Hole Sheller, with fan, feed table and pulley. Weight, 225 lbs... 15.45
70438 Hocking Valley Two-Hole Sheller, complete with fan, feed table, pulley and cob carrier. Weight, 325 lbs.............. 18.75

New Famous Sheller.

Shipped Third-class.

70440 We have made a great improvement in our famous corn sheller, increased the size and weight and doubled the capacity of the machine. It will now shell, if turned rapidly, thirty ears of corn a minute, or as fast as any large and expensive one-hole sheller. No better implement for the price was ever offered. Weight, 15 pounds. Price $1.00
Per dozen, in full dozen lots...................... 11.00
Balance wheel and pulley adds to price each.......$0.75

All Steel Road Scrapers.

Shipped Third-Class.

70442 No 1 carries 7 feet of earth; weight, complete, 110 lbs. Price, each..$5.40

70444 No. 2 carries 5½ feet of earth; weight, 100 lbs. Price, each..$4.90

70445 No. 3 carries 4 feet of earth; weight, about 90 lbs.............................. 4.40

All our scrapers are furnished with runners on bottom without charge; these increase durability and ease of hauling.

Spray Pump—The Advance.

70446 Outfit consisting of pump (barrel not included); 6 feet of hose fitted with couplings and brass spray nozzle. Price......$11.90

This pump can be attached to any good, sound barrel and the barrel hung on either of our barrel carts and used for spraying plants, shrubbery, vines and trees, washing buggies, watering gardens, lawns, etc. It has an agitator which commences as soon as the pump-handle is worked, preventing the settling of any mixture with which the water is charged.

Shipped First-class.

70447 Combination Barrel and Utility Cart. Weight, 100 lbs. Price, with box and irons for 1 barrel.......$6.00
Irons for each additional barrel..... 1.00

Barrels have iron gudgeons bolted to each side. Cart will pick up barrel or body in a moment; change instantaneous. One cart answers for any number of barrels required.

Barrel Carts, for use in the garden and for feeding purposes; can be attached to any good sound barrel; one cart required for each barrel used.

Height of wheels 3 ft. axle stubs bolted direct to barrel. Wood or iron frame. Wood wheels and frame probably strongest. Weight, 65 lbs.

70448 Barrel Cart, steel wheels. Price..............$3.25

70449 Barrel Cart, wood wheels. Price 3.25

Hand Carts.

70450 36-inch wheels, box 24x36, 10 inches deep. Weight, 85 lbs. Removable end boards, bent handles, iron foot rest, iron hubs, well painted and striped. A first-class job. Very useful about barn, stable or garden. Price.................$5.00

Steel Hand Cart Wheels.

Shipped First-class.

70451 We furnish a pair of light steel wheels suitable for hand cart and other purposes. Tire, 1¼ inch, half oval. 38 inches high, to fit 1¼ axle. Weight, 40 lbs. Price, per pair..................$2.50

70451½ Iron Axles for above wheels. Weight, 15 lbs. 75 cents each.

PLOWS.

We publish a special plow, cultivator and general implement catalogue of nearly 225 pages. Postage, 4 cents. This gives complete illustrations and descriptions of Plows, Cultivators, etc. Our moldboards on our steel plows, double board, are double thickness on the wearing edge, rolled in when made, and are far superior to the common double shin. Right hand plows shipped in every case unless left hand is specially ordered. Whiffletrees and neck yoke and rolling coulter furnished with sulky plows. All Walking Plows set up, shipped first class; K. D., second-class. Coulter and extra share with breaking plows.

Our Chilled Plows are of the latest and most improved pattern, and sold at a price that barely pays for handling.

70452 M. W. & Co.'s Full Chilled Plows. In all sections where chilled plows are used, our plows will be readily recognized, and our price on plows and repairs appreciated. See the following prices;

	Turns furrow, inches.	Depth of furrow.	Weight, pounds.	Price.
A Right..................	8	4½	50	$3.60
B Right..................	10	5	65	4.80
10 Right..................	11	5¼	70	5.25
13 Right or left..........	11	6	80	6.00
19 Right or left..........	12	6¼	100	6.25
20 Right or left..........	14	7	112	6.50
E1 Right or left..........	14	7	125	6.75
40 Right or left..........	16	9	130	6.75

Price of jointer.................................. 1.50
Lead wheel and standard.......................... 1.00

70453 Price of repairs for the Oliver Chilled Plows, warranted to fit any of the chilled plows we send out.

Be sure and state whether plows or shares are wanted to turn furrow to the right or to the left.

		Standard.	Moldboard.	Lan'side	Shares, plain
A	Right.	$0.95	$0.95	$0.30	$0.20
B	"	1.13	1.32	.45	.20
10	"	1.50	1.50	.45	.25
13	Right or left	1.68	.68	50	.25
19	"	1.68	.88	.56	.25
20	"	1.68	2.10	.56	.25
E1	"	1.88	2.25	.56	.25
40	"	1.88	2.25	.56	.25

Jointer Points, 15c. Moldboards, 40c.

70454 Breaking Plow, solid cast steel moldboard; share unhardened, but of high natural temper, wood beam furnished with gauge wheel, rolling coulter, patent three-horse adjustable clevis, extra share.

Size, inches..........................	12	14	16
Weight, lbs..........................	112	125	135
Each..................................	$10.60	11.60	13.20

70454½ Sod Breakers, steel beam, 2 shares, 2 fine cutters, gauge iron. 12 in. $5.75; 14 in. $6.00; 16 in. $6.25.

70456 Stubble Plow. Wood beam, capped standard welded handle brace, wrought frog and welded bar and hardened steel share; beam adjustable for 2 or 3 horses; medium landside. Warranted to scour in any soil.

Size.	Single Shin.	Double Shin.	Weight.
10½ in.	$5.25		70 lbs.
11 in.	6.10		75 lbs.
12 in.	6.50	$7.10	80 lbs.
14 in.	7.50	8.00	90 lbs.
16 in.	8.55	9.00	110 lbs.

70458 Stubble Plow, steel beam, very strong, will stand the greatest strain without bending and so curved as not to foul, or choke in weedy land; all parts carefully fitted; no chance for it to become rickety; medium landside.

Size.	Single Shin.	Double Shin.	Weight.
10½ in.	$6.46	$8.40	80 lbs.
12 in.	7.88		98 lbs.
13 in.	8.55	8.87	
14 in.	9.31	9 83	101 lbs.
16 in.	10.75	11.35	115 lbs.
18 in.		12.42	120 lbs.

Plows—Continued.

70460 Brush or Timber Land Plow, also used as a road plow, works well in all kinds of land, strong and durable, all steel.

10 inch, 75 lbs.....$7.50 | 12 inch, 88 lbs.....$8.00
11 inch, 83 lbs.....7.75 | 14 inch, 100 lbs.....8.75

Subsoil Plows.

70461 Indispensable for fruit culture and deep cultivation, should be used on every farm.

Weight 90 lbs.
Price.....$8.00

Light All-Steel Plows.

70463 Designed for either stubble or light sod, doing both kinds of work in the most perfect manner; very light draft; scours in any soil. Is also adapted to the cultivation of corn, cotton, and fruit orchards. This plow does decidedly more work than its width of cut would indicate. Has a curved steel standard and cap, an extra steel share furnished with every one of these plows.

Price.
Pony, 7 inch share, 10¼ moldboard, 38 lbs.....$3.90
A, O, 8 inch share, 11 moldboard, 42 lbs.....3.50
B, O, 8 inch share, 12 moldboard, 50 lbs.....4.25
C, O, 9 inch share, 14 moldboard, 60 lbs.....5.00
D, O, 9½ inch share, 15½ moldboard, 65 lbs.....5.50

Sulky Plows.

All sulky and gang plows K. D. Third-class.

On account of the hard times, and poor collections, one of the principal plow companies of the west offers us the larger part of their output for the coming year, at prices, for "spot cash," far below any figures ever reached before by dealer or jobber. This enables us to furnish our customers the best steel plows manufactured. Warranted to scour in any soil, at prices much lower than the dealer pays for the same plows at wholesale. A double shin, wood beam 12 in. plow, best make for $7.10, or steel beam for $7.85. Plows usually sold for $11.00 to $12.00. Compare our prices with those of your local dealer. We will guarantee quality, and let our plows side by side with any plow manufactured.

For illustration of our New Three-Wheel Sulky see our special implement Catalogue for 1894. All plows furnished with rolling coulters, whiffletrees, evener and yoke.

THE NATIONAL TWO-WHEEL SULKY.
70464 Has 40 inch steel wheels, 16 inch cutters. New spring lift, land side cut out and no friction in bottom of furrow. Prices: 14 inch 2 wheel sulky, weight, 500 lbs. $27.50 16 inch 2 wheel sulky, weight, 505 lbs. $27.50

70465 The Plow Boy Three wheeled Sulky Plow, 12 in., $25.50; 14 in., $26.50; 16 in., $27.50. If turf and stubble bottom is wanted it adds $1.00 to above prices. Has all the points of excellence of any three-wheeled plow; turns square corners. Complete with whiffletrees and yoke steel share and mold-board.

Gang Plows.

All gang plows shipped as Third-class freight.
For cuts showing the latest improvements in our gang and wheel plows, see our Agricultural Catalogue.

National Three-Wheel Gang.

70468 The above cut shows our Improved Old Reliable Gang, which works perfectly with four horses abreast or with two ahead of two. Has large steel wheels, spring lifts, is very easy to handle, is perfectly carried on three wheels. Old Reliable Gang with two 12-inch plows, weighs 600 lbs.....$40.25
Old Reliable Gang, with two 14-inch plows, weight 620 lbs.....41.50

70468½ Steel Frame Walking Gang Plow, weight 390 pounds, turns 27 inches. Price with steel moldboards and shares.....18.90
With chilled cast moldboards and shares.....15.00

70469 This cut represents our New Wheel Gang Plow which works perfectly with four horses. Gang Walking Wheel Plow, two 12-inch plows; weight, 480 lbs.....$41.00
Gang Walking Wheel Plows, two 14-inch plows; weight, 480 lbs.....43.00
Single Walking Wheel Plow, one 14-inch plow, weight, 310 lbs.....24.00
Single Walking Wheel Plow, one 16 inch plow, weight, 315 lbs.....25.00
Riding attachment to above plow.....8.00

70470 Shovel Plow, with hinged wings; can be adjusted to suit any width of row. Wood beam, is well made and strongly put together. weighs about 65 lbs. Price.....$3.50

70472 Double Shovel Plow, wood beam, weighs 35 lbs. Price.....$2.50

Contractors' Plows.

70473 This is built especially for road and contract work; it is very strong and durable, used by the principal contractors in the United states. Weight, 155 lbs. Price.....$10.00

Clipper Potato Digger.

70474 These diggers are put up with three rods on each side, with extra plates attached for two rods, which are sometimes used where the soil is heavy. The depth of digger is regulated by the rod from heel of shoe through end of beam. Weight, 75 lbs. Price.....$7.00

Ditching Plows.

70475 Will loosen the dirt in the bottom of ditch 4 ft. deep; use long evener, one horse on each side of ditch Price.....$10.00

Cultivators.

All cultivators shipped as First class freight.

70478¼ Five tooth cultivator, steel teeth; with heavy braced standards, the teeth are reversible and the frame can be expanded or contracted Weight 60 lbs. Price.....$3.50

70479 Hand Cultivator, "Queen of the Garden" steel wheel, wrought iron shafts. With combination shovel-mold-board, shovel weeder. Weight, 28 lbs. Price.....$4.00

70480 Dexter cultivator, similar to Queen, but lighter. Weight, 23 lbs. With all attachments Price.....3.00

70482—Our Handy Steel Beam Cultivator. Has coil spring lift. Weight, 180 lbs. Price.....$15.50

Tongueless Cultivator, best pattern, steal beam. Price.....$10.50
Six styles of walking and riding cultivators in our Agricultural Catalogue. Prices ranging from $13.50 to $22.50.

Mowers.

Mowers shipped Third-class.

70484—The Advance Iron Mower. Weight, 500 lbs. Price, 4 feet cut, 4 ft. 6 in. cut, Weight, 540 lbs Price.....$37.00

70486 Wide Cut Mower, with bar carrying spring. This is a heavier and wider cut machine than above. Pressure of bar on ground relieved by spring. It has many advantages. See cut in Agricultural Catalogue; weight, 675 lbs. Price, 4 ft. 6 in. cut, $40.00; 5 ft. cut, $42.00; 6 ft. cut, $45.00

The Boss Sickle Grinder.

Shipped as Second-class.

70488 The Boss Sickle Grinder, one of the most successful grinders made. It costs but little more than an ordinary mounted grindstone and can be used for all grindstone purposes; size of stone 18 in. diameter, 2¾ thick; weight, 130 lbs. Price.....$3.50
70489 Perfection Emery Wheel, sickle grinder, light and handy; weight, 18 lbs. Price.....$3.00
70490 The well-known Dutton Sickle Grinder, latest pattern. Wgt. 16 lbs $6.00

Hay Rakes.

All Hay Rakes and Hay Tedders shipped First-class.

70492 The revolving Horse hay rake, turned head and teeth. Weight 70 lbs., 13 teeth.
Weight, 80 lbs. Price.....$4.00

Rider Hot Air Pumping Engine.

70557 The Rider Hot Air Pumping Engine. Burns coal, wood, kerosene or gas.

PRICE LIST AND APPROXIMATE CAPACITY PER HOUR IN GALLONS.

SIZE OF CYLINDER.	50 feet	100 feet	Price	Weight.
4 inch	150		$150.00	400 lbs
5 "	350	200	225.00	900 "
6 "	1,000	800	300.00	1,200 "
8 "	2,000	1,200	400.00	2,000 "
10 "	3,500	2,000	500.00	2,500 "

Extra, for well deeper than 25 feet, 5 inch and 6 inch engines, $15.00; 8 inch and 10 inch engines..$20.00
Extra, for Kerosene Burner and Tank, $10.00 for 4 inch and 5 inch; $12.00 for 6 inch; and $15.00 for 8 inch and 10 inch engines.

Stump Pullers.

70558 Benett's Stump Puller and Rock Extractor. One man can lift 20 tons.
No. 1 machine, 15 inch wheel, complete for 1 man ....
No. 2 machine, 18 inch wheel, complete for two men ....
No. 3 machine, 20 inch wheel, complete for three men ....
No. 4 machine, 23 inch wheel, complete for four men ....
Large cut of this machine in Agricultural Catalogue. Prices quoted on application.

The Screw Power Stump Puller. Wrought screw, four sizes. Weight, 1,000 to 2,850 pounds. The most powerful machine made. Prices quoted, and special circular mailed on application.

The Montgomery Ward & Co.'s Windmill.

70560 This is a solid wood wheel with the proper dish to secure strength, maintained by iron rods. To put the mill out of motion the vane is swung around parallel with the wheel, which turns edge to the wind and remains firm and motionless. Price, complete, except tower, 10 foot mill..$26.00 Price, complete, except tower, 12 foot mill..$30.00

Shipping weight of mill, 574 pounds. Will furnish complete tower for 10 foot mill at 35 cents per foot. 12 " " 45 cents "

Montgomery Ward & Co.'s All Steel Mill.

70561 This mill is geared back one-half so that it makes two turns to one stroke of the pump. Diameter of wheel, eight feet. It is very simple in construction; any one can put it together. It is made of the best material and hand painted. Guaranteed to stand the test of all kinds of weather and to equal in power any other make of mill of similar size.
Weight about 300 lbs.
Price $26.00
Gas pipe tower 30 feet high 22.00
Additional height of tower, 75 cents per foot.
Metal anchor posts, set of four 3.00
Wind mills shipped as first-class freight. Towers second class.

All lines of merchandise very generally reduced in price.

Pumping Jacks.

70563 Pumping Jack. For operating wind mill pump in times of light wind or calms; can be connected to any horse power, stroke 4 to 16 inches; balance wheel. 300 pounds com. Jack weight 600 lbs.
Price $18.00

70564 Our $10.00 Wind Mill Grinder. We furnish an elbow to connect this mill to the pump rod. Adapted to a large farm with 50 head of cattle. Weight, 75 lbs.
Price $10.00
70566 Tallerday Automatic Wind Mill Regulator. Weight, 50 lbs.
Price $4.00

Broom Machinery.

70568 Broom Corn and Hay Press, Bales 30x24x45 inches; weight, 300 lbs. Weight of press, 1,300 lbs.
Price $74.00
70570 Hand Broom Corn Scraper; weight, 185 lbs.
Price $5.00
70572 Power Broom Corn Scraper, 5 cylinder, weight, 600 lbs.

Wagon Jacks.

70574 The Eclipse Wagon Jack, strong and substantial, good enough for all practical purposes, weight, 7 lbs. Each $0.70
A wagon jack is made only to raise the axle of a wagon. Elevating capacity limited to about 3 in. by one stroke of lever. To raise buildings, buy a Jack Screw or use our Maxon Lever Jack. Wagon Jack shipped third class.

70575 The Miller Wagon Jack, can be moved and adjusted with one hand; many prefer it to all others.
No. 1 weight 10 lbs.
Price $1.00
No. 2 weight 13 lbs.
Price $1.25

70576 The Improved Meeker Wagon Jack, strongest and lightest, most compact and made the handle. It has a perfectly straight lift; will lift more and is easier to operate than any other jack made.
No. 1, for threshers and portable engines; weight 40 lbs. This jack lifts 3,500 lbs. This is only a wagon jack, lifts high enough to remove wheel for greasing. Price................$3.40
No. 2, heavy trucks; weighs 24 lbs., will lift 3,000 lbs.
Price $2.90
No. 3, farm wagons; weighs 13 lbs. will lift 2,000 lbs. Price......$1.20
No. 4, carriages and light wagons; 7 lbs. Price.................. 1.00

70577 The Maxon lever Jack. This jack differs from a wagon jack. The weight can be lifted 10 to 12 inches, capacity 2 to 6 tons, lower claw can be inserted under a sill or stone in a 2 inch space.

No.	Tons.	Height inches.	Rise inches.	Weight pounds.	Price.
1	2	16	10	32	$6.50
3	6	19	12	60	10.00

No. 1 is for threshing machines, portable engines etc.
No. 3 is for buildings, stone yards and heavy work.

Our Dress Making Department will interest the ladies. Send for Special Catalogue E (free). We can make a dress for less than you can yourself.

Portable Farm and Dairy Scales.

Made on our special order. Branded with the name of our firm. Freight prepaid by us to all points in the United States east of the west line of Kansas and Nebraska, North and South Dakota and Louisiana.
We guarantee these scales to be as accurate and as well made as any standard scale sold in the country and warrant them fully for five years. You can get no better, more durable or accurate scale. If you pay a higher price you are paying for a name only.

Portable Platform Scales.

All scales are shipped as 2nd class freight.

Order No. 70578   WITH WHEELS.

No.	Capacity.	Platform.	Price
74	¼ to 600 lbs	16x24	$13.80
75	¼ to 800 lbs	16x25	15.00
76	¼ to 1,000 lbs	17x25	16.25
77	¼ to 1,200 lbs	17x26	17.50
78	¼ to 1,400 lbs	19x28	21.25
79	¼ to 1,600 lbs	20x29	23.75
80	¼ to 2,000 lbs	21x29	27.50

Dairymen's Scales.

WITH DOUBLE BEAM.   NO WHEELS.

No.	Capacity ¼		Price.
No. 81	Capacity ¼ to 600 lbs		$13.90
No. 82	Capacity ¼ to 800 lbs		15.25
No. 83	Capacity ¼ to 1,000 lbs		16.30

DOUBLE BEAM WITH WHEELS.

No.			Price.
No. 84	Capacity ¼ to 600 lbs		14.08
No. 85	Capacity ¼ to 800 lbs		16.00
No. 86	Capacity ¼ to 1,000 lbs		17.25

Montgomery Ward & Co.'s 5-Ton Hay and Stock Scale.

Montgomery Ward & Co.'s Wagon Scales.

Price, delivered, $53.50.

70582 Send all cash with the order which will bring this 5-ton scale to the low price (net)....$51.90
We prepay the freight.
We are now turning out the strongest, heaviest and most reliable hay and stock scale ever offered to farmers and ranchmen at the low price here named. We sell these high grade scales for $51.90 net, cash with order. The regular manufacturers sell this grade of scales, made from precisely the same patterns and exactly the same weight and capacity at an average price of $110.00. We ship these scales, freight paid by us, to any railroad station or steamboat landing in the United States east of the west line of Kansas and Nebraska, North and South Dakota and Louisiana. To points farther west we pre-pay the freight to the west line of the above states, which amounts to $5.00. To remote points wherever the freight is in excess of $5.00, we apply this amount on the freight bill and the purchaser pays any balance of freight over this $5.00 paid by us on receipt of scale. No such value for this amount of money has ever before been offered the purchaser of scales. We furnish a highly finished, double brass beam and a neatly painted beam box. Our scales have double truss rods on the levers. The cheap scales sold throughout the country have single truss rods with light beams about one-half the weight of ours, which imparts a trembling and uncertain motion to the scale beam. A heavy scale is positive and accurate in its movement, and has none of the vibrating motion of a cheap scale. Platform, 8x14 feet.
Shipping weight, 780 lbs., including beam box.
70584 A 50-lb. test weight, sealed and strictly accurate. Furnished on cars at Chicago, for...$2.75

Montgomery Ward & Co.'s Wagon Scale.

F. O. B., Chicago, Purchaser pays Freight on this scale.

To meet the demand for a low priced but reliable scale adapted to the use of farmers and stock growers, we have arranged with one of the best known scale manufacturers, whose name is a sufficient guarantee, to furnish us at a moderate price the STANDARD SCALE.

We sell this scale, *free on board at Chicago*, the purchaser paying freight from this point.

The weights of three sizes of these scales are here given. They are shipped at second-class freight, actual weight. We will omit freight rates to any one interested.

These scales are, of course, a lighter scale than our special 780 lb. 5-ton scale, but are perfectly reliable and trustworthy, furnished with single beam and nice beam box.

70582 2 Ton. Platform 7x13. Weight of scale, 500 lbs. Price........................$38.00
70583 3 Ton. Platform 7x13. Weight of scale, 550 lbs. Price........................41.50
70584 4 Ton. Platform 8x14. Weight of scale, 600 lbs. Price........................45.00
Double beam extra........................2.00

Scale Books.

Howe U. S. Standard and Fairbanks' Scale Books (600 tickets each) post paid, 68 cents.

Howe Trucks.

70594—The Howe Daisy Truck, for bags, barrels and general purposes. Weight, 25 lbs. Price........................$1.75

The Howe Warehouse Truck.

Shipped First-Class.

Order No. 70595
No. 1, weight, 43 lbs. Length 3½ ft. Price....$3.00
No. 2, weight 56 lbs. Length, 4 ft. Price....4.00
No. 3, weight, 77 lbs. Length, 4½ ft. Price....5.50

The Montgomery Ward & Co.'s Road Grader.

Shipped First-class.

70596 Weight, about 1,500 lbs. Price, without trucks........................$100.00

We warrant this grader to be strong and durable, and to stand any strain that can be brought to bear on it. Warranted a perfect and thoroughly made implement, or no sale.

This road grader with two men and four horses will do more work, and far better in the same time, than the full road district crew of a dozen men and half dozen teams, working with a common scraper, plow, shovel, and hoe in the usual manner. Save the money from delinquent road taxes and buy Montgomery Ward & Co.'s road grader.

Good roads render farming profitable; you can market your products at good prices when others cannot move a mile from home. Good roads enhance the value of your property, invite strangers to travel over it and settle in your community, and are the best evidence of an intelligent, wide awake and progressive community.

We would like to correspond with the Chairman of any Town Board whose town could be interested in profitable road working machinery. Please send your address. Special circular mailed free on request.

Write your name and Address on package returned to us if you want it to have attention; send letter of instructions by mail; do not put it in package.

Fruit Dryers and Evaporators.

Shipped Second-class.

70600 No. 6 Cook Stove Dryer; weight, 40 lbs. Price....$5.00 Capacity, about one bushel per day. Sets on back of cook stove, leaves room for cooking at same time; desirable for small family; has 12 trays, fine galvanized wire cloth 10x11, suitable for berries and fruit.

70601 No. 1 Dryer and Baker; weight 175 lbs. Price....$25.00 Capacity, 3 to 5 bushels per day, 24 in. deep, 23 in. wide, 4 feet high, 6 trays, 32x32, giving 20 feet of surface; will also bake 10 loaves of bread or 30 pies at a time.

70602 No. 2 Dryer and Baker; weight, 225 lbs. Price........................$30.00 Capacity, 5 to 7 bushels apples per day; 24x26 in., 5½ feet high, takes 12 in. wood; 12 trays, 24x32, 40 feet of drying surface.

70603 No. 3 Dryer only; weight, 600 lbs. Price........................$85.00 Capacity, 15 to 20 bushels apples per day. Size, 44x37, 6 ft. high, 24 trays, 15x34, 85 feet surface, coal or wood.

70604 No. 4 Factory Dryer; weight, 1,000 lbs. Price........................$150.00 Capacity, 20 to 30 bushels per day, 48 trays, 15x34, 177 feet surface, 44x37, 10 feet high.

The Celebrated Gasoline Engine.

Below is our net price, f. o. b. cars, Chicago.

70608—

	Horse power.	Floor Space.	Height.	Weight.	Price.
1	1	36x22	40	500	$130.00
2	4	44x24	48	700	180.00

We carry in stock shafting, Hangers and pulleys to ship with engines at a very low cost. Write for price on complete outfit. Descriptive circulars sent free upon request.

"Otto" Gasoline Engine.

70610 The use of gasoline in the engine is far more safe than in an ordinary gasoline cook stove. The average amount of gasoline consumed in 10 hours for one horse power is one gallon. The economy of gasoline engines surpasses almost any system of power production.

Size.	Actual H. P.	Pounds Weight.	Price.
No. 2	2	950	$ 295.00
" 3	4	1,250	420.00
" 4 a	6½	1,650	540.00
" 4 b	8	1,725	630.00
" 5 a	10.5	2,825	740.00
" 5 b	13	3,000	810.00
" 6	17	4,100	1,025.00
" 7	23	5,500	1,437.00
" 8	29.6	8,000	1,887.00
" 9	36	12,300	2,343.00

Always be sure to state the amount of money enclosed with order.

BARB WIRE.

Send for our latest price list of Barb Wire and you will see that our prices are low. Worth your while to write us before buying elsewhere.

Kane's Electro Vapor Engine.

GAS OR GASOLINE FOR FUEL.

70612 No fire; no boiler; no engineer; no danger. You turn the switch engine does the rest. Engine run by spark from small battery. The cost of running: In computing the cost of running, the following facts should be taken into consideration.

I. No expense until started.
II. No necessity of starting until the power is required.
III. Expense while running always in exact proportion to amount of power used.
IV. The moment engine does all expense stops.

When running at maximum speed and power, our engine consumes about one eighth a gallon of gasoline per horse-power per hour, or, when illuminating gas is used, twenty cubic feet of gas per indicated horse-power per hour.

PRICE OF ENGINE ALONE.

No.	Actual H. P.		Floor Space.	Revolutions per Minute.	Shipping Weight.	Price.
1	½	25 x 40 in.		250	600	$150.00
2	2	31 x 51		240	870	250.00
3	3	38½x 35½		250	1291	350.00
4	4	40 x 64		225	1954	450.00
5	6	57 x 82		200	2265	600.00
6	8	61 x 90		209	3097	700.00
7	10	76 x105		200	4402	800.00

Engine and Pump combined on one base.

No.	Actual H. P.		Floor Space.	Shipping Weight.	Capacity Gallons per Hour.	Price.
1	½	25 x40 in.		700	500	$175.00
2	2	31 x51		1127	1000	300.00
3	3	38½x35½		1501	2500	400.00
4	4	40 x64		2054	4500	500.00
5	6	57 x82		2703	10000	700.00

Large Illustrations of above engine mailed on application.

Horizontal Centrifugal Pump.

With Primer for Suction Pipe.

70620 Lifts water only 25 feet. Additional height to be forced through discharge pipe. No. 8 to 15 will lift 25 feet and force 15 feet more in quantity named.

	Capacity per Minute.		Size of Engine Cylinder.	Price.
No. 4.	450 gallons		5x5	$271.25
No. 5.	700	"	5x5	293.25
No. 6, 1000		"	8x8	333.50
No. 8, 1800		"	8x8	362.25
No. 10, 2500		"	10x10	635.50
No. 12, 3500		"	12x10	801.25
No. 15, 8000		"	12x12	1000.00

70621 Horizontal Centrifugal Pump, mounted with Upright Boiler on wheels. With this outfit water can be taken from different wells or sources of supply. Several farmers can join in the purchase and the pump moved from farm to farm as required.

Size A, 4-in. pump, 450 gallons per minute, $920.00
Size B, 6-in. pump, 1000 gallons per minute, 1075.00
Size C, 8-in. pump, 1800 gallons per minute, 1454.00

All orders are filled from the latest Catalogue. We shall, whenever possible, on orders from old Catalogues, give the nearest we have, and wish to explain that we change our quotations so as to be able to give the latest styles and better values.

Montgomery Ward & Co.'s Perfection Cane Mill.

NO EXPENSIVE BREAKAGES.

Both top and bottom journals run in brass boxes. The gearing is encased.

Order No. 70622. SIZES, WEIGHT AND PRICES.

No.	Power.	Size of rolls in inches.			Estimated capacity not guarant'd gallons per hour.	Shipping weight, pounds	Prices.
		Diam. large.	Diam. small.	Length.			
0	Light One-Horse	8¼	5½	5⅝	40 to 50	400	$16.00
1	One-Horse	9½	6⅛	6	50 to 60	500	20.00
2	One-Horse	11½	6¾	6⅝	60 to 75	625	25.00
3	Two-Horse	13	7⅓	7⅜	75 to 90	800	31.00
4	Two-Horse	13	7⅓	8¾	90 to 100	850	35.00
5	Heavy Two-Horse	14	8¾	9¼	100 to 120	1,150	43.00
6	Extra Heavy Two-Horse	14	8¾	11¼	120 to 140	1,250	48.00

Cane mills are shipped at third-class rates. Observe that we are furnishing these mills, on an average, at less than 4 cents per pound, actual weight.

Order No. 70625. PRICES FOR COPPER AND GALVANIZED IRON PANS, WITH TWO SKIMMERS.

No.	Size of pan, inches.	Estimated capacity for day of 12 hours, gallons syrup.	Weight, pounds.		Price of heavy copper pans.	Price of galvanized iron pans.
			Copper.	Galvanized iron.		
1	44x 66	20 to 30	97	71	$ 9.00	$ 4.00
2	44x 72	30 to 40	110	84	9.60	4.30
3	44x 90	40 to 52	135	101	12.00	5.40
4	44x108	50 to 80	150	119	14.40	6.50
5	44x126	75 to 120	165	137	16.80	7.60
6	44x144	100 to 140	195	155	19.20	8.60
7	44x180	125 to 175	....	191	24.00	10.80

Nos. 4 and 5 pans, for brick arch, have one gate and one high ledge.
Nos. 6 and 7 pans, for brick arch, have two gates and two high ledges.

CARRIAGE HARDWARE AND SUPPLIES.

Carriage Trimmers', Wagon Makers', Blacksmiths' and Farriers' Hardware, Wood Stock and Supplies.

Special Notice.

The weights given in the following pages are ESTIMATED SHIPPING weights and are not guaranteed to be accurate. The weight of timber depends so much on its dryness and the weight of metal on its density and form that it is impossible to give weights that would be correct in all cases, even where the dimensions of articles are the same.

We make our figures as close to the average as we can to give you an idea of what transportation charges will be and of the character of the goods.

Buggy Tops, Bodies and Cushions.

No. 1.

No. 2

Carried in stock and furnished only as described below. For special sizes and grades see 70702 to 70720.

70699 Special lined rubber buggy tops, for one-seated buggy, made in large lots on special contract. Steel bow sockets, rubber top, lined with good cloth, rubber curtains (see cut No. 1) carried in stock, ready for immediate shipment. This special top made only to fit buggies with seat out to out on top of flare 33 to 36 inches. No other sizes of this grade furnished.
Price, only.......... $8.50

70700 Leather quarter-top, lined with good broadcloth, except curtains, which are of rubber. Top for single seated buggy 33 to 36 inches.
Price only.......... $13.75

70701 Full leather top, lined rubber side curtains, all lined with heavy broadcloth, padded top, handstitched front and back, 33 to 36 inches. Top for single seated buggy. Price, only $21,90

Price List of Buggy Tops.

MADE TO ORDER ONLY.

We will fill no orders for buggy tops or cushions unless measurement is sent according to the following

Instructions for Measuring Seat.

For tops, backs, cushions and falls as here stated.

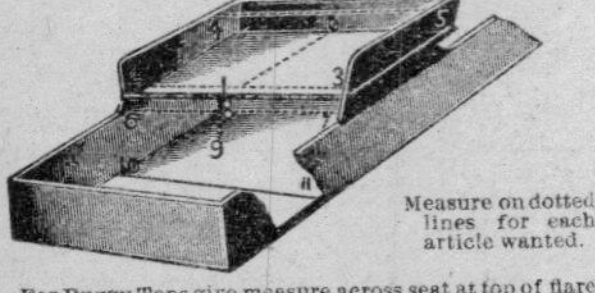

Measure on dotted lines for each article wanted.

For Buggy Tops give measure across seat at top of flare as per dotted line between figures 4 and 5 in cut. For cushions, give measure on bottom of seat as per dotted lines between figure 0....1 and 2....3. For falls to cushions give measure as per dotted lines between 6-7, 8-9 10-11. State if seat is round or square corner.

In measuring for extension tops give measure from out to out on top of seat same as you see in cut from 4....5; then give measure from the back of the back seat to the front of the front on top, and state if front seat is higher than back seat at level of seat.

These tops are made in a special factory in Chicago. If wanted to fit jobs we advertise without tops, customers will have to bolt the rails and irons on to the seats of such vehicles, which can readily be done.

Buggy Tops to Order.

Allow one week to have made.

Tops for two seated carriages weigh about 50 lbs.
Tops for single seated buggies weigh about 35 lbs.

The following prices are for *tops and rails alone without seat, lazy back or cushion*, as shown in cut No. 1. If irons and lazy back woods are required malleable, see 70722.

70702 Unlined Top, steel bow sockets, malleable end joints; covered with a good quality of colored back rubber, with side curtains to match.
Top for single seated buggy.......... $8.25

70706 Same as 70702, but better rubber, and has japanned or silvered prop nuts and rivets.
Single seat, $10.00 Double seat.......... 15.00

70708 Rubber Top, made of 24 ounce rubber, lined with a good quality of broadcloth except curtains, which are made of colored rubber; back stays stiffened with buckram and made to show no raw edges, enameled front valance, silver or japanned nuts and rivets, steel bow sockets, malleable rails and joints, top nicely padded.
Top for single seated buggy.......... 12.50
Top for two-seated buggy.......... 17.00

70712 Rubber Top, same as above, made of 26 ounce rubber, back curtains and top lined with a high grade of broadcloth.
Top for single seated buggy.......... 15.00
Top for two seated buggy.......... 25.00

70714 Leather Quarter Top, lined with good broadcloth, except curtains which are of rubber. Top for single seated buggy.......... 18.00
Top for two seated buggy.......... 30.00

70716 Same top as above, except is better made, has better broadcloth lining, top handstitched welts inside and side laced pinked.
Top for single seated buggy.......... 22.00
Top for two seated buggy.......... 36.00

70718 Full Leather Top, same as above, all lined with heavy broadcloth, padded top, hand stitched front and back. Top for single seated buggy.......... $24.80
Top for two seated buggy.......... 38.00
We cannot furnish covers to fit old tops. They must be sent to us to be re-covered.

70720 Canopy tops, made of solid bent wood, corners slightly rounded, covered with 8 oz. black enameled cloth, 4 iron props well braced, made only with straight standards. Give width and length of top and length of each standard.
Price, scalloped cloth fringe.. $16.00 } Weight, crated.
Price, with fancy cord fringe. 19.00 } 100 lbs.
Side and back curtains, extra. 5.00

All buggy tops have to be made to order to fit the measurement sent. Other goods ordered with tops will be detained about one week until top is finished.

Above tops are made by a special carriage top maker. If ordered to fit any of our wagons, customers have to screw irons (all of which we furnish) to the seats they are ordered to fit.

70722 Lazy back, woods and irons, alone, $1.00; trimmed in rubber, $1.50; trimmed in leather. $2.00 where a full lazy back is desired add $1.00 for wood and irons, and the cost of the **back cushion**, which is the same price as seat cushions without falls. Weight, about 10 lbs.

West's Carriage Top Dressing.

Makes an old top look as good as new.

70723 A Top Dressing of just sufficiant body to render the leather waterproof and no more. A goods that will not accumulate a hard substance on the leather after repeated applications. An article that will dry in a few hours with a natural leather finish and not be sticky. A jet black waterpoof finish which will not crack, harden or injure the finest leather or rubber top.

	Price, each.
¼ pint cans will dress 1 buggy top..........	$0.40
1 " " " " 2 " "	.80
1 quart " " " 4 " "	1.50

Wagon, Buggy or Cart Tops.

No. 4.

This is the latest, strongest and most durable top of this kind ever produced, and a most handsome shaped top. It does not require the services of a mechanic to attach them to the seat. You can do the work yourself in a very few minutes' time, and when the top is attached to the seat, you can, while sitting in the seat, lower, raise or close the top from the inside. It is not necessary to leave the seat to operate this top. You can throw this top forward or backward, or leave it standing straight up. It will stand in any position you desire to put it WHEN OPEN OR CLOSED. The top is furnished complete with irons ready to attach to the seat. The irons will fit any kind of a seat. *In ordering tops give length of seat on top.* The sizes we keep in stock are for seats measuring from 32 to 44 inches. For extra wide tops the additional cost of making will be added. Weight about 20 lbs.

PRICES:

70724 Covered with Brown Duck and Fringed, see cut No. 4.......... $3.75
70726 Covered with Awning Strip and Fringed, see cut No. 4.......... 4.25
70728 Covered with Enameled Drill and Fringed, see cut No. 4.......... 3.85
70730 Covered with Rubber and Fringed.......... 4.50

Wagon Umbrella with Fixtures and Socket.

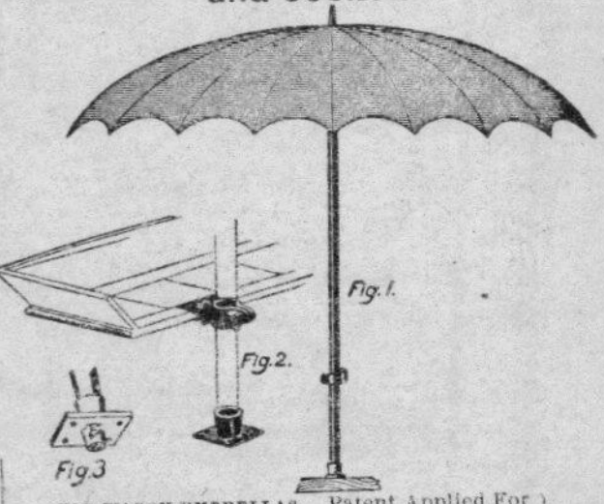

FOR WAGON UMBRELLAS. Patent Applied For)

70731 The most complete fixture yet produced. Made of the best malleable iron, light and strong, quickly applied, and holds the umbrella secure. Our umbrellas are all supplied with these fixtures without extra charge.

PRICE LIST OF UMBRELLAS WITH SOCKET AND SEAT FIXTURES COMPLETE.

Size.	Covers.	Colors.	Price 10 Ribs
40 Inch.	Heavy Muslin.	White Only.	$2.30
40 Inch	Heavy Close Cloth. Waterproofed.	Green, Blue.	$2.90
40 Inch	Heavy Drill.	White.	$2.60
40 Inch.	Heavy Drill.	Blue.	$3.00
40 Inch.	Fancy Stripe Double Face Duck.	Blue.	$3.20

Best quality heavy steel ribs and fixtures Handles 1¼ in. white ash, oiled and varnished.

Patent Leather Dashes.

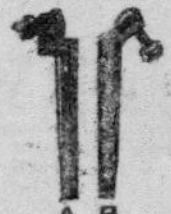
A B

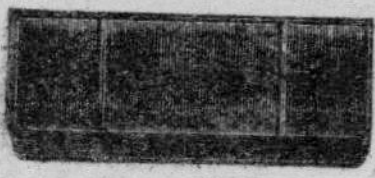

70732 For Piano Box Buggies, we send dash irons A. For Flaring End Buggies, we send angled irons B. State which is wanted.

Will fit any wagon or buggy; state size wanted. These are fine dashes, 10 stitches to the inch, dash, feet irons and bolts included in price. We send irons for square bodies, unless ordered for flaring end.

Dash Price List.

Size.	Price	Size.	Price	Size.	Price	Size.	Price
21x11	$1.19	21x13	$1.29	21x15	$1.43	21x17	$1.59
22x11	1.22	22x13	1.33	22x15	1.48	22x17	1 65
23x11	1.25	23x13	1.37	23x15	1.53	23x17	1.71
24x11	1.27	24x13	1.41	24x15	1 59	24x17	1.77
25x11	1.32	25x13	1.48	25x15	1.66	25x17	1.84
26x11	1 36	26x13	1.53	26x15	1.71	26x17	1.90
27x11	1.39	27x13	1.58	27x15	1.77	27x17	1.97
28x11	1.43	28x13	1.62	28x15	1.81	28x17	2.02
29x11	1.49	29x13	1 68	29x15	1.86	29x17	2.08
30x11	1 54	30x13	1.73	30x15	1.92	30x17	2.12
31x11	1 60	31x13	1.78	31x15	1.98	31x17	2.20
32x11	1.63	32x13	1.82	32x15	2.04	32x17	2.25
33x11	1 66	33x13	1.86	33x15	2.10	33x17	2.33
34x11	1.71	34x13	1.91	34x15	2.16	34x17	2.39
35x11	1.75	35x13	1.96	35x15	2.22	35x17	2.45
36x11	1 80	36x13	2.02	36x15	2.28	36x17	2.51
37x11	1.84	37x13	2.07	37x15	2.34	37x17	2.58
38x11	1.89	38x13	2.12	38x15	2.39	38x17	2.64
39x11	1 93	39x13	2.17	39x15	2.45	39x17	2.70
40x11	1.98	40x13	2.22	40x15	2.51	40x17	2.76
41x11	2.02	41x13	2.27	41x15	2.56	41x17	2.83
42x11	2.05	42x13	2.32	42x15	2.63	42x17	2.91

Dash Leather and Whip Sockets.

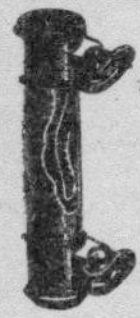

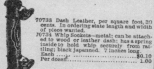

70733 Dash Leather, per square foot, 30 cents. In ordering state length and width of piece wanted.

70734 Whip Sockets—metal; can be attached to wood or leather dash; has a spring inside to hold whip securely from rattling; black japanned. 7 inches long.
Each $0.10
Per dozen 1.00

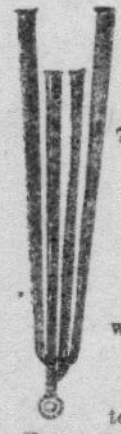

Bow Sockets.

70735 Black Enameled Steel Tubular Bow Sockets.
3 Bow, Buggy (one seat). Per set....$1.25
4 Bow, Buggy (one seat). Per set..... 1.50
4 Bow, Extension Top (two seat). Per set.. 1.75
Back Tubes, with steel. Each.......... .30
All other tubes for buggies. Each.... .25
Main Irons for Extension Tops. Each. .30
Always state whether right or left hand are wanted, and whether for 3 or 4 bow top.

We measure bows from center of pivot hole to the top of middle or shortest bow.

Be careful to use for the back bow the tube marked "Back Bow," as it has a steel strip welded in to prevent bending at the prop.

70738 Top Props, without nuts, 4 to a set, 2 long and 2 short.

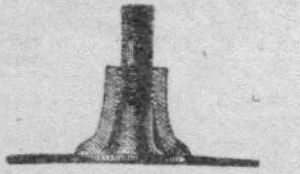

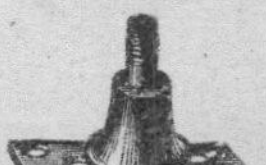

Malleable, ⅝ and ⅞ shank. Each..................$0.04
Per set.. .15
If less than a full set is wanted, state whether long or short shanks are needed.

Cushions, Falls and Full Backs.

The following Cushions, Falls, and Curtains are made only to order.

Buggy cushions, square cornered. Come 26, 28, 30 or 32 inches in length. All sizes the same price.

☞ *We will fill no order for cushions unless length of seat on bottom is given.*

	Without falls.	With falls.
70740 Buggy Cushions, rubber drill..	$1.05	$1.88
70742 Buggy Cushions, enameled duck..	1.57	2.32

Cushions—Continued.

	Without falls.	With falls.
70744 Buggy Cushions, enameled leather....	$2.75	$3.50
70746 Buggy Cushions, Corduroy..	1.62	2.47
70748 Buggy Cushions, cloth good quality....	3.50	4.25

Plain Full Backs to match above cushions cost *extra* the same price as the cushions. This does not include lazy backs, irons or wood, for which we make an additional charge of $1.00.

(EXAMPLE.) Suppose you wish to furnish a plain seat with cushion No. 70740, $1.05. Back cushions to match, $1.05, woods and irons to back, $1.00; the amount to remit would be $3.10; or if only the *back* and seat *cushion*, $2.10.

Curtains.

Side curtains for buggy tops.
70750 Side Curtains, made of 18 oz. rubber drill, colored back; weight, 18 oz. Each..............$1.25
70752 Side Curtains, made of rubber drill, lined with cloth; weight, 21 oz. Each.............. 1.87
70754 Side Curtains, made of leather, lined with cloth; weight, 36 oz. Each.............. 4.12
Back Curtains to match side curtains, same price and weight as one side curtain. Send paper patterns of both back and side curtains, showing position of eye let holes.

Storm Aprons.

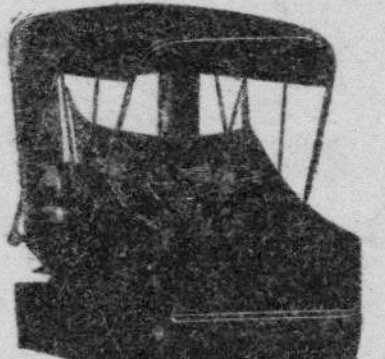

These aprons are held firmly in position on the dash by two oil tempered steel springs attached to the underside, thus forming an unbroken water-shed over front of dash. No mud, snow or rain can settle inside of carriage.

Warranted to fit the dash of any wagon, carriage or buggy; 42 inches usual length.
70755 Best Rubber Drill, each..................$1.50
70756 Good Grade Rubber Drill, each........... 1.00

Curtain Lights.

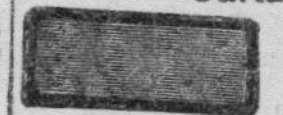

70759 Buggy Curtain Lights, square corners, Japaned, 1¼x5 inch opening.
Each..............$0.07
Per doz.............. .75
1⅜x5½. Each.............. .10
Per doz.............. 1.00

Button Holes.

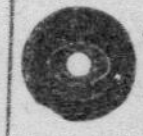

70760 Talcott's Elastic Button holes for Carriage or Wagon Curtains, oval hole.
Per dozen..............$0.30
Per gross.............. 3.24

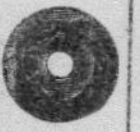

Knob Eyelets--With Leather Centers.

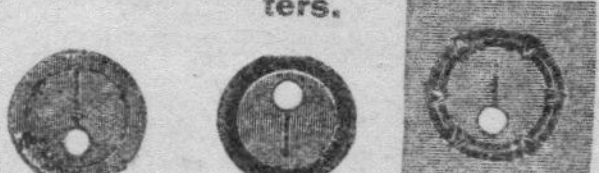

Front View. Reverse. Showing Fastener.

70760½ Knob Eyelets consist of a black japanned Metal Fastener, with outside prongs to pass through the curtain, and inside prongs to hold the leather eyelet, also a black japanned ring on which the outside and inside prongs are clinched. Best Goat Leather Centers. Per doz..$0.10
Per gross.............. .95

Patent Buckle and Strap Loops.

70761 Double Buckle Loop.
Each..............$0.05
Per dozen.............. .40

Curtain Straps and Fasteners.

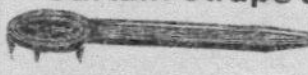

70761½ Each.......$0.03
Per dozen.............. .25

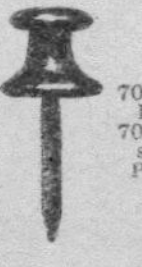

Carriage Knobs.

70762 To drive, per doz..............$0.05
Per gross.............. .45
70764 To screw, for double or single curtains, per doz.. .... .08
Per gross.............. .80

Tufting Buttons and Lining Nails.

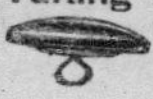

70766 Japanned Tufting Buttons. 22 line.
Per paper of one gross $0.20
Per dozen papers.............. 2.10
Weight per dozen, 3 oz.

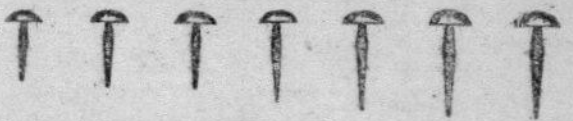

70768 Lining Nails, japanned.
Per paper, 4, 6, 8, 10, 12 oz..............$0.04
14 and 16 oz.............. .05

Imitation Covered Nuts.

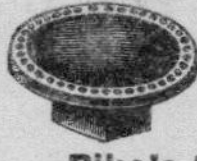

70769 Black Japan Finished Top Prop Nuts.
1 inch Capped Nuts, per doz. 15c.
1⅛ inch Capped Nuts, per doz. 16c.
1¼ inch Capped Nuts, per doz. 17c.

Pike's Patent Nut Locks.

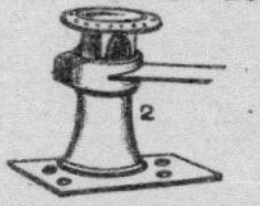
2

70769¼ Can be used on any buggy or carriage top and absolutely insures against loosing top nuts. Bend lock over the end of prop socket so that prop bolt will pass through both holes of lock. Screw nut up to place and bend lugs on lock up on opposite sides of nut. Price, per doz........$0.08

Rubber Drill.

70770 Rubber Drill, for covering or patching buggy tops, cushions, etc. Per yard.
18 oz. 50 in. wide..............$0.38
28 oz. very heavy, 50 in. wide.............. .50
18 oz. green back, 50 in. wide.............. .48
28 oz. green back, 50 in. wide.............. .60
70771 Flock Back Drill, 36 insides wide under surface finished to represent fine broadcloth. No lining needed. Per yard.............. .58
Flock Back Drill, 50 inches wide. Per yard.............. .70

Enameled Cloth.

Per yd.
70771½ Black Muslin, Glazed, Shot or Leather Grain, 45 inch wide..............$0.15
Imitation Rubber muslin Smooth Glazed, Shot or Leather Grain 45 inches wide.............. .15
Black Drill, Glazed, Shot, Pebble or Leather Grain 45 inches wide.............. .19
Black Drill, Glazed, Shot, Pebble or Leather Grain, 50 inches wide.............. .21
Black Drill, Glazed, Shot, Pebble or Leather Grain, 54 inches wide.............. .26
Black, Glazed, Shoe Drill, 45 inches wide....... .24
Tan Back, Glazed, Drill, 45 inches wide.......... .28
Tan Back, Glazed, Drill, 50 inches wide.......... .27
Tan Back, Glazed, Drill, 54 inches wide.......... .30
Tan Back, Glazed, Mole Skin, 36 inches wide.... .54
Tan Back, Glazed, Mole Skin, 45 inches wide.... .64

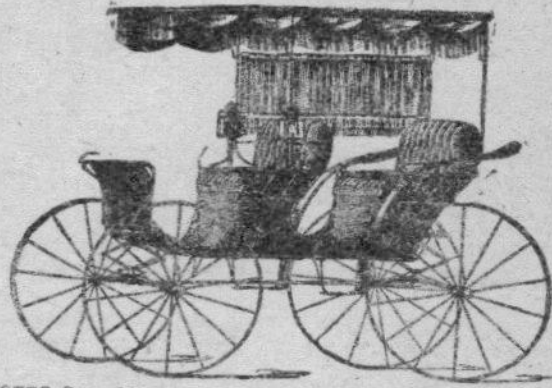

70772 Sun Shade Curtains for canopy top surreys, 60 inches long; fit any canopy top. No surrey complete without one.
Silesia, each..............$1.00
Sateen, each.............. 1.25
Cloth, each.............. 1.50

Carriage Lamps.

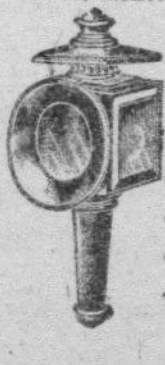

70773 Carriage Lamp, square body with round flange, round cornered head, with fancy canopy and bright cap, side glass beveled and grooved, candle burners, size of side glass 3⅛x 3½; diameter of flange, 4½ inches.
Per pair..............$2.60
70774 Better quality, size 3⅛x 3½; flange, 4½. Price.............. 3.00
70775 Better quality, size 3⅛x3½; flange 4½. Price.............. 4.00
70776 Better quality, size 3¾x4¾; flange 5. Price.............. 4.50
70777 Better quality, round side light; flange 5 in. Price.............. 4.90

FURNITURE DEPARTMENT.

We are the Cheapest House in America for Furniture.

Send for our new special Furniture Catalogue. It is the latest and most complete in the world. It contains cheap, medium and fine furniture. Mailed upon receipt of 8 cents to pay postage.

Upholstered Parlor Furniture.

All parlor furniture is made "to order." This insures clean, fresh goods, made exactly as wanted. It usually takes two to six days to complete furniture orders, depending upon the amount of work required on the goods ordered.

Explanation of Grades of Upholstering.

The prices of upholstered furniture are designated by letter. The letters represent the various grades of covering. Under each article will be found the price and quality of cover.

Grade A. Ramie or Raw Silk.

Grade D. Hair cloth, embossed or crushed wool plush, and cotton tapestries.

Grade E. Domestic crushed plush or silk tapestry.

Grade F. Best imported crushed plush, plain mohair plush, marbleized silk plush, heavy wool and silk tapestries, satin damask and brocatelle, or mottled corduroy.

Grade H. Best imported plain mohair (car) plush, silk faced tapestry, heavy wool tapestry, fine marbleized silk plush, silk damask and brocatelle.

Grade K. Best tapestry and a good quality of brocatelle.

Grade N. Best imported brocatelle.

Specify exactly what colors are wanted.

Be very particular to specify style of covering wanted from the grades you order, as you will see under some grades we quote several different coverings. Countermands will not be considered after work has commenced, as we make all upholstered furniture to order.

We make no charge for cartage or for burlaps.

Any single piece furnished out of a parlor suit at prices given, unless otherwise stated. We can furnish all the standard colors in upholstery.

Samples of upholstery sent free upon request. State what you want samples of clearly, or we shall have to guess at it.

Casters furnished with all furniture requiring same.

A parlor suit weighs about 220 pounds, as follows: sofa, 55 pounds; arm-chair, 35 pounds; rocker, 40 pounds; divan, 50 pounds; two parlor chairs, 40 pounds.

A Bargain.

72000 Five-piece Parlor Suit, well made, of SOLID OAK and neatly carved; seats are covered with cotton tapestry, and backs are upholstered with silk plush. We can furnish above in all standard colors. Samples of covering sent free upon application. We do not separate above suit. Suit includes packing, castered and delivered to freight house here. This is good value and a bargain. Suit consists of sofa, rocker, armchair and two parlor chairs, same as above cuts, except backs are plain in place of tufted. Price complete, 5 pieces, only........................$14.75

72001 Five-Piece Parlor Suit. This is the greatest bargain ever offered in a parlor suit. Frame is made of solid oak, richly carved and has a good gloss finish; every piece has spring seats, is covered with a good grade of domestic crushed plush or cotton tapestry, and trimmed with silk plush; is well made and very comfortable. Samples of coverings of above suit sent upon application free of charge. We can furnish above in all standard colors. Where can you buy such a suit in the world at this price? Weight, about 170 pounds. We will sell above suit complete, or either piece separate, at the following prices:

Sofa	$ 5.73
Arm chair	3.12
Rocker	4.76
Parlor chair	2.07
Parlor chair	2.07
Suit complete, 5 pieces	**$17.50**

72002 Parlor Suit. This suit is nicely upholstered in plush or tapestry and trimmed in good silk plush; richly fringed, very handsome and durable. Weight, about 200 pounds. The corner chair in this suit is very artistic and pretty. This is the cheapest suit of this style on the market. Consists of five pieces, as follows:

	Grade D.	Grade E.	Grade F.
Sofa	$5.75	$6.75	$11.00
Rocker	5.85	6.85	7.45
Corner chair	6.85	7.45	8.10
Parlor chair	3.45	3.90	4.20
Parlor chair	3.45	3.90	4.20
Suit complete, 5 pieces	**$28.35**	**$31.85**	**$34.95**

72003 Parlor Suit, made of solid oak, richly carved and highly polished; covered in plush or tapestry, has all spring seats and edges; weighs 225 pounds. This new style we consider one of our best bargains.

	Grade E.	Grade F.	Grade H.
Sofa	$9.45	$10.40	$10.75
Arm Chair	4.25	4.55	5.20
Rocker	6.50	7.15	7.50
Divan	7.15	7.80	8.15
Two Parlor Chairs	5.20	5.50	5.75
Suit complete, 6 pieces	**$32.55**	**$35.40**	**$37.35**

72004 Parlor Suit, made of oak. Spring seats and edges, covered in tapestry, brocatelle or plush with silk plush trimming on front. The backs of this suit are handsomely carved. We also call your special attention to our price on this suit; frames, polished, weight, 225 pounds.

	Grade D.	Grade E.	Grade F.	Grade H.	Grade K.
Sofa	$10.20	$10.80	$12.00	$14.40	$16.80
Arm Chair	5.10	5.40	6.00	7.50	9.30
Rocker	6.30	6.60	7.20	8.70	10.50
Divan	7.50	8.10	8.70	10.20	12.00
Two Parlor Chairs	9.00	9.60	10.20	11.40	13.20
Suit comp., 6 pcs.	**$38.10**	**$40.50**	**$44.10**	**$52.20**	**$61.80**

A handsome line of Lodge and Church Furniture in our new special Furniture Catalogue, mailed upon receipt of 8 cents to pay postage.

Parlor Furniture—Continued.

72005 Parlor Suit. This suit is well made in solid oak, richly hand carved and polished; spring seats and edges; well made and very showy; is upholstered in crushed plush or silk tapestry. Weight, 225 pounds.

Note price.	Grade F.	Grade H.
Sofa	$12.05	$12.35
Arm Chair	6.90	6.50
Rocker	8.15	8.45
Divan	9.45	8.75
2 Parlor Chairs	8.45	8.75
Suit complete, 6 pieces	$44.30	$45.80

72006 Parlor suit. *A bargain.* This suit is extra large and well made; is very highly polished and hand carved; the arms are supported by heavy brackets; length of sofa, 4 feet 2 inches; length of divan, 3 feet 1 inch; upholstered in crushed plush or silk tapestry and trimmed in silk plush; weight 225 pounds; spring seats and edges. We will send you samples of covering on every piece. Our prices are extremely low on this suit.

	Grade F.	Grade H.
Sofa	$11.70	$12.35
Arm chair	5.85	6.30
Rocker	8.45	8.95
Divan	9.10	9.75
2 Parlor Chairs	7.80	8.45
Suite complete, 6 pieces	$42.90	$46.00

37—6th

Parlor Furniture—Continued.

Designs of frames subject to manufacturer's change on this set.

72007 Parlor Suit made of solid oak, finished antique or walnut, and hand rubbed; not polished. Has spring edge, which is very comfortable. This is good value. Weight, 225 lbs.

	Grade D.	Grade E.	Grade F.	Grade H.
Sofa	$9.10	$9.20	$10.10	$11.00
Arm Chair	4.55	4.90	5.40	6.00
Rocker	5.95	6.45	6.95	8.00
Divan	6.00	6.65	7.35	7.75
Two Par. chairs	6.90	7.50	8.10	9.50
Suit comp.6 pcs.	$32.90	$34.00	$37.00	$42.00

We can furnish above suit $4.00 less in hardette.

Students' Chairs.

72020 Students' Chair, a popular pattern at a very low figure, walnut, upholstered in ramie cloth, tufted. Weight, 60 pounds........$4.50
Grade D................ 7.65
Grade E................ 9.65

72021 Arm Chair, walnut, oak or imitation mahogany, handsomely engraved, polished, spring seat and back. Weight, 80 pounds.
Grade D................ $7.20 | Grade E...... $9.70
Grade F................ 10.50 | Plain Leather...... 15.00
Wilton Rug.................................... 15.00

72023 Large Student Chair with head-rest, spring seat, back and edges, tufted arms, walnut, oak or imitation mahogany. Weight 80 pounds.
Grade D........ $11.50
Grade E........ 12.45
Grade F........ 13.90
Grade H........ 16.65

Chairs—Continued.

72024.   72030

72024 Arm Chair, spring seat, back and edges, frames walnut, oak or imitation mahogany. Weight 80 pounds.
Grade D............$14.40 | Grade H......$20.70
Grade E............ 15.90 | Grade K...... 22.50
Grade F............ 16.50
72030 Rocker, made of walnut or oak, spring seat and back. Weight, 80 pounds.
Grade D.............................$9.30
Grade E............................ 10.35
Grade F............................ 11.65

72031   72032

72031 Patent Rocker; a model; walnut, oak or imitation mahogany, spring seat and back. Weight, 80 pounds.
Grade D............$9.30 | Grade H.........$12.85
Grade E............ 10.35 | Wilton rug...... 16.80
Grade F............ 11.65
72032 Rocker, spring seat and back, tufted in middle, walnut, oak finished, antique. Weight, 45 pounds.
Grade E............$8.70 | Grade H......$11.40
Grade F............ 9.30 | Grade K...... 13.20

72035   72036

72035 Patent Rocker, a model of elegance and comfort; nothing made in the way of chairs begins to approach this for luxury and positive ease; has spring edges, spring seat and spring back. Frames, oak finished, antique. Weight, 80 pounds.
Grade D.............................$12.50
Grade E............................ 13.45
Leather............................ 20.70
Grade F............................ 16.45
Grade H............................ 17.65
72036 Patent Rocker, spring seat and back. Walnut, oak or imitation mahogany. Weight, 80 pounds.
Grade D.............................$15.00
Grade E............................ 15.90
Grade F............................ 17.10
Grade H............................ 21.30
Grade K............................ 23.10

Do not pay agents big prices for books before consulting us.

Bedsteads—Continued.

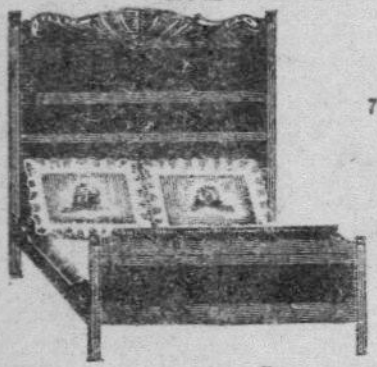

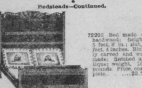

72202 Bed made of hardwood; height, 5 feet, 8 in.; slat, 4 feet, 4 inches. Richly carved and well made; finished antique; weight, 100 pounds. Price, complete.......$3.75

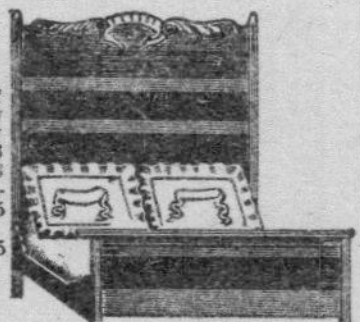

72203 Bed made of solid oak, richly carved and nicely finished. Height, 6 feet; slat, 4 feet 6 inches; finished antique; weight, 105 pounds.
Price,complete,$4.65

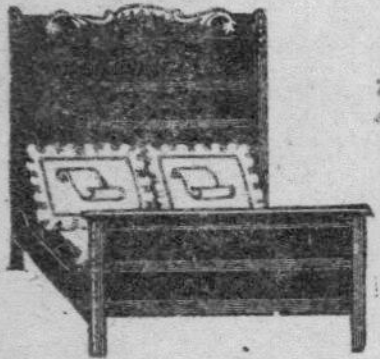

72204 Bed made of solid oak, richly carved. Very showy and pretty. Height, 6 feet 2 inches; slat, 4 feet 6 inches; weight, 105 pounds.
Price, complete, ...$5.00

We can furnish above beds in ½ or ¾ sizes, if desired, at same prices.

Iron Beds and Cribs.

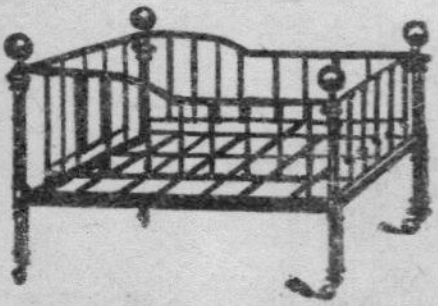

72225 Child's Iron Crib. Made entirely of iron, enameled white and ornamented with brass knobs. Size, 2 feet 6 inches wide, 4 feet 6 inches long. Very pretty and clean. Weight, 50, pounds. Price complete with slats......$8.75

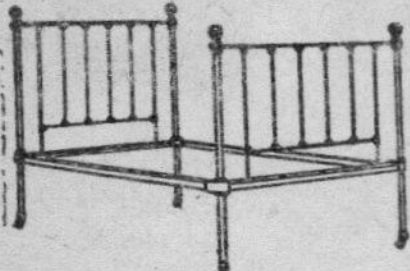

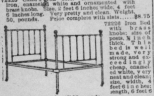

72226 Iron Bed with brass knobs; size of posts, ⅜ inch thick. This bed is well made, very strong and exceedingly cheap, enameled white, very neat and clean; size, width, 4 feet 6 inches; length, 6 feet 6 inches; weight about 100 pounds.
Price only.......................................$5.85
We do not furnish slats with above bed; if desired, 50 cents extra.

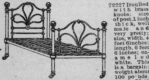

72227 IronBed with brass knobs; size of post,1 inch thick, well made and very pretty; size, width, 4 feet 6inches; length, 6 feet 6 inches; enameled white. This is a bargain; weight about 100 pounds.
Price, only.......................................$6.40
We do not furnish slats with above iron beds; if desired, 50 cents extra.

Bedsteads—Continued.

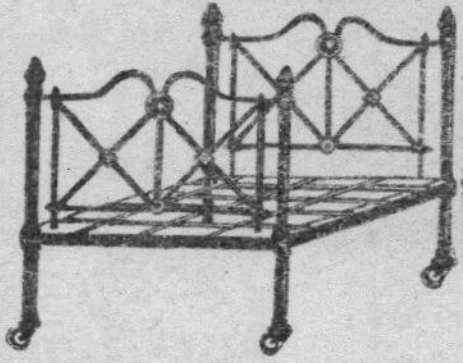

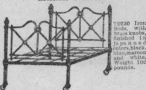

72230 Iron Beds, with brass knobs, finished in japanned colors, black, blue, maroon and white. Weight 100 pounds.

Size, 3x6½ ft.......................................$5.65
Size, 3½x6½ ft.......................................6.65
Size, 4x6½ ft.......................................6.80
Size, 4½x6½.......................................6.90
We do not send slats with iron beds; if desired, 50c. extra.

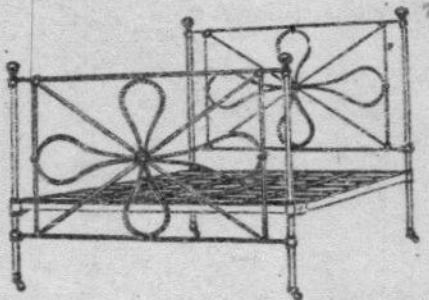

72231 Iron Bed, with brass knobs and extended foot rail; size of posts, 1 inch thick; size, width, 4 feet 6 inches; length, 6 feet 6 inches; enameled white; very fancy, well made and cheap; weight, about 100 lbs.
This is the best iron bed we have for the money.
Price, only.......................................$8.00.
We do not furnish slats with above bed; is desired, 50 cents extra.

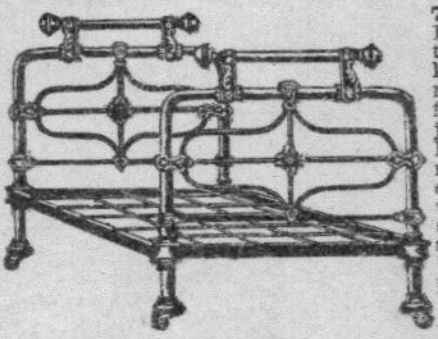

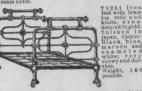

72251 Iron Bed with brass top rods and knobs, ornamented in gold; finished in japan. Colors: Black, blue, maroon and enameled white; very showy and durable. Weight, 100 pounds.

Size, 3x6½ ft.......................................$9.25
Size, 3½x6½ ft.......................................9.75
Size, 4x6½ ft.......................................9.90
Size, 4½x6½ ft.......................................10.00
Above prices do not include slats to iron bed. If desired, 50c. extra.

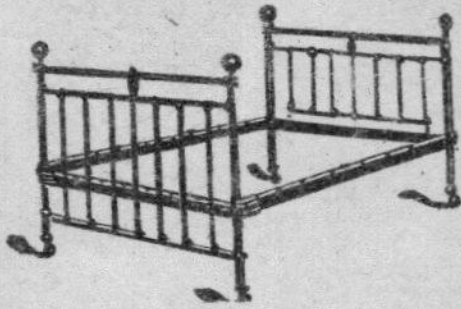

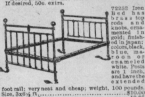

72252 Iron Bed has brass top rods and knobs, ornamented in gold; finished in japan; colors, black, blue, maroon or enameled white. Posts are 1 inch, and have the extended foot rail; very neat and cheap; weight, 100 pounds.
Size, 3x6½ ft.......................................$10.00
Size, 3½x6½ ft.......................................10.25
Size, 4x6½ ft.......................................10.50
Size, 4½x6½ ft.......................................10.75

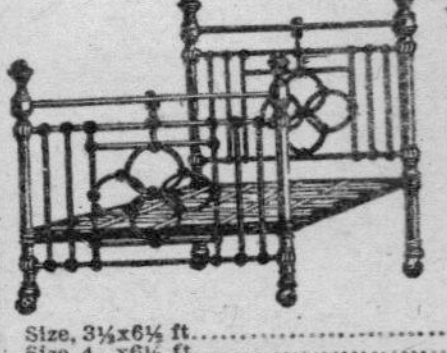

72253 Iron Bed with brass top rods, knobs and brass rosettes ornamented in gold. Finished in japan colors, black, blue and maroon, enameled white. A beauty. Weight, 1 60 pounds.

Size, 3½x6½ ft.......................................$13.50
Size, 4 x6½ ft.......................................13.75
Size, 4½x6½ ft.......................................14.00
We can furnish No. 72253 bed with canopy, if desired, for $4.00 extra.
Above prices do not include slats to iron bed. If desired, 50c extra.

Write out what you want, enclose the money, tell where to send and we do the rest. Easiest thing in the World.

Child's Folding Beds and Cribs.

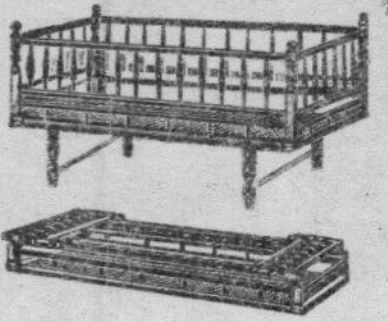

72275 Child's crib. Has folding sides and ends which contain the bedding when folded. The legs fold under, which enables us to ship it K. D. All castings are malleable iron. Frame is made of kiln-dried hard maple, and supplied with a steel woven wire mattress and patent adjustable brace for legs. Finished in natural maple. Weight, 25 pounds. Size 30x54 inches.
Price.......................................$3.25
72280 Child's crib. Same style as 72275, only larger. Size, 36x60 inches. Weight. 30 lbs.
Price.......................................3.75

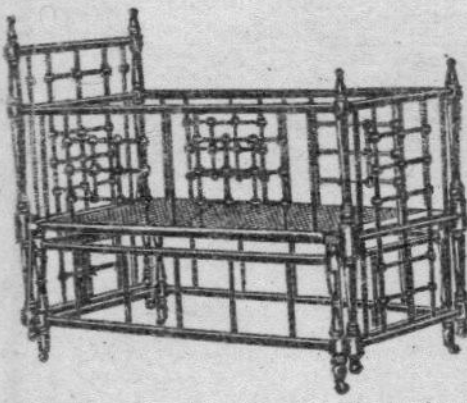

72285 Cradle made of hardwood. Has a gloss finish in natural maple, imitation walnut or mahogany. Is very rigid and strong. The cradle rocks perfectly level, is mounted on casters and easily moved about. Fitted with a fine woven wire mattress bottom. Size 24x44 inches. Weight, 25 lbs. Price only.....$3.75

FOLDING BEDS FOR CHILDREN.

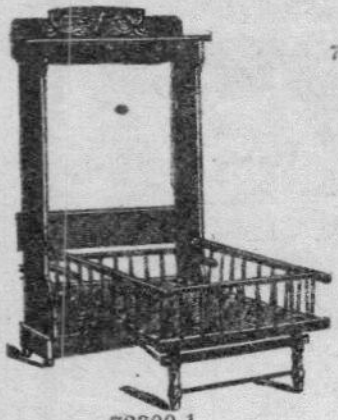

72300-1

72300 This bed is made for curtain front, and has all the advantages of a full sized folding bed; has a woven wire mattress. It is light, neat, tasteful and substantial. Size of bed when open, 30x54 in. outside measure, height 60 in.; width, 34 inches; depth, 14 inches; finished in antique only. Weight, 55 pounds.
Price complete..$6.25

72301 Folding Bed same as No. 72300, except in larger size—36x60 inches. Weight 60 pounds. Price complete.......................................$7.50

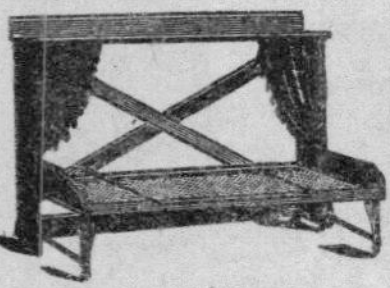

72302 Curtain Mantel Bed. Size when open, 3 ft. 9 in wide, 6 feet long. Size when closed, 4 ft. 4 in. high, 6 ft. 6 in. long. Made of hardwood, with woven wire mattress. Has brass rod for curtain. Finished in antique only.
Weight 125 pounds.
Without curtain, only.......................................$7.00

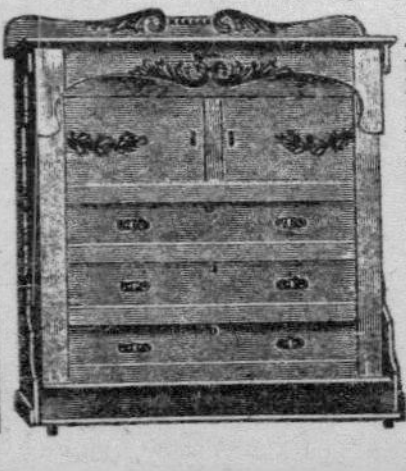

72303 Mantle Bed made of Elm Inside measure: 4 feet wide, 6 feet long. Outside measure when closed: height 5 feet; width, 4 feet 4 in. It has the woven wire supported spring and mattress holders attached. Finished in antique only. Weight 190 pounds. Price complete..$15.00

Wardrobe Folding Bed.

72305 Combination Wardrobe and Folding Bed Combined. The front view shows a very handsome wardrobe, which has 6 large hooks, is 4 ft. wide, 6 ft. high, 14 in. deep. By turning the article around you let the bed down as any ordinary folding bed, whereby you have two very handsome pieces of furniture in one at the cost of one piece; made of hard wood. Has 18x40 in. bevel mirror. Inside measure when open, 3 ft. 9 in. wide, 6 ft. long. Size when bed is closed, 4 ft. wide 6 ft. high. Finished in antique only. Weight, about 400 pounds.
Each.......................$25.00
Same without mirror....... 20.00

72306 Combination Folding Bed, Wardrobe, Bookcase and Desk combined; neatly carved and nicely finished. Made on the same principle as No. 72305 bed. Has 18x 20 inch German bevel mirror. Size of bed when open, 4 feet wide, 6 feet 3 inches long. Made in elm and finished antique. Weight about 400 pounds.
Price, complete, only..$24.50

72307 Combination Folding Bed, Wardrobe and Book Case combined; made on the same principle as 72305 bed. Except is much finer. Richly carved and highly polished; has 18x40 inch German bevel mirror. Extra fine woven wire mattress. Size of bed when open, 4 feet by 6 feet 3 in. Weight about 450 pounds.
Made of ash, price...$33.75
Made of oak, price... 36.00

72308 Combination Folding Bed, Wardrobe and Desk combined; made of solid oak, richly hand carved and hand polished. Has 20x48 inch French bevel mirror, and 3 large drawers as shown is cut, made on the same principle as No. 72305 bed, except is a much finer bed. Size of bed when open, 4 feet 2 inches wide, 6 feet 3 inches long. Has a fine woven wire mattress; finished antique; weight, about 525 pounds.
Price complete.....$52.00

Upright Folding Beds.

We show a larger variety of folding beds in our new special Furniture Catalogue. The cheapest line of folding beds in the market. There is nothing made to compare with them in price, make or finish.

72400 Upright Folding Bed, made of elm and finished antique. Very richly carved, and has a fine gloss finish; has a good woven wire supported spring. Size of bed when open, 4 feet 2 inches wide; 6 feet 3 inches long; weight, 425 pounds.
Price with 18x40 inch German bevel mirror, only.$24.70
Price, with panel front only 20.90

72401 Upright Folding Bed, made of solid oak, richly carved and hand polished. Has 18x40 inch German beveled glass mirror and a woven wire supported spring. Size of bed when open, 4 feet 2 inches wide; 6 feet 3 inches long. Finish antique; good value; weight, 425 pounds.
Price, complete.......$29.75

Folding Beds—Continued.

72402 Upright Folding Bed, made of solid oak, richly carved and polished. Has 18x40 inch German bevel mirror, and a woven wire supported spring. Size of bed when open, 4 feet 2 inches wide 6 feet 3 inches long; finished antique; cheap; weight, 425 pounds.
Price, complete.........$33.80

72403 Upright Folding Bed, made of solid oak, richly carved and polished; finished antique; has a fine woven wire supported spring, and 18x40 German bevel plate mirror. Size of bed when open, 4 feet 2 inches wide. 6 feet, 3 inches long. Very showy and rich; weight. 425 pounds.
Price, complete.......$36.90

72404 Upright Folding Bed made of solid walnut, richly hand carved and polished; has a fine woven wire supported spring, and a good 18x40 inch German bevel mirror. Size of bed when open, 4 feet, 4 inches wide; 6 feet, 3 inches long. An extra fine piece of furniture for little money; weight, 425 lbs.
Price, complete.......$44.00

Chiffoniers.

We show a beautiful line of chiffoniers in our new Furniture Catalogue.

72500 Chiffonier, made of solid oak, neatly carved and polished; has 6 large drawers. Height, 60 inches; size of top, 20x40 inches; finished antique; extra large and cheap; weight, 150 pounds.
Price......... $10.75

72502 Chiffonier, made of solid oak, richly carved and highly hand polished; has 5 extra large drawers; a fine 18x24 French bevel plate mirror; size of top, 24x38 inches; very stylish and cheap. Finished antique; weight, 104 pounds.
Price.....................$17.55

Bureaus, Dressers.

72550 Bureau antique finish; four drawers, no mirror; height 3 ft. 7 in.; width, 3 ft. 1 in.; weight about 75 pounds.
Price, complete.....$5.90

72551 Dresser, made of hardwood; finished antique; size of dresser top, 20x40 inches; has a 16x28 inch plain German mirror, and three large drawers; weight, 85 pounds. Price, only....$6.75

If the description of any article is not sufficient for your information, write us and we will cheerfully give further facts.

Dressers—Continued.

72552 Dresser, made of solid oak nicely finished antique; size of dresser top, 21x42 inches; has a good 24x30 inch German bevel mirror, and three large drawers; well made and cheap. Weight, 100 pounds.
Our price.. ....$11.80

72553 Cheval Dresser, made of solid oak. Richly hand-carved and nicely finished antique; size of dresser top, 21x42 inches; has a fine 18x40 inch German bevel mirror. Retails for double our price.
Price....................$13.50

72554 Dresser, made of solid oak, carved and polished; size of dresser top, 21x42 inches; has a good 24x 30 inch German bevel mirror and three large drawers; finished antique, weight, 100 lbs.
Price, only.............$12.80

72554 Dresser, richly carved and made of solid oak, with a fine 18x40 inch German bevel mirror; size of dresser top, 21x42 inches; finished antique; weight, 110 pounds.
Price, only..............$14.80

72555 Cheval Dresser

Washstands.

72600 Washstand, hardwood top 16x30 in., 3 large drawers only. Weight, about 35 pounds.
Price each.................$2.95

72600-1

72602 Washstand hardwood top 16x30 inches, one large and two small drawers and single door. Weight, about 35 pounds.
Each....................$3.25

72602

72603 Washstand, hardwood, one drawer, 16x23 in. top. Weight, about 20 pounds.
Each....................$1.30
Above washstands furnished in antique finish.

72604 Toilet Washstand, well made of solid oak; size of top, 18x32 in. Has one large drawer, two small and a door. Also has a good large 18x20 in. German bevel mirror. Finished Antique. Weight about 75 pounds.
Price.........$6.50

72605 Toilet Washstand, made of solid oak, richly carved, and nicely finished. Has large 18x20 in. German bevel mirror; size of top, 18x 32 inches, well made and cheap. Finished antique. Weight, about 75 pounds. Price $7.75

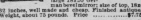

FOLDING BOOK RACKS.

72960 Folding Book Rack, made of oak; finished antique. Height, 34 inches; width 19 inches; depth, 9 inches. Hangs on the wall and is very strong. Three shelves fold and close automatically. Weight, 13 pounds.
Price, each.............$1.50

72965 Folding Book Case, made of solid oak. Height, 55 inches; width, 28 inches; depth, 10 inches. Four shelves fold and close automatically. Entirely new; very handy and cheap. No screws or nails needed. Finished antique. Weight, 30 pounds.
Price.....................$2.50

Book Cases.

73000 Curtain Library Case, made of hardwood, finished antique; brass rods and rings for curtain, adjustable shelves, polished finish; height, 5 ft.; width, 2 ft. 8in Weight, about 80 pounds.
Price complete.............$4.80

73001 Curtain Book Case, made of solid oak, neatly carved and polished; height, 5 ft. 2 in.; width, 2 ft. 9 in.; has French mirror, 6x10 in.; brass rod and rings for curtain; adjustable shelves. Weight about 90 pounds.
Price.....................$6.00

73002 Book Case, made of quarter-sawed oak, neatly carved and highly hand polished. width, 33 inches; depth, 12 inches; height, 6 feet; has one door and shelves are adjustable; well made and cheap. We consider this a bargain. Weight about 100 pounds.
Our price only.............$10.50

 73002½

73002½ Book Case, made of quarter sawed oak, richly carved and polished. Width, 3 feet 6 inches; depth, 12 inches; height, 5 feet 5 inches; has two doors with lock and shelves are adjustable. This is a beautiful large case for the money, and exceedingly cheap. Weight about 175 pounds. Price only.....$11.20

73002

73003 Book Case. Here is a fine book case for the library or sitting room; made of quarter-sawed oak, highly hand polished and neatly carved. Height, 5 feet 6 inches; width, 5 feet; has three doors with locks; shelves are adjustable. Very large. Weight about 200 pounds. Price only.... $14.50

73003

Book Cases—Continued.

73003½ Book Case, made of quarter-sawed oak, richly carved and highly hand polished. Height, 5 feet 5 inches; width, 3 feet 5 inches; depth, 13 inches; has two door with locks, and shelves are adjustable; has a fine French mirror 12x24 inches. Very ornamental, and well made. Note low price on this book case. Weight about 200 pounds.
Our price only.........$16.80

73003½

73004 Book Case, made of quarter-sawed oak, highly hand polished and richly hand carved. Height, 6 feet 6 inches; width, 4 feet; depth, 13½ inches; has two large glass doors with locks; shelves are adjustable; has a fine French bevel mirror, 16x24 inches. This is a beautiful book case and is extra good value. Is extra well made. Weight about 200 pounds.
Our price, only......$19.20

73004

73006 Book Case, made of solid oak, highly polished and carved. Height, 6 feet 2 inches; width, 3 feet 10 inches; has two doors and lower drawer; shelves are adjustable; French bevel mirror, extra inches. This book case is well made and a bargain. Weight, 200 pounds.
Price.............$17.25

73006

73007 Book Case, made of solid oak. Richly carved and polished. Has a French bevel mirror 10x 24 in. Extra heavy glass in the door, and two small drawers. Height, 6 ft. 6 in. Width, 4 ft. 2 in. Finished antique. Useful and ornamental. Weight,140 pounds.
Price..............$21.00

73007

73008 Book Case. Made of solid oak, quarter-sawed front; height, 6 ft. 4 in.; width 5 ft. 3 in. Has 16x20 inch French bevel mirror. Has 3 large doors with good heavy glass; shelves are adjustable. Finished antique. Note size and low price. Weight, 275 pounds.
Price.......$25.00

Combination Book Cases.

A BARGAIN.

73009 Combination Book Case and Writing Desk, made of solid oak, neatly carved and highly polished; height, 5 feet 6 inches; width, 3 feet 6 inches; has French bevel mirror 16x14 inches; shelves are adjustable; desk is nicely partitioned with pigeon holes and drawers; cheapest on the market; weight about 150 lbs.
Price, only.............$12.95

Combination Book Cases—Cont'd.

73011 Combination Book Case and Writing Desk, made of solid oak, highly polished and richly carved; interior of desk is fitted with pigeon holes and drawer; height, 6 feet; width, 3 feet 5 inches; finished antique; weight, about 150 pounds; has a fine French bevel mirror 12x16 inches; well made and cheap.
Our price, only.......$17.50

73015 Combination Book Case and Writing Desk, made of solid oak; richly hand carved and highly polished; height, 5 feet 8 inches; width,3 feet 8 inches; has a drop leaf desk nicely partitioned with pigeon holes and drawers; shelves are adjustable; French bevel mirrors 6x6 inches and 12x16 inches; finished antique; weight, 150 lbs; very ornamental; cheap. Price.......$19.50

73016 Combination Book Case and Writing Desk, made of solid oak, richly hand carved and polished; height, 5 feet 7 inches; width, 3 feet 6 in. Desk is nicely partitioned with pigeon holes and drawers; has a fine fancy French bevel mirror 16x16 inches; finished antique; weight, about 150 pounds.
Price, only...........$21.75

73019 Combination Book Case and Writing Desk, made of quarter-sawed oak. Richly hand carved and highly polished. Height,5 feet, 11 in.; width, 3 feet 10 in. Desk is nicely partitioned with pigeon holes and drawers; has a French bevel mirror 16x16 in.; shelves are adjustable; very ornamental and nice enough for any house. Weight about 175 pounds.
Price..............$24.30

73020 Combination Book Case and Writing Desk, made of quarter-sawed oak, richly carved and polished. Height, 5 feet, 9 inches; width, 3 feet, 9 inches; desk is partitioned with pigeon holes and drawers; shelves are adjustable; has a fine, fancy French bevel mirror 12x16 inches; 4 large drawers with locks. Weight about 200 pounds. Our price on this case is only...............$27.90

73021 Combination Book Case and Writing desk, made of solid oak neatly carved and highly polished. Height, 5 feet, 5 in.; width, 3 feet, 10 in. All shelves are adjustable. Desk is nicely partitioned with pigeon holes and drawers; has 7 inch bevel mirror 14x18 in; weight about 250 pounds; finished antique; very large, well made and cheap.
Price, only.....$28.00

ombination Bookcases—Continued

73028   73029

73028 Combination Bookcase and Writing desk, made in solid oak, neatly carved and polished, height 6 feet 10 inches; width 3 feet; size of glass in doors, 14x30 inch. Has a drop leaf desk with 3 large drawers. shelves are adjustable. Finished antique. The best and cheapest combination book case in the market; weight, 175 pounds. Price, only......**$15.75**

73029 Combination Bookcase and Writing Desk, made in walnut or solid oak, richly carved and nicely polished; height, 7 feet, 2 inches; width, 2 feet, 11 inches. Has a cylinder desk nicely partitioned with pigeon holes and drawers; shelves are adjustable; size of glass in doors, 13x30 inches; well made and cheap. Weight, 175 pounds. Price........................**$21.75**

73031 Combination Bookcase and Writing Desk, made in walnut or solid oak; richly carved and polished; height, 7 feet, 6 inches; width, 3 feet, 4 inches; size of glass in doors 15x32 inches; has a cylinder desk nicely partitioned with pigeon holes and drawers; shelves are adjustable; weight, 200 lbs. Price...................**$24.90**

73031

Ladies' or Parlor Desks.

73100 Ladies' Desk, made of solid oak; richly carved. Height, 46 in.; width, 26 in.; depth, 15 in. Has a French bevel mirror 6x16 inches. Inside is nicely partitioned with drawers. Weight, about 50 pounds.
Price only.................**$6.95**

73101 Parlor or Ladies' Desk, made of solid oak; richly carved and highly hand-polished. Height, 50 inches; width, 30 inches. Has a French bevel mirror 6x16 inches. The drop leaf has lock, and the inside is nicely partitioned with pigeon holes and drawers. This desk is one of the best bargains we have. Weight, about 75 pounds ..**$10.98**

73102 Parlor or Ladies' Desk, made of solid oak: richly carved and polished. Height, 52 inches; width, 26 inches. Inside is nicely partitioned with pigeon holes and drawers; a good, durable desk. Weight, about 75 lbs. Price...................**$10.50**

73104 Parlor or Ladies' Desk, made of select oak; hand carved and highly polish d. Height, 52 inches; width, 26 inches. Has large drawer and drop-leaf, nicely partitioned with pigeon holes and drawers. French bevel mirror. Very ornamental and well made. Weight, about 80 pounds.**$13.50**

73105 Ladies' Parlor Desk, made of quarter-sawed oak; hand carved and highly polished. Height, 54 inches; width, 28 inches. Has a beautiful French bevel mirror. Inside of desk is nicely partitioned with pigeon holes and drawers. Extra large and showy. Weight, about 100 pounds. Price..........**$16.25**

Ladies' Desks—Continued.

73107 This is a beautiful Ladies' Desk, richly hand carved. The polish on this desk is as fine as a piano finish. Height, 4 feet 9 inches; width, 24 inches; depth 17 inches. Has a fine French bevel mirror 10x18 inches. Inside is nicely partitioned with pigeon holes and drawers. The wood used in this desk is very select and handsome. Very ornamental. Weight, about 80 pounds.
Price, made of quarter-sawed oak.................**$15.70**
Price, made of solid mahogany **$18.90**
Price, made of curly birch, 18.30

Office Desks.

We wish to call your special attention to our extremely low prices on office desks.

73125 Office Desk, made of oak, highly polished. Has one extension slide combination lock and the perfect working flexible slide roll top. Length, 3 feet 6 inches; width, 2 feet 6 inches. Well made and cheap. Finished antique. Weight, about 165 pounds.
Price..........**$14.70**

73126 Office Desk, made of oak, highly polished. Has one extension slide, combination lock and the perfect working flexible slide roll top. Length, 3 feet 4 inches; width, 2 feet 6 inches. Finished antique. Weight, about 175 pounds.
Price.........**$16.80**
We can furnish above desk with cabinet in place of drawers, if desired, at same price

73127 Office Desk, made of solid oak and highly polished. Has two extension slides combination lock, and the perfect working flexible slide roll top. Writing bed is highly polished. Length, 4 ft, width, 2 ft. 8 inches; height, 3 ft. 9 inches.
Finished antique; weight, about 265 pounds.
Price only **$15.75**
We can furnish above desk with drawers on both sides, if desired, at same price.

73128 Office Desk, same as 73127, except is 4 feet 6 inches long and has closed back. well made and a bargain. Weight, about 280 lbs. Price only ..**$18.00**

73129 Office Desk, same as 73127, except is 5 ft. long and has closed back. Weight, about 290 pounds.
Our price is only **$19.75**

73130 High Curtain Office Desk, made of solid oak and highly polished. Has two extension slides, combination lock and the perfect working slide roll top. Writing bed is highly polished. Length, 4 ft., width, 2 ft. 8 inches; height, 4 feet 2 inches. Finished antique; very roomy; well made and cheap. Same as cut except has closed back. Weight, about 280 pounds. This is a bargain. Price only....................**$17.50**

73131 High Curtain Office Desk, same as 73130, except is 4 feet 6 inches long and has closed back. Price is only **$18.50**

73132 High Curtain Office Desk, same as 73131, except is 5 feet long and back is closed. This desk is large enough for anyone. We consider it a great bargain. Weight about 290 lbs. Price only ..**$20.50**

Office Desks—Continued.

73135 Office Desk. This cut shows the desk open, which you can see is very handy and convenient. Made of oak and nicely finished. All the doors and drawers have locks. Length, 4 ft. 4 in; width, 2 ft. 7 in. Writing bed is covered with cloth or imitation leather. Has slant top. Finished antique. Weight, 200 pounds.
Price, only.....**$21.00**

73140 Flat Top Office Desk, made of oak. Length, 4 feet 2 inches; width, 2 feet 6 inches. Has two extension slides. Finished in polished wood top, or covered with cloth or imitation leather. Weight, 200 lbs. Same as cut, except back is closed. Price..................**$9.50**
We can furnish No. 73140 desk with drawers on both sides, if desired, at same price.

73141 Flat Top Office Desk, same as 73140, except is 4 feet 6 inches long, and has closed back. Weight about 210 pounds. This is well made and bargain.
Price only **$10.00**

73142 Flat Top Office Desk, same as 73140, except is 5 ft. long and has closed back. Weight about 225 pounds, very large and exceedingly cceap. Price only....**$10.50**

73159 Men's Drop Leaf Desk, nicely partitioned with pigeon holes and drawers. Made of hardwood and finished antique. Height, 5 feet 6 inches; width, 2 feet 6 inches. A very convenient article to have in any house. Weight, 100 pounds.
Price..................**$9.50**

73159

73160 Desk, made of oak, finished antique. Has all the conveniences of a large, expensive desk. Takes up no floor space, can be set on a shelf, table, or can be fastened to the wall with two screws. Height, 29 inches; width, 25 inches; depth, 10 inches; size of drop leaf, 17x22 inches. Weight, 35 pounds.
Price, only......**$4.95**

Hat Racks.

73177 Hat Rack, made of solid oak rubbed and polished, 36 in. long, 15 in. high; 10 brass plated hooks. It can be folded flat for packing.
French bevel mirror. Price, each..............**$2.25**
Weight, about 10 pounds.

73178 Hat Rack, made of solid oak, finely finished antique; size, 16x28 inches, with 4 large hooks, and a French bevel mirror 10x14 inches. Very neat, cheap and well made. Weight, 8 pounds.
Price only..................**$2.50**

73179 Hat Rack, made of solid oak, finished antique; size 13x36 inches. Has 6 large hooks and a French bevel mirror 6x6 in.
Weight, 6 pounds   Each, only..................**$1.60**

Folding Tables—Continued.

73411 Folding Table, much finer than 73410, is made of ash, finely finished antique and mounted on casters; size 36 inches long, 30 inches wide and 26 inches high. The folding device is constructed in such a manner as to form a complete brace from the leg to the center of the table, rendering great strength. Weight, about 15 pounds.
Price..$1.25

Dining Room Tables.

(We wish to call special attention to our prices.)

73500 Extension Table, oval drop leaves, 28x42 inch, top closed, made of hardwood and finished in antique only. Comes in 6, 8, 10 or 12 foot lengths.

Weight, 10 foot table, 100 pounds. Price, per foot..$0.58

73501 Extension Table square, 29x42 in. top, closed made of hardwood and finished in antique only. Comes in 6, 8, 10 or 12 foot lengths.

Weight, 10 foot table, 100 pounds. Price, per foot, $0.58

73502 Extension Table, made of oak, size of top when closed 42x44 inches. Finished antique carved and well made, a bargain. Weight, 10 foot table, 125 pounds.
Price, 8 ft table..$6.25
" 10 ft. " 7.75
" 12 ft. " 9.25

73503 Extension Table, made of oak, richly carved and polished, size of top when closed 42x48 inches, finished antique, a beauty and very cheap. Weight, 10 foot table, 125 pounds.
Price, 8 foot table..................$8.50
Price, 10 foot table..................$7.90
Price, 12 foot table..................$9.50

73504 Extension Table, made of quarter-sawed oak, hand carved and highly polished, size of top 42x42 inches when closed. Weight, 10 foot table, 125 pounds. This table is a bargain at the price we offer it.
Price, 8 foot table..................$8.25
Price, 10 foot table..................9.75
Price, 12 foot table..................11.50

Dining Room Tables.—Continued.

73505 Extension Table, made of quarter-sawed oak, highly polished and richly carved. It has 6 large heavy legs; size of top when closed 42x 42 in. Weight, 10 foot table, 125 pounds. Well made and rich.
Price, 8 foot table..................$9.25
Price, 10 foot table..................10.75
Price, 12 foot table..................12.35

73506 Extension Table, made of fine quarter-sawed oak highly polished and richly carved, very heavy and well made. Weight, 10 foot table, 125 pounds. Size of top when closed 42x 42 inches.
Price, 8 foot table..................$10.25
Price, 10 foot table..................12.00
Price, 12 foot table..................14.00

73507 Extension Table, made of quarter-sawed oak. The finish on this table is as fine as a piano polish. Size of top, when closed, 44x44 inches. Has six extra large, heavy legs, which are highly polished. Weight, 10-foot table, 160 pounds. Fine enough for any dining room.
Price, 8-foot table..................$12.25
Price, 10-foot table..................14.00
Price, 12-foot table..................16.00

Kitchen Tables.

                                     Each

73515 Kitchen Table, all hardwood, turned legs, molded edge with dr wer..................$1.30
73516 Fall-Leaf Table, square leaf at each end, folds down, made of hardwood; size, open, 42x52 inches..................2.40
73517 Same as 73516, round leaf, making an oval table when all leaves are up; made of hardwood; size, open, 42x62..................3.50

73518 Kitchen Cabinet Table. The most handy household article we have. Made of elm, with maple top. Has a molding board, spice and cutlery drawer, sugar and groceries drawer, flour drawer with zinc bottom that holds 100 pounds of flour, and a cupboard for cooking utensils. Finished antique. Length, 5 feet; width, 2 ft. 4 in.; height, 2 ft. 8 in. Well made and cheap. Price only..................$6.95

WASHING MACHINES.

No lady will appreciate a good Washer until she has tried one. We advise her to try an Anthony Wayne or Western Star. See Index for quotations.

Invalid Rolling Chairs.

We are prepared to supply our customers with Invalid Chairs of all kinds at manufacturers' prices We illustrate some of the styles most commonly used, but our limited space prevents our showing more of the extensive line which we carry. For the benefit of those who cannot find here what they think would suit their particular ailment we will mail on application a special catalogue.

73550 An Invalid's' Commode or Sick Room Chair, has large arms, very strong and made of hardwood, finished light, dark or antique. No sick room should be without it. A door on the back of it will admit any ordinary commode. Weight, 20 pounds.
Price..$2.40

73550½ A very commonly used chair for out or in door use. Iron boxed hickory wheels, oak frame, cane seat and back. Best malleable iron castings, strong enough for the heaviest adult; will pass through any door 28 in. wide; weight, 45 pounds.
Price..$18.00
Hand rims, same as on 73555, can be placed on the wheels of 73550 chair for $2.00 extra.

73551 Same pattern as 73550 for children, age 13 or 14 and under. Weight, 30 pounds. Price, $16.00

73552—The World's Fair Rolling Chair. Here is a bargain in an invalid chair. These were used at the World's Fair. Have all been put in good shape and are almost as good as new. They have a shellaced reed body, ball-bearing cushioned rubber tired bicycle wheels, on springs, with a push handle. These sold at the World's Fair for $65.00, and our customers can have them until they are all sold for only..$24.00

73553 Invalid or Reclining Chair. You can lie down or sit up in it at any angle. This is the best, most comfortable, cheapest and the one used more than any other for invalids. Height of back from seat, 33 inches; width of seat inside, 19 inches. Will pass through a door 28 inches wide. It is made of antique oak, hickory and oak, iron boxed wheels. Weight, 50 lbs.
Each..$25.00
With outside hand rims, same as 73555, for $2.00 extra.
Springs can be had on this chair same as shown on 73555 at an additional cost of $3.00.

73554 Child's Invalid or Reclining Chair, same as 73553 for children of 15 years or younger. Weight, 35 pounds.
Price..$20.00
73555 Invalid's or Reclining Chair. The above chair, while being the same as 73553, is a better chair; the particular advantage is in the easy manner in which invalids can change to different positions and still be very comfortable. Otherwise it is the same in all particulars as 73553. Weight, 35 pounds. Price, complete, as shown in cut..................$37.00
Price, with hand rims, and without springs..$35.00
Price, with springs and without hand rims....34.00
Price, without springs and without hand rims. 32.00

Invalid Rolling Chairs—Continued.

shown on 73555, $2.00 extra.

73556 A new Invalid or Reclining Chair. You can lie down or sit up tip at any angle. Made of solid oak with rubber-tired bicycle wheels. A model invalid's chair; seat, 19 in. wide; will pass through a door 32 in. wide; strong and easy running. Weight, about 50 pounds.
Price only..$35.00
With side hand rims, same as

Hand rims can be placed on the wheels same as on 73555 for $2.00 extra.

73557 A new style of Invalid Chair. Cane Seat, polished antique, solid oak bolted frame, has cushion tired ball bearing bicycle wheels. Back is high enough to rest anyone's head on. Very comfortable, strong and one of the best and cheapest chairs ever made for the money. Large size for adults' use; will pass through a door 31 inches wide. Weight, about 35 pounds.
Price only..$23.50

Chairs.

Chairs are shipped to best advantage when tied in pairs, hence it is the best not to order less than two of a kind. This, of course, does not apply to arm chairs, rockers, rattan goods, etc. We fill orders for any quantity and see that they are packed in good shape for shipping. The risk of break and damage is very slight, but such as it is, it must be assumed by the purchaser. Our responsibility ceases when we have obtained a clean receipt from the transportation company. Quarters or half dozen lots may be had at dozen rates.

Kitchen and Dining Chairs—All Wood.

73600 Bent Back Dining Chair, has 3 spindles, made of hardwood, scooped seat, double stretchers all around, plain light, dark or antique finish. Weight, about 10 pounds.
Each.........................$0.40
Per dozen........................4.50
Above chair in lots of 100 or more. Per dozen...........$4.00

73601

73601 Our Columbian Diner, very stylish, medium high back, strong and very cheap. Made of hardwood, finished antique. Weight, 10 pounds.
Each.....................$0.52
Per dozen........................5.80

73601½ Ladies' Wood Seat Rocker to match 73601 chair, very comfortable. Finished antique.
Weight, 13 pounds. Each......................82

73602 Bent Back Dining Chair, same size as 73600 chair, has 4 spindles, is striped and decorated and better finished; antique, light or dark. Weight, 10 pounds.
Each..........$0.42 Per dozen........4.75

73603 Ladies' Rocker to match No. 73602. Light or dark finish. Weight, 12 lbs.......65

Always write your name the same way.

Chairs—Continued.

73604   73605

73604 Pioneer Dining Wood, seat beaded, double bent bow 5 spindles, extra heavy and strong, light or dark finish. Weight, 11 pounds. Each........$0.60 Per dozen...$6.75
73605 Perforated seat and back double bent bow 5 spindles, made in imitation walnut and light finishes, antique oak finish. Weight, 9 lbs. Each......$0.67 Per doz...7.50
73606 Same chair as No. 73605 except has beaded spindle. Weight, 9 pounds. Each..........72
Per dozen........................8.00

73655 Dandy High Back, perforated seat and back, made in imitation walnut, antique and light finish; weight, 11 pounds.
Each.....................$0.80
Per dozen........................9.00

73655

73660 Double Back Wood Seat Chairs light or dark finish. Weight, 10 pounds.
Each.....................$0.62
Per doz.........................7.00

73660

Cane-Seated Dining and Cottage Chairs.

73700 Half Grecian Cottage or Dining Chairs, cane seat, finished in imitation walnut, and light and antique finish; weight, 9 pounds.
Each.....................$0.68
Per doz.........................8.00
73705 Same as 73700, but made in solid oak and carved top; weight, 11 pounds.
Each.....................$0.90
Per doz.........................11.00

73720 Very attractive cane seat Dining and Chamber Chair, made of hardwood and finished imitation antique oak, carved top; weight, 12 pounds. Price only each..$0.90
Per dozen........................10.00
73721 Same as 73720 only has plain top instead of carved.
Each.....................$0.80
Per dozen........................9.00

73722 A strong and attractive Ladies Rocker. Made of hardwood and finished imitation antique oak to match 73721; weight, about 15 pounds.
Plain top...................$1.20
Covered top.................1.30

Chairs—Continued.

73723 A large and very attractive Dining or Chamber Chair; cane seat, made of hardwood, finished antique; weight, 12 pounds; very strong and durable
Each.....................$6.90
Per dozen........................10.00

73724 Large, strong and attractive Ladies' Rocker to match 73723 chair; weight, 15 pounds.
Price, only..........$1.30

73725 Very large and attractive cane seat Dining Chair, made of hardwood and finished antique; weight, 12 pounds.
Each.....................$0.95
Per dozen........................11.00

73726 A very showy Dining and Sitting Room Chair, cane seat, made of hardwood, richly carved and nicely finished; very durable; weight, about 12 pounds; has brace arms.
Each.....................$1.20
Per dozen........................13.50

73727 A beautiful Ladies' cane seat brace arm Rocker, high back and very strong, made of hardwood and finished antique; weight, 15 pounds; a bargain. Only.........$1.80

73730 New High Back Dining Chair with brace arms, carved top, comfortable and very showy. A fine sitting room or dining room chair, made of hardwood; finished antique. Weight, 12 pounds.
Each.....................$1.20
Per dozen........................13.25
73735 Rocker to match 73730. Fine and comfortable for Ladies; finished antique. Weight, 15 pounds.
Price.....................$1.60

73730

73736   73736

73736 How is this for the money? A set of hardwood, antique finish dining room chairs, cane seat; the cheapest and best made for the money, exceedingly comfortable and very strong.

	Each	Per doz.
Dining chair; weight, 10 lbs.	$1.10	$12.00
Arm chair; weight, 16 lbs.	2.00	
One set, 5 chairs and 1 arm chair to match.		7.00

73737 Rocker to match 73736 chair; finished antique; very comfortable; weight, 15 pounds.
Price.....................1.50

Chairs—Continued.

74426 Man's Large Arm Rocker. This is one of the most attractive and positively good rockers we show this season. A man's delight and lady's household comfort; very large, and has extra high back. This is a beauty. Weight about 18 pounds.
Natural reed............$6.65
New shellac finish......7.55

74427   74429
74427 An extra fine pattern of gentleman's very large arm rocker. If you want the best for all purposes, buy this. Weight, 16 pounds.
Price in natural reed.................$7.55
New shellac finish....................8.45
74428 Lady's Reed Rocker, same style and quality as 74427. Very comfortable. Weight, about 12 pounds.
Natural reed, only........5.75
New shellac finish........6.65
74429 Gentleman's Rocker. Best quality, very fancy and durable. Extra high back. Never sold for less than $10.00. Weight, 16 pounds.
Natural reed.................7.55
New shellac finish..........8.45
74430 Lady's Fine Reed Rocker, same pattern and quality as 74429; exceedingly comfortable; you make no mistake by ordering this rocker. Weight, 13 pounds.
Natural reed, only.........5.75
New shellac finish.........6.65

74430½ A gentleman's big high back easy arm chair. Just the thing to take comfort in. Well made and cheap. Weight about 18 pounds.
Natural reed............$6.25
New shellac finish.. 7.10

74430½ A beautiful reception, hall or corner chair. Very ornamental, comfortable and strong. A bargain, never sold before for less than $7.50. Weight about 15 pounds. Our price, in natural reed, only................$4.45
New shellac finish........5.35
Finished in gold leaf......7.30

74432 Corner or Odd Chair. Made of reed, exceedingly showy. Considering the work, style and durability it is very cheap. Weight about 16 pounds.
Natural reed.............$5.35
New shellac finish........6.25
Finished in gold leaf.. 8.25

74432

74433 Child's Reed Rocker, strong and comfortable; hardwood frame. weight 6 pounds. Price, natural Reed.................$1.35
74434 High chair with table to match 74433. Has same kind of table as shown on 74439 chair. Weight about 12 pounds. Natural reed, only.................$1.75

Chairs—Continued.

74435 Child's Fancy Reed Rocker; a little beauty; very comfortable; Best quality; weight, 7 pounds. Price, in natural reed, only..$2.45

74436 A very attractive Child's Reed Rocker. Durable and comfortable. Weight, 6 lbs. Price of natural reed, only.................$2.00
74437 Child's High Chair, to match 74436, with table same pattern as shown on 74439, strong and durable. Weight, 10 pounds. Natural reed...$2.65

74438 A very pretty Child's Reed Rocker. A good pattern strong and comfortable. Weight, about 10 lbs.
Price, natural reed.................$2.45

74439 Child's Reed High Chair, with table. A perfect chair. The table is the best made. New feature with bent arms, so it swings high over the head of the child. No fear of ever unfastening. The legs have a wide spread, so there is no tipping over; weight, 10 pounds. Price in natural reed only $2.45
74440 Child's Reed Rocker to match 74439; an attractive pattern; very comfortable; weight, about 10 pounds. Price in natural reed....$1.75

74441 Child's Chair with table; reed back and solid oak frame; same table, spread of legs as on 74439 chair. This chair is a bargain. Weight, 10 pounds. Finished in antique oak.
Only.................$1.50

74550 Baby Walker, made of willow, on casters. Just the right size and thing for a baby when learning to walk. An article that everyone should have in their home. Weight about 10 pounds. Each $1.75

74551 Baby Walker, made of hardwood with shelf. If you want to teach your baby how to walk without trouble and at the same time, get one of these. All colors. Weight about 15 pounds. Each.................$2.40

74555 Chair. Cabinet Nursery Chair; willow, with shelf and seat. Our sales on this chair are so great that it is almost impossible to supply the demand. Weight, about 5 pounds. Each.................$0.75
Per dozen.................8.00

Work Baskets.

74560 A very showy and handy work basket made of the best Reed. Should be in every household. Weight, 4 pounds.
Price, only..$1.35

74561 Fancy Reed work basket. A lady's delight. Weight, 4 pounds. Price, only $1.40

74560   74561

74561½ Bamboo Easel Work Stand. made of bamboo; height, 43 inches; very artistic and well made; a very useful hall or parlor ornament. Price, only.................$3.00

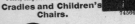

74562 Reed and Rattan Music Stand, very durable and ornamental; weight about 8 pounds. Each.................$2.00

74565 Work Basket; very fancy; made of reed with cover to basket; very pretty and good size. Weight about 5 pounds. Price, only.................$1.30

74565

74566 Fancy Reed Work Basket very large and showy. Weight about 7 pounds.
Price, only.................$1.75

Cradles and Children's Chairs.

74635 Cradle, bent wood ends. plain spindles, well made and substantial. Finished in light or dark wood. Weight 15 pounds. Price $1.25

74650 Child's High Chair, wood seat with table; light, dark or in colors. Weight, 15 pounds.
Each.................$0.85
74651 Same with perforated veneer back. Weight. 11 pounds. Each $0.95. Either of above, without table, 20 cents less.
74653 Child's High Chair; cane seat with table; made of solid oak, antique finish. Weight, 14 pounds.
Each.................$2.00

74653

74566

Chairs—Continued.

74654 Child's High Chair. A beauty. Finished in all colors: Red, light, antique and dark. Very strong, wood seat. Weight, 12 pounds.
Each..........$1.20
Cane seat. Each..........1.40

74655 Child's High chair, with table; made of hardwood; finished antique. Weight, 12 pounds.
Price, cane seat..........$1.20
Price, wood seat..........1.00

74656 A very showy cane and wood seat high chair; bent arm, carved back, strong and good. Weight, 12 pounds
Wood seat..........$1.40
Cane seat..........1.60

74658

74658 Child's Rocker. A beautiful little rocker for the money. Large enough for a child of 10 years. Cane seat; antique finish. Weight, 8 pounds.
Each..........$1.50

74659

74659 Child's Fancy Rocker; has silk plush or silk tapestry seat and back. Very pretty. Finished antique. Weight 9 pounds.
Each..........$2.50

74660 Child's Rocker. Very strong and durable; weight, 7 pounds.
Price, cane seat..........$1.00
Price, wood seat..........90

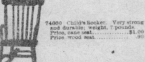

74661 A Child's beautiful Rocker; large size; strong and made of solid oak; cane seat; weight, 10 lbs.
Price..........$1.70

Chairs—Continued.

74665 Child's Nursery Chair, wood seat, light, dark or in colors. Weight, 6 pounds.
Each..........$0.65
74670 Same with shelf (or table) in front. Weight, 8 pounds.
Each..........$0.85

74675

74675 Child's Rocker, wood seat, bent pillars, striped and ornamented; finished light, dark or in colors. Weight, 8 lbs.
Each..........$0.95
74680 Same as 74675; cane seat. Weight, 6 pounds.
Each..........$1.25

74685.

74685 Kindergarten Chair, finished in red, light, antique and dark; made in two heights. Height of seat from floor, 14 in; height of seat from floor, 10 inches. Weight, 6 lbs.
Each..........$0.45
Per doz..........5.00

74690 Child's Toy Chair, ornamented in colors Weight 3 pounds.
Each..........$0.30

Combined Chair and Ladder.

74695

74695 The above cut fully illustrates our combination Step Ladder and Chair. The one on the left is the form of a step ladder, and the one on the right that of a chair, which you will see at once is a neat and convenient article, and useful in many ways in every household and office.

The chair is made of dried elm, finished in natural wood with two coats of varnish, every joint glued and nailed, making it a strong and safe ladder, when in use for that purpose. Weight, about 20 pounds. Price each..........$1.00
Per doz..........11.50

Cold Blast Feathers.

74700 Odorless Feathers, one-half feathers and one-half down oooo grade.
Per lb..........$0.75
74701 Odorless Feathers, very choicest extra selected prime live geese feathers ooo grade.
Per lb..........$0.72
74702 Odorless Feathers, selected prime live geese feathers, oo grade.
Per lb..........$0.60
74703 Odorless Feathers, prime live geese feathers, o grade.
Per lb..........$0.58
74704 Odorless Feathers, fair prime geese feathers, L grade.
Per lb..........$0.55
74705 Odorless Feathers, slightly mixed duck and geese feathers, M grade. Per lb..........$0.45
74706 Domestic Geese Down Extra No. 1. Per lb. 2.25
74707 Domestic Geese Down No. 1. Per lb...... 1.25
74708 Domestic Geese Down No. 2. Per lb...... 1.00
Odorless feathers will be put in sacks containing one pound and upward, no extra charge for sacks.

Down Sofa Pillows.

In Domestic Sateen.

74710 Size	15x15	18x18	20x20
Price, each	$1.25	$1.75	$2.25

Pillows.

74712 Size..........	20x26,	22x27,	24x28,	24x29	24x30
Weight of each pillow.	2	2½	3	3½	4
With (OO) Grade of feathers. Price each	$1.14	1.42	1.71	2.00	2.28
74713 Size..........	20x26,	21x27,	22x28,	23x28	24x30
Weight of each pillow.	2	2½	3	3½	4
With (O) Grade of feathers. Price, each.	$1.10	1.38	1.65	1.93	2.20
74714 Size..........	19x27,	20x27,	21x27,	22x28,	24x28
Weight of each pillow.	2	2½	3	3½	4
With (L) grade of feathers. Price each.	$1.04	1 30	1.56	1.82	2.08
74715 Size..........	19x26,	20x27,	21x27,	22x28,	24x28
Weight of each pillow.	2	2½	3	3½	4
With (M grade of feathers. Price	$0 96	1.20	1.44	1.68	1.92
74716 Size..........		17x26,	20x27,	22x27,	23x28
Weight of each pillow.		2	2½	3½	4
With N grade of Duck feathers.		$0.95	1.14	1.33	152
74717 Size..........			18x25,	20x26,	22x27
Weight of each pillow..........			3.	3½	4
With hen feathers Price, each....			$0.70	.80	.90

Only good quality of ticking used with our pillows.

Wire Mattresses.

74740

74740 The Regular Standard Corded Steel wire Woven Mattresses. Perfectly tight joint between end rail and bottom. No putty used. A good clean mattress Weight, 40 pounds. Each..........$1.25

74741 Woven Wire Mattress supported by heavy steel, spiral springs, resting upon slats, not connected with the side rails, but attached securely to strips of iron, which are firmly fastened to the end rails. It will not sag. Weight, 50 pounds.
Price, only..........$1.95
Be sure to send length of slats when ordering springs.

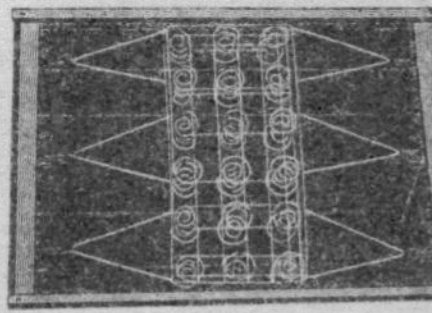

74742 Woven Wire Mattress, supported by 3 rows of heavy steel springs. The fabric is of the best mattress wire, finely woven. The frame is made of kiln-dried hard maple, finely finished. This spring will give perfect satisfaction. Be sure to give size of slat. Weight, 50 pounds.
Price only..........$2.65

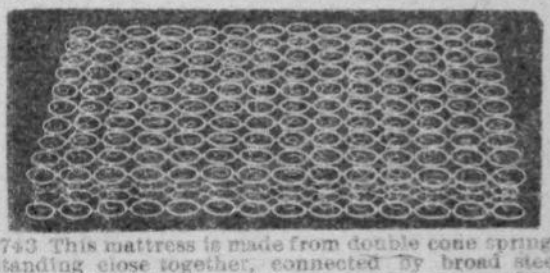

74743 This mattress is made from double cone springs standing close together, connected by broad steel clasps. The top and bottom surfaces are alike. The bed is elastic and yielding in all its parts, conforming perfectly to the form and weight of the sleeper, and is very durable. A full size has 117 springs, Leave all slats in bedstead Weight, 40 pounds. Each..........$1.95

74743½ Spring, same style as 74743, except is made of much finer wire, and has 140 springs, also folds in the center, which is much easier to handle. Weight, 40 pounds. Price, only..........$2.75

M. W. & Co.'s Harvester Oil.

	Per can.	Per doz.
G2490 For threshing machines, wind mills, harvesters, mowers and heavy farm machinery of all kinds. Is highly recommended by those who have used it. Quart cans, 1 dozen in case	$0.21	$2.50
G2491 Gallon cans, 6 in case, price per case	.55	6.20
G2492 Five gallon cans, two in crate; price per case of ten gallons		4.35
G2493 5 gal. can, in 1 case, price for 5 gal.		2.30

G2494 ½ bbl., 28 gallons, no charge for pkgs., 33 cents per gallon. Bbls., 52 gallons, price per gallon 29 cents.

Pure Colors Ground in Oil.

Ready for use with addition of oils, etc., for thinning.

		1 lb. cans.	5 lb. cans.
G2640	Drop Black	$0.16	$0.75
G2645	Ivory Black	.16	.75
G2646	Coach Black	.16	.75
G2647	Prussian Blue	.26	1.65
G2648	Ultramarine Blue	.20	.95

*** And the kitchen furnishings! A treat for a woman to give an order there—Anything—Everything.

*** Our next Catalogue will be sent only to those who send us 15 cents for postage.

Colors Ground in Oil—Continued.

		1 lb. cans.	5 lb. cans
G2649	Italian Sienna, Raw or Burnt	$0.14	$0.65
G2650	Turkey Umber, Raw or Burnt	.12	.55
G2651	Van Dyke Brown	.14	.65
G2652	Chrome Green	.16	.75
G2653	Scarlet Vermilion	.26	1.20
G2654	Tuscan Red	.20	.95
G2655	Venetian Red	.08	.35
G2656	Indian Red	.15	.70
G2657	Chrome Yellow	.20	.90
G2658	Yellow Ocher	.10	.45
G2660	Graining Colors (Antique, Mahogany, Cherry, Walnut)	.15	.70
G2661	Red Lead	.13	.30

Lime, Cement, Tar, Etc.

		Per bbl.
G2770	Lime	$1.10
G2771	Cement, natural	1.25
G2772	Portland Cement, imported	3.40
G2773	Plaster Paris	2.00
		Per bushel.
G2774	Hair, washed	$0.30
G2775	Pine Tar, Carolina, bbls. only, per bbl. about 30 gallons	3.50
G2776	Coal Tar, per bbl	7.50

Axle Grease.

M. W. & Co.'s Perfection Axle Grease.

We have secured control of the total product of the best equipped axle grease factory in the United States, and can now offer you a grease that will outwear by 5 to 15 days any grease in the market. No matter how this price may seem to you, we have faith enough in the goods to place *our name on every package*, and if not satisfactory, you may return the goods at *our expense*.

		Per case.	Each.
G2800	Trial box 1 doz. 1¼ lb. boxes	$0.55	$0.05
G2801	2 doz. in case 1½ lb. boxes	1.00	.05
G2802	4 doz. in case 1½ lb. boxes	1.95	.05
G2803	½ doz in crate 12½ lb. bkts	2.90	.50
G2804	1 doz. in crate 12½ lb. bkts	5.75	.50
G2805	½ doz. in crate 25 lb. bkts	5.00	.90
G2806	1 doz. in crate 25 lb. bkts	9.00	.90
G2807	Kegs, about 60 lbs		2.10
G2809	100 lb. kegs		3.25
G2810	200 lb. kegs		6.00
G2811	400 lb. bbls		12.00

We Carry a Complete Line of

MUSIC BOXES VIOLINS, BANJOS, ZITHERS, GUITARS, ACCORDIONS, FLUTES, BAND INSTRUMENTS, ETC.

And sell them from 25 to 50 per cent. less than what other dealers ask for the same quality of goods.

VARNISHES, COLORS IN OILS, STAINS, ETC., ETC.

WOOD STAINS.

No charge for package.

	Pt cans ea.	Pint cans, per doz.	Qt. cans ea.	Qt. cans Per doz.	½ gal. can each	½ gal. can per doz.	1 gal. cans each	1 gal. cans per doz.	5 gal. cans each.	10 gal. cans each.	½ bbls, 25 gal. per gal.	Bbls. 50 gal. per gal.
G2619 Oil stains, new line. In all colors as follows; Walnut, Mahogany, Cherry, Rosewood, Light oak and Dark oak.	25	2.50	.44	4.80	78	8.50	1.44	16.00	6.25	11.50	1.10	1.00

Chicago Varnish Co.'s Varnishes, Etc.

We have obtained the agency for this celebrated brand of goods, which are guaranteed equal in quality to any like goods made, and have placed them on the market at prices that will at once command your attention. Put up in all sizes, from pts. to 50 gallon barrels. No charge for packages.

	Pints, each.	Pints, doz.	Quarts, each.	Quarts, doz.	½ gal. each.	½ gal. doz.	1 gal. each.	5 gal. each.	10 gal. each.	½ barrel, 25 gallons, Per gal.	Barrels, 50 gallons, Per gal.
G2620 Outside Body Varnish	$0.55	$6.00	$1.00	$11.00	$1.60	$18.00	$3.00	$12.50	$25.00	$2.40	$2.55
G2621 Inside Coach Rubbing Varnish	35	3.75	.65	6.25	1.00	11.00	1.80	8.00	16.00	1.55	1.50
G2622 Benzine Dryer	.18	2.00	.25	2.50	35	3.60	.60	2.25	4.50	.40	.35
G2623 No. 1 Coach Varnish	.25	2.50	.45	4.25	.85	8.50	1.60	6.25	12.50	1.05	1.00
G2624 No. 1 Furniture Varnish	.22	2.25	.40	3.50	.60	6.00	1.00	4.50	9.00	.80	.75
G2625 Light Hard Oil Finish	.25	2.35	.45	4.00	.80	8.25	1.50	6.00	12.00	1.15	1.10
G2626 Extra Light Coach Varnish	.30	3.00	.55	5.50	.90	9.25	1.60	7.00	14.00	1.35	1.30
G2627 Coach Body Varnish	.50	5.00	.85	8.50	1.50	15.00	2.75	13.00	25.50	2.45	2.40
G2628 Rubbing Body Varnish	.40	3.50	.75	7.00	1.30	12.50	2.55	11.50	23.00	2.20	2.15
G2629 Supremis Floor Varnish	.35	3.25	.65	6.25	1.20	11.50	2.30	10.50	21.00	2.00	1.95
G2630 Pure T'rp'ntine Demar Varnish	.30	3.20	.55	5.50	.90	9.50	1.60	7.50	15.00	1.45	1.40
G2631 No. 1 Black Asphaltum	.20	2.20	.30	2.50	.50	4.75	.80	3.50	7.00	.65	.60
G2632 Turpentine Japan Dryer	.25	2.35	.35	3.00	.60	6.00	.90	4.50	8.25	.75	.70
G2633 Enamel Leather Top Dressing, ½ pts. 25c. each, $2.50 per doz	.40	4.00	.75	7.75	1.35	13.00	2.59	10.00	20.00	2.20	2.10
G2634 Shellac Varnish, Orange, Grain Alcohol	.50		.85				3.15				
G2634½ Shellac Varnih, Orange, Wood Alcohol	.40		.75				2.50				

For prices of paint and varnish brushes, see Index.

MRS. HANNAH COBB'S

Improved Home Made Soap

FOR HOUSE AND LAUNDRY USE.

Strictly pure, and we guarantee it to give satisfaction. If not, return at our expense, and we will refund full price paid, and pay transportation charges both ways.

100 12-oz. bars in box, 75 lbs. net	$3.35
30 12-oz. bars in box, trial or family size	1.15
M. W. & Co.'s Old Fashioned Mottled Soap—Dirt Killer—60 1-lb. bars in box	2.10

To convince you that this is the best soap in the market for the money, we will furnish with all orders

ONE SAMPLE CAKE FREE

— OF THE —

Improved Hannah Cobb

— OR THE —

Old Fashioned Mottled Soap.

We can not send it by mail; only with freight and express orders. Mention in your order *one cake soap free.* Until April 1, 1895.

FOR INDEX SEE PINK PAGES

In Middle of Book.

COAL!

If you want any coal you should by all means write for our prices, delivered at your nearest railroad station, in cars of from 12 to 18 tons. We can supply several kinds of both hard and soft coal, and we think that we can discount any price that you can otherwise secure.

If you cannot use a carload, get your neighbors to club with you.

TWO NEW DEPARTMENTS

Dressmaking Department.

This department is in charge of an experienced designer and fitter, with a force of competent dressmakers as assistants. We publish a special catalogue showing a number of styles of dresses and wraps, and giving prices on each in various qualities. We can, however, duplicate any dress shown in fashion magazines or catalogues published by other houses, and will be pleased to quote prices and send samples, if you will send us an illustration and state about the kind of material preferred.

Custom Tailoring Department.

Gentlemen residing in any section of the country can now procure clothes MADE TO FIT THEM, thus securing the latest prevailing styles in both cut of garments and pattern of cloth, at prices but a trifle higher than the ordinary ready-made clothing. Suits and Overcoats at from $15.00 to $25.00. Pants from $4.00 to $6.00.

Our cutters are expert, and we can fit you if any one can.

Write for Tailor-Made Clothing Pamphlet. It contains descriptions, prices, samples of cloths, and rules for self-measurement.

Montgomery Ward & Co.

111 to 116
Michigan Ave., Chicago.

INDEX.